42nd European Photovoltaic Solar Energy Conference and Exhibition (EU PVSEC 2025)

Bilbao, Spain
22-26 September 2025

Volume 5 of 6

ISBN: 979-8-3313-2987-7

42nd European Photovoltaic Solar Energy Conference and Exhibition

Proceedings of the International Conference

22 September – 26 September 2025

Edited by:

C. DEL CAÑIZO
Solar Energy Institute
UPM
Spain

R. KENNY
European Commission
Joint Research Centre
Italy

J. BERGMILLER
WIP Renewable Energies
Germany

J. DE GREGORIO
WIP Renewable Energies
Germany

Edition Team:

B. Yildiz
L. Großhans
A. Michaelsen
U.E. Birgi
WIP Renewable Energies
Germany

Photos at:

Coordination of the Technical Programme:

European Commission Joint Research Centre
Via E. Fermi 1
21020 Ispra (VA)
Italy

Institutional Support:

European Commission

Institutional PV Industry Cooperation:

SolarPower Europe

ESMC – European Solar Manufacturing Council

Supporting Organisations:

AUSTRALIAN PV INSTITUTE

ASOM – Alliance for Solar Mobility

BASQUE ENERGY CLUSTER

BILBAO CONVENTION BUREAU

EASE – European Association for Storage of Energy

ETIP PV – European Technology & Innovation Platform PV

GÜNDER – Turkish Solar Energy Society

IEA PVPS - IEA Photovoltaic Power Systems Programme

INSTITUTO SOLAR DE ENERGÍA SOLAR

LDES – Long Duration Energy Storage Council

NSEFI – National Solar Energy federation of India

NUS /SERIS – National University of Singapore / Solar Energy Research Institute of Singapore

UPM - Polytechnic University of Madrid

Supporting Associations:

EERA – European Energy Research Aliance

EREF – European Renewable Energies Federation

EUREC – The Association of European Renewable Energy Research Centres

VDMA Photovoltaic Equipment

Local Support:
ENTE VASCO DE LA ENERGÍA
EUH – University of the Basque Country

EU PVSEC 2025 realised by:

WIP Renewable Energies
Sylvensteinstr. 2, 81369 Munich, Germany
Tel: +49 89 720 12 735, Fax: +49 89 720 12 791
Email: pv.conference@wip-munich.de
www.eupvsec.org
www.wip-munich.de

Proceedings produced and published by:

WIP Renewable Energies
Sylvensteinstr. 2, 81369 Munich, Germany
Tel: +49 89 720 12 735, Fax: +49 89 720 12 791
Email: pv.conference@wip-munich.de
www.eupvsec.org
www.wip-munich.de

42nd EUROPEAN PHOTOVOLTAIC SOLAR ENERGY CONFERENCE AND EXHIBITION
22 SEPTEMBER – 26 SEPTEMBER 2025

EU PVSEC 2025 COMMITTEES

INTERNATIONAL SCIENTIFIC ADVISORY COMMITTEE (ISAC)

Chair

P. Szymanski, European Commission Joint Research Centre, Director of Energy, Transport and Climate, Petten, The Netherlands

Committee Members

V. Bermúdez Benito, Founder & Principal Consultant, Berbetin, Antibes, France

G.C. Eder, OFI, Vienna, Austria

P. Frankl, Head of the Renewable Energy Division, International Energy Agency, France

M. Getsiou, European Commission, DG RTD, Brussels, Belgium

S.W. Glunz, Head of Division Photovoltaics - Research, Fraunhofer ISE, Freiburg, Germany

N.M. Haegel, Director of the National Center for Photovoltaics, NREL, Golden, USA

R. Kenny, European Commission Joint Research Centre, Directorate for Energy and Transport and Climate, Ispra, Italy

S. Nowak, Managing Director of NET Nowak Energy & Technology, St. Ursen, Switzerland

R. Schlatmann, Chairman of ETIP PV, Head of the Solar Energy Division at Helmholtz-Zentrum Berlin, Germany

W.C. Sinke, TNO Energy Transition, The Netherlands

M. Topič, Head of Laboratory of Photovoltaics and Optoelectronics of the University of Ljubljana, Slovenia

P. Verlinden, Director at Amrock, Visiting Professor at Sun Yat-Sen University, Guangzhou, China

E. Voroshazi, Head of PV module process laboratory, CEA, Le Bourget-du-Lac, France

J. Bergmiller, Managing Director Events & Knowledge Transfer, WIP Renewable Energies, Munich, Germany

J. de Gregorio, Head of Unit, Scientific Services and Cooperation, WIP Renewable Energies, Munich, Germany

CONFERENCE EXECUTIVE COMMITTEE

Conference General Chair

C. del Cañizo, UPM, Madrid, Spain

Technical Programme Chair

R. Kenny, European Commission Joint Research Centre, Directorate for Energy and Transport and Climate, Ispra, Italy

Committee Members

W.C. Sinke, Program Development Manager, TNO Energy Transition, The Netherlands

S. Nowak, Managing Director of NET Nowak Energy & Technology, St. Ursen, Switzerland

M. Topič, Head of Laboratory of Photovoltaics and Optoelectronics of the University of Ljubljana, Slovenia

V. Bermúdez Benito, BERBETIN, France

E. Voroshazi, Head of PV Module Process Laboratory, CEA, Le Bourget-Du-Lac France

H. Ossenbrink, Former European Commission Joint Research Centre, Germany

J. Bergmiller, Managing Director Events & Knowledge Transfer, WIP Renewable Energies, Munich, Germany

J. de Gregorio, Head of Unit, Scientific Services and Cooperation, WIP Renewable Energies, Munich, Germany

2025 SCIENTIFIC COMMITTEE

Programme Technical Chair

R. Kenny, European Commission, Joint Research Centre, Italy

Topic Chairs

Topic 1: Silicon Materials and Cells
F. Schindler, Fraunhofer ISE, Germany

Topic 2: Thin Films and New Concepts
I. Gordon, imec, Belgium

Topic 3: Photovoltaic Modules and BoS Components
T. Barnes, NREL, USA

Topic 4: PV Systems Engineering, Integrated/Applied PV
A.M. Gracia Amillo, FUNDACION CENER, Spain

Topic 5: PV in the Energy Transition
C. Agraffeil, CEA / INES, France

Topic Organisers and Paper Review Experts

Topic 1: Silicon Materials and Cells
F. Schindler, Fraunhofer ISE, Germany
C. Fischer, Wacker Chemie, Germany
G. Hahn, University of Konstanz, Germany
K. Ding, Forschungszentrum Jülich, Germany
P. Roca i Cabarrocas, CNRS-LPICM, France
A. W. Weeber, TNO Energy Transition, The Netherlands
D. Muñoz, CEA / INES, France
S. W. Glunz, Fraunhofer ISE, Germany
K. Bothe, ISFH, Germany
M. Topic, University of Ljubljana, Slovenia
P. Fath, RCT-Solutions, Germany
S. Peters, Hanwha Q CELLS, Germany

M.P. Bellmann, SINTEF, Norway
A. Ciesla, UNSW, Australia
C. Hagendorf, Freiberg Instruments, Germany
X. Yu, Zhejiang University, China
J.S. Lee, KIER, South Korea
R. Brendel, ISFH, Germany
T. Dullweber, ISFH, Germany
J. Horzel, Fraunhofer ISE, Germany
W. Nemeth, NREL, United States of America
R. Turan, METU, Türkiye
F. Menchini, ENEA, Italy
W. Favre, CEA, France

J. Meier, Meier Technologies, Switzerland
J. Schmidt, ISFH, Germany
M. Wright, University of Oxford, United Kingdom
J. Zhao, CSEM, Switzerland
A. Morisset, CSEM, Switzerland
A. Richter, Fraunhofer ISE, Germany
J. Linke, ISC Konstanz, Germany
B. Geerligs, TNO Energy Transition, The Netherlands
S. Dubois, CEA, France
M. Hermle, Fraunhofer ISE, Germany
B. Terheiden, University of Konstanz, Germany
P. Delli Veneri, ENEA, Italy
T. Matsui, AIST, Japan
Y. Ohshita, Toyota Technological Institute, Japan
E. Bruhat, HOLOSOLIS, France
A. Augusto, Dalarna University, Sweden
F. Ferrazza, ENI S.p.A., Italy
A. Otaegi, UPV/EHU, Spain
M.C. Schubert, Fraunhofer ISE, Germany
H. Duman, KalyonPV, Türkiye
N. Usami, Nagoya University, Japan
Y. Zhu, UNSW, Australia
D. Brunner, RENA Technologies, Germany
A. Danel, CEA, France
C. Gerardi, 3Sun, Italy
H.J. Nonnenmacher, Meyer Burger, Germany
P. Verlinden, AMROCK, Australia
Q. Wang, Wang, Qi, China
W. Zhang, Zhang, Weiming, China
Y. Chen, Trina Solar Energy, China
E. Krassowski, CE Cell Engineering, Germany
M. Foti, 3Sun, Italy
D.L. Bätzner, Meyer Burger Research, Switzerland

Topic 2: Thin Films and New Concepts
I. Gordon, imec, Belgium
J.C. Goldschmidt, Marburg University, Germany
F. Schoofs, Oxford PV, United Kingdom
N. Kyranaki, Hasselt University, Belgium
S. Veenstra, TNO Energy Transition, The Netherlands
T. Aernouts, imec, Belgium
A.N. Tiwari, SOLTIWA, Switzerland
G. Siefer, Fraunhofer ISE, Germany
M. Edoff, Uppsala University, Sweden
A. Martí Vega, UPM, Spain
J. Poortmans, imec, Belgium
I. Ramiro, UPM, Spain
T. Magorian Friedlmeier, ZSW, Germany

S. Albrecht, HZB, Germany
S. Berson, CEA, France
P. Carroy, CEA, France
C. Case, Oxford PV, United Kingdom
G. Coletti, FuturaSun, Italy
S. De Wolf, KAUST, Saudi Arabia
U.W. Paetzold, KIT, Germany
H. Sivaramakrishnan Radhakrisnan, imec, Belgium
P. Schulze, Fraunhofer ISE, Germany
L. Wang, Technology Innovation Institute, United Arab Emirates
Y. Smirnov, Applied Materials, United States of America
B. Stannowski, HZB, Germany
F. Fertig, Hanwha Q CELLS, Germany
L. Lancellotti, ENEA, Italy
S. Cros, CEA, France
S. Hayase, The University of Electro-Communications, Japan
S. Huang, Macquarie University, Australia
M. Khenkin, HZB, Germany
C. Lin, National Taiwan University, Taiwan

M.S.H. Norton, University of Cyprus, Cyprus
P. Pistor, Pablo de Olavide University, Spain
W. Tress, Zurich University of Applied Sciences, Switzerland
A. Aguirre, imec, Belgium
D. Lan, UNSW Sydney, China
M. Saliba, University of Stuttgart, Germany
P. Manshanden, TNO Energy Transition, The Netherlands
L. Vesce, University of Rome II, Italy
I. Dogan, TNO Solliance, The Netherlands
Y. Kuang, imec, Belgium
M. Al Katrib, IPVF, France
M.I. Hossain, QEERI, Qatar
W.H. Chiu, Chang Gung University, Taiwan
C. Chen, Ming Chi University of Technology, Taiwan
C. Fell, CSIRO Energy Technology, Australia
G. Brammertz, imec, Belgium
T. Dalibor, Avancis, Germany
S. Ishizuka, AIST, Japan
A. Redinger, University of Luxembourg, Luxembourg
A. Romeo, University of Verona, Italy
V. Sittinger, Fraunhofer IST, Germany
M. Theelen, TNO/Solliance, The Netherlands
G. Timò, RSE, Italy
A. Kanevce, ZSW, Germany
A. Pérez-Rodríguez, IREC, Spain
R. Gutzler, ZSW, Germany
W. Witte, ZSW, Germany
T. Nishimura, Tokyo Institute of Technology, Japan
C. Qian, University of New South Wales, Australia
J.P. Connolly, CentraleSupelec, France
J.P. Kleider, CNRS/GeePs, France
I. Konovalov, University of Applied Sciences Jena, Germany
Y. Okada, University of Tokyo, Japan
M. Rusu, HZB, Germany
H. Meddeb, DLR, Germany
E. Saucedo, Universitat Politècnica de Catalunya (UPC), Spain
P. Vidal-Fuentes, FUNDACIÓ INSTITUT DE RECERCA EN ENERGIA DE CATALUNYA, Spain
C. Malerba, ENEA, Italy
C. Becker, HZB, Germany
D. Kuciauskas, NREL, United States of America
M. Ochoa, University of Cantabria, Spain
T. Tayagaki, AIST, Japan
S. Wasmer, WAVELABS Solar Metrology Systems, Germany
S. Zandi, UNSW, Australia
C. Messmer, University of Freiburg, Germany
J.B. Puel, Institut Photovoltaïque d'Ile de France (IPVF), France
S. Ternes, University of Rome II, Italy

Topic 3: Photovoltaic Modules and BoS Components
V. Bermúdez Benito, BERBETIN, France
R. Preu, Fraunhofer ISE, Germany
R. Gottschalg, Fraunhofer CSP, Germany
T. Barnes, NREL, United States of America
G. Friesen, SUPSI, Switzerland
G. Bardizza, TÜV Rheinland Solar, Italy

V. Barth, CEA, France
A. Faes, CSEM, Switzerland
A. Lennon, Sundrive Solar, Australia
M. Mittag, Fraunhofer ISE, Germany
M.A. Muñoz-Garcia, UPM, Spain
H. Nagel, Fraunhofer ISE, Germany
S. Pietralunga, CNR, Italy
T. Timofte, ISC Konstanz, Germany

S. Feldbacher, PCCL, Austria
A. Halm, ISC Konstanz, Germany
H. Hanifi, AESOLAR, Germany
E. Warren, NREL, United States of America
S. Zhang, Trina Solar Energy, China
X. Zhen, Canadian Solar, China
G. Beaucarne, Dow Silicones Belgium, Belgium
T. Bejat, CEA, France
C. Camus, LayTec, Germany
U. Jahn, Fraunhofer CSP, Germany
G. Oreski, PCCL, Austria
M. Pander, Fraunhofer CSP, Germany
T. Sample, European Commission JRC, Italy
A. Morlier, imo-imomec, Belgium
C. Barretta, PCCL, Austria
P. Gebhardt, Fraunhofer ISE, Germany
C. Sen, UNSW, Australia
O. Arriaga Arruti, CSEM, Switzerland
X. Gu, NIST, United States of America
C. Xiao, Chinese Academy of Sciences, United States of America
R. Aninat, TNO/Solliance, The Netherlands
S. Mitterhofer, NIST, United States of America
B. Hoex, UNSW, Australia
E. Özkalay, SUPSI, Switzerland
M. Bokalič, University of Ljubljana, Slovenia
S. Bordihn, ISFH, Germany
M. Despeisse, CSEM, Switzerland
J. Govaerts, imec, Belgium
J. Lopez-Garcia, STS-Certified, Spain
M. Pravettoni, Technology Innovation Institute, United Arab Emirates
T. Stoyanova Lyubenova, Joint Research Centre, Italy
C. Ulbrich, HZB, Germany
J. Moereke, Avancis, Germany
Y.S. Long, ITRI, Taiwan
D. Pavanello, European Commission JRC, Italy
A.K. Vidal de Oliveira, UFSC, Brazil
J. Bengoechea, CENER, Spain
M. Ernst, ANU, Australia
H. Ellis, European Commission JRC, Italy
B. Mihaylov, European Commission JRC, Italy
G. Chowdhury, 3E, Belgium
B. Aissa, QEERI - Qatar Environment and Energy Research Institute, Qatar

Topic 4: PV Systems Engineering, Integrated/Applied PV
A. Gracia Amillo, CENER, Spain
W.G.J.H.M. van Sark, Utrecht University, The Netherlands
K. Lappalainen, Tampere University, Finland
J.M. Almeida Serra, University of Lisbon, Portugal
I. Tsanakas, CEA, France
C. Buerhop-Lutz, HI ERN, Germany
D. Moser, Becquerel Institute Italia, Italy
F. Frontini, SUPSI, Switzerland
G.C. Eder, OFI, Austria
A. Scognamiglio, ENEA, Italy
A. Chatzipanagi, European Commission JRC, Italy
I. Antón Hernández, UPM, Spain
R.M.E. Valckenborg, TNO, The Netherlands
T. Reindl, SERIS, Singapore
J.R. Gonzalez, European Space Agency, The Netherlands
G. Mütter, Gerhard Mütter e.U., Austria
T. Merdzhanova, Forschungszentrum Jülich, Germany

V. Lara-Fanego, Solargis, Spain
A. Louwen, Eurac Research, Italy
A. Martinez Fernandez, European Commission JRC, Italy
T. Oozeki, AIST, Japan

J. Remund, Meteotest, Switzerland
M. Sengupta, NREL, United States of America
M. Zehner, Rosenheim Technical University of Applied Sciences, Germany
B. Nouri, German Aerospace Center, Spain
S. Poddar, UNSW, Australia
D. Bachour, HBKU/ Qatar Foundation, Qatar
J. Yang, NREL, United States of America
S. Bouguerra, imo-imomec, Belgium
C. Alonso-Tristán, UBU, Spain
M. Carbone, ENEL Green Power, Italy
M. Dennenmoser, BayWa r.e. Solar Projects GmbH, Germany
C.W. Hansen, Sandia National Laboratories, United States of America
A. Neubert, DNV Maritime Software GmbH, Germany
D. Berrian, Belectric, Germany
M. Oliosi, PVsyst, Switzerland
J. Moschner, KU Leuven / EnergyVille, Belgium
C. Bucher, BUAS, Switzerland
B. Wittmer, PVsyst SA, Switzerland
M. Bolen, SB Energy, United States of America
D. Daßler, Fraunhofer CSP, Germany
R. Einhaus, ZSW, Germany
P. Hacke, NREL, United States of America
A. Heimsath, Fraunhofer ISE, Germany
J. Lin, PV Guider, Taiwan
A. Migan-Dubois, GeePs, France
M. Rinio, University of Karlstad, Sweden
J.S. Stein, Sandia National Laboratories, United States of America
D. Stellbogen, ZSW, Germany
M. Theristis, Sandia National Laboratories, United States of America
A. Virtuani, CSEM, Switzerland
A. Driesse, PV Performance Labs, Germany
M. Øgaard, IFE, Norway
A. Nobre, SERIS, Singapore
T. Trupke, UNSW, Australia
C. Cornaro, University of Rome II, Italy
G. A. dos Reis Benatto, DTU, Denmark
S. Malik, Fraunhofer CSP, Germany
S. Lindig, Univers SAS, France
M.M. Nygård, Institute for Energy Technology, Norway
P. Alonso Gomez, BayWa r.e., Germany
Y. Assoa, CEA, France
P. Bonomo, SUPSI, Switzerland
V. D'Ambrosio, University of Naples Federico II, Italy
E. Román Medina, Tecnalia, Spain
L.H. Slooff, TNO Energy Transition, The Netherlands
S. Villa, TNO, The Netherlands
M. La Rosa, Glass to Power, Italy
T. Del Caño, Onyx Solar Energy, Spain
X. Zhihao, AIST, Japan
P. Sharif, ODTU-GUNAM, Türkiye
K. Umeda, TAISEI CORPORATION, Japan
S. Boddaert, CSTB, France
N. Lysgaard Andersen, DTU, Denmark
K. Meyer, ISFH, Germany
T. Biel, NET Nowak Energy & Technology, Switzerland
F. Colucci, ENEA, Italy
A. Pascaris, NREL, United States of America
C. Dupraz, INRAE, France
C. Alonso-García, CIEMAT, Spain
A. Lefort, BayWa, Germany
H.N. Riise, IFE, Norway
M.A. Schüler, Next2Sun Technology GmbH, Germany
P.J. Pérez-Higueras, University of Jaén, Spain
K. Oda, Agritree,

M. Berwind, Fraunhofer ISE, Germany
M. Dörenkämper, TNO, The Netherlands
M. Heinrich, Fraunhofer ISE, Germany
B. Newman, Lightyear, The Netherlands
A. Reinders, Eindhoven University of Technology, The Netherlands
T. Tanahashi, AIST, Japan
J. Leloux, LuciSun, Belgium
E. Shirazi, University of Twente, The Netherlands
K. Araki, University of Miyazaki, Japan
K. Nishioka, University of Miyazaki, Japan
R. Campesato, CESI, Italy
V. Khorenko, Azur Space, Germany
G. Kakoulaki, European Commission Joint Research Centre, Italy
H. Toyota, JAXA, Japan
P. Garcia-Linares, UPM, Spain
I. Weiss, Weiss, Ingrid, Germany
A. Hensel, Fraunhofer ISE, Germany
J.S. da Fernandes, Hochschule Offenburg, Germany
Y. Ueda, Tokyo University of Science, Japan
J. Braid, Sandia National Laboratories, United States of America

Topic 5: PV in the Energy Transition
J. Stierstorfer, WIP Renewable Energies, Germany
R. Pestana, R&D Nester, Portugal
P.J. Alet, CSEM, Switzerland
C. Agraffeil, CEA, France
K. WAMBACH, Wambach-Consulting, Germany
C. del Cañizo, UPM, Spain
L. Großhans, WIP Renewable Energies, Germany
M. Getsiou, European Commission DG RTD, Belgium
S. Nowak, NET Nowak Energy & Technology, Switzerland
C. Breyer, LUT University, Finland
I. Kaizuka, RTS Corporation, Japan
G. Masson, Becquerel Institute, Belgium
P. Baliozian, VDMA, Germany
L. Großhans, WIP Renewable Energies, Germany
C. Candelise, Bocconi University, Italy
S. Caneva, WIP Renewable Energies, Germany

G. Barchi, Eurac Research, Italy
R. Bründlinger, AIT, Austria
V. Efthymiou, University of Cyprus, Cyprus
M. Centeno Brito, University of Lisbon, Portugal
F. Carigiet, ZHAW, Switzerland
B. Gaiddon, HESPUL, France
F.Z. Ouchani, Green Energy Park, Morocco
M. Rennhofer, AIT, Austria
G. Adinolfi, ENEA, Italy
W. Schaffer, Salzburg Netz, Austria
A. Haber, e-control, Austria
G. Heilscher, Technische Hochschule Ulm, Germany
A. Anctil, Michigan State University, United States of America
S. Arancón, Plug and Play, Spain
S. Capaccioli, ETA - Florence Renewable Energies, Italy
V. Fthenakis, Columbia University, United States of America
G. Heath, NREL, United States of America
K. Komoto, Mizuho Research & Technologies, Ltd., Japan
W. Palitzsch, LuxChemtech, Germany
S. Ovaitt, NREL, United States of America
M. de Wild-Scholten, SmartGreenScans, The Netherlands
S. Herceg, Fraunhofer ISE, Germany
C. Polacchi, Eurac Research, Italy
N. Espinosa, Universidad de Murcia, Spain
E. Drahi, TotalEnergies OneTech, France
S. Guastella, RSE, Italy

H. Ossenbrink, Band Gap, Germany
D. Polverini, European Commission DG GROW, Belgium
N. Taylor, European Commission JRC, Italy
K.A. Weiß, Fraunhofer ISE, Germany
I. Kafedjiska, Helmholtz Zentrum Berlin, Germany
P. Malbranche, Solar Action, France
S. De Iuliis, ENEA, Italy
T. Haarberg, BNW-Energy, Norway
A. Nayfeh, Khalifa University, United Arab Emirates
E. Vartiainen, Fortum Renewables Oy, Finland
E. Veronese, Eurac Research, Italy
P. Sanchez-Friera, Solkeys, Spain
N. Cherradi, Desert Technologies, Saudi Arabia
S. Nold, Fraunhofer ISE, Germany
H.J.J. Yu, CEA, France
M. Beck, U.S. Department of Energy, United States of America
M. Woodhouse, NREL, United States of America
A.B. Cristóbal, UPM, Spain
G. Ruggieri, Insubria University, Italy
S. Tay, NUS, Singapore

Awards Coordinators

Student Awards Coordinator
A.H.M. Smets, Delft University of Technology, The Netherlands

Student Awards Committee
R. Kenny, EU PVSEC Technical Programme Chair, Italy
C. del Canizo, Conference Chair, UPM, Spain
E. Voroshazi, CEA, France
J. Poortmans, imec, Belgium
P.J. Alet, CSEM, Switzerland
S. Caneva, WIP Renewable Energies, Germany
A. Romeo, University of Verona, Italy
G. Friesen, SUPSI, Switzerland
F. Schindler, Fraunhofer ISE, Germany
J.C. Goldchmidt, Marburg University, Germany
D. Moser, Becquerel Institute, Italy
K. Ding, FZJ, Germany
W.C. Sinke, TNO Energy Transition, The Netherlands
M. Topic, University of Ljubljana, Slovenia
R. Schlatman, HZB, Germany
S. Glunz, Fraunhofer ISE, Germany
A.M. Vega, UPM, Spain
I. Kaizuka, RTS, Japan
P.D. Veneri, ENEA, Italy
J. Bengoechea, CENER, Spain

Poster Awards Coordinator
P. Malbranche, Solar Action, France

Poster Awards Committee
R. Kenny, European Commission JRC, Italy
C. del Canizo, UPM, Spain
W. van Sark, Utrecht University, The Netherlands
I. Tsanakas, CEA INES, France
L. Miranda, Oxford PV, United Kingdom
D. Munoz, CEA INES, France
I. Gordon, imec, Belgium
E. Roman, Tecnalia, Spain
G. Eder, OFI, Austria
I. Antón, UPM, Spain
S. Veenstra, TNO, The Netherlands
J.M. Almeida Serra, University of Lisbon, Portugal
T. Magorian Friedlmeier, ZSW, Germany
J. Stierstorfer, WIP Renewable Energies, Germany

SUBJECT INDEX

Silicon Materials and Cells

Sessions 1CP.1, 1EP.3, 1AO.4, 1AO.5, 1AO.6, 1BO.1, 1BO.2, 1BO.3, 1BO.4, 1DO.9, 1BV.5, 1CV.2

Thin Films and New Concepts

Sessions 2CP.2, 2BO.1, 2CO.1, 2CO.2, 2DO.9, 2DO.6, 2DO.7, 2DO.8, 2AO.2, 2AO.3, 2AO.1, 2BO.8, 2BO.9, 2BO.10, 2BV.1, 2BV.2, 2CV.3

Photovoltaic Modules and BoS Components

Sessions 3CP.1, 3CP.3, 3CO.10, 3CO.11, 3DO.12, 3DO.16, 3DO.19, 3DO.20, 3BO.11, 3BO.12, 3BO.14, 3BO.15, 3AV.1, 3AV.2, 3AV.3

PV Systems Engineering, Integrated/Applied PV

Sessions 4AP.1, 4AO.7, 4AO.8, 4AO.9, 4DO.1, 4DO.3, 4BO.6, 4BO.7, 4CO.8, 4CO.9, 4DO.10, 4DO.17, 4BO.5, 4BO.16, 4BO.17, 4DO.2, 4DO.4, 4DO.5, 4CO.3, 4EO.2, 4BV.3, 4BV.4, 4CV.1, 4DV.1, 4DV.4,

PV in the Energy Transition

Sessions 5CP.1, 5CP.2, 5DO.14, 5DO.15, 5CO.4, 5CO.5, 5CO.6, 5DO.18, 5CO.4, 5CO.5, 5CO.6, 5DO.18, 5EO.3, 5EO.1, 5DV.2, 5DV.3,

---

Topic Code	Session Type	Day Codes
1 Silicon Materials and Cells	P = Plenary Session	A = Monday, 22 September 2025
2 Thin-Films and New Concepts	O = Oral Session	B = Tuesday, 23 September 2025
3 Photovoltaic Modules	V = Visual Session	C = Wednesday, 24 September 2025
4 Photovoltaic Systems		D = Thursday, 25 September 2025
5 Photovoltaics in the Energy Transition		E = Friday, 26 September 2025

e.g. 1AO.4 ⇒ 1= Silicon Materials and Cells, A=Monday, O=Oral session, 4=Session 4

FOREWORD

The European Photovoltaic Solar Energy Conference and Exhibition (EU PVSEC) stands as the World's leading and most renowned forum for PV research and development and the biggest conference on PV solar energy. In 2025, celebrating its 42nd edition, the EU PVSEC was the essential meeting and exchanging point for global PV experts from research, development, and industry.

Held from 22–26 September 2025 in Bilbao, Spain, the EU PVSEC 2025 was a resounding success, showcasing a wide range of cutting-edge research results. Bringing together both the Conference and the Exhibition, this edition attracted more than 1600 participants from 61 countries who contributed over 1000 presentations across various fields of science and technology. The event provided an essential platform for the exchange of knowledge and ideas on photovoltaic research, innovations, and applications. In the exhibition area 51 companies from all parts of the world welcomed visitors and presented their products and services.

Conference Highlights

The EU PVSEC covered a broad range of topics with an extensive programme that offers an opportunity for workers from across the entire field of photovoltaics to share their findings, as well as an opportunity for multidisciplinary learning. Rapid advances in materials, designs, and manufacturing processes reflect the accelerating expansion of the global PV market. The programme was arranged into 5 topics as follows:
- Silicon Materials and Cells;
- Thin Films and New Concepts;
- Photovoltaic Modules and Balance of System Components;
- PV Systems Engineering, Integrated/Applied PV;
- PV in the Energy Transition.

Communicating the key messages from the conference, not only to participants, but also to other researchers, key stakeholders, policy makers and the general public was an important added value. We thank the Highlights Committee, composed of selected members of the Scientific Committee, as well as the Session Chairs, for providing a comprehensive summary of the findings and state of the art research that were delivered during this year's event. Some key highlights are listed below, while further details may be found in the dedicated highlights presentation in the annex of these proceedings.

Cross-cutting themes:

- Demonstrated the versatility of solar technologies, spanning traditional and emerging application areas.
- Sustainability and circularity remain central, with research focused on reducing material use, such as replacing silver with copper, and advancing end-of-life management of modules.
- Ensuring long-term stability and predictable energy yield is equally essential, with many examples of studies on degradation mechanisms and efforts to elucidate their root-causes, such as in the case of UVID.

- The role of artificial intelligence across the PV value chain is rapidly expanding, from design to operations and maintenance, including among many others drone applications.

Latest Solar Innovations in Materials, Cells, Modules and PV Systems:

While silicon solar cells remain the cornerstone of PV technology, perovskite solar cells continue to stand out as the leading complementary technology to silicon, both as standalone devices and in tandem configurations. Research efforts are increasingly focused on enhancing stability, understanding degradation mechanisms, improving durability and scalability, and ensuring full industrial compatibility.

Many companies presented impressive results on industrial-size single-junction perovskite modules as well as perovskite-based tandem modules, and several new efficiency records were announced during the event. The rapid pace of innovation in cell and module architecture underscores the need for accelerated and more robust testing and qualification methodologies. Both the industry and the research community are moving swiftly to assess and improve reliability in this fast-evolving PV landscape.

A major focus in module research remains the optimisation of materials and packaging to ensure long lifetimes and predictable energy yields from high-efficiency cells. In parallel, many innovative advances in the operation and maintenance (O&M) of PV systems were presented and discussed.

Applications, Grid Integration and Storage

"PV can be deployed everywhere": from space applications to agrivoltaics, PV noise barriers, building-integrated photovoltaics (BIPV), floating PV systems, and even vehicles. Among these, agrivoltaics is gaining momentum as a promising dual land use approach, offering economic benefits for farmers while increasing resilience to climate change.

Flexibility solutions, particularly through battery storage, were recognised in many technical presentations as essential to accommodate higher PV penetration levels and to reduce energy curtailment. At the same time, strengthening grid infrastructure and enhancing grid management capabilities remain critical to enable the next phase of large-scale PV integration.

Photovoltaics in the Energy Transition

Options for re-establishing competitive module manufacturing in Europe were extensively analysed, including detailed policy recommendations for industrial support and market growth. Currently, a mismatch persists between global PV module installation rates and production rates, resulting in growing inventories and sharply reduced prices.

Finally, inclusiveness, diversity, citizen participation, awareness, education, and social engagement were underlined as vital dimensions of the sector's long-term sustainability and innovation capacity.

EU PVSEC 2025 Proceedings

Selection for inclusion in the conference was made by the Scientific Committee's paper review experts and topic organisers (see the listing on pages 010002-001-005), to whom we express our sincere gratitude for their comprehensive review work and overall contribution to the success of the conference.

The EU PVSEC 2025 Proceedings contain the full papers covering most of the highlights described above and more. The Proceedings provide a comprehensive overview of the PV solar sector, its current status and future prospects in science, research, innovation, development and deployment extending to 3,750 pages. In addition to the 299 submitted papers, the proceedings include 101 presentations (slides) shown during the plenary and oral presentations as well as 176 poster files of the visual presentations. In total this amounts to 576 publications.

The Conference Proceedings are published as downloadable files and are also fully accessible online. A DOI code (Digital Object Identifier) has been assigned to each paper. This ensures unequivocal and permanent identification and full citability. The EU PVSEC 2025 papers can be viewed and downloaded in a full free open access from the EU PVSEC's Proceedings website https://userarea.eupvsec.org/proceedings.

The proceedings of the EU PVSEC 2025 strengthen the commitment to providing quick and open access to high quality scientific results. This is a powerful source for targeted and quick information search and retrieval, enabling you to search by topic, keywords, paper title, DOI, author, or organization.

We are confident that these Proceedings will play an important role in providing a comprehensive overview of the current actors and activities in the global PV sector and that they will disseminate information on the state-of-the-art of technologies and applications. This can generate further research, add momentum to innovation and promote interest in PV worldwide.

We would like to cordially thank all authors and participants of the EU PVSEC 2025 for their contributions and look forward to welcoming you in Rotterdam, The Netherlands from 14 – 18 September 2026 at the EU PVSEC 2026, the 43rd European Photovoltaic Solar Energy Conference and Exhibition

The Editors

TABLE OF CONTENTS OF EU PVSEC 2025 PROCEEDINGS PAPERS

Oral SESSION 1AO.5 Si TOPCon Solar Cells and Related Processing Steps

Jiahui Xu[1], Yuxuan Li[2], Wenjing Zhang[1], Geng Zhang[3], Pierre Verlinden[1], Cui Liu[2], Zhenjue Shen[1], Xiao Yuan[1]
[1] YIST, Jiangyin, China; [2] East China University of Science and Technology, Shanghai, China; [3] Jolywood (ShanXi) Solar Technology, Taiyuan, China

Jan Lossen[1], Justus Carstens[1], Mertcan Comak[1], Apoorva Gattu[1], Dominik Rudolph[1], Pirmin Preis[1], Lejo Joseph Koduvelikulathu[1]
[1] ISC Konstanz, Konstanz, Germany

Oral SESSION 1BO.2 Characterisation and Modelling of Si Solar Cells

Marko Turek[1], Stefan Eiternick[1], Jonathan Linke[2], Jan Hoß[2]
[1] Fraunhofer CSP, Halle (Saale), Germany; [2] ISC Konstanz, Konstanz, Germany

Oral SESSION 1BO.3 Si Solar Cell Manufacturing Processes

Julian Reichle[1], Sraisth[1], Mehul Raval[1], Gourab Das[1], Andreas Teppe[1], Wolfgang Jooss[1], Peter Fath[1]
[1] RCT Solutions, Konstanz, Germany

Thorsten Dullweber[1], Yevgeniya Larionova[1], Philip Jäger[1], Verena Mertens[1], Sabrina Schimanke[1], Melanie Ripke[1], Ulrike Baumann[1], Alaa Osman[1], Udo Römer[1], Robby Peibst[1], Rolf Brendel[1], Özlem Coşkun[2], Gamze Çekerek[2], Meriç Çalışkan Arslan[2], Geoffrey Gregory[3], Erik Hoffmann[3], Massimo Centazzo[3]
[1] ISFH, Emmerthal, Germany; [2] Kalyon PV, Ankara, Türkiye; [3] EnPV, Karlsruhe, Germany

[1] *Anhalt University of Applied Sciences, Köthen, Germany;* [2] *Fraunhofer CSP, Halle, Germany*

Oral SESSION 2AO.2 Advances in Chalcogenide Devices

2AO.2.3 A New Method for Sb-doped CdSeTe/CdTe Devices with Superior Stability   020057

Elisa Artegiani[1], Mariyam Mukhtar[1], Alessandro Romeo[1]
[1] *University of Verona, Verona, Italy*

Oral SESSION 2AO.3 III-V Based Devices | Tandem and Perovskite Solar Cells

2AO.3.3 Micro-Crystal GaAs Array Sub-Cells for Si Tandem Solar Cells   020058

James Patrick Connolly[1], Ahmed Nejim[2], Alexandre Jaffré[1], José Alvarez[1], Jean-Paul Kleider[1], Denis Mencaraglia[1], Laurie Dentz[3], Géraldine Hallais[3], Frederic Hamouda[3], Laetitia Vincent[3], Daniel Bouchier[3], Charles Renard[3]
[1] *CNRS, Gif-sur-Yvette, France;* [2] *SILVACO, St. Ives, United Kingdom;* [3] *CNRS, Palaiseau, France*

2AO.3.5 Multiscale Models for Perovskite Optimisation   020060

Philippe Baranek[1], James Patrick Connolly[2], Antoine Gissler[1], Philip Schulz[3], Michel Rerat[4], Roberto Dovesi[5]
[1] *EDF R&D, Palaiseau, France;* [2] *CNRS, Gif-sur-Yvette, France;* [3] *IPVF, Palaiseau, France;* [4] *IPREM, Pau, France;* [5] *Academy of Sciences of Turin, Torino, Italy*

2AO.3.6 Modelling Recovery in Perovskite Solar Cells under Light and Dark to   020062
Address Stability Challenges

Guillem Álvarez-Pérez[1], Jean Baptiste Puel[1], Jean François Guillemoles [1]
[1] *IPVF, Palaiseau, France*

Oral SESSION 2BO.10 Advanced Modelling and Characterisation of Perovskite Solar Cells

2BO.10.2 On Perimeter Losses in Perovskite Top- and Poly-Si-Passivated Silicon   020063
Bottom Cells – Do Small Area Tandems Reveal the Full Efficiency Potential?

Felix Haase[1], Lukas Brockmann[1], Annika Raugewitz[1], Verena Steckenreiter[1], Verena Barnscheidt[1], Roland Clausing[1], Sara Baumann[1], Joachim Vollbrecht[1], Welmoed Veurman[1], Johannes Löhr[1], Dongyang Liu[1], Mircea Turcu[1], Lasse Nasebandt[1], Udo Römer[1], David Sylla[1], Jessica Strey[1], Martha Löhning[1], Larissa Mettner[1], Renate Winter[1], Anja Christ[1], Heike Kohlenberg[1], Cornelia Marquardt[1], Emanuel Brueckner[1], Hossein Rabiei[1], Michael Rienäcker[1], Sarah Kajari-Schröder[1], Tobias Wietler[1], Robby Peibst[1]
[1] *ISFH, Emmerthal, Germany*

2BO.10.5 In-depth Characterization and Simulation Approach for the Understanding of   020064
In- and Outdoor Degradation of Perovskite Solar Cells

Jonathan Parion[1], Amit Kumar Harit[1], Elias Peraticos[2], Vasiliki Paraskeva[2], Maria Hadjipanayi[2], Aranzazu Aguirre[1], Filip Duerinckx[1], Hariharsudan

Sivaramakrishnan Radhakrishnan[1], Jef Poortmans[1], Johan Lauwaert[3], Bart Vermang[1]
[1] *Hasselt Unversity, Genk, Belgium;* [2] *University of Cyprus, Nicosia, Cyprus;* [3] *Ghent University, Ghent, Belgium*

Oral SESSION 2BO.8 Advanced Conversion Devices

Visual SESSION 2BV.1 New Materials, Devices and Conversion Concepts | New Modelling and Characterisation Techniques

Nathan Roosloot[1], Harsha Walpita[2], Christoph Seiffert[1], Jean Thomas[3], Maarten Dörenkämper[4], Minne M. de Jong[4], Josefine H. Selj[1], Gaute Otnes[1]
[1] Institute for Energy Technology, Kjeller, Norway; [2] University of Oslo, Kjeller, Norway; [3] Ciel et Terre, Lille, France; [4] TNO, Eindhoven, The Netherlands

Visual SESSION 3AV.3 PV Modules Characterisation and Performances Assessment

Nikolina Pervan[1], Jutta Geier[1], Christian Veas[1], Gernot Oreski[1]
[1] PCCL, Leoben, Austria

Oral SESSION 4CO.8 Soiling and Snow Effects in PV Systems

Oral SESSION 4CO.9 Data-driven and AI-based O&M of PV Systems

Srijani Mukherjee[1], Laurent Vuillon[2], Liliane Bou-Nassif[3], Stephanie Giroux-Julien[4], Herve Pabiou[3], Denys Dutykh[5], Ioannis (John) A. Tsanakas[1]
[1] CEA / INES, Le Bourget-du-Lac, France; [2] CNRS, Chambery, France; [3] CETHIL, Villeurbanne, France; [4] CNRS, Villeurbanne, France; [5] Khalifa University, Abu Dhabi, United Arab Emirates

Oral SESSION 4DO.1 PV Tracking and Simulation

*Marcus Rennhofer[1], Philipp Mayer-Ullmann[1], Diana Maria Krainer[1],
Gusztav Ujvari[1], Janine Lichtenberger[1], Konrad Kainz[1], Vassilissa Neussl[1],
Bernhard Kubicek[1]*
[1] AIT, Vienna, Austria

Visual SESSION 4DV.4 PV System Engineering

¹ Luxembourg Institute of Science and Technology, Esch-sur-Alzette, Luxembourg; ² University of Lisbon, Lisbon, Portugal

4EO.2.6 Optimizing Angular Performance of Curved VIPV Modules   020459

Francisco José Martín[1], Rebeca Herrero[1], Ignacio Antón[1]
[1] UPM, Madrid, Spain

Oral SESSION 5CO.4 Life Cycle Assessment of Silicon and Perovskite-based Cells and Modules

5CO.4.1 Towards Low-Impact Triple-Junction Perovskite/Silicon Tandem Modules: 020461
LCA of Precursor Materials to Describe the Influence of Background Data
Sources

Alejandra Galarza[1], Sebastian Nold[2], Lars Oberbeck[3]
[1] IPVF, Palaiseau, France; [2] Fraunhofer ISE, Freiburg, Germany; [3] TotalEnergies OneTech, Paris, France

5CO.4.3 Sustainability Assessment of Perovskite/Silicon Tandem Solar Modules: from 020462
Laboratory Scale to Industrial Implementation

Elisabetta Brivio[1], Andrea Danelli[1], Sofia Spagnolo[1], Pierpaolo Girardi[1]
[1] RSE, Milan, Italy

5CO.4.4 LCA Learning Curve for Crystalline Silicon Solar Technologies based on   020463
Technology Improvements

Julian Reichle[1], Moritz Fath[1], Sraisth[1], Amish Kumar Sinha[1], Mehul Raval[1], Wolfgang Jooss[1], Peter Fath[1], Gourab Das[1]
[1] RCT Solutions, Konstanz, Germany

Oral SESSION 5CO.5 Life Cycle Assessment of New PV Applications and Recycling

5CO.5.1 Optimizing AgriPV: A Comprehensive Assessment Framework for   020464
Sustainable Energy and Agriculture

Ana Patricia Lopes[1], Bruno Barrionuevo[2], Daniel P. Albuquerque[3], Diogo Cordeiro[4], Cláudia Fernandes[3], Athanasios T. Balafoutis[2], Rui Castro[1]
[1] University of Lisbon, Lisbon, Portugal; [2] CERTH, Athens, Greece; [3] Centre for New Energy Technologies, Sacavém, Portugal; [4] EDP, Lisbon, Portugal

5CO.5.2 Environmental Sustainability Assessment of Agrivoltaic Systems: a Life   020466
Cycle Approach

Maria Anna Cusenza[1], Andrea Danelli[1], Pierpaolo Girardi[1], Sofia Spagnolo[1]
[1] RSE, Milan, Italy

5CO.5.4 Closing the Circle: Integrating the Circular Footprint Formula into   020467
Photovoltaic System Life Cycle Assessment

Alexis Barrou[1], Selin Kandiyoti-Eskenazi[1], Jacques Levrat[1], Bertrand Paviet-Salomon[1], Christophe Ballif[1]
[1] CSEM, Neuchâtel, Switzerland

MODEL TESTS ON WATERLILY SHAPED OFFSHORE PV SYSTEM

Linda Kemp[1], Patrick Schrijvers, Naman Baderiya, William Otto
Maritime Research Institute Netherlands (MARIN)
(1) l.j.kemp@marin.nl

ABSTRACT: The European Union funded NATURSEA-PV project aims to develop a lily-inspired PV substructure solution to meet the specific needs for Offshore Floating PV. The substructure will be manufactured of a flexible, light and ecofriendly type of concrete which will give the substructure the advantages of flexibility and lightness to withstand offshore conditions. As part of the project, model scale tests on the flexible substructure are performed to capture the behavior of the substructure to waves. These basin tests are conducted in the MARIN shallow water basin at scale 1:30. To allow for numerical model validation, the tests are conducted using two sets of soft-mooring system to ensure that there is no interaction between the natural periods of the mooring system and wave frequencies. During irregular wave tests, different vertical behavior is observed at the outer ring of the substructure compared to the inner ring. Wave response is more extreme in high frequency ranges (smaller wave length) for the outer ring, which is related to the number of beams connected to the floater constraining the vertical motion. Strain measurements perpendicular to the longitudinal axis show the largest deformations, but this is not observed along the longitudinal axis. There is no exceedance of the air gap for the tested wave conditions. These basin tests demonstrate the validity of the original design, and serve as input for future numerical model validation.
Keywords: floating PV, basin test, validation, flexibility

1 INTRODUCTION

The European Union funded NATURSEA-PV project aims to develop a lily-inspired PV substructure solution to meet the specific needs for Offshore Floating PV. The lily's concept of radial and tangential girders is researched and engineered using flexible eco-Ultra High Performance Concrete (eco-UHPC) elements. The concrete girders will provide support to a lightweight sheet, which spans the construction like an umbrella. This sheet will have openings to ensure sufficient sunlight reaches the water surface, and it will provide sufficient carrying capacity for the PV panels as well as maintenance technicians [1].

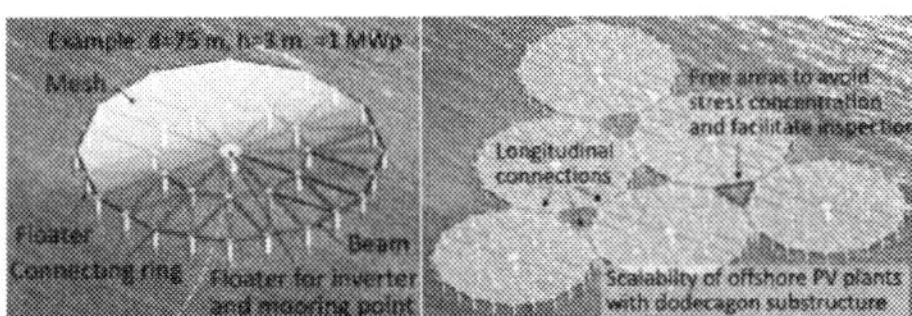

Figure 1: Conceptual Offshore floating PV (left) and scalability of the solution (right)

A conceptual and global design of the substructure was made, which serves as starting point of the prototype that is tested in a wave basin test campaign [2].

The main objectives of the test campaign are to validate the overall concept's performance, model the dynamic and flexible response of the floater and provide validation data for numerical tools [3].

Within the floating offshore PV different technologies are used, to harvest solar energy in harsh wave environments and strong winds [4]. To better understand the floating PV technologies, the concepts can be roughly distinguished into flexible membrane type concepts and hinge connected fixed floaters as well as into floating PV at the water surface or PV panels elevated above the water surface level. For example, the Solar@Sea concept consists of flexible floaters, where the PV panels are glued on top of the floaters [5]. Another membrane type floating PV on the water level is installed by company Ocean Sun in Norway inspired by fish farms [6]. The tested NATURSEA-PV concept is a combination of the a

flexible structure by the use of UHPC as the main material and an elevated shield of solar panels. The eco-UHPC is considered as an effective material with improved reliability and maintainability for offshore floating PV substructures [1].

2 EXPERIMENTAL SET-UP

2.1 Flexible model and instrumentation

The basin tests are conducted at a scale of 1:30, based on the general dimensions of the floater and the wave maker capabilities. The structure is a combination of 21 floaters, connected with two layers of beams to create an orthogonal design. The numbering of the floaters, and location of instrumentation is shown in Figure 2.

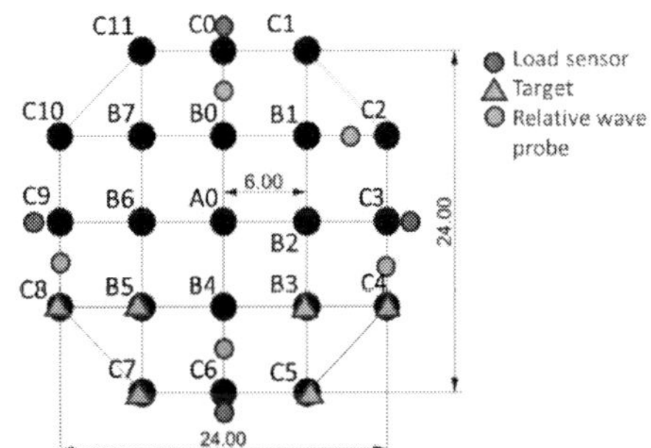

Figure 2: Floater numbering used for the substructure layout

The scale model is designed based on the required flexibility, dimensions and weight distribution of the prototype substructure. The material and dimensions of the beams are carefully selected to match the bending stiffness. PVC beams are used with a slightly smaller width at model scale, as this provided the closest match in the desired bending stiffness. The small deviation of 0.03m in beam width is considered acceptable at this stage of the project, since it is expected that modelling the correct bending stiffness is vital to the objectives of this project.

Bending tests are conducted on the individual beams to document the corresponding stiffness, which is used as input for the numerical modelling. In addition, a bending test on the complete substructure has been performed for numerical model validation (see Figure 3). The global flexibility of the model in the basin is shown in Figure 4.

Figure 3: Bending test on the global substructure

Figure 4: Flexibility of the global substructure shown in the basin (still from model test video, available at https://youtu.be/DLAIcCs89J8?si=1_RINsoFnwlfCwAV)

The instrumentation on the model consisted of motion measurement on 6 floaters, depicted by the green triangles in Figure 2. The NDI contact-less optical measurement system is used. Since the floater is flexible, the motions are measured at multiple locations. Resistance type wave probes are used to directly measure the airgap, and ring-shaped strain gauge force transducers are used to measure the loads from the soft-mooring system.

An optical fiber is used to directly measure strain differences on the flexible model. These optical fiber sensors have brass gratings at a specific position along the fiber, which reflects a specific wavelength of the incoming light. The remaining light travels to the next bragg grating with a slightly different bragg grating wave length. Since the wavelength changes when the fiber is stressed or compressed, this allows for a direct measurement of the strain.

2.2 Mooring system

During the model tests, a so-called horizontal soft spring mooing system was used to keep the model in position and at the specified heading. The system consists of 4 steel wired including linear springs. The lines are identical to avoid undesired coupling effects between modes of motion. The lines are oriented horizontally to a pulley and vertically up to the mooing points.

Two sets of springs are used. Set 1 has a theoretical horizontal stiffness of 41.5 kN/m and pretention of 271.5kN (surge and sway), which results in natural periods

of 14.0s. These periods are within the wave period for a white noise wave and two irregular waves. Therefore, the drift forces on the model may not be captured well.

A second set of springs has been used with stiffness of 7.5kN and a pretension of 135.7kN. These softer springs increase the natural periods to 24.1s, which is outside the wave frequency range and therefore won't affect the motion behavior of the model.

In order to achieve different model headings, the model is rotated. Two relative wave headings are considered during the tests.

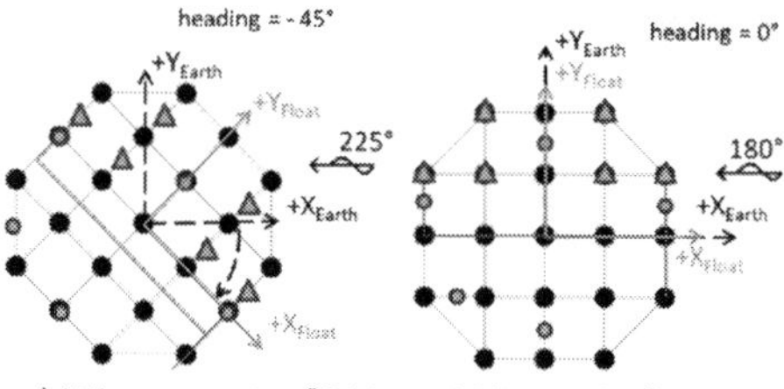

Figure 5: Floater with heading of -45 and 0 degrees.

2.3 MARIN's shallow water basin

Tests are conducted in the MARIN shallow water basin. The basin is 220m long, 15,8m wide and has a water depth of 1.0m. Waves can be generated from one side using a wave board. Both regular and irregular waves can be generated. The experiments are conducted at a fixed location, 30m from the wave generators. More information on the shallow water basin can be found at https://www.marin.nl/en/about/facilities-and-tools/basins/shallow-water-basin

2.4 Environmental conditions

Seven (7) regular waves are generated, ranging from H = 3.5m with period T of 5.7s to H=7.0m with T = 8.6s. Five (5) irregular JONSWAP waves are calibrated for a duration of 3½ hour, ranging from Hs = 0.8m with Tp = 4.5s to Hs = 5.3m with Tp = 12.50s. In addition, two white noise tests are generated with Hs = 2.0 and 4.0m

Table I: Calibrated Regular and Irregular waves

Environment	Duration	Wave characteristics		
Regular waves		H [m]	T [s]	
Reg. wave 5		3.52	5.7	
Reg. wave 6		4.50	6.4	
Reg. wave 7	~20 oscillations	5.40	7.0	
Reg. wave 8		6.26	7.6	
Reg. wave 9		7.06	8.1	
Reg. wave 10		6.86	9.0	
Reg. wave 11		7.04	8.6	
Irregular waves		H_s [m]	T_P [s]	γ [-]
Irreg. wave 1		5.416	12.566	3.3
Irreg. wave 2		3.329	12.566	3.3
Irreg. wave 3	½ + 3 hr	3.807	10.472	3.3
Irreg. wave 4		1.824	8.490	3.3
Irreg. wave 5		0.771	4.525	3.3
White noise 1	½ + 1 hr	1.965	5-20	1.0
White noise 2		3.987	5-20	1.0

The calibrated regular and irregular wave conditions (see Table I) are calibrated prior to the actual model tests, without the model in the basin. The wave elevations are measured by means of resistance wire wave probes, placed at the centre of the test set-up and at one additional reference position. The reference wave probe remains at its location in the test set-up for the entire duration of the model test project. The deviations between requested and measured wave height was less than 2% for all waves.

3 BASIN TEST RESULTS

3.1 Verification tests

The mooring stiffness was verified using static pull out tests, where a surge offset is applied to the substructure in three distinct steps. The applied external load, loads in the mooring lines and global translation and rotation are measured. The measured inline mooring forces and pull out force magnitudes are reported in figure 6. The mooring forces show linear trends with increasing external load, and the theoretical stiffness of 41.5 kN/m is matching well with the as-build mooring system.

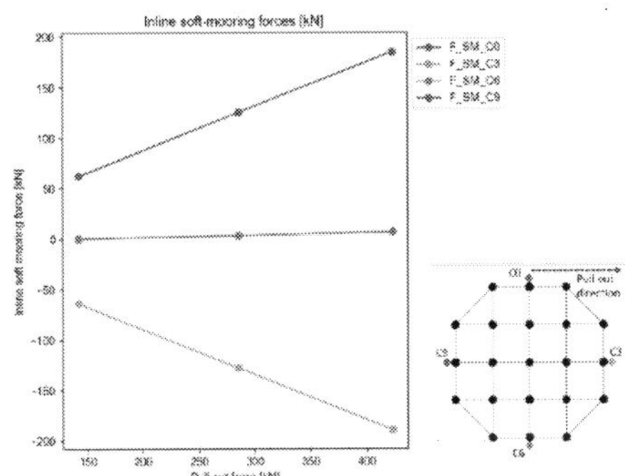

Figure 6: Soft-mooring forces during pull-out tests.

Decay tests were conducted to verify the natural periods. Two free floating heave decays were conducted, surge, sway and heave decay tests are conducted for the moored system. From these tests, the natural periods and where possible the linear and quadratic damping were analyzed. The free floating heave decays show a clear damped oscillation for the first four to five oscillations, after which non-linear response of the system affects the heave oscillations at the floaters in the first ring (B3 and B5) around the initial position of the decay.

During the decay tests, the oscillations of the different instrumented targets do not show clear differences. Figure 7 shows the heave response of the 6 instrumented floaters in one of the performed heave decay tests. The natural heave periods of the individual floaters are within 2% of the average value of the floaters. Also, the linear damping (P) and quadratic damping (Q) coefficients show a clear relation to the floater positions or motions. The heave decays are initialized by a positive heave offset, applied to the middle floater (A0). This initial offset causes a high strain value at the optical fiber measurement locations close to the attachment point. The strain magnitude decreases for measurement points further from the attachment point. No clear bending eigenmodes of the substructure are observed during the heave decay tests.

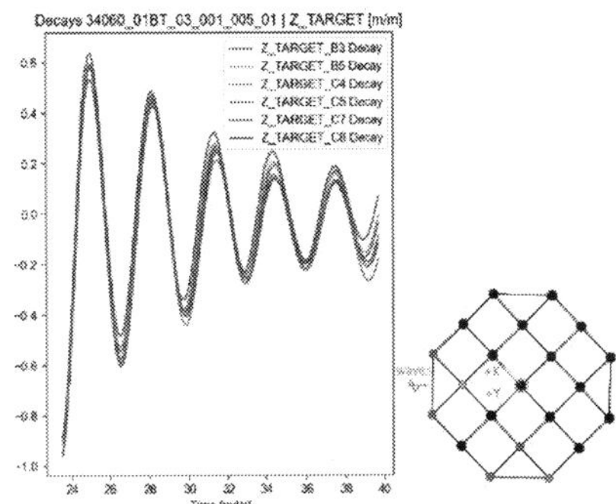

Figure 7: Heave decay measured at 6 floater positions, heave applied to floater C0 with a +Z offset

3.1 Motions and deformation

The Response Amplitude Operator (RAO) of the different floaters within one test are compared. For a model heading of 0 degrees, the substructure shows rigid body pitch, surge and yaw response. For heave, there is a clear distinction between the outer ring floaters and inner ring floaters (see figure 8). For low frequencies, the RAO is approximately 1 m/m, but increases for the higher frequency range for floaters C4 and C8 in the outer ring. This difference is related to the beam layout of the individual floaters. The floaters in the outer ring are restrained by 3 beams, while the floaters in the inner ring are restrained by 4 beams, limiting the vertical motion of these floaters.

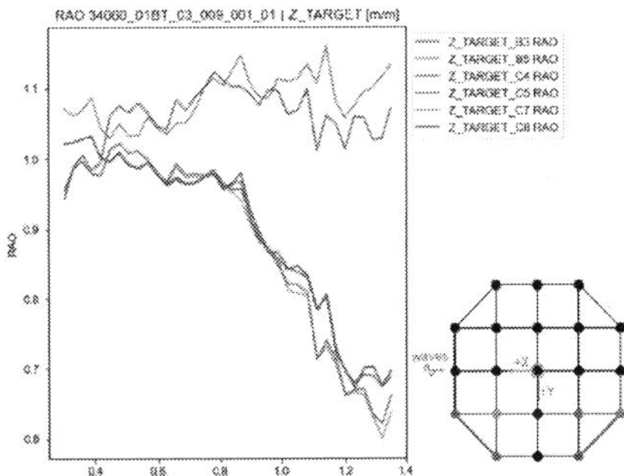

Figure 8: Heave RAO for a white noise test.

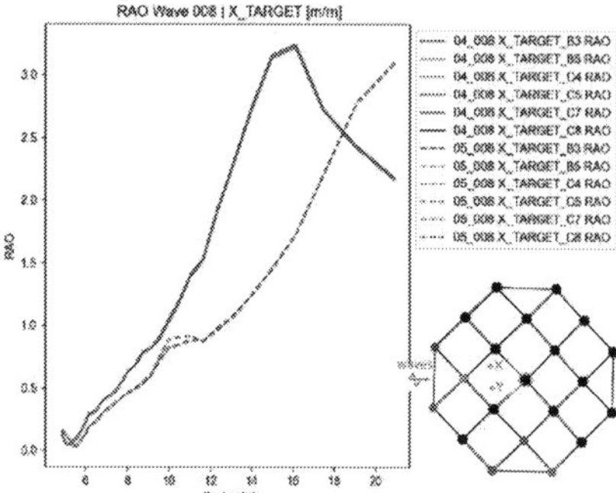

Figure 9: Surge RAO for a white noise test as a result of different soft mooring systems. The solid line represents the soft mooring system with eigen period of 14.0 s, while the dashed line represents the system with eigen period of 24.1s.

In Figure 9 the RAO of body surge is compared for two different set of soft mooring spring systems. The natural period for surge of the original soft mooring system with a stiffness of 41.5 kN/m (indicated by solid lines) shows a clear response around 14.0 seconds. The second set of springs with surge stiffness of 17.0 kN the natural period is outside the wave frequent period, around 24.1 seconds and is therefore not visible in Figure 9.

3.2 Relative wave elevations

One of the design constraints was a positive air gap, meaning that there is no impact or green water event on the solar panel system. For each irregular wave test, the airgap is calculated, which shows a positive value for each tests. The smallest recorded airgap was 1.32m at the leading side of the substructure. A still of the video recording is shown in Figure 10.

Figure 10: still of wave test recording with smallest positive airgap.

3.3 Measured strain

The FBG optical fiber is used to measure microstrain in the centerline of the substructure. The strain response is converted to a RAO along this centerline per meter incoming wave. The overall strain response on the top beam is higher for 0 degree heading, when the bending strain is in-line with the wave direction (see Figure 11). The highest strain is measured at the waveward side of the substructure (the 'bow'), and decreases further for the locations further towards the 'stern'. Based on the motion response in regular waves, no clear resonance in bending motions is observed.

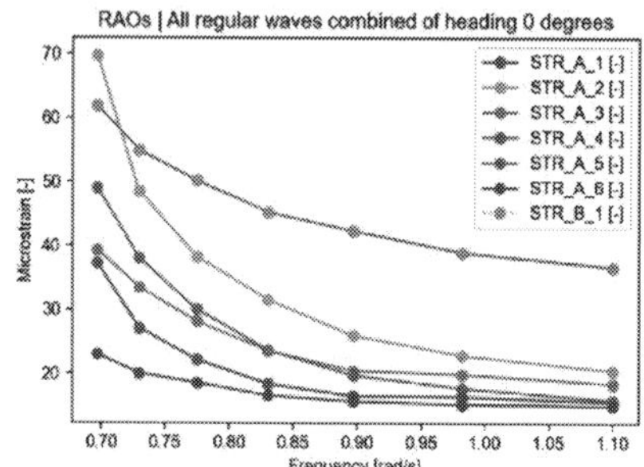

Figure 11: Microstrain response to the incoming regular wave at 7 different positions.

4   CONCLUDING REMARKS

Basin tests were executed to test and validate the lily-shaped floating offshore PV system in relevant environmental conditions. A flexible model-scale substructure was engineered, closely representing the overall concept. The beams were build from PVC with a slightly smaller width at model-scale, such that the bending stiffness of the beams matched between model-scale and prototype scale.

The basin tests demonstrated that the overall concept performance is as expected from the general design. The flexible model-scale substructure did not experience any wave impact loads on the solar deck, with a positive airgap of at least 1.3m. The dynamic beam loads remained below the capacity of the beam - in other words: the substructure did not break.

Emphasis was placed during the basin tests on verification tests, to ensure that the obtained dataset can be used for numerical model calibration and validation. In addition to multiple motion sensors, a novel fiber optical measurement system was used to directly measure the strain in the substructure. This high quality dataset allows to further improve the numerical model that was used for the first design. This work is ongoing.

FUNDING

This work is part of the NATURSEA-PV project, funded by the HORIZON-CL5-2021-D3-03-10 program with grant agreement number 101084348. MARIN would like to thank all parties in the NATURSEA-PV project for their valuable contributions and discussions in the design and testing of the substructure.

DATA AVAILIBITY STATEMENT
The full dataset of the model tests can be accessed through https://doi.org/10.5281/zenodo.17047051 (accessed on 4/9/2025).

5   REFERENCES

[1] Fundación Tecnalia Research and Innovation, "Proposal NATURSEA-PV - Part B," Derio, 2022.

[2] N. Baderiya and W. Otto, "D1.2 Design of Substructure," NATURSEA-PV, Wageningen, 2024.

[3] L. Kemp, N. Baderiya, R. Heijmen and E. Linnartz, "D4.1 Substructure Model Tests," NATURSEA-PV, Wageningen, 2024.

[4] E. Solomin, E. Sirotkin, E. Cuce, S. Selvanathan and S. Kumarasamy, "Hybrid Floating Solar Plant

Designs: A Review," *Energies,* vol. 14, no. 2751, 2021.

[5] W. Otto, T. Bunnik and L. Kaydihan, "Hydro-Elastic Behavior of an Inflatable Mattress in Waves," in *9th International Conference on Hydroelsticity in Maritime Technology*, Rome, 2022.

[6] Ocean Sun, "About Ocean Sun," Ocean Sun, [Online]. Available: https://oceansun.no/about/. [Accessed 22 08 2025].

NATURSEA-PV

NOVEL ECO-CEMENTITIOUS MATERIALS AND COMPONENTS FOR DURABLE, COMPETITIVE, AND BIO-INSPIRED OFFSHORE FLOATING PV SUBSTRUCTURES

EU PVSEC | Session 4DO.4

25th September 2025 | Bilbao, Spain

Linda Kemp
(MARIN)

"Funded by the European Union. Views and opinions expressed are however those of the author(s) only and do not necessarily reflect those of the European Union or the European Climate Infrastructure and Environment Executive Agency (CINEA). Neither the European Union nor the granting authority can be held responsible for them."

Funded by the
European Union

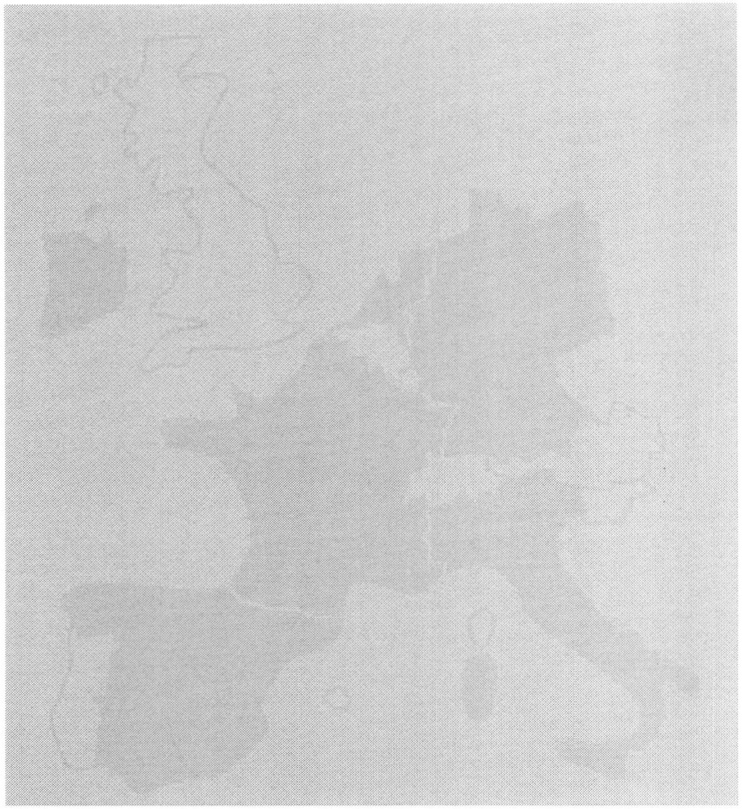

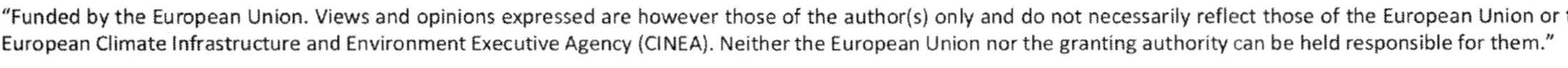

Partners

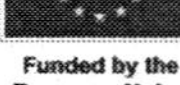
"Funded by the European Union. Views and opinions expressed are however those of the author(s) only and do not necessarily reflect those of the European Union or the European Climate Infrastructure and Environment Executive Agency (CINEA). Neither the European Union nor the granting authority can be held responsible for them."

NATURSEA-PV

Our approach

The substructures will be built using newly developed environmentally friendly low carbon **ultra-high performance concrete**, and it will be coated with new biobased antifouling and anticorrosive coatings.

The lily's concept of radial and tangential girders will take advantage of the **flexibility and lightness** of the new eco-concretes to withstand the harsh offshore metocean conditions.

The computational toolkit will serve to optimize materials properties and plan timely maintenance operations.

Victoria Amazonica (left) showing underside of a leaf (right)

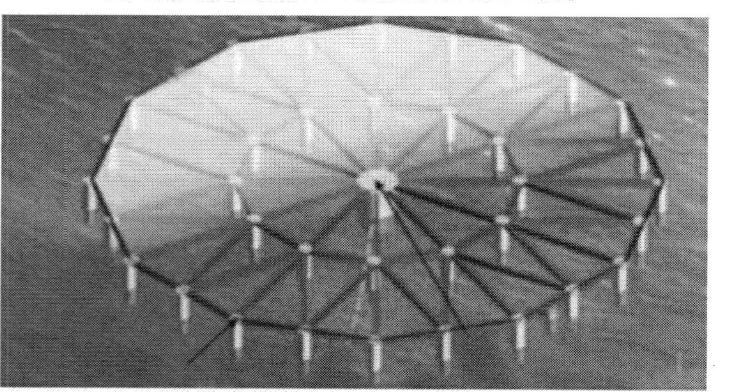

Conceptual Offshore Floating PV sideview

"Funded by the European Union. Views and opinions expressed are however those of the author(s) only and do not necessarily reflect those of the European Union or the European Climate Infrastructure and Environment Executive Agency (CINEA). Neither the European Union nor the granting authority can be held responsible for them."

Funded by the European Union

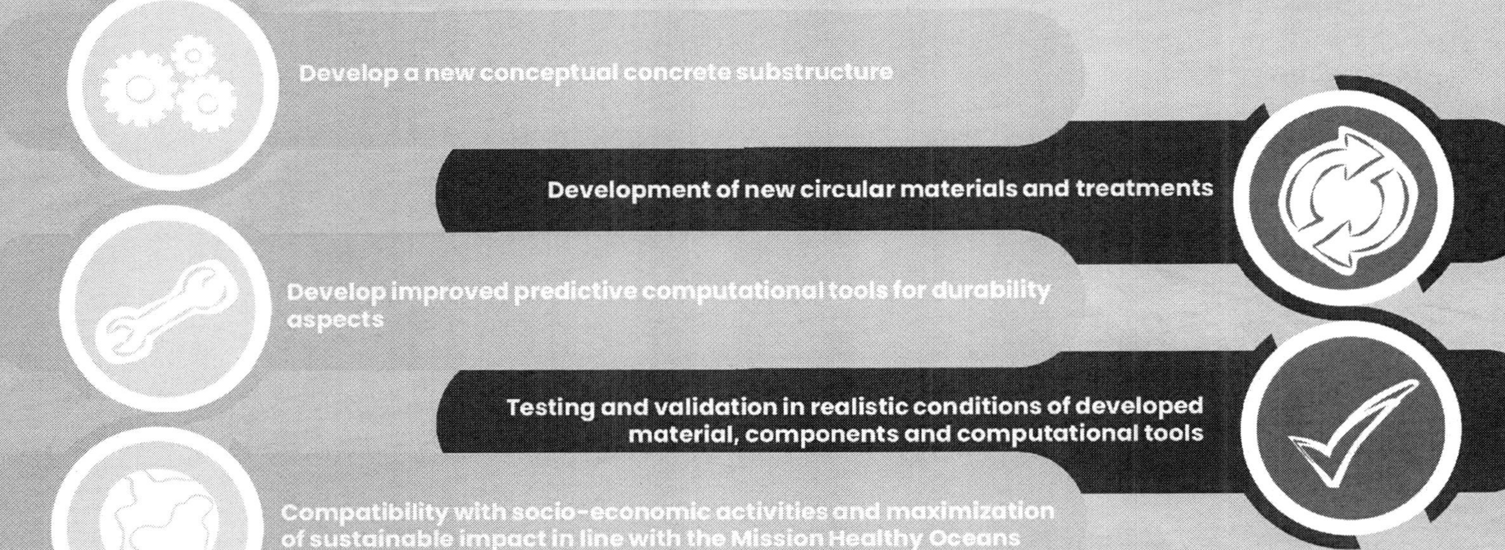

Objectives
NATURSEA-PV
Develop a new conceptual concrete substructure
Development of new circular materials and treatments
Develop improved predictive computational tools for durability aspects
Testing and validation in realistic conditions of developed material, components and computational tools
Compatibility with socio-economic activities and maximization of sustainable impact in line with the Mission Healthy Oceans

Funded by the
European Union

Experimental setup
Model and instrumentation

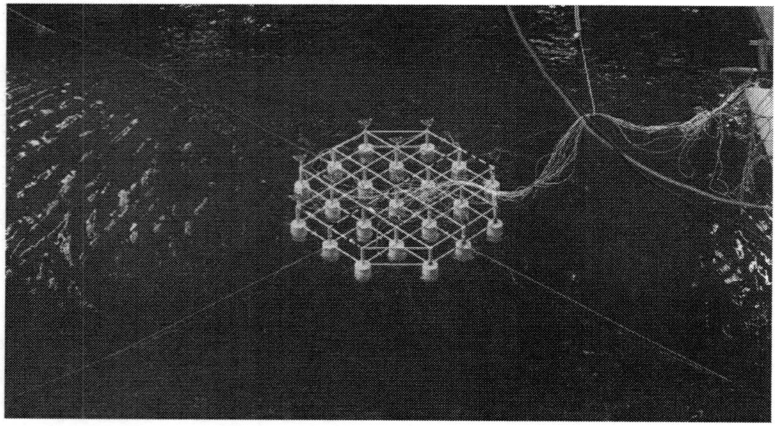

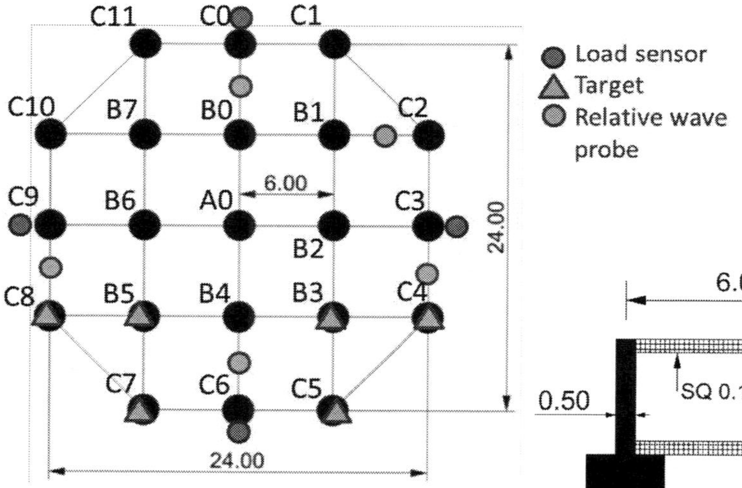

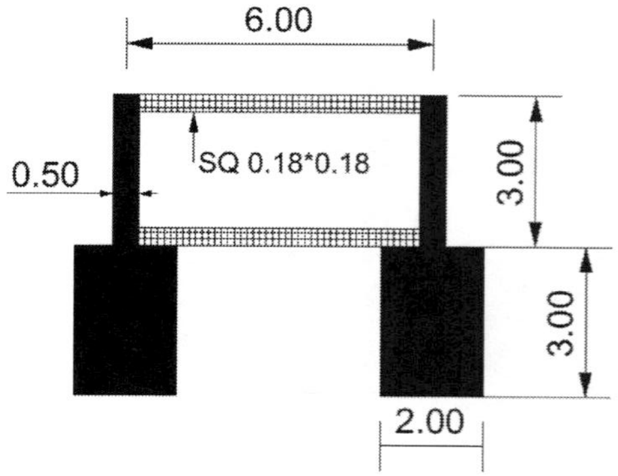

NATURSEA-PV

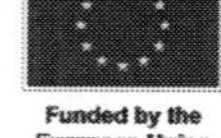

"Funded by the European Union. Views and opinions expressed are however those of the author(s) only and do not necessarily reflect those of the European Union or the European Climate Infrastructure and Environment Executive Agency (CINEA). Neither the European Union nor the granting authority can be held responsible for them."

Funded by the
European Union

NATURSEA-PV

Experimental setup
Flexibility modelling

(Dry) Flexibility Test

(Wet) Flexibility demonstration

Experimental setup
Test Basin & Wave Conditions

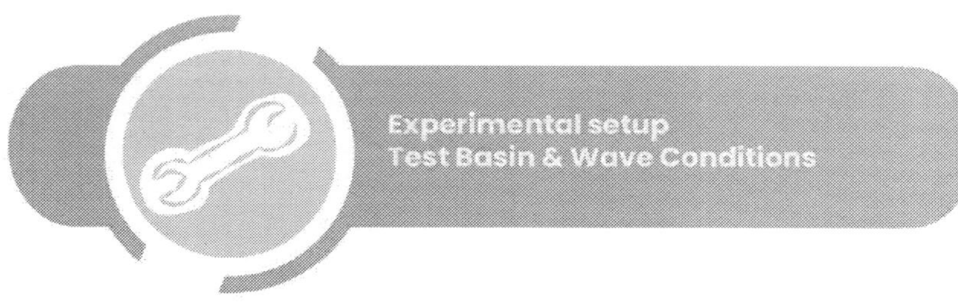

Environment	Duration	Wave characteristics		
Regular waves		H [m]	T [s]	
Reg. wave 5	~20 oscillations	3.52	5.7	
Reg. wave 6		4.50	6.4	
Reg. wave 7		5.40	7.0	
Reg. wave 8		6.26	7.6	
Reg. wave 9		7.06	8.1	
Reg. wave 10		6.86	9.0	
Reg. wave 11		7.04	8.6	
Irregular waves		H_s [m]	T_p [s]	γ [-]
Irreg. wave 1	½ + 3 hr	5.416	12.566	3.3
Irreg. wave 2		3.329	12.566	3.3
Irreg. wave 3		3.807	10.472	3.3
Irreg. wave 4		1.824	8.490	3.3
Irreg. wave 5		0.771	4.525	3.3
White noise 1	½ + 1 hr	1.965	5-20	1.0
White noise 2		3.987	5-20	1.0

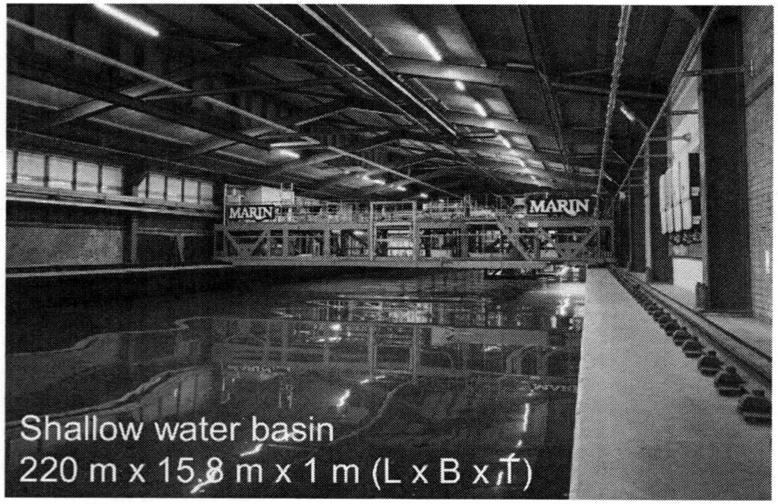

"Funded by the European Union. Views and opinions expressed are however those of the author(s) only and do not necessarily reflect those of the European Union or the European Climate Infrastructure and Environment Executive Agency (CINEA). Neither the European Union nor the granting authority can be held responsible for them."

Funded by the European Union

MARIN
NATURSEA-PV

Heave decay tests – Offset applied to floater A0 (+Z)

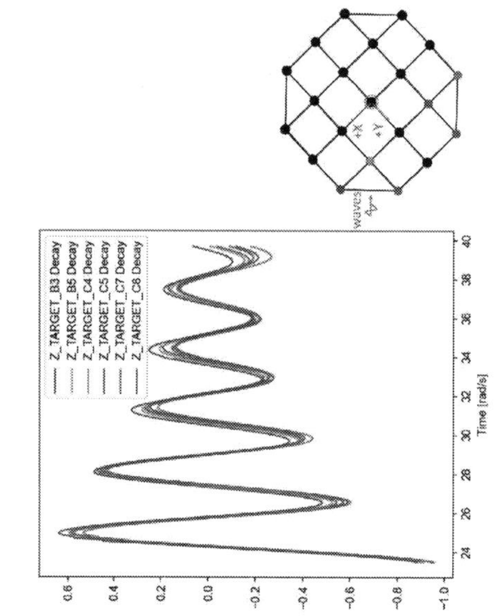

Mooring system verification – Pull out tests

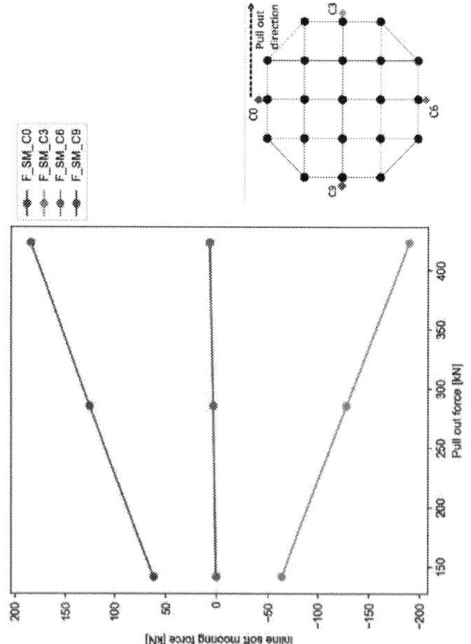

"Funded by the European Union. Views and opinions expressed are however those of the author(s) only and do not necessarily reflect those of the European Union or the European Climate Infrastructure and Environment Executive Agency (CINEA). Neither the European Union nor the granting authority can be held responsible for them."

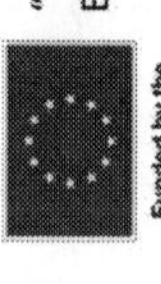

020391-009

42nd European Photovoltaic Solar Energy Conference and Exhibition

Relative Amplitude Operator – Horizontal motions (surge) in two different mooring systems

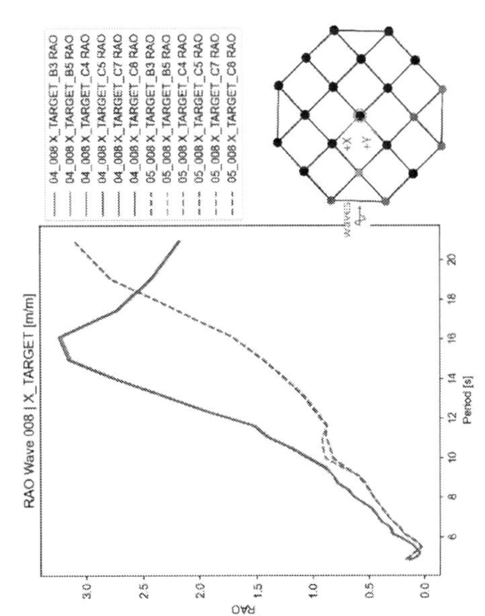

Relative Amplitude Operator – Vertical motions (heave)

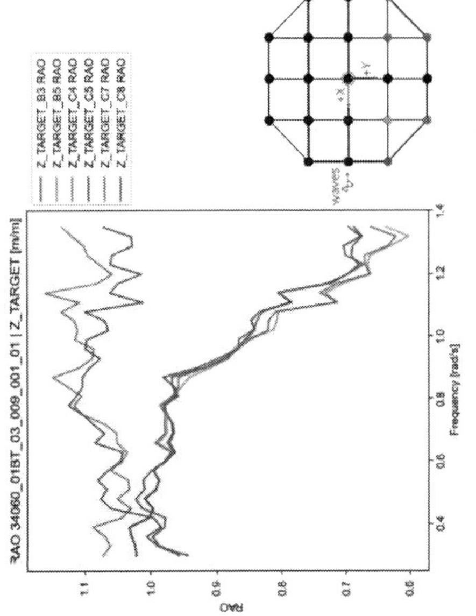

"Funded by the European Union. Views and opinions expressed are however those of the author(s) only and do not necessarily reflect those of the European Union or the European Climate Infrastructure and Environment Executive Agency (CINEA). Neither the European Union nor the granting authority can be held responsible for them."

020391-010

42nd European Photovoltaic Solar Energy Conference and Exhibition

NATURSEA-PV

Basin Test Results
Relative wave elevations & Strain

Strain measurements in Regular Wave tests

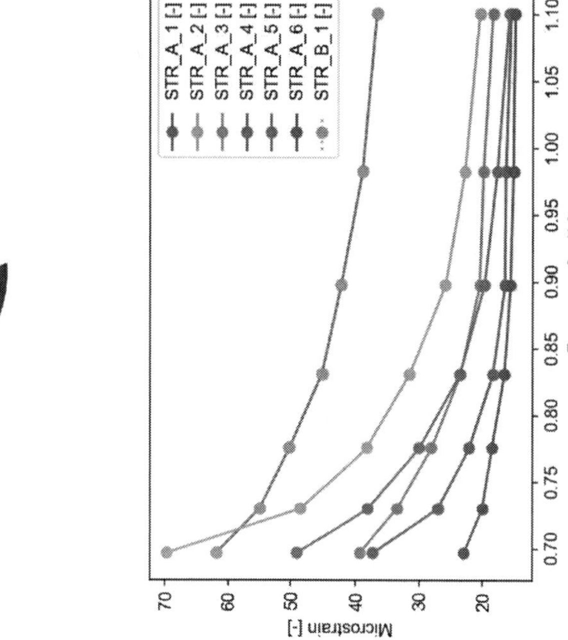

Still from model test with airgap minimum

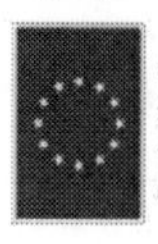

"Funded by the European Union. Views and opinions expressed are however those of the author(s) only and do not necessarily reflect those of the European Union or the European Climate Infrastructure and Environment Executive Agency (CINEA). Neither the European Union nor the granting authority can be held responsible for them."

Funded by the European Union

020391-011

Concluding remarks

- A flexible model-scale substructure was engineered, closely representing the overall concept.

- The basin tests demonstrated that the overall concept performance is as expected from the general design.

- Emphasis was placed during the basin tests on verification tests, to ensure that the obtained dataset can be used for numerical model calibration and validation. This high-quality dataset allows to further improve the numerical model that was used for the first design. This work is ongoing.

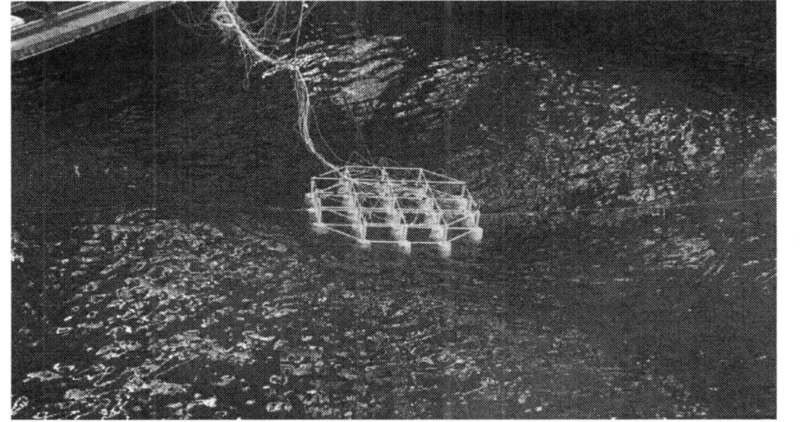

"Funded by the European Union. Views and opinions expressed are however those of the author(s) only and do not necessarily reflect those of the European Union or the European Climate Infrastructure and Environment Executive Agency (CINEA). Neither the European Union nor the granting authority can be held responsible for them."

Funded by the
European Union

NATURSEA-PV

NOVEL ECO-CEMENTITIOUS MATERIALS AND COMPONENTS FOR DURABLE, COMPETITIVE, AND BIO-INSPIRED OFFSHORE FLOATING PV SUBSTRUCTURES

THANKS FOR YOUR ATTENTION

Visit our website!

www.natursea-pv.eu

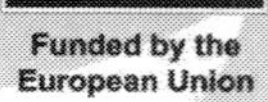 "Funded by the European Union. Views and opinions expressed are however those of the author(s) only and do not necessarily reflect those of the European Union or the European Climate Infrastructure and Environment Executive Agency (CINEA). Neither the European Union nor the granting authority can be held responsible for them."

Funded by the European Union

DEVELOPMENT AND EVALUATION OF AGRIVOLTAIC SYSTEMS IN OLIVE GROVES BASED ON A NOVEL SMART TRACKING ALGORITHM

Ildefonso Muñoz[1], Irati Amatriain[1], Gregorio Olivares[1], Gillen Abrego[2], Eusebio Gainza[2], Iñaki Cornago[1]

[1] CENER, National Renewable Energy Centre
[2] ALLOTARRA, Association for Organic Agriculture and Livestock

42nd European Photovoltaic Solar Energy Conference and Exhibition
25.09.2025

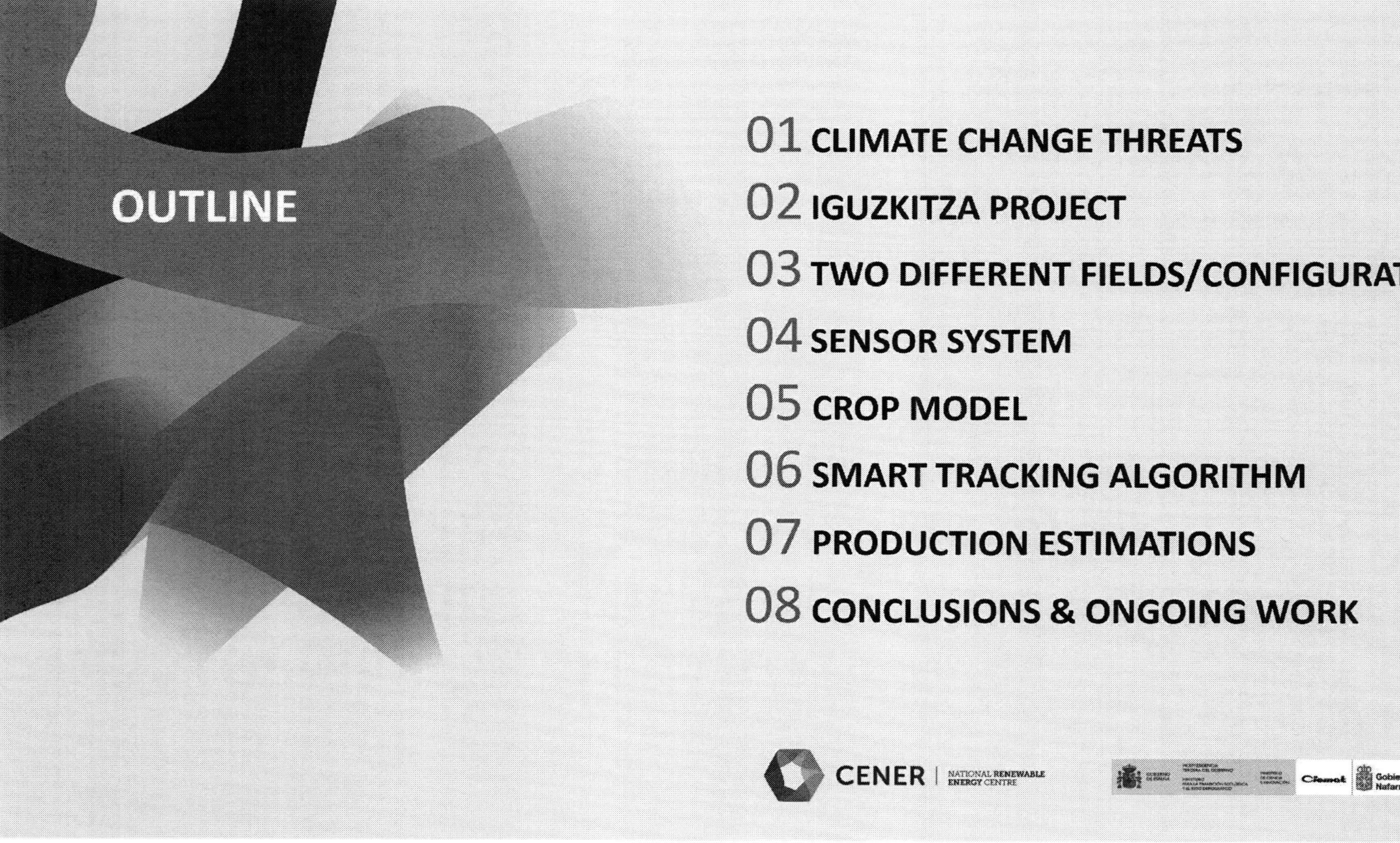

OUTLINE
01 CLIMATE CHANGE THREATS
02 IGUZKITZA PROJECT
03 TWO DIFFERENT FIELDS/CONFIGURATIONS
04 SENSOR SYSTEM
05 CROP MODEL
06 SMART TRACKING ALGORITHM
07 PRODUCTION ESTIMATIONS
08 CONCLUSIONS & ONGOING WORK
CENER | NATIONAL RENEWABLE ENERGY CENTRE
Gobierno de Navarra
Nafarroako Gobernua

01 CLIMATE CHANGE THREATS

- Olive Groves: Well adapted to Mediterranean climate and resilience to water scarcity
- However, olives trees are being affected by effects of climatic change:
  - Increase of solar irradiance
  - Higher temperatures
  - Extreme weather events (droughts, heavy rainfall, hailstorms)

- AgriPV techniques could mitigate this effects

CENER | NATIONAL RENEWABLE ENERGY CENTRE

Gobierno de Navarra Nafarroako Gobernua

020392-003

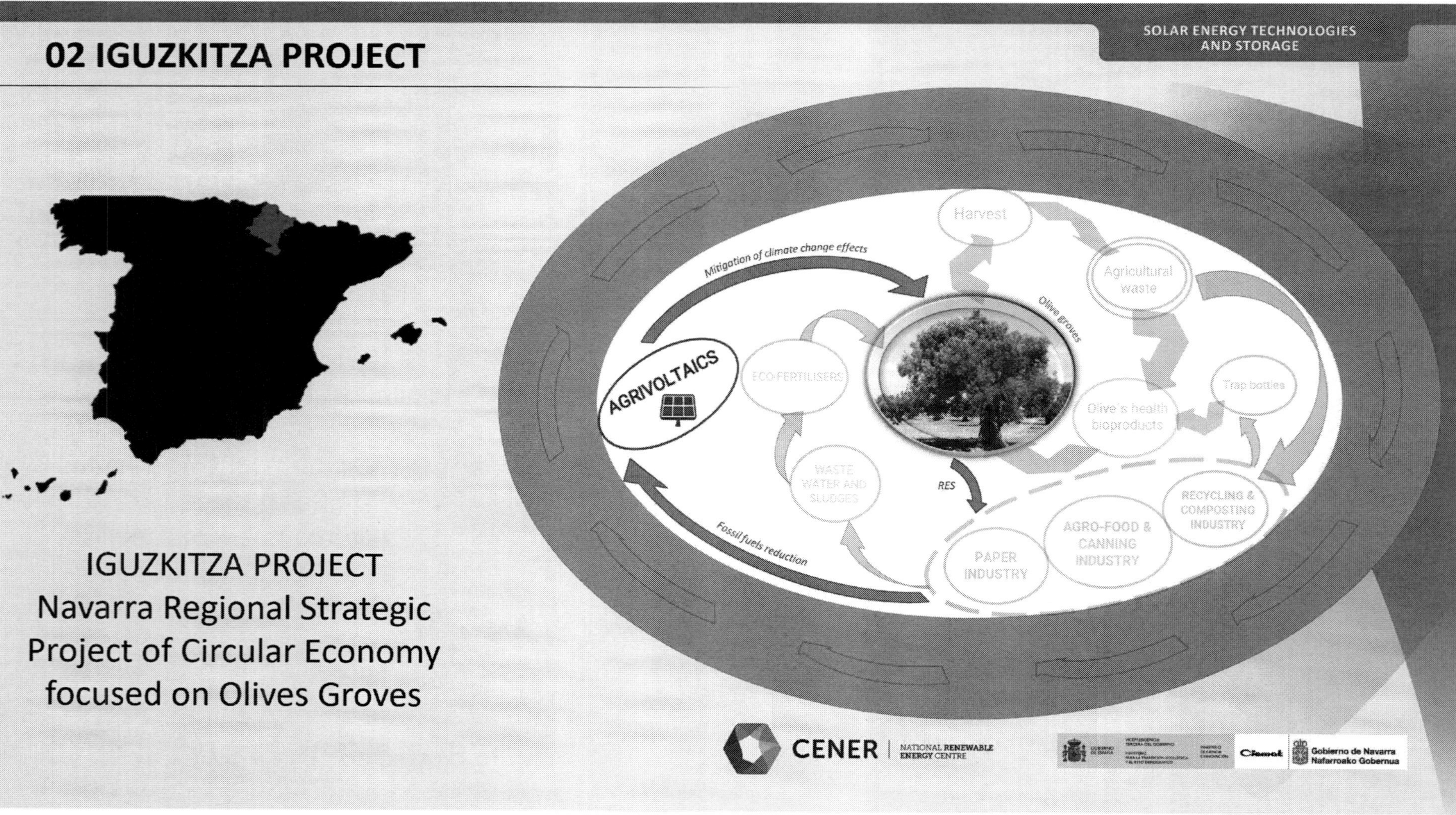

02 IGUZKITZA PROJECT
SOLAR ENERGY TECHNOLOGIES AND STORAGE
IGUZKITZA PROJECT
Navarra Regional Strategic Project of Circular Economy focused on Olives Groves
Mitigation of climate change effects
Olive groves
Harvest
Agricultural waste
Trap bottles
Olive's health bioproducts
RES
RECYCLING & COMPOSTING INDUSTRY
AGRO-FOOD & CANNING INDUSTRY
PAPER INDUSTRY
WASTE WATER AND SLUDGES
ECO-FERTILISERS
AGRIVOLTAICS
Fossil fuels reduction
CENER | NATIONAL RENEWABLE ENERGY CENTRE
Gobierno de Navarra Nafarroako Gobernua

03(1) TWO DIFFERENT FIELDS

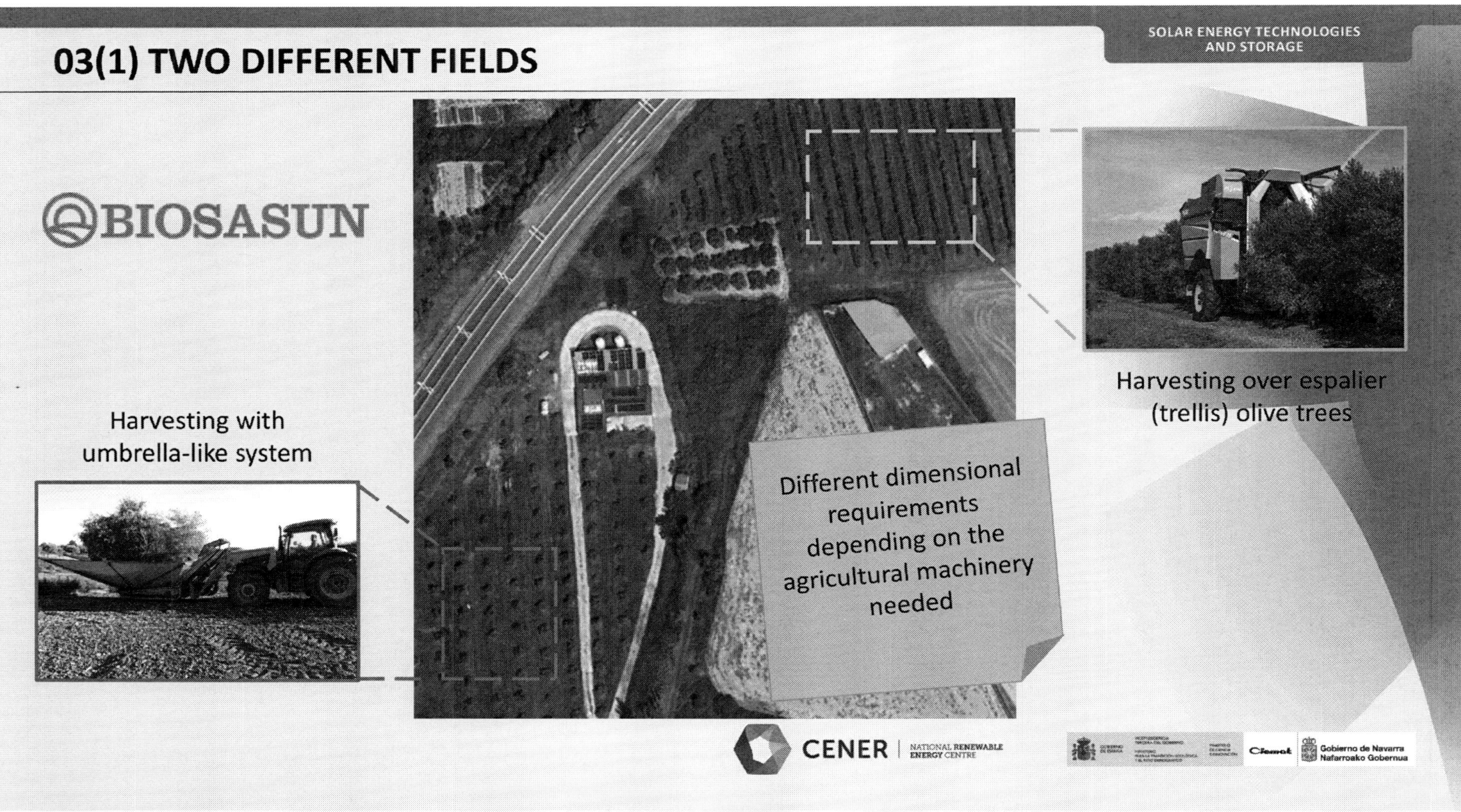

020392-005

03(2) TWO DIFFERENT CONFIGURATIONS

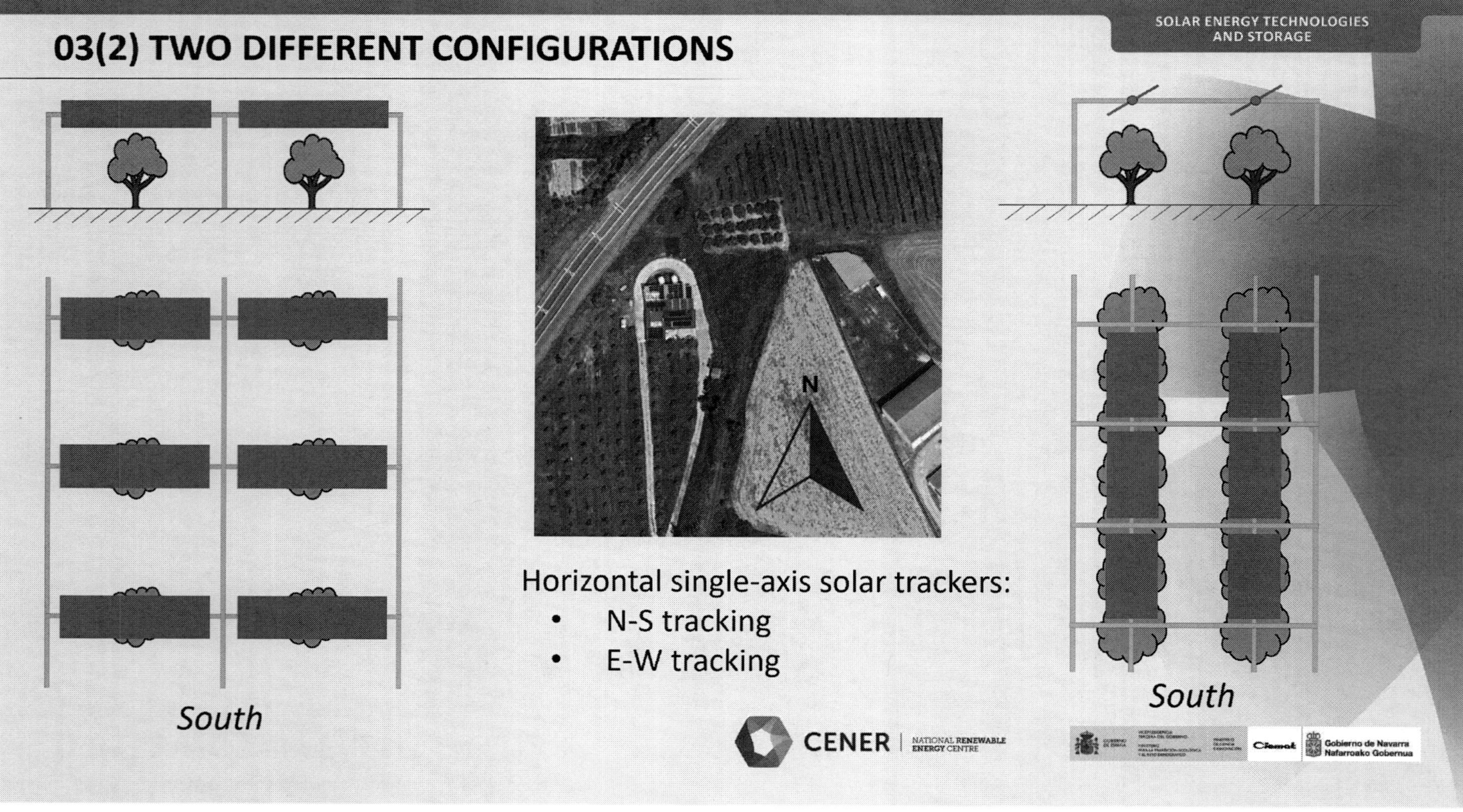

03(3) TWO DIFFERENT MECHANICAL DESIGNS

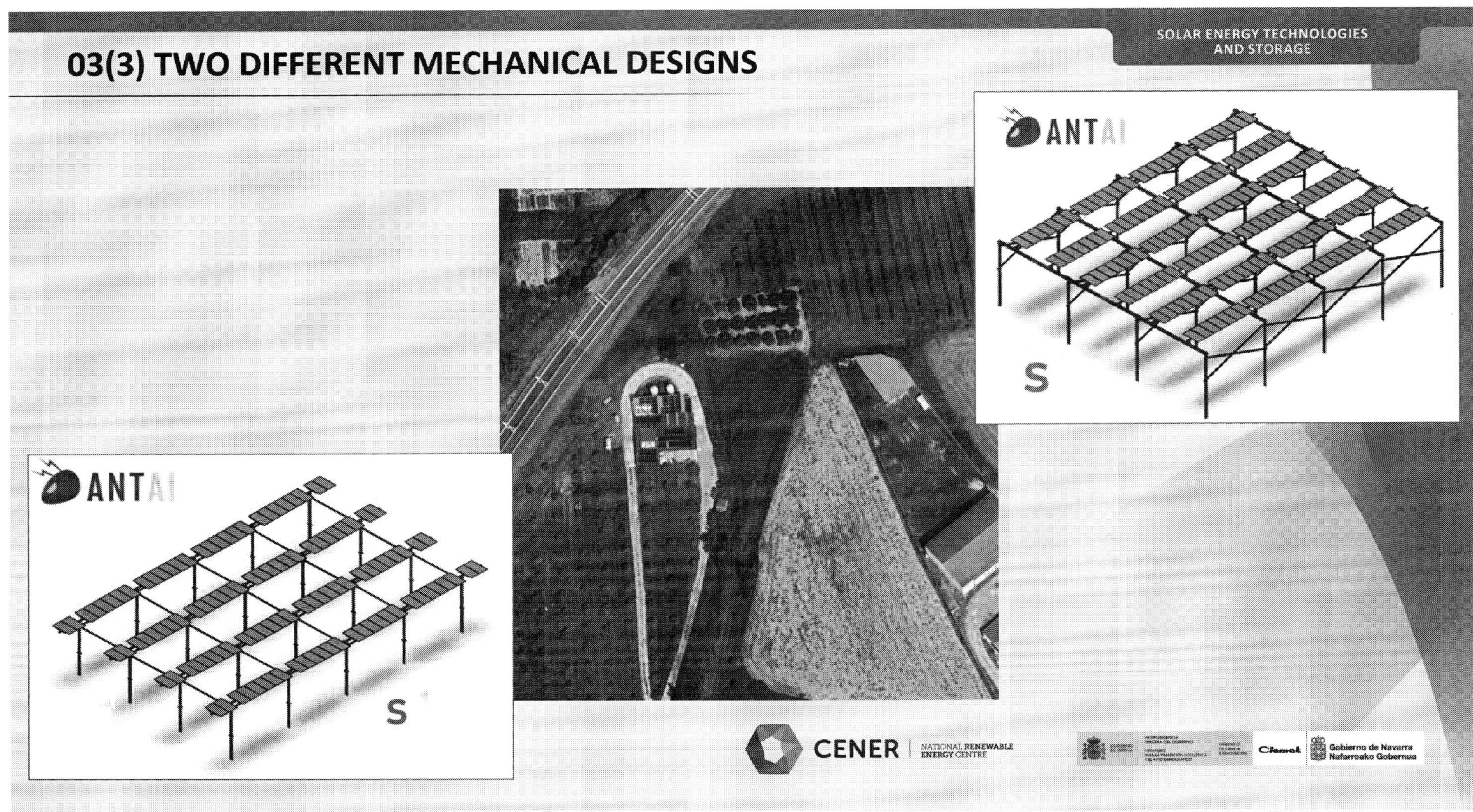

04 SENSOR SYSTEM

- 5 pyranometers
- 5 PAR
- 2 wind speed and direction
- 1 precipitation
- 1 snow
- 5 ambient temperature & RH
- 6 soil temperature & RH
- 8 dendrometers

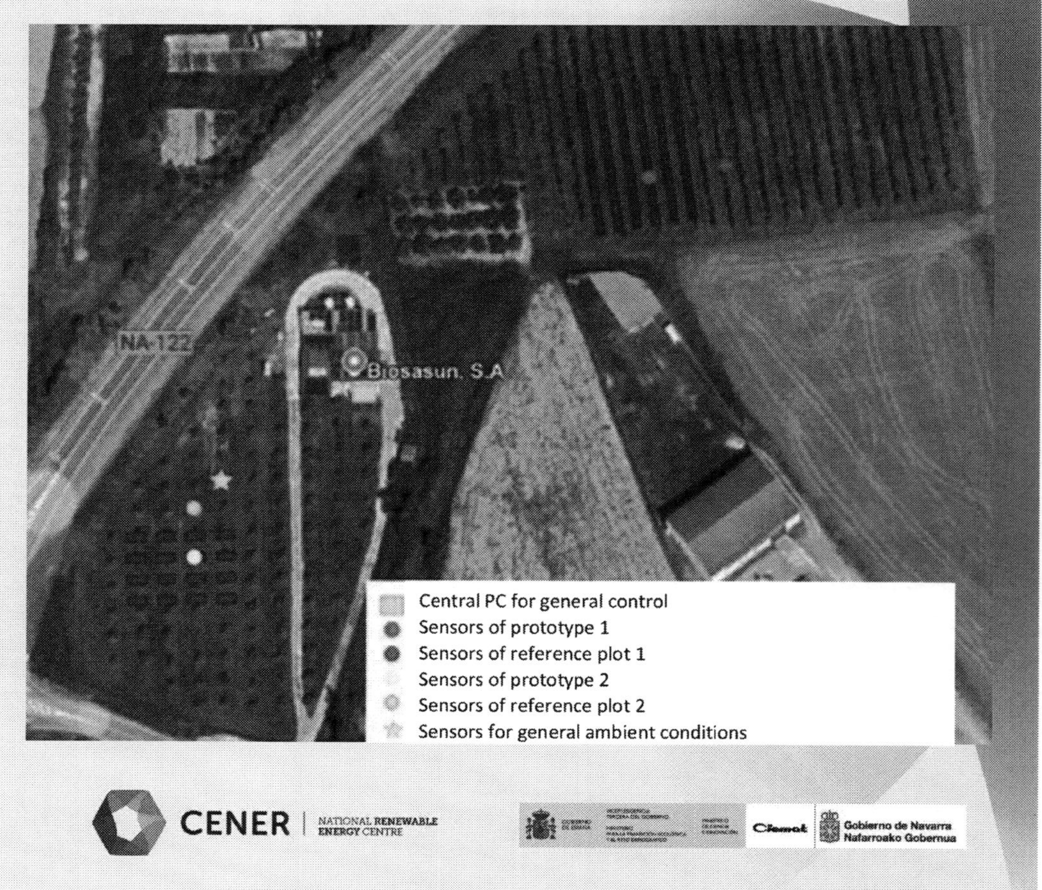

CENER | NATIONAL RENEWABLE ENERGY CENTRE

Gobierno de Navarra
Nafarroako Gobernua

05(1) CROP MODEL

SIMPLE model (C. Zhao et al. 2019) adapted to project needs

$$Biomass_{rate} = Radiation \cdot fSolar \cdot RUE \cdot f(CO_2) \cdot f(Temp) \cdot \min[f(Heat), f(Water)]$$

- PAR $\rightarrow$ A. García-Rodríguez methodology
- $fSolar$ $\rightarrow$ F. Orgaz model
- RUE $\rightarrow$ F. J. Villalobos proposal
- $f(Temp)$ $\rightarrow$ SIMPLE model from C. Zhao et. Al.
- $\min[f(Heat), f(Water)]$ $\rightarrow$ SIMPLE model from C. Zhao et. Al.
- $f(PAR)$ $\rightarrow$ IdAB-CSIC (project partner)

$$Biomass_{rate} = PAR \cdot fSolar \cdot RUE \cdot f(Temp) \cdot \min[f(Heat), f(Water)] \cdot f(PAR)$$

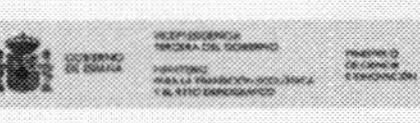

CENER | NATIONAL RENEWABLE ENERGY CENTRE

Gobierno de Navarra
Nafarroako Gobernua

05(2) CROP MODEL

Olive trees shading approach (PAR collected by olive tree surface)

1. Geometric representation of polygonal spheres

2. Calculation of shading for every polygon, which are considered different planes

3. Weighted sum of all planes

06 SMART TRACKING ALGORITHM

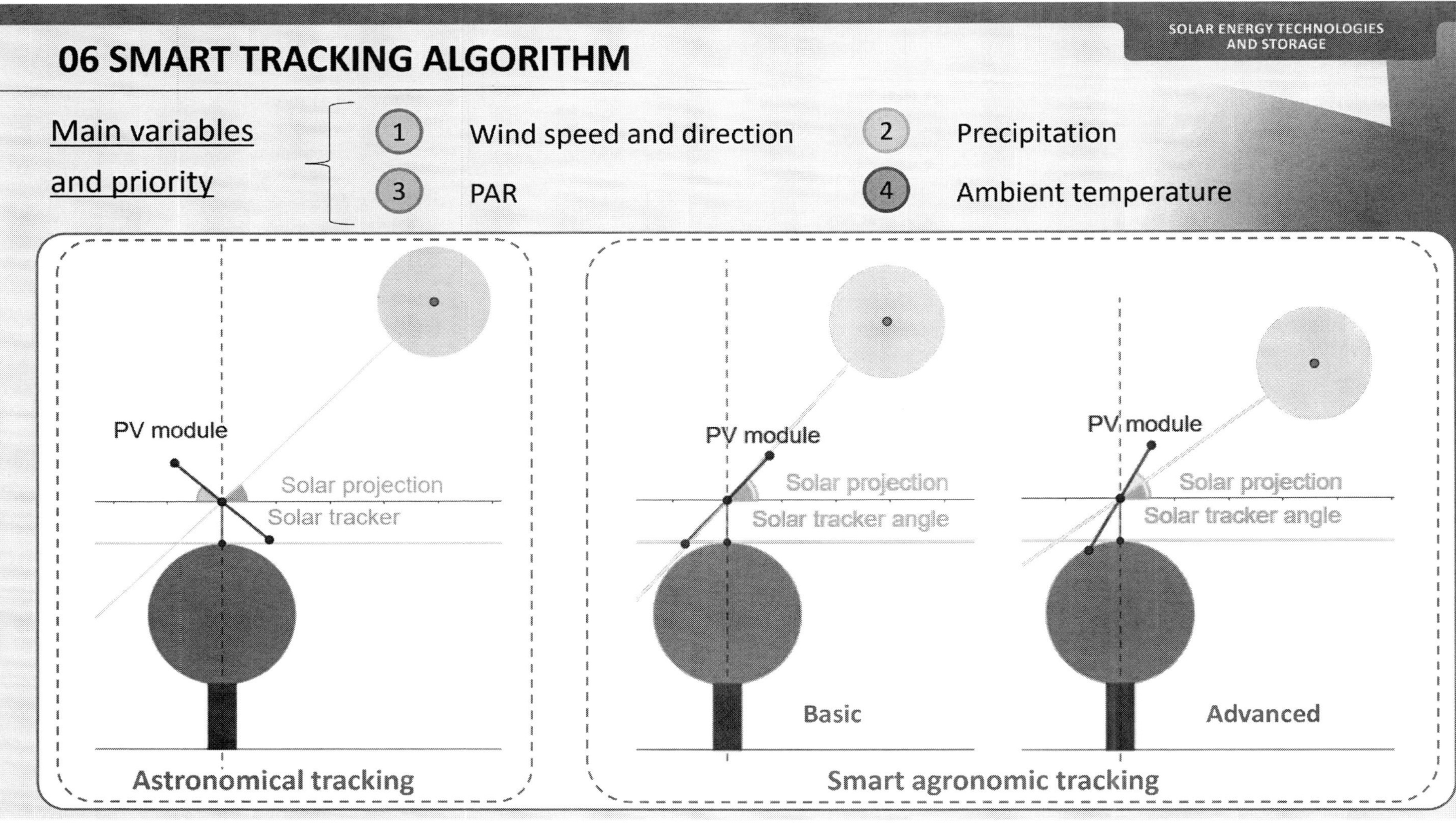

07 PRODUCTION ESTIMATIONS

CENER | NATIONAL RENEWABLE ENERGY CENTRE

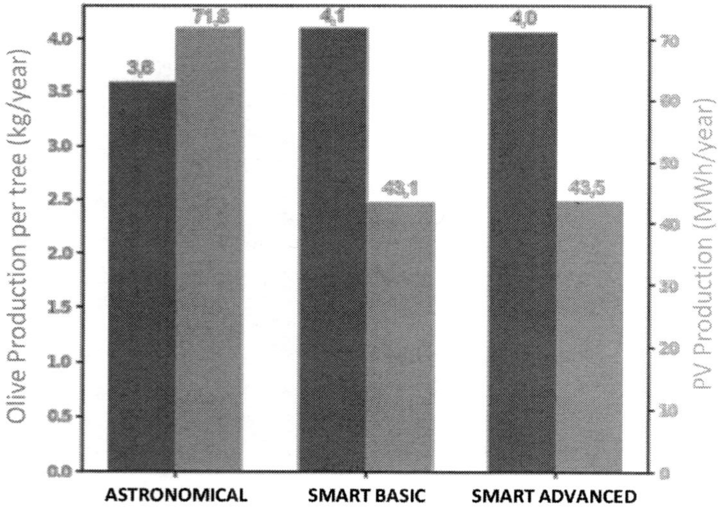

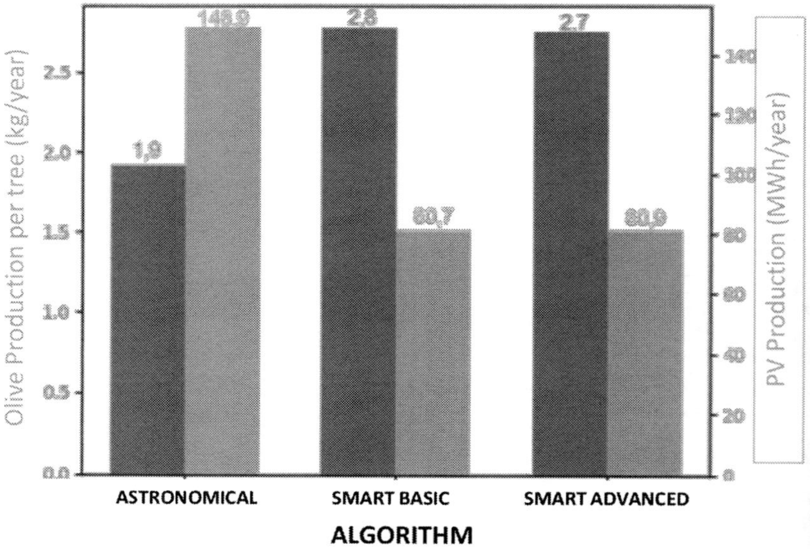

Gobierno de Navarra
Nafarroako Gobernua

020392-012

08 CONCLUSIONS & ONGOING WORK

➤ Two overhead 1-axis tracking agrivoltaic systems designed according to the needs of two different olive groves.

➤ Two agrivoltaic prototypes to be installed in the upcoming weeks, including a comprehensive sensor system to assess their performance.

➤ Crop growing model adapted to project needs.

➤ Development of two smart tracking algorithms (N-S & E-W), prioritising olive trees needs over PV production in terms of light and protection.

➤ Preliminary production estimations. Need to fine-tune crop model and tracking algorithm after prototype implementation and experimentation.

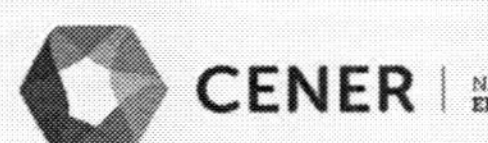

CENER | NATIONAL RENEWABLE ENERGY CENTRE

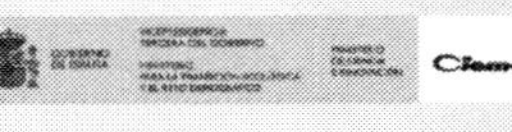

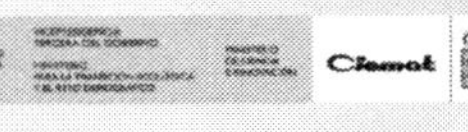

Gobierno de Navarra
Nafarroako Gobernua

DEVELOPMENT AND EVALUATION
OF AGRIVOLTAIC SYSTEMS IN OLIVE
GROVES BASED ON A NOVEL SMART
TRACKING ALGORITHM

THANKS A LOT.

www.cener.com
info@cener.com
T +34 948 25 28 00

Ildefonso Muñoz
imunoz@cener.com

Iñaki Cornago
icornago@cener.com

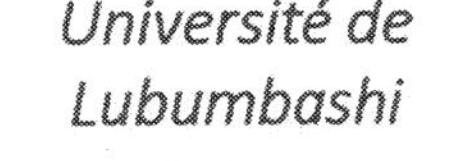

Université de Lubumbashi

Adoption and Optimisation Analysis of Agrivoltaic Systems for Horticultural Production and Energy Autonomy in Lubumbashi/DR Congo

Eddie Bilitu[1,2,3], Shu-Ngwa Asaa[3], Sara Bouguerra[2,3], Nikoleta Kyranaki[2,3], Ismail Kaaya[3], Yannick Useni[4], Michael Daenen[2,3]

[1] University of Lubumbashi, Electrical Engineering Department, Lubumbashi P.O. Box 1825, Democratic Republic of the Congo;

[2] Hasselt University, Institute for Materials Research (imo-imomec), Martelarenlaan 42, B-3500 Hasselt, Belgium;

[3] Energyville, imo-imomec, Thor Park 8320, B-3600 Genk, Belgium;

[4] University of Lubumbashi, Faculty of Agronomic Sciences, Ecology, Ecological Restoration and Landscape Unit, Lubumbashi P.O. Box 1825, Democratic Republic of the Congo;

OUTLINE

 1. Context

 2. Objectives

 3. Methodology

 4. Preliminary Results

5. Conclusions

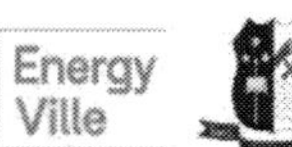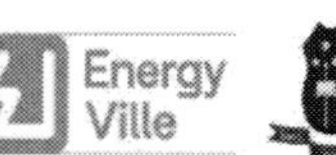

020393-002

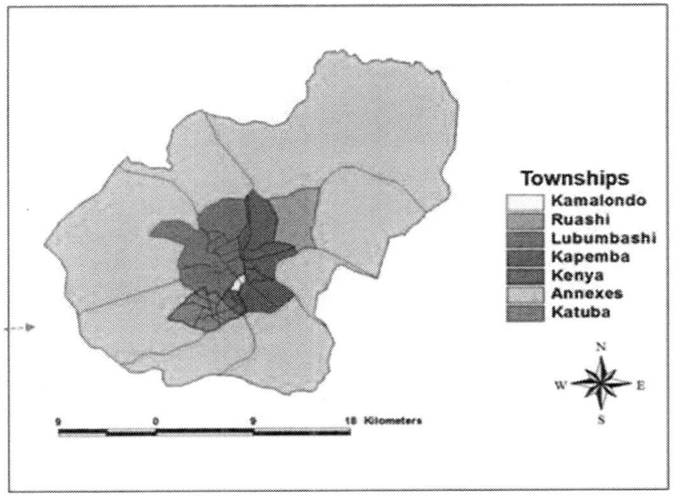

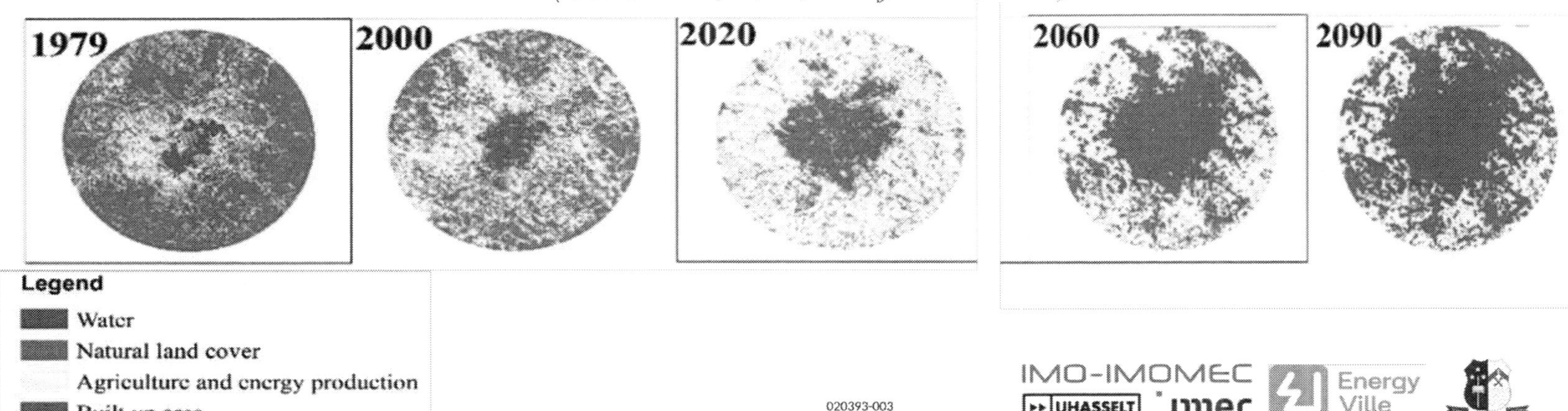

Irradiance level : $\sim 6\text{kWh}/m^2 d$
PV potential: 1753 kWh/kWp *(solagis.com)*

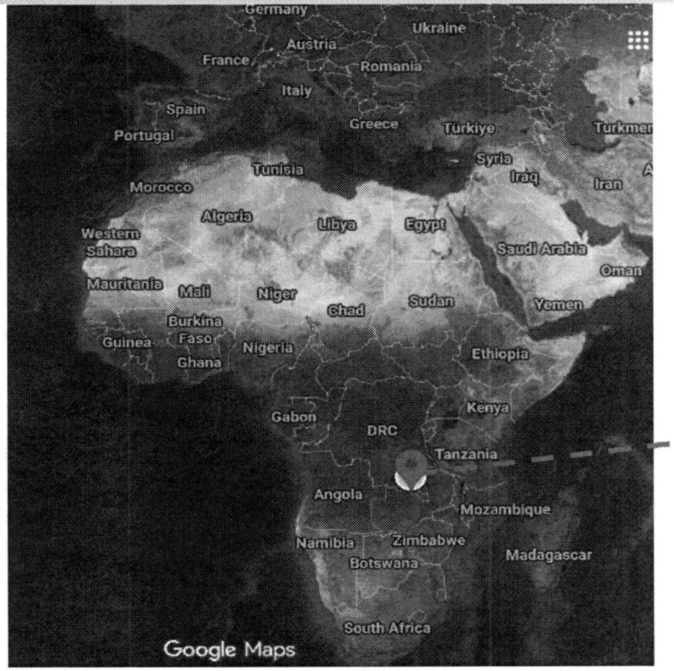

Lubumbashi is facing rapid and unplanned urban spatial growth (more than 5% / year)
(Useni et al., 2020, Khoji et al., 2022)

① Context: Energy deficit and Food insecurity in Lubumbashi

Lubumbashi

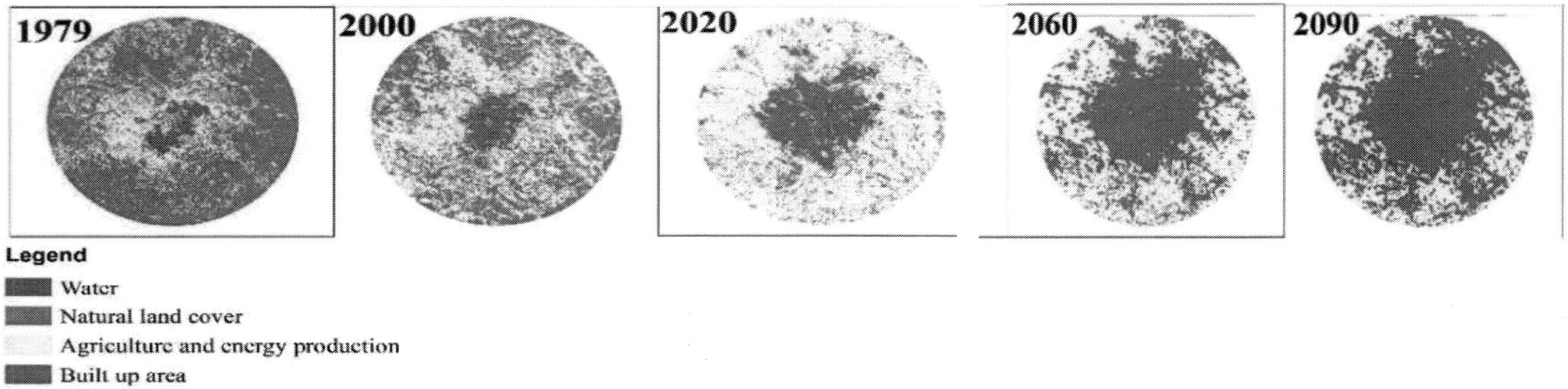

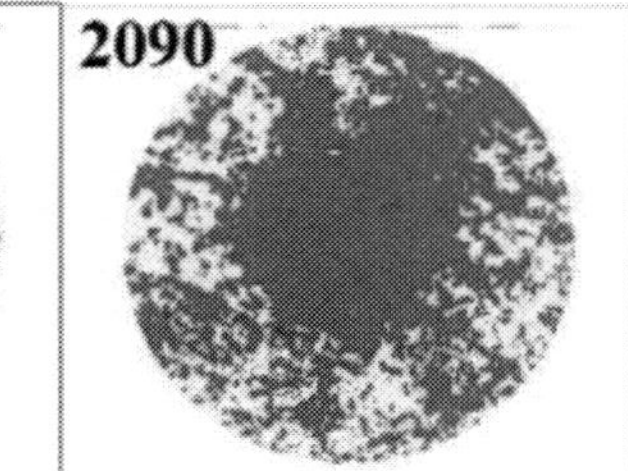

Legend
- Water
- Natural land cover
- Agriculture and energy production
- Built up area

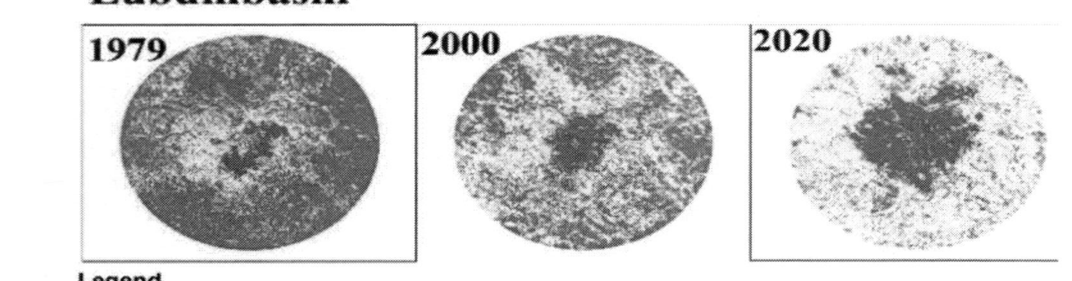

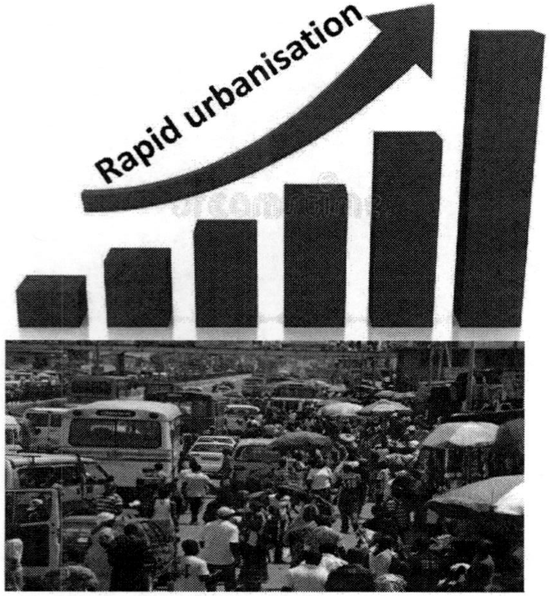

Challenges

1) Context: The Population of Lubumbashi facing the challenges arising from urbanisation.

Challenges

Population solutions

Consequences

Energy deficit
(Currently estimated at **24.8%** and projected to reach **73.3%** by 2050)

(Nkulu et al., 2022)

Food Insecurity
(28million or 25.5% of people in DR Congo)

(WFP, 2025; Nghonda et al., 2024)

Intensive use of generators

Market gardening

Atmospheric and noise pollution

Main survival activity hampered by rainfall deficit
(Kesonga, 2024)

Low crop yield

Manual irrigation
(Kesonga, 2024)

1) Conext:

These two problems are traditionally addressed separately, whereas an integrated and innovative approach could offer a synergistic solution. *Agrivoltaics (AVS) represents such an opportunity.*

Agrivoltaic systems

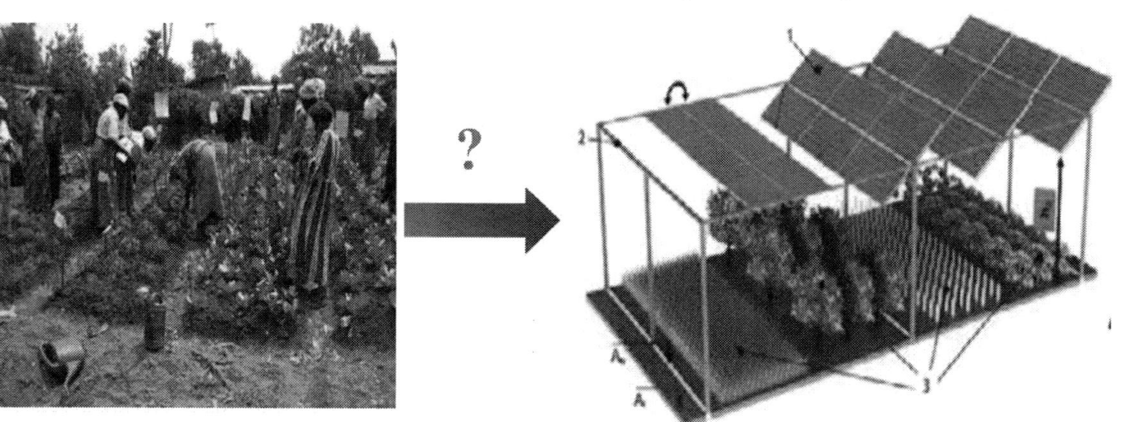

Despite the **high irradiance level** ($\sim 6\,kWh/m^2d$) **in the city**, AVS application, effectiveness, and specific impacts within the socio-economic and climatic context of Lubumbashi have not been studied and remain unknown.

Research question:

*"**How** can PV modules **be integrated into market gardening** to **optimally** produce both **electrical energy and vegetable crops** under the farming practices, climatic and socio-economic context of Lubumbashi?"*

Examining the **potential** for the synergistic **integration of AVS** into market gardening practices to address the **interconnected challenges of energy crisis** and **low crop yield** in the local socioeconomic and climatic context of Lubumbashi.

Specifically, we:

1. Evaluate urban agriculture (UA) stakeholder perceptions on AVS benefits and adoption barriers.

2. Simulate optimal AVS configurations for main crops within the local climatic conditions of Lubumbashi.

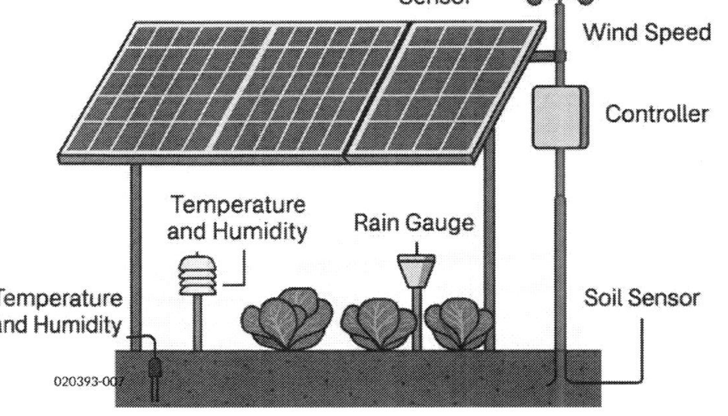

3.1. Stakeholders perception analysis

Random & convenience sampling of stakeholders:

- **157 farmers from 7 main sites**
- **26 experts from Energy, Research & UA sectors**

Surveys on AVS adoption by interviews from April to July 2025 using **Kobo Collect**

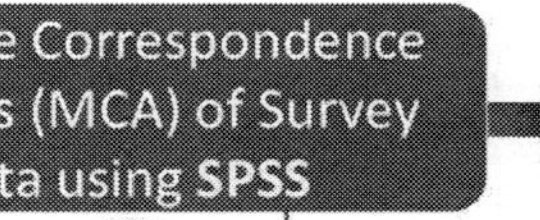

Multiple Correspondence Analysis (MCA) of Survey Data using **SPSS**

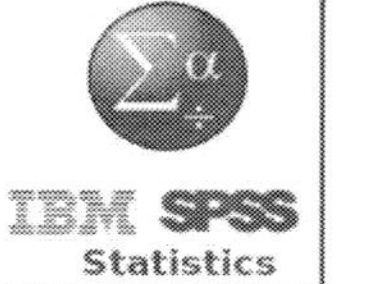

Identification of farming practices, factors influencing AVS adoption, drivers and barriers in Lubumbashi

3.2. Identification of optimal configurations of AVS

Energy yield modelling of bifacial tilted & vertical modules (455Wp) (Simplified SAM model)

Input: Meteorological data of Lubumbashi, site size, cultivar, etc.

Crop yield modelling of cabbage (Stress-based DSSAT model)

Multi-objective optimisation using **NSGA-II method**

Analysis of the irradiation distribution using the **imec Framework**

Output: Tilt, height, spacing, nr. of modules, energy & crop yields, LER, shading, PAR

Identification & comparison of **Optimal solutions**

42nd European Photovoltaic Solar Energy Conference and Exhibition

4.1. Farming practices

Frequency Diagram of Agricultural Practices in Lubumbashi

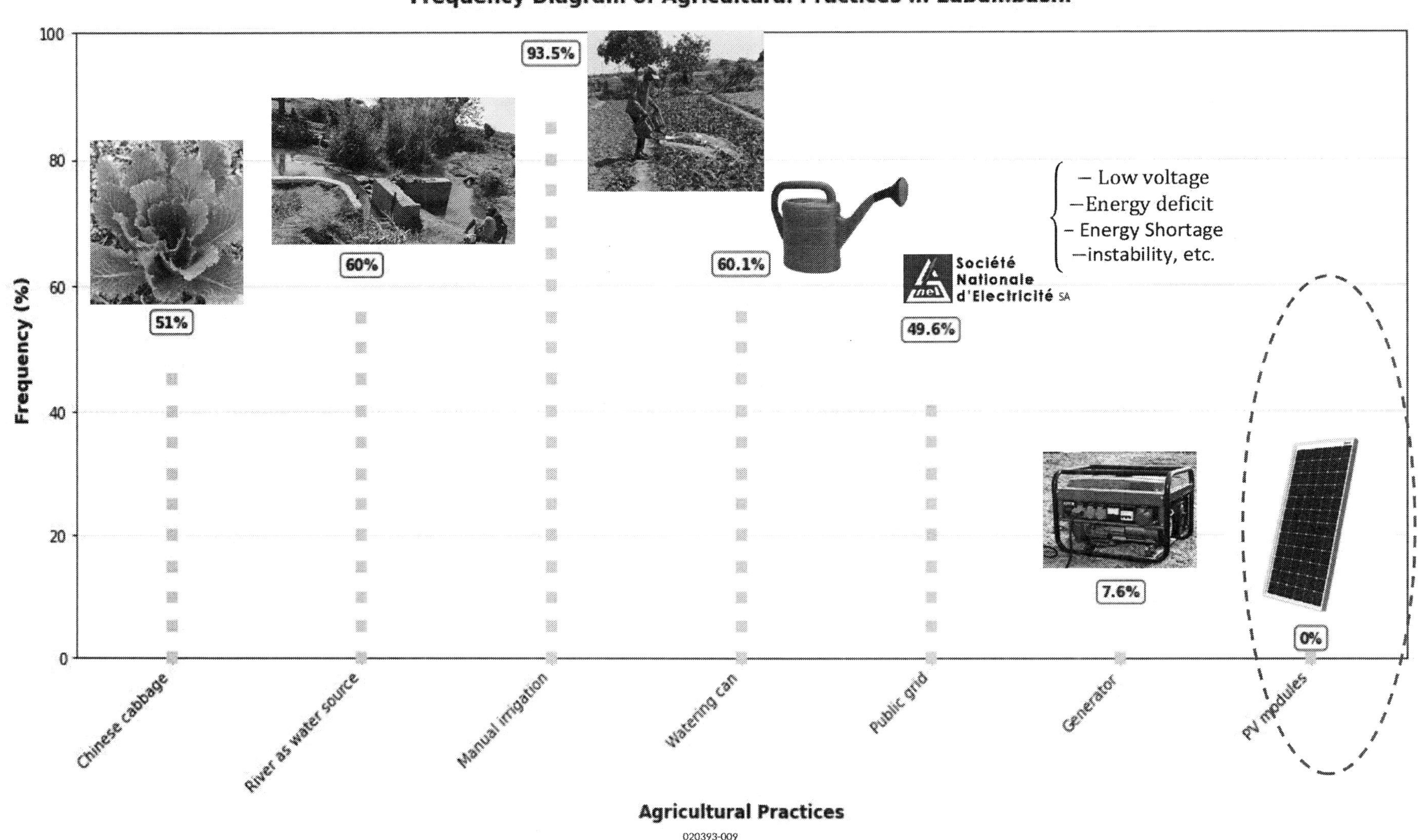

4.2. Cross-Comparison of stakeholders' views on the adoption of AVS (Response variable)

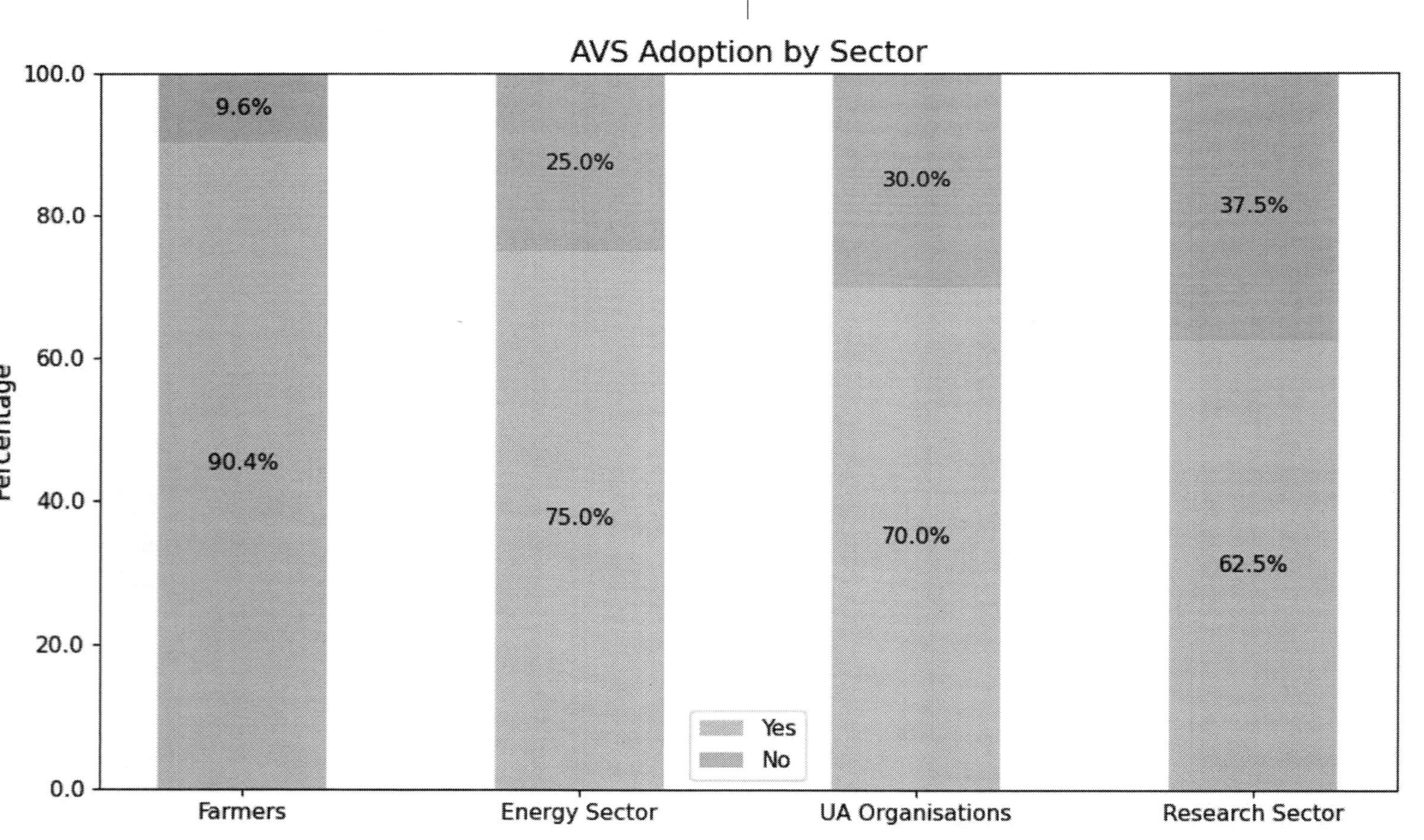

4.3. Motivations & barriers to AVS adoption

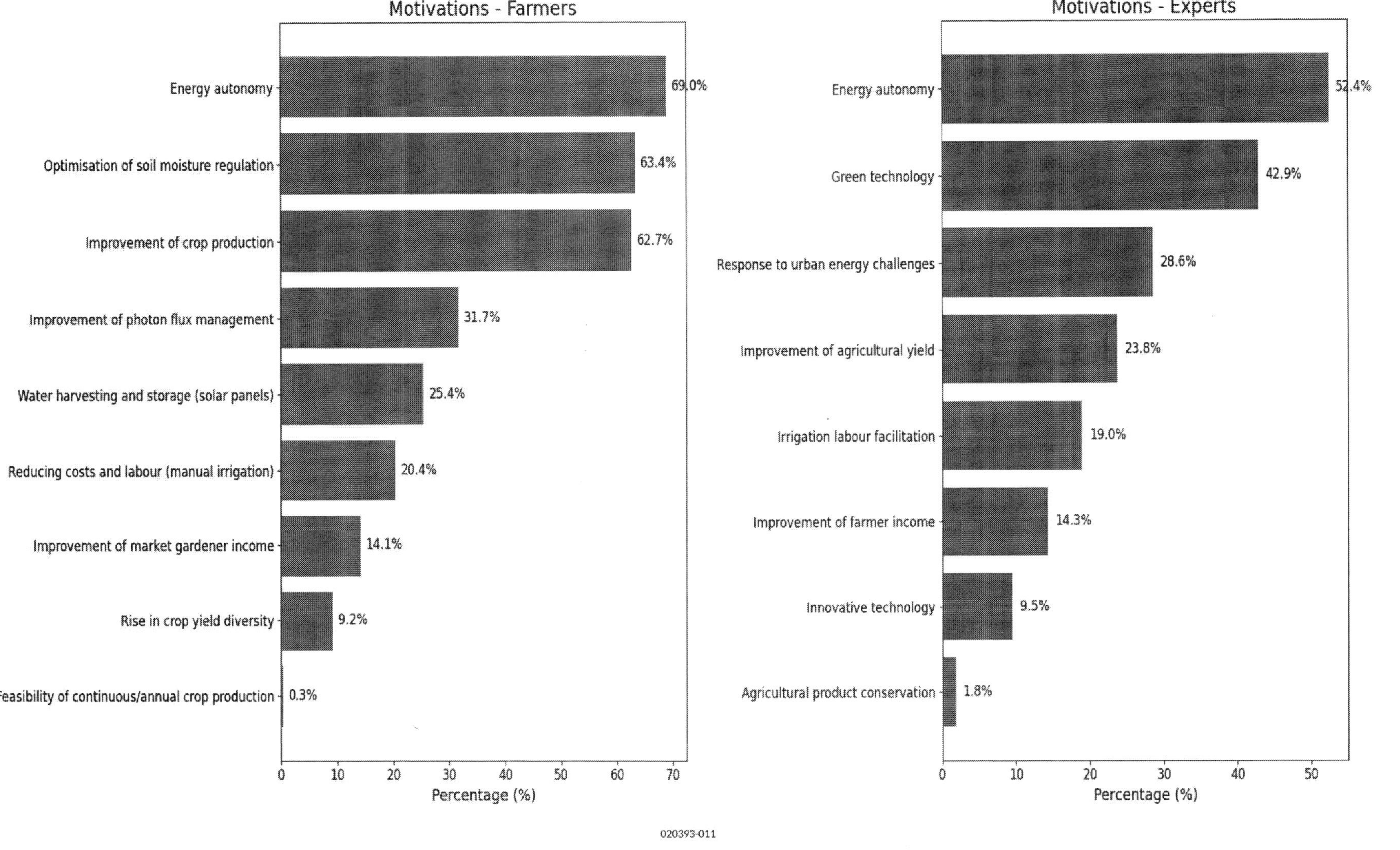

020393-011

Barriers - Farmers

Barriers - Experts

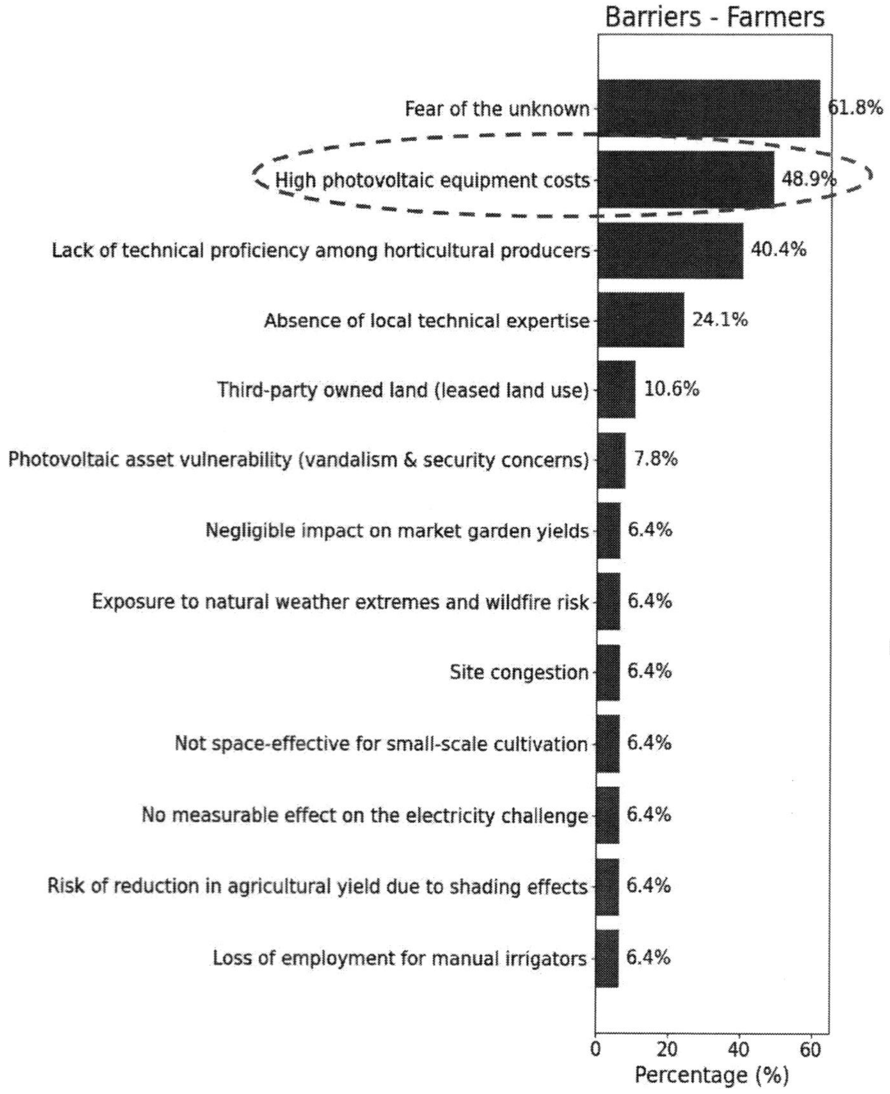

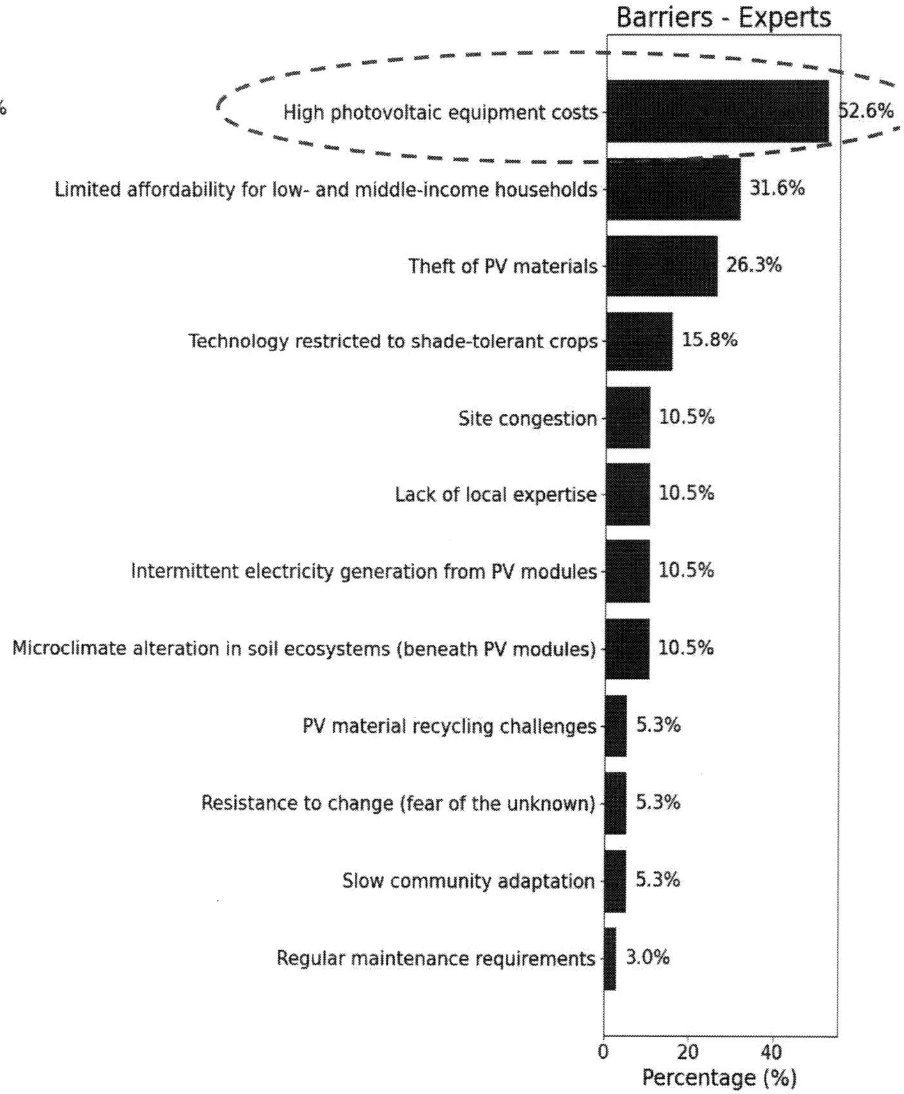

4.4. Factors influencing AVS adoption by farmers

Discrimination diagram

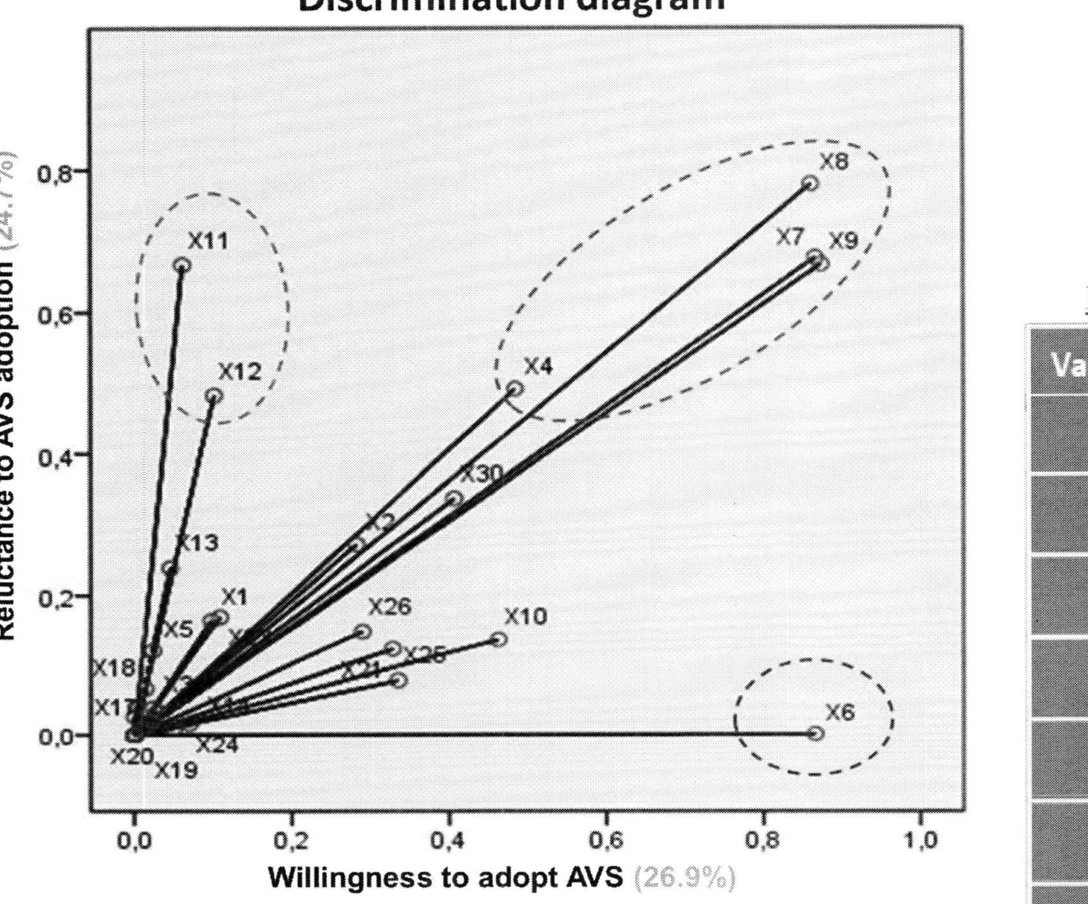

Most influential explanatory variables

Variable	Label
X4	Difficulties_faced
X6	Availability_Power_Supply
X7	Electricity_Source_Type
X8	Usefulness_Power_source
X9	Reason_Lack_Power_Source
X11	Irrigation_Type
X12	Means_of_manual_irrigation

4 Results : Stakeholders' perception analysis

IMO-IMOMEC UHASSELT imec EnergyVille

4.5. Key levers and public policies to encourage AVS Adoption

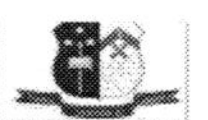

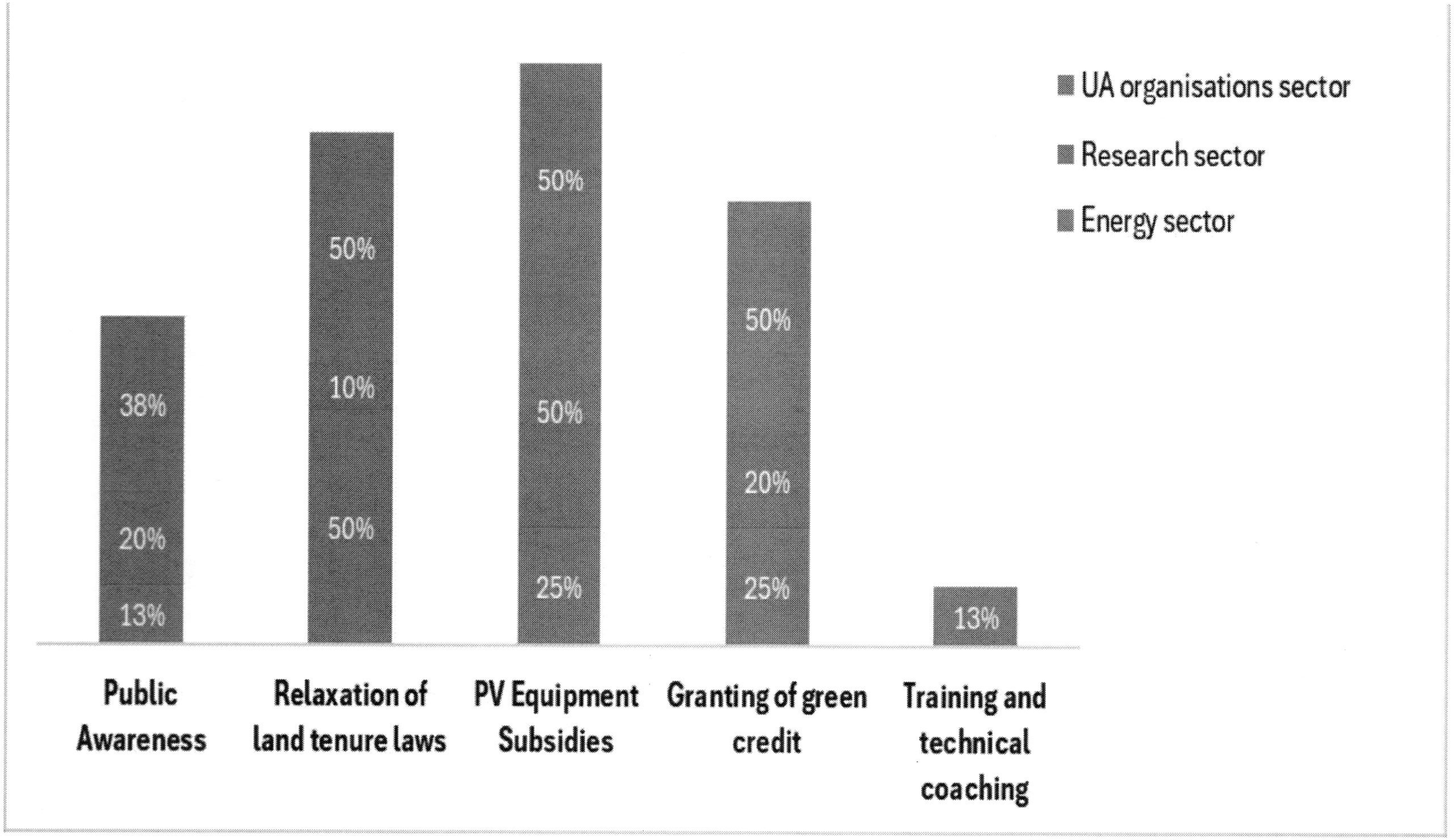

4.6. IRRADIATION DISTRIBUTION

Tilted modules (12° facing north)

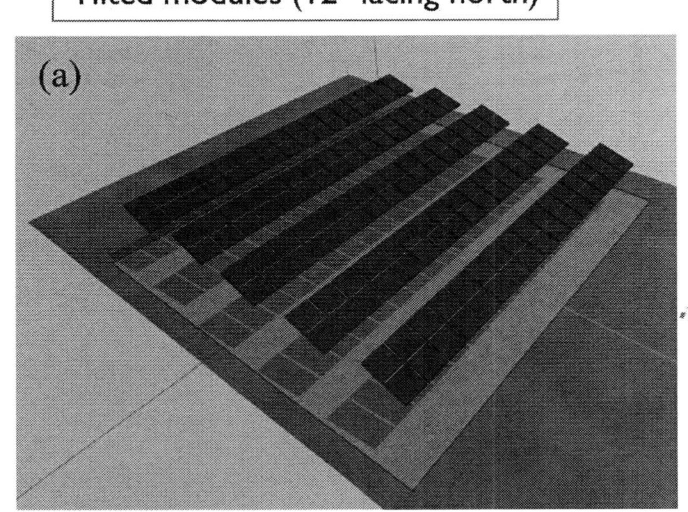

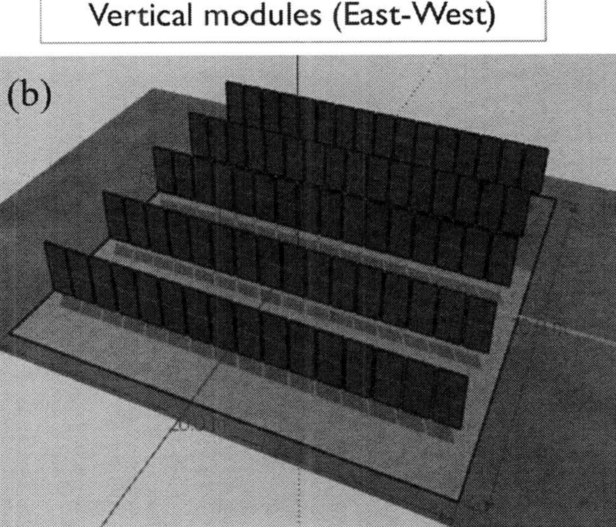

Vertical modules (East-West)

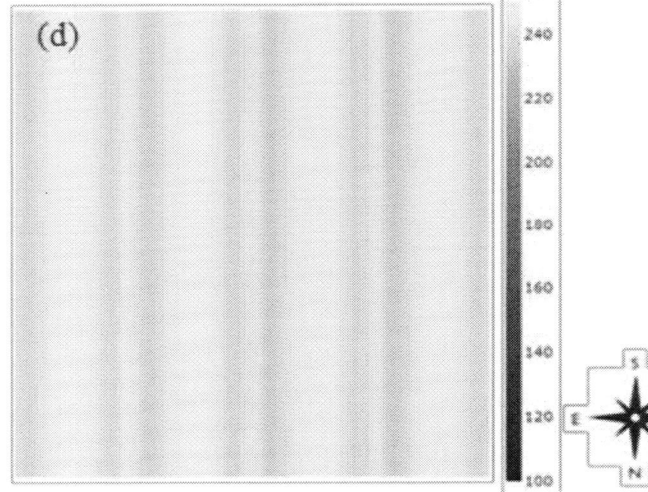

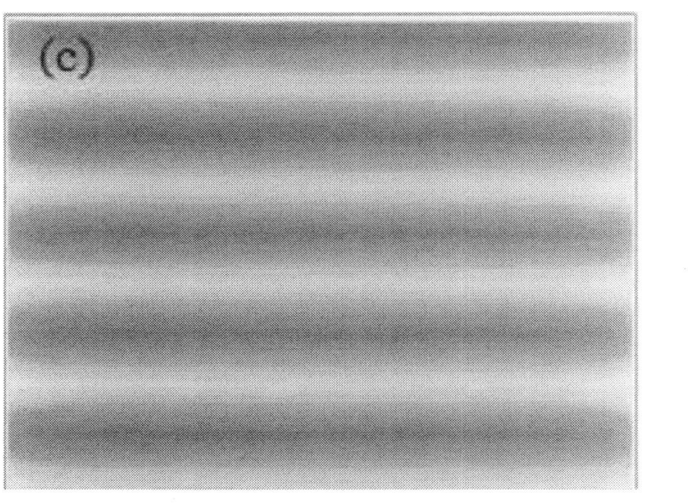

Parameters	Optimal confugurations	
	Tilted modules	Vertical modules
Electricity production (kWh/year)	63395	51221
Energy yield (kWh/kWp)	**1741**	**1407**
Agricultural yield (kg/m^2)	**1.79**	**1.9**
Modules(455Wp)	80(5 rows × 16 modules)	80 (5 rows × 16 modules)
Installed capacity (kWp)	36.4	36.4
Tilt angle (°)	12	90
Mounting height (m)	2	1
Shading ration (%)	40	6
LER	**1.32**	**1.29**

④ Results : Identification of optimal configurations of AVS

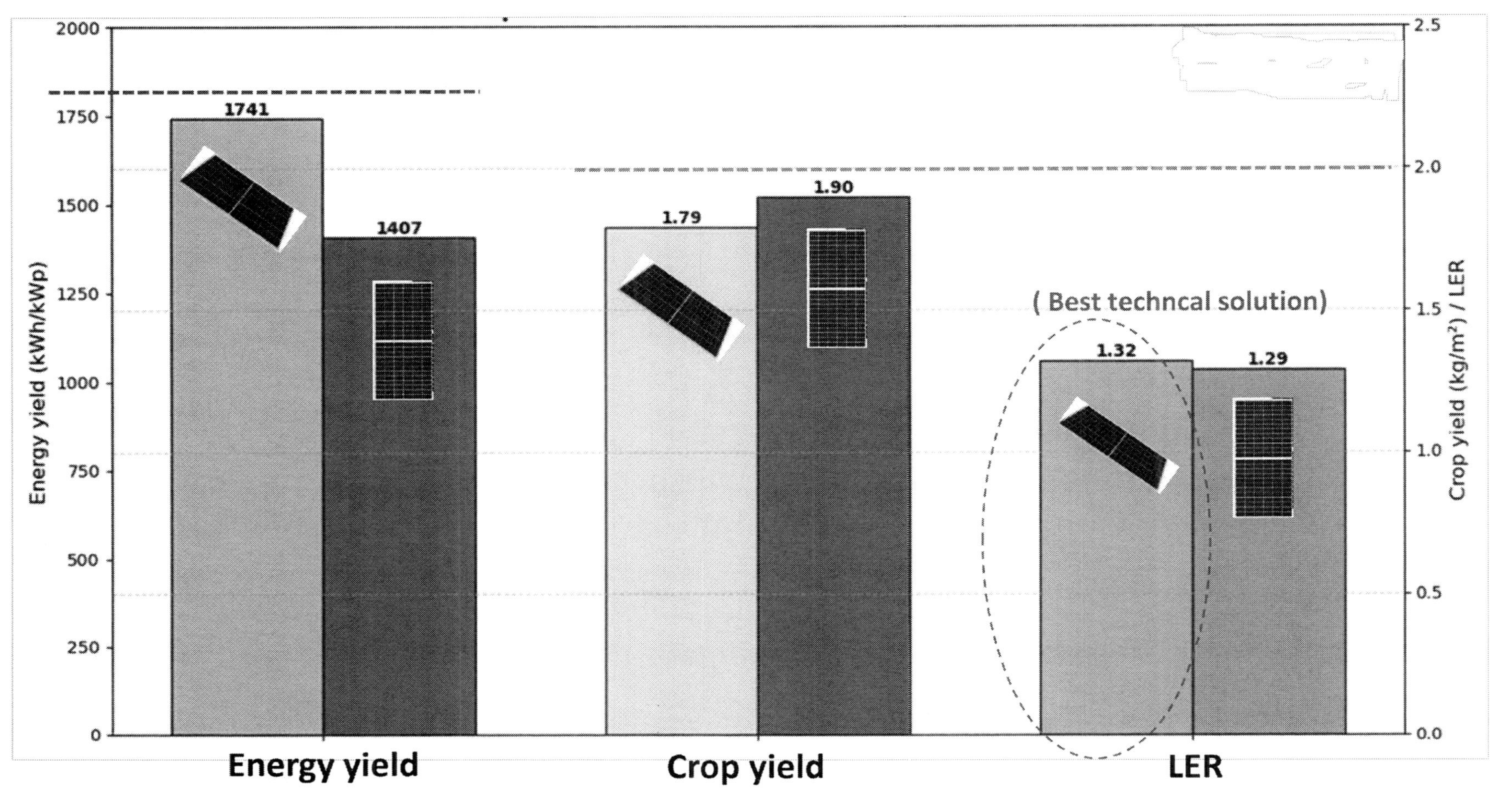

---------- Average yearly energy yield in Lubumbashi: **1753 kWh/kWp** *(solagis.com)*

--------- Average cabbage yield in Lubumbashi: **2 kg/m²** *(https://agrovolaille.com)*

020393-017

- **Stakeholder Support:** Strong support from stakeholders, driven by the prospect of energy autonomy.
- **Identified Barriers:** The main perceived obstacles are the **high initial cost, fear of the unknown** and the **lack of local expertise**.
- **Policies to encourage AVS Adoption:** The majority of experts advocate for PV equipment subsidie and granting green credit
- **Optimal Configuration:** Simulations identify tilted configuration at 12° facing the north as the better technical solution to optimise both energy and Chinese cabbage production by a **LER of 1.32**, demonstrating a **32% increase** in the overall land productivity.

Agrivoltaics (AVS) → **Possible solution** to **simultaneously** address the energy deficit and food insecurity in Lubumbashi.

Further research: **Economic analysis**

MAXIMIZING ECONOMIC PERFORMANCE OF AGRIVOLTAIC SYSTEMS THROUGH MODULE ARRAY DESIGN

Habeel Alam[1,2,3*], Jenny Nelson[2], Alona Armstrong[3], Duncan Whyatt[3] and Nauman Butt[1]
[1]Department of Electrical Engineering, Lahore University of Management Science, Lahore, Pakistan
[2]Department of Physics, Imperial College London, London, United Kingdom
[3]Lancaster Environment Centre, Lancaster University, United Kingdom
Tel: +923132251333, *h.alam@lancaster.ac.uk

ABSTRACT: Growing demand for food and energy has prompted the need for an efficient utilization of the land resources which are globally under increasing stress due to climate change and population growth. Agrivoltaics (*AV*) offers a dual use of land for harvesting food and solar energy. The design of module arrays in *AV* must achieve an optimal balance between food and energy production while ensuring an economic viability. We explore techno-economic effects of module array density, hardware infrastructure cost, land specific soft costs, and the net crop income on the AV system design. A variety of module technologies including fixed tilt and tracking modules with standard tracking (*ST*) and anti-tracking (*AT*) are explored. We show that both fixed tilt and tracking systems can be designed for an optimal yield and economic viability, the latter provides best flexibility for various types of crops. While *ST* maximizes the energy conversion, agriculture yield may significantly decrease. *AT* on the other hand, maximizes agricultural production, but the energy conversion can drop by ~60% making it economically infeasible. An optimal tracking system for *AV* can therefore use a combination of *ST* and *AT* to meet the yield and economic targets.
Keywords: agrivoltaics, food-energy yield, economic feasibility, module array design

1 INTRODUCTION

The adverse effects of climate change have prompted the utilization of renewable sources to meet global energy demand. The issue with renewables, specifically solar, is the huge land requirement for adequate generation which leads to conflict of land usage between agriculture (food) and energy production. Agrivoltaics (*AV*) is a type of dual land usage system which solves this conflict by elevating the *PV* panels above ground (for maneuvering of agricultural machinery) and utilizing the same land for both energy and crop(food) production [1-3]. The crop cultivation under the *PV* modules can provide economic benefits including increased revenue and higher land usage efficiency[4]. It can also enable favorable microclimatic conditions including protection of crops from heat stress via shading and water savings by reducing evapotranspiration under *PV* modules in hot arid and semi-arid regions [2]. In some cases, *AV* can provide protection to vulnerable crops from hail, wind, heavy rainfall and snow. Favorable microclimate resulting in reduction in temperatures due to crop cultivation underneath the modules can also result in increased performance of *PV* during hot temperatures [5]. The energy production from *AV* can meet local agricultural demands, increase self-consumption and diversify farmers income through additional revenue stream. [3].
The economic viability is highly dependent on the module array design optimization which is crucial for maximizing solar *PV* and agricultural production. Several factors including the tilt angle, orientation, row to row distance, crop selection and elevation of the modules play a vital role in determining both the crop and energy yield. Optimizing these design parameters is essential to maximize the overall benefits and achieve economic feasibility for *AV* systems. The economic feasibility also dependent on high initial capital costs associated with *AV* in comparison with Ground mounted Photovoltaics (*GMPV*) due to mounting structure and customization requirements[6]. Thus, optimization of *AV* design and careful selection of crops which can tolerate shading without significantly reducing the yield is crucial as its

revenue can offset the initial capital costs. The additional revenue can also provide an opportunity to invest in automation of agricultural machinery which will further increase their revenue [7].

Despite many commercial and academic installations having demonstrated the promising potential of *AV* across various global locations, comprehensive modeling quantifying economic aspects for a variety of module array configurations, crops, and associated impacts has not been reported. Here, we present a techno-economic framework to evaluate the relative economic performance of *AV* farms relative to ground mounted *PV* for different bifacial *AV* systems including a) conventional North/South faced b) East/West faced vertical, c) Standard solar tracking and d) Anti-tracking modules. We have used the location of Lahore (31.5204° N, 74.3587° E) for illustration throughout the simulations. We used the crop rotation of tomato, cauliflower, and garlic over a complete year. The rest of the paper includes mathematical modeling in Section II, results and discussion describing relative food-energy productivity, and economic trends in Section III. Finally, conclusions are presented in Section IV.

2 MODELING APPROACH

2.1 *PV* Energy and incident *PAR* over crops

The modelling framework for food-energy yields and economics have been discussed in detail in [8] and [9]. A view factor approach validated by field experiments is used [8], [10-11]. *PV* yield is calculated by sunlight interception by *PV* panels including the contributions from direct beam, diffused light and albedo. We evaluate the shading for the direct beam and diffused light caused by the solar panels to calculate the available *PAR* at any horizontal surface on the ground or at an elevation underneath the panel arrays. Diffuse and direct components of global horizontal irradiation are estimated by using typical meteorological conditions [12]. An isotropic model is assumed for diffused light. Computations are carried out on 1-minute resolution. Fig 1. shows the *AV* systems for which the analysis is

10.4229/EUPVSEC2025/4DV.1.5
020394-001

Nomenclature			
		M_L	Module hardware to soft cost ratio
AT	Anti-tracking	n	Number of solar tracking hours
AV	Agrivoltaics	p	Pitch between the module rows
CGR	Crop growth rate	p_r	Price
$CAPEX$	Capital expenditure	pb	Performance
CT	Customized tracking	P_C	Normalized crop profit
FIT	Feed in tariff	ppr	Price performance ratio
$GMPV$	Ground mounted photovoltaics	PV	Photovoltaics
h	Height	ST	Standard tracking
κ_L	Normalized soft cost ratio	Y_{Crop}	Biomass/crop yield
κ_M	Hardware cost ratio	Y_{PAR}	PAR yield
$LCOE$	Levelized cost of electricity	Y_{PV}	Energy ratio

performed which includes (a) fixed tilt 40° N/S faced, (b)E/W faced vertically installed, (c) standard solar tracking (ST) and (d) anti/back (AT) tracking systems. AT is opposite of ST in such a way that in AT, module face is kept parallel to direct beam throughout the day prioritizing agricultural production rather than maximizing electricity generation.

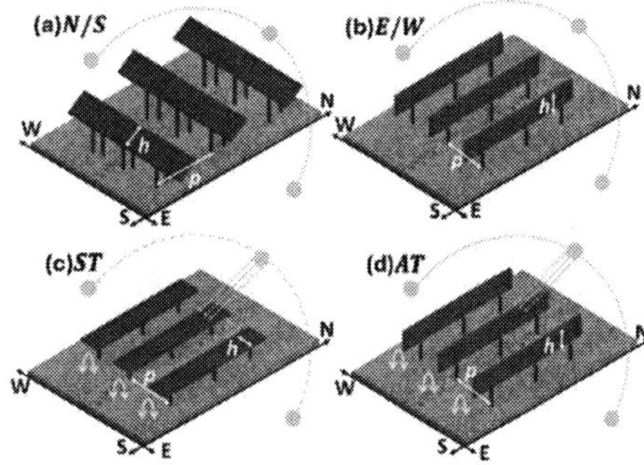

Figure 1: Schematic of modelled agrivoltaic systems including a) N/S facing fixed tilt b) E/W facing vertical bifacial c) Standard solar tracking (ST) and d) Anti-tracking (AT) systems. Row to row distance (p) which is an important design parameter along with height (h) of modules is also shown.

2.2 Useful PAR & Relative Crop Yield

While the incident PAR intensity over crops can provide an indication of the shading related impact due to modules, the actual impact depends on the shade sensitivity of the specific crop as defined by the threshold PAR (PAR_{th}) above which the PAR intensity does not contribute to photosynthesis. The crop dependent useful PAR at any point (y) across the pitch is calculated across the day as:

$$PAR_{u,open}(y) = \int_{tr}^{ts} PAR_0(x,t)\,dt; \quad PAR_0 \leq PAR_{th} \quad (1)$$

where t_r and t_s are the times for sunrise and sunset, respectively, and PAR_0 is the incident PAR under open sun. The PAR underneath the panel shades is smaller relative to the open farm. PAR_u for AV is calculated as:

$$PAR_{u,AV}(y) = \int_{tr}^{ts} PAR_{AV}(x,t)\,dt; \quad PAR_{AV} \leq PAR_{th} \quad (2)$$

where PAR_{AV} is the incident PAR on ground.

2.3 Relative Crop-Energy Yields

The relative crop yield (Y_{PAR}) for a given crop over its cycle and the relative AV energy yield (Y_{PV}) are calculated as [8]:

$$Y_{PAR} = \frac{PAR_{u,AV}}{PAR_{u,open}} \quad (3)$$

$$Y_{PV} = \frac{I_M(AV)}{I_M(GMPV)} \quad (4)$$

where I_M is energy output. Y_{PAR} and Y_{PV} can be useful metrics for the early assessment of the crop-energy yields and overall farm productivity. Using these, [5] provides a holistic view of the AV performance for various module configurations.

2.4 Economic Performance

We explore when a module configuration, designed for an AV system, could be profitable relative to a standard ground mounted PV ($GMPV$) system. The answer depends on the quantitative balance between a higher CAPEX needed for an elevated mounting and the net income from the crops. The economic performance for an AV system is evaluated by comparing the profits from energy and crops of an AV system with individual profits from $GMPV$ and that for an open agricultural farm. The model is described in detail in [9],[13]. For a better economic performance as compared to $GMPV$:

$$P_{AV} + P_{c,AV} \geq Max\left(P_{GMPV}, P_{c,full\,sun}\right) \quad (5)$$

where P_{AV}, P_{GMPV} are the annual energy profit from AV and $GMPV$, respectively, and $P_{c,AV}$ and $P_{c,full\,sun}$ denote the crop profits for AV and full sun, respectively. We assume that the energy profit per unit land area is higher as compared to that from crop. For AV, an economic performance equivalent or better than $GMPV$ requires:

$$(FIT_{GMPV} - FIT_{AV} + LCOE_{AV} - LCOE_{GMPV}) \times YY_T \leq P_{C,AV} \quad (6)$$

where YY_T is the total annual energy production taken to be the same for AV and $GMPV$ and $P_{c,AV}$ is assumed to scale linearly with Y_{PAR}.

After solving and re-arranging (6), for the same FIT for AV and $GMPV$, the condition to have economic equivalence or improvement over $GMPV$ can be written as:

$$\kappa_M + \kappa_L - Y_{PV}' \leq (Y_{Crop} \times P_C) \quad (7)$$

where the 1st two terms (κ_M & κ_L) on the left-hand side represent difference in hardware and soft costs for AV modules relative to ground mounted PV representing customized module technology for land preservation. Y_{PV}' represents normalized annual energy produced per unit module area for AV relative to that for $GMPV$. P_C is the normalized crop profit, and Y_{crop} denotes crop yield. The terms on left hand side of (7) can be termed as price(p_r) while the right-hand side terms can be termed as performance(p_b), thus making economic viability condition for AV as

$$ppr \overset{\text{def}}{=} \frac{p_r}{p_b} \leq 1 \qquad (8)$$

A price performance ratio of less than one ($ppr \leq 1$) is desirable for economic feasibility.

3 RESULTS AND DISCUSSION

3.1 Food-energy yield for different module configurations.

Fig. 2 shows the effect of module density ratio (p/h) on food (Y_{PAR}) and energy (Y_{PV}) yields for bifacial modules under the 4 different configurations. A tradeoff between the module collected light and the PAR incident to the ground can be seen on the plots. It can be noted that the result for different configurations deviates strongly at higher density ($p/h \leq 2$) but come closer at higher array densities. Both Y_{PV} and Y_{PAR} tends to saturate at lower module densities ($p/h \sim 6$).

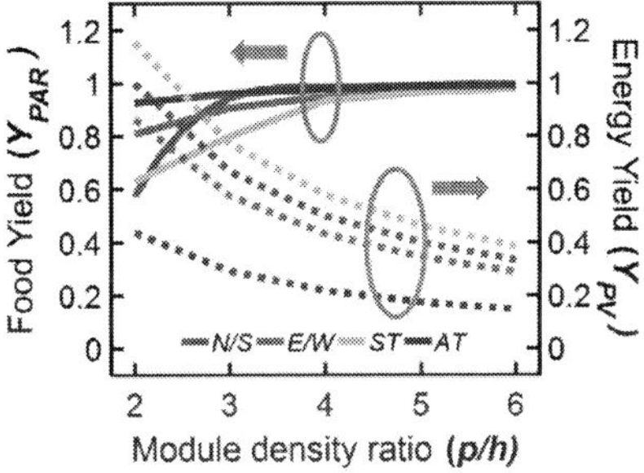

Figure 2: Normalized food (Y_{PAR}) and energy yield (Y_{PV}) is plotted as a function of module array density for fixed tilt (N/S), vertical (E/W) faced, solar tracking (ST) and anti-tracking (AT) orientations. Food yield decreases while energy yield increases by reducing the module density.

3.2 Effect of module density ratio on techno-economics.

Fig. 3 shows the effect of module density ratio (p/h) on different parameters in (7) which makes price, performance and ppr. Capital cost ratio is highest for ST and AT followed by N/S and vertical E/W faced orientations. Energy yield ratio is highest for ST and lowest for AT as it prioritizes food over energy production. Crop profit ratio increase with increase in p/h due to increased sunlight availability to crops translating into higher yield and thus higher profits.

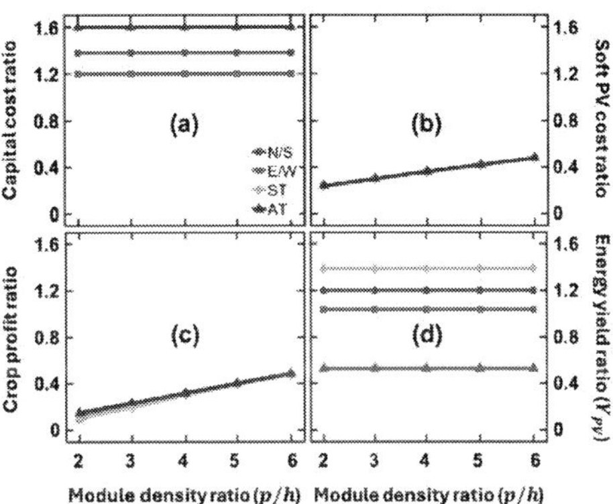

Figure 3: Effect of module density ratio(p/h) on various techno-economic parameters including a) capital cost ratio, b) soft PV cost ratio, c) Crop profit ratio and d) energy yield ratio. Crop profit ratio increase with increase in p/h due to increased sunlight availabilty to crops.

Fig. 4 shows the effect of module density ratio (p/h) on price, performance and ppr. For high row to row distance ($p/h \geq 6$), the economic feasibility is achieved for N/S, E/W and ST orientations. The economic feasibility is not achieved for AT and it might require policy intervention to achieve economic equivalence.

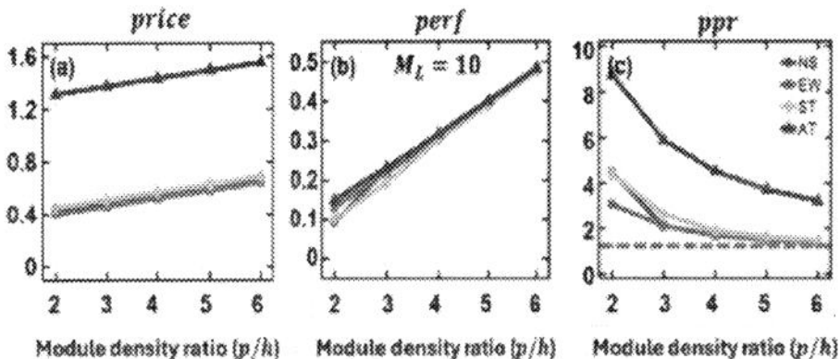

Figure 4. Effect of module density ratio (p/h) on price (p_r), performance(p_b) and price performance ratio (ppr) for $N/S, E/W$, ST and AT. The horizontal dotted line represents economic feasibilty condition ($ppr = 1$). For high $p/h(p/h \geq 6)$, the economic feasibilty is achieved for $N/S, E/W$ and ST orientations.

3.3 Customized tracking for Agrivoltaics

Fig. 5 shows the conceptual schematic of customized tracking (CT) scheme which can be defined by multiplexing ST, which maximizes the energy, with anti-tracking (AT) which maximizes the agricultural yield. CT incorporates both ST and AT such that ST is implemented for n hours with $n/2$ number of hours on each side of midday (noon) while AT is implemented.

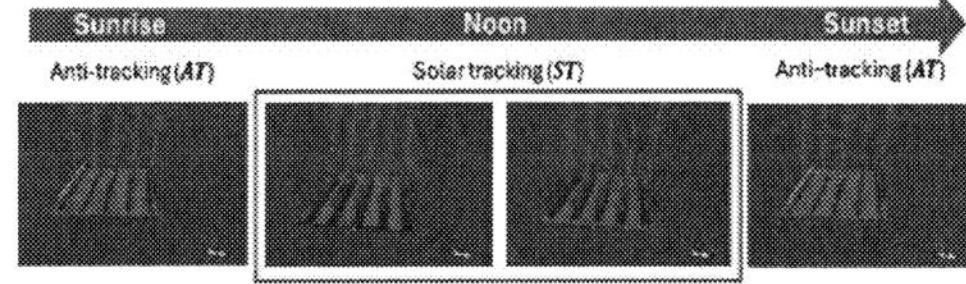

Figure 5. Schematic of customized tracking (CT) which time multiplexes ST and AT by performing ST at noon and AT for the remaining hours.

Fig. 6 shows the number of standard tracking hours on price, performance and ppr for $p/h = 3$ and $M_L = 10$. As we go from anti tracking (ST hours=0) to standard tracking (ST hours=12), price decreases which results in reduction in ppr. The economic feasibility is not achieved for this case and policy intervention might be required.

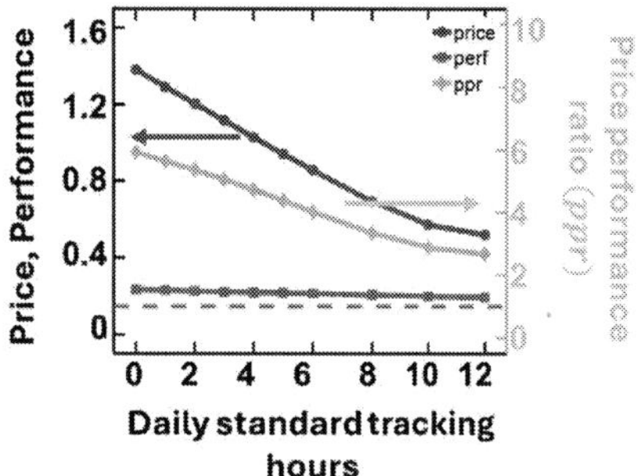

Figure 6. Effect of daily standard tracking hours on price (p_r), performance(p_b) and price performance ratio (ppr) for $N/S, E/W, ST$ and AT. The horizontal dotted line represents economic feasibilty condition ($ppr = 1$).

3.4 Effect of feed-in-tariff

F To make AV economically feasible, policy interventions in the form of subsidies or feed in tariff (FIT) might be needed. Fig. 7 shows the threshold feed-in tariff requirements for different AV orientations for $M_L = 10$. Due to its lowest energy contribution, AT requires the highest FIT. N/S fixed tilt, E/W vertical bifacial and ST require additional FIT between 7-13% relative to ground mounted PV.

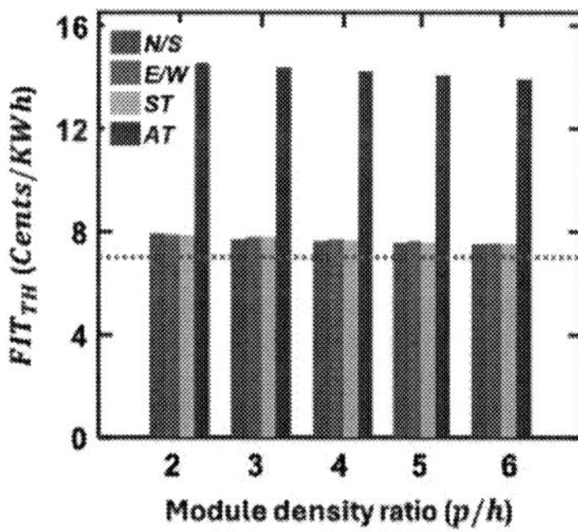

Figure 7: Effect of module density ratio (p/h) on threshold feed in tariff (FIT) requirement for $N/S, E/W, ST$ and AT orientations. The horizontal dotted line shows the FIT for ground mounted PV. AT requires highest FIT due to lowest energy contribution and highest CAPEX requirements.

4 CONCLUSIONS

Food-energy yield and economic performance for agrivoltaics are evaluated using a techno-economic framework. For high module density ($p/h\sim2$), anti-tracking bifacial modules can provide highest crop yield but at a reduced energy generation while standard solar tracking modules can provide highest energy yield but at

reduced crop yield. The economic equivalence for AV relative to ground mounted PV was evaluated in terms of price performance ratio. The economic competitiveness for AV relative to ground mounted PV requires a module array design at a reduced array density. At a lower module density ($p/h \geq 6$) related to land acquisition, taxes, and overheads along with a significant crop income, E/W faced vertical bifacial, N/S faced, and standard solar tracking systems can have an equivalent or economic feasibility relative to ground-mounted PV. Anti tracking systems produce the lowest energy and hence require the highest feed-in tariff to achieve economic equivalence. A customized approach where the standard tracking is applied only for a selected number of hours before and after the noon can provide a high flexibility in terms of food-energy yield and can be designed to obtain best economic trade-offs while satisfying minimum crop yield threshold. The proposed framework can be utilized to facilitate economic assessments and guide policy formulation across various global locations.

5 REFERENCES

[1]   Sacchelli, S., Garegnani, G., Geri, F., Grilli, G., Paletto, A., Zambelli, P., Ciolli, M. and Vettorato, D., 2016. Trade-off between photovoltaic systems installation and agricultural practices on arable lands: An environmental and socio-economic impact analysis for Italy. *Land Use Policy, 56,* pp.90-99.

[2]   Barron-Gafford, G.A., Pavao-Zuckerman, M.A., Minor, R.L., Sutter, L.F., Barnett-Moreno, I., Blackett, D.T., Thompson, M., Dimond, K., Gerlak, A.K., Nabhan, G.P. and Macknick, J.E., 2019. Agrivoltaics provide mutual benefits across the food–energy–water nexus in drylands. *Nature Sustainability, 2*(9), pp.848-855.

[3]   Schindele, S., Trommsdorff, M., Schlaak, A., Obergfell, T., Bopp, G., Reise, C., Braun, C., Weselek, A., Bauerle, A., Högy, P. and Goetzberger, A., 2020. Implementation of agrophotovoltaics: Techno-economic analysis of the price-performance ratio and its policy implications. *Applied Energy, 265,* p.114737.

[4]   Giri, N.C. and Mohanty, R.C., 2022. Agrivoltaic system: Experimental analysis for enhancing land productivity and revenue of farmers. *Energy for Sustainable Development, 70,* pp.54-61.

[5]   Weselek, A., Ehmann, A., Zikeli, S., Lewandowski, I., Schindele, S. and Högy, P., 2019. Agrophotovoltaic systems: applications, challenges, and opportunities. A review. *Agronomy for sustainable development, 39*(4), p.35.

[6]   Feuerbacher, A., Herrmann, T., Neuenfeldt, S., Laub, M. and Gocht, A., 2022. Estimating the economics and adoption potential of agrivoltaics in Germany using a farm-level bottom-up approach. *Renewable and Sustainable Energy Reviews, 168,* p.112784.

[7]   Lowenberg-DeBoer, J., Huang, I.Y., Grigoriadis, V. and Blackmore, S., 2020. Economics of robots and automation in field crop production. *Precision Agriculture, 21*(2), pp.278-299.

[8]   Riaz, M.H., Imran, H., Alam, H., Alam, M.A. and Butt, N.Z., 2022. Crop-specific optimization of bifacial PV arrays for agrivoltaic food-energy production: The light-productivity-factor approach. *IEEE Journal of Photovoltaics, 12*(2),

pp.572-580.

[9]   Alam, H., Alam, M.A. and Butt, N.Z., 2022. Techno economic modeling for agrivoltaics: Can agrivoltaics be more profitable than ground mounted PV?. *IEEE Journal of Photovoltaics*, *13*(1), pp.174-186.

[10]   Riaz, M.H., Imran, H., Younas, R., Alam, M.A. and Butt, N.Z., 2021. Module technology for agrivoltaics: Vertical bifacial versus tilted monofacial farms. *IEEE Journal of Photovoltaics*, *11*(2), pp.469-477.

[11]   Patel, M.T., Khan, M.R., Sun, X. and Alam, M.A., 2019. A worldwide cost-based design and optimization of tilted bifacial solar farms. *Applied Energy*, *247*, pp.467-479..

[12]   PV performance modeling collaborative | an industry and national laboratory collaborative to improve photovoltaic performance modeling, https://pvpmc.sandia.gov/2016

[13]   Alam, H. and Butt, N.Z., 2024. How does module tracking for agrivoltaics differ from standard photovoltaics? Food, energy, and technoeconomic implications. *Renewable Energy*, *235*, p.121151.

Maximizing Economic Performance of Agrivoltaic Systems through Module Array Design

Habeel Alam[1,2,3*], Jenny Nelson[2], Alona Armstrong[3], Duncan Whyatt[3] and Nauman Z. Butt[1] *(h.alam@lancaster.ac.uk)

[1] Department of Electrical Engineering, Lahore University of Management Sciences, Pakistan
[2] Department of Physics, Imperial College London, United Kingdom
[3] Lancaster Environment Centre, Lancaster University, United Kingdom

Introduction

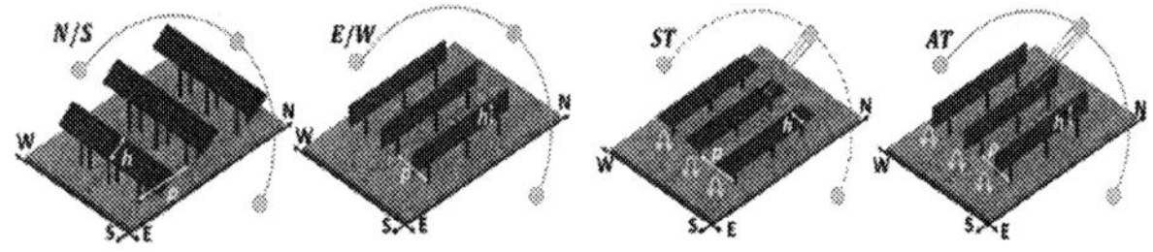

- Selection of an optimal module array density (p/h) for agrivoltaics (AV) can be non-trivial
- Various performance metrics and constraints may need to be met
  - **Food-energy yields, available land area, and economics**
- North/South faced fixed tilt, vertical East/West faced bifacial, standard tracking and anti tracking orientations are studied
- Economic constraints are explored for high and low value crops.

Sunrise   Noon   Sunset

Anti-tracking (AT)   Solar tracking (ST)   Anti-tracking (AT)

Performance Metrics & Economic Constraints

- Energy yield ratio [1]:
$$= \frac{Annual\ energy/\ unit\ farm\ area\ for\ AV}{Annual\ energy/\ unit\ farm\ area\ for\ standard\ PV}$$

- Sunlight availability to crops (PAR ratio) [1]:
$$= \frac{PAR\ available\ to\ crop\ for\ a\ given\ AV\ system}{PAR\ available\ to\ crop\ for\ the\ reference\ full\ sun\ condition}$$

- Crop(biomass) yield ratio (Y_{PAR}) [2]:
$$= \frac{Biomass\ yield\ for\ a\ crop\ in\ AV\ system}{Biomass\ yield\ for\ the\ same\ crop\ in\ full\ sun\ condition}$$

- Economic constraints [2]:
$$price(p'_r) = Hardware\ costs + Soft\ PV\ costs - Energy\ yield\ ratio$$
$$performance\ benefit(pb') = crop\ profit$$
$$price\ performance\ ratio(ppr) = \frac{price\ (p'_r)}{performance\ benefit\ (pb')}$$
$$\mathbf{ppr \leq 1}\ is\ desired\ for\ economic\ feasibility$$

- In case of feed in tariff, performance benefit becomes:
$$performance\ benefit(pb') = crop\ profit + \Delta FIT$$

Food-Energy Yield for different crops

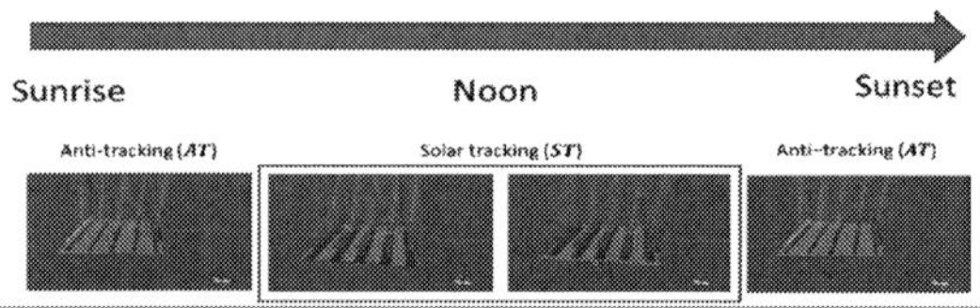

(i) **shade susceptible** (S) ⇒ highly susceptible to shade
(ii) **shade tolerant** (T) ⇒ moderately affected by shade
(iii) **shade benefiting** (B) ⇒ mildly affected by shade

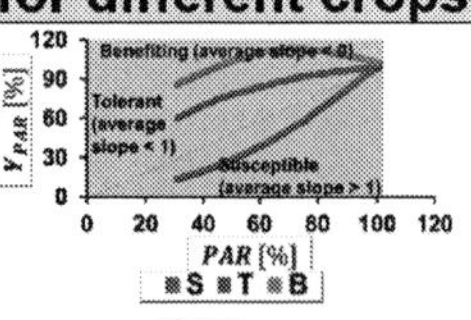

a)N/S b)E/W
c)ST d)AT

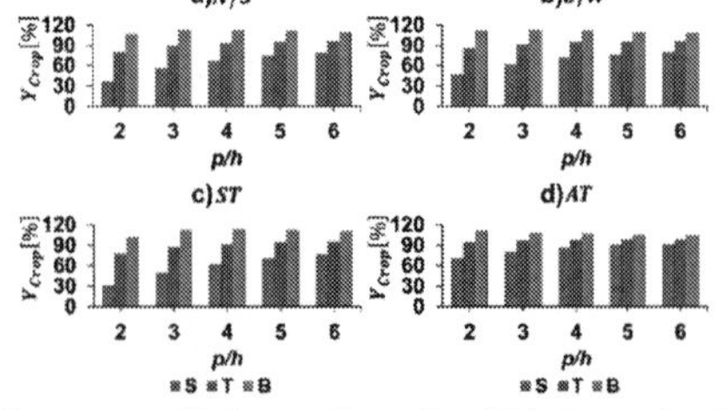

- Y_{Crop} increases with increasing p/h which is most evident in the crop type S.
- ST is not recommended for crop type S at $p/h \leq 4$.

CT for various crop types and seasons.

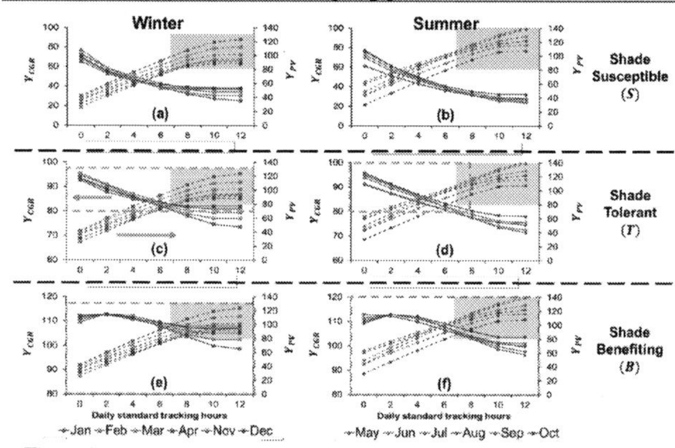

- The yellow dotted box and green shaded box show the space where the value of ST hours can meet 80% value for Y_{CGR} and Y_{PV}, respectively.
- For shade sensitive crops, the assumed threshold limit of $Y_{CGR} = 80\%$ is not met at any value for ST hours.
- The required yield limits are met for the crop type T and B for a range of ST hours.

Economic Feasibility Relative to Standard PV

- Lower ppr (lower module density) requires more land for the same energy capacity but reduces crop shading losses..
- Except for AT, all other module configurations become economically viable for $\Delta FIT \geq 10\%$.

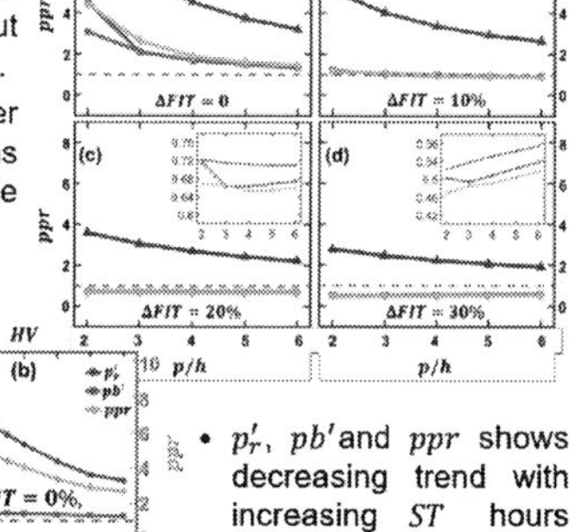

- p'_r, pb' and ppr shows decreasing trend with increasing ST hours when $\Delta FIT = 0$.
- At higher ΔFIT, pb' increases with increasing p/h.

Conclusions

- Requirements for lower ppr and higher land equivalent ratio (LER) often contradict each other.
- Economic scenario shown assumes single ownership of energy and crop revenues; partnerships require mutual contracts to ensure feasibility for each stakeholder

References

[1] H. Alam *et al.*, IEEE Journal of Photovoltaics (2023)

[2] H. Alam *et al.*, Renewable Energy (2024)

[3] M. Laub, *et al.* Agronomy for Sustainable Development (2022).

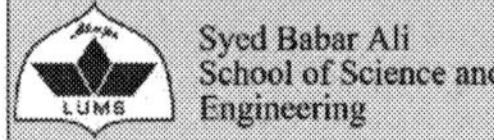

BIFACIAL AND MISMATCH FACTORS OF AGRI-PHOTOVOLTAICS SYSTEMS

Keith R. McIntosh, Solomon Freer, Bastien J.J. Ardissone, S. Ramirez, Ben A. Sudbury and Malcolm D. Abbott
PV Lighthouse
Coledale, NSW, Australia

ABSTRACT: We use ray tracing and circuit simulation to examine bifacial and mismatch factors in three very different types of Agri-PV systems: (A) east–west waves with semi-transparent modules above crops; (B) single-axis trackers with greenhouses between the rows; and (C) east–west facing vertical modules. We determine the annual bifacial gain to be 6%, 4% and 70%, respectively, where the gain for Systems A and B is considerably reduced by crop absorption, and where the gain for System C is close to the bifaciality of the modules. We quantify the shading and transmission factors of the Agri-PV systems, finding them to be significantly higher than for equivalent conventional systems, largely due to extra shading from crops and greenhouses, extra spacing between modules and bays, and, in the case of System A, semitransparent modules. We also quantify the electrical mismatch loss that arises from non-uniform irradiance, finding it to be moderate for System A (0.8%), small for System B (0.3%) and very high for System C (3.9%), primarily due to row-to-row shading when the sun is low in the sky. In addition to quantifying their annual values, we show that these factors depend strongly on the solar position and the diffuse fraction (cloudiness), and we quantify the error introduced into forecasts of output power when this dependence is neglected.
Keywords: agri-photovoltaics, bifacial, yield, mismatch, ray tracing, systems

1 INTRODUCTION

The development of an Agri-PV system requires an understanding of its energy gains and losses, both for the PV modules and the crops. This understanding is assisted by simulation tools that are fast and accurate at quantifying system parameters that cannot easily be measured or calculated. Such parameters include module yield Y_{mod}, bifacial gain g_B, and factors that are used in yield forecasting software: the rear-side shading f_S, the transmission factor f_T, and the electrical mismatch factor f_M, which some split into front f_{MF} and rear f_{MR} components.

The determination of these system parameters tends to be more difficult for Agri-PV than for regular utility-scale systems—especially for bifacial modules—because Agri-PV often includes one or more of the following complications: semitransparent modules, large spacing between modules, custom configurations, additional shading from structural supports or greenhouses, and crops that grow below and between the modules [e.g., 1–4].

The most common way to determine Y_{mod} and g_B involves modelling the optics of the system with a view-factor approach. It solves the optical behavior of an ideal system and then modifies the rear irradiance by the three factors, f_S, f_T and f_{MR}. PVsyst [5] is the best-known software that follows this approach. One of its drawbacks is that it requires the user to know (or guestimate) values for f_S, f_T and f_{MR}, which are exceedingly difficult to measure.

The bifacial factors for Agri-PV systems tend to be quite different from those for conventional utility-scale systems. For example, f_S can be much higher due to shading from crops, greenhouses, or additional structural supports; f_T can be much higher due to the use of semitransparent modules or additional spacing to allow light to pass through to the crops; and f_M can be much higher due greater non-uniformity of the rear irradiance, both in terms of cell-to-cell non-uniformity and module-to-module non-uniformity. These parameters are very different again for Agri-PV systems with vertically mounted modules. Thus, one cannot simply assume default or typical values of f_S, f_T and f_M when forecasting the yield of bifacial Agri-PV systems.

Another way to determine Y_{mod} and g_B is to model the optics with ray tracing, and the mismatch with SPICE modelling. This accounts directly for the complicated geometry of the system, avoiding any need to determine f_S, f_T and f_M.

Moreover, ray tracing and SPICE modelling can used to determine f_S, f_T and f_M for the view-factor programs [6–15]. This is achieved by solving simulations with and without structural supports, with and without transmission through and between modules, and with and without stringing the cells within the module and the modules within the system.

In this work, we determine the system parameters for three very different Agri-PV systems shown in Fig. 1: (a) an east–west wave orientation with semitransparent modules above tall crops, (b) a single-axis tracker (SAT) with greenhouses between its rows, and (c) vertically mounted modules facing east–west and supported by vertical posts.

With the assistance of irradiance maps generated by ray tracing, and with plots of g_B, f_S, f_T and f_M against solar position, day of year, and diffuse fraction, we describe and quantify the major trends for these Agri-PV systems. The results illustrate how the factors for Agri-PV systems differ markedly from those of conventional utility-scale systems, both in terms of magnitude and variability. We also compute the subsequent error that arises in yield forecasting when constant values of f_S, f_T and f_M are used in conventional view-factor programs.

The approach and procedure contained in this paper can be applied to determine the parameters for any Agri-PV configuration and location.

2 SIMULATION DETAILS

Fig. 1 presents the three types of Agri-PV systems examined in this work. The left-hand images are photos of real systems, and the right-hand images show the results of simulations at one timestep during the year, where the color of each solar cell represents its generation current J_G, and where redder/bluer cells indicate a higher/lower J_G.

The colored modules in Fig. 1 are within the simulated unit-system; that is, the set of modules that represents a repeatable unit within the full system. Thus, the simulations account for local edge effects like the spacing

10.4229/EUPVSEC2025/4DV.1.7
020396-001

Figure 1: (a) Actual and **(b)** simulated view of System A: Bifacial semitransparent modules (with 50% cell area) installed in a fixed east-west wave configuration above tall crops.

Figure 2: (a) Actual and **(b)** simulated view of System B: Bifacial modules installed on a two-in-portrait single axis tracker with semi-cylindrical greenhouses between rows. At the example timestep, a strip of cells has a higher J_G (i.e., the redder cells) due to reflection from the top of the greenhouse onto the modules.

Figure 3: (a) Actual and **(b)** simulated view of System C: Bifacial modules installed in a vertical north-south configuration. Tractor omitted from yield simulations. Shading from neighboring rows is evident. Fig. 3(a) reprinted with permission from Raphael Faschang.

between bays, but not the global edge effects at the boundaries of the system.

We simulate the systems with SunSolve Yield [18], which harnesses 600 parallel cores in the cloud to solve the annual yield within minutes (see Table I). The assigned computing power makes this endeavor much less time-consuming than prior studies [6–11] and capable of accounting for more effects, like spectral dependencies, frames, cell optics, crops, large unit systems, and stringing.

Moreover, for System A, the ray tracing extends into the module, accounting for the complicated optics of modern cells and modules (anti-reflection coatings, surface texture, etc.), as well as the cell layout, permitting light to pass between the cells. Their inputs are very similar to those listed in [6] except that the cells are

separated such that they encompass 50% of the module area. For Systems B and C, we emulate a Longi LR5 530 W bifacial module with 144 half-cut cells but the raytracing extends only to the surface of the module. It has a bifaciality of 70%.

The wavelength-dependent optical behavior of the albedo (green grass) and galvanized steel is identical to that shown in Fig. 3 of [15]; the crops of System A assume the reflectance of green grass, and the greenhouses of System B assume the reflectance of glass.

After the ray tracing has computed J_G in every cell of the unit system, the electrical circuit is solved with a SPICE model. This circuit accounts for the conventional stringing of cells within the module (including bypass diodes), as well as the stringing of the modules within the unit system as shown in Fig. 4. The electrical calculations account for thermal effects as described in [6].

We situate all three systems in the same location: Santiago do Cacém, Portugal (38° N, 8.7° E), where Europe's largest PV power plant (1.2 GW) is planned [16]. We use the same weather and atmospheric conditions as described in [15]. The tracking algorithm for the SATs includes conventional backtracking.

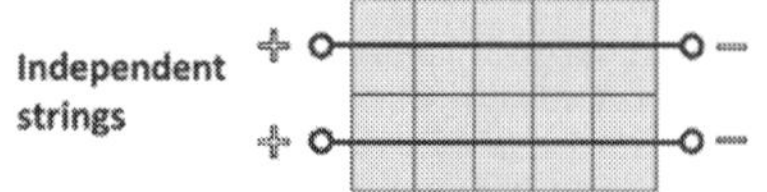

Figure 4: Module rows are connected independently in this study to minimize module-to-module mismatch within strings.

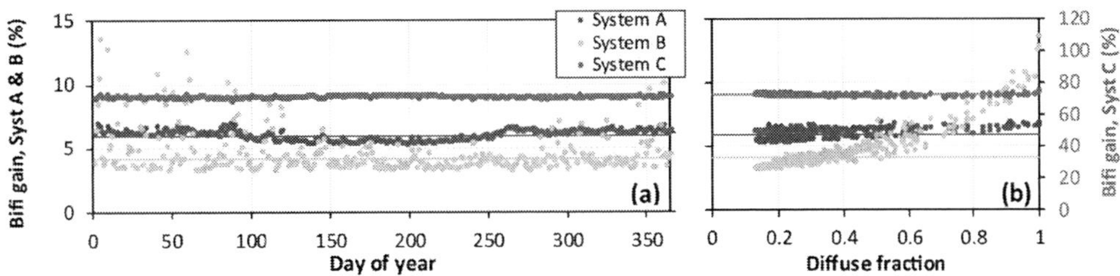

Figure 5: Bifacial gain vs (a) day of year and (b) diffuse fraction. Symbols show the daily g_B, lines show the annual g_B. Data for System C plotted on the right-hand y-axis, whose scale 10× larger than the left-hand y-axis.

3 RESULTS

The results of the simulations are summarized as follows: Table I lists the annual results, Fig. 5 plots the daily bifacial gain against day of year and diffuse fraction, Fig. 6 plots the shading factor f_S at every timestep against the solar zenith angle θ_s, Fig. 7 plots daily factors against day of year, and Fig. 8 plots the factors at each timestep on a single day that contains periods of clear, cloudy and overcast skies. We now describe the major conclusions from the simulations.

3.1 Annual yield

Table I indicates that the energy yield per module Y_{mod} is highest for System B (SAT) because it tracks the sun, and its cells have a high packing density. The yield is the lowest for System A (waves) because its modules are semi-transparent and widely spaced.

TABLE I

ANNUALISED SIMULATION RESULTS

System	A	B	C
N_{mod}	8	80	16
Sim time (min)	3	7	1
Y_{mod} (kWh)	317	1239	815
g_B	6.0%	4.1%	72.8%
f_S	46.9%	52.70%	2.4%
f_T	174.2%	8.6%	0.9%
f_{MR}	0.5%	1.2%	−1.3%
f_M	0.8%	0.3%	3.9%

3.2 Bifacial gain

The bifacial gain g_B is determined by comparing the yield of the full simulation Y_1 to the yield of a simulation that neglects any rays that impinge on the rear-side of the module Y_2. The gain is then given by $g_B = Y_1/Y_2 - 1$. Being the gain in yield, rather than irradiance, it considers the effects of temperature and mismatch.

Table I indicates that g_B of Systems A and B is small but sufficiently large that it should be accounted for in any energy-yield calculation. A gain of 4.1% for System B is smaller than the 5–9% typical of SATs with moderate albedo because the greenhouses absorb some of the light that would otherwise have reflected from the ground onto the rear of the modules. The greenhouses also reflect some light away from the modules.

By contrast, g_B for System C is very large because its modules are vertically mounted and facing east–west [2], and thus, direct sunlight impinges on the rear of the modules after midday. Moreover, like practical vertical PV systems, the module orientation is alternated for each row in the system (i.e., the front side is alternated from being east-facing to west-facing); thus, in the simulated scene, there must be the same irradiance on the front and rear of all modules combined. We find that the bifacial gain in yield is 73%, close to the bifaciality of the modules (70%), but a little higher due to the non-linear dependence of module power on irradiance.

Fig. 5 plots the daily g_B vs day of year and diffuse fraction, exhibiting informative trends that would be difficult to determine experimentally:

System A displays weak dependencies of g_B on season and diffuse fraction, where g_B is higher in winter than summer, and higher in cloudy skies than in clear skies.

System B exhibits almost no dependence on season, but a strong dependence on diffuse fraction. In fact, g_B is 13% when completely overcast and 3.5% under clear skies. That is, the fraction of diffuse sunlight that reaches the rear of the module is much greater than the fraction of direct light. Thus, the value of bifacial modules is much greater on days with low irradiance, when solar electricity is more valuable.

System C exhibits no dependence on season or diffuse fraction, and little scatter in g_B. This is due to the alternating orientation of the front-side of the module

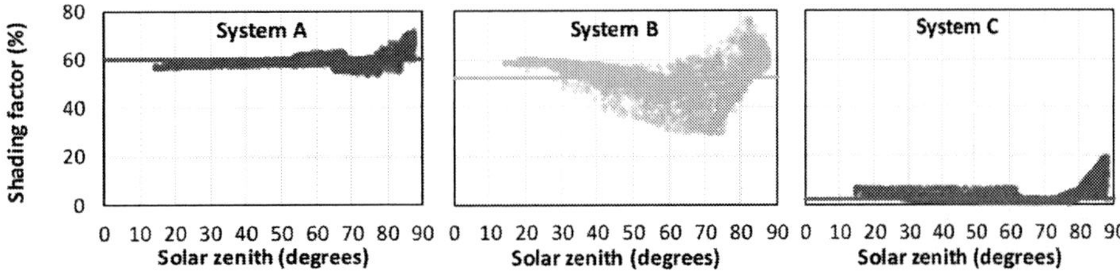

Figure 6: Shading factor vs solar zenith. Symbols show the hourly f_S, lines show the annual f_S.

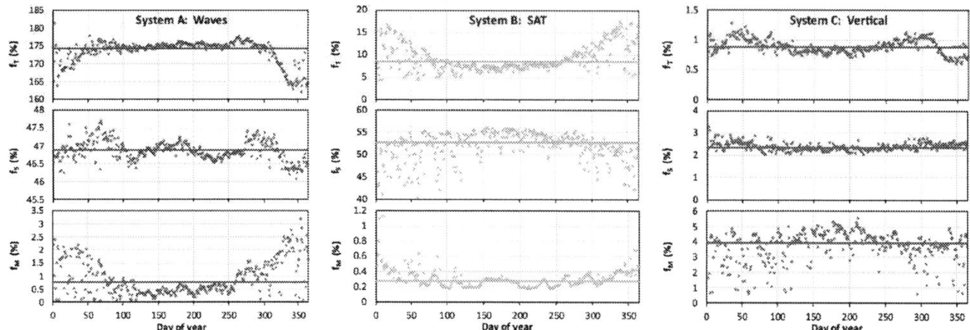

Figure 7: Bifacial factors, f_T, f_S and f_M, for Systems A, B and C. Symbols show daily factors, lines show annual factors.

3.3 Shading factor

The irradiance impinging on the rear surface of the modules is attenuated by shading from structural supports, crops and greenhouses. As in [9, 10], we quantify that shading by solving the rear irradiance I_R with and without those features that shade the rear, $f_S = 1 - I_{R3}/I_{R1}$, where I_{R1} represents the full simulation and I_{R3} represent the simulation without the features. (As described in the appendix, an alternative approach must be applied for wave configurations in PVSyst V8, but we maintain this equation here because it is more informative when comparing configurations.)

The results in Table I indicate the following: In System A, the structural supports and crops approximately halve the rear-side irradiance. In System B, the annual f_S is 47%, which is much higher than f_S for a regular SAT (about 5–10%) [9], indicative of the large impact of the greenhouses. In System C, f_S is much smaller but non-zero, where the shading arises primarily from the posts, which shade the modules when the sun is due south.

We learn more with Fig. 6, which plots f_S vs solar zenith θ_S at every timestep. The large variations in f_S, particularly for System B, indicate that the rear-side irradiance depends strongly on solar position and other factors like the diffuse fraction. Thus, although an energy-weighted annual value of f_S can be determined for simple yield forecasts of Agri-PV (i.e., the lines in Figs. 6 and 7), it introduces error, as quantified in Section 4.

Finally, Fig. 7 shows that f_S is relatively constant over the course of a day for System A. By contrast, for System B, f_S varies strongly since the fraction of light shaded by the greenhouses depends on how much direct light falls between the rows.

3.4 Transmission factor

The transmission factor defines the extra light that reaches the ground due to the semi-transparent nature of modules, or due to spacing between modules—both of which are omitted from idealized view-factor calculations. Thus, those calculations account for these effects by multiplying their ground irradiance by f_T (neglecting any spatial dependence to the light). As in [9, 10], we calculate the factor as $f_T = 1 - I_{R4}/I_{R3}$, where I_{R4} represents the simulation without module spacing and with opaque gaps between the cells of the module (as well as without the features that shade the rear).

Table I indicates that f_T differs greatly between systems. It is very high (174%) for System A because it contains large gaps between semi-transparent modules, making f_T a very

important correction factor for view-factor models (see appendix regarding the calculation of f_T for waves in PVsyst). For System B, the value of f_T is greater than is typical of SATs due to the large bay spacing, and for System C, f_T is very small because the gaps between the posts and modules is small.

We observe in Figs. 7 and 8 that f_T varies with season and time of day, indicating that f_T depends strongly on the

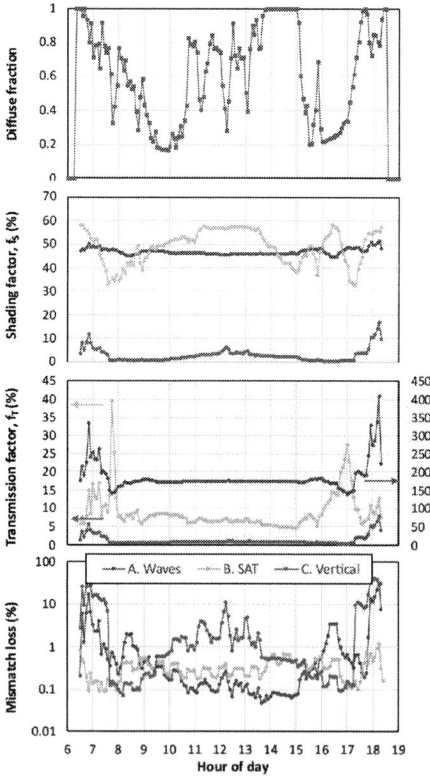

Figure 8: One of day data with 5-minute intervals showing (a) diffuse fraction, (b) f_M (c) f_T and (d) f_S for Systems A, B and C. As evident from the diffuse fraction, the sky is clear during the periods 9h–10.5h and 16h–17h, overcast at 14h–15h, and otherwise partly cloudy.

position of the sun in the sky. Interestingly, f_T is lowest in the winter for System A but highest in the winter for System B. This arises due to the systems having very different dependencies on direct and diffuse light.

Once again, there is a large amount of variation in the data, suggesting that the use of annual values (lines) introduce significant error into yield simulations—as will be quantified in Section 4.

3.5 Mismatch factor

The factor f_M quantifies the relative reduction in yield caused by the electrical mismatch arising from non-uniform irradiance. In this work, f_M includes both cell-to-cell and module-to-module mismatch and does not distinguish between front and rear non-uniformity. (It is determined in the manner described in [6, 14].)

Table I indicates that f_M is small for System B, moderate for System A, and very large for System C. It is highest for System C due to the row-to-row shading of direct light that occurs when the sun is low in the sky, and to a lesser extent from the non-uniformity arising from ground reflection.

Fig. 7 shows that there are strong seasonal dependencies in all factors for all systems—moreso than for conventional utility-scale systems [13]. They arise primarily from changes in the solar position and the resulting introduction of row-to-row shading of direct light for Systems A and C, and also due to changes in non-uniformity on the rear. The scatter about those trends is mostly due to variation in diffuse fraction.

4 ERROR WHEN ASSUMING CONSTANT VALUES OF f_S, f_T and f_M DURING A YIELD FORECAST

Many yield forecasting programs (e.g., PVSyst, SAM, Solar Farmer) solve the system optics with a view-factor model. The model computes the irradiance on the front and rear of the modules for the ideal scenario of opaque modules, no space between modules, and no structural supports. The programs then modify the rear irradiance by multiplying it by $(1 + f_T)$ and $(1 - f_S)$ to account for additional light impinging on the ground and shading from structural supports. These programs also account for electrical mismatch due to non-uniformity by multiplying the yield by $(1 - f_M)$. This approach provides a fast optical model but requires the user to input values of f_T, f_S and f_M, which can either be guesstimated or determined by ray tracing.

Current versions of these programs restrict the user to entering constant values of f_T, f_S and f_M to represent all timesteps. As evident above, however, these values can vary substantially over the course of the day and year,

whether due to their dependence on the position of the sun, or on the atmosphere (changing the diffuse fraction or, to a lesser extent, the incident spectra). Thus, the 'constant-factor' assumption introduces error into yield forecast.

We now investigate the error at each timestep introduced by the constant-factor assumption. Fig. 9 presents the results, plotting the absolute error in module power at every timestep for each of our example agri-PV systems. To put the error into context, the average output power per module during daylight hours $P_{mod\ av}$ is (a) 70 W, (b) 276 W and (c) 172 W. (Note that the sum of the absolute errors of each plot in Fig. 9 is zero because the constant value of f_S, f_T and f_M are energy-weighted averages that ensure there is no error in the annual yield.)

Fig. 9 demonstrates that the error (i) is not insignificant and (ii) exhibits very different trends for each system, indicative of very different dependencies on the position of the sun in the sky.

For System A (waves, $P_{mod\ av}$ = 70 W), the yield from each module is underestimated by between 0 and 1 W when $\theta_s < 65°$, and overestimated by as much as 6 W when $\theta_s > 65°$ (i.e., when the sun is low in the sky). In short, the forecast of System A tends to be significantly overestimated at the shoulders of the day.

System B (SAT, $P_{mod\ av}$ = 276 W) follows a different trend. Its error is within ±5 W, where it tends to overestimate when $\theta_s < 50°$ and overestimate when $\theta_s > 55°$.

System C (vertical, $P_{mod\ av}$ = 172 W) exhibits the greatest error and the greatest scatter. It overestimates the yield by as much as 50 W, particularly when the sun is low in the sky (primarily due to an underestimation of electrical mismatch due to row-to-row shading) and underestimates by as much as 30 W, particularly when the sun is high in the sky. Unlike the other systems, the error also depends strongly on the diffuse fraction.

For both System A and B, the error is predominantly due to the variation in structural shading that is not captured when assuming a constant f_S. For System C, the error is predominantly due to the variation in electrical mismatch.

5 CONCLUSION

With ray tracing and SPICE solving, we calculated the bifacial and mismatch factors of three types of Agri-PV systems. We found the factors vary greatly for each system and exhibit markedly different trends. We demonstrated that the factors depend strongly on the position of the sun in the sky and cloud cover—more than is typical for utility-scale non-Agri-PV systems. We found that the application of the 'constant-factor assumption'

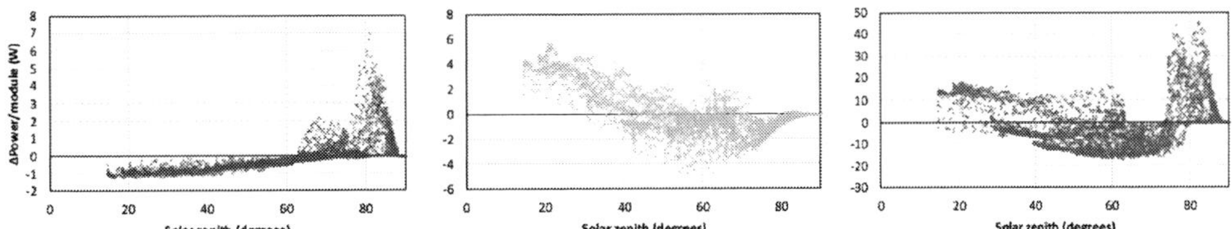

Figure 9: Absolute error in the module power vs solar zenith when annual energy-weighted values of f_T, f_S and f_M are used. Results plotted for Systems (a) A, (b) B and (c) C. For context, the average daytime output power per module is (a) 70 W, (b) 276 W and (c) 172 W.

leads to significant errors, particularly during the shoulders of the day for wave systems due to structural shading, and in vertical systems due to electrical mismatch.

These results underscore the complexity of simulating bifacial Agri-PV systems and demonstrate how insights can be gained by studying the systems with a combination of ray tracing and SPICE modelling.

6 APPENDIX

At the time of writing, the simulation of bifacial wave systems with PVsyst necessitates a complicated procedure. Although PVsyst (V 8.0.15) contains the option to simulate 'domes' (a waves system), it does not permit the modules to be bifacial. Consequently, a bifacial wave system must create two separate 'infinite-shed' systems—one for the east-facing and another for the west-facing modules—where the bifacial option is selected for both.

PVsyst's optical model then computes the irradiance on the rear of the module as if (i) there are no lateral gaps between modules, (ii) the modules are opaque, and (iii) the neighbouring rows of modules are exclusively of the same type of system. Thus, to simulate the east–west waves structure of Figure 1(a), PVsyst simulates the rear optics of the east-facing modules as if the west-facing modules were not present as shown in Figure 4(b), and the equivalent case for the west-facing.

The procedure for determining f_S and f_T must therefore change to accommodate this approach. Remember that the purpose of f_S and f_T is to modify the optics such that the configuration simulated by PVsyst emulates the actual configuration as simulated by the ray tracing.

In the new procedure, the approach to determine the baseline current I_{R1} remains the same, and the full simulation is solved as normal. However, I_{R3} and I_{R4} must be determined by removing the structures *and* the neighbouring row; thus to determine f_S and f_T for the east-facing modules, the west-facing modules are omitted from the ray tracing simulation; and vice versa. The determination of I_{R4} also requires (i) the removal of the spacing between modules and (ii) converting any semi-transparent regions in the module to be opaque.

Finally, we note that the recommended procedure to determine the bifacial factors for PVsyst might have to adapt to future versions of PVsyst. Refer to [18] for updates.

TABLE II

ANNUALISED SIMULATION RESULTS FOR SYSTEM A

	Standard approach	Modified approach for PVsyst V8
f_S	46.9%	60.3%
f_T	174.2%	34.8%

7 ACKNOWLEDGEMENT

This project received funding from the Australian Renewable Energy Agency (ARENA) as part of ARENA's Advancing Renewables Program. The views expressed herein are not necessarily the views of the Australian Government, and the Australian Government does not accept responsibility for any information or advice contained herein.

8 REFERENCES

[1] B. Staie, Agrivoltaics Technical Assistance in the United States, NREL Report PR-6A20-90143 (2024).

[2] S. Ovaitt, A. Kinzer, M. Boyd, J. Jones, C. Deline, J. Macknick, "Viewfactor and Raytracing for AgriPV Modeling", NREL Report PR-5K00-86631 (2023).

[3] M. H. Riaz, H. Imran, N. Z. Butt, "Optimization of PV Array Density for Fixed Tilt Bifacial Solar Panels for Efficient Agrivoltaic Systems," IEEE PVSC, 2020, pp. 1349–1352.

[4] Y. Hu, X. Zhang, X. Ma, "Agrivoltaics with semitransparent panels can maintain yield and quality in soybean production," Solar Energy 282 (2024) 112978.

[5] PVSyst, http://pvsyst.com/

[6] K. R. McIntosh, M. D. Abbott, B. A. Sudbury, J. Meydbray, "Mismatch loss in bifacial modules due to nonuniform illumination in 1-D tracking systems," IEEE Journal of PV 9 (2019) 1504.

[7] S. A. Pelaez, C. Deline, J. S. Stein, B. Marion, K. Anderson, M. Muller, "Effect of torque-tube parameters on rear-irradiance and rear-shading loss for bifacial PV performance on single-axis tracking systems," Proceedings 46th IEEE PVSC (2019).

[8] C. Deline, S. A. Pelaez, S. MacAlpine, C. Olalla, "Estimating and parameterizing mismatch power loss in bifacial photovoltaic systems," Progress in Photovoltaics 28 (2020) 691.

[9] K. R. McIntosh, M. D. Abbott, B. A. Sudbury, "How the PVSyst inputs for bifacial systems depend on conditions," Bifacial Workshop 2020, Virtual Proceedings.

[10] C. Zhao, J. Xiao, Y. Yu, J. N. Jaubert, "Accurate shading factor and mismatch loss analysis of bifacial HSAT systems through ray-tracing modeling," Solar Energy Advances 1 (2021) 100004.

[11] G. Raina, S. Sunanda, "A comprehensive assessment of electrical performance and mismatch losses in bifacial PV module under different front and rear side shading scenarios," Energy Conversion and Management 261 (2022) 115668.

[12] A. C. Russell, C. E. Valdivia, C. Bohémier, J. E. Haysom, K. Hinzer, "DUET: A Novel Energy Yield Model With 3-D Shading for Bifacial Photovoltaic Systems," IEEE Journal of PV 12 (2022) 1576.

[13] A. Calcabrini Andres, R. Cardosso, D. Gribnau, P. Babal, P. Manganiello, M. Zeman, O. Isabella, "Time-varying, ray tracing irradiance simulation approach for photovoltaic systems in complex scenarios with decoupled geometry, optical properties and illumination conditions," Progress in Photovoltaics 31 (2023) 134–148.

[14] PV Lighthouse, "Step-by-step guide to determine PVSyst bifacial inputs with SunSolve," 2024.

[15] K. R. McIntosh, M. D. Abbott, B. A. Sudbury, "Quantifying Inherent Sources of Electrical Mismatch in Utility-Scale Bifacial Systems," Proceedings 40th EU PVSEC, Lisbon (2023).

[16] https://taiyangnews.info/markets/europes-largest-solar-power-farm-planned-in-portugal/, Taiyang News, 1-Feb-2023.

[17] Pelaez, S.A., C. Deline, P. Greenberg, J. Stein, and R.K. Kostuk. 2018. "Model and Validation of Single-Axis Tracking with Bifacial Photovoltaics: Preprint." NREL/CP-5K00-72039.

[18] https://sunsolve.com/
[19] Mahim, T.M., Rahim, A.H.M.A, Mosaddequr
      Rahman, M., "Review of Mono- and Bifacial
      Photovoltaic Technologies: A Comparative Study,"
      IEEE Journal of Photovoltaics 14 (2024) 375.
[20] Toqueboeuf, C., "Comparative Modeling And
      Validation Of Bifacial Gains In PV Power Plants",
      Dissertation, 2025.
[21] Benbba, R., Akhsassi, M., El mouden, H., Wifaya,
      A., and Outzourhit, A., "View Factors Approach for
      Bifacial Photovoltaic Array Modeling: Bifacial Gain
      Sensitivity Analysis." J. Sol. Energy Eng., 147
      (2025) 021008.

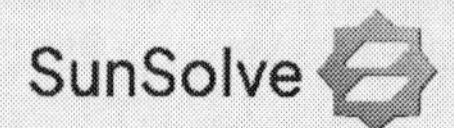

SunSolve

Bifacial factors for AgriPV

K.R. McIntosh, S. Freer, B. Ardissone, S. Ramirez, B.A. Sudbury and M.D. Abbott

An optical challenge

Bifacial modules provide a significant boost to the electrical yield from AgriPV.

What is the bifacial gain? How does it depend on time of day, time of year, weather?

View-factor (VF) approaches struggle to answer those questions due to the complexity of AgriPV. E.g.,

- semitransparent modules,
- large spacing between modules,
- shading from supports or greenhouses,
- crops that grow below and between modules.

VF programs account for complexity with correction factors for the bifacial irradiance, like transmission f_T, shading f_S, and mismatch due to non-uniformity f_M.

Findings

Ray tracing (RT) can solve complex systems to give:

- electrical yield — annual, daily, hourly;
- bifacial gain;
- bifacial factors for VF programs like PVsyst.

Modern RT programs solve those systems in 1–10 mins, using cloud processing and tuned algos. We find:

AgriPV bifi factors depend greatly on configuration.

Results give useful insights. E.g., for our location, f_M is

- 10× higher for vertical PV than SATs,
- Variability for vertical PV is due mostly to cloud,
- Variability for waves, SATs due more to season.

The paper quantifies the error from assuming f_S, f_T and f_M are constants. It depends strongly on zenith angle.

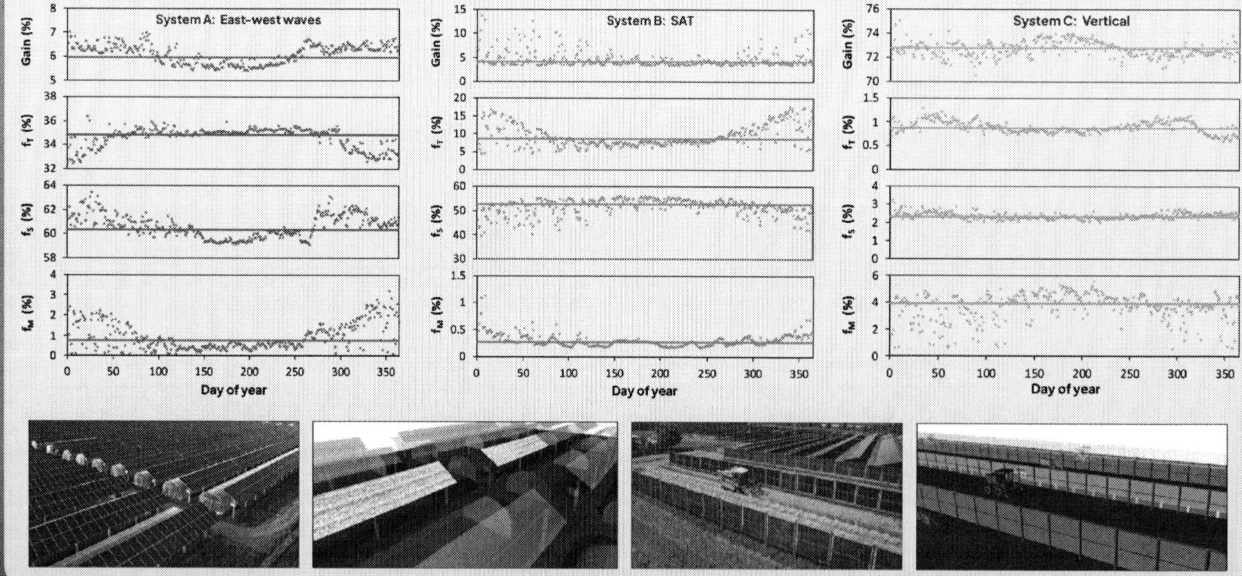

Conclusions

- AgriPV systems are optically complex.
- Modern ray tracers can solve their bifacial gain and annual yield in 1–10 minutes.
- RT can also determine the bifacial factors (f_S, f_T and f_M) required by PVsyst and other VF programs.
- The factors vary with site, weather, time of day and year.

020397-001

PERFORMANCE ANALYSIS OF AGRIVOLTAIC SYSTEM CONFIGURATIONS IN NORDIC CONDITIONS

Magda Szarek[1], Sami Jouttijärvi[1], Lauri Karttunen[1], Samuli Ranta[2], Kati Miettunen[1]
[1]Department of Mechanical and Materials Engineering, University of Turku, Vesilinnantie 5, 20500 Turku, Finland
[2]Turku University of Applied Sciences, Joukahaisenkatu 7, 20520 Turku, Finland

ABSTRACT: This study compares the energy yields, ground shading, and financial impacts of several agrivoltaic (APV) system layouts in high-latitude conditions. APV systems allow farmland to be combined with energy production, thus reducing the land-use conflict between photovoltaic systems and food production. APVs have been gaining popularity worldwide, including in Nordic countries and other high-latitude locations where solar energy has received little attention until recently. High latitude locations face different conditions than low latitude locations because of different sun elevation angles, day length, and weather patterns. Because of this, system configurations must be optimized for these conditions. We analyzed three APV configurations of 1 MW that include 1) vertically mounted east-west facing bifacial panels, 2) a single-axis tracker system, and 3) a south-facing overhead system at separations of 8, 10, 15, and 30 m. The tracker system had the highest specific yield (1.26–1.39 kWh/kW). However, the two production peaks of the vertical system more closely matching high spot prices of electricity resulted in the highest capture price of electricity produced by the vertical system (43.77–43.83 EUR/MWh).
Keywords: photovoltaic, agrivoltaic, land use

1 INTRODUCTION

The need for renewable technologies continues to grow as the environment and society change. Cheap renewable energy offers opportunities for economic gain, resilience through local energy production, and reduced emissions. To compound, solar photovoltaic (PV) technologies have become cheaper, making them attractive prospects in a wide range of applications and climates. Until recently, wide-scale implementation of solar installations in the Nordic countries has been limited compared to other regions of the world. This was, in part, due to the solar energy conditions being less favorable at high latitudes. In recent years, this trend has shifted, and solar installations have seen rapid growth in the Nordic countries [1].

Until recently, investments were primarily in small personal installations; however, a significant number of large-scale installations are currently in various stages of planning and implementation [2]. This booming interest has created an opportunity and a need for research on the suitability of various system designs in high latitude conditions. Differences between high and low-to-mid latitude conditions entail a need for different design approaches and types of systems analyses. Lower temperatures, typical of higher latitudes, result in reduced heat loss. However, the highly variable yearly irradiance, low sun elevation angles, and snow cover pose challenges to creating optimal systems [3]. In addition, electricity prices in the Nordic countries are typically low, especially during the summer months. As a result, efficient designs tailored to local conditions are needed to ensure the profitability of solar energy production [4]. For example, bifacial panels, especially when combined with vertical placements that allow both sides direct access to irradiance, may be particularly well suited to high latitudes, as they can make use of long periods of low solar elevation [5].

One of the challenges of PV energy production is ensuring the efficient use of available land. A potential solution is to place solar panels in actively used locations. Agrivoltaics (APVs), which combine agricultural land with PV installations, are a notable form of dual land use. APVs have been implemented in many locations around the world and have already been successfully tested in high-latitude locations, though in a limited capacity [6], [7]. Because APV land can produce more combined value than dedicated agricultural or PV land, it is attractive as both a means of supplementary income for farmers and a means of preserving land for other uses, including biodiversity [8], [9]. APV can also decrease evaporation, improving crop yield during drought years [10], though this positive effect is likely limited in typical high-latitude conditions.

Our previous studies have already shown how bifacial technologies can be efficiently utilized in high latitude conditions [5] and the benefits of east-west facing vertical bifacial (VBPV) systems in APV applications [11] and the higher value for self-consumption of produced electricity [12]. This study expands on previous research by analyzing tracker systems and comparing three types of systems using bifacial panels in a high-latitude location. Specifically, a VBPV system, a tracker system, and a south-facing overhead (SO) system are compared in terms of their total produced energy, ground shading, revenue, and the value of produced electricity based on Nordpool spot prices. Several row separations (8, 10, 15, and 30 m) were analyzed to compare the impact of varying row separation. The albedo values used in simulations are typical of crops grown in high-latitude conditions.

2 METHODOLOGY

2.1 Meteorological and environmental data

The study was conducted in high latitude Nordic conditions, specifically in southwestern Finland in the area of Turku at 60° N. To determine the systems' performance in that area's meteorological and solar conditions, satellite weather data and measured albedo from a site at a similar latitude were used. Satellite data were obtained from Copernicus Atmosphere Monitoring Service (CAMS), and the output was analyzed for the 2024 calendar year [13]. Barley is the most common crop grown in Finland, and planting in the spring is the most common method. Thus, the albedo for the system surroundings was chosen from a measured spring barley albedo. The location at which it was measured is situated at a similar latitude in Sweden

[14]. The albedo in high latitudes, especially cropland, is highly varied, as it can go from as low as 0.08 in October to as high as 0.74 in December when snow cover is significant.

2.2 Spot price data

The electricity price in Finland is updated on an hourly basis, so the value of the electricity produced at any given hour is determined by the current market price. That price depends on multiple factors, including the variable renewable electricity production in Finland as well as prices in neighboring electricity markets. To determine the profitability of the different configurations, the Nordpool tax-free spot price in the day-ahead market for the 2024 calendar year was used [12], [15]. Finland is covered by a single price zone, with no price differences for different regions. The electricity value was determined as the total revenue divided by the production of the given system. The total revenue was calculated using the following formula:

$$revenue = \sum_{t=1}^{n}\left(p_{spot,t} \cdot E_{PV,t}\right), \quad (1)$$

where p_{spot} is the spot price, t is the hour of the year, and $E_{PV,t}$ is the energy output of the PV system at t.

2.3 System design

The simulations were completed using PVsyst® [16] software, which was previously found to be capable of creating accurate simulations for high latitude locations [9]. A generic bifacial panel offered by the program was used for all system types, with the built-in bifaciality function of "unlimited sheds" for the SO and VBPV systems and "unlimited trackers" for the tracker system. The panel parameters are depicted in Table I.

Table I: Selected generic bifacial solar panel parameters

Parameter	Mono 700 Wp Twin half-cells bifacial
Rated power (W)	700
Rated voltage (V)	42.60
Rated current (A)	16.43
Open circuit voltage (V)	50.59
Short circuit current (A)	17.33

The nominal power of the created systems was 1 MW. A generic "1,000 kWac central inverter" was used. Ground shading is the difference between irradiance reaching the agriculturally usable ground between solar rows and the total GHI. The formula for ground shading is as follows:

$$irradiance = \frac{\sum_{t=1}^{n}\left(GHI_t - I_{ground,t}\right)}{\sum_{t=1}^{n}\left(GHI_t\right)} \cdot 100\%, \quad (2)$$

where GHI is the global horizontal irradiance, t is the hour of the growing season in Southern Finland (27.04–17.10), and $I_{ground,t}$ is the irradiance at ground level at t.

The unused space around PV panel rows is 0.5 m on each side of the VBPV and SO panels. The ground shading of the tracker system was omitted due to program limitations. The effects of snow cover, which primarily affect SO systems, were omitted [17]. Due to snow being present during low irradiance months, the effect is limited, especially for vertical and tracker systems, as their tilt significantly reduces the likelihood of snow cover. All systems were created in a configuration of 19 rows of 40 × 2 panels.

The VBPV system is placed 1 m above ground level and consists of two horizontally situated solar panels, and

0.5 m of clearance space is left unused on each side of solar rows, resulting in 1 m of unused land per row (see Fig. 1).

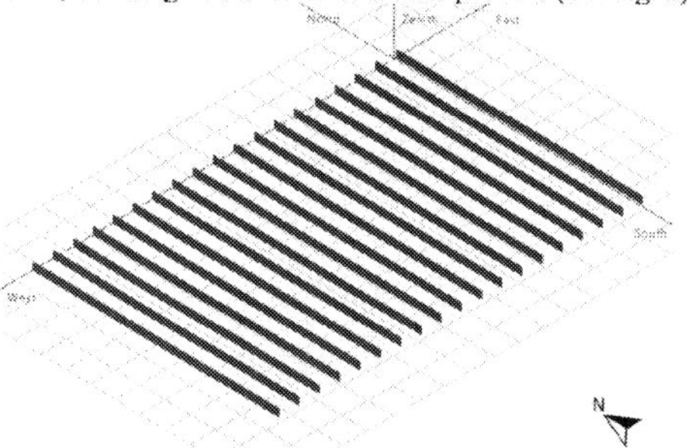

Figure 1: VBPV system (created with PVsyst®)

The tracker system was designed as a standing ground system raised 1 m above ground level (see Fig. 2).

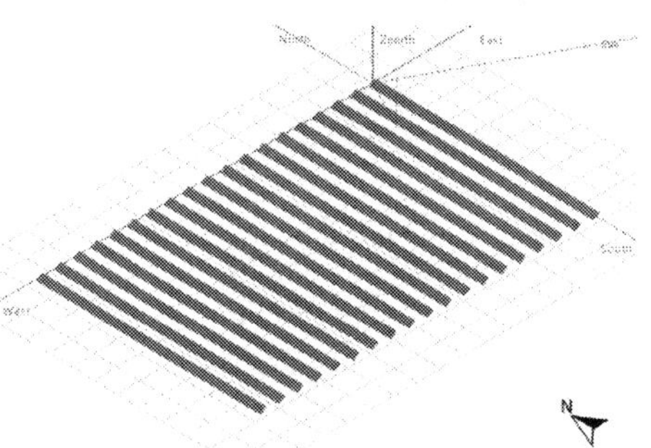

Figure 2: North-south axis bifacial tracker system (created with PVsyst®)

The SO system was designed as an overhead system placed 5 m above ground level to leave space for agricultural activity (see Fig. 3). To account for the large beams typically used in overhead systems, 0.5 m of unused space was left as clearance on each side.

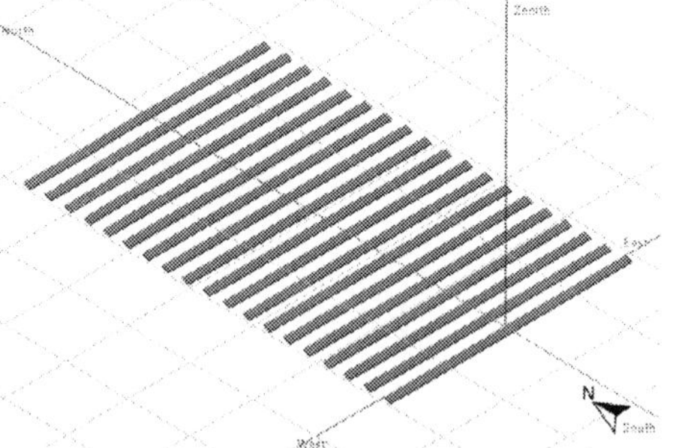

Figure 3: Bifacial south-facing overhead (SO) system (created with PVsyst®)

For each system, four different row separations (8, 10, 15 and 30 m), and for the ground shading three row separations (8, 10 and 15 m) were analyzed as large-scale farming equipment may necessitate significant clearance. The PV systems at a 30 m separation were assumed to be a case with minimal self-shading. In the case of very large farming vehicles, even over 20 m of clearance could be necessary; however, APV systems with such a scale are not currently utilized at high latitudes and thus were not taken into consideration. The 8 m separated variant occupied 14,112 m², the 10 m separated variant occupied 17,640 m², and the 15 m variant occupied 26,460 m².

3 RESULTS

Three types of PV systems were analyzed to compare their outputs, production times, value of produced electricity, and ground shading. A comparison of the average power production in each month of 2024 is shown in Fig. 4. The SO installation performed best at noon when electricity prices are typically lower. The tracker system performed well throughout the day and was characterized by the most consistent energy production as well as the highest performance overall. The VBPV system had two production peaks, one in the morning and one in the evening, which matches energy use peaks than the other systems[18].

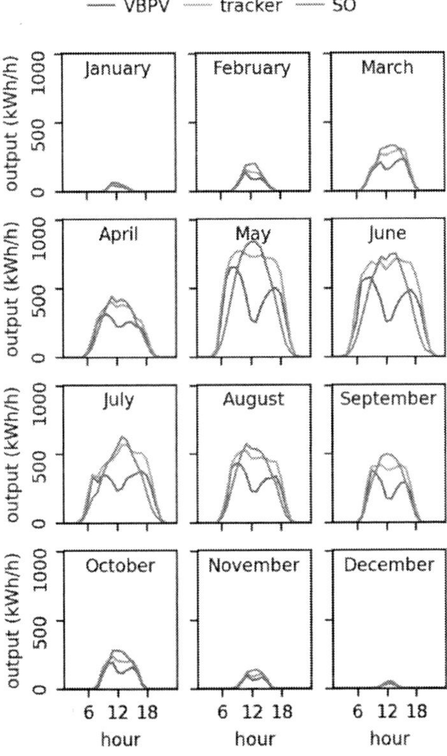

Figure 4: Average power production of the VBPV, SO, and tracker systems for each month in Turku, Finland in 2024 at a row distance of 15 m

The total energy production in 2024 for each system at 8, 10, 15 and 30 m separations is shown in Fig. 5. In all cases, increasing row separation in the analyzed range resulted in increased energy output. Tracker panels had the highest output in all cases. The SO systems outperformed the VBPV system at the analyzed row distances. However, the performance of the SO panels remained constant at above 10 m separation, and they received no further benefit from increasing row separation, while the VBPV system's output continued to increase.

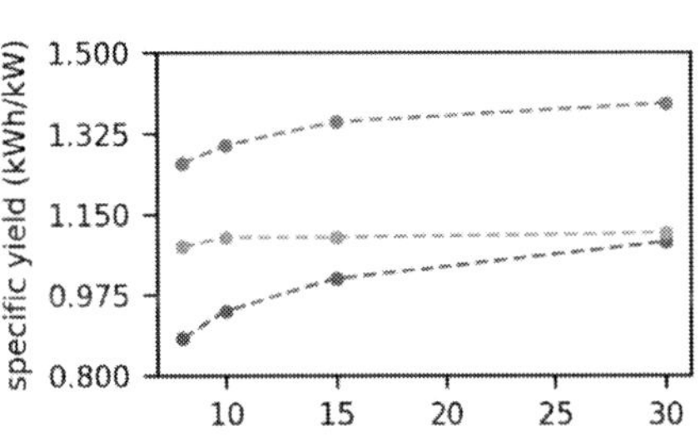

Figure 5: Specific yield of three agrivoltaic systems utilizing trackers, a VBPV configuration, and an SO installation in Finland in 2024

A comparison of the hourly energy output and spot price for selected summer days containing both sunny and cloudy conditions is shown in Fig. 6.

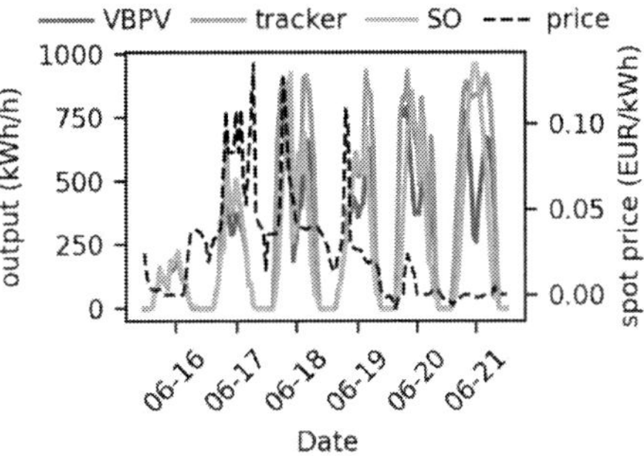

Figure 6: Output of the analyzed systems at a 15 m separation and spot price in 2024. Chosen days are summer days with both sunny and cloudy conditions as well as varied spot-price

The irradiance reaching the ground in the analyzed systems for row separations of 8, 10, and 15 m is depicted in Fig. 7. In the cases of both the VBPV and SO systems, the irradiance reaching the ground increased rapidly with increased row separation, which resulted in reduced crop impact. It is estimated that a roughly 25% reduction in irradiance reaching crops results in minor losses only [2]. The exact value depends on both the exact growth conditions and the crop; thus, the threshold is only a generalized estimate. At low row separations, VBPV allows more light to reach the ground, resulting in a lower crop impact than an SO system. At large row separations, shading from both types of systems is minimal and should have no significant impact on the crops.

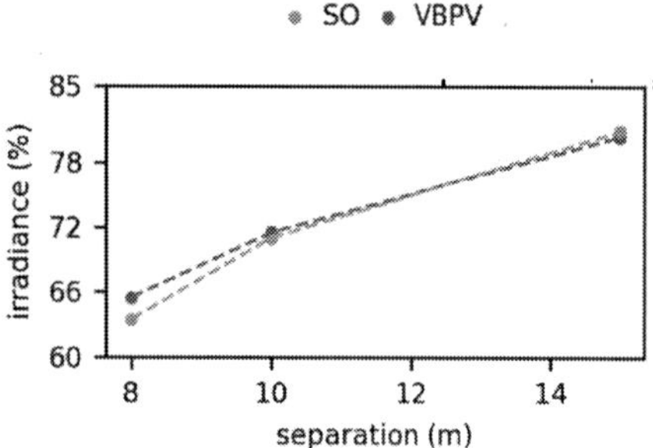

Figure 7: Irradiance reaching the ground for an SO system and a VBPV installation in Finland in 2024

The revenue and value of electricity based on the Nordpool spot price for each system are depicted in Fig. 8. Revenue increases with an increase in PV energy output. The tracker system had the highest revenue and energy yield per panel. Although the VBPV system had a higher revenue than the SO system at high row separations, at low separations, the SO system had a higher revenue. However, electricity prices from 2024 are still only affected by existing PV systems to a small degree due to a small number of PVs in the Finnish energy grid. In the future south facing PV systems will drive the electricity prices down, which can be seen in countries like Germany where PV adoption is much further ahead. By contrast, the value of the energy in the VBPV system was the highest due to the difference in price between different times of day and two-peak production profiles of the VBPV systems [4].

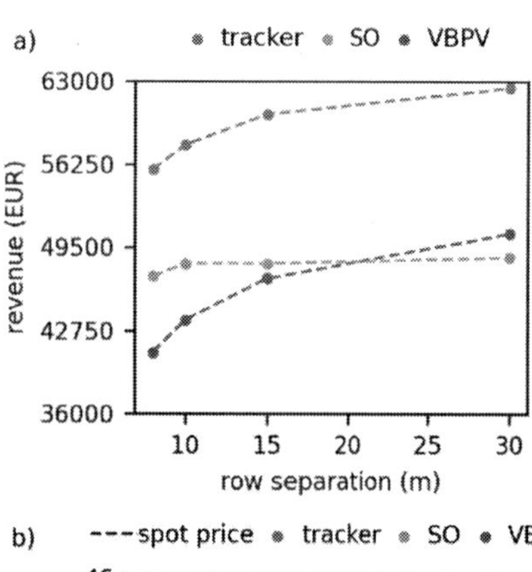

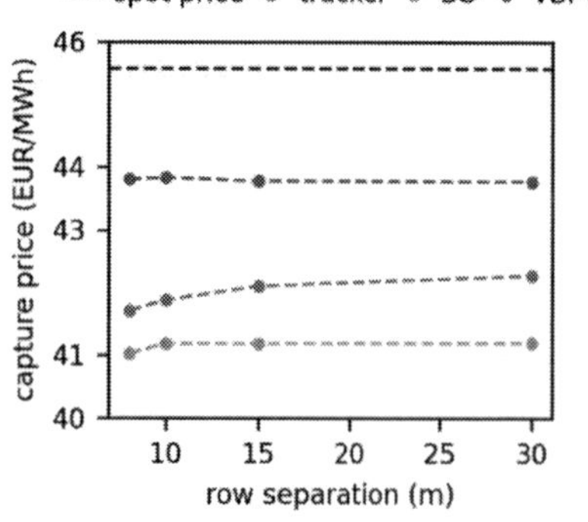

Figure 8: Graphs showing a) revenue (EUR) and b) capture price (EUR/MWh) for tracker, SO, and VBPV installations based on Nordpool spot prices for Finland in 2024

4 CONCLUSIONS

This study compared the performance of three types of high-latitude APV systems. All the systems had an equal number of bifacial panels to ensure comparability. The total yearly output based on meteorological data from 2024 was determined for VBPV, SO, and tracker systems at three row separations (8, 10, and 15 m) with an additional comparison of PV output of a 30 m separated system for an unshaded scenario. Ground shading for the SO and VBPV systems was comparable at larger row distances; however, at 8 m, the VBPV installation was favored because it shaded the ground less than the SO system, and a PV system's negative impact on crop yield is primarily due to shading. The tracker system had the highest production and revenue. Although the VBPV system notably had the highest value of electricity produced, in terms of output, it was outperformed by the tracker and SO systems.

While the VBPV system had the highest capture price per MWh, it only resulted in a higher revenue at very large row separation. The difference in revenue stemming from increased production in the case of the tracker and SO systems at this time outpaces the difference in capture price between the systems at lower row separations. However, as the share of solar energy in the energy market continues to grow, the value of electricity produced around noon is expected to drop further, which can put SO systems at a greater disadvantage, which would favor VBPV systems, which are expected to be less affected due to different peak production times matching demand and thus daily price peaks. Additionally, SO systems are the most vulnerable to snow cover during winter, when electricity prices are typically higher than in the summer months, which can further decrease the value of the electricity they produce. Note that, although these calculations omitted snow cover losses, vertical and tracker systems are less prone to snow cover, which gives them an advantage in snow-heavy regions.

Overhead and tracker systems are more expensive than VBPV systems; although, SO systems can also be installed directly on the ground, giving VBPV an advantage in the form of lower investment costs and increased resilience to the effects of the growing share of PV in the energy market. Based on 2024 prices, the VBPV systems require large row separation to result in higher revenue than an SO system due to their lower energy production. Designs that reduce self-shading can result in a higher specific yield, but the main draw of a vertical system remains its synergy in dual land-use scenarios. While the revenue from SO systems is likely to plummet in the future, which will favor vertical systems, the most valuable system type is still likely to be the one that produces energy at times when it can be self-consumed on site rather than sold.

ACKNOWLEDGMENTS

This project was funded by the Strategic Research Council established within the Research Council of Finland Decision No. 358542 (KM, SJ, MS, LK), Decision No. 359141 (SR), University of Turku Graduate School (LK) and the city of Salo and University of Turku HEMS-project (LK).

REFERENCES

[1] V. Olkkonen, A. Lind, E. Rosenberg, L. Kvalbein, "Electrification of the agricultural sector in Norway in an effort to phase out fossil fuel consumption," Energy 276 (2023) 127543, doi: 10.1016/J.ENERGY.2023.127543.

[2] "RENEWFM: EUR 27.5 million supporting 7 solar power plants in Finland - European Commission", [Online]. Available: https://cinea.ec.europa.eu/news-events/news/renewfm-eur-275-million-supporting-7-solar-power-plants-finland-2024-05-29_en.

[3] J. Viitanen, A. Amogpai, M. Puolakka, L. Halonen, "Photovoltaic production possibilities and its utilization in office buildings in Finland," Int. J. Eng. Appl. IREA 2 (2011), doi: 10.15866/irea.v7i1.17186.

[4] S. Jouttijärvi et al., "Sensitivity of electricity price in the Finnish market conditions with increasing solar energy production," doi: 10.4229/EUPVSEC2024/5DV.3.27.

[5] S. Jouttijärvi, G. Lobaccaro, A. Kamppinen, K. Miettunen, "Benefits of bifacial solar cells combined with low voltage power grids at high latitudes," Renew. Sustain. Energy Rev. 161 (2022) 112354–112354, doi: 10.1016/J.RSER.2022.112354.

[6] S. Völler, M.D. Sabatino, R.J. Randle-Boggis, G. Stokkan, "AgriPV in Norway: evaluating the initial performance and lessons learned," EU PVSEC (2024), doi: 10.4229/EUPVSEC2024/4DV.1.10.

[7] P.E. Campana et al., "Experimental results, integrated model validation, and economic aspects of agrivoltaic systems at northern latitudes," J. Clean. Prod. 437 (2024) 140235–140235, doi: 10.1016/J.JCLEPRO.2023.140235.

[8] A.K. Schneider et al., "Drawing transformation pathways for making use of joint effects of food and energy production with biodiversity agriphotovoltaics and electrified agricultural machinery," J. Environ. Manage. 335 (2023) 117539, doi: 10.1016/J.JENVMAN.2023.117539.

[9] P.E. Campana, B. Stridh, S. Amaducci, M. Colauzzi, "Optimisation of vertically mounted agrivoltaic systems," J. Clean. Prod. 325 (2021), doi: 10.1016/J.JCLEPRO.2021.129091.

[10] S. Touil, A. Richa, M. Fizir, B. Bingwa, "Shading effect of photovoltaic panels on horticulture crops production: a mini review," Rev. Environ. Sci. Biotechnol. 20, no. 2 (2021) 281–296, doi: 10.1007/S11157-021-09572-2/FIGURES/10.

[11] M. Szarek, S. Jouttijärvi, L. Karttunen, T. Hynnä, S. Ranta, K. Miettunen, "Performance evaluation of high-latitude agrivoltaic systems with vertically mounted bifacial panels.," under Review for Applied Energy (2025).

[12] S. Jouttijärvi, L. Karttunen, S. Ranta, K. Miettunen, "Techno-economic analysis on optimizing the value of photovoltaic electricity in a high-latitude location," Appl. Energy 361 (2024) 122924, doi: 10.1016/J.APENERGY.2024.122924.

[13] "CAMS solar radiation time-series", [Online]. Available: https://ads.atmosphere.copernicus.eu/datasets/cams-solar-radiation-timeseries?tab=overview.

[14] P. Sieber, S. Böhme, N. Ericsson, P.A. Hansson, "Albedo on cropland: field-scale effects of current agricultural practices in Northern Europe," Agric. For. Meteorol. 321 (2022) 108978, doi: 10.1016/J.AGRFORMET.2022.108978.

[15] "Nord Pool | Data Portal", [Online]. Available: https://data.nordpoolgroup.com/auction/day-ahead.

[16] "PVsyst – Photovoltaic software", [Online]. Available: https://www.pvsyst.com/.

[17] S. Tsuchida, Y. Tsuno, D. Sato, T. Oozeki, N. Yamada, "Power generation characteristics of vertical bifacial photovoltaic arrays in heavy snow regions," EPJ Photovolt. 15 (2024) 32, doi: 10.1051/EPJPV/2024029.

[18] A. Meriläinen, P. Puranen, A. Kosonen, J. Ahola, "Optimization of rooftop photovoltaic installations to maximize revenue in Finland based on customer class load profiles and simulated generation," Sol. Energy 240 (2022) 422–434, doi: 10.1016/J.SOLENER.2022.05.057.

PERFORMANCE ANALYSIS OF AGRIVOLTAIC SYSTEM CONFIGURATIONS IN NORDIC CONDITIONS

Magda Szarek[1]*, Sami Jouttijärvi[1], Lauri Karttunen[1], Samuli Ranta[2], Kati Miettunen[1]

[1]Department of Mechanical and Materials Engineering, University of Turku, Vesilinnantie 5, 20500 Turku, Finland
[2]Turku University of Applied Sciences, Joukahaisenkatu 7, 20520 Turku, Finland
*email: magda.szarek@utu.fi

Tracker systems have the highest output, vertical systems have the highest energy value in high-latitudes

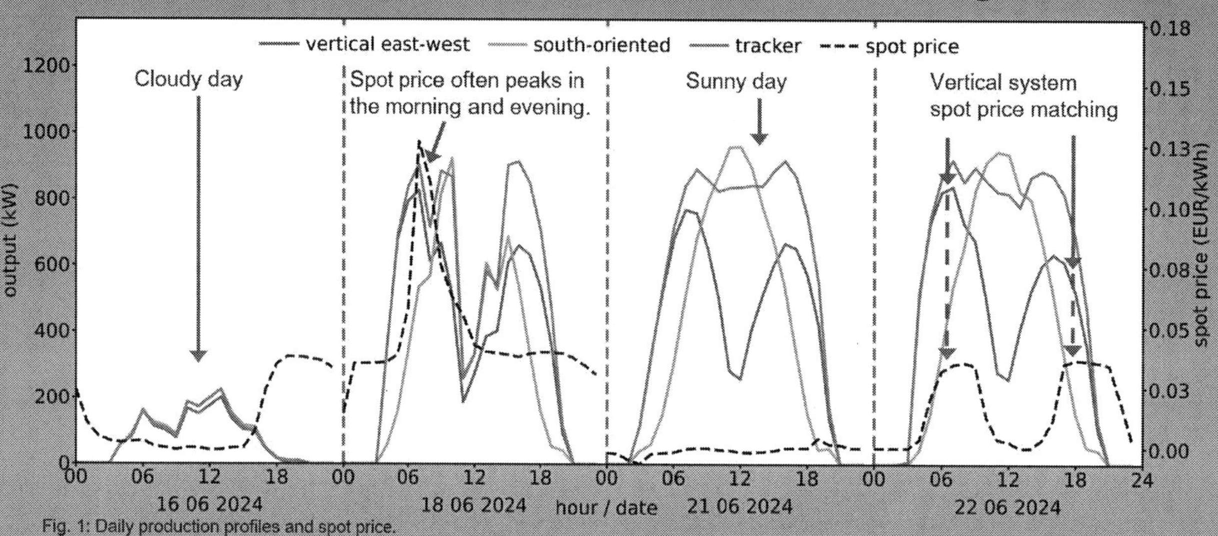

Fig. 1: Daily production profiles and spot price.

Aim and context

- **Comparing performance of three types of bifacial systems in high-latitude conditions in Turku, Finland.**

- Solar energy in the Nordics is developing rapidly, local energy market has a high fraction of renewables and high-latitude conditions.

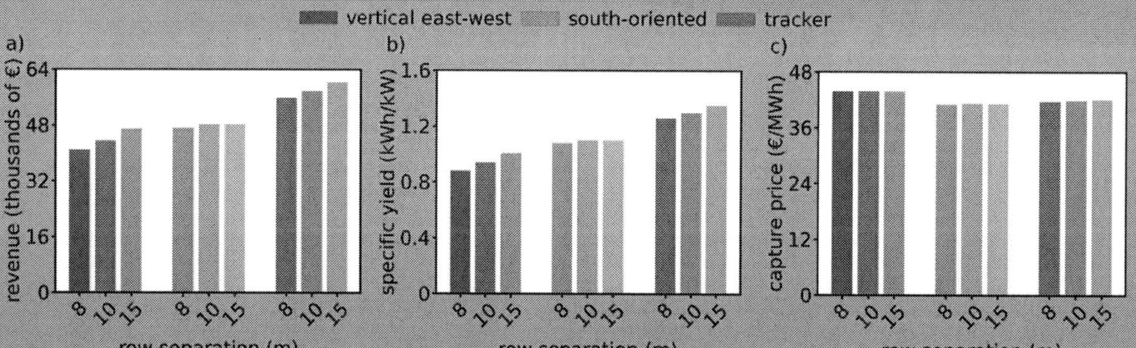

Fig. 2: Comparison of three 1 MW bifacial systems for different row separations a) revenue, b)specific yield, c) capture price.

Tracker systems
- Highest yield and revenue.
- Capture price is less sensitive to low spot prices at noon than south oriented panels.
- High system cost.

Vertical east-west systems
- Highest benefit from increased row distance.
- Resilient to low spot prices at noon.
- High capture price due to a better spot-price match [1].
- Lower output than other types.

South-oriented systems
- Higher yield and revenue than vertical for closely situated rows.
- Little benefit from increased row distance.
- Lowest capture price, expected to drop even further as the share of PV in the market grows [2].

References

[1] S. Jouttijärvi, L. Karttunen, S. Ranta, and K. Miettunen, "Techno-economic analysis on optimizing the value of photovoltaic electricity in a high-latitude location," Appl. Energy, vol. 361, p. 122924, May 2024

[2] S. Jouttijärvi et al., "SENSITIVITY OF ELECTRICITY PRICE IN THE FINNISH MARKET CONDITIONS WITH INCREASING SOLAR ENERGY PRODUCTION", 41st EU-PVSEC, Vienna (2024)

Acknowledgements

The work was funded by the Strategic Research Council Finland Decision No. 358542 (project RealSolar).

IRRADIANCE MANAGEMENT IN AGRIVOLTAIC SYSTEMS WITH VARYING DESIGNS ACROSS LATITUDES: TOWARD FINLAND'S FIRST SIGNIFICANT DEMONSTRATION

Shuo Wang[1*], Soroush Moradi Zavie Kord[2], Hugo E Huerta[1], Antti Lajunen[2], Samuli Ranta[1]
1. New Energy Research Group, Turku University of Applied Sciences, 20520 Turku, Finland
2. Department of Agricultural Sciences, University of Helsinki, 00790 Helsinki, Finland
*Corresponding author: shuo.wang@turkuamk.fi

ABSTRACT: This study performs irradiance management in AgriPV systems with varying design parameters to support the development of Finland's first significant AgriPV demonstration project. Using ray-tracing simulations at three locations with distinct latitudes, we analyzed annual solar insolation on PV modules and ground level. Within the azimuth-tilt iterations, maximum module insolation occurs with a southwest orientation, corresponding to minimal ground insolation. Due south orientation induces the strongest non-uniformity in ground irradiance. For more balanced distribution between PV modules and crops, a southeast-facing configuration is preferred. Height-GCR iterations show that increasing installation height or reducing GCR enhance both module and ground insolation. Height controls the shading extent beneath the mounting structure, whereas GCR modulates the spacing between shaded regions. Accordingly, two different optimization strategies can be suggested for overhead and vertical configurations. Overhead systems benefit primarily from optimizing installation height, enabling more uniform irradiance distribution under the PV modules, while vertical systems require low mounting height and tuned GCR to achieve shading-free areas between PV arrays. Latitude-dependent effects have also been identified. For overhead systems, higher latitudes allow lower installation heights to achieve a given ground uniformity, while for vertical systems, lower latitudes tolerate higher GCRs without sacrificing the uniformity.
Keywords: Agrivoltaics, irradiance management, vertical PV, overhead PV, high latitude

1 INTRODUCTION

Solar energy plays an important role in the transition to a sustainable energy system, reducing dependence on fossil fuels, and lowering CO_2 emissions in Finland. It requires innovative solutions to balance renewable energy production with land use efficiency. Agrivoltaics (AgriPV), which combines solar energy generation with agricultural activities, presents a promising approach to optimizing land use while supporting climate goals. Given Finland's high latitude, seasonal variations in solar irradiance, and challenging weather conditions, research on AgriPV is crucial to understanding its feasibility, productivity, and potential benefits for farmers and energy producers. One of the biggest challenges is to understand how the crops are influenced by the shading effect from PV modules and how to balance or optimize the irradiance distribution between crops and PV modules.

To address this challenge, several simulation models and methods have been proposed, such as decomposition models [1], transposition models [2], view-factor analysis [3], and ray-tracing techniques [4]. In this study, we investigated the irradiance distribution for both PV modules and crops in high-latitude AgriPV systems using ray-tracing modeling tools. The shading effects of PV modules at ground level were analyzed in detail under different system parameters. A comparison was also made between Helsinki, where the first significant AgriPV demonstration project in Finland is planned, and lower-latitude locations with different irradiance conditions. The findings will support the design of the upcoming demonstration project, with validation to follow once the system is operational.

2 METHODOLOGY

2.1 Pilot site and solar irradiance

The planned AgriPV pilot site is located in Viikki, Helsinki, Finland, covering an area of 3.5 hectares. It is adjacent to the Viikki campus of the University of Helsinki. Detailed onsite crop assessments will be conducted in the future. Two types of AgriPV configurations, overhead and vertical PV, will be implemented and tested on two approximately equal portions of the site, labeled Areas A and B in Figure 1, respectively. Area C will be maintained as a reference area without any PV arrays.

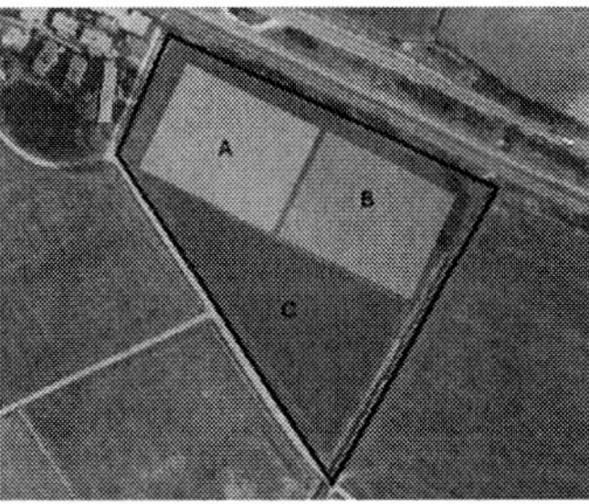

Figure 1: Satellite photo of the pilot site in planning in Viikki Helsinki. Area A and B are planned to host overhead and vertical PV arrays, respectively. Area C will be kept free of PV as a reference.

Solar irradiance data were obtained from the SARAH3 dataset via the PVGIS platform [5]. In addition to Helsinki (60.222° N, 25.026° E), the primary site for high-latitude analysis, this study considered two other locations: Murcia, Spain (37.917° N, 1.478° W), and Katibougou, Mali (12.501° N, 8.091° W). These lower-latitude sites provide a broad range for comparative analysis. AgriPV pilot systems have been established in these regions, offering opportunities to potentially validate the modeling results.

2.2 Irradiance modeling

The irradiance modeling was performed using the bifacial_radiance toolkit [6], which is a peer-reviewed open-source Python wrapper based on the ray-tracing software Radiance [7]. The tool was further developed to enable efficient irradiance sampling on both the surface of PV modules and ground level. With the solar irradiance as the input data, five rows of PV modules were created in the model with different system configurations. The irradiance on both sides of PV modules and at ground level was simulated within one run of simulation. Accumulative simulations were used for the annual insolation modelling. The key parameters and their default values used for modeling are summarized in Table 1. Azimuth is defined as the angle clockwise from north and Ground Covering Ratio (GCR) is calculated by dividing the array width by the row pitch.

Table 1: Key parameters and the default values for modeling

Item	Value	Item	Value
Azimuth	135°	Module length	2.38 m
Tilt	40°	Module width	1.3 m
Hub height	5 m	Row number	5
Pitch	15 m	Module per row	20×2
GCR	0.18	Ground albedo	0.2

2.3 Evaluation indicator

The irradiance harvested by PV modules is evaluated by the annual average solar insolation on both sides of the modules, $\bar{I}_m$.

$$\bar{I}_m = \frac{\sum_{i=1}^{M} I_{mi}}{M} \tag{1}$$

where I_{mi} is the sum of annual front- and back-side insolation on module i. M is the total number of PV modules in the simulation.

To illustrate the solar irradiance at ground level, Figure 2 (a) shows a heat map of annual ground insolation within the AgriPV system as described in Table 1. Shading from the PV modules reduces irradiance available for crop growth, with the worst-affected areas experiencing losses of up to about 25% in this case. The detailed profile along the central line can be found in Figure 2(b).

Peaks in ground insolation occur between the rows, while valleys can be observed near the PV module mounting positions. This variation is qualified using two indicators. $\bar{I}_{gn}$ evaluates the solar irradiance that is reserved for crops at ground level in AgriPV systems.

$$\bar{I}_{gn} = \frac{\sum_{i=1}^{N} I_{gi}}{N \, I_{gmax}} \tag{2}$$

where $\bar{I}_{gn}$ is defined as the average ground insolation over the central sampling positions, normalized to the maximum value of the sampling points I_{gmax} (the reference ground insolation clear of shading). I_{gi} is the annual insolation at ground position i. N is the total number of the sampling positions along the central line.

Another indicator σI_{gn} is used to evaluate the variation of irradiance at ground level over the central line as shown in Figure 2(a).

$$\sigma I_{gn} = \frac{1}{\bar{I}_g} \sqrt{\frac{\sum_{i=1}^{N} |I_{gi} - \bar{I}_g|^2}{N}} \tag{3}$$

where σI_{gn} is defined as the root mean square deviation (RMSE) of the annual ground insolation, normalized to the average value over the sampling positions. $\bar{I}_g$ is the average ground insolation over the central sampling positions without normalization.

With these indicators, the optimization of an AgriPV system aims to high $\bar{I}_m$, high $\bar{I}_{gn}$, and low σI_{gn}, though in practice a compromise between these factors is often required.

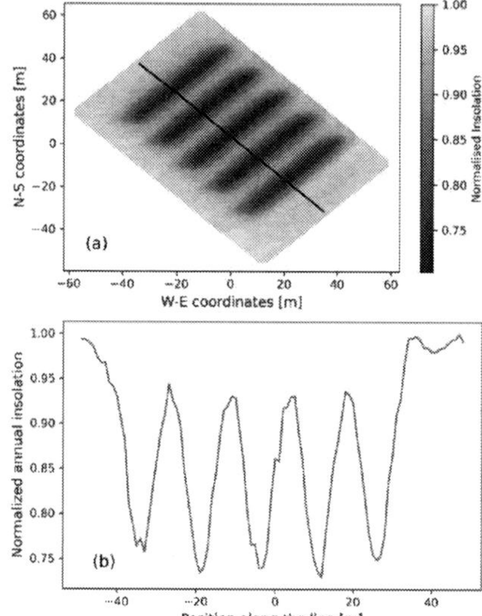

Figure 2: Exemplary results of annual ground-level insolation with the parameters as listed in Table 1. (a) heat map of the ground-level insolation normalized to the maximum, (b) normalized annual insolation profile along the central line as labeled in (a).

3 RESULTS

The AgriPV system was modeled by varying key parameters, including azimuth, tilt angle, GCR, and hub height of the PV arrays. Unless otherwise specified, the values listed in Table 1 were used for the simulations.

3.1 Azimuth – tilt angle evaluation

To determine the proper orientation of PV arrays, the influence of azimuth and tilt angle were investigated for Helsinki, as shown in Figure 3.

Figure 3 (a) shows the variation of $\bar{I}_m$ for different azimuth and tilt combinations, normalized to the maximum value within the investigated range to highlight deviations from the locally optimized. The optimization for module irradiance occurs at an azimuth of 225° (southwest) and a tilt of 50°. Correspondingly, as more sunlight is captured by the PV modules, the minimal ground irradiance for crops is observed at this configuration, with about 15% of solar energy lost compared to the unshaded reference, as shown in Figure 3(b). Figure 3(c) indicates that the highest ground irradiance variation (σI_{gn}) occurs at an azimuth of 180° (due south), suggesting that south-facing modules produce the most non-uniform ground irradiance, potentially leading to the greatest deviation in crop quality.

Simulations for the other two locations with lower latitudes produced results similar to those for Helsinki. AgriPV system optimization can vary depending on objectives, such as maximizing profit, solar generation, or crop yield. In this study, to achieve a more balanced irradiance between PV modules and crops and minimize the nonuniformity of ground irradiance, an azimuth of 135° and a tilt angle of 40° were selected for the overhead

AgriPV system in the following simulations. For the vertical AgriPV system, the same azimuth of 135° was used, with the tilt angle fixed at 90°.

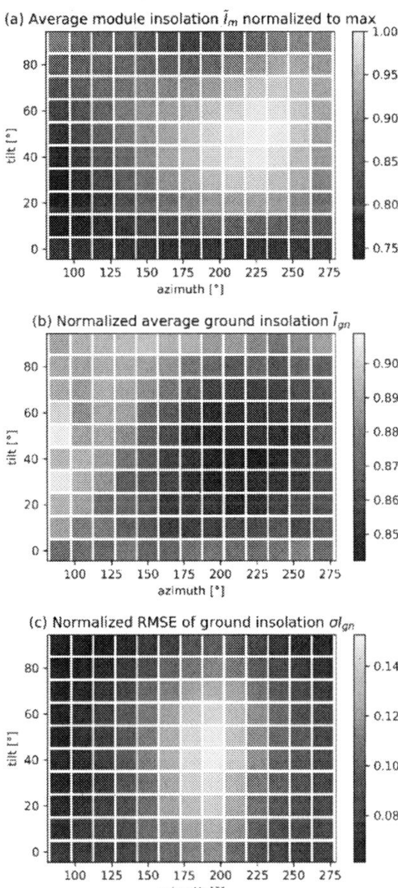

Figure 3: Evaluation of the three indicators with different combinations of the azimuth and tilt angle of the PV arrays. (a) average annual insolation on PV modules $\bar{I}_m$ normalized to the maximum value within the investigated range, (b) normalized average annual insolation at ground level $\bar{I}_{gn}$, and (c) normalized RMSE of ground-level insolation σI_{gn}.

3.2 GCR – hub height evaluation

Figure 4 illustrates the influence of GCR and hub height on the evaluation indicators. The results show that lower GCR consistently improves system performance, yielding higher $\bar{I}_m$, higher $\bar{I}_{gn}$, and lower σI_{gn}. A similar, though less pronounced, improvement is observed with increasing hub height.

However, note that in practice these parameters need to be balanced with installation constraints. Low GCR reduces land-use efficiency, while high hub height increases structural costs. Therefore, the ground irradiance distribution is further analyzed under varying GCR and hub height.

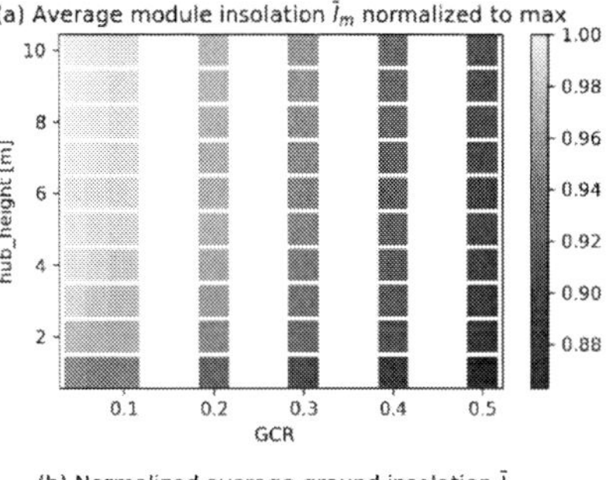

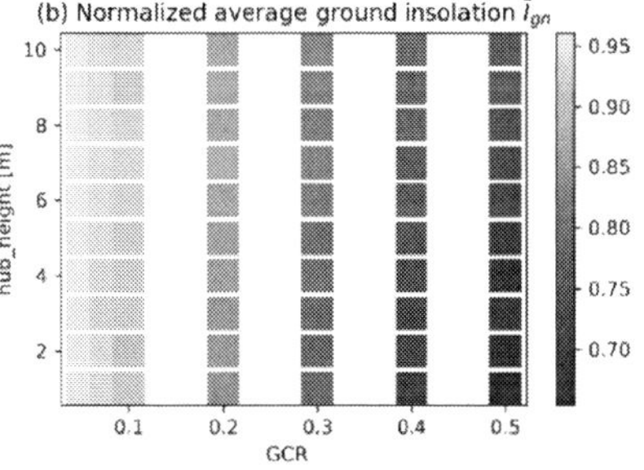

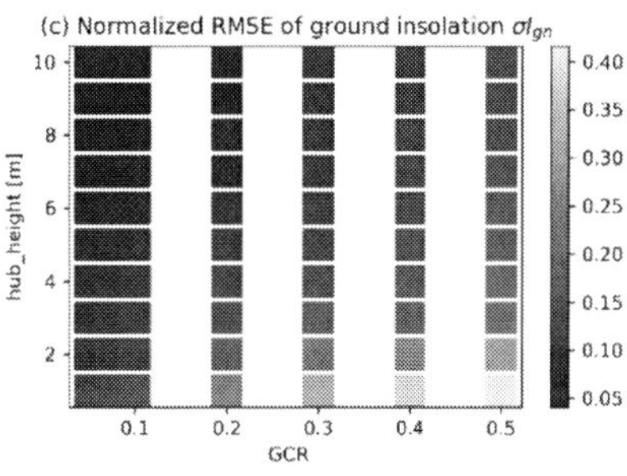

Figure 4: Evaluation of the three indicators with different combinations of the hub height and GCR of the PV arrays. (a) average annual insolation on PV modules $\bar{I}_m$ normalized to the maximum value within the investigated range, (b) normalized average annual insolation at ground level $\bar{I}_{gn}$, and (c) normalized RMSE of ground-level insolation σI_{gn}.

3.2.1 Effect of hub height on ground-level irradiance profile

The annual ground insolation along the central line was simulated for varying hub heights in both overhead and vertical systems. In overhead systems, as shown in Figure 5(a), the area between PV rows can clearly be identified as shaded and unshaded zones at low hub heights. Shading is confined to a narrow band near the module mounting position, with irradiance reduced to about 20% of the reference value, while the unshaded areas retain insolation comparable to the reference. As hub height increases, the shaded zone broadens, but irradiance within it also improves. Beyond 7 m hub height in this case, the ground insolation becomes nearly uniform, with no clear distinction between shaded and unshaded areas, averaging the insolation around 80% of the reference value.

The vertical system, shown in Figure 5(b), exhibits similar trends with increasing hub height as the overhead system. However, at low heights the contrast between shaded and unshaded areas is less pronounced, and irradiance losses in shaded zones are significantly smaller than in the overhead configuration.

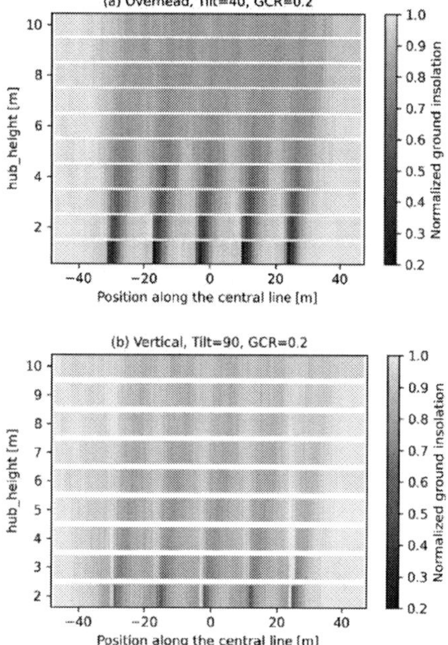

Figure 5: Detailed ground-level insolation profiles along the central line of systems with varying hub height of PV arrays. (a) overhead system with tilt angle of 40° and GCR of 0.2, (b) vertical system (tilt angle of 90°) and GCR of 0.2.

3.2.2 Effect of GCR on ground-level irradiance profile

The influence of GCR on ground irradiance profile is similar for both system types, as shown in Figure 6. At high GCR, the row spacing is small, causing extensive shading under the PV array. As GCR decreases, unshaded areas emerge between the PV rows, with annual insolation approaching that of the reference area, while confining shaded areas near the module rows.

3.3 Optimization strategies for different types of systems

Based on these observations, different optimization strategies can be suggested for different AgriPV system configurations.

For overhead systems, the supporting structure must be sufficiently high to allow agricultural activities beneath, with optimization favored on achieving uniform ground irradiance across the area. This makes hub height the critical parameter, while GCR remains relatively flexible. For example, Figure 7(a) shows the annual ground-level insolation profile at a hub height of 8 m and GCR of 0.2. In this case, ground insolation remains within 80-100% of the reference across the entire area, ensuring uniform crop quality and yield. Such conditions are suitable for crops requiring slightly less irradiance than open-field reference.

For vertical systems, agricultural activities are arranged between PV module rows, requiring a relatively low GCR. In this configuration, optimization could aim to confine shading close to the module rows, which necessitates a low hub height. At the same time, an

appropriate GCR ensures that the inter-row space remains largely free from shading. Figure 7(b) illustrates such a case with a hub height of 2 m and GCR of 0.1. Here, areas receiving less than 80% of the reference insolation are restricted to within ±2 m of the mounting position, while the remaining space maintains sufficient irradiance, with most of it completely free from shading. This case is particularly suitable for crops sensitive to irradiance.

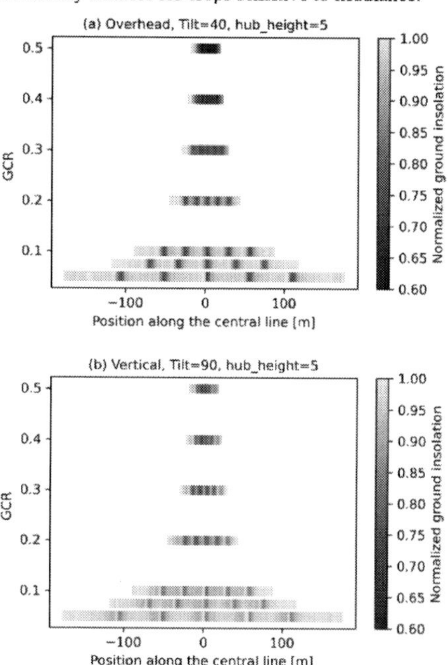

Figure 6: Detailed ground-level insolation profiles along the central line of systems with varying GCR of PV arrays. (a) overhead system with tilt angle of 40° and hub height of 5 m, (b) vertical system (tilt angle of 90°) and hub height of 5 m.

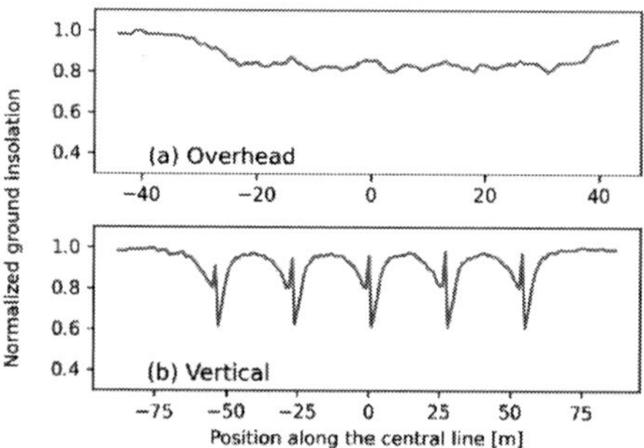

Figure 7: Ground-level insolation profile along the central line optimized following different strategies for (a) overhead system with hub height of 8m and GCR of 0.2, (b) vertical system with hub height of 2m and GCR of 0.1.

3.4 Comparison of different locations

Since the low latitude location usually has better solar radiation than the high latitude area for PV production, the comparison on absolute PV generation among different locations is not critical. The discussion in this section focuses on the influence of various locations on ground-level irradiance distribution.

As demonstrated in the previous sections, hub height is the critical parameter in the overhead system. To minimize the influence of PV shading on crops and achieve balance between energy production and crop yield, one needs to find compromise among ground irradiance, agricultural requirements and construction costs. Low height is preferred if it ensures good ground irradiance distribution to save costs. Figure 8 (a) and (b) show the influence of hub height on the $\bar{I}_{gn}$ and σI_{gn} in different locations. The low latitude locations show higher $\bar{I}_{gn}$ in the investigated range of hub height. However, high-latitude areas achieve lower σI_{gn} at relatively modest hub heights, indicating more uniform ground irradiance with less structural height.

The investigation on GCR in vertical systems is shown in Figure 9. Low-latitude locations outperform high latitudes again in terms of $\bar{I}_{gn}$. At the same GCR, they also exhibit lower σI_{gn}, demonstrating both higher ground irradiance and greater uniformity.

These findings can be explained by differences in solar position across latitudes. At high latitudes, the lower solar elevation enables sunlight to reach beneath overhead arrays more effectively, reducing ground irradiance variation. At low latitudes, the higher solar elevation keeps shading closer to the modules, producing more uniform ground irradiance.

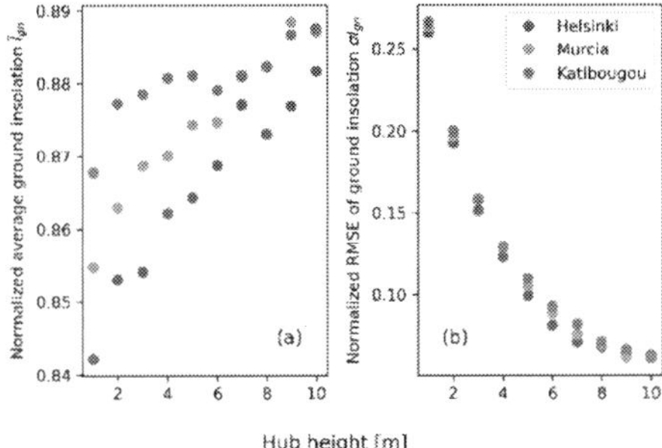

Figure 8: Ground-level insolation indicators evaluated for overhead systems with varying hub heights across different locations. (a) normalized average annual insolation at ground level $\bar{I}_{gn}$, and (b) normalized RMSE of ground-level insolation σI_{gn}.

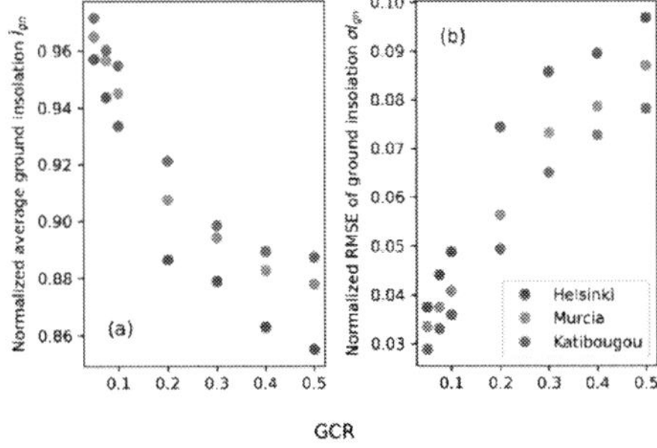

Figure 9: Ground-level insolation indicators evaluated for vertical systems with varying GCR across different locations. (a) normalized average annual insolation at ground level $\bar{I}_{gn}$, and (b) normalized RMSE of ground-level insolation σI_{gn}.

4 CONCLUSION

In this work, we performed irradiance management in AgriPV systems with varying design parameters, providing guidance for the design of the first significant AgriPV demonstration system in Finland. Using ray-tracing simulations at three locations with different latitudes, we analyzed the distribution of annual solar insolation on both PV modules for power generation and ground for crop growth.

From the azimuth-tilt iteration, we identify a trade-off between module and ground insolation. Maximum module insolation is achieved with a southwest azimuth and a tilt angle of around 50°, which corresponds to minimal ground insolation. However, the greatest non-uniformity in ground insolation does not occur under this configuration, but instead with a due south orientation. A southeast-facing configuration emerges as a compromise, offering a more balanced distribution between PV modules and crops.

From the height-GCR iteration, we find that higher installation heights and lower GCRs increase insolation for both modules and ground. However, their effects on ground irradiance distribution differ. Height determines the breadth of shading area beneath the mounting position, while GCR modulates the spacing between adjacent shaded zones. The findings suggest two different optimization strategies for overhead and vertical configurations. For overhead systems, optimizing the installation height is more critical for achieving uniform insolation beneath the modules. For vertical systems, a low mounting height is essential to confine the shading area near the installation point. At the same time, optimizing the GCR is crucial to obtain shading-free zones between adjacent PV arrays.

Finally, comparison among the three locations reveals latitude-dependent effects. Low-latitude location offers higher average ground insolation in all cases. However, the uniformity of ground insolation varies by system type. For overhead systems, higher latitudes allow lower installation heights to achieve a given uniformity, while for vertical systems, lower latitudes tolerate higher GCRs without sacrificing the uniformity.

ACKNOWLEDGEMENTS

The work is funded by the Strategic Research Council (SRC) established within the Research Council of Finland under project RealSolar 359141, and European Regional Development Fund (ERDF) under the project Aurinkoenergiapelto A81526.

REFERENCES

[1] Y. Elamri, B. Cheviron, A. Mange, C. Dejean, F. Liron, and G. Belaud, "Rain concentration and sheltering effect of solar panels on cultivated plots," Hydrology and Earth System Sciences, vol. 22, no. 2, pp. 1285–1298, Feb. 2018, doi: 10.5194/hess-22-1285-2018.

[2] P. E. Campana, B. Stridh, S. Amaducci, and M. Colauzzi, "Optimisation of vertically mounted agrivoltaic systems," Journal of Cleaner Production, vol. 325, Nov. 2021, doi: 10.1016/j.jclepro.2021.129091.

[3] P. E. Campana et al., "Solar irradiance distribution under vertically mounted agrivoltaic systems-Model development, validation, and applications for microclimate assessment," EarthArXiv, 2022. doi: 10.31223/X5G07D

[4] O. A. Katsikogiannis, H. Ziar, and O. Isabella, "Integration of bifacial photovoltaics in agrivoltaic systems: A synergistic design approach," Applied Energy, vol. 309, Mar. 2022, doi: 10.1016/j.apenergy.2021.118475.

[5] "Photovoltaic Geographical Information System." Accessed: Sep. 17, 2025. [Online]. Available: https://re.jrc.ec.europa.eu/pvg_tools/en/

[6] S. Ayala Pelaez and C. Deline, "bifacial_radiance: a python package for modeling bifacial solar photovoltaic systems," Journal of Open Source Software, vol. 5, no. 50, p. 1865, Jun. 2020, doi: 10.21105/joss.01865.

[7] G. J. Ward, "The RADIANCE Lighting Simulation and Rendering System," in 21st Annual Conference on Computer Graphics and Interactive Techniques, 1994, pp. 459–472. doi: 10.1145/192161.192286.

IRRADIANCE MANAGEMENT IN AGRIVOLTAIC SYSTEMS WITH VARYING DESIGNS ACROSS LATITUDES:
TOWARD FINLAND'S FIRST SIGNIFICANT DEMONSTRATION

Shuo Wang[1*], Soroush Moradi Zavie Kord[2], Hugo E Huerta[1], Antti Lajunen[2], Samuli Ranta[1]

1. New Energy Research Group, Turku University of Applied Sciences, 20520 Turku, Finland
2. Department of Agricultural Sciences, University of Helsinki, 00790 Helsinki, Finland

Contact: shuo.wang@turkuamk.fi

Objective

- Perform irradiance management for bifacial AgriPV systems using ray-tracing modeling
- Various system design parameters
- Different latitude locations
- Provide design guidance for demo site

Methodology

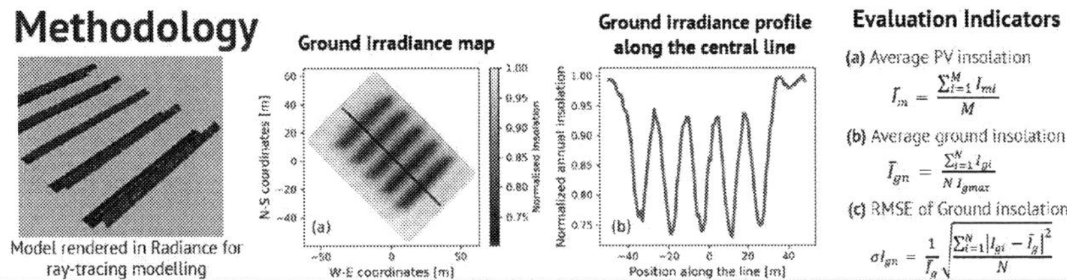

Model rendered in Radiance for ray-tracing modelling

Ground irradiance map

Ground irradiance profile along the central line

Evaluation Indicators

(a) Average PV insolation

$$\bar{I}_m = \frac{\sum_{i=1}^{M} I_{mi}}{M}$$

(b) Average ground insolation

$$\bar{I}_{gn} = \frac{\sum_{i=1}^{N} I_{gi}}{N\, I_{gmax}}$$

(c) RMSE of Ground insolation

$$\sigma I_{gn} = \frac{1}{\bar{I}_a}\sqrt{\frac{\sum_{i=1}^{N}\left|I_{gi}-\bar{I}_g\right|^2}{N}}$$

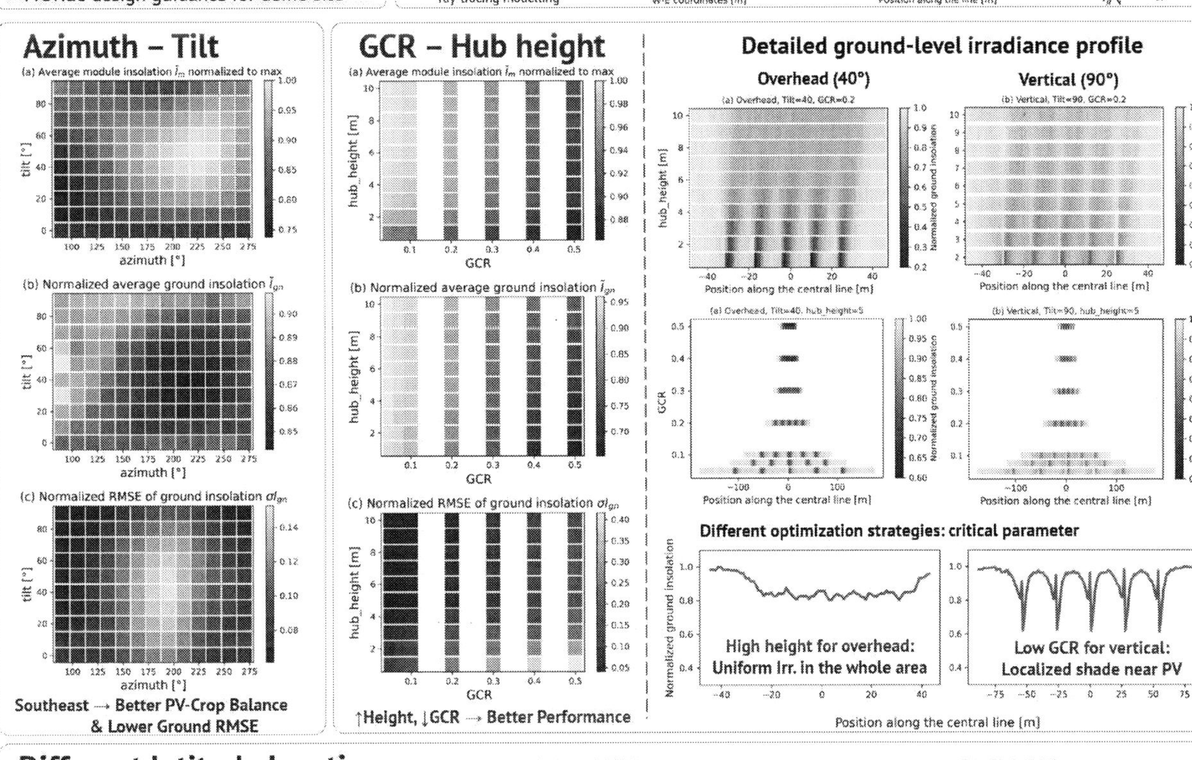

Azimuth – Tilt

(a) Average module insolation $\bar{I}_m$ normalized to max

(b) Normalized average ground insolation $\bar{I}_{gn}$

(c) Normalized RMSE of ground insolation σI_{gn}

Southeast → Better PV-Crop Balance & Lower Ground RMSE

GCR – Hub height

(a) Average module insolation $\bar{I}_m$ normalized to max

(b) Normalized average ground insolation $\bar{I}_{gn}$

(c) Normalized RMSE of ground insolation σI_{gn}

↑Height, ↓GCR → Better Performance

Detailed ground-level irradiance profile

Overhead (40°) — (a) Overhead, Tilt=40, GCR=0.2

Vertical (90°) — (b) Vertical, Tilt=90, GCR=0.2

(a) Overhead, Tilt=40, hub_height=5

(b) Vertical, Tilt=90, hub_height=5

Different optimization strategies: critical parameter

High height for overhead: Uniform Irr. in the whole area

Low GCR for vertical: Localized shade near PV

Different latitude locations

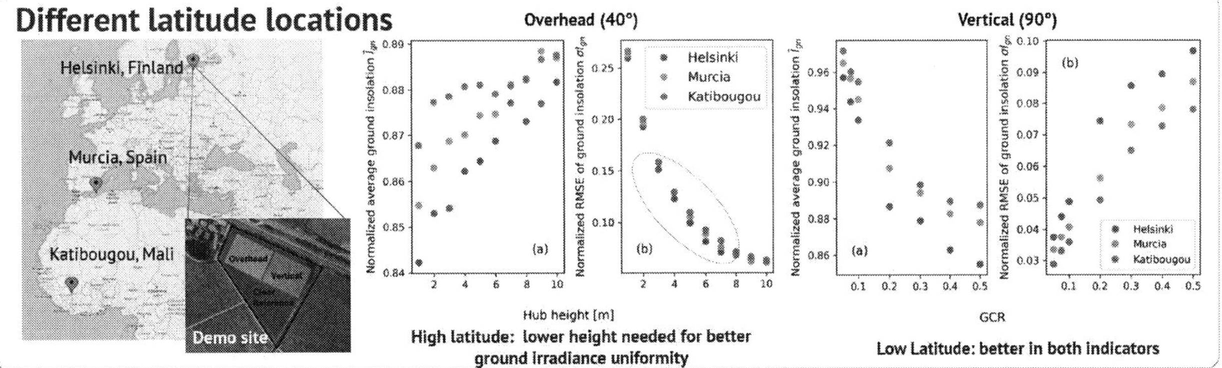

Overhead (40°)

Helsinki / Murcia / Katibougou

Vertical (90°)

Helsinki / Murcia / Katibougou

High latitude: lower height needed for better ground irradiance uniformity

Low Latitude: better in both indicators

Conclusion

- Panels facing southeast help with the irradiance balance between PV and crops, as well as the ground irradiance uniformity
- Considering the ground irradiance, different strategies for GCR-hub height optimization for overhead and vertical system: hub height for overhead system and GCR for vertical system are more critical for the optimization
- High latitudes favor overhead systems, where lower height is sufficient for uniform ground irradiance, while low latitudes favor vertical systems, providing higher ground irradiance with more uniform distribution.

Acknowledgement

The work is funded by the Strategic Research Council (SRC) established within the Research Council of Finland under project RealSolar 358141, and European Regional Development Fund (ERDF) under the project Aurinkoenergiapelto A81526.

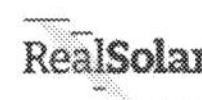

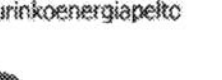

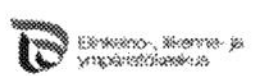

AN INNOVATIVE AGRIVOLTAIC SYSTEM FOR DESERT CLIMATES WITH ANTI-SOILING, IRRADIANCE CONTROL, AND WATER MANAGEMENT

Sagarika Kumar[1], Min Hsian Saw[1], Ahmed Shaaban[1], Kamil Jaworczak[1], Nursulu Kuzhagaliyeva[1], Carlos G. Parrilla[2], Francois M. Tsombou[2], Fouad Lamghari[2], and Mauro Pravettoni[1]
[1]Technology Innovation Institute, Renewable and Sustainable Energy Research Centre, Abu Dhabi, UAE
[2]Fujairah Research Centre, Fujairah, UAE
Sagarika.Kumar@tii.ae

ABSTRACT: The need to balance renewable energy generation and sustainable agriculture in arid regions is of global interest, due to water scarcity in many regions, and intensified heat by climate change. Conventional agrivoltaic (agri-PV) systems fall short under desert conditions. GROOViD (Green, Robust & Optically-Optimised agriVoltaics in Deserts) was conceived to overcome some of these limits by integrating conventional solar tracking with dual-use water systems for irrigation and module cleaning. The aim is to reduce water demand, enhance solar efficiency, and protect crops, supporting the UAE's Food Security 2051, Water Security 2036, and Net Zero 2050 goals while creating a scalable model for desert agriculture. In this paper, the authors focus on the concept of the GROOViD solution, introducing the methodology, and presenting the performance and preliminary reliability findings after the first 6 months of operation. They also present a quantitative analysis of the shading benefit to the photosynthetically active radiation (PAR) and to the crops evapotranspiration. They finally show the advantages of the combined cleaning-irrigation system in terms of antisoiling.
Keywords: agrivoltaics, climate change, arid regions, antisoiling, tracking systems

1 INTRODUCTION

The increasing global demand for renewable energy and sustainable food production has intensified the competition for land resources, particularly in arid and semi-arid regions. Climate change further exacerbates these challenges, driving higher temperatures, more frequent extreme weather events [1], and severe water scarcity. Conventional agrivoltaic (agri-PV) systems, originally designed for temperate climates, often fail to deliver optimal performance under desert conditions [2], where high irradiance, dust accumulation (soiling), and limited freshwater availability constrain both solar and agricultural outputs. In the United Arab Emirates (UAE), these challenges are critical, given the country's reliance on food imports and limited arable land [3]. National initiatives such as the Food Security Strategy 2051, the Water Security Strategy 2036, and the Net Zero by 2050 commitment highlight the need for innovative, climate-resilient solutions.

The GROOViD project (an acronym for Green, Robust and Optically-Optimised agriVoltaics in Deserts) was conceived to address this gap by combining advanced photovoltaic (PV) technologies with smart agricultural practices. The system integrates the PV energy production of bifacial modules on single-axis trackers with crop shading and a dual-use water system for irrigation and PV cleaning, and complimentary water generation via atmospheric water harvesting (AWH). This holistic approach aims at reducing water consumption, improving crop resilience, and sustaining solar efficiency in extreme desert environments.

This paper presents the first results from the prototype deployed at Masdar City in Abu Dhabi, UAE. The efficacy of the system against soiling is illustrated, comparing the performance of GROOViD modules with that of modules exposed to natural soiling. The study also illustrates the benefit of the prototype in terms of reduced crop evapotranspiration, and a preliminary analysis of few reliability indicators, thus providing a basis for scaling up the system in rural and agricultural settings.

2 THE GROOVID PROJECT

2.1 The prototype at Masdar City

The GROOViD prototype (Fig. 1) was designed to test an integrated agri-PV system optimized for desert conditions. The small-scale prototype consists of four bifacial n-type TOPCon PV modules (144 M10 half-cut cells, with nominal 570 W and >80% bifaciality, see Tab. I) mounted on a single-axis tracker, operating within an angular range of $-60°$ to $60°$ over the day with a GPS-time-based control system. The modules are installed in 2-P (portrait, 2×2 modules) configuration.

Figure 1: The GROOViD prototype at Masdar City, Abu Dhabi.

Table I: Technical specifications of the tested modules.

Parameter	Tech. Spec.	Tech. drawing
Cell type	TOPCon	
Cell size [mm]	182 (M10), half-cut	
Cell number	144	
Dimensions [mm]	2278×1113	
Weight [kg]	30	
Bifaciality [%]	>80	
P_{max} [W]	570	
δ [%/K]	-0.30	

A dual-use water distribution system was implemented, serving both crop irrigation and module cleaning. In parallel, a condensation-based AWH unit was integrated to supplement irrigation in water-scarce conditions.

In the 2.28 kWp system, modules have been divided into two pairs, labelled as:

- AA02 and AA03 (east side of the tracker), uncleaned (benchmark);
- AA04 and AA05 (west side), with GROOViD integrated cleaning and irrigation system.

The system also incorporates light diffusing panels to protect the crops from direct irradiance, thus creating a microclimate with reduced evapotranspiration and heat stress while ensuring adequate photosynthetically active radiation (PAR). Crops tested included mint and basil, selected for shade tolerance and relevance to UAE agriculture.

Irradiance and temperature sensors for PV yield analysis; thermistor probes and infrared (IR) thermometers to monitor the crop evapotranspiration (ET_C); a volume meter for measurements of water-use efficiency; a 4-quadrant bipolar power supply for current-voltage (IV) characterization of the PV modules; IR thermography to detect hotspots; and UV fluorescence imaging for early signs of encapsulant degradation form the comprehensive monitoring system of the testbed.

2.2 Operating principle

Fig. 2 illustrates the operating principle of GROOViD.

During the day (Fig. 2a), the single-axis solar tracker follows the sun, allowing the system to maximize solar power generation while simultaneously protecting the crops from direct irradiance in most of the time, while a portion of the directly sunlight only occasionally enters the crops area to enhance photosynthesis.

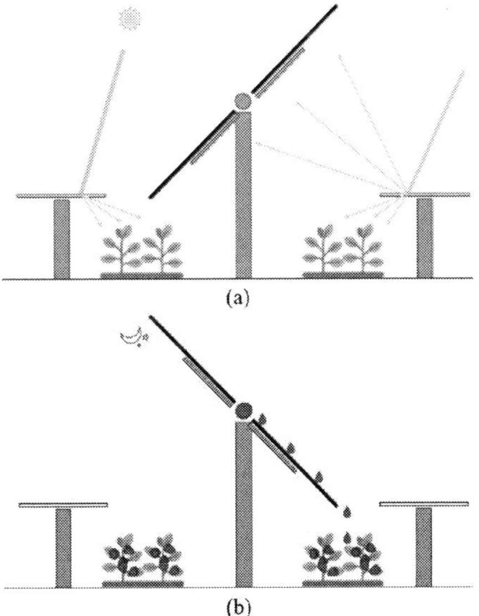

Figure 2: Concept diagrams of: (a) day and (b) night operations.

A system of white diffusers positioned to the east and west side of the installation enhances albedo, thus helping to improve solar power generation. Overall, the shading effect reduces crop heat stress and water evaporation, lowering evapotranspiration rates (see section 4). The design ensures that plants receive sufficient photosynthetically active radiation (PAR) for healthy growth, while the PV system delivers enhanced albedo-driven energy yield.

At night (Fig. 2b), the tracker repositions the modules first to stow, then to east, while a battery-powered system pumps water through the irrigation system on the top of the module and in axis with the tracker: the system serves both irrigation of crops and cleaning of PV modules. This process ensures uniform water distribution across the agricultural rows while removing accumulated dust and soiling from the panels, which is a major performance concern in desert regions. In addition, the integration of AWH provides a supplementary water source, reducing water consumption in water-scarce areas.

3 ELECTRICAL AND CLEANING PERFORMANCE

3.1 Electrical measurement setup

IV measurements of the PV modules were performed with a 4-quadrant programmable bipolar power supply by Kepco (BOP-ME 1000W).

Plane-of-array, GHI irradiance and albedo was monitored by EKO MS-80SH Class A pyranometers (response time: <0.5 s; 285-3000 nm responsivity; <0.7% calibration uncertainty).

Module temperature was recorded at the centre, at the sides and at the corner of the testing module by Pt100 probes sticked at the rear side. An offset temperature of 5 °C was derived from measured temperature and cell temperature, based on IR thermographic imaging measurements.

No spectral correction was performed on measurements that were always performed at approximately AM1.5 conditions and in clear-sky. No irradiance correction was performed; temperature correction was performed based on the nameplate relative temperature coefficient for maximum power, reported in Tab. I.

3.2 Results

The four PV modules were measured at various tilt angles, corresponding to various in-plane irradiances from 700 to 1100 W/m^2. IV measurements were performed after installation. After a pre-conditioning period of about 1 month, modules were deeply cleaned and remeasured; successively, modules were remeasured 1, 4, 5 and 6 weeks after cleaning, respectively.

Maximum power (P_{max}, in W), temperature corrected to 25 °C, are reported in Fig. 3 as a function of the plane-of-array irradiance G_{POA} (in W/m^2): T-corrected P_{max} measurements of the two benchmark modules AA02 and AA03 are reported in Fig. 3a and 3b, respectively; the performance of the GROOViD-treated modules AA04 and AA05 are shown in Fig. 3c and 3d, respectively. The charts show also the isolines corresponding to a module efficiency η_{mod} of 12%, 17% and 22% respectively.

Fig. 4 summarises the module efficiency trend: data at each measurement condition are distributed in box-and-whiskers and plotted as a function of time.

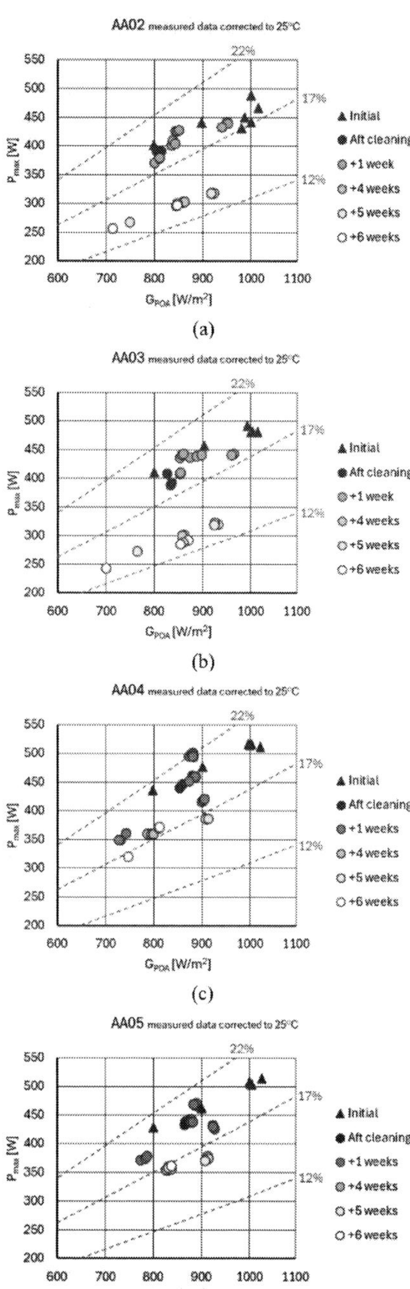

(a)

(b)

(c)

(d)

Figure 3: Electrical performance of the benchmark modules: (a) AA02, and (b) AA03; and of the GROOViD treated modules: (c) AA04 and (d) AA05. Maximum power (P_{max}) data have been corrected to 25 °C and plotted as a function of the plane-of-array irradiance G_{POA}. Measurements were performed after installation (dark-coloured triangles), after cleaning (dark-coloured circles) and 1, 4, 5 and 6 weeks after cleaning, respectively (lighter-coloured circles).

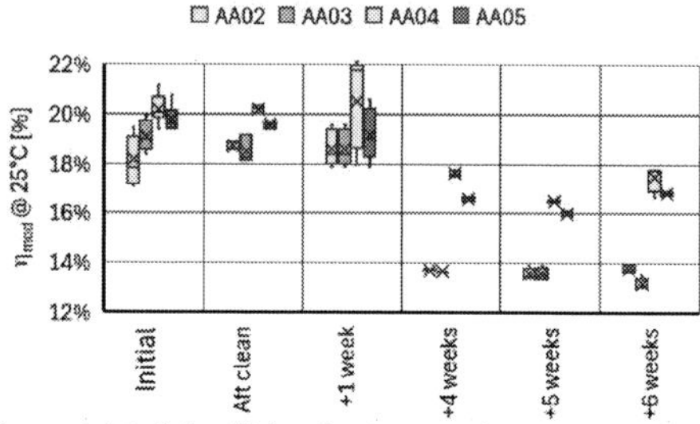

Figure 4: Module efficiencies (corrected to 25 °C), plotted as a function of time for benchmark modules (AA02 and AA03) and for GROOViD-treated modules (AA04 and AA05).

3.3 Discussion

The measurement results shows that the initial performance of modules AA02 and AA03 (benchmark modules not connected to the GROOViD cleaning and irrigation system, Fig. 3a and 3b, respectively) lay in an efficiency range 17-20%: considering measurement uncertainty and the module technology this is broadly consistent with the nameplate efficiency. After the first week of exposure, no significant reduction in P_{max} was observed. By week 4 and until week 6, however, the temperature-corrected P_{max} points felt in the 12-14% efficiency region, indicating substantial power losses due to soiling accumulation, primarily dust and organic deposits, which are known to be severe in desert environments.

Modules AA04 and AA05 (Fig. 3c and 3d, respectively) showed initial performance in line with modules AA02 and AA03. However, maintained under the GROOViD cleaning-irrigation solution, they sustained efficiencies in the 16-18% module efficiency range, confirming that the integrated cleaning and irrigation solution is functional to ensure stable, long-term operation of solar arrays in the desert environments.

4 EVAPOTRANSPIRATION AND CROP HEALTH MONITORING

4.1 Crop selection and measurement approach

Basil and mint were selected for the GROOViD prototype as shade-tolerant, fast-growing, and water-sensitive crops, making them ideal indicators of microclimate effects in agri-PV systems. Their moderately high commercial value in the UAE, combined with measurable responses in evapotranspiration and yield stability, makes them excellent pilot crops for evaluating GROOViD's dual benefits in desert farming.

The crop evapotranspiration value ET_C was estimated using the FAO-56 Penman-Monteith equation [4], which incorporates temperature, wind speed, humidity, and solar radiation to derive a reference evapotranspiration ET_0, which later was corrected to ET_C with a crop-specific correction factor.

Site-specific climatic data were used to simulate the effect of different shading levels – with direct irradiance reduction from 10% to 100%. Measurements of spectral irradiance were used for the solar irradiation input in an unshaded scenario and in the shaded case of GROOViD system. These measurements and simulations were crucial in predicting water needs for the crops under varying levels of solar exposure.

Fig. 5 shows the results for the calculated ET_C (in mm/d, equivalent to l/m²/d) for mint (Fig. 5a) and basil (Fig. 5b) in 4 crop growing phases: initial, development, mid-season and late season. The cases of 100% (unshaded) irradiance, 25% irradiance (partial shading) and GROOViD measured data (indicated by stars) are shown.

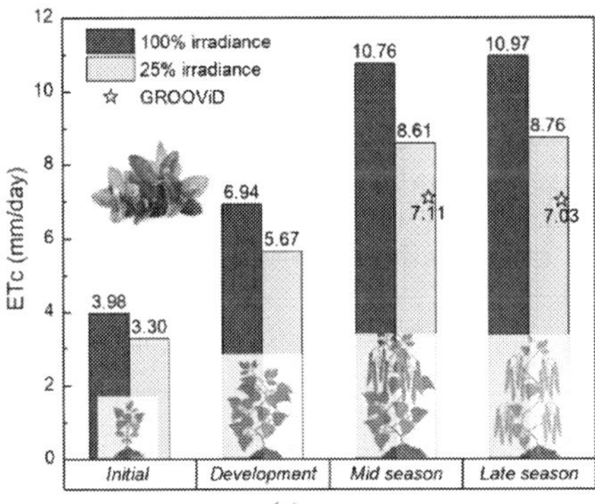

(a)

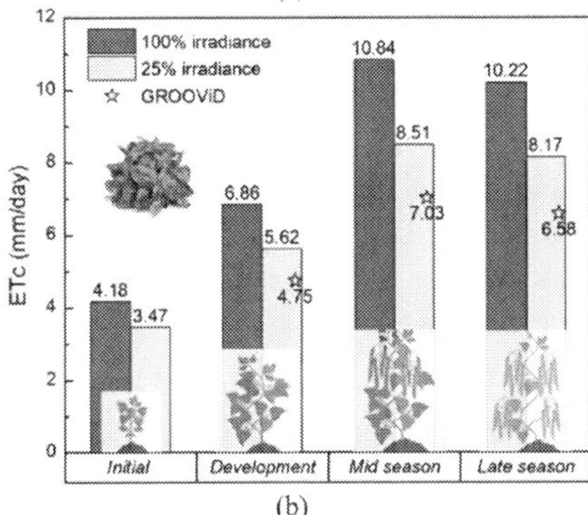

(b)

Figure 5: Crop evapotranspiration for: (a) mint, and (b) basil. Shown data (in mm/d) are based on site-specific climatic data, with 100% and 25% irradiance, and with the directly measured irradiance under GROOViD system.

4.2 Results

GROOViD shaded irradiance generates ~30% decrease in crop evapotranspiration ET_C down to about 7 mm/day in the mid and late seasons for the two case studies (mint and basil). The microclimate created by the GROOViD solution has been confirmed by observed crop resilience during the hottest season, as presented by M. H. Saw et al. in [5].

5 PRELIMINARY RELIABILITY RESULTS

5.1 Visual inspection

The 4 modules have been regularly inspected during the first 6 weeks of monitoring after cleaning. Tab. II shows the visual aspect of the modules in the various phases.

The visual inspection of benchmark modules AA02 and AA03 highlighted significant soiling accumulation, both sand dust and bird droppings, more evident after week four. These deposits reduced optical transmission and contributed to efficiency losses over time, as observed in section 3 above.

Table II: Visual inspection of the 4 tested modules: after cleaning, and after 1, 4 and 6 weeks, respectively.

	Aft cleaning	+1 w	+4 w	+6 w
AA02				
AA03				
AA04				
AA05				

After 6 weeks of exposure, the repeated accumulation and subsequent wash-off of morning dew resulted in a distinct arrow-shaped deposition pattern on benchmark modules AA02 and AA03.

In contrast, GROOViD-treated modules AA04 and AA05, leveraging on the integrated cleaning-irrigation system, showed consistent reduction of soiling, which sustained the higher and more stable performance highlighted in section 3. Evidence of non-uniform cleaning can be observed in AA04 and AA05, due to the non-optimised position of water sprinklers: this has left stains of dirt particularly accumulated to the long sides of the modules that increased the risk of hot-spot.

5.2 IR thermography

Tab. III shows IR thermography imaging after 6 weeks of exposure. Measurements were performed at 900 ± 100 W/m² plane-of-array irradiance and with the testing module kept in short-circuit conditions for 5 minutes.

Table III: Visual inspection of the 4 tested modules: after cleaning, and after 1, 4 and 6 weeks, respectively.

	+6 weeks	
Benchmark	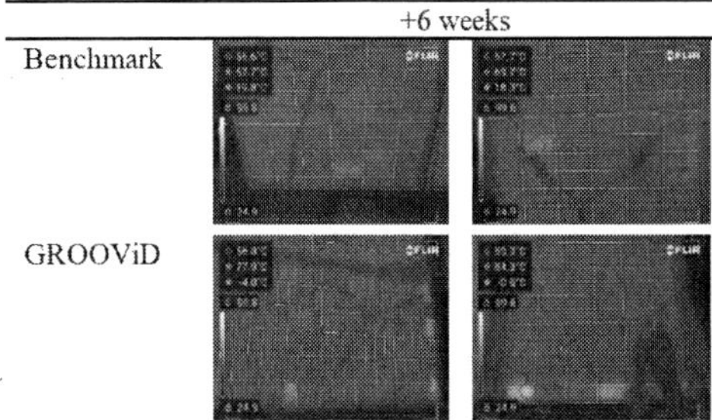	
GROOViD		

The benchmark modules AA02 and AA03 presented mild hot-spot findings, with up to +12 °C deviations between the coldest and the hottest area in the modules. GROOViD modules AA04 and AA05, instead, presented more distinct hot spots in correspondence to the partial shading areas caused by non-uniform cleaning. In this case, the deviations between the coldest and the hottest areas in the modules raised to +25 °C, with hottest areas in the range of 80-90 °C. Hot spots caused by non-uniform cleaning require more attention in the future development of GROOViD solution.

5.3 UV fluorescence imaging

UV fluorescence imaging highlighted organic soiling deposits and bird droppings (Fig. 6a) and fluorescent streaks along cell edges in the shortest side of the modules, with no significant difference between the modules treated with GROOViD irrigation-cleaning system and the benchmark modules. This may indicate an early EVA encapsulant degradation, exacerbated by UV exposure and extreme heat. Oxygen and moisture ingress, likely enhanced by thermomechanical stresses, are under investigation as possible causes.

 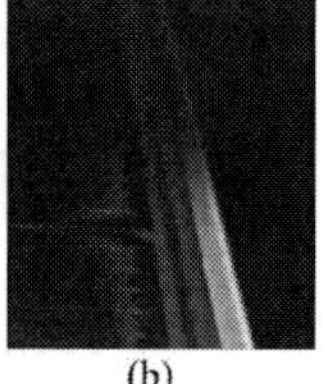

(a)   (b)

Figure 6: UV fluorescence imaging: (a) organic deposits and bird drops; (b) fluorescence streaks along cell edges.

6 FUTURE WORKS

A 4-times scaled-up GROOViD pilot system is under development in collaboration with the Fujairah Research Centre at its Honey Park in Dibba, Fujairah (UAE), with a nominal capacity of 9.12 kWp . The system will consist of sixteen bifacial TOPCon modules of Tab. I, arranged in one string, extending the design of the Masdar City prototype, with diffuser and water management systems that are scaled up based on insights gained from observations and measurements conducted at Masdar City.

7 CONCLUSIONS

GROOViD project demonstrates that agri-PV can be effectively adapted to desert conditions by integrating PV tracking, dual-use of water management, and optimized shading. Results showed reduced evapotranspiration with improved crop health, and stable power performance of the solar modules against soiling. This integrated approach can support the UAE's food, water, and energy security strategies, while offering a scalable model for arid regions worldwide. Future work will focus on improved cleaning uniformity, the pilot expansion in Fujairah, and long-term reliability studies, reinforcing GROOViD's role as a climate-resilient solution for sustainable agriculture in arid regions.

REFERENCES

[1] S. Kumar, M. H. Saw, S. L. Heng, A. Sinha, S. W. Leow, L. Wang, M. Pravettoni, Proceedings of the 52nd IEEE Photovoltaic Specialist Conference (PVSC), (2024) 1487-1492.

[2] B. Adothu, S. Kumar, J. J. John, G. Oreski, G. Mathiak, B. Jäckel, V. Alberts, J. Bin Jahangir, M. A. Alam, R. Gottschalg Prog. Photovolt: Res. Appl., 32(8) (2024) 495-527.

[3] US-UAE Business Council, "The U.A.E.'s Food Security Vision: Innovation, Investment, and Partnerships", policy reports (2024).

[4] R. G. Allen, L. S. Pereira, D. Raes, M. Smith, Crop evapotranspiration - Guidelines for computing crop water requirements, FAO Irrigation and drainage paper 56 (1998).

[5] M. H. Saw, S. Kumar, S. Singh, C. G. Parrilla, F. Lamghari, M. Pravettoni, Proceedings of the Agrivoltaics World Conference (2025).

REVIEW OF SENSOR TECHNOLOGIES FOR MONITORING AGRIVOLTAIC SYSTEMS

Sara Pereira[1], José A. Silva[1], Luís Fialho[2], Pedro Horta[1]

[1]Applied Research in Solar Energy for the Energy Transition (SOL4R), University of Évora, Polo da Mitra da Universidade de Évora, Edifício Ário Lobo de Azevedo, 7000-083 Nossa Senhora de Tourega, Portugal.

[2]Eurac Research-Institute for Renewable Energy, 39100 Bolzano, Italy

ABSTRACT: Agrivoltaics (AgriPV) co-locates photovoltaic generation with crops, coupling microclimate, plant physiology and power conversion. This paper assembles an empirical baseline of current monitoring practice via a systematic review of 123 experimental studies (2014–2024). It presents what is measured across meteorological, energy-performance and agricultural domains, how measurements are acquired (manual, automated, hybrid), and how research themes co-occur. The literature shows a higher volume of papers addressing agronomic/environmental effects, frequently studied alongside system integration/design and energy performance. Meteorological sensing is most prevalent (102 papers), followed by energy-performance (53) and agricultural variables (41). Acquisition is predominantly hybrid: 65.0% combine automated logging (weather/power) with targeted plant measurements; 21.1% are automated-only; 13.8% manual-only. Documentation gaps cluster in operational metadata, such as maintenance/durability, power supply/autonomy, data transmission and calibration/accuracy. Where PAR/PPFD is explicitly measured or robustly derived and co-reported with module temperature and inverter telemetry on a shared time base, studies can trace causal chains from forcing to conversion and crop response, enabling quantitative, design-relevant comparisons. By consolidating what AgriPV studies actually measure and pinpointing concise, high-impact co-measurements and reporting items (timekeeping, calibration, placement, power/telemetry), this review provides the practical foundation for portable, cross-site synthesis and supports emerging data-driven analysis and control in AgriPV.

Keywords: agrivoltaics, sensors, monitoring, microclimate, soil

1 INTRODUCTION

The rapid expansion of photovoltaic (PV) capacity is intensifying pressure on land, particularly where food production and energy security are both strategic priorities. Agrivoltaics (AgriPV), which is the co-location of PV generation and crop cultivation, offers a path to dual productivity per unit area and has been repeatedly proposed as a land-sharing solution with agronomic and energetic co-benefits [1], [2]. By altering the radiation field, wind exposure, and surface energy balance, AgriPV structures can moderate heat and water stress and create distinctive microclimates that influence canopy function and soil–plant water fluxes. Evidence spans greenhouse and open-field contexts: spatial photosynthetic photon flux density (PPFD) mapping under PV roofs quantifies light gradients that guide planting geometry and crop placement [3], while instrumented open-field pilots couple plane-of-array or global irradiance, air temperature/humidity and power telemetry to link microclimate with energy conversion in situ [4]. Crop responses are system and species dependent. Multi-crop field studies document both neutral and beneficial outcomes for shade-tolerant vegetables under moderate coverage and more stringent thresholds for cereals [5].

The measurement challenge is therefore central to AgriPV research and practice. Physiological monitoring in perennial systems has demonstrated how shading alters leaf temperature and gas exchange, reinforcing the need to synchronize plant with meteorological data [6]. Sensor-rich tomato deployments show how coordinated monitoring of atmosphere, soil and canopy enables mechanistic interpretation of yield and quality outcomes [7]. Beyond agronomy, optical and spectral design choices can produce hydrological co-benefits, plot-scale experiments report measurable reductions in surface evaporation under tailored PV/glazing configurations [8]. At the water–energy–food nexus, integrated pilots highlight how harmonized data collection supports operational control and policy-relevant assessment [9].

In this work we assemble and organize the experimental AgriPV literature into an empirical baseline of current monitoring practice, mapping which variables are measured across meteorological, energy-performance and agricultural domains, how they are acquired and documented, and highlighting concise, high-impact reporting items and co-measurements that make studies portable across crops, layouts and climates enabling for researchers and practitioners to move from isolated case studies to reproducible, design-relevant synthesis and, in turn, to more credible evidence for AgriPV deployment and management.

2 METHODOLOGY

This study follows a systematic review protocol tailored to experimental AgriPV research. The objective was to map how sensors are used to monitor meteorological conditions, agricultural variables, and energy-performance metrics in AgriPV deployments, and to assess the degree of automation, time synchronization, and reporting completeness.

2.1 Literature selection

Scientific papers were extracted from Scopus, Google Scholar, and IEEE Xplore using keyword combinations such as "agrivoltaics", "monitoring", "sensors", "soil", "IoT", "case study" and "pilot" published from 2014 to 2024. Only peer-reviewed conference and journal papers published in English and explicitly describing AgriPV systems with identifiable sensor-based monitoring were considered. Purely simulation-based or review papers, and studies lacking experimental data were excluded. Records were deduplicated, screened by title/abstract, and full texts assessed for eligibility. 123 studies met the criteria and were retained for analysis.

2.2 Data extraction and classification

Studies were systematically examined using a structured data extraction protocol. For each publication, metadata and descriptive information when available were compiled into a database, including research questions addressed, system characteristics, deployment scale, sensor categories, automation and control mechanisms, sensor accuracy and calibration methods, IoT and machine learning use, sensor power supply details, data collection and transmission details, frequency and duration of data collection, as well as maintenance and durability aspects of the monitoring system.

Monitoring variables were systematically classified into three key categories: meteorological, energy performance, and agricultural monitoring. Particular care was taken to distinguish between fully automated sensor-based monitoring and manual field data collection, with the latter categorized separately to maintain consistency. Information was only included when explicitly mentioned in the source document.

Each paper was tagged against six research questions: RQ1—meteorological impacts on PV shading; RQ2—energy generation performance; RQ3—AgriPV impacts on environment or agriculture; RQ4— the roles of digital and automated technologies (IoT/control/ML); RQ5—economic and policy considerations; RQ6— system integration and design strategies. Papers could map to multiple RQs.

Given the heterogeneity of systems and metrics, this classification methodology was designed to allow for cross-study comparison and to highlight both the technological heterogeneity and reporting gaps in AgriPV monitoring research.

3 RESULTS AND DISCUSSION

The systematic literature review analyzed 123 peer-reviewed studies on AgriPV, with a specific focus on monitoring systems.

3.1 Thematic focus of AgriPV Studies

The reviewed AgriPV studies span a broad range of research objectives. As shown in Fig. 1, RQ3 (the impacts of AgriPV on the environment and agriculture) appears in 105 papers, followed by 87 for RQ6 (system integration/design) and 63 for RQ2 (energy performance), while RQ1 (impacts of meteorological factors on PV), RQ4 (digital/automation) and RQ5 (economics/policy) are comparatively less represented. Studies frequently straddle multiple RQs (Fig. 2): the most common pairing is RQ3 + RQ6 (31 papers), reflecting the tight coupling between crop outcomes and design/layout choices, and a substantial number of RQ2 + RQ3 + RQ6 (17 papers) mirrors the need to evaluate energy yield, agronomy and geometry together.

The emphasis on RQ3 is evident in field and greenhouse experiments that quantify how partial shading modulates microclimate and plant function, often linking soil moisture dynamics, gas exchange and biomass or quality metrics. Rice studies explore yield responses across coverage regimes and altered light fields,

highlighting threshold behavior and the need for crop-specific photosynthetically active radiation (PAR) targets [10]. In greenhouses, tomato experiments track microclimate and plant performance under PV roofing, demonstrating how localized radiation and humidity patterns translate into physiology and quality traits [11]. These investigations place measurement at the center of interpretation: without time-synchronized meteorological and plant data, it is difficult to distinguish beneficial microclimate control from unintended stress.

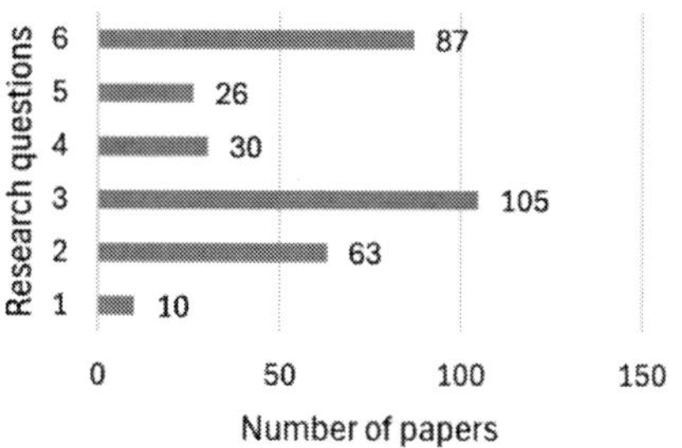

Figure 1: Number of papers addressing each research question.

Under RQ6, researchers increasingly treat layout as a control knob. Algorithmic approaches for semi-transparent or patterned PV optimize shading geometry and spectral transmission to stabilize plant light regimes through the season, connecting optical design with agronomic targets [12]. This design lens extends into open fields, where geometry (row spacing, tilt, vertical vs tilted) is treated as part of an agronomic–energetic trade-off, with instrumentation used to capture wind shelter, shade dynamics and their implications for both plants and power (the latter often appearing under RQ2) [13].

Energy performance (RQ2) in AgriPV is typically assessed through inverter telemetry coupled with module temperature and irradiance proxies, either in situ or inferred for the plane-of-array. Studies that co-report agricultural outputs and AC generation are particularly informative because they expose the simultaneity of benefits and trade-offs—e.g., rice–PV configurations that quantify electricity production alongside yield stability under different layouts [14].

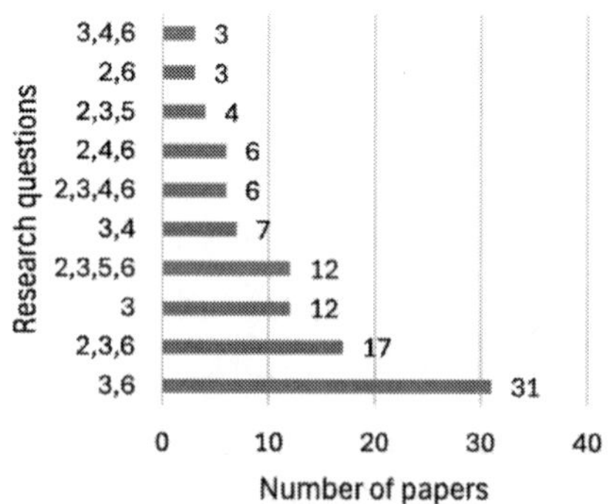

Figure 2: Most frequent combinations of research questions addressed in individual papers.

Digital and automated technologies (RQ4) are emerging. IoT-based fertigation platforms demonstrate how soil-moisture-driven control loops and low-power telemetry can stabilize water status while creating reproducible data streams for agronomic analysis, but such implementations remain the exception rather than the rule [15]. Finally, RQ5 (economics/policy) appears in techno-economic assessments that relate module transparency/coverage and crop response to levelized metrics and payback, providing a first link between sensor-evidenced agronomy and investment logic [16].

Taken together, the pattern in Fig. 1–2 suggests a maturing field that already recognizes the need to co-measure energy, environment and crop physiology.

3.2 Categories of sensors

Across literature, meteorological monitoring dominates (Fig. 3) with 102 studies reporting meteorological variables, typically global or plane-of-array irradiance and PAR/PPFD, air temperature and humidity, wind and precipitation. Open-field pilots that log plane-of-array irradiance alongside air temperature and humidity provide the basic scaffold for linking microclimate to agronomy and power, typically with dataloggers appropriate for long-term deployments [4]. Where geometry itself is the treatment, multi-station layouts capture gradients in wind, radiation components and PAR across vertical versus tilted arrays, enabling design-level inference [13].

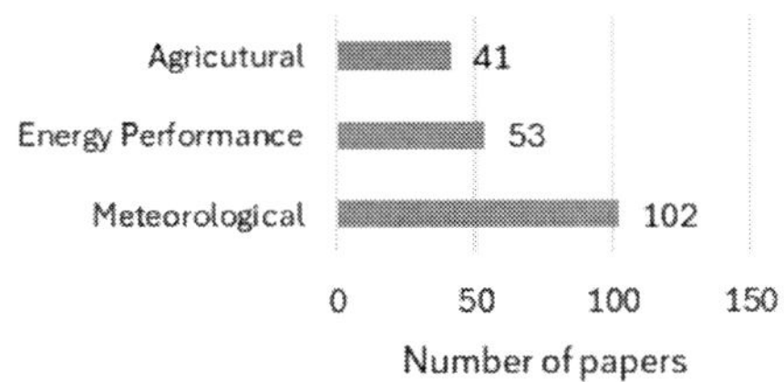

Figure 3: Number of papers with automated sensors by monitoring category.

Energy-performance sensing appears in 53 papers and most often comprises inverter telemetry coupled with back-of-module temperature, with occasional string-level current/voltage or I–V traces for detailed diagnostics. Greenhouse-integrated studies often access AC output through manufacturer platforms, which are helpful for continuity even when internal climate is sparsely documented [17]. Studies that time-align the electrical stream with radiation and temperature offer clearer attribution of transient behavior (e.g., cloud-edge events), a practice increasingly visible in geometry-comparison pilots that record power at short intervals [13] and in field trials where PV–crop co-location is evaluated with concurrent weather logging [4].

Papers using automated agricultural sensors are the fewest in number (41 papers) yet they ultimately validate AgriPV's agronomic value. The most common variables are soil moisture and temperature at depth, soil pH/EC/NPK, and leaf or canopy indicators such as chlorophyll indices or NDVI. Where physiological mechanisms matter, campaigns with portable gas-exchange (e.g., LI-6400) are used to connect microclimate to photosynthesis and stomatal control, generally layered

onto the automated weather baseline [7]. Chlorophyll-a fluorescence is also applied to track photo-physiological status in crop-specific contexts (e.g., tomatoes or cereals), tying light regime and plant performance to yield and quality outcomes [11], [14]. Greenhouse and semi-transparent configurations, in particular, show how spectral control reshapes plant light budgets and physiology, underscoring the need to report sensor placement and heights relative to canopy [11], [18].

Acquisition modes mirror field reality (Fig. 4): 65.0% of studies combine manual and automated measurements, 21.1% are automated-only, and 13.8% remain manual-only. This hybrid pattern works provided two basics are met: time-synchronization across streams and explicit metadata on sensor siting (heights, within vs inter-row, above/below canopy). Where calibration or accuracy is reported (particularly for PAR/PPFD or soil moisture) comparability improves substantially. Recent IoT-enabled systems document calibration steps, telemetry, and low-power autonomy, illustrating a reproducible template for field deployments [15].

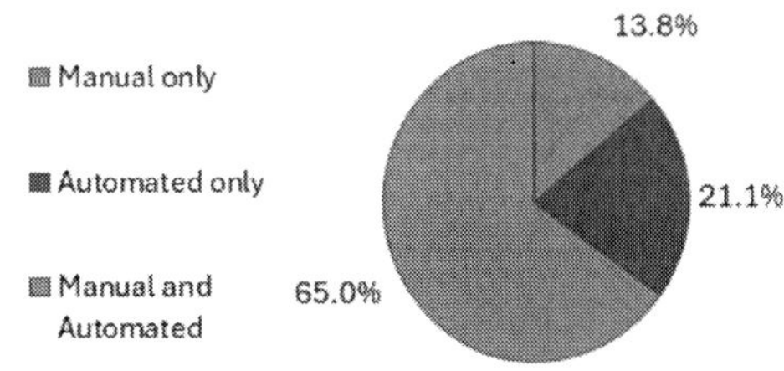

Figure 4: Percentage of papers by acquisition method.

Taken together, Fig. 3–4 indicate a field that already measures the dominant forcing (meteorology) and the electrical conversion stream, but still under-instruments continuous plant-side responses and under-reports the metadata that make results transferable.

3.3 Data acquisition practices

Fig. 5 reports gaps (number of papers lacking each item) across the 123 studies. The largest omissions are maintenance/durability (missing in 116 papers) and power supply/autonomy (105), followed by data-transmission method (102) and sensor accuracy/calibration (93). By contrast, only 28 papers fail to describe data-acquisition/processing, indicating that most studies now state sampling and basic processing, whereas operational metadata remain under-reported.

These omissions matter for reproducibility: without maintenance logs or power/telemetry descriptions, drift, dropouts and soiling effects are hard to interpret. Positive exemplars show what helps: explicit soiling/cleaning records alongside short-interval power and microclimate logging in geometry trials [13]; clear PAR to PPFD conversion and calibration notes where the photosynthetic light environment is central [19]; and concise statements of logger cadence and channels in pilot deployments [4]. Where telemetry is used, a one-line "how data leave the field" (e.g., LoRaWAN to cloud or inverter portal) plus time-synchronization notes makes datasets portable and auditable [15]. In short, most studies already state how they sampled, what is still missing, and most useful to add, are the operational details (power, transmission, calibration, maintenance), that make AgriPV monitoring comparable across sites and seasons.

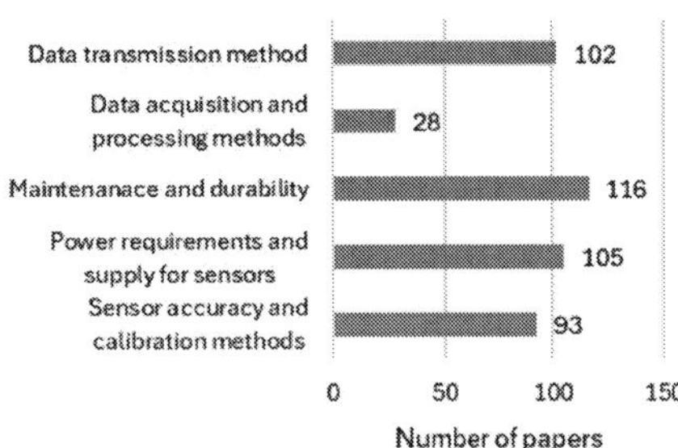

Figure 5: Number of papers missing information on key aspects of data acquisition.

4   CONCLUSIONS

This review of 123 experimental AgriPV studies shows a field converging on an integrated treatment of crops, climate and power. Most studies prioritize agronomic effects while layout and energy performance are co-determinants, and the prevailing hybrid acquisition model (continuous logging of weather and electrical variables complemented by targeted plant measurements) now enables causal chains from forcing to conversion and crop response to be traced with increasing confidence. Where photosynthetic light is explicitly resolved through PAR/PPFD sensing or robust irradiance-to-PPFD conversions, crop outcomes are interpretable in terms of the light budget rather than generic "shade," and geometry can be evaluated as a control parameter in its own right, from vertical/tilted rows in open fields to spectral tailoring in protected cultivation [3], [13], [19]. The literature also reveals that operational details such as timekeeping, calibration/uncertainty, placement relative to canopy and rows, and simple notes on power/telemetry and maintenance, remain the information most likely to be omitted, yet they are precisely the details that make results portable across sites and seasons.

Consolidating the evidence across studies, three elements of current practice consistently underpin credible AgriPV inference. First, co-reporting PAR/PPFD, inverter telemetry and module temperature on a shared time base provides a direct bridge from light environment to electrical conversion and plant response. When this triad is present, attribution improves, and design comparisons become quantitatively defensible. Second, pairing microclimate with soil-water information (at minimum, soil moisture at two or more depths and simple irrigation volumes) connects radiation and wind to water status and yield, enabling the interpretation of crop outcomes beyond instantaneous weather. Third, when layouts are the experimental treatment, multi-station measurements that resolve spatial gradients in wind and illumination across rows or panel orientations capture the heterogeneity that drives both physiology and power.

To make results truly portable, the most effective step is not more instrumentation but concise, high-impact documentation that standardizes what studies already do. At minimum, papers should specify logger clocks and time zones, sampling and aggregation intervals for each stream, sensor models and stated accuracies, exact placement relative to canopy height, row position and panel geometry, and one-line statements on power supply, telemetry and cleaning/maintenance. Providing these items in a machine-readable appendix with consistent variable names and SI units allows cross-site synthesis without reinterpretation. With such documentation and the co-measurement choices outlined above, the community can progress from coverage counts to transferable response functions that inform positioning, geometry and optical choices by crop and climate, and assess when simple automation (e.g., moisture-triggered fertigation) delivers operational benefit.

ACKNOWLEDGMENTS

This research was partly funded by the PRR Mobilizing Agendas, project Alliance for Energy Transition (ATE) with Grant agreement ID C644914747-00000023.

REFERENCES

[1] H. J. Williams, K. Hashad, H. Wang, and K. Max Zhang, "The potential for agrivoltaics to enhance solar farm cooling," *Appl Energy*, vol. 332, p. 120478, Feb. 2023, doi: 10.1016/j.apenergy.2022.120478.

[2] M. Jordan *et al.*, "Sonoran Desert Photovoltaics Laboratory and Growing Green: A Networked Regional Approach to Agrivoltaics Citizen Science," in *2024 IEEE 52nd Photovoltaic Specialist Conference (PVSC)*, IEEE, Jun. 2024, pp. 1465–1467. doi: 10.1109/PVSC57443.2024.10749646.

[3] S. Castellano, P. Santamaria, and F. Serio, "Solar radiation distribution inside a monospan greenhouse with the roof entirely covered by photovoltaic panels," *Journal of Agricultural Engineering*, vol. 47, no. 1, p. 1, Mar. 2016, doi: 10.4081/jae.2016.485.

[4] P. Gese, F. M. Martínez-Conde, G. Ramirez-Sagner, and F. Dinter, "Agrivoltaic in Chile - Integrative solution to use efficiently land for food and energy production and generating potential synergy effects shown by a pilot plant in Metropolitan region," in *Proceedings of the ISES Solar World Congress 2019 and IEA SHC International Conference on Solar Heating and Cooling for Buildings and Industry 2019*, International Solar Energy Society, 2020, pp. 1016–1024. doi: 10.18086/swc.2019.19.04.

[5] H. J. Lee, H. H. Park, Y. O. Kim, and Y. I. Kuk, "Crop Cultivation Underneath Agro-Photovoltaic Systems and Its Effects on Crop Growth, Yield, and Photosynthetic Efficiency," *Agronomy*, vol. 12, no. 8, p. 1842, Aug. 2022, doi: 10.3390/agronomy12081842.

[6] G. Ferrara, M. Boselli, M. Palasciano, and A. Mazzeo, "Effect of shading determined by photovoltaic panels installed above the vines on the performance of cv. Corvina (Vitis vinifera L.)," *Sci Hortic*, vol. 308, p. 111595, Jan. 2023, doi: 10.1016/j.scienta.2022.111595.

[7] S. Mohammedi, G. Dragonetti, N. Admane, and A. Fouial, "The Impact of Agrivoltaic Systems on Tomato Crop: A Case Study in Southern Italy," *Processes*, vol. 11, no. 12, p. 3370, Dec. 2023, doi: 10.3390/pr11123370.

[8] A. Ali Abaker Omer *et al.*, "Water evaporation reduction by the agrivoltaic systems development," *Solar Energy*, vol. 247, pp. 13–23, Nov. 2022, doi: 10.1016/j.solener.2022.10.022.

[9] J. Fleischmann *et al.*, "Guiding the data collection for integrated Water-Energy-Food-Environment systems using a pilot smallholder farm in Costa Rica," *Energy Nexus*, vol. 13, p. 100259, Mar. 2024, doi: 10.1016/j.nexus.2023.100259.

[10] S. S. Joy, I. Khan, and A. M. Swaraz, "A non-traditional Agrophotovoltaic installation and its impact on cereal crops: A case of the BRRI-33 rice variety in Bangladesh," *Heliyon*, vol. 9, no. 7, 2023, doi: 10.1016/j.heliyon.2023.e17824.

[11] R. Bulgari, G. Cola, A. Ferrante, G. Franzoni, L. Mariani, and L. Martinetti, "Micrometeorological environment in traditional and photovoltaic greenhouses and effects on growth and quality of tomato (Solanum lycopersicum L.)," *Italian Journal of Agrometeorology*, vol. 20, no. 2, pp. 27–38, 2015, [Online]. Available: https://www.scopus.com/inward/record.uri?eid=2-s2.0-84942313617&partnerID=40&md5=c0475f81f29e22209ba8305f7a69710f

[12] T. Petrakis, V. Thomopoulos, and A. Kavga, "Algorithmic advancements in agrivoltaics: Modeling shading effects of semi-transparent photovoltaics," *Smart Agricultural Technology*, vol. 9, p. 100541, Dec. 2024, doi: 10.1016/j.atech.2024.100541.

[13] K. A. Khan Niazi and M. Victoria, "Field Characterization of Vertical and Tilted Agrivoltaic Installations," in *2024 IEEE 52nd Photovoltaic Specialist Conference (PVSC)*, IEEE, Jun. 2024, pp. 410–410. doi: 10.1109/PVSC57443.2024.10749577.

[14] S.-W. Park, S.-M. Yun, D.-G. Seong, J. J. Lee, and J.-S. Chung, "Rice yield and electricity production in agro-photovoltaic systems," *Chil J Agric Res*, vol. 84, no. 5, pp. 674–685, Oct. 2024, doi: 10.4067/s0718-58392024000500674.

[15] F. Zito, N. I. Giannoccaro, R. Serio, and S. Strazzella, "Analysis and Development of an IoT System for an Agrivoltaics Plant," *Technologies (Basel)*, vol. 12, no. 7, p. 106, Jul. 2024, doi: 10.3390/technologies12070106.

[16] U. R. Patel, G. A. Gadhiya, and P. M. Chauhan, "Techno-economic analysis of agrivoltaic system for affordable and clean energy with food production in India," *Clean Technol Environ Policy*, vol. 26, no. 7, pp. 2117–2135, Jul. 2024, doi: 10.1007/s10098-023-02690-1.

[17] M. Torres *et al.*, "The Photovoltaic Greenhouse as Energy Hub for a More Sustainable Agriculture," in *2022 IEEE International Conference on Automation/25th Congress of the Chilean Association of Automatic Control: For the Development of Sustainable Agricultural Systems, ICA-ACCA 2022*, Institute of Electrical and Electronics Engineers Inc., 2022. doi: 10.1109/ICA-ACCA56767.2022.10006135.

[18] T. Hickey, M. Uchanski, and J. Bousselot, "Vegetable crop growth under photovoltaic (PV) modules of varying transparencies," *Heliyon*, vol. 10, no. 16, p. e36058, Aug. 2024, doi: 10.1016/j.heliyon.2024.e36058.

[19] D. Yajima, T. Toyoda, M. Kirimura, K. Araki, Y. Ota, and K. Nishioka, "Agrivoltaic system: Estimation of photosynthetic photon flux density under solar panels based on solar irradiation data using all-climate solar spectrum model," *Clean Eng Technol*, vol. 12, p. 100594, Feb. 2023, doi: 10.1016/j.clet.2022.100594.

Review of Sensor Technologies for Monitoring Agrivoltaic Systems

Sara Pereira[1], José A. Silva[1], Luís Fialho[2], Pedro Horta[1]

[1]Applied Research in Solar Energy for the Energy Transition (SOL4R), University of Évora, Portugal
[2]Eurac Research-Institute for Renewable Energy, 39100 Bolzano, Italy

Introduction

Agrivoltaics (AgriPV) co-locates PV generation with crops, coupling microclimate, plant physiology, and power conversion. Robust, time-aligned monitoring is central to interpreting crop–climate–power interactions and to comparing layouts across sites and crops.

Objectives

- Systematically review sensor types and monitoring strategies used in research on AgriPV.
- Identify and analyze current practices and gaps in AgriPV monitoring setups.

Methods

- Literature search: IEEE Xplore, Scopus, Google Scholar (2014–2024).
- Criteria: AgriPV-specific, included sensor use, peer-reviewed, English. Resulted in the selection of 123 studies.
- Classify sensors by manual vs automated and by monitoring objectives: environmental, energy performance, and agricultural.
- Data extracted: system type, deployment scale, sensor type, calibration, data acquisition, data transmission, power supply, etc.

Results

Research questions addressed

RQ1	Impact of the environment on AgriPV systems [1].	RQ4	Roles of digital and automated technologies [4].
RQ2	Energy generation performance [2].	RQ5	Economic and policy consideration [5].
RQ3	Impact of the AgriPV system on the environment or agriculture [3].	RQ6	System integration and design strategies [6].

Research questions (Number of papers):
- 6 — 87
- 5 — 26
- 4 — 30
- 3 — 105
- 2 — 63
- 1 — 10

Number of papers mentioning automated sensors by category:
- Agricultural — 41
- Energy Performance — 53
- Meteorological — 102

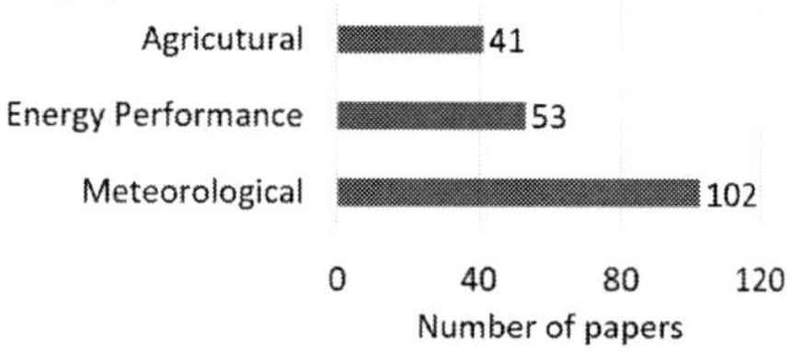

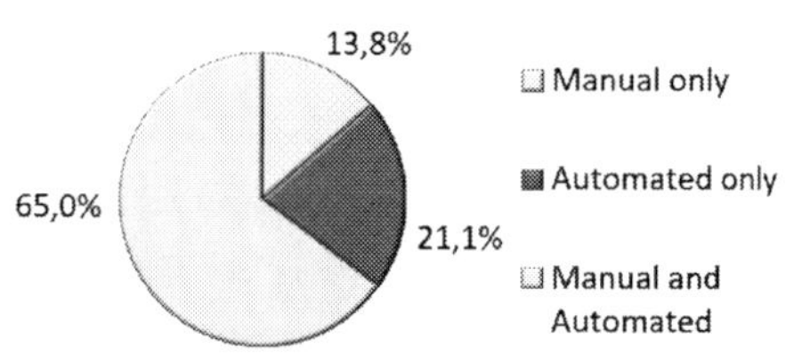

- Manual only — 13,8%
- Automated only — 65,0%
- Manual and Automated — 21,1%

Categories of sensors

Category	Measured Variable	Sensors reported
Meteorological	Global / plane-of-array irradiance	Pyranometers: Kipp & Zonen CMP11, CMP22, CMP3; Hukseflux SR20, SR11; EKO
	PAR / PPFD (crop height)	Quantum sensor
	Spectral distribution	Spectroradiometer: Ocean Optics USB2000+
	Air temperature / relative humidity	Shielded thermo-hygrometer
	Wind speed/direction	Cup/ultrasonic anemometers: RM Young 05103
	Precipitation	Tipping-bucket rain gauge
Energy Performance	Inverter AC power / telemetry	Inverter-based loggers
	String DC / I-V	I–V curve tracer; string monitoring unit (Hall-effect or shunt); DC power analyzer
	Module temperature	T/K thermocouples, PT100
Agricultural	Soil moisture / temperature	TDR/FDR/capacitance probes: Campbell CS650/CS655
	Leaf temperature	Thermography: Apogee SI-111/IRT; FLIR cameras
	Gas exchange	IRGA-based portable photosynthesis system: LI-COR LI-6400/LI-6800
	Chlorophyll-a fluorescence	PAM fluorometer: Walz MINI-PAM / PAM-2500
	Canopy indices (chlorophyll/NDVI/PRI)	Chlorophyll meter / proximal multispectral sensor: SPAD-502, GreenSeeker
	LAI / light interception	Ceptometer / canopy analyzer: LI-COR LAI-2200, AccuPAR LP-80, Delta-T SunScan

Critical research gaps

Number of studies lacking information on key aspects of data collection:
- Data transmission method — 102
- Data acquisition and processing methods — 28
- Maintenanace and durability — 116
- Power requirements and supply for sensors — 105
- Sensor accuracy and calibration methods — 93

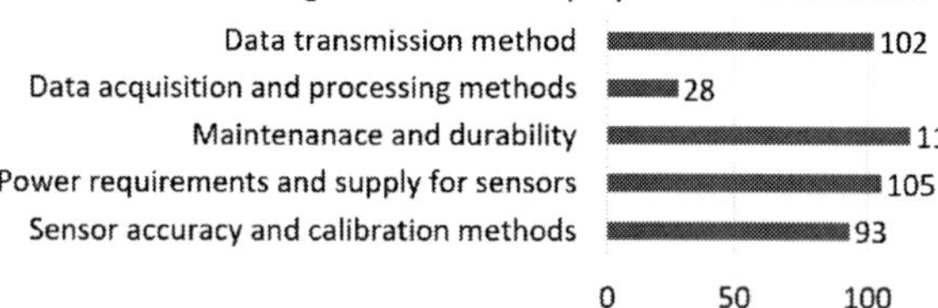

- Operational metadata underreported, timekeeping and precise sensor placement seldom specified.
- PAR/PPFD often absent or conversions undefined.
- Plant-soil responses under-instrumented, irrigation volumes frequently missing.
- Spatial under-sampling and limited automation.

Conclusion

This review turns a scattered literature into a usable baseline of how AgriPV is actually monitored. By quantifying what is measured, how it is acquired, and where key operational metadata are missing, it enables portable, cross-site comparisons of crop–climate–power interactions. The results point to simple, high-impact practices: co-reporting PAR/PPFD, module temperature, and inverter telemetry on a shared clock and documenting timekeeping, calibration, placement, power and telemetry. This transforms isolated case studies into design-relevant evidence for geometry, optics, and emerging data-driven control.

References

[1] H. J. Williams et al., (2023). doi: 10.1016/j.apenergy.2022.120478

[2] K. A. Khan Niazi and M. Victoria, (2024). doi: 10.1109/PVSC57443.2024.10749577

[3] H. J. Lee et al., (2022). doi: 10.3390/agronomy12081842

[4] F. Zito et al., (2024). doi: 10.3390/technologies12070106

[5] U. R. Patel et al., (2024). doi: 10.1007/s10098-023-02690-1

[6] T. Petrakis et al. (2024). doi: 10.1016/j.atech.2024.100541

Contact me:

Commercially viable solar parks with improved soil quality

A.R. Burgers, B.B. Van Aken, K.M. de Groot, G.J. de Graaff, B.W.J. Kikkert, I. Cesar, TNO solar energy, Petten
F.F. van der Zee, Wageningen University and Research
S. Leone, Novar

E/W facing systems and soil quality

- Typical E/W solar parks NL: high ground coverage ratio (> 90%)
- Vegetation:
  - in aisles, extending 50-100 cm under lower edges
  - Very little vegetation elsewhere
- **Idea**: concentrate crest opening light to create central zone with conditions viable for plant growth

Funnel view 08-2025

Experiment

- Optical element installed Sep-2024
  - So far been in-place for about 1 ½ grow season
- Irradiance on ground measured with sensor arrays
- Vegetation assessment squares
  - Monitoring by Wageningen University
  - Assess vegetation at intervals, statistical evaluation.
  - requires time, maybe multiple growth seasons

key

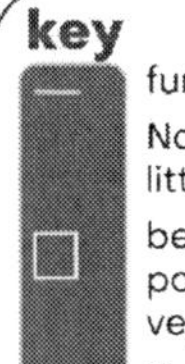

regular crest, crest with funnel

Design of optical elements

- Funnel limiting spread of light entering through crest opening
  - Non-imaging concentration of light
  - Parameters such as tilt of mirror, height of mirror.
- bigeye view factor approach extended with ray tracing.
- Calculations validated with on-site measurements
- Comparing measured and simulated irradiance on a clear day:
  - Sun rays: direct, 1 reflection (E-face or W-face), detectors registering sun multiple times
  - Each color: time series per sensor.

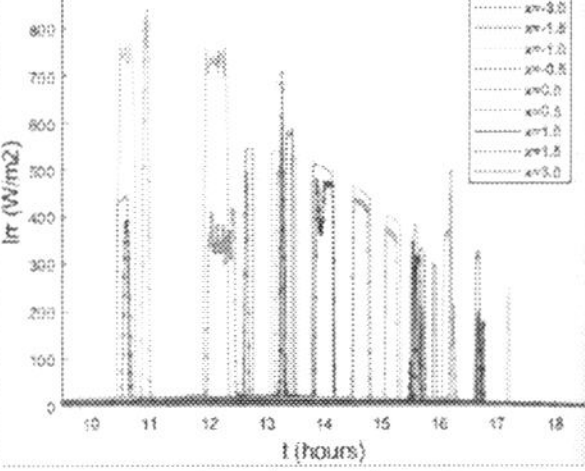
measured and simulated irradiance on a clear day.

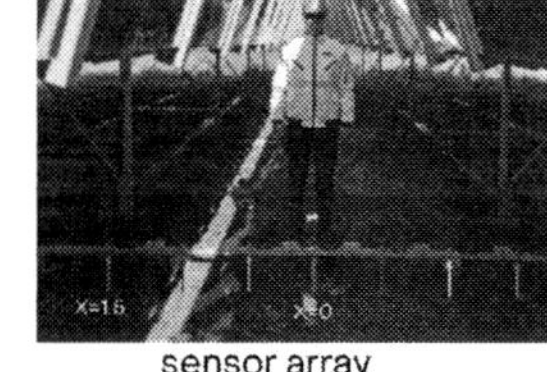
sensor array
(wet circumstances 09-2024)

Carbon fixation model calibration and "hairline"

- Vegetation present from aisle up to "hairline"
- steep decrease in irradiance below lower edge of table
- Realise conditions below crest opening better than "hairline" to extend vegetation coverage
- Funnel: more peaked irradiance profile than open crest reference case

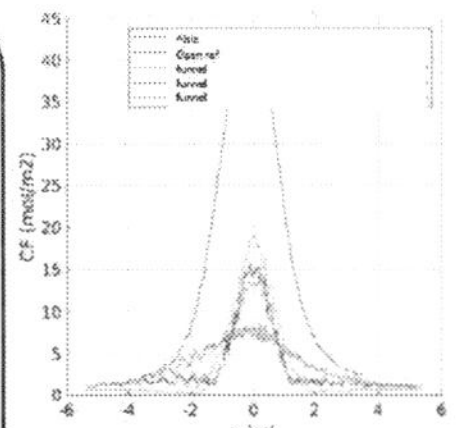
Calculated crop yield: open ref, aisle, funnel

Grass growth in aisle extending below PV

Conclusions

- Designed and realized optical elements to boost the vegetation growth conditions below densely packed PV
- Validated the irradiance with and without these elements below the tables and in the aisle
- Improved irradiance conditions below the crest: should lead to more vegetation growth, but needs longer observation period

- Mirrors have withstood near 2 years of operation well.
- Comprehensive approach: optical elements, irradiance measurements, vegetation assessment
- Geometry of this system (narrow crest opening) was critical with respect to gains

42nd European Photovoltaic Solar Energy Conference and Exhibition

Meira Itzel Torres Aguilar[1], Shusen YU[2], Anne MIGAN-DUBOIS[1,3], Vincent BOURDIN[3,4], Jordi Badosa FRANCH[2], Johan PARRA[2], Bouchra MEKHALDI[2]

[1] Université Paris-Saclay, CentraleSupélec, CNRS, Laboratoire de Génie Électrique et Électronique de Paris, 91192 Gif-sur-Yvette, France
[2] LMD/IPSL, Ecole Polytechnique, IP Paris, Sorbonne Université, ENS, PSL University, CNRS – 91128 – France
[3] Sorbonne Université, CNRS, Laboratoire de Génie Électrique et Électronique de Paris, 75252 Paris, France
[4] CNRS, LISN, Bâtiment 507, Rue du Belvédère, 91405 Orsay, France

Power Output Modelling of a Single-Axis Backtracking Bifacial Module in an Agrivoltaic System in Palaiseau, France

Introduction (1)

In recent years, the use of land for both agricultural crop production and photovoltaic (PV) solar energy conversion has gained considerable attention, leading to an accelerated growth of agrivoltaics.

New bifacial technologies and larger utility-scale PV arrays result in a growing need for models that can more accurately account for the multiple diffuse light components and reflections incident on various surfaces of a PV array. For this reason, integrated modelling, simulation, and optimisation of systems are fundamental.

Together, new bifacial technologies and models, aim to develop a better understanding of how the shading produced by PV modules impacts solar irradiation distribution on the ground, the microclimate beneath the PV modules, how this microclimate influences crop growth, and, in turn, how microclimate and crop growth affects PV production.

This work presents initial results of a modelling chain starting from tracker angles up to power output while considering the impact of a variable albedo due to the presence of plants under the PV installation.

Installation (2)

Figure 1 Layout of agripv installation located on the campus of Ecole Polytechnique in Palaiseau, France.

- North-South orientation with single-axis tracking (East-West)
- 72 TOPCon half-cell bifacial modules (555 Wp, 560 Wp, 565 Wp)
- 36 modules equipped with individual optimizers
- 4 inverters (1 per row)
- Meteorological variables: wind, air temperature, precipitation, among others

Methodology (3)

- 4 c-Si reference cells on module A8 (2 front/2 back)
- 4 temperature probes (2 on A8)

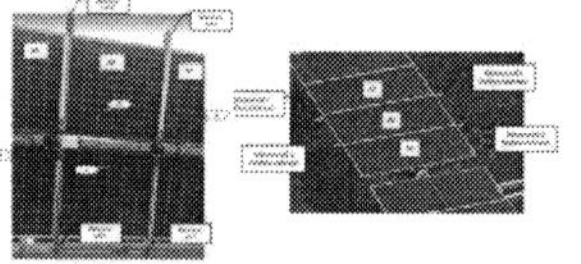

Figure 2 Location of temperature probes (left) and of reference cells on module A8 (right).

- 2 periods of PV tracking: fixed horizontal and backtracking

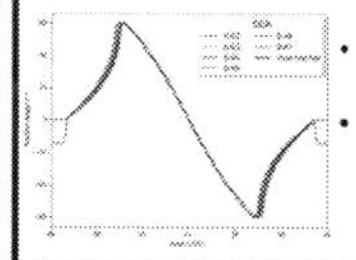

Figure 3 Photos of installation at two different periods: horizontal position (left) and backtracking (right)

- 3 alfalfa cycles:
  - June 10th – August 29th 2024
  - August 30th – November 12th 2024
  - November 14th – May 27th 2025

Models used

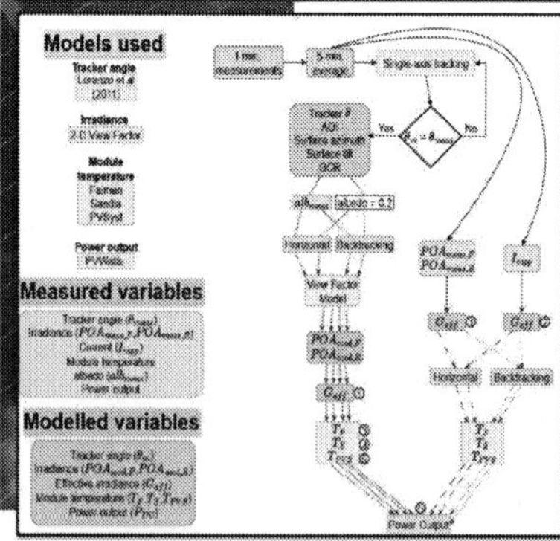

Models used

Measured variables

Modelled variables

Models (4)

$$G_{eff} = POA_{front} + (POA_{back} * \varphi_{Pmax}) \quad (1)$$

$$G_{eff} = \frac{I_{MPP}}{I_{mpp,STC}} \quad (2)$$

$$T_F = T_a + \frac{POA}{U_0 + U_1 * WS} \quad (3)$$

$$T_S = POA * \exp(U_0 + U_1 * WS) + T_a \quad (4)$$

$$T_{PVS} = T_a + \frac{\alpha\, POA\,(1-\eta)}{U_0 + U_1 * WS} \quad (5)$$

$$P_{DC} = \frac{POA}{G_{STC}} P_{STC}(1 + \gamma(T_m - T_{STC})) \quad (6)$$

α: absorption coefficient
γ: power temperature coefficient
η: module efficiency
Φ: bifaciality factor
I_{mpp}: current at maximum power point
$I_{mpp,STC}$: current at maximum power point under STC
P_{STC}: power output at STC
POA: plane-of-array irradiance
T_a: air temperature
T_m: measured module temperature
T_{STC}: module temperature at STC
U_0: heat loss factor
U_1: heat loss factor influenced by wind
WS: wind speed

Results (5)

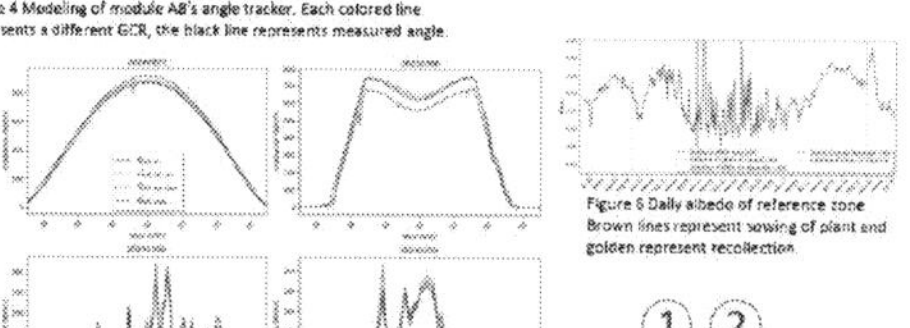

- GCR that best models measured tracker angle is 0.44
- Falls within the 10% tolerance of module size with respect to the GCR value provided by the installer of 0.407

Figure 4 Modeling of module A8's angle tracker. Each colored line represents a different GCR, the black line represents measured angle.

Figure 5 Comparison between measured and modeled front and rear irradiance for sunny and cloudy days during period in horizontal position and backtracking. Blue corresponds to measured value, orange to modeled value considering a fixed albedo of 0.2, and green to a modeled value considering a variable albedo

Figure 6 Daily albedo of reference zone. Brown lines represent sowing of plant and golden represent recollection

Figure 7 Comparison between different calculated G_{eff}. For the blue curve, on-site measurements were used. For orange, modeled values considering a fixed albedo, for green a variable albedo was considered. The brown curve was calculated using only the module's I_{mpp}.

- There is a maximum relative mean bias error (rMBE) of 2.22% for the front side irradiance and of -40.91% for the back.
- The large error is suspected to be partly due to spectral and engle-of-incidence effects not being considered by the model
- The presence of plants results in a an albedo variation of ~4%

- The uncertainty associated to the modeled rear irradiance does not have a strong impact on the calculated effective irradiance (G_{eff}) due to the bifaciality factor (75%) and low irradiance values
- The most impactful factor is the front irradiance measurements used
- Calculated G_{eff} using the module's current at maximum power point (I_{mpp}), is lower than the others because it corresponds to the irradiance truly absorbed by the module.

Figure 8 Comparison between different module temperatures calculated with different G_{eff}. The bar pattern indicates type of day and the bar color indicates the model used.

- Even large errors when modeling T_p have a negligible impact on the modeled power output
- The determining factor is the irradiance used
- Utilizing measured instead of fixed albedo for modelling irradiance provides an improvement of up to 2.88%
- For cloudy conditions all temperature models give similar results, for sunny days there is a difference of up to 1.82%
- The best result is obtained when using a G_{eff} calculated from the module's own I_{mpp}.

Figure 9 Comparison between modeled and measured power output using different T_p and G_{eff} as input. Bar pattern indicates type of day and color the module temperature used.

- There is good agreement between modeled and measured module temperature (T_p), specially for the Faiman and Sandia models
- Large errors for the PVSyst model are due to low values of U_0 and U_1 estimated with local wind measurements
- The free air flow due to module rotation in backtracking mode keeps the modules cooler
- The smaller difference for cloudy days is due to overall lower temperatures.

Conclusions (6)

- Even though a model is capable of accurately modelling incident irradiance on the front side of modules, there is increased difficulty for a moving surface
- Adding a changing albedo due to the presence of plants in the model for the back irradiance is complex and will require furrther work
- Despite large errors when using a specific temperature model, the defining factor is the irradiance data used for modelling
- The best power output modelling results are obtained when using an effective irradiance calculated with the module's I_{mpp}

Acknowledgements

This work is part of the AgriPV-ER project (22-PETA-0007), which contributes to the "Pole National de Recherche sur l'Agriphotovoltaïsme" from INRAE. The project is supported by France 2030, the PEPR TASE (https://www.pepr-tase.fr/), as well as the 3rd Programme d'Investissements d'Avenir (ANR-18-EUR-006-02), and the Foundation of Ecole polytechnique (Chaire "Défis Technologiques pour une Energie Responsable") financed by TotalEnergies.

020406-001

YIELD AND PR ESTIMATION FOR VERTICAL AGRIVOLTAICS SYSTEMS

[1]Guillermo P. Moreda (gullermo.moreda@upm.es), [2]Miguel Ángel Egido (egido@ies-def.upm.es) , [3]Valero Pascual Gallego (valero.pascual@upm.es), [4]Delia Rodriguez Lucas, (delia@ekilabs.com), [1*]Miguel A. Muñoz-García (miguelangel.munoz@upm.es)

[1] Dep. Ing. Agroforestal. ETSIAAB. Universidad Politécnica de Madrid. R&D group: LPF-Tagralia. Av. Puerta de Hierro, 2. 28040. Madrid, Spain. Tel.: +34 91 06 70968.
[2] Instituto de Energía Solar. Universidad Politécnica de Madrid.
[2] Dep. Estructuras y Física de la Edificación. Universidad Politécnica de Madrid.
[3] EkiLabs CORP.

ABSTRACT: Photovoltaic systems interspersed with cropland are gaining ground. Since both elements compete for radiation, determining the amount of light that reaches each of them is of great interest. Vertical agrivoltaic systems are an alternative to other systems installed in crop fields, which interfere less with tillage and machinery. When these systems consist of bifacial panels, energy capture is almost twice that of monofacial system. To determine profitability, measurements of both actual production and expected output or performance ratio (PR) must be obtained. Likewise, if the system is agrivoltaic, agricultural production must not be substantially reduced, and regulations set different limits depending on the country, with an extended objective of not assuming a reduction greater than 20%. The calculation of the PR in a vertical system is something that is still open to debate when the panels are bifacial. In addition, when the system is oriented with a north-south axis, the maximum radiation can be strongly affected by nearby shadows, both from other parallel strings and from nearby obstacles. Given the sensitivity of a vertical system to these aspects, in this work we address the elements that will affect the correct understanding and design of vertical agrivoltaic plants.
Keywords: Photovoltaic, bifacial, performance ratio, agrivoltaic

1 INTRODUCTION

Agrivoltaics (AV), the dual use of agricultural land to produce crops and photovoltaic (PV) power in the same plot, is a hot topic of research. A key aspect in AV is that both the crop and the PV plant can mutually benefit if the materials are adequately selected, and the geometry of the system is well designed. The crop can be inside a greenhouse or in open-field, what gives rise to different designs of the PV plant.

In the last years, two open-field AV geometries have been proposed: The South-facing tilted static panels arranged on a gantry-type shed structure and the static vertical East-West facing bifacial panels assembled on a fence-type structure. The research reported here is in the context of how well vertical bifacial AV will serve as the generator for electric-powered pump irrigation.

The calculation of the performance ratio (PR) in a vertical system is something that is still open to debate when the panels are bifacial. In addition, when the system is oriented with a north-south axis, the maximum radiation can be strongly affected by nearby shadows, both from other parallel strings and from nearby obstacles. Given the sensitivity of a vertical system to these aspects, in this work we address the elements that will affect the correct understanding and design of vertical agrivoltaic plants.

In this regard, the following points should be discussed:

- Is the peak power indicated by the manufacturer or should both sides be taken into account?
- If both sides are included, what bifaciality coefficient should be applied?

The objective of this work is to compare the model-based estimates of incident solar radiation on the active faces of bifacial solar panels placed vertically, with the actual radiation received by them. In this way, it will be possible to determine which parameters come into play when using radiation databases.

2 MATERIALS AND METHODS

To carry out this task, a real vertical installation (Figure 1, Figure 2) was instrumented with bifacial panels, with the intention of measuring the real radiation on both sides and at different heights. On the other hand, the electrical production on both sides was monitored.

Figure 1: Agrivoltaic system with vertical bifacial PV panels

10.4229/EUPVSEC2025/4DV.1.22
020407-001

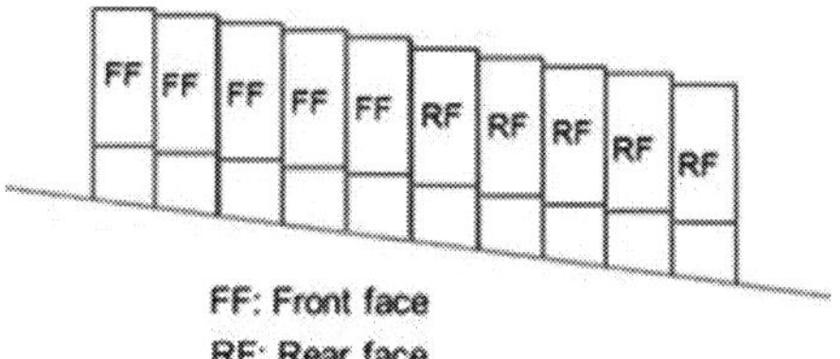

Figure 2: Vertical bifacial PV panels, where FF is the main side and RF is the rear side.

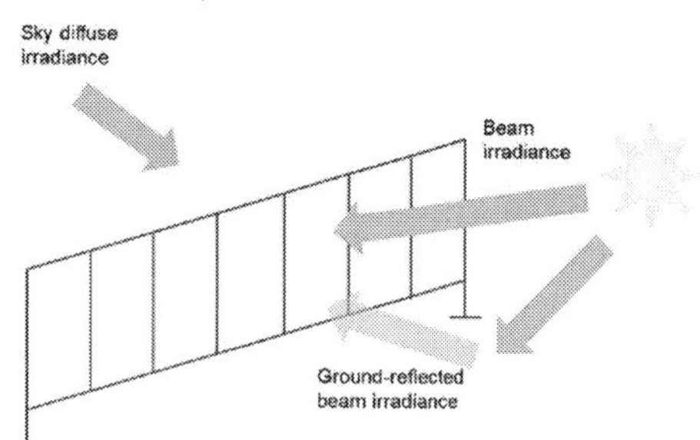

Figure 3: Main radiation sources for bifacial PV panels

Determining the quality of the data obtained from databases such as CAMS, PVGIS SARAH-2, or Solargis is of vital importance to calculate the yield of agrivoltaic plants with vertical installation.

On the other hand, the Performance Ratio (PR) would be the most commonly used parameter to determine the proper functioning of a conventional plant. However, if we look at the formula for obtaining it (Eq. 1), in a bifacial panel there would be a discussion about whether the radiation to be measured should be taken from the most exposed side, as well as whether the peak power should include both sides.

Eq. 1:

$$PR = \frac{Yield\ (kWh)}{PSH\left(\frac{kWh}{1\ kW}\right) \cdot P_p\ (kW)}$$

The bifaciality of a bifacial PV panel is measured with the bifaciality coefficients. The bifaciality coefficient prescribed by the technical specification IEC 60904-1-2: 2024 is the bifaciality of current, φ_{Isc}, defined as the ratio between the short-circuit current (I_{sc}) generated exclusively by the rear face of the panel and the I_{sc} generated exclusively by the front face, with the condition that both currents are measured at STC (irradiance of 1000 $W \cdot m^{-2}$, panel temperature of 25 °C, and with the IEC 60904-3 reference solar spectral irradiance distribution). To determine the φ_{Isc}, bifacial PV panels can be tested as showcased in Figure 4.

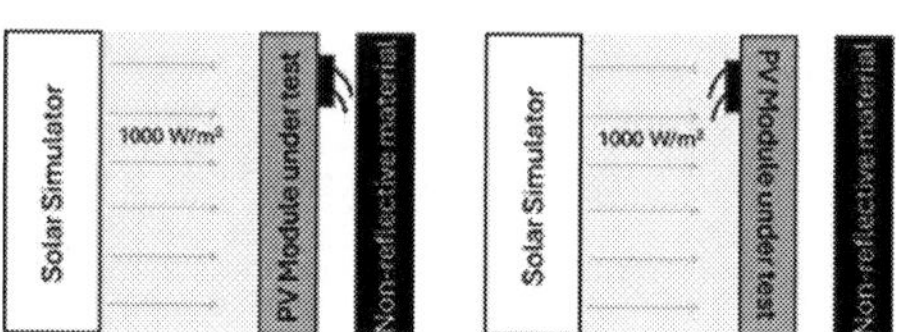

Figure 4: Single-side illumination test method for bifacial PV panels.

To qualify bifacial panels, the so-called bifacial standard test condition (BSTC) applies, characterized by a front irradiance of 1000 W/m^2, a rear irradiance of 135 W/m^2 and an equivalent irradiance G_E defined [1] in Eq.2, where $\varphi_{Isc} = I_{sc,rear} / I_{sc,front}$

Eq. 2:

$$G_E = (1000 + \varphi_{Isc} \cdot 135)\ W/m^2$$

If our solar simulator can only illuminate the tested panel from one side, then the rear irradiance is transferred to the front by using an G_E higher than 1000 $W \cdot m^{-2}$ (Eq. 1). The bifacial power gain or BiFi [2] is determined from solar simulator test as the slope of the linear fit that corresponds to plotting $P_{max.}$ against G_{rear}.

The conventional PR is given by Eq.1, where PSH is the Peak Solar Hours (kWh/m^2) on the generator's plane and Pp is the generator peak power.

In the case of vertical system, with main axis North-South and two parallel rows (strings), connected to independent MPPT, where one row has the main face oriented to the East and the other one to the West, we propose the PR expression of Eq.3, where the index 1 or 2 represents the Yield, PSH, Pp and bifaciality coefficient (φ_{Isc}) for each string.

Eq. 3:

$$PR = \frac{\dfrac{Yield_{(1)}}{PSH_{(1)} \cdot P_{p1} \cdot (1 + \varphi_{Isc(1)})} + \dfrac{Yield_{(2)}}{PSH_{(2)} \cdot P_{p2} \cdot (1 + \varphi_{Isc(2)})}}{2}$$

3 RESULTS AND DISCUSSION

IEC 61724-1:2021 proposes to calculate PR of a bifacial array by Eq. 4:

$$PR_{BIF} = \sum \frac{P}{\sum \dfrac{C \cdot P_0 \cdot G_{front} \cdot BIF}{1000\ W \cdot m^{-2}}}$$

where P is the system AC power output, P_0 is the system DC power rating at STC, C is a temperature correction factor and BIF, that stands for bifacial irradiance factor, is equal to $1 + \varphi \cdot (G_{rear} / G_{front})$

Karttunen et al. (2023) proposed a temperature-corrected PR [5].
Little information is available on the measurement of

bifaciality coefficient under real operating conditions. An exception is the work by Muñoz-Cerón et al. (2024), who for outdoor conditions found that the bifaciality coefficient increases with increasing irradiance. They recommended assessing the bifaciality coefficient preferably in the central hours of sunny days. But in our case the greatest impact would be at the beginning and end of the day, so we propose a more direct method, which applies different coefficients to each string depending on its orientation (Eq.).

Starting from the estimated radiation data, both for clear and average days (Figure 5), and measuring the real radiation, it will be possible to validate the method for the real calculation and minimize the error applied in the estimation of bifacial vertical agrivoltaic systems.

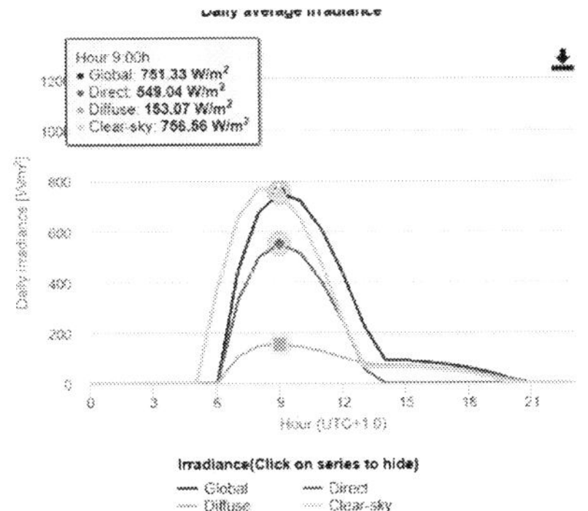

Figure 5: PVGIS estimated radiation on one side of a vertical east-oriented PV panel.

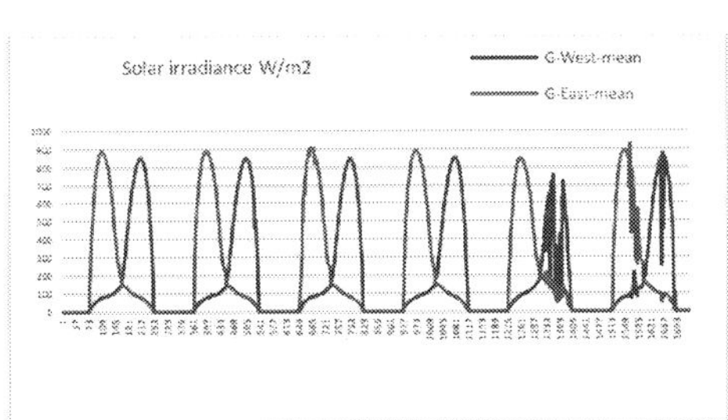

Figure 6: Radiation measured on both sides (east and west) of a vertical mounted solar panel.

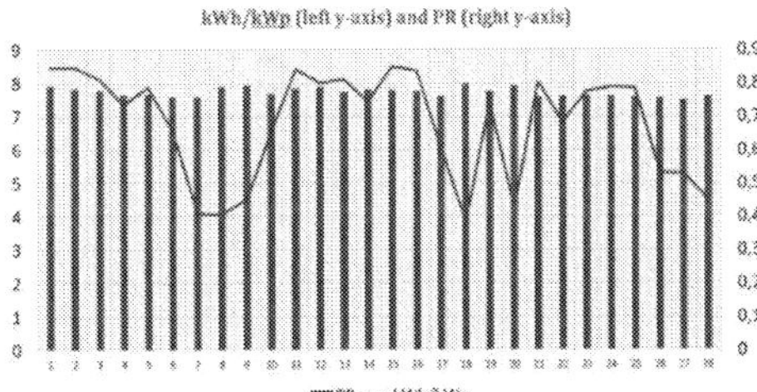

Figure 7: June 2024 daily specific yield (kWh/kWp) and Performance Ratio of vertical bifacial system.

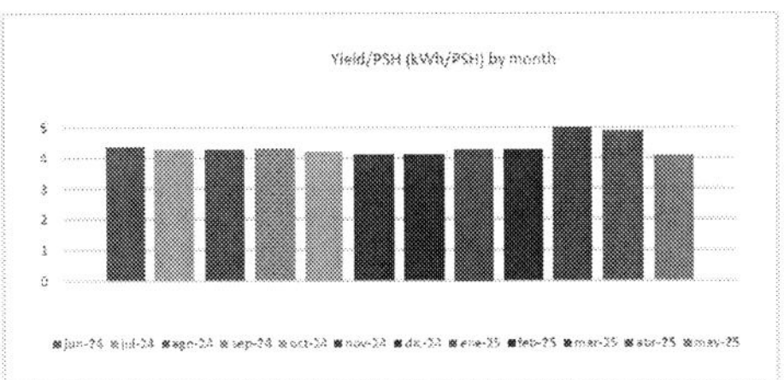

Figure 8: Yield per peak solar hour, monthly average, from June 2024 to May 2025.

For a vertical bifacial array of HJT photovoltaic panels, Badran and Dhimish [3] found that increased diffuse irradiance correlated with higher bifacial gain. Nonetheless, Muñoz-Cerón et al. [4] reported lower bifaciality coefficient for cloudy day (more diffuse irradiance) with respect to sunny day (less diffuse irradiance), although the bifacial panels in [4] were not vertical.

4 CONCLUSIONS

The following conclusions can be drawn:

- Diffuse irradiance plays a major role in vertical bifacial PV systems.
- A vertical system presents the question of radiation to be taken into account. In this work, we considered that radiation should be the sum of that captured on both sides, but applying a bifaciality coefficient.
- More research is needed on outdoor characterization of bifaciality, especially for vertical bifacial systems.

5 Acknowledgements

This work is partially funded by the grant 'PID2023-147841OB-C22' of Spain MCIN/AEI (10.13039/501100011033): Studies on emerging photovoltaic technologies for pumping hydrants adapted to irrigation needs and distribution network characteristics. (EMERPVPUMP), and by European Union 'NextGeneration'.

6 References

[1] X. Zhang, C. Monokroussos, M. Schweiger, M. Heinze. (2018). Power rating and qualification of bifacial PV modules. *Photovoltaics International*, 40: 90- 96.

[2] International Energy Agency-Photovoltaic Power Systems Programme. (2021). Bifacial photovoltaic modules and systems: Experience and results from international research and pilot applications.

[3] G. Badran & M. Dhimish. (2024). Comprehensive study on the efficiency of vertical bifacial photovoltaic systems: a UK case study. *Scientific Reports*, 14: 18380.

[4] E. Muñoz-Cerón, S. Moreno-Buesa, J. Leloux, J.

Aguilera, D. Moser. (2024). Evaluation of the bifaciality coefficient of bifacial photovoltaic modules under real operating conditions. *Journal of Cleaner Production*, 434: 139807.

[5] Karttunen et al. (2023). Comparing methods for the long-term performance assessment of bifacial photovoltaic modules in Nordic conditions. *Renewable Energy*, 219: 119473.

YIELD AND PR ESTIMATION FOR VERTICAL AGRIVOLTAICS SYSTEMS

G.P. Moreda[1], Miguel Ángel Egido[2], Valero Pascual Gallego[3] D. Rodríguez-Lucas[4], M.A. Muñoz-García[1]*

1 Dep. Ing. Agroforestal. ETSIAAB. Universidad Politécnica de Madrid. R&D group: LPF-Tagralia. Av. Puerta de Hierro, 2. 28040. Madrid. Spain. Tel.: +34 91 06 70968.
2 Instituto de Energía Solar. Universidad Politécnica de Madrid.
3 Dep. Estructuras y Física de la Edificación. Universidad Politécnica de Madrid.
4 EkiLabs CORP.
*Corresponding author. E-mail: miguelangel.munoz@upm.es

Introduction

Photovoltaic systems interspersed with cropland are gaining ground. Given that both elements compete for radiation, determining the amount of light that reaches each of them is a matter of great interest. Vertical agrivoltaic systems (Figure 1) are presented as an alternative to other systems installed in crop fields, which interfere less with tillage and the passage of machinery. When these systems are composed of bifacial panels (Figure 2, Figure 3), energy capture increases to almost double that of a non-bifacial system.

To determine the profitability of a photovoltaic system, measurements of both actual production and expected output or performance ratio (PR) must be obtained. Likewise, if the system is agrivoltaic, agricultural production must not be substantially reduced. In this case, regulations set different limits depending on the country, with an extended objective of not assuming a reduction of agricultural production greater than 20%.

The calculation of the PR in a vertical system is something that is still open to debate when the panels are bifacial. In addition, when the system is oriented with a north-south axis, the maximum radiation can be strongly affected by nearby shadows, both from other parallel strings and from nearby obstacles. Given the sensitivity of a vertical system to these aspects, in this work we address the elements that will affect the correct understanding and design of vertical agrivoltaic plants.

Materials and Methods

The bifaciality of a bifacial PV panel is measured with the bifaciality coefficients. The bifaciality coefficient prescribed by the technical specification IEC 60904-1-2: 2024 is the bifaciality of current, φ_{Isc}, defined as the ratio between the short-circuit current (I_{sc}) generated exclusively by the rear face of the panel and the I_{sc} generated exclusively by the front face, with the condition that both currents are measured at STC (irradiance of 1000 W·m^{-2}, panel temperature of 25 °C, and with the IEC 60904-3 reference solar spectral irradiance distribution). To determine the φ_{Isc}, bifacial PV panels can be tested as showcased in Figure 4.

To qualify bifacial panels, the so-called bifacial standard test condition (BSTC) applies, characterized by a front irradiance of 1000 W/m^2, a rear irradiance of 135 W/m^2 and an equivalent irradiance G_E defined [1] in Eq.1, where $\varphi_{Isc} = I_{sc\,rear} / I_{sc\,front}$

$$Eq.1.\ G_E = (1000 + \varphi_{Isc} \cdot 135)\ W/m^2$$

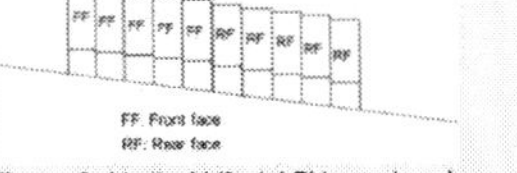

Figure 2: Vertical bifacial PV panels, where FF is the main side and RF is the rear side.

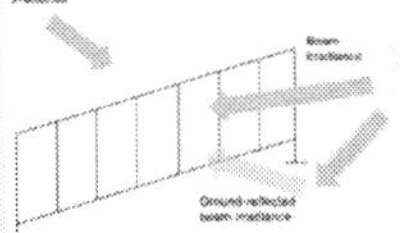

Figure 3: Main radiation sources for bifacial PV panels.

If our solar simulator can only illuminate the tested panel from one side, then the rear irradiance is transferred to the front by using an G_E higher than 1000 W·m^{-2} (Eq. 1). The bifacial power gain or BiFi [2] is determined from solar simulator test as the slope of the linear fit that corresponds to plotting P_{max} against G_{rear}.

The conventional PR is given by Eq.2, where PSH is the Peak Solar Hours (kWh/m^2) on the generator's plane and Pp is the generator peak power.

$$Eq.2.\ PR = \frac{Yield\ (kWh)}{PSH\left(\frac{kWh}{1\ kW}\right) \cdot P_p\ (kW)}$$

In the case of vertical system, with main axis North-South and two parallel rows (strings), connected to independent MPPT, where one row has the main face oriented to the East and the other one to the West, we propose the PR expression of Eq.3, where the index 1 or 2 represents the Yield, PSH, Pp and bifaciality coefficient (φ_{Isc}) for each string.

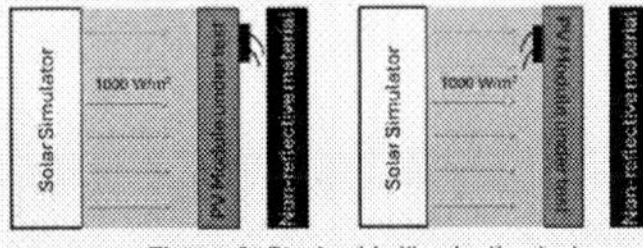

$$Eq.3.\ PR = \frac{\dfrac{Yield_{(1)}}{PSH_{(1)} \cdot P_{p1} \cdot (1+\varphi_{Isc(1)})} + \dfrac{Yield_{(2)}}{PSH_{(2)} \cdot P_{p2} \cdot (1+\varphi_{Isc(2)})}}{2}$$

Note that in Eq.3., PSH is the daily irradiation in kWh/m^2 but taking into account both sides of the solar panel (main and rear), for each string.

Figure 4: Single-side illumination test method for bifacial PV panels.

Figure 1: Agrivoltaic system with vertical bifacial PV panels.

Results and Discussion

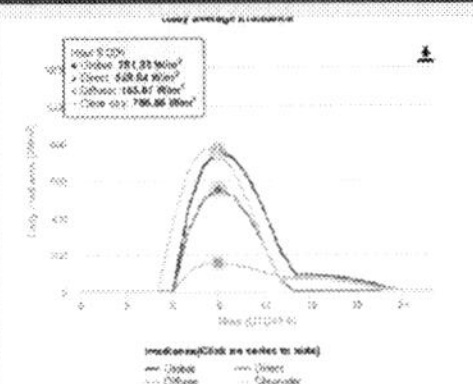

Figure 5: PVGIS Stimated radiation on one side of a vertical east-oriented PV panel.

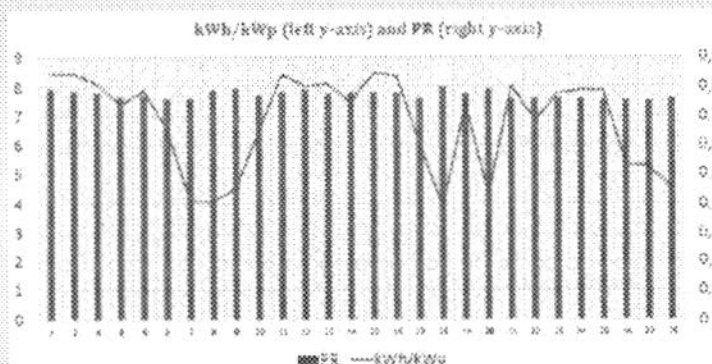

Figure 6: June 2024 daily specific yield (kWh/kWp) and Performance Ratio of vertical bifacial system.

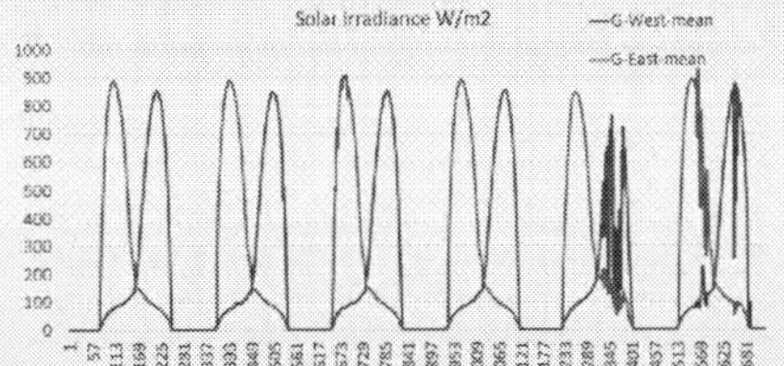

Figure 7: Radiation measured on both sides (east and west) of a vertical mounted solar panel.

For a vertical bifacial array of HJT photovoltaic panels, Badran and Dhimish [3] found that increased diffuse irradiance correlated with higher bifacial gain. Nonetheless, Muñoz-Cerón et al. [4] reported lower bifaciality coefficient for cloudy day (more diffuse irradiance) with respect to sunny day (less diffuse irradiance), although the bifacial panels in [4] were not vertical.

IEC 61724-1:2021 proposes to calculate PR of a bifacial array by Eq. 4:

$$Eq.4.\ PR_{BIF} = \sum \frac{P}{\sum \frac{C \cdot P_0 \cdot G_{front} \cdot BIF}{1000\ W \cdot m^{-2}}}$$

where P is the system AC power output, P_0 is the system DC power rating at STC, C is a temperature correction factor and BIF, that stands for bifacial irradiance factor, is equal to $1 + \varphi \cdot (G_{rear} / G_{front})$

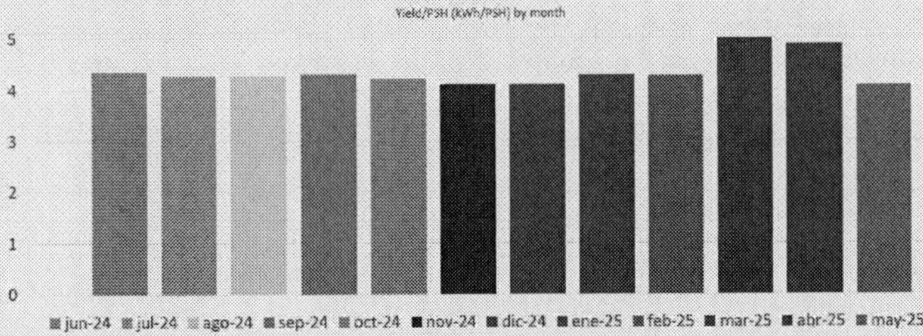

Figure 8: Yield per peak sun hour, monthly average, from June 2024 to May 2025.

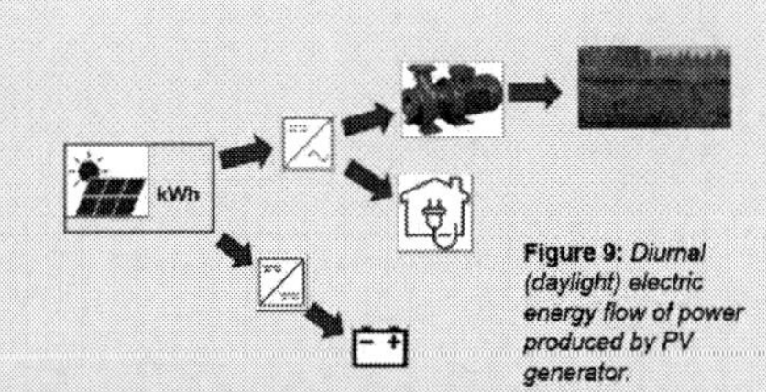

Figure 9: Diurnal (daylight) electric energy flow of power produced by PV generator.

Conclusions

- Diffuse irradiance plays a major role in vertical bifacial PV systems.
- A vertical system presents the question of radiation to be taken into account. In this work, we considered that radiation should be the sum of that captured on both sides, but applying a bifaciality coefficient.
- More research is needed on outdoor characterization of bifaciality, specially for vertical bifacial systems.

References

[1] X. Zhang, C. Monokroussos, M. Schweiger, M. Heinze. (2019). Power rating and qualification of bifacial PV modules. Photovoltaics International, 40: 90- 96.
[2] International Energy Agency-Photovoltaic Power Systems Programme. (2021). Bifacial photovoltaic modules and systems: Experience and results from international research and pilot applications.
[3] G. Badran & M. Dhimish. (2024). Comprehensive study on the efficiency of vertical bifacial photovoltaic systems: a UK case study. Scientific Reports, 14: 18386.
[4] E. Muñoz-Cerón, S. Moreno-Buesa, J. Leloux, J. Aguilera, D. Moser. (2024). Evaluation of the bifaciality coefficient of bifacial photovoltaic modules under real operating conditions. Journal of Cleaner Production, 434: 139867.

Acknowledgements

This work is partially funded by the grant "PID2023-14784105-C22" of Spain MCIN/AEI (10.13039/501100011033) Studies on emerging photovoltaic technologies for pumping hydrants adapted to irrigation needs and distribution network characteristics.(EMERPVPUMP), and by European Union "NextGeneration".

AGRIVOLTAIC – STUDY OF THE POTENTIAL IN PORTUGAL CONTINENTAL

Jeremias dos Santos [1], José A. Silva[1], Luís Fialho [2], Pedro Horta[1]
[1]Renewable Energies Chair, University of Évora. Pólo da Mitra da Universidade de Évora, Edificio Ario Lobo de Azevedo, 7000-083 Nossa Senhora da Tourega, Portugal
[2]Institute for Renewable Energy, Eurac Research, Via Alessandro Volta, 13ª, 39100 Bolzano BZ, Itália

ABSTRACT: The objective for the share of renewable energy in Portugal's total energy consumption was raised from 47% to 51% in the revised National Energy and Climate Plan for 2030, highlighting Portugal's commitment to reducing emissions, enhancing renewable energy usage, and improving energy efficiency. Agrivoltaics systems can be one of the strategies to accomplish this goal. These systems allow the combination of food and energy production in the same space in a synergistic way, avoiding land-use competition between PV and agriculture. This study analyzes the technical potential of agrivoltaics in mainland Portugal, a country particularly suitable for its implementation due to its high solar potential and diversified agriculture. The study used public geographic information system databases to perform systematic mapping of the viable areas. The methodology used was based on a multicriteria geospatial analysis, which included the identification of agricultural and pasture areas (based on the 2023 Land Use Charter), the exclusion of zones with legal restrictions such as National Agricultural Reserve (RAN), National Ecological Reserve (REN), and Natura 2000 Network, and the areas with a terrain slope >10%. The analysis revealed that the Alentejo region has the greatest technical potential, due to its predominantly flat topography, high solar radiation, and low density of environmental restrictions. The study estimated the potential for installed photovoltaic (PV) power through overhead configuration.
Keywords: agrivoltaics; photovoltaic energy; agriculture; sustainable development; territorial planning

1 INTRODUCTION

Over the last few decades, the ongoing climate changes, combined with the increasing need for energy production and growing pressure on natural resources, has imposed considerable challenges on the sustainability of economic, social, and environmental systems. While the energy sector seeks to transition to clean and renewable sources, the agricultural sector faces challenges such as water scarcity, soil degradation, reduction of biodiversity, and the search for greater resilience and efficiency in production systems [1].

In this scenario, agrivoltaics or AgriPV presents itself as a promising solution, allowing for the combined use of the same area of land for agricultural production and electricity generation through photovoltaic solar panels. By combining energy and food production in the same location, this strategy fosters a more efficient use of rural land, reducing land-use conflicts and promoting synergies between strategic sectors [2].

The adoption of agrivoltaics has increased in European countries with a Mediterranean climate, such as France, Italy, and Spain. In Southern Europe, the high levels of solar radiation and the strong agricultural traditions make this technology particularly promising [3,4]. In addition, countries with more temperate climates, such as Germany and the Netherlands, are also developing agrivoltaic solutions adapted to their specific climatic conditions. In these countries, public policies, incentive programs, and specific regulations have helped to consolidate the agrivoltaic model as a viable option for achieving climate goals and strengthening food security [5, 6, 7, 8].

In Portugal, the outlook is also promising: the country has high levels of solar radiation (>1,800 kWh/m²/year in most of the territory), extensive coverage of agricultural areas, and solid commitments to decarbonization, established in the National Energy and Climate Plan (PNEC 2030), which foresees a significant increase in the contribution of photovoltaic (PV) energy to the country's energy matrix [9]. However, there are still important gaps to be solved at the national level, such as the lack of

specific regulations for the agrivoltaic sector, the scarcity of applied technical-scientific studies, and the lack of a systematic mapping of the territory to identify areas with technical, legal, and environmental viability for the implementation of this type of system.

Identifying these areas is essential to boost the adoption of agrivoltaics in Portugal, contributing to more sustainable territorial energy planning that considers legal constraints of the lands, as well as their potential to be used in AgriPV projects. Thus, this study aims to fill this gap through a multicriteria geospatial analysis that examines the agrivoltaic viability of the territory in the different regions of mainland Portugal, considering criteria such as legal constraints on land use, as well as its current use and slope.

2 METHODOLOGY

2.1 Definition of Criteria for the Selection of Potential Areas.

To define the areas suitable for the installation of agrivoltaic systems, it's necessary to consider criteria that encompass agronomic, environmental, and technical-spatial dimensions [2, 10, 11].

In this analysis, the selection criteria were divided into three main categories:

- Current land use: The selection of eligible areas was based on vector data from the Land Use Map of 2023 (COS 2023), where classes with the greatest compatibility with agrivoltaic systems were selected: agricultural use and pasture [12].
- Legal and environmental restrictions: Areas that intersect with the Natura 2000 Network, the National Agricultural Reserve (RAN), and the National Ecological Reserve (REN) were excluded due to legal restrictions that make the installation of energy infrastructures unfeasible [13, 14, 15].

- Topographic conditions: Two slope categories were analyzed (≤10% and >10%) based on the methodology for assessing agricultural suitability and the installation of photovoltaic panels [16, 17].
- The analysis consisted of:
- Intersection between agricultural and pasture areas (COS 2023) with the restriction layers (Natura 2000, RAN, and REN).
- Topographic filtering to retain areas within slopes categories ≤10%.
- Calculation of the potential photovoltaic energy installation capacity in the identified useful areas, based on simulations using the PVSyst 8.0.13 software [18].

2.1.1 Land Use: Classification by COS 2023

The first spatial selection criterion used in this analysis was the current land use designation. Areas designated for agriculture and pasture were selected, as recorded in the 2023 Land Use Map (Carta de Ocupação do Solo, COS) [12]. This map represents the most recent cartographic database for mainland Portugal. Figure 1 presents the land use classification map, which shows the spatial distribution of the main land use and land cover categories for mainland Portugal.

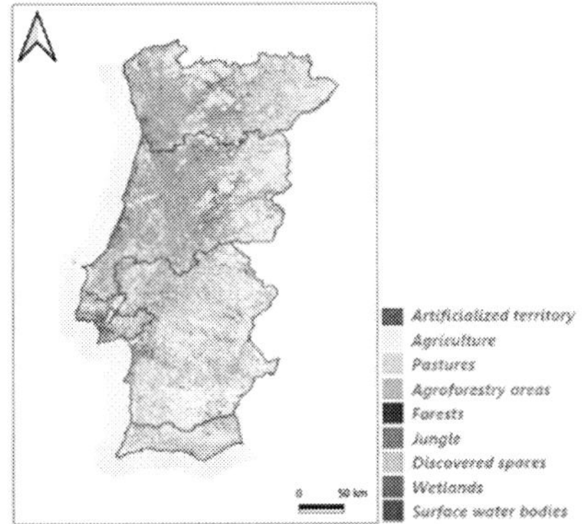

Figure 1: Land Use and Land Cover Map according to COS 2023.

The land use categories selected for agrivoltaic use in this project were:
- Agriculture: This class or category of land use and cover includes the crop regions shown on this land use and land cover map.
- Pasture: This class or category includes all regions occupied by pasture.

Figure 2 shows the eligible areas for pasture and agriculture in mainland Portugal.

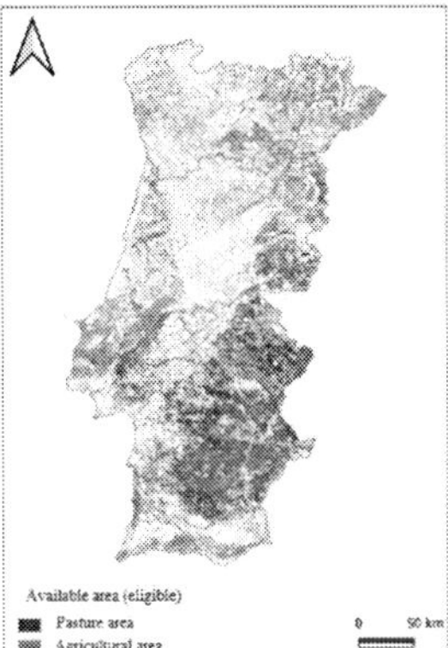

Figure 2: Combination of the map of eligible areas (pasture and agriculture)

The selection of these land use classes was based on their technical and ecological feasibility for integration with photovoltaic systems. These uses allow for the continuation of agricultural or livestock activities with controlled levels of shading, without significantly affecting productivity [10, 19].

2.1.2 Map of areas with legal restrictions.

The second step involved removing areas that intersect with zones of legal restrictions (Rede Natura 2000, REN, RAN) to ensure that the agrivoltaic systems comply with land-use planning regulations. This removal is essential for the development of agrivoltaic systems to comply with the legislation governing environmental preservation and sustainable land use, ensuring territorial compatibility with current public policies.

Figure 3 shows the areas occupied by each of these protection zones.

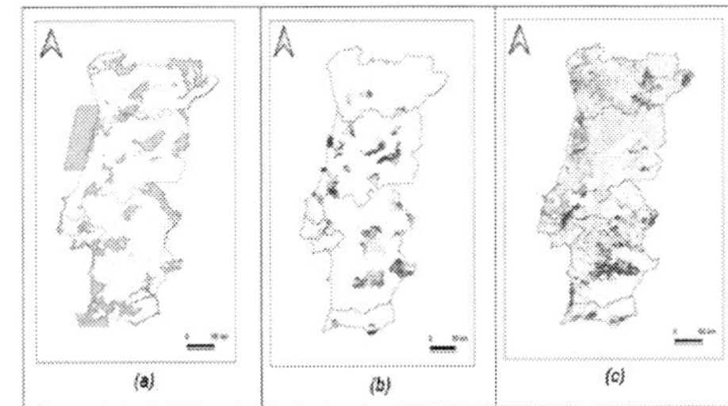

Figure 3: Map of the Natura 2000 Network (a); REN (b); and RAN (c).

2.1.3 Slope of the Land.

Land slope was the third criterion evaluated to identify suitable areas for agrivoltaic systems. The energy and economic sustainability of agrivoltaic installation is heavily affected by the terrain's inclination. Land with steep slopes presents technical challenges for both the installation of photovoltaic panels with ideal orientation and for agricultural activity.

The exclusion of regions with a slope above 10% is intended to ensure:
- That the orientation and inclination of the photovoltaic modules are ideal to maximize solar radiation capture [16].

- A decrease in system installation costs, by reducing the need for earthmoving and land leveling services.
- Improved accessibility and safety during operations, facilitating the movement of agricultural machinery and the maintenance of the energy infrastructure [19].

This technical criterion is essential to ensure the technical and economic viability of agrivoltaic projects, especially when implemented on a large scale in rural regions. There are various technical and scientific studies that discuss the definition of a slope threshold for land slopes. Some studies indicate that land with slopes up to 3% are ideal for agrivoltaic projects with high agro-productive integration, as it reduces the need for earthworks and maximizes land use [2, 20]. According to the U.S. Environmental Protection Agency and the National Renewable Energy Laboratory, conventional ground-mounted photovoltaic solar plants can accommodate slopes up to 10%, although this increases project costs and complexity [16]. In this study, a threshold of 10% slope was used to determine whether land is suitable for AgriPV projects or not. Figure 4 presents the map with areas with slopes ≤10 and >10% in mainland Portugal.

Figure 4: The map of the areas with the two different slopes ≤10% and >10% in mainland Portugal.

2.2 Estimation of the potential for PV installation capacity.

Determining the potential for photovoltaic energy installation capacity is a fundamental step in analyzing the economic potential of agrivoltaic systems. This allows for the quantification of the installed potential capacity of the areas considered technically viable. In this sub-chapter, we present the methodology used to determine the photovoltaic installation potential, expressed in kilowatt-peak (kWp), based on the useful area identified in each region.

2.3.1 Technical Reference Parameters

The potential for photovoltaic energy installation capacity was calculated based on a standard configuration of a monocrystalline Trina Solar microcrystalline silicon bifacial module with a nominal power of 655 Wp and a total area of 3.106 m² [21]. This value indicates the ground area required for each panel, excluding additional structural spaces.

The potential for photovoltaic energy installation capacity was calculated using the following equations:

$$Nm = Int\,\frac{Au}{Am} \quad (Eq1)$$

$$PPV = Nm * Pm \quad (Eq2)$$

Where: Nm is the number of modules, which is given by the integer quotient between the useful area, Au (m2), and the module area, Am (m2).
PPV is the total photovoltaic potential (kWp).
Pm is the nominal power of each module (kWp).

This calculation was performed for all analyzed regions, based on the useful area values obtained after applying the geospatial criteria previously mentioned. The results are presented in gigawatt-peak (GWp).

2.3.2 Structural Configurations

In this analysis an agrivoltaic plant with an overhead configuration was considered.

Overhead configuration: In this setup, the modules are raised relative to the ground typically > 3 m, allowing for agricultural or grazing activities to take place underneath the photovoltaic systems. Figure 6 shows the PVsyst design of the elevated configuration analyzed in this study, which considered the following parameters:

- Alignment and Orientation: The photovoltaic array was oriented to the south (azimuth = 0°).
- Module Tilt: A fixed tilt of 25° was adopted.
- Installation Height: The modules were installed at a height of 4.0 m above the ground, and the spacing between rows is 5 m.
- Bifacial Photovoltaic Module: A dual-glass monocrystalline silicon bifacial PV Trina Vertex module with a nominal power of 655 Wp an area of 3.106 m² per module [21].
- Total Area Occupied: The simulation considered a plot of 1 hectare (10,000 m²).
- A reference location in the Central region of mainland Portugal was selected for the simulations in the PVsyst software. This location was chosen to adequately represent the average solar irradiation and climate conditions of mainland Portugal.

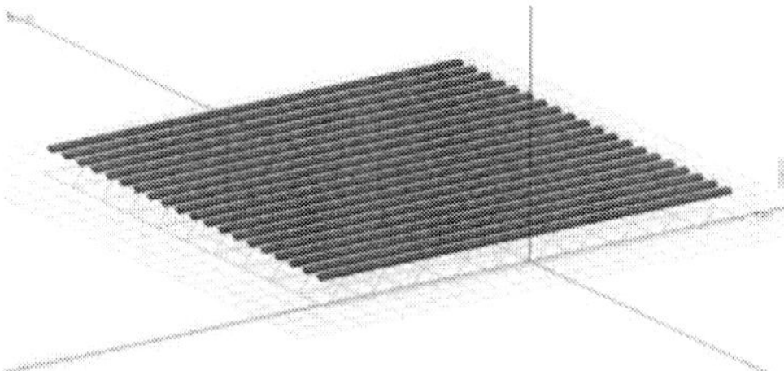

Figure 6: Schematic drawing of the elevated configuration considered in PVsyst [18].

3   RESULTS AND DISCUSSION

The geospatial analysis showed that a total of 1263 kha area suitable to be used for AgriPV, the analysis evidenced significant regional variations in the distribution of suitable areas between the different regions.

3.1 Area affected by legal restrictions.

Figure 7 presents the fractions of the agricultural and pasture areas affected by legal limitations in each region of Portugal's mainland.

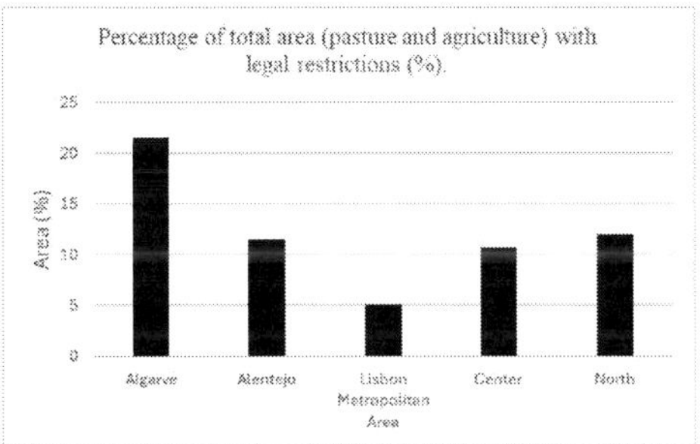

Figure 7: Percentage of agricultural and pasture areas affected by legal restrictions in each region.

It can be observed that Algarve has the highest percentage of areas impacted by legal restrictions with 22% areas intercepting protected zones, while the Lisbon Metropolitan Area has the lowest percentage, with only 5% of its agricultural and pastureland subject to legal restrictions.

3.2 Pasture and agricultural area with a slope >10%.

The analysis of agricultural and pasture areas excluded due to slopes greater than 10% indicates that there are significant topographical restrictions for implementing agrivoltaic systems in mainland Portugal.

Figure 8 shows the percentages of the total agricultural and pasture area excluded for having slopes >10% in each region of mainland Portugal.

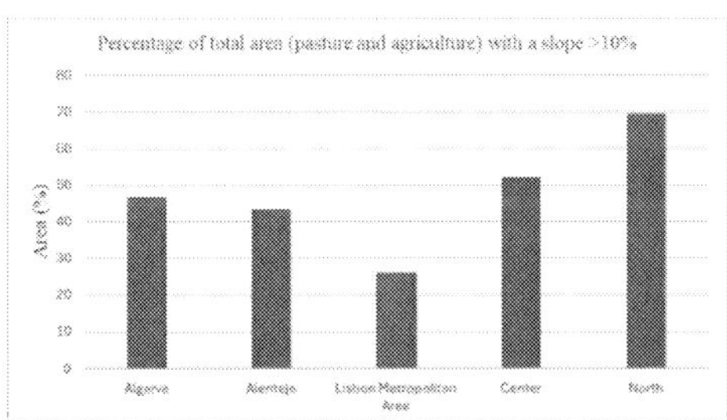

Figure 8: Percentage of total agricultural and pasture areas excluded due to a slope >10% in each region.

It's observed that the North region has the largest area excluded (69.9%), reflecting the strong presence of steep terrains. Center (51%) and the Algarve (46.6%) regions also have very significant areas excluded due to their high slope. The Alentejo registers 43.0% of area excluded, while the Lisbon Metropolitan Area has the lowest percentage of area excluded due to the slope with 26%.

3.3 Analysis of the useful areas.

Figure 9 shows the regional distribution areas (agricultural and pasture) which are considered suitable for agrivoltaic projects in mainland Portugal.

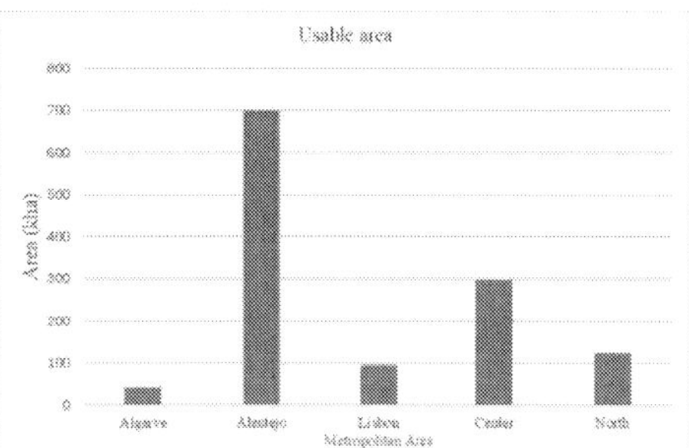

Figure 9: Areas of agriculture and pasture are usable for AgriPV.

Figure 9 indicates that, in the Algarve, the availability of area for agrivoltaic implementation is quite restricted compared to other regions, having 44 kha considered usable for AgriPV. Alentejo stands out as the region with the greatest potential, with a total area of 700 kha. This result is particularly interesting due to the high solar potential available in this region. In Lisbon Metropolitan Area, there are 96 kha considered usable for AgriPV, while Center and North regions of respectively 299 kha and 124 kha are usable for agrivoltaic projects.

3.4 Estimation of Photovoltaic Installation Potential

The analysis focused on the overhead configuration, considering the usable areas previously determined for each region.

3.4.1 Calculation of the potential for photovoltaic energy installation capacity in the useful areas.

> Calculation of the potential for photovoltaic energy installation capacity of the elevated configuration.

To determine the number of PV panels and PV power that can be installed on a specific plot of land, equations 1 and 2 were used.

Considering the bifacial PV panels above described, and assuming a maximum ground coverage ratio (GCR) of 35%, it was concluded that it is possible to install 1,125 modules on a 10,000 m2 area, which results in a total installed capacity of 736.9 kWp. Using this feature and considering the usable area for each region, the respective potential for PV capacity installation was obtained.

Table 1 shows the distribution of the potential for PV capacity installation with overhead configuration (GCR=35%) by region. The results show the significant differences in the potential available in the different regions.

Table 1: Potential for PV capacity installation in each region.

Region	PV capacity (GWp)
Algarve	32
Alentejo	515
Lisbon Metropolitan Area	71
Center	220
North	92

As expected, Algarve shows lowest potential, while concentrates the largest PV installation potential reaching 515 GWp, which reflects both the vast available area and favorable topographic conditions. The Center region stands out as the second most relevant in terms of PV installation potential with 220 GWp. While Lisbon Metropolitan Area and North region have a moderate potential for the installation of PV capacity.

4 CONCLUSIONS

The analysis of the energy production potential proved to be a fundamental step to evaluate the technical potential of agrivoltaic systems in mainland Portugal. The integration of geospatial criteria, such as land use, slope, and legal restrictions, and considering an overhead structure with a GCR=35%, enabled a detailed regional analysis of the potential for PV capacity installation. This approach also allowed for an assessment of the impact of the legal constrains and terrain slopes, on the usability of agricultural and pasture areas for agrivoltaics.

The Alentejo region stood out, the region with highest potential with 515 GWp, confirming its leadership potential for large-scale agrivoltaic deployment. The Center region followed with 220 GWp, while the North and Lisbon Metropolitan Area registered 92 GWp and 71 GWp, respectively. The Algarve presented the lowest value, with 32 GWp. These results show that the Alentejo and Center together account for the largest share of the national potential, making them key territories for the expansion of overhead agrivoltaic systems in Portugal.

5 REFERENCES

[1] Intergovernmental Panel on Climate Change (IPCC), *Climate Change 2022 – Impacts, Adaptation and Vulnerability: Working Group II Contribution to the Sixth Assessment Report of the Intergovernmental Panel on Climate Change.* Cambridge: Cambridge University Press, 2023. doi: 10.1017/9781009325844.

[2] S. Amaducci, X. Yin, e M. Colauzzi, «Agrivoltaic systems to optimize land use for electric energy production», *Appl. Energy*, vol. 220, pp. 545–561, jun. 2018, doi: 10.1016/j.apenergy.2018.03.081.

[3] Agenzia per le Erogazioni in Agricoltura [AGEA], "Guida agli incentivi agrivoltaici in Italia", Agenzia per le Erogazioni in Agricoltura, 2023. Accessed: 8 August 2025. [Online]. Available at: https://www.agea.gov.it/portale-agea/

[4] IDAE – Instituto para la Diversificación y Ahorro de la Energía, "Estrategia de energías renovables y uso del suelo agrícola". Accessed: 8 August 2025. [Online]. Available at: https://www.idae.es/

[5] Bundesnetzagentur, Renewable Energy Sources Act (EEG). Accessed: 8 August 2025. [Online]. Available at: https://www.bundesnetzagentur.de/

[6] Fraunhofer ISE, "Agrivoltaics - Electricity and Agriculture", Fraunhofer Institute for Solar Energy Systems ISE. Accessed: 8 August 2025.

[7] RVO – Netherlands Enterprise Agency, "Stimulation of sustainable energy production and climate transition (SDE++)", RVO.nl. Accessed: 8 August 2025. [Online]. Available at: https://english.rvo.nl/en/subsidies-financiering/sde

[8] C. Jjls. C. S. Wageningen University & Research, Wageningen Solar Research Programme, WUR. Accessed: 8 August 2025. [Online]. Available at: https://www.wur.nl/en/research-results/research-institutes/environmental research/projects/wageningen-solar-research-programme.htm

[9] "PNEC 2030." Accessed: Aug. 13, 2025. [Online]. vailable: https://www.dgeg.gov.pt/pt/destaques/pnec-2030/

[10] C. Dupraz, H. Marrou, G. Talbot, L. Dufour, A. Nogier, e Y. Ferard, «Combining solar photovoltaic panels and food crops for optimizing land use: Towards new agrivoltaic schemes», *Renew. Energy*, vol. 36, n.º 10, pp. 2725–2732, oct. 2011, doi: 10.1016/j.renene.2011.03.005.

[11] A. Weselek, A. Ehmann, S. Zikeli, I. Lewandowski, S. Schindele, e P. Högy, «Agrophotovoltaic systems: applications, challenges, and opportunities. A review, *Agron. Sustain. Dev.*, vol. 39, n.º 4, p. 35, Aug 2019, doi: 10.1007/s13593-019-0581-3.

[12] Direção-Geral do Território (DGT), "COSc2023 – Carta de Ocupação do Solo Conjuntural de 2023 | DGT." Accessed: Aug. 13, 2025. [Online]. Available: https://www.dgterritorio.gov.pt/COSc2023-Carta-de-Ocupacao-do-Solo-Conjuntural-de-2023

[13] Comissão Nacional do Território (CNT), "Reserva Ecológica Nacional (REN)." Accessed: Aug. 13, 2025. [Online]. Available: https://cnt.dgterritorio.gov.pt/ren-pagina

[14] Direção-Geral de Agricultura e Desenvolvimento Rural (DGADR), "Reserva Agrícola Nacional (RAN)." Accessed: Aug. 13, 2025. [Online]. Available: https://www.dgadr.gov.pt/pt/reserva-agricola-nacional-ran

[15] Instituto da Conservação da Natureza e das Florestas (ICNF), "Rede Natura 2000." Accessed: Aug. 13, 2025. [Online]. Available: https://www.icnf.pt/conservacao/redenatura2000/a redenatura2000

[16] EPA & NREL, Best practices for siting solar photovoltaics on municipal solid waste landfills. Accessed: August 13, 2025.

[17] S. G. Simões, T. Simões, J. Barbosa, *et al.*, "Estimativa de potenciais técnicos de energia renovável em Portugal...," LNEG, Amadora, Portugal. Accessed: August 13, 2025.

[18] PVsyst SA. "PVsyst 8." Accessed: August 19, 2025. [Online]. Available: https://www.pvsyst.com

[19] G. A. Barron-Gafford *et al.*, «Agrivoltaics provide mutual benefits across the food–energy–water nexus in drylands», *Nat. Sustain.*, vol. 2, n.º 9, pp. 848–855, set. 2019, doi: 10.1038/s41893-019-0364-5.

[20] T. Sekiyama e A. Nagashima, Solar Sharing for Both Food and Clean Energy Production: Performance of Agrivoltaic Systems for Corn, A Typical Shade-Intolerant Crop, *Environments*, vol. 6, n.º6, p.65, jun. 2019, doi: 10.3390/environments6060065.

[21] Trina solar TSM-XXXDEG21C.20 product datasheet, URL:https://static.trinasolar.com/sites/default/files/Vertex_DEG21C.20_EN_2021_Aus_A_web_1.pdf

AGRIVOLTAIC – STUDY OF THE POTENTIAL IN PORTUGAL CONTINENTAL

Jeremias dos Santos[1], José Silva[1], Luís Fialho[2], Pedro Horta[1]

[1] Renewable Energies Chair, University of Évora, Portugal
[2] Eurac Research-Institute for Renewable Energy, 39100 Bolzano, Italy

ABSTRACT

The objetive for the share of renewable energy in Portugal's total energy consumption was raised from 47% to 51% in the revised National Energy and Climate Plan for 2030, highlighting Portugal's commitment to reducing emissions, enhancing renewable energy usage, and improving energy efficiency. Agrivoltaics systems can be one of the strategies to accomplish this goal. These systems allow the combination of food and energy production in the same space in a synergistic way, avoiding land-use competition between PV and agriculture. This study analyzes the technical potential of agrivoltaics in mainland Portugal, a country particularly suitable for its implementation due to its high solar potential and diversified agriculture. The study used public geographic information system databases to perform a systematic mapping of the viable areas. The methodology used was based on a multicriteria geospatial analysis, which included the identification of agricultural and pasture areas (based on the 2023 Land Use Charter), the exclusion of zones with legal restrictions such as National Agricultural Reserve (RAN), National Ecological Reserve (REN), and Natura 2000 Network, and the areas with a terrain slope >10%.

METHODOLOGY

- Identification of eligible areas using the Land Use chart (COS 2023)
- Application of legal restrictions to eligible areas (Natura 2000 Network, RAN and REN)
- Intersection of eligible areas with slope ≤10%
- Definition of useful areas for slope ≤10%
- Calculation of the potential FV (photovoltaic) installation capacity in the identified useful areas

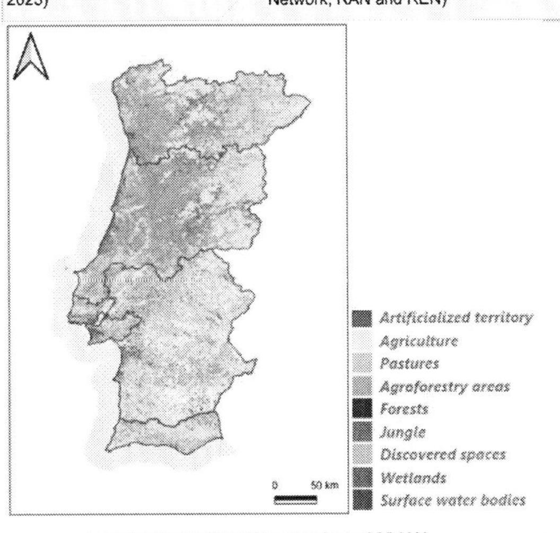

Land Use and Land Cover Map according to COS 2023.

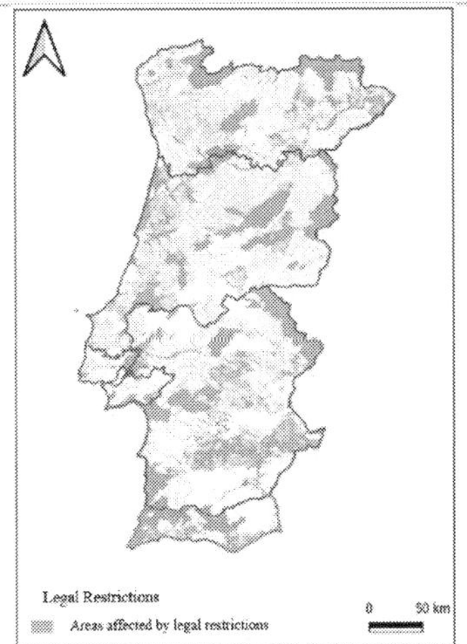

Map of the areas affected by legal restrictions (Natura 2000 Network, REN and RAN)

Map of the area with slope ≤10% and >10% in mainland Portugal

RESULTS

Total area (pasture and agriculture) with area affected by legal restrictions, the area with slope >10% and the total usable area

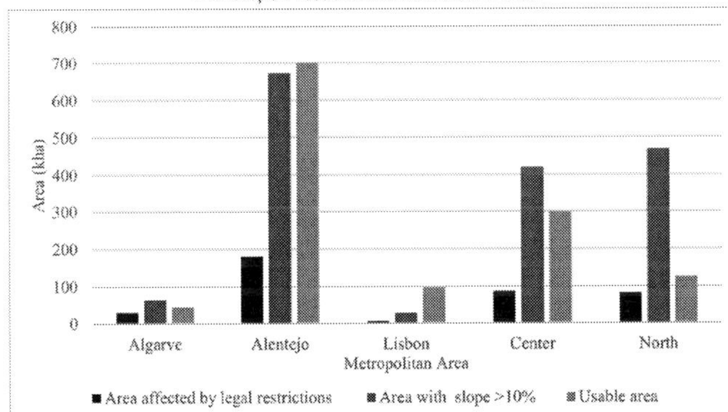

Potential for photovoltaic energy installation capacity of each region in the useful areas with an overhead configuration

Region	Potential for PV energy installation capacity in useful areas (GWp)
Algarve	32
Alentejo	515
Lisbon Metropolitan Area	71
Center	220
North	92

Conclusion

- ❖ Integration of geospatial criteria (land use, slope, legal restrictions) enabled the assessment of agrivoltaic technical potential in mainland Portugal.
- ❖ Alentejo: largest potential, 515 GWp, confirming national leadership.
- ❖ Center: second highest, 220 GWp
- ❖ North: 92 GWp.
- ❖ Lisbon Metropolitan Area: 71 GWp.
- ❖ Algarve: lowest potential, 32 GWp.
- ❖ Alentejo and Center together account for the majority of the national potential, making them priority regions for the expansion of agrivoltaic systems.

Acknowledgements

The authors would like to thank the project AGROVOLTEP for supporting and funding this project.

Levelized Cost of Electricity

and its limitations to consider the value of electricity

Fabian Spera[1], Simon Lahr[1] and Marc Andre Schüler[1]
[1] Department of Research Next2Sun Technology GmbH. Franz-Meguin-Str. 10a, 66763 Dillingen (Germany)

Introduction

European climate targets drive a steady expansion of PV capacity. With increasing PV penetration, day-ahead market prices around midday decrease and even turn negative [1]. Conventional PV (C-PV) mainly generate electricity during these low-price hours. Vertical PV (VB-PV) shifts generation to the morning and evening, when higher prices are usually achieved. The aim of this study is to highlight that LCOE neglects generation profile characteristics. Hence, market revenues are evaluated as a complementary indicator reflecting the real value of different PV approaches.

Assumptions

Seven locations were analyzed. An overview of the sites is provided in Table 1 and Figure 1.

Table 1: Overview of the analyzed sites including their latitudes

Site	Latitude
Oulu (Finland)	64.9468
Kärrbo (Sweden)	59.5525
Milkowice (Poland)	51.2552
Aasen (Germany)	47.9949
Bologna (Italy)	44.5352
Toulouse (France)	43.5968
Valencia (Spain)	39.5021

Figure 1: Geographical distribution of the analyzed sites

Table 2 shows the system parameters for VB-PV and C-PV. Both systems were simulated with the same installed capacity of 15 MWp. Due to the lower power density of the VB-PV system (384 kWp/ha) compared to the C-PV system (1050 kWp/ha), the required land area differs significantly. For the given capacity, VB-PV requires ca. 39 ha, while C-PV requires 14 ha. Operational costs are split into fixed OPEX, representing standard operational PV expenses, and variable OPEX, describing land related costs.

Table 2: Overview of the considered system and investment parameters

System	Tilt (°)	Orientation	Module	Pitch (m)	GCR (%)
Vertical-PV	90°	East/West	560 Wp Bifacial (95%)	12	18
Conventional-PV	25°	South	565 Wp Monofacial	-	50

System	CAPEX (€/kWp)	OPEX fix (€/kWp*a)	OPEX var. (€/kWp*a)
Vertical-PV	565 [1*]	15 [2]	2,000
Conventional-PV	450	16.5 [2*]	3,000

Results

The VB-PV system was simulated using the in-house simulation tool from Next2Sun, based on Python and pvlib, while the C-PV system was modeled in PVsyst. Specific yield and LCOE were determined using TMY data. Market revenues for 2024 were simulated with historical weather data, considering hourly spot market prices. Negative hours were included, with no curtailment applied to the systems.

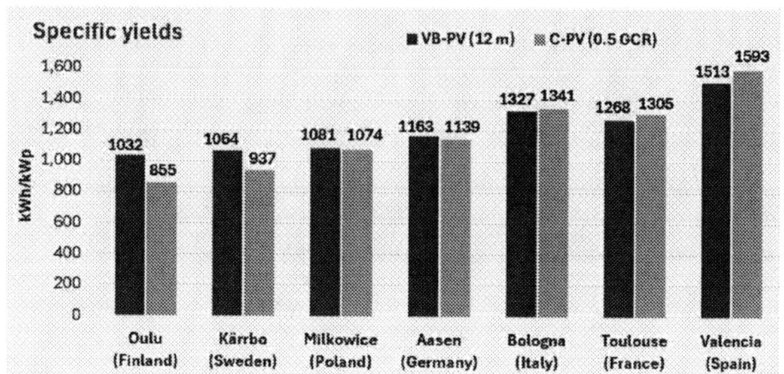

* VB-PV shows higher specific annual yields than C-PV at all locations north of a transition point between Aasen and Bologna, which aligns with findings from other scientific studies [3].

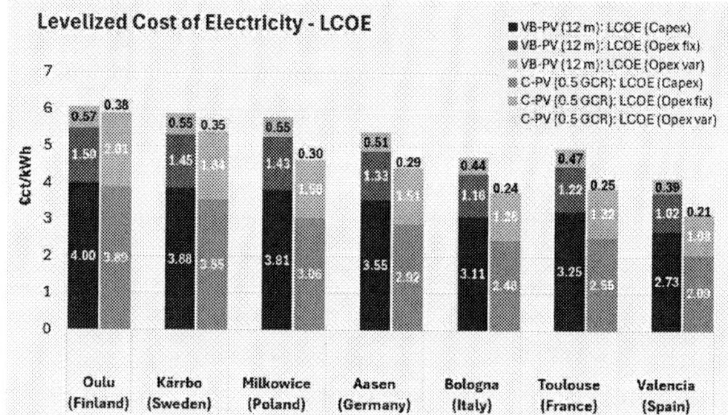

* While CAPEX optimizations have reduced the LCOE gap between VB-PV and C-PV, higher variable OPEX - driven by land related costs due to lower specific installed capacity - remain a key economic drawback.

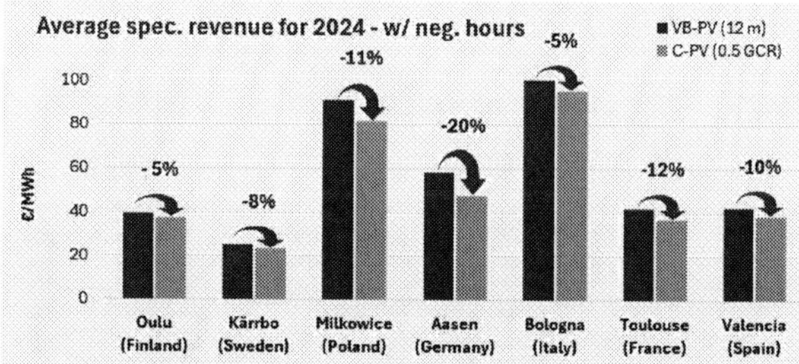

* VB-PV generates significantly higher spec. revenues than C-PV at all studied locations due to its grid friendly generation profile. Disadvantages in terms of LCOE can thus be at least partially offset over the lifetime of the plant even in southern latitudes, while at the same time reducing the risk of producing renewable electricity at negative electricity prices.

Summary

* **LCOE will underestimate the economic performance** of systems with grid friendly generation profiles like **VB-PV**

* To make an informed investment decision, the achievable **market revenue**, considering the **specific generation profile**, should be **taken into account**.

* Land related **variable OPEX remain a key challenge** for **VB-PV** due to the lower power density

Outlook

* **Future assessment** of C-PV should be done with **bifacial module deployment**

* **VB-PV** is expected to **achieve even higher market revenue in the future** in EU states due to increasing PV penetration & negative electricity prices

1* Assumption: CAPEX VB-PV = CAPEX C-PV + 25.5%; 2* Assumption: OPEX fix C-PV = OPEX fix VB-PV + 10%

[1] Fraunhofer ISE (2025). Aktuelle Fakten zur Photovoltaik in Deutschland. Fraunhofer Institute for Solar Energy Systems ISE. Freiburg, Germany. https://www.ise.fraunhofer.de/de/veroeffentlichungen/studien/aktuelle-fakten-zur-photovoltaik-in-deutschland.html
[2] Böhm (2024). Wirtschaftlichkeit verschiedener Agri-PV Konzepte Impuls aus der Forschung. Presentation at the 2nd National Agri-PV Forum, Leibniz Centre for Agricultural Landscape Research (ZALF), Müncheberg, Germany.
[3] Chudinzow, D., Nagel, S., Güsewell, J., & Eltrop, L. (2020). Vertical bifacial photovoltaics – A complementary technology for the European electricity supply? Applied Energy, 264. https://doi.org/10.1016/j.apenergy.2020.114782

020411-001

Fabian Spera
Next2Sun Technology GmbH
Franz-Meguin-Str. 10a,
66763 Dillingen (Germany)
f.spera@next2sun.de

DEVELOPMENT OF A SIMPLE TOOL FOR ESTIMATING IRRADIATION REDUCTION IN AGRIVOLTAIC GREENHOUSES

Paula Sánchez-Friera[1], Guillermo Correa[2], Luis Pérez[2], Baurin Leza[2], Tomás Pernas[3], Jairo Pérez[3], Jorge Pérez[3]
[1] Solkeys, Mar Cantábrico 16, 33204 Gijón, Spain
[2] Gonvarri MS R&D, PI Cancienes, 33470 Corvera de Asturias, Spain
[3] Gonvarri AgroTech, PI Cancienes, 33470 Corvera de Asturias, Spain
e-mail: paula@solkeys.com

ABSTRACT: Agrivoltaic greenhouses combine photovoltaic (PV) energy production with horticultural cultivation, but their success depends on maintaining sufficient light transmission to crops. Current modelling tools provide accurate projections of PV performance yet are often too complex for early-stage design or regulatory assessments. This work presents PASSIFLORA, a simplified but physically consistent framework for estimating both crop-level irradiation and PV energy yield in greenhouses. The model reuses and adapts geometric ray-casting and hemispherical sampling algorithms originally developed in PASE, enabling efficient calculation of direct and diffuse irradiance beneath PV-covered roofs. A graphical interface allows users to configure greenhouse geometry, roof layouts and cover properties, with automatic module placement and an option to sweep module coverage to achieve a target irradiation reduction factor. Validation against PVsyst was carried out for a Gothic tunnel greenhouse in the region of Toledo (Spain). The results showed excellent agreement in crop-level irradiation (<0.5% difference) and close agreement in PV yield (within 3%). Case studies further demonstrated the application of the tool to assess different factors such as tunnel configuration, layout patterns, and greenhouse orientation. PASSIFLORA provides a fast, transparent and regulation-oriented approach for pre-design of agrivoltaic greenhouses, complementing detailed engineering software in later project stages.
Keywords: agrivoltaics; greenhouses; solar irradiation; shading analysis; PV simulation.

1 INTRODUCTION

The accelerating deployment of renewable energy systems and the parallel demand for sustainable food production have placed agrivoltaics (AV)—the combined use of land for photovoltaic (PV) energy generation and agriculture—at the center of current research and policy agendas. First proposed by Goetzberger and Zastrow in 1982 [1], the concept has since evolved from an academic idea into a recognized strategy for addressing the food–energy–land nexus, with pilot projects emerging across Europe, Asia, and North America. By co-locating PV with crops, AV systems promise higher overall land productivity and resilience against climate change. Their success, however, hinges on the careful distribution of solar radiation between energy and agriculture.

A central challenge in AV research is the accurate quantification of the solar irradiation reaching the crop zone. While the calculation of plane-of-array irradiance on PV modules is well established in design tools such as PVsyst, PV*SOL, or SAM, these tools were developed primarily for energy applications and are not specifically designed to simulate ground-level shading or the complex distribution of transmitted light. As a result, specialized models or adaptations are required to evaluate the availability of light for crops in AV settings.

Over the past decade, a wide spectrum of approaches has been proposed to address this need [2]. On one side, empirical or semi-empirical indicators such as the ground coverage ratio (GCR) or shading factors have been used as proxies for crop irradiation. These allow quick assessment of average irradiation reduction and have been incorporated into design guidelines, but they provide limited insight into the heterogeneity of light distribution. More recent work has refined these approaches by introducing dedicated shading-factor models, based on analytical projections of regular module geometries [3].

At the opposite end of the spectrum are high-accuracy frameworks [4]. Ray-tracing methods, such as radiance-based, have long been applied to PV system analysis, and in the AV field they are increasingly used to resolve 3D light distribution with spatial and temporal detail. GPU-accelerated approaches such as LuSim [5], [6] extend this capability by providing fast and accurate calculations of light interception in large, heterogeneous scenes, enabling applications to complex AV scenes [7]. Module-level multi-physics detailed models [8], illustrate the depth of resolution achievable when intra-module shading and temperature effects are explicitly considered. These methods capture the full angular structure of diffuse irradiance and complex module geometries, but their computational and/or data and design requirements make them more suitable for advanced engineering studies than for early project exploration.

Greenhouse-based AV has attracted specific attention, as roof-integrated PV modifies not only light availability but also the microclimate within the enclosure. A number of studies [9], [10], [11], [12], [13] have examined how PV integration affects transmitted light and crop performance within greenhouses, addressing aspects such as maximum feasible cover ratios, the effects of shading on yield and quality, and the use of coupled light–climate–crop models to validate growth responses. These works highlight both the opportunities and agronomic risks of PV greenhouse integration, and underline the importance of reliable light-distribution modelling for design and regulation.

Despite this progress, the field continues to face a trade-off between accuracy and usability. The current gap lies in tools that are user-friendly, transparent, fast, physically consistent, and able to deliver reliable estimates of crop-level irradiation without requiring extensive modelling expertise—particularly at the early stages of project development.

This need is reinforced by the evolving regulatory context. In Catalonia, technical guidelines issued in 2023 [14] stipulate that agricultural yield in AV systems must be at least 60% of reference levels, supported by studies quantifying irradiation reduction inside the protected cultivation area. In France, the April 2024 national decree on agrivoltaics [15] requires agricultural yields to remain above 90% of comparable control zones. Similar regulatory frameworks are being debated in other European regions. Such rules necessitate practical modelling tools that can quickly inform design decisions, support compliance assessments, and facilitate dialogue between developers, farmers, and regulators.

In this study, we introduce the streamlined tool PASSIFLORA for estimating the reduction of solar irradiation under PV-covered greenhouses. Our tool builds on validated algorithms to compute direct and diffuse irradiance on the ground, reusing modules from the open-source framework Python Agrivoltaic Simulation Environment (PASE) [16], which has been adapted to integrate specific features for PV greenhouses. By abstracting material properties into global transmission coefficients (e.g., [17]), the approach minimizes input requirements while retaining sufficient physical realism.

The main objectives of this work are therefore: i) to develop a computationally efficient and user-friendly tool for estimating irradiation reduction under PV greenhouse configurations; ii) to validate its predictions against more advanced modelling approaches and reference scenarios; iii) to demonstrate its applicability as a pre-design decision-support tool for regulatory compliance and project development.

By addressing the need for a balance between accuracy and simplicity, this work aims to complement the suite of available AV models, providing a practical solution that supports the early design and approval phases of greenhouse-based agrivoltaic projects.

2 METHODOLOGY

2.1 General approach

The framework developed in this work is designed to provide a fast and user-friendly means of estimating the reduction in solar irradiation reaching the crop zone under photovoltaic (PV) greenhouse systems.

The modelling strategy is based on algorithms developed within the open-source Python Agrivoltaic Simulation Environment (PASE) [16]. Rather than employing full optical ray-tracing—which can capture every reflection and scattering event within the greenhouse system but at significant computational cost—the tool relies on efficient geometric ray-casting algorithms. For each point on the crop zone, rays are traced toward incoming light directions and tested for obstruction by PV modules. The direct component corresponds to the sun vector at each timestep, while the diffuse component is obtained by sampling multiple directions across the sky dome and scaling the diffuse irradiance according to the unobstructed fraction.

In addition to these PASE-based algorithms, PASSIFLORA also makes extensive use of the open-source pvlib Python library [18], which ensures consistency with widely used PV modelling practices.

By integrating these modules into a streamlined workflow (see Figure 1), the tool requires only a limited number of user inputs yet produces physically meaningful outputs that are directly interpretable in the context of agrivoltaic regulation. The primary model output is the transmitted irradiation available to crops, provided both as an hourly time series and as aggregated seasonal or annual totals.

2.2 Set-up of the 3D scene: greenhouse and PV module layout

The first step in the workflow is the definition of the physical scene, which establishes the geometry of the greenhouse and the placement of the photovoltaic (PV) modules. To make the process accessible to non-specialist users, the tool provides automated routines that generate realistic greenhouse models and PV layouts from a limited number of high-level inputs.

Greenhouse geometry: The tool can represent both single-tunnel and multi-tunnel structures, reflecting the two main categories of commercial greenhouses. Each tunnel can be defined with a flat sloped roof or a curved roof, as shown in Figure 2. In the curved case, the radius or curvature factor can be adjusted by the user, enabling the representation of roof types ranging from shallow arcs to sharply vaulted profiles such as Gothic or parabolic designs. Roof height, window gap, span, tunnel length and number of parallel tunnels are also user-defined, which allows the geometry to be scaled to match commercial dimensions.

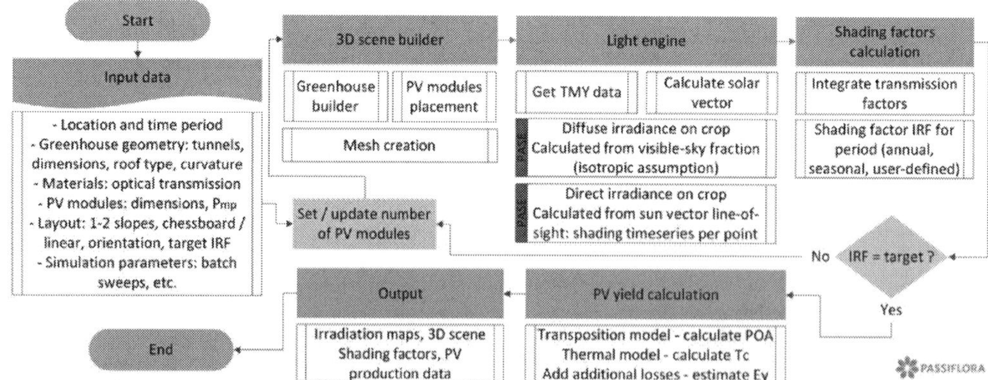

Figure 1: Simulation workflow for the determination of optimal PV capacity on a greenhouse roof to reach the target irradiation reduction factor (IRF)

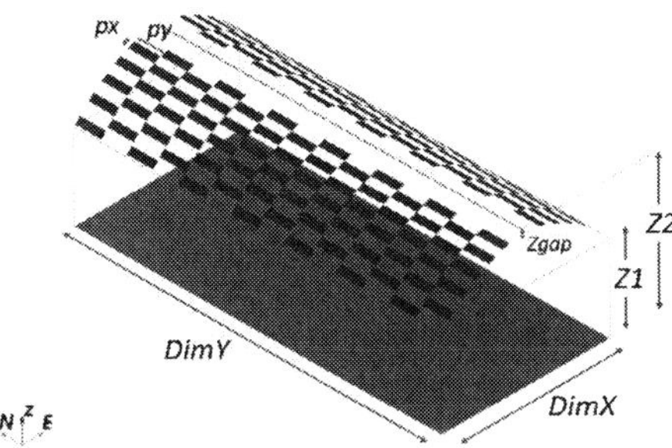

Figure 2: Example of a 3D scene with single-tunnel gothic-arc greenhouse and relevant geometry variables

The orientation of the greenhouse is another key parameter, as it determines how both PV generation and crop light distribution align with the sun's path. The tool allows users to set the azimuth of the greenhouse's longitudinal axis, enabling the simulation of common north–south or east–west orientations as well as any arbitrary angle required by local site constraints.

PV module properties: the type of PV module is defined by its dimensions, peak power and weight. This enables detailed shading calculations as well as the determination of the energy production during the time period specified by the user. The total additional weight of the PV system is also calculated.

PV module layout: The tool automatically generates a PV module arrangement on the roof surface. Several layout strategies are implemented to capture typical design options. In particular, modules can be installed on one slope only (e.g. the south-facing side of an east–west oriented greenhouse) or on both slopes simultaneously. The modules can be arranged in linear rows or in chessboard patterns, the latter often used to improve spatial homogeneity of transmitted light on the crop zone. Finally, the fraction of the roof covered with modules can be adjusted by the user, either directly by specifying the desired ground coverage ratio (GCR) or indirectly by setting a target shading factor on the crops. The tool then determines the appropriate number and spacing of modules to meet this specification.

The output of the scene set-up stage is a fully defined 3D representation of the greenhouse and PV system, which serves as the geometric basis for the subsequent irradiance calculations.

2.3 Weather and irradiance data

Accurate weather inputs are essential for quantifying both the reduction of irradiation in the crop zone and the potential photovoltaic output. In PASSIFLORA, the default workflow retrieves a Typical Meteorological Year (TMY) dataset from PVGIS using the default database for the site (usually SARAH3 for most European locations). The user specifies the geographical location, and the file is automatically downloaded through the pvlib interface. Alternatively, the user may provide a local weather file in CSV format, which is read by the same routines. This dual option ensures that the tool can be applied both in early design stages, when site-specific measurements may not yet be available, and in detailed analyses where local meteorological records are accessible.

In all cases, the model expects the standard irradiance components—global horizontal irradiance (GHI), diffuse horizontal irradiance (DHI), and direct normal irradiance (DNI)—to be explicitly included in the dataset. Solar position parameters, namely zenith and azimuth angles, are calculated with pvlib's astronomical routines to guarantee consistency across irradiance processing and geometric evaluation of shading and sky obstruction.

2.4 Calculation of irradiation on the crop zone

For each timestep, the model evaluates both the direct and diffuse contributions of solar radiation reaching the ground beneath the PV structure.

The direct beam irradiance is determined by tracing a virtual line from the sun's position to the ground plane and checking whether this line intersects any PV module. If the point is shaded, the direct component is set to zero; if unshaded, the component is calculated as the product of DNI and the cosine of the solar zenith angle. This binary shading logic, adapted from PASE's ray-casting module, provides a computationally efficient means of generating shading masks without requiring full 3D rendering.

The diffuse irradiance is estimated with an isotropic sky model in combination with a hemispherical sampling approach. For each point in the crop zone, a set of uniformly distributed rays is generated over the upper hemisphere using a Fibonacci-sphere method, which ensures a nearly even angular coverage. Each ray is then tested for visibility: if it exits unobstructed to the sky it contributes to the diffuse component, whereas rays that intersect a PV module are counted as blocked. The ratio of visible to total rays provides a numerical estimate of the sky view factor, which is used to scale the diffuse horizontal irradiance to the ground level. Although the model assumes isotropic diffuse conditions and therefore neglects anisotropic effects such as horizon or circumsolar brightening, the method offers a good compromise between accuracy and computational efficiency for agrivoltaic applications.

The global irradiance at the crop zone is obtained as the sum of the direct and diffuse components. Finally, the effect of the greenhouse covering material is represented by a single transmission factor (τ). In the reference case, based on literature values for multilayer polyethylene–EVA films, a transmission of 90% in the photosynthetically active radiation (PAR) range is assumed [17]. The transmitted irradiance is then calculated as the product of τ and the global irradiance beneath the modules.

Finally, to quantify the impact of the PV installation, the tool computes the irradiation reduction factor (IRF) for the specified time period, defined as the relative difference between the transmitted irradiation under PV coverage and the reference irradiation without modules (but including cover transmission). This ratio directly expresses the fraction of light lost to the crops due to PV integration, and can be compared against regulatory thresholds. Note that this ratio in our model is independent of the global optical transmission coefficient.

2.5 Photovoltaic energy production

In addition to estimating the irradiance available to crops, the PASSIFLORA tool calculates the energy yield of the installed PV system. This step makes use of the irradiance components (GHI, DNI, DHI) from the weather dataset together with the geometric layout of the modules defined in the scene.

The first step is the computation of irradiance on the plane of array (POA) for each module. The tool makes use of the Reindl transposition model, as implemented in pvlib. Compared to purely isotropic approaches, the Reindl model provides a more realistic representation of diffuse irradiance under a wide range of sky conditions and is widely used in PV performance modeling.

Once the POA irradiance is determined, the module operating temperature is estimated using the SAM temperature model implemented in pvlib, which relates cell temperature to ambient conditions and incident irradiance. The effective POA irradiance and cell temperature are then combined with the module's electrical parameters to compute the energy output in the defined time period. To approximate additional losses not explicitly modelled, a global loss factor is applied. This term accounts for effects such as angular losses, spectral variations, mismatch, soiling, cabling resistance, and inverter conversion, thereby yielding the final system energy production. Results are generated as hourly time series and aggregated into annual or seasonal indicators such as total yield and performance ratio. These outputs are presented alongside the crop-level irradiation reduction, enabling an integrated assessment of agrivoltaic system performance.

2.6 Framework and user interface

A distinctive feature of this modelling framework is its emphasis on accessibility. The computational routines are implemented in Python, but they are embedded within a graphical user interface (GUI) that allows users to configure greenhouse dimensions, PV layout, and material properties without requiring programming skills. Input parameters are organised in simple forms, and results are displayed both as numerical values (annual irradiation totals, reduction percentages) and as graphical outputs such as time series plots and shading maps.

By default, the tool can be run in an automatic sweep mode where the number of PV modules is varied until the simulated irradiation reduction factor matches, as closely as possible, a user-defined target. This feature is particularly relevant in contexts where regulatory frameworks prescribe a maximum allowable reduction in transmitted light, as it enables the user to directly identify a compliant configuration without trial-and-error adjustments.

This design choice serves two purposes. First, it makes the tool usable by a broad range of stakeholders—including farmers, project developers, and regulators—who may not have expertise in simulation software. Second, it facilitates potential deployment as a web-based application, where the GUI could be adapted into an online interface enabling interactive design studies. By combining simplified but validated algorithms with a user-friendly interface, the framework ensures that reliable irradiation reduction assessments can be carried out quickly and consistently at the earliest stages of project planning.

3 VALIDATION

3.1 Case definition

The reference system is a commercial Gothic-tunnel greenhouse supplied by Gonvarri AgroTech, located in the region of Toledo (Spain). The site has no PV cover at present; the PV layout described below is a controlled configuration used for validation.

Although the greenhouse is multitunnel, for the validation we have focused on a single-span Gothic tunnel,

with dimensions 30 m length and 9.6 m span, channel height 5.0 m, and ridge height 7.8 m. The impact of multiple tunnels is analysed in section 4. The curved roof is represented by circular arcs of 10 m radius, yielding a mean roof slope of ~30°. The greenhouse longitudinal axis is north–south, so the roof slopes face east and west. A vent opening at the top is modelled by using a maximum z value for the positioning of the modules. Other elements such as the greenhouse structure are neglected.

The enclosure is treated as a typical multilayer LDPE/EVA greenhouse film; a PAR transmission factor of 0.90 is adopted for the baseline, consistent with values reported for commercial films.

For roof integration we consider narrow crystalline-Si modules of 1.00 m × 0.25 m and 35 Wp, aligned with the roof arcs. These lightweight units were selected because they had been used previously in a small laboratory prototype test, and their reduced width facilitates uniform coverage along the curved roof geometry. Although their efficiency is lower than that of standard PV modules, they provide a representative case for evaluating the modelling framework.

3.2 PASSIFLORA and PVsyst configuration

For the geometry of the greenhouse described above and the type of PV module, PASSIFLORA was used to generate automatically PV modules on the roof with a target of 20% irradiation reduction factor. The positions, tilts and azimuths of the PV modules were exported to a file for later use in PVsyst. The weather data was ingested from PVGIS.

In PVsyst, the roof-mounted modules are modelled in the 3D scene for the energy-yield run, employing the same reference PV module as in the PASSIFLORA simulation. The positions, tilts and azimuths of the PV modules are input in the 3D scene using the exported values from PASSIFLORA. The electrical model includes standard PVsyst loss mechanisms (IAM, temperature, wiring/mismatch, soiling, inverter behaviour).

To obtain crop-level irradiation under the canopy, a second variant is used: the roof modules are converted into opaque shading objects, and a horizontal "virtual array" is defined at crop height over the greenhouse floor. PVsyst's hourly shading engine (direct, diffuse sky, circumsolar) then returns transmitted ground irradiation and shading factors on that horizontal plane, while the regular variant provides the PV production of the roof array. This enables the calculation of the irradiation values on the crop area for direct comparison with PASSIFLORA.

3.3 Results

The results of this simulation with both modeling approaches are shown in Table I. The annual ground-level global irradiation agrees to better than 1 kWh m^{-2}. The irradiation reduction factors were essentially identical in both simulations (0.1775), which corresponds to a ratio of 0.52 for a ground cover ratio of 0.3448.

The annual energy delivered by the system differs by 1.38%. This is partially due to small differences in the plane-of-array irradiance, which arise from the different transition methods employed in the two simulations, and to the simplification of loss factors in PASSIFLORA.

The validation confirms that the easy-to-use approach in PASSIFLORA reproduces crop-level irradiation beneath a PV greenhouse with negligible bias relative to PVsyst. Differences in PV energy yield remain small (≤ ~3%) and trace primarily to the distinct loss and transposition treatments. Taken together, these results support the use of PASSIFLORA for rapid, regulation-oriented pre-designs of solar PV greenhouses.

Table I: Comparison of PVsyst and PASSIFLORA for the simulation of a single-tunnel PV greenhouse

Variable	PASSIFLORA	PVsyst	Diff.
Irradiation reduction factor (IRF)	0.1775	0.1779	-0.22%
PV energy yield [kWh kWp^{-1}]	1382.1	1363.3	1.38%

4 CASE STUDIES

Following the validation against PVsyst, a series of case studies were conducted to illustrate the capabilities of PASSIFLORA in exploring different design options for agrivoltaic greenhouses. These examples are not intended as detailed engineering designs but rather as demonstrations of how the tool can be applied to support early-stage decisions and regulatory compliance. Each case highlights a different design variable and its impact on both crop-level irradiation and PV production.

4.1 Multi-tunnel configuration

The influence of adjacent tunnels on crop-level irradiation was analysed by simulating an increasing number of identical Gothic tunnel units placed side by side. Each tunnel retained the same geometry and PV layout as in the reference case; only the number of lateral repetitions was varied, as shown in Figure 3. Irradiation was then evaluated at the ground level in the central tunnel, so that the results reflect the effect of neighbour shading.

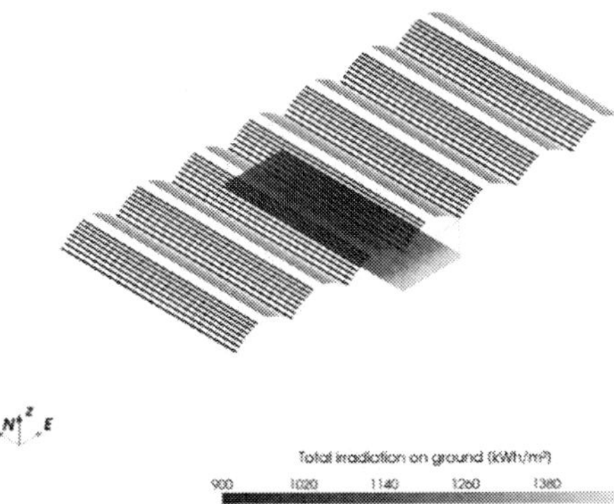

Figure 3: Representation of a 3D scene with 7 tunnels to assess the impact on the irradiation on crop for the central tunnel

Figure 4 shows the variation of the ratio of annual irradiation reduction to geometric cover (IRF/GCR$_x$) as a function of the total number of tunnels in the greenhouse. A sharp increase occurs when moving from an isolated tunnel to configurations with three or more tunnels. This is caused by lateral shading from neighbouring roofs, which diminishes both the visible fraction of sky and the direct beam component. Beyond approximately seven tunnels, the shading factor stabilises, indicating that the central tunnel has reached a "pseudo-infinite" condition where side effects become negligible. In this situation the value of IRF/GCR$_x$ reaches 0.87, which is consistent with

values reported in previous studies [9], [19]. This demonstrates that multi-tunnel arrangements accentuate shading effects and must be accounted for when modelling large-scale greenhouse blocks.

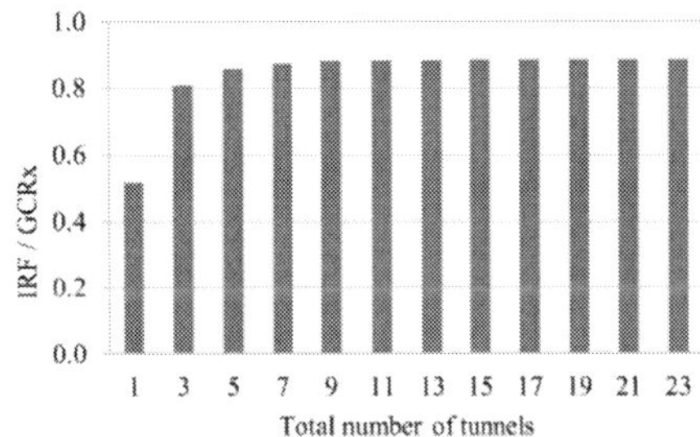

Figure 4: Impact of the number of tunnels on the irradiation on crop at a central tunnel

4.2 Alternative module arrangements

PASSIFLORA allows testing of different roof layouts beyond the baseline linear configuration. To illustrate this, two roof patterns were compared: linear rows and a chessboard arrangement. In both cases the number of modules per tunnel and the overall ground coverage ratio were kept identical. Results show that the chessboard pattern produces negligible changes in annual IRF and PV yield when compared to the linear layout. However, the irradiation distribution at crop level becomes slightly more homogeneous in the chessboard case, with lower contrasts between shaded and unshaded zones. This suggests that, while energy metrics remain unaffected, the chessboard pattern may provide agronomic benefits in terms of spatial light uniformity.

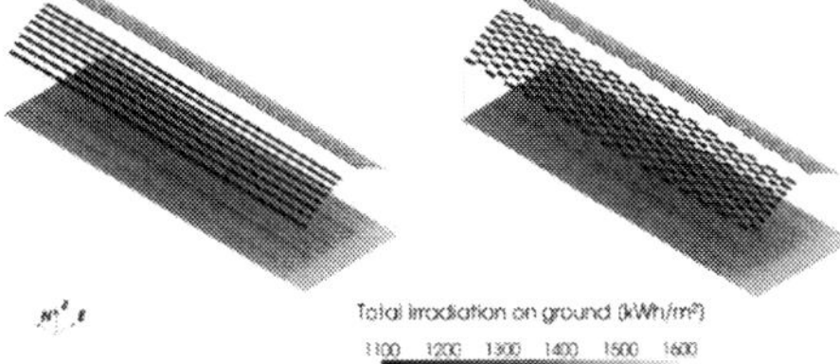

Figure 5: Comparison of linear (left) versus chessboard (right) patterns for the PV modules layout on the greenhouse roof

4.3 Impact of orientation

The effect of greenhouse orientation was evaluated by comparing a north–south (N–S) ridge, with PV modules placed on both roof slopes facing east and west, against an east–west (E–W) ridge, with PV modules placed only on the south-facing slope, as shown in Figure 6. Both configurations used the same greenhouse geometry and the same number of PV modules (300), corresponding to a total installed capacity of 10.5 kWp. The geometric ground cover ratio was 0.22 in both cases.

The results are shown in Table II. The crop-level irradiation is lower in the E-W case, with a nearly 30% higher irradiation reduction factor.

In terms of electricity generation, the E-W ridge PV greenhouse delivers around 20% more energy. Despite the lower production, the N-S greenhouse produces a more homogeneous daily output. Moreover, shading on the crop is more evenly distributed temporally and spatially in the N-S orientation, while the E-W orientation presents stronger asymmetries. These differences underline that orientation affects not only the balance between energy yield and crop irradiation but also the diurnal and seasonal light patterns experienced by crops, which may be critical depending on crop sensitivity.

Table II: Comparison of N-W vs E-W orientations for a PV greenhouse

Variable	N-S	E-W	Diff.
Irradiation reduction factor (IRF)	0.1118	0.1571	-28.8%
PV energy yield [kWh kWp^{-1}]	1391.3	1712.5	-18.8%

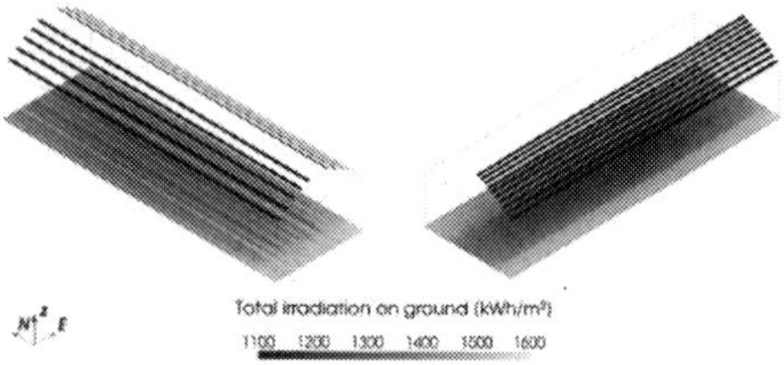

Figure 6: Comparison of N-S (left) versus E-W (right) greenhouse orientation with same total number of PV modules

5 CONCLUSIONS

This work presented the development and first validation of PASSIFLORA, a simplified modelling framework for estimating irradiation reduction and PV energy yield in agrivoltaic greenhouses. By adapting geometric shading and light-sharing algorithms originally developed in PASE, the tool provides physically consistent estimates of transmitted irradiation without relying on computationally intensive ray-tracing methods. A graphical interface and automated layout routines make the framework accessible for non-expert users, supporting early-stage design and compliance with emerging agrivoltaic regulations.

Validation against PVsyst for a real Gothic tunnel greenhouse at the region of Toledo (Spain) showed excellent agreement in crop-level irradiation, with annual differences below 0.5%, and close agreement in PV energy yield, within approximately 3%. These results confirm that the simplified ray-casting and hemispherical sampling approach implemented in PASSIFLORA can reproduce the outputs of a reference engineering tool with negligible bias, while requiring significantly less design effort.

The case studies further illustrated how the framework can be applied to explore practical design variables. Multi-tunnel arrangements introduced additional shading due to neighbouring tunnels reduced the light available in the central tunnel, while alternative layouts such as chessboard arrangements improved homogeneity without altering annual totals. The comparison between north–south and east–west ridge orientations showed that in this case the east-west orientation offers more homogeneity and more irradiation for the crops while lowering the PV yield.

Overall, PASSIFLORA demonstrates that simplified yet physically grounded methods can provide reliable and transparent estimates of both crop irradiation and PV

performance. Its ease of use and ability to deliver regulation-oriented metrics position it as a valuable decision-support tool for developers, farmers and policymakers, complementing but not replacing detailed simulation software in later design stages.

ACKNOWLEDGEMENTS

This work has been partially funded by the Agencia SEKUENS through the FLORA project (reference IDE/2024/000462). The authors gratefully acknowledge the PASE development team for making their open-source algorithms publicly available, which provided the foundation for part of the modelling framework presented here.

REFERENCES

[1] A. Goetzberger and A. Zastrow, 'On the Coexistence of Solar-Energy Conversion and Plant Cultivation', *International Journal of Solar Energy*, vol. 1, no. 1, pp. 55–69, Jan. 1982, doi: 10.1080/01425918208909875.

[2] S. Zainali *et al.*, 'Modelling, simulation, and optimisation of agrivoltaic systems: a comprehensive review', *Applied Energy*, vol. 386, p. 125558, May 2025, doi: 10.1016/j.apenergy.2025.125558.

[3] S. Zainali *et al.*, 'Direct and diffuse shading factors modelling for the most representative agrivoltaic system layouts', *Applied Energy*, vol. 339, p. 120981, Jun. 2023, doi: 10.1016/j.apenergy.2023.120981.

[4] S. P. Rajan, S.-N. Asaa, A. Katsikogiannis, J. Robledo, J. Leloux, I. Kaaya, G. Bosco, 'Validation and benchmark of modelling tools for light assessment using ray-tracing and GPU-based method', Deliverable 2.2 - Symbiosyst - Horizon Europe EU project - Grant Agreement No. 101096352, Dec. 2024.

[5] J. Robledo, J. Leloux, E. Lorenzo, and C. A. Gueymard, 'From video games to solar energy: 3D shading simulation for PV using GPU', *Solar Energy*, vol. 193, pp. 962–980, Nov. 2019, doi: 10.1016/j.solener.2019.09.041.

[6] J. Robledo Bueno *et al.*, 'Lessons Learned from Simulating the Energy Yield of an Agrivoltaic Project with Vertical Bifacial Photovoltaic Modules in France', *38th European Photovoltaic Solar Energy Conference and Exhibition; 1588-1595*, p. 8 pages, 7533 kb, 2021, doi: 10.4229/EUPVSEC20212021-6CV.4.41.

[7] I. El Boujdaini *et al.*, '3D Modelling of Light-Sharing Agrivoltaic Systems for Orchards, Vineyards and Berries', *40th European Photovoltaic Solar Energy Conference and Exhibition*, pp. 020430001–020430010, 2023, doi: 10.4229/EUPVSEC2023/4DO.2.3.

[8] H. Goverde *et al.*, 'Energy Yield Prediction Model for PV Modules Including Spatial and Temporal Effects', *29th European Photovoltaic Solar Energy Conference and Exhibition; 3292-3296*, 2014, doi: 10.4229/EUPVSEC20142014-5CV.2.28.

[9] M. Cossu *et al.*, 'Assessment and comparison of the solar radiation distribution inside the main

commercial photovoltaic greenhouse types in Europe', *Renewable and Sustainable Energy Reviews*, vol. 94, pp. 822–834, Oct. 2018, doi: 10.1016/j.rser.2018.06.001.

[10] M. Cossu *et al.*, 'Agricultural sustainability estimation of the European photovoltaic greenhouses', *European Journal of Agronomy*, vol. 118, p. 126074, Aug. 2020, doi: 10.1016/j.eja.2020.126074.

[11] C. J. Torrente, J. Reca, R. López-Luque, J. Martínez, and F. J. Casares, 'Simulation model to analyze the spatial distribution of solar radiation in agrivoltaic Mediterranean greenhouses and its effect on crop water needs', *Applied Energy*, vol. 353, p. 122050, Jan. 2024, doi: 10.1016/j.apenergy.2023.122050.

[12] M. E. Evans, J. A. Langley, F. R. Shapiro, and G. F. Jones, 'A Validated Model, Scalability, and Plant Growth Results for an Agrivoltaic Greenhouse', *Sustainability*, vol. 14, no. 10, pp. 020430-001-020430–010, 2022, doi: https://doi.org/10.3390/su14106154.

[13] G. López-Diaz, A. Carreño-Ortega, H. Fatnassi, C. Poncet, and M. Díaz-Pérez, 'The Effect of Different Levels of Shading in a Photovoltaic Greenhouse with a North–South Orientation', *Applied Sciences*, vol. 10, no. 3, p. 882, Jan. 2020, doi: 10.3390/app10030882.

[14] Generalitat de Catalunya Departament d'Acció Climàtica, Alimentació i Agenda Rural Direcció General d'Agricultura i Ramaderia., *Instrucció tècnica que estableix els criteris d'agrovoltaisme a Catalunya*. 2023.

[15] Journal Officiel de la République Française, *Décret no 2024-318 du 8 avril 2024 relatif au développement de l'agrivoltaïsme et aux conditions d'implantation des installations photovoltaïques sur des terrains agricoles, naturels ou forestiers*. 2024.

[16] R. Bruhwyler *et al.*, 'Modelling light-sharing in agrivoltaics: the open-source Python Agrivoltaic Simulation Environment (PASE 1.0)', *Agroforest Syst*, vol. 98, no. 8, pp. 2747–2764, Dec. 2024, doi: 10.1007/s10457-024-01090-8.

[17] H.-J. Tantau *et al.*, 'Solar Transmittance of Greenhouse Covering Materials', *Acta Hortic.*, no. 956, pp. 441–448, Oct. 2012, doi: 10.17660/ActaHortic.2012.956.51.

[18] K. S. Anderson, C. W. Hansen, W. F. Holmgren, A. R. Jensen, M. A. Mikofski, and A. Driesse, 'pvlib python: 2023 project update', *Journal of Open Source Software*, vol. 8, no. 92, p. 5994, Dec. 2023, doi: 10.21105/joss.05994.

[19] N. Hanrieder, A. Kujawa, A. B. Seychelles, M. Blanco, J. Carballo, and S. Wilbert, 'Estimation of maximum photovoltaic cover ratios in greenhouses based on global irradiance data', *Applied Energy*, vol. 365, p. 123232, Jul. 2024, doi: 10.1016/j.apenergy.2024.123232.

Development of a simple tool for estimating irradiation reduction in agrivoltaic greenhouses

Paula Sánchez-Friera[1], Guillermo Correa[2], Luis Pérez[2], Baurin Leza[2], Tomás Pernas[3], Jairo Pérez[3], Jorge Pérez[3]

[1] Solkeys, Mar Cantábrico 16, 33204 Gijón, Spain

[2] Gonvarri MS R&D, PI Cancienes, 33470 Corvera de Asturias, Spain

[3] Gonvarri AgroTech, PI Cancienes, 33470 Corvera de Asturias, Spain

E-mail: paula@solkeys.com

CONTEXT AND OBJECTIVES

- **Regulatory context:** constraints on maximum shading factors and/or maximum yield reduction inside the greenhouse due to PV
- **Challenge:** Standard PV simulation tools lack features to model in detail irradiation at the crop level, while more sophisticated tools exist but require a high-level of modeling expertise / cost
- **Need:** fast, accurate and transparent tool for early-stage design and regulation compliance

Key objectives:

- Development of a computationally efficient and user-friendly tool for estimating irradiation reduction under PV greenhouse configurations
- Validation against other modelling approaches
- Demonstration as a pre-design decision-support tool for regulatory compliance and project development

METHODOLOGY

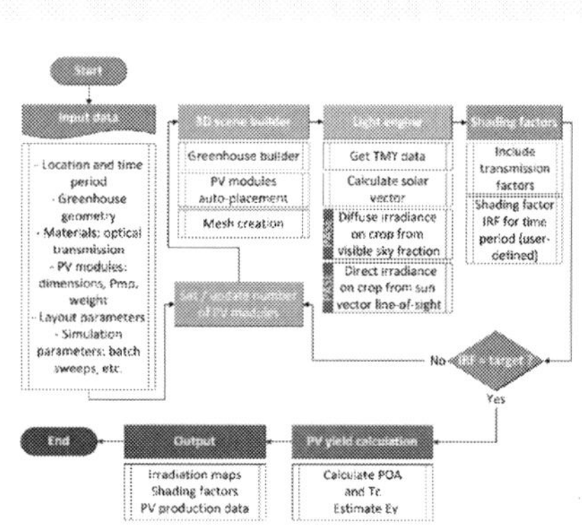

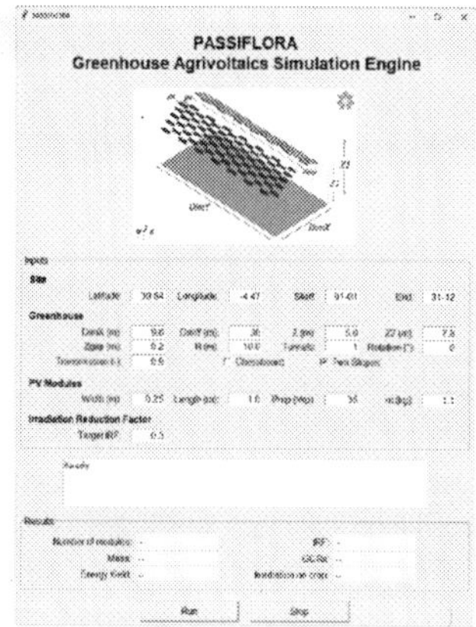

VALIDATION

- Comparison with PVsyst simulation results
- Gothic tunnel greenhouse (30 m × 9.6 m)
- Modules: linear layout, 8 rows per slope, 0.25 m
- PVsyst variants:
    A. PV roof: positions of tables input from PASSIFLORA
    B. Sensor field: PV modules transformed to objects and virtual PV field created at crop level
- Results show very good agreement

Variable	PASSIFLORA	PVsyst	Diff.
Irradiation reduction	0.1775	0.1779	-0.22%
PV energy yield [kWh/kWp]	1382.1	1363.3	1.38%

CASE STUDIES

Impact of number of parallel tunnels

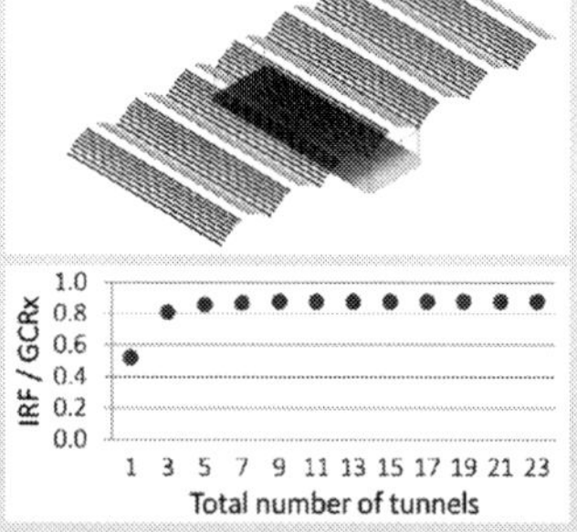

- Irradiation on crop stabilizes after 2-3 tunnels on each side

Impact of N-S vs E-W orientation

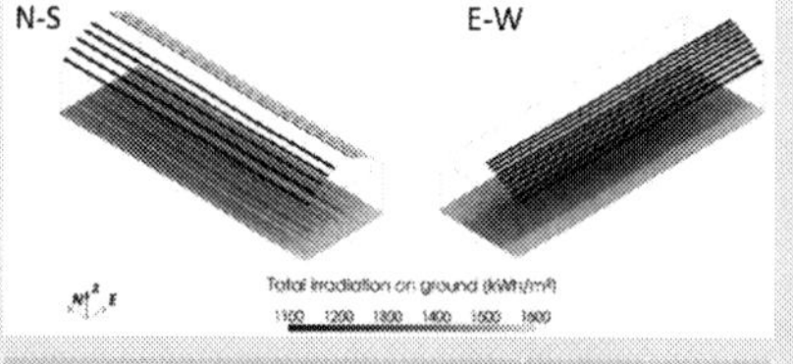

Variable	N-S	E-W	Diff.
Irradiation reduction [%]	0.1118	0.1571	-28.8%
PV energy yield [kWh/kWp]	1391.3	1712.5	-18.8%

- N-S ridge orientation favours higher irradiation on crop, more uniformity and better-balanced diurnal PV production

Impact of PV module layout

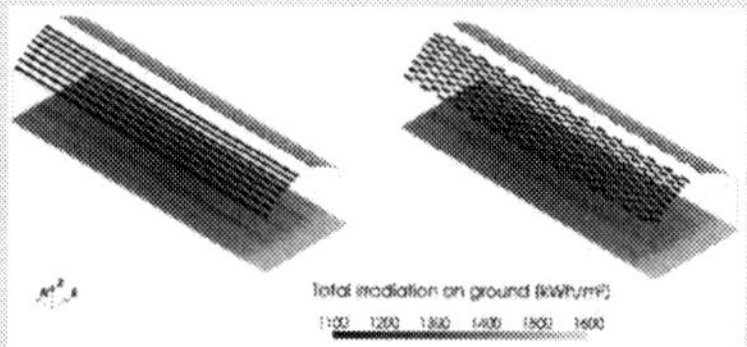

- Linear vs chessboard lay-out comparison
- IRF and PV yield almost unchanged
- Chessboard slightly more uniform light distribution

CONCLUSIONS AND OUTLOOK

- PASSIFLORA enables fast, regulation-oriented design of AV greenhouses
- Validated against PVsyst with excellent agreement

- Flexible for geometry, layout, orientation
- Accessible through GUI
- Minimal inputs needed

Future work:

- Integration of additional models
- Further validation including real greenhouse
- Online deployment for interactive design

This work has been partially funded by the Agencia SEKUENS through the FLORA project (reference IDE/2024/000462). The authors gratefully acknowledge the PASE development team for making their open-source algorithms publicly available, which provided the foundation for part of the modelling framework.

020413-001

PV AND PVT SYSTEMS DESIGN FOR "RASPA Y AMAGADO" GREENHOUSES

Author(s): José Manuel Naveiro[1,*], Beatriz Muñoz Vidal[2], Eduardo Pardo[3], María Miguel Laborda[2], Ana Escudero[2], Gonzalo Brun[1], Raquel Simón-Allué[1], Raúl Villén[1], Yolanda Lara[1]
Company / Institute(s): (1) Endef; (2) IaSol; (3) Fundación Tecnova
Address(es): josemanuel.naveiro@endef.com , beatrizmunoz@iasol.es , ingenieria@fundaciontecnova.com ,
mariamiguel@iasol.es , anaescudero@iasol.es , gonzalo.brun@endef.com, raquel.simon@endef.com,
raul.villen@endef.com , yolanda.lara@endef.com

ABSTRACT: **Achieving symbiosis between agriculture and photovoltaic production** is one of the most critical aspects of developing agrivoltaic technology (Agri-PV), being the integration with greenhouses one of the main research lines. Among greenhouses, Almería's region, in Spain, shows a unique typology known as "raspa y amagado" (or Almería-type) characterized by lightweight removable plastic covers.

The present study is part of the Agrisol project; a Spanish-national project that seeks to implement Agri-PV in Almería-type greenhouses. Within this project, options for achieving an efficient and simple installation of solar systems in this type of greenhouses have been studied.

Innovation was also achieved with the integration of photovoltaic-thermal air-based solar panels, which generate hot air that can contribute to general heating, ventilation, or cooling consumption, depending on the greenhouse and crop requirements.

This paper presents the studies and designs developed for the Agri-PV system. **It is the first study conducted on "raspa y amagado" greenhouses with photovoltaic and hybrid (PVT) panels.**

1 INTRODUCTION

Agrivoltaics (Agri-PV), also known as agrophotovoltaics, involves harnessing a single area of land to produce both solar energy and agricultural products. In other words, solar panels coexist with crops on the same surface. This technique was originally conceived by Adolf Goetzberger and Armin Zastrow in 1981, but the concept only became popular in the last decade. According to a study published by Nature [1], if just 1% of arable land were dedicated to solar electricity production, it would be possible to meet global energy demand.

One of the aspects to be considered is the amount of shading provided by the solar panels that may be acceptable for the crops. Studies reported no significant effects of 20% coverage with photovoltaic panels on growth, yield, and quality in a greenhouse in Greece [2]. In Italy, pepper species were found to be compatible within photovoltaic greenhouses with a shading rate of 25%, causing limited yield reduction below this value [3].

The most characteristic greenhouse in Almería is the so-called "raspa y amagado" greenhouse (Figure 1), which occupies approximately 96% of the total greenhouse surface area [4]. This type of greenhouse consists of a wooden or steel structure covered by a lightweight plastic cover that is replaced every 2 years. These greenhouses have narrow windows in the roof to allow for ventilation, covered with a more durable plastic than the rest of the structure, which is replaced every 8 years.

Figure 1 "raspa y amagado" greenhouse.

The electricity consumption required by this type of greenhouse is around 15,000–30,000 kWh per hectare per year, being the highest consumption due to the water pumping systems and the motors for opening and closing windows. These characteristics of low-energy greenhouses represent, a priori, the potential to cover greenhouse demand with photovoltaic energy, improving the farmer's operating account and reducing the carbon footprint of Almería's products [5].

The purpose of the Agrisol project is to research and develop new methodologies, processes, and components for optimizing the implementation and operation of Agri-PV technology, resulting from the integration of photovoltaic generation facilities in greenhouse crops.

To achieve this objective, the project seeks to install photovoltaic modules adapted to the layout and structure of Almería-type greenhouses without affecting the development of the crops.

Agrisol incorporates two types of infrastructure innovation within the framework of Agri-PV technology: the support structure for the photovoltaic panels and the implementation of a hybrid system that generates both electricity and heat.

2 DESIGN PROCESS

For the design process, aspects such as the structural requirements, the weight of the system, and the replacement of the plastic cover needed to be considered together with global Agri-PV aspects such as shading.

The replacement of the plastic envelope was one of the limitations found during the study. After the assessment of several options, it was decided the most adequate location for the solar system was the greenhouse roof windows. This offered a standard and more solid structure, although narrow surface to work on, with lower replacement frequency of the plastic cover. Additionally, the windows are yet considered as shading area in these greenhouses, so the shading percentage is not increased.

There are two window orientations (East and West) and two main positions for the windows: closed (0% aperture, 11° tilt) or opened (100% aperture, 52° tilt). A representation of the East-faced window is shown in Figure 2.

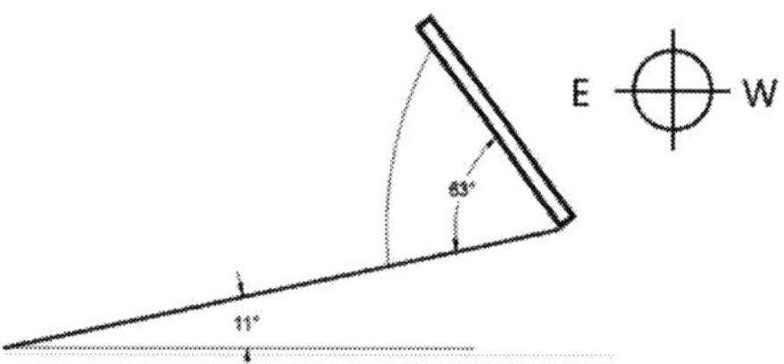

Figure 2 East-faced window tilt 100% aperture.

The evaluation and selection of photovoltaic modules to be used in the PV and PVT systems were framed by the windows area and the weight limitations. Thus, flexible photovoltaic modules were adopted for both systems.

2.1. PV Fastening system.

In a photovoltaic installation, the mounting structure is a mechanical component responsible for securing the modules by fixing them to the roof either through anchoring or ballast. The structure allows for setting the panel's orientation and tilt parameters and angles that determine the plant's final energy output.

The fastening system employed had to enable anchoring the modules to the window frame structure. To achieve this, a structural analysis of the components was performed using a FEM-based software and assembly tests were carried out on a replica of the greenhouse window where the modules would be installed.

For the photovoltaic system, two distinct anchoring methods were proposed:

1. Hook-type component; commonly used for anchoring lightweight modules on balconies. The proposed components are very lightweight, made of aluminium 5005-T5, and consist of three elements: (1) a small curved L-, (2) a larger flat rectangular (3) the joining mechanism. This three individual pieces interlock to create a hook-shaped structure.

2. Sheet Metal Threaded Profile; which involves attaching three very lightweight aluminium profiles per module to the window structure using sheet metal screws. The distribution of these profiles matches that of the hooks, as both are arranged according to the module's mounting holes.

For the structural assessment of each component under system loads, the Finite Element Method (FEM) was employed. The showed results are the ones from the final selected structure for the PV system: sheet metal threaded profile. The location of the threaded profiles is presented in Figure 3 below:

Figure 3 Structure design (threaded profiles in pink colour).

The sheet metal threaded profile method requires drilling the base window structure. The most relevant element for this method is the window structure itself and how the incorporation of these profiles and their corresponding drilled holes affect it. The distribution of 5.5 kg among six supports of the photovoltaic modules is accounted for in the FEM analysis. In addition, the weight

of the profile between the two supports in the structure is considered, resulting in a point load of 9.77 N. This point load is transmitted through the 12 module mounting holes distributed along the longitudinal window profiles. The analysis indicates that the maximum resulting longitudinal displacement of the window is 0.422 mm.

In Figure 4 the result of the Finite Element Analysis (FEA) is shown. The FEA allows to dimension the critical points of the structure and to decide if it is necessary to reinforce the structure or change to another attaching system.

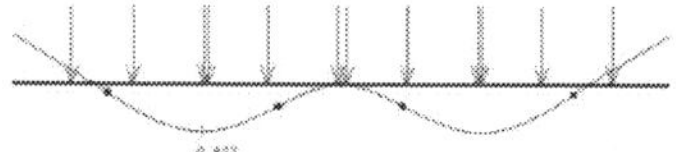

Figure 4 Finite Element Analysis applied to the longitudinal profile of the window.

The stress analysis performed yielded values that were practically negligible, indicating that the induced stresses do not significantly compromise the structural integrity of the window. Furthermore, the displacement results corroborate the minimal influence of this fastening method on the overall load-bearing behaviour of the system. Based on these findings, it can be concluded that the implementation of Sheet Metal Threaded Profiles provides sufficient stability, thereby eliminating the necessity for additional structural reinforcement.

As part of the validation process, a series of assembly tests were conducted at Endef's facilities. The objective of these tests was to evaluate the technical feasibility and compatibility of the two proposed structural systems for securing the photovoltaic panels on the greenhouse window under study. A photography of the assembly test appears in Figure 5.

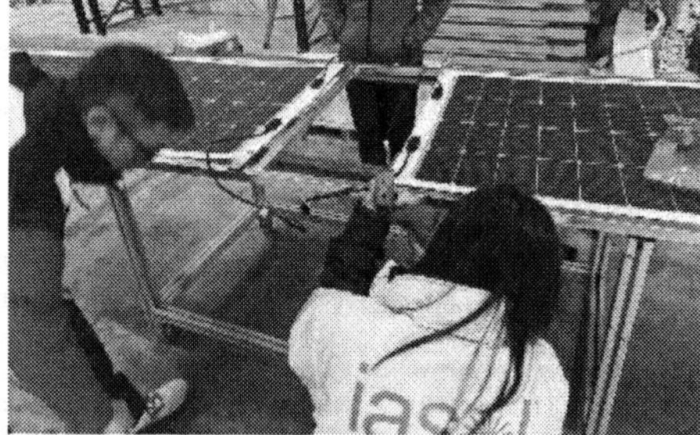

Figure 5 Assembly test of the sheet metal threaded profile method.

The tests enabled identification of potential design adjustments, confirmed the mechanical and functional suitability of the structures for future implementation, and allowed selection of the structure type with the simplest assembly. This, in turn, helps to reduce assembly times and associated costs. During assembly, the evaluated aspects included time required, personnel needed, and tools used.

For the sheet metal threaded profile method, only one installer was required, with an estimated assembly time of approximately 15 minutes per module. The assembly process was simpler and safer, and it reduced the buckling effect that was observed in the photovoltaic module when hook-type components were used.

2.2. PVT system

As for the integration of hybrid photovoltaic-thermal (PVT) panels into agricultural structures, this technology adds a unique and innovative element to the Agrisol project. These panels combine the production of thermal energy with the generation of electrical energy. This dual functionality enables the system's energy efficiency to be maximised.

The PVT-system requires the creation of a channel for the air to flow under the photovoltaic modules. This air, which passes between the photovoltaic modules and the plastic, comes from inside the greenhouse and returns to it at a higher temperature. In order to create this channel within the available surface, taking into account the weight and structural requirements, numerous hybrid system configurations and concepts were explored throughout the process in order to arrive at the final solution. Figure 6 shows the design's evolution regarding materials and distribution.

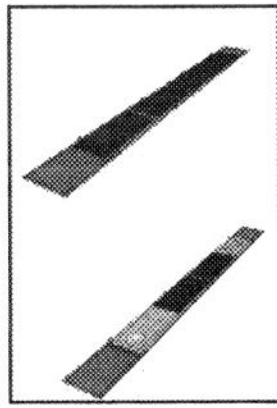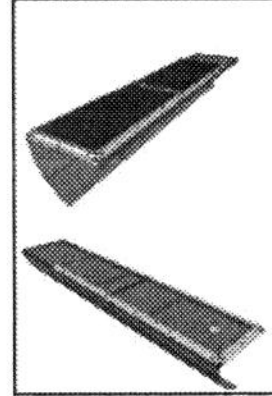

Figure 6 PVTs design evolution.

The final design presents the easiest mounting system of the explored concepts and is also the most resistant one thanks to the employed materials and structure.

An aluminium mounting structure bolted to the roof windows that creates a channel for the air flow between the photovoltaic modules and window surface was designed (Figure 7). This structure also underwent through the FEM analysis as well as through a series of assembly tests at Endef's facilities to check the technical feasibility of the process.

Figure 7 First assembled PVT system prototype at Endef's facilities.

The end result of the design process is a small, light, and effective system that maximizes the use of the available space, makes mounting easier, and minimizes the need for new structural elements.

3 INSTALLATION PROCESS AND TESTING

Both systems, PV and PVT, were installed in Almería during the spring-summer of 2025 on a "raspa y amagado" greenhouse. The installed systems were located over the greenhouse windows, as seen in Figure 8.

Figure 8 Photovoltaic modules installed on the "raspa y amagado" roof windows.

Two of the three available windows on the roof of the demonstrator greenhouse were used to install the PV system (East- and West-faced windows), while the remaining window was assigned to the PVT system (East-faced window).

The commissioning and first data acquisition were done on summer 2025. During this period, thermal performance data have been gathered in order to prepare for the final testing phase which will take place during the pepper planting season, in autumn.

The working hours for the initial testing were between 8 a.m. and 1 p.m. This initial testing allowed to analyse the performance and the hardiness of the PVT system as a preparation for the full testing.

Figure 9 shows temperature and irradiance data for July 28th. This situation is the worst-case scenario because the data were gathered with the window totally opened, facing the west orientation in the morning and with crops inside the greenhouse. In this scenario, an increment of 8.2 °C over the greenhouse internal temperature was observed.

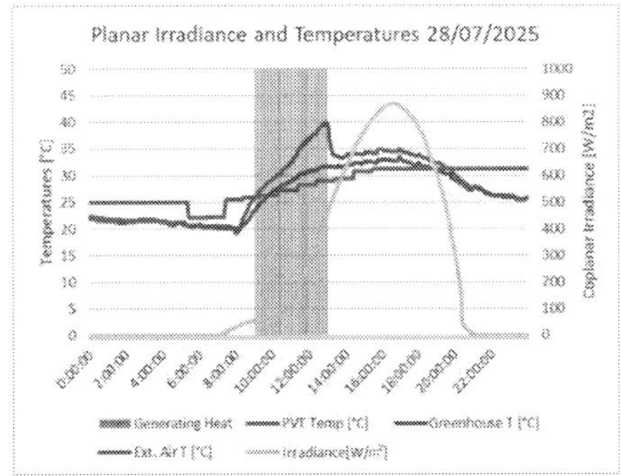

Figure 9 Temperatures and irradiance.

The blue background colour represents the working hours of the fan (from 8 a.m. to 1 p.m.). The blue line is the temperature of the air at the exit of the PVT system. As shown in the figure, while the fan is turned on, this temperature reaches a sharper increase than the greenhouse one (red line) as well as the ambient one (grey line). Once the fan is turned off the temperature of the PVT decreases and becomes similar to the temperature of the greenhouse.

The shape of the irradiance curve (yellow line) corresponds to the 100% opened window (52° tilt and west orientation), and does not reach the maximum values during the working time. Higher temperatures are expected during peak irradiation hours, and future test data will be used to clarify this expectation.

Data collection will be performed during autumn to determine performance during the crop season. Through that time the fan of the PVT system will be working all the day continuously.

4 CONCLUSSIONS

Two small, light, and effective structures for installing PV and PVT technologies in Almería-type greenhouses have been designed.

The designed configurations have been installed in Almería in spring-summer 2025. Performance data will be collected in autumn 2025.

The worst-case scenario during the summer obtained an increase of 8.2 °C in the PVT air temperature over the internal greenhouse temperature.

The project provides a previously unexplored component in Almería-type greenhouses. The developed systems allow to find more efficient and widespread applications of these technologies and reduce the CO_2 emissions.

5 ACKNOWLEDGEMENTS

This publication is part of the R&D&I project AGRISOL, funded by MCIN/AEI (CPP2021-008521) and the European Union Next Generation EU/PRTR.

6 REFERENCES

[1] Adeh, E. H., Good, S. P., Calaf, M., & Higgins, C. W. (2019). Solar PV power potential is greatest over croplands. Scientific reports, 9(1), 1-6.

[2] Kavga, A., Trypanagnostopoulos, G., Zervoudakis, G., & Tripanagnostopoulos, Y. (2018). Growth and physiological characteristics of lettuce (Lactuca sativa L.) and rocket (Eruca sativa Mill.) plants cultivated under photovoltaic panels. Notulae Botanicae Horti Agrobotanici Cluj-Napoca, 46(1), 206-212.

[3] Cossu, M., Yano, A., Solinas, S., Deligios, P. A., Tiloca, M. T., Cossu, A., & Ledda, L. (2020). Agricultural sustainability estimation of the European photovoltaic greenhouses. European Journal of Agronomy, 118, 126074.

[4] Céspedes, A. J., García, M. C., Pérez-Parra, J. J., & Cuadrado, I. M. (2010). Caracterización de la explotación hortícola protegida almeriense. Almería, España: FIAPA.

[5] López-Díaz, G., Carreño-Ortega, A., Fatnassi, H., Poncet, C., & Díaz-Pérez, M. (2020). The effect of different levels of shading in a photovoltaic greenhouse with a north–south orientation. Applied Sciences, 10(3), 882

PV and PVT systems design for "raspa y amagado" greenhouses

Author(s): José Manuel Naveiro[1,*], Beatriz Muñoz[2], Eduardo Pardo[3], María Miguel Laborda[2], Ana Escudero[2], Gonzalo Brun[1], Raquel Simón-Allué[1], Raúl Villén[1], Yolanda Lara[1]
Company / Institute(s): (1) ENDEF; (2) IASOL; (3) Fundación Tecnova
*corresponding e-mail address(es): josemanuel.naveiro@endef.com

INTRODUCTION: AGRISOL Project

The work is part of the **Agrisol** project; a Spanish-national project that seeks to **implement agrivoltaics technology (Agri-PV) in Almería-type greenhouses.** Thus, we have designed the implementation of two technologies for this type of greenhouses: **photovoltaic (PV) and photovoltaic thermal (PVT)** for electricity (with PV and PVT) and heat generation (with PVT), to maintain the greenhouse temperature above 25 °C.

"Raspa y amagado" greenhouse

- The most characteristic greenhouse in Almería
- Wooden or steel structure .
- Lightweight plastic cover, replaced every 2 years.
- Narrow windows in the roof to allow for ventilation (their plastic is replaced every 8 years).

Design process: decisions

- To use narrow windows for solar installation due to its plastic cover replacement frequency.
- Narrow windows are already considered shaded space.
- Flexible PV modules are selected due to the structural requirements and the modules lightweight.

PVT SYSTEM

Objective: To create a channel below PV modules for enable forced air circulation and heat the greenhouse.

ANALYSIS

Solar energy: Estimation of electrical and thermal production

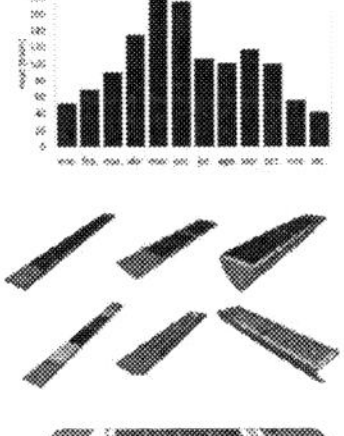

CONCEPT

Redesign: Generation of different designs that accomplishes the requirements

PROTOTYPE

Resulting system: Compact solution that is simpler to assemble. It recirculates the air from the greenhouse

PV FASTENING SYSTEM

Objective: To enable anchoring the modules to the window though a low weight and easy-to-install grip.

ANALYSIS

Structural: Strains and deformations

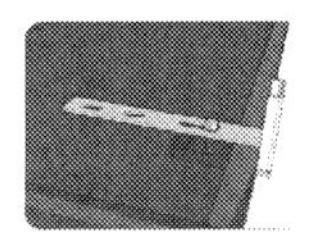

CONCEPT

Anchoring methods: two proposed :
- Hook-type component
- Sheet Metal Threaded Profile

PROTOTYPE

Resulting system: Simpler and safer solution to install. Reduction of the buckling effect

INSTALLATION AND TESTING

INSTALLATION PROCESS: 1 PVT and 2 PV systems were installed in Almería, during the spring-summer of 2025 on a "raspa y amagado" greenhouse.
- Commissioning and first data acquisition: summer, without crop.
- Two position for windows: open (11° tilt, east) / closed (52° tilt, west).
- Working hours for initial testing: 8 a.m. to 1 p.m.

PRELIMINARY RESULTS: **Increase of 8.2 °C over internal temperature**, in the worst-case scenario (summer, open window facing west, morning operation and with crops)
Data collection will be performed **during autumn** to determine performance during the crop season.

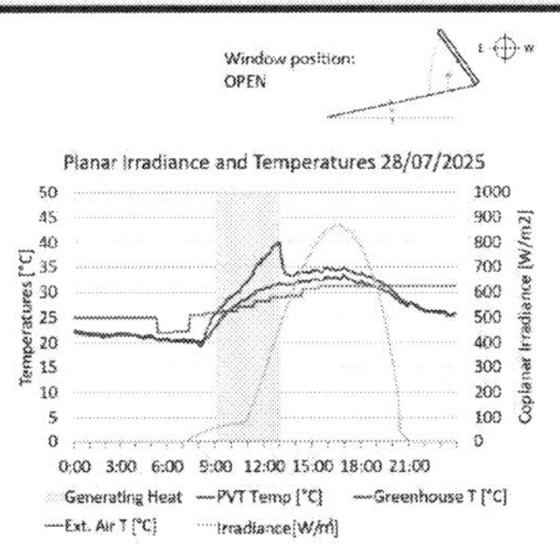

CONCLUSIONS

- The designed configurations have been **installed in Almería** in spring-summer 2025. Thermal data will be collected in autumn 2025.
- The end result of the design process is a **small, light, and effective structure** for each technology, the PV and the PVT technologies.
- The worst-case scenario during the summer obtained **an increase of 8.2 °C over the internal greenhouse temperature**.
- The project provides a previously unexplored component in Almería-type greenhouses. The developed systems allow to find more efficient and widespread applications of these technologies and reduce the CO_2 emissions.

This publication is part of the R&D&I project AGRISOL, funded by MCIN/AEI (CPP2021-008521) and the European Union NextGenerationEU/PRTR.

020415-001

INVESTIGATING SPECTRAL, THERMAL AND POSITIONAL EFFECTS ON THE PERFORMANCE OF 5-JUNCTION CPV CELLS

Elizabeth M Hagemann[1], Frederik J Vorster[1], E Ernest van Dyk[1], Ruediger F Loeckenhoff[2]

[1] Physics, Nelson Mandela University, University Way, Summerstrand, Port Elizabeth, 6031, South Africa
[2] AZUR SPACE Solar Power GmbH, Theresienstr. 2 74072 Heilbronn, Germany

Corresponding author e-mail address: s221440003@mandela.ac.za

ABSTRACT: Concentrator photovoltaic (CPV) cells are sensitive to environmental conditions, including solar spectral composition and operating temperature, as well as cell alignment relative to the Fresnel lens. Using a research-based CPV module, provided by AZUR SPACE Solar Power and deployed in South Africa, the study provides insights into the effects of spectral composition, operating temperature and cell misalignment on the performance of two variations of the 5C46 cell under operational conditions. Solar spectral data, using Average Photon Energy, indicated that Port Elizabeth is predominantly blue-rich relative to AM1.5d, with seasonal variations. Measurements revealed temperature differences of approximately 10 °C between cells along the edge and in the centre of the module, resulting in power variations of up to 0.328 W. Positional displacement showed that small lateral x–y misalignments had a limited effect on Voc and Isc, but a noticeable influence on power. Variations in cell height with respect to the Fresnel lens affected all electrical parameters. Spectral analysis confirmed that a version of the 5C46 cell performed as designed with improved performance in red-rich spectra. These findings emphasise the importance of spectral considerations, effective thermal management, and accurate optical alignment in the design of CPV modules.
Keywords: Concentrator Photovoltaics, Multi-junction Solar Cell, Spectral Composition, Thermal Effects, Positional Effects

1 INTRODUCTION

Most concentrator photovoltaic (CPV) systems utilise multi-junction solar cells (MJSCs) to efficiently convert solar energy to electricity. MJSCs are sensitive to a variety of factors, including environmental conditions and the cell's position within the module, which influence their behaviour under real-world operational conditions. Thus, to evaluate the MJSCs performance under realistic conditions, AZUR SPACE Solar Power developed and provided a research-based CPV test module, referred to as the Analysis Module [1].

The Analysis Module is deployed at the Outdoor Research Facility of Nelson Mandela University (NMU) in Port Elizabeth, South Africa. Mounted on a dual-axis tracker, the Analysis Module is adjacent to the modules it replicates. The baseline modules form part of a C3PV system which is a commercial 4 kW CPV system franchised by AZUR SPACE Solar Power [2], [3]. To provide a detailed comparative performance analysis of MJSCs, the Analysis Module contains sixty MJSCs manufactured by AZUR SPACE Solar Power, which vary in the number of junctions, subcell current balance and position within the module. This study focuses on the performance of two variations of the 5C46 CPV cell (5-Ja and 5-Jf) under varying spectral, temperature, and positional conditions.

MJSC performance depends on both the magnitude of the direct normal irradiance (DNI) and its spectral composition. Spectral composition, impacted by time of day, season and atmospheric conditions, influences the photon flux incident on each subcell and consequently affects overall MJSC power output.

Port Elizabeth is well-suited for studying the impact of solar spectrum on MJSCs due to its geographical position as a coastal town producing variability in the environmental conditions. Despite frequent cloud cover limiting the power production from CPV systems, the area experiences variations in temperature, aerosol concentrations and water vapour concentration, which make it ideal for MJSCs and CPV system testing.

In addition to the impacts of DNI and spectral composition, the operating temperature plays a critical role in determining MJSC performance. Although MJSCs are typically made from materials with larger band gaps than silicon cells, an increase in operating temperature causes a narrowing of the band gap in the semiconductor material and ultimately reduces the open-circuit voltage (Voc) of MJSCs [4]. Thus, higher operating temperatures lead to a loss of power for the MJSC.

Beyond environmental influencing factors, positional variations of the MJSCs relative to the Fresnel lens may occur during the assembly of the module and can impact the performance of the MJSCs. Misalignments of the enhanced Fresnel assembly (EFA), comprising the MJSC and secondary lens, can be both an x–y positional displacement on the module backsheet or a variation in the cell- Fresnel lens distance. Both types of displacement can alter the spectral and thermal conditions experienced by the cell, ultimately impacting its power.

Thus, the purpose of this study is to investigate the influence of environmental and positional conditions on the performance of two variations of the 5C46 cell. The research focuses on the influence of spectral composition, operational temperature variations, and cell position in the module during operational conditions.

2 THEORY

Average Photon Energy (APE), Equation 1, is a simple, single-unit measurement used to classify the solar spectral composition by comparing the integral of spectral composition $E(\lambda)$ to the integral of photon flux $\varphi(\lambda)$ [5]. Spectra can be compared to a reference spectrum, where spectra with higher APE values are considered blue-shifted, whilst lower APE values are considered red-shifted. A comparison can be IEC standard spectral composition AM1.5d, with APE = 1.545 eV for the wavelength range of 290-1800 nm.

10.4229/EUPVSEC2025/4DV.1.41
020416-001

$$APE = \frac{\int_{\lambda_a}^{\lambda_b} E(\lambda)\, d\lambda}{q \times \int_{\lambda_a}^{\lambda_b} \varphi(\lambda)\, d\lambda} \quad (eV) \tag{1}$$

Although APE values provide a convenient single-value metric for complex spectral comparison and are indicative of spectral shifts, it does not directly translate to photovoltaic power output [6], [7]. This limitation arises because APE values average the spectral information, masking variability and ultimately obscuring the effects of features such as water vapor absorption and aerosol optical depth on the spectral composition. Consequently, APE values can be used as a qualitative measurement and must be complemented with detailed spectral and performance analyses.

APE values vary by region, reflecting the local atmospheric and environmental conditions. Desert locations often exhibit red-rich spectra with lower APE values, whereas high-altitude or low-aerosol regions, such as Lima, Peru, are characterised by blue-rich spectra with APE values as high as 1.920 to 1.930 eV [8].

The operating temperature of a solar cell has a well-established effect on performance. In single-junction solar cells, elevated temperatures reduce both the open-circuit voltage (Voc) and fill factor (FF) due to an increased intrinsic carrier concentration and enhanced recombination rates within the semiconductor material [4]. For MJSCs, these thermal effects are even more pronounced. Because each subcell operates at a different band gap, temperature-induced changes can lead to current mismatch among subcells, thereby adding to the overall power loss. Additionally, an increase in operating temperature results in an increase in the current at the maximum power point (Imp) of a solar cell.

Finally, positional displacement of MJSCs relative to the focal point can affect device performance. Displacement may occur during module assembly, from mechanical stress or from thermal warping of the module backsheet. Such misalignments can manifest either as x-y displacements on the module backsheet or as deviations in the cell–lens distance. In both cases, the spectral distribution on the cell surface and the cell's thermal conditions are altered, ultimately influencing its electrical output [9].

3 EXPERIMENTAL PROCEDURE

To evaluate the performance of the 5C46 cells, producing approximately 7 W of power under full concentrated sunlight, both electrical and environmental parameters were measured using the Analysis Module. The collected data were subsequently filtered and analysed to determine the impact of spectral composition, operational temperature and cell displacement on MJSC performance.

3.1 Analysis Module

Designed and provided by AZUR SPACE Solar Power, the Analysis Module replicates the base structure of a C3PV module, a commercial CPV system. It is a compound refractive module consisting of sixty EFAs, a Fresnel lens and an aluminium module housing [1]. Each MJSC varies in the number of junctions, subcell current balance and position within the module. This study focuses on 2 variations of the 5C46 illustrated in Figure 1. These are the 5-Ja and 5-Jf, adapted for AM1.5d and red-rich

spectra according to AZUR SPACE Solar Power.

To monitor positional displacement of the MJSCs as a height variation from the Fresnel lens, the Analysis Module is constructed with 4 separate panels, which are indicated in Figure 1. The panels are 0 mm (no deviation from a C3PV module), -1.8 mm (decreased MJSC to Fresnel lens distance), +2.2 mm (increased MJSC to Fresnel lens distance), and +4.4 mm (further increased MJSC to Fresnel lens distance).

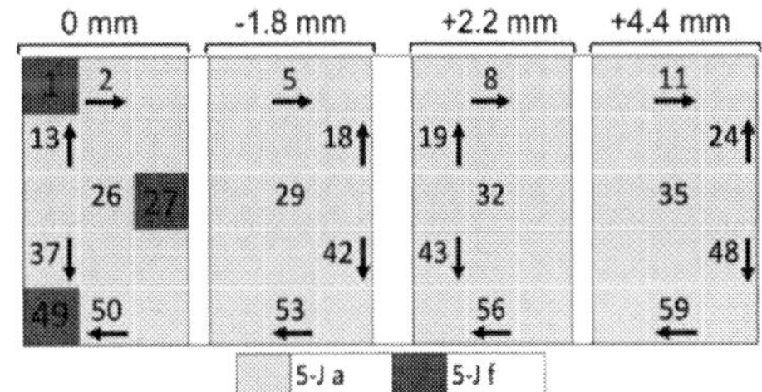

Figure 1: Simplified diagram of the cells within the Analysis Module.

Due to the construction of the Analysis Module, panels -1.8 mm and +2.2 mm are partially thermally isolated from the module housing, whereas the cells on panels $\Delta 0$ mm and +4.4 mm are secured directly to the backsheet of the aluminium housing and thus benefit from the heat-sinking capabilities of the surrounding housing. Additionally, unlike power-producing C3PV modules, the Analysis Module does not deliver electricity to a load. As a result, the MJSCs operate at different temperatures within the Analysis Module and operate at temperatures higher than those observed in the adjacent C3PV modules.

For the temperature analysis, the 5C46 cells, 5-Jf in Figure 1, are examined. The cells are located on the $\Delta 0$ mm panel and positioned on the outer edge (cells 1 and 49) and towards the centre (cell 27) of the panel.

For the cell displacement and spectral analysis, the 5C46 5-Ja cells, in Figure 1, are examined. The x-y-displacement consists of cells that have a ±2 mm shift, as well as a reference cell on the panel that has no shift from the position optimised during the design of the C3PV modules. Replicating possible variations that could occur in the placement of the MJSC in a CPV module during the assembly or due to a mechanical strain of the backsheet allows for an understanding of the tolerances of cell misalignment.

3.2. Experimental Method

Measured data was collected from the Analysis Module, including electrical measurements comprising Voc, short-circuit current (Isc), Imp and the voltage at the maximum power point (Vmp). Simultaneously, it records environmental parameters, such as backsheet temperature and, using a Spectrafy D2 sensor, it determines DNI and solar spectral composition.

Following data collection, APE was calculated for every solar spectrum, using equation 1, and the measurement data was then filtered to remove incorrect measurements and false readings. The data is limited to above 500 W/m², after 09h00 and before 15h00. Due to the placement of the Analysis Module at the bottom of the tracker, the data was limited to remove data entries with module or Spectrafy D2 sensor shading.

For the temperature analysis, thermal images were taken of the Analysis Module at 14h30 on 17 January 2025 under clear sky conditions. The three 5C46 cells, 1, 27, and 49, were identified, and the corresponding backsheet temperatures and electrical data were compared.

To evaluate positional misalignment effects, both lateral displacement and height variation to the Fresnel lens, 20 cells with 5 cells per panel were examined. The data was compared to understand the impact of positional tolerances on MJSC performance.

For the spectral analysis, two reference spectra, whose APE values are shown in Figure 2, were selected to represent red-shifted and blue-shifted spectral conditions in Port Elizabeth. These were defined as the median spectra of all data entries with APE values below and above AM1.5d, respectively. All measurement data were filtered relative to these reference spectra. Pmp normalised by DNI (a proxy for efficiency) was then compared against the cell performance at AM1.d.

4 RESULTS AND DISCUSSION

Port Elizabeth provides an ideal testing ground due to the wide range of solar spectral compositions experienced. In this section, the impacts of spectral composition, operating temperature, and positional displacement on MJSC performance are presented.

4.1 Solar Spectrum in Port Elizabeth

The distribution of APE values for Port Elizabeth, shown in Figure 2, was determined from January 2024 to August 2025, with data recorded between 09h00 and 15h00. The yearly APE values for Port Elizabeth are clustered around AM1.5d, with the yearly median APE slightly above the APE value of AM1.5d (1.545 eV). Thus, Port Elizabeth is a predominantly blue-rich region, for data entries above 500 W/m², when compared to AM1.5d. However, when compared to sites such as Lima, Peru, with APE values as high as 1.930 eV [8], Port Elizabeth appears relatively red-rich.

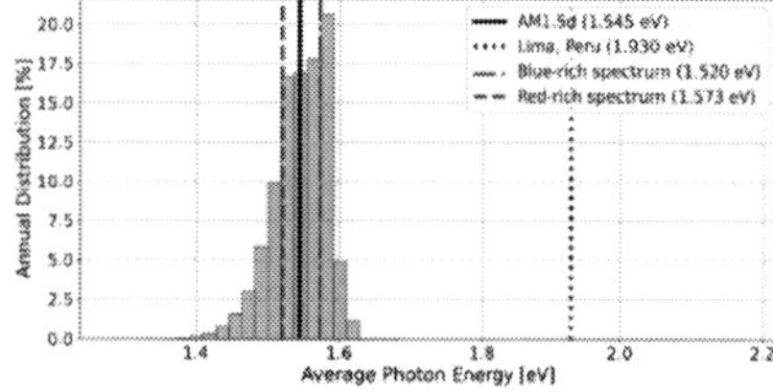

Figure 2: Distribution of APE values for Port Elizabeth. For comparison, the APE of AM1.5d, the maximum APE reported for Lima, Peru [8], and the representative red-rich and blue-rich spectra for Port Elizabeth are shown.

Table I provides a comparison of the median monthly APE values for Port Elizabeth. There is a seasonal variation with an APE difference of 0.063 eV between the highest and lowest months. This indicates measurable seasonal spectral shifts, making Port Elizabeth a suitable environment for the spectral analysis of MJSCs and CPV modules.

Table I. Median monthly APE values for Port Elizabeth, with comparison to AM1.5d.

Month	Median APE [eV]	Comparison to AM1.5d [%]
January	1.578	2.129
February	1.580	2.281
March	1.576	2.040
April	1.570	1.579
May	1.541	-0.269
June	1.525	-1.282
July	1.526	-1.237
August	1.517	-1.795
September	1.526	-1.223
October	1.532	-0.831
November	1.570	1.647
December	1.573	1.815

4.2 Temperature Variations on MJSC Performance

Temperature measurements of three 5C46 cells (cells 1, 27, and 49), on the Δ0 mm panel, revealed operating temperature differences. These differences are illustrated in the thermal image of the back of the Analysis Module, Figure 3, captured at 14h30 on 17 January 2025. The cells near the edges (cells 1 and 49) exhibited lower operating temperatures due to additional heat sinking from the module housing, while the central cell (cell 27) was approximately 10 °C hotter. This temperature distribution is noticed in the C3PV module, where the cells on the outer edge are cooler than the central cells.

Additionally, visible in Figure 3 is the increased temperature of the cells on the -1.8 mm panel. The -1.8 mm and +2.2 mm exhibited increased temperatures because of poor thermal contact with the aluminium housing. As such, the MJSCs on panel -1.8 mm operate at temperatures hotter than those on the Δ0 mm panel.

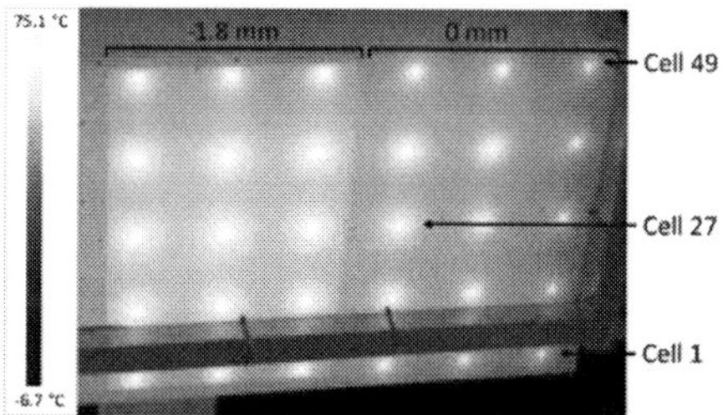

Figure 3: Thermal image of the Analysis Module taken at 14h30 on 17 January 2025. The investigated cells, 1, 27 and 49 are shown with temperatures of 66.5 °C, 76.7 °C and 66.1 °C respectively.

The operating temperatures are confirmed by the electrical performance of cells 1, 27, and 49. Table II summarises Isc, Voc, Imp, Vmp, and Pmp, expressed as a difference relative to cell 27. The edge cells, approximately 10 °C cooler, achieved significantly higher Voc values and improved Pmp.

The reduction in Imp for Cell 49 was within measurement uncertainty and is considered negligible compared to the strong impact of temperature on Voc and Vmp.

Furthermore, solar cells commonly increase in Imp with an increase in temperature, and the situation is more complex for MJSCs. In this case, the 5-Jf, adapted for red-rich spectra, was mostly used under blue-rich conditions.

Consequently, the uppermost solar cell, which benefits most from the bandgap shift at elevated temperatures, was seldom current limiting. Under red-rich spectra, the Imp and temperature relationship may show a strong positive relation.

Table II. Electrical parameters for cells 1, 27, 49 on the $\Delta 0$ mm panel. The parameters are given as a percentage difference to cell 27. Data was taken between 14h15 and 14h45 on the 17 January 2025 at a DNI of 886.59 W/m^2.

		Cell		
Parameter		1	27	49
Isc	[A]	0,014	0,000	0,014
Voc	[V]	0,180	0,000	0,187
Imp	[A]	0,015	0,000	-0,004
Vmp	[V]	0,186	0,000	0,190
Pmp	[W]	0,328	0,000	0,250
FF	[-]	0,006	0,000	-0,005

These results confirm the sensitivity of MJSC performance to operating temperature. Thus, emphasis must be placed on the importance of thermal management in CPV module design, as the location of the cell within the module can impact its performance.

4.2 Spectral and Positional Variations on MJSC Performance

To assess the effect of MJSC displacement, five cells were analysed on each panel corresponding to a 2mm shift up, right, down and left. The electrical characteristics, including Voc, Isc and Pmp were considered for the filtered data.

Positional displacement had minimal impact on Voc, as shown in Figure 4. The cells, on the 0 mm panel, showed maximum Voc variations of approximately 1 %. The altered panels showed a maximum variation of approximately 3 %. Additionally, the effect of an increased operational temperature is further illustrated for the Voc of cells 26, 32, 35. Situated in the middle of their respective panel, they performed worse than the surrounding cells.

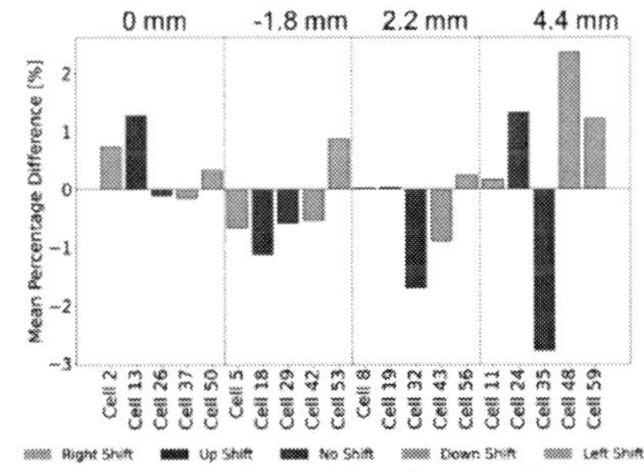

Figure 4: Voc of displaced 5-Ja cells at AM1.5d.

With an average Isc of approximately 1.3 A, the variations in current were varied across all panels. The cells on the 0 mm panel experienced the lowest variations in Isc, indicating the 0 mm panel has the best tolerance for misalignment. Additionally, the -1.8 mm panel showed an increased Isc for all cells indicating an improved performance for shorter variations of heights between the Fresnel lens and MJSC.

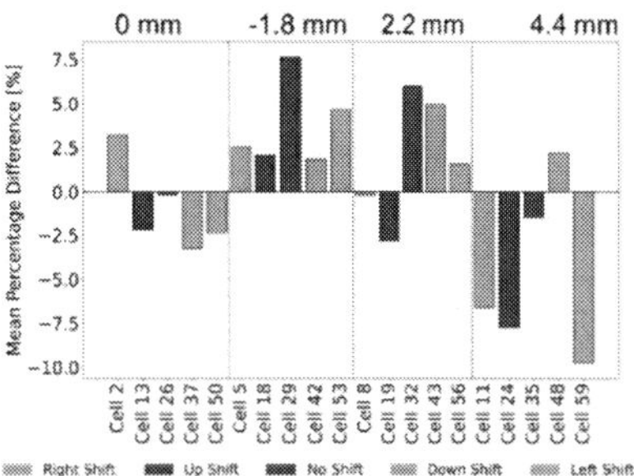

Figure 5: Isc of displaced 5-Ja cells at AM1.5d.

Pmp was sensitive to displacement as a combination of both Imp and Vmp. On the 0 mm panel, differences of less than 8 % were observed, whilst a maximum approximately 13 % was observed on the adjusted panels.

These findings highlight the importance of precise cell placement during module assembly. Small misalignments can cause significant performance variations and significant influences on electrical output.

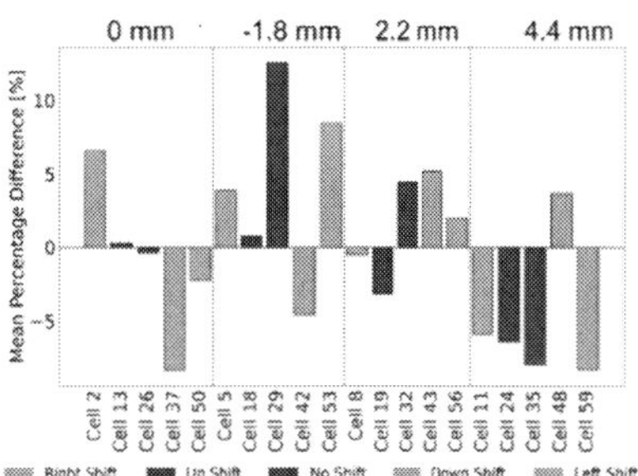

Figure 6: Pmp of displaced 5-Ja cells at AM1.5d.

Finally, the influence of the spectrum is shown for the Pmp normalised by DNI (a proxy for efficiency) of the displaced cells, 5-Ja, which are adapted for current matching at AM1.5, in Figure 7. As expected, the 5C46 generally performed well at AM1.5d, with little performance variation shown for any cell in the red-rich spectrum.

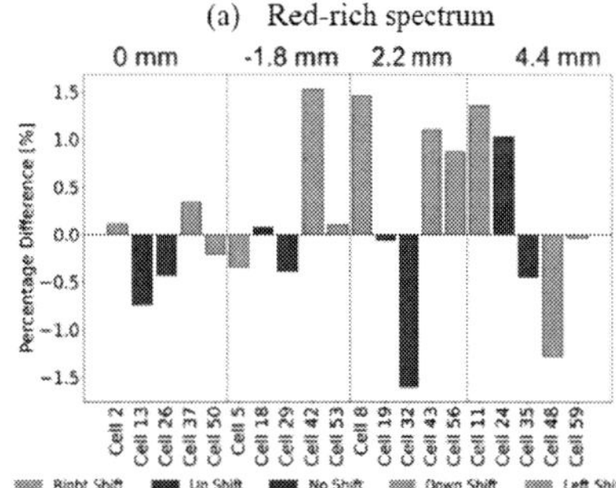

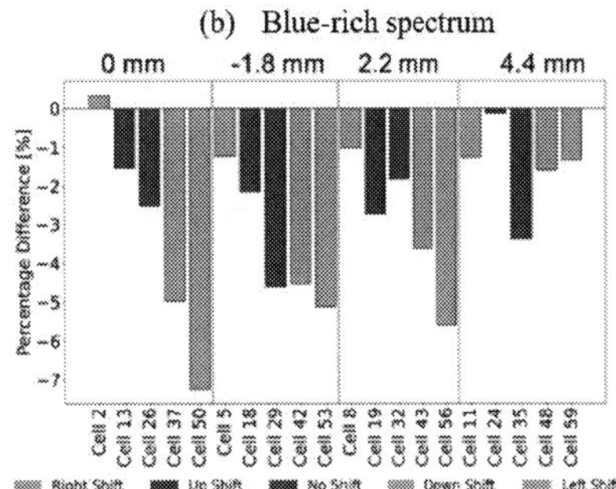

Figure 7: Impact of spectral composition Pmp normalised to DNI of the displaced 5-Ja cells under (a) red-rich and (b) blue-rich conditions as compared to AM1.5d.

5 CONCLUSION

Utilising the Analysis Module, built and provided by AZUR SPACE Solar Power and deployed in Port Elizabeth, the electrical and environmental parameters for the 5C46, an MJSC manufactured by AZUR SPACE Solar Power, were analysed. This study focused on the influence of spectral composition, operating temperature, and positional alignment on the performance of the 5C46 cell.

The solar spectral data and the respective APE values determined that Port Elizabeth is a blue-rich region compared to AM1.5d, however, when compared to other sites such as Lima, Peru, it tends to be quite red. Additionally, seasonal shifts in APE highlight the region's suitability for spectral studies.

Thermal imaging and electrical measurements confirmed the temperature dependence of an MJSC. A temperature difference of approximately 10 °C between central and edge cells led to power variations up to 0.328 W, primarily driven by changes in Voc. These results underline the importance of thermal management in CPV module design.

Positional displacement experiments revealed that small misalignments in the x–y plane had minimal influence on Voc and Isc, but more significant effects on power output (Pmp). Variations in cell-Fresnel lens distance also altered both spectral distribution and thermal conditions, resulting in electrical parameters varying across the panels in the Analysis Module. The results confirm that the C3PV module is well aligned.

Spectral effects showed that the 5-Ja variation of the 5C46 cell performed as expected. As it was adapted for AM1.5d, it performed well under these conditions. Additionally, little variation was shown for red-rich conditions, and a reduced performance is noted under blue-rich conditions.

Overall, this study underscores the importance of accounting for spectral composition during MJSC design, operating temperatures during the module design and the importance of accurate cell placement during assembly of the module.

6 ACKNOWLEDGEMENTS

The authors wish to acknowledge assistance from colleagues and financial support from Nelson Mandela University and AZUR SPACE Solar Power.

7 REFERENCES

[1] R. F. Loeckenhoff and P. Schroth, "Comprehensive analysis of the interactions between a concentrating photovoltaics (CPV) module and 5-junction solar cells: indoor and outdoor sub-cell current measurements," in *40th European Photovoltaic Solar Energy Conference and Exhibition*, 2023. doi: 10.4229/EUPVSEC2023/4CP.3.3.

[2] AZUR SPACE Solar Power GmbH, "C3PV Concentrator PV System - 5C37S," Feb. 2021.

[3] R. F. Loeckenhoff, A. Endress, and W. Bensch, "C3PV: Mass Produced EFA Receivers for a Franchised Module Technology," Mar. 2021. Accessed: Mar. 06, 2025. [Online]. Available: https://www.azurspace.com/index.php/en/company/company-publications

[4] V. M. Andreev, V. A. Grilikhes, and V. D. Rumyantsev, *Photovoltaic conversion of concentrated sunlight*. Chichester: John Wiley and Sons, 1997.

[5] L. A. Conde, J. R. Angulo, M. Sevillano-Bendezú, G. Nofuentes, J. A. Töfflinger, and J. de la Casa, "Spectral effects on the energy yield of various photovoltaic technologies in Lima (Peru)," *Energy*, vol. 223, May 2021, doi: 10.1016/j.energy.2021.120034.

[6] G. Nofuentes, C. A. Gueymard, J. Aguilera, M. D. Pérez-Godoy, and F. Charte, "Is the average photon energy a unique characteristic of the spectral distribution of global irradiance?" *Solar Energy*, vol. 149, pp. 32–43, 2017, doi: 10.1016/j.solener.2017.03.086.

[7] E. M. Hagemann, F. J. Vorster, and E. Ernest Van Dyk, "A methodology for evaluating the performance of a concentrator photovoltaic module," in *SASEC 2024 Proceedings*, SPRINGER Energy Proceedings, 2025.

[8] C. Cornaro and A. Andreotti, "Influence of Average Photon Energy index on solar irradiance characteristics and outdoor performance of photovoltaic modules," *Progress in Photovoltaics: Research and Applications*, vol. 21, no. 5, pp. 996–1003, Aug. 2013, doi: 10.1002/PIP.2194.

[9] F. Vorster, "On the evaluation of a photovoltaic concentrator system," Magister Scientiae, University of Port Elizabeth, 2001.

EPOXY RESIN AND FIBERGLASS TO INTEGRATE PV INTO TERRESTRIAL ELECTRIC VEHICLES

Fernando Castro-Gallardo[1, 2]* Jorge Rabanal-Arabach[1, 2], Sebastían Rodríguez-Romero[1, 2], Sonia Beltran-Condori[1, 2], Natalia Videla-Magnata[1, 2] and Edward Fuentealba-Vidal[1, 2]

[1] University of Antofagasta, Av. Angamos 601, 1270300 Antofagasta, Chile.
[2] Solar Energy Research Center, Tupper 2007, 8370451 Santiago, Chile.
* email: fernando.castro.gallardo@ua.cl

ABSTRACT: Epoxy–fiberglass laminates are evaluated as glass-free encapsulation for vehicle-integrated photovoltaics (VIPV). Two commercial epoxies were characterized on cured films (FT-IR, ASTM E96 WVTR at 40 °C, push-rod dilatometry CTE, and ASTM D638 tensile). Six back-contact c-Si cells (Maxeon Gen III) were encapsulated between epoxy layers on a fiberglass backing to build 2×3 mini-modules (MIMOs). Outdoor I–V and electroluminescence (EL) were recorded before and after single-axis vibration. MEPSOLARIS-1350 exhibited ~ 4× lower WVTR than MEPOX-441; MEPOX-441 showed a linear CTE of 48.2 ± 15.9 ppm K^{-1} (25–60 °C). The MEPOX-441 MIMO retained $\approx$97% of HALM-translated P_{MPP} post-vibration with unchanged EL maps, indicating no electrically active cracking at the tested excitation. Results support epoxy–fiberglass glass-free stacks as a viable path for VIPV prototypes and highlight barrier/thermomechanical trade-offs for scaling.
Keywords: VIPV, glass-free laminate, epoxy–fiberglass, I–V and EL, vibration durability

1 Introduction

Vehicle-integrated photovoltaics (VIPV) aims to harvest solar energy directly on the vehicle envelope (roof, hood, body panels) to extend range and reduce grid dependence [1, 2]. Unlike building-integrated modules, VIPV requires lightweight constructions, tight curvature conformity, and resistance to vibration and thermal cycling, eliminating the glass cover is attractive for mass and integration, but raises challenges in barrier performance, adhesion, and mechanical reliability [3].

Epoxy systems are promising encapsulants for glass-free laminates due to their processability, adhesion and stiffness, especially when combined with fiberglass reinforcement [4]. However, moisture ingress (quantified by water vapor transmission rate, WVTR) and thermo-mechanical mismatch with crystalline silicon can limit durability through corrosion, debonding, and micro-cracking [5]. A materials stack must therefore balance: (i) low WVTR; (ii) compatible coefficients of thermal expansion (CTE) with c-Si; and (iii) adequate strength and stiffness under dynamic loads [6].

This work evaluates two epoxy formulations MEPOX 441 and MEPSOLARIS 1350. We first characterize moisture barrier via ASTM E96 water-cup test at 40 °C [7], and assess CTE [8] and tensile properties [9]. We then fabricate six-cell MIMOs with IBC cells and evaluate electrical performance (I–V, EL) before and after vibration. The results quantify trade-offs between barrier and mechanical behavior and demonstrate feasibility for VIPV prototypes.

The manuscript is structured as follows: Section 2 describes materials and methods, including WVTR testing; Section 3 presents results and discussions; Section 4 summarizes conclusions and implications for full-size panels.

2 Materials and Methods

This work comprises three methodological blocks. First, the encapsulation materials are characterized chemically and physico-mechanically (FT-IR, WVTR, CTE, uniaxial tensile) on cured epoxy specimens. Second, glass-free mini-modules (MIMOs) are fabricated by encapsulating six back-contact c-Si cells between epoxy layers with a fiberglass backing. Third, the MIMOs are evaluated electrically and for durability by pre-

and post-vibration I–V and EL under controlled conditions.

2.1 Materials characterization
2.1.1 Materials and specimen preparation

Two commercial epoxy systems were investigated as encapsulants: MEPOX 441 Cristal and MEPSOLARIS 1350. Resins and hardeners were mixed according to the manufacturers' instructions, cast on flat glass molds and cured at 60 °C for 8 h, followed by >24 h at room temperature before machining. Unless otherwise noted, coupons were taken from the same cast sheets to ensure comparable thermal and curing history.

Specimens for each characterization were prepared as follows: (i) FT-IR (ATR): flat films (~1 mm) with smooth surfaces; contact area was cleaned with isopropyl alcohol prior to measurement. (ii) WVTR: circular discs (film thickness ~1 mm) sized to seal a 3D-printed ASTM E96 cup (effective inner diameter 50 mm) using a TPU gasket; an ABS polymer disc was used only as a methodological reference. (iii) CTE: cylindrical pins with flat, parallel ends (reference length L_0 measured to ±0.01 mm), suitable for push-rod dilatometry. (iv) Tensile: ASTM D638 type IV dog-bones cut from the cast sheets (thickness ~1 mm).

For prototype mini-modules, six back-contact c-Si cells (SunPower Maxeon Gen III) were encapsulated between epoxy layers with a fiberglass fabric backing acting as a glass-free structural substrate. All dimensions reported in the analysis correspond to the measured values of each specimen.

2.1.2 Fourier-transform infrared spectroscopy (FT-IR)

FT-IR spectra were recorded in attenuated total reflectance (ATR) on a Nicolet Avatar 330 (Thermo Electron). Cured epoxy films (flat surfaces, thickness ~1 mm) were pressed against a diamond ATR crystal (45°). For each resin, at least $n = 2$ spectra were measured and averaged (32 scans per spectrum, $4\,cm^{-1}$ resolution) over $4\,000\,cm^{-1}$ to $600\,cm^{-1}$. A fresh background was acquired before each series; spectra were baseline-corrected and ATR-corrected. To enable between-material comparison, intensities were normalized to the aromatic ring band at $1\,508\,cm^{-1}$.

2.1.3 Water Vapor Transmission Rate (WVTR)

WVTR was measured according to ASTM E96/E96M [7] in the upright *water-cup* configuration. 3D-printed cups with an effective inner diameter of 50 mm ($A = 1.9635 \times 10^{-3}$ m^2) were used; the water level was kept 10–15 mm below the specimen. Epoxy films (thickness ~1 mm) were sealed with a TPU gasket and weighed on an analytical balance, with the assembly placed on a 40 °C hot plate. After discarding the initial transient, a linear model $m(t) = a+bt$ (least squares) was fitted to the steady regime; the slope $|b|$ (g h^{-1}) was converted to

$$\text{WVTR} = \frac{|b|}{A} \times 24 \quad \left[\text{g m}^{-2}\,\text{day}^{-1}\right].$$

For each material we report WVTR and the fit coefficient R^2. An ABS polymer was included as a methodological reference.

2.1.4 Coefficient of thermal expansion (CTE)

Linear CTE was measured with a push-rod dilatometer (Orton DIL 1412 STD) according to ASTM E228 [8]. Cylindrical specimens with flat, parallel ends (reference length $L_0 \approx 25$ mm, measured to ±0.01 mm) were ramped at $3\,°\text{C min}^{-1}$. The instrument records ExpPLC (percent linear change) versus temperature. CTE was obtained from a least-squares fit of the linear region (25–60 °C, below T_g), converting percent to fraction as

$$\alpha\,[\text{ppm/K}] = \frac{1}{100}\,\frac{d(\text{ExpPLC})}{dT} \times 10^6.$$

Instrument performance was verified with the supplied reference. Results are reported as mean ± SD over n replicates.

2.1.5 Uniaxial tensile testing (ASTM D638)

Uniaxial tensile tests were performed according to ASTM D638 [9] on a Zwick/Roell Z50 universal testing machine (50 kN) with flat grips. Type IV dog-bone specimens were cut from cast sheets (thickness ~1 mm). Tests were run at a crosshead speed of 1 mm min^{-1} under laboratory conditions. Engineering stress–strain curves were computed from force and grip-to-grip displacement. Young's modulus E was obtained by a least-squares fit to the initial linear region (typically 0.05–0.25% strain), and the yield strength σ_y was determined by the 0.2% offset method. At least $n = 2$ replicates were tested per resin; outliers were screened with a median–absolute–deviation (MAD) criterion and discarded when $|z_{\text{MAD}}| > 3$.

2.2 Mini-module fabrication

2.2.1 Stack architecture

Six back-contact c-Si cells (SunPower Maxeon Gen III; $125 \times 125 \times 0.175$ mm) [10] were arranged in a 2×3 matrix with 1 mm inter-cell gaps and a 10 mm perimeter margin, giving an internal footprint of 273×401 mm. The glass-free laminate—from front (exposed side) to back—consisted of: epoxy encapsulant (front layer) / solar cells / epoxy encapsulant (rear layer) / fiberglass backing acting as a structural substrate and backsheet substitute. An RTV silicone casting mold with internal dimensions $273 \times 401 \times 5$ mm (external $293 \times 421 \times 10$ mm) controlled geometry, providing nominal epoxy cover layers of ~1 mm above and below the cell matrix and a fiberglass backing thickness of 1 mm (shown Fig.1).

2.2.2 Encapsulation process and curing

Only the epoxy system (MEPOX 441) was used for MIMO encapsulation. The RTV mold was conditioned with release wax and PVA. Resin and hardener were mixed at 2:1 (A:B) by weight, stirred for ~3 min while scraping the cup walls, and

Fig. 1: Exploded view of the glass-free MIMO

allowed to rest for 2–3 min to promote bubble release. A first ~1 mm epoxy layer was poured slowly (edge-to-center) to wet the surface; the pre-interconnected 2×3 cell matrix was aligned on the wet epoxy; a second ~1 mm epoxy layer was applied; and the pre-molded fiberglass backing (1 mm) was placed onto the rear wet layer to achieve bonding. Air entrapment was minimized by slow pouring and a short dwell before handling; critical surfaces were cleaned with isopropyl alcohol. Laminates were cured for **24 h at 27 °C** under laboratory conditions (20–25 °C, 40–60 % RH). After cure, modules were demolded, edge-trimmed and visually inspected (voids/delamination); thickness and mass were recorded for traceability. (show Fig. 2).

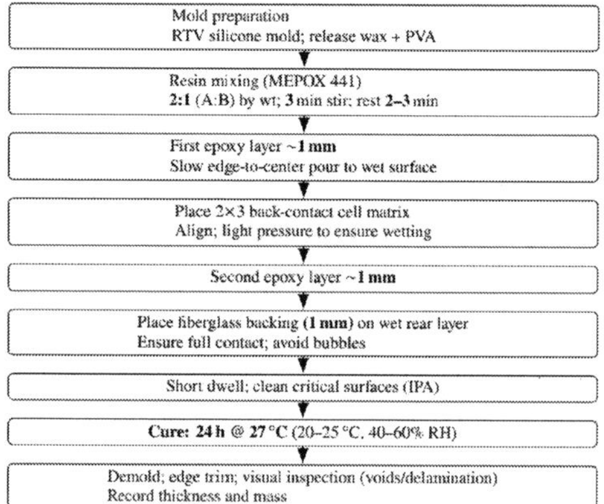

Fig. 2: Encapsulation process and curing workflow for epoxy–fiberglass MIMOs (MEPOX 441).

2.3 Performance and durability assessment

2.3.1 Electrical performance (I–V)

I–V curves were measured with a H.A.L.M. *cetisPV Outdoortest* tracer under natural sunlight in accordance with IEC 60904-1 [11]. Plane-of-array irradiance was monitored by a calibrated c-Si reference cell mounted coplanar with the MIMO, and the back-surface temperature T_{mod} by a PT1000 bonded at the laminate center. The module was connected in four-wire to the tracer. For each MIMO, three single sweeps were recorded within ≤1 min to limit irradiance drift (sweep time ≈0.1–0.2 s, ≥500 points). From each curve we obtained I_{SC}, V_{OC}, P_{MPP} and FF. The measurement setup is shown in Fig. 3.

2.3.2 Electroluminescence (EL) imaging

EL was recorded in a dark enclosure by forward-biasing the mini-modules. Each specimen was imaged *before* and *after* vibration at 2, 3, and 4 A using identical camera settings. Images were saved as 16-bit grayscale without tone mapping; only frames at matching current/exposure were compared.

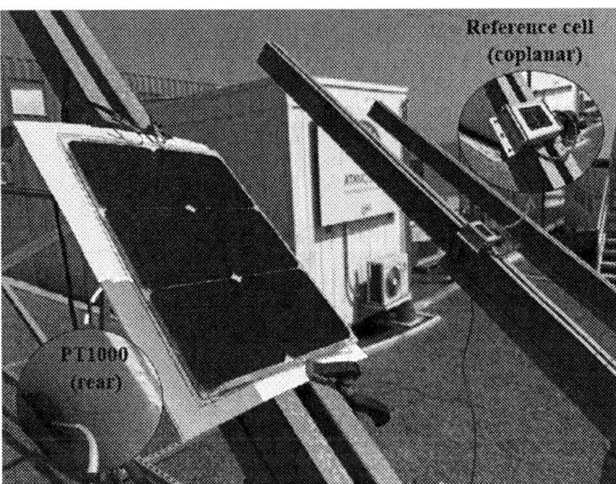

Fig. 3: Outdoor I–V setup with HALM tracer: coplanar reference cell and rear PT1000; four-wire connection to the mini-module.

2.3.3 Vibration test

Mechanical excitation was applied on a custom frame using an unbalanced-mass motor. A module-fixed coordinate system was used with X along the long edge (401 mm), Y along the short edge (273 mm), and Z normal to the laminate. A smartphone accelerometer (iPhone 13, phyphox) was rigidly fixed on the support plate and aligned with X (Table I).

At the selected dial setting, the dominant frequency was $f_0 = 72.4$ Hz with peak (RMS) acceleration $a_{pk} = 1.01$ g ($a_{rms} = 0.68$ g) along X; transverse and out-of-plane components were much smaller (Y: $a_{rms} = 0.13$ g; Z: $a_{rms} = 0.068$ g). Each specimen was exposed for 12 min under X excitation only. Immediately before and after the exposure, I–V and EL were recorded with identical settings.

Table I: Single-axis vibration measured with smartphone (phyphox, iPhone 13).

Axis	a_{rms} [g]	a_{pk} [g]	f_0 [Hz]
X	0.677	1.009	72.4
Y	0.130	0.215	72.4
Z	0.068	0.131	72.4

2.3.4 Post-vibration re-evaluation and acceptance criteria

Immediately after vibration, I–V and EL were repeated with the same protocols and settings. Acceptance was defined a priori as P_{MPP} retention $\geq 90\%$ relative to baseline (same reporting basis: as-measured or IEC 60891-translated) [12] and absence of critical EL-visible defects (e.g., cell fragmentation, extensive dark areas crossing busbars). Statistics are reported as mean ± SD over available replicates.

3 Results and Discussion

3.1 Materials characterization

3.1.1 WVTR at 40°C

Mass–time series exhibited steady-state behavior (linear fits with $R^2 \geq 0.998$). Table II summarizes the slope and the area-normalized WVTR (film thickness ~1 mm).

Under identical conditions (40 °C, Ø 50 mm, $e \approx$ 1 mm), MEPSOLARIS 1350 shows the lowest WVTR (~ 86.7 g m^{-2} day^{-1}), about 4× lower than MEPOX 441, indicating a superior moisture barrier. ABS is reported only as a methodological control and not as an encapsulation candidate.

Table II: WVTR at 40 °C (water-cup, Ø 50 mm).

Material	e (mm)	n (–)	Slope (g h^{-1})	WVTR (g m^{-2} d^{-1})	R^2 (–)
MEPSOLARIS 1350	1.00	1	0.007 10	86.73	0.999 7
MEPOX 441	1.00	1	0.028 66	350.33	0.999 0
ABS (reference)	1.00	1	0.034 09	416.68	0.998 3

Note: ABS was used only as a methodological control (not an encapsulation candidate).

3.1.2 FT-IR results

Both resins exhibit the typical features of cured epoxy networks (Fig. 4). A broad O–H band at $3\,200$ cm^{-1} to $3\,600$ cm^{-1} is present in both materials, consistent with hydroxyl formation upon curing.

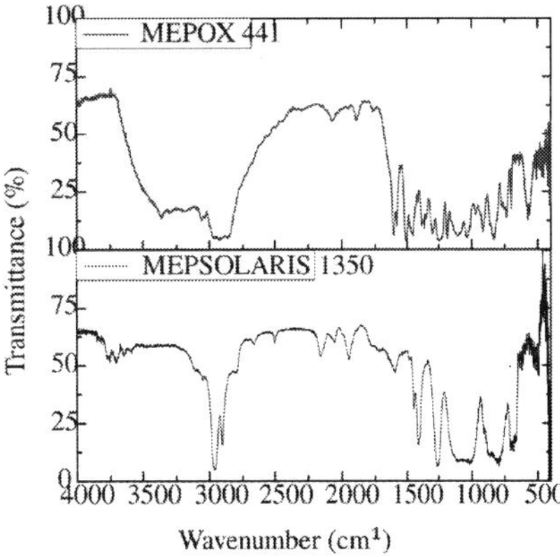

Fig. 4: FT-IR (ATR) of cured resins. Spectra baseline- and ATR-corrected, normalized to the aromatic band at 1508 cm^{-1}.

The ether-related C–O–C band near $1\,240$ cm^{-1} confirms epoxy ring opening. The epoxy-ring breathing at ~ 910 cm^{-1} shows low relative intensity in both spectra, indicative of a high degree of cure under the selected schedule. Compared with MEPOX 441, MEPSOLARIS 1350 displays stronger aliphatic C–H stretching at $2\,925\,2850$ cm^{-1} and an additional carbonyl band near $1\,720$ cm^{-1}, suggestive of ester-containing modifiers. Selected bands and assignments are summarized in Table III.

Table III: Selected FT-IR bands (ATR) and assignments for cured resins. Spectra normalized at 1508 cm^{-1}.

Wavenumber (cm^{-1})	Assignment	Obs.[1]	Note
3200–3600	O–H stretching (hydroxyl, curing)	Both	Broad band.
2925 / 2850	Aliphatic C–H stretching	MS1350	Stronger vs. M441[2].
1720	C=O stretching (ester/additive)	MS1350	Present.
1600	Aromatic C=C stretching	M441	Higher aromatic content.
1508	Aromatic C–H bending (reference)	Both	Normalization band.
1240	C–O–C (ether linkages)	Both	Cure confirmation.
910	Epoxy ring breathing (residual)	Both	Weak in both[3].

[1] Obs.: M441 = MEPOX 441; MS1350 = MEPSOLARIS 1350.
[2] Relative intensity after normalization at 1508 cm^{-1}.
[3] Low 910 cm^{-1} indicates high degree of cure in both resins.

These qualitative differences indicate a more aromatic backbone in MEPOX 441 and a higher aliphatic/ester contribution in MEPSOLARIS 1350. While FT-IR confirms curing and network chemistry, moisture-barrier performance is addressed separately by the WVTR results in Section 3.

3.1.3 CTE results

Table IV summarizes the linear CTE of MEPOX 441 in the 25–60 °C window. The mean value is 48.2 ± 15.9 ppm/K ($n = 3$), which is in the expected range for unfilled epoxies and implies a positive mismatch of ≈46 ppm/K relative to c-Si (~2.6 ppm/K).

Table IV: Linear CTE of MEPOX 441 in 25–60 °C.

Specimen	α (ppm K^{-1})
MEPOX441#1	31.3
MEPOX441#2	50.5
MEPOX441#3	62.8
Mean ± SD ($n = 3$)	**48.2 ± 15.9**

3.1.4 Tensile results

Table V summarizes tensile metrics for the epoxy matrix. For MEPOX 441 ($n = 2$ after MAD screening) we obtained $E \approx 0.438$ GPa and $\sigma_y \approx 1.59$ MPa. MEPSOLARIS 1350 is not reported here because specimens failed at the grips prior to loading; new tests will be performed with soft jaw pads and end tabs to prevent pre-damage.

Table V: Tensile properties of cured epoxy matrix (ASTM D638).

Material	n	E (GPa)	σ_y (MPa)
MEPOX 441	2	0.438	1.59

In the context of the mini-module, these values are typical of unreinforced epoxy networks: the laminate stiffness will be dominated by the fiberglass backing, while the matrix provides adequate elastic response provided operational stresses remain well below ~1 MPa during vibration.

3.2 Mini-module performance

3.2.1 Baseline I–V and EL (pre-vibration)

Figure 5 (gold trace) shows the pre-vibration sweep. The EL map at 4 A (bottom-left panel of Fig. 6) is largely uniform: the consistently brighter top-right cell serves as a visual marker. A representative surface temperature during the acquisition is shown in the top-left panel of Fig. 6.

3.2.2 Post-vibration I–V and EL; P_{MPP} retention

The post sweep (blue in Fig. 5) was taken under different outdoor conditions, hence the as-measured current is lower; a fair comparison uses HALM's STC translation. Relative to baseline, P_{MPP}^{*} is retained at **97%** (14.76 W vs. 14.35 W). Small shifts appear in V_{OC}^{*} (+2.1%), I_{SC}^{*} (+3.2%), and FF^{*} (−2.4%). The post-vibration EL at 4 A (bottom-right panel of Fig. 6) remains qualitatively unchanged, indicating no electrically active cracks at the tested excitation. The corresponding surface temperature is shown in the top-right panel of Fig. 6.

4 Conclusions

We fabricated glass-free epoxy–fiberglass 2 × 3 IBC mini-modules and combined a simple materials screen with a pre/post vibration check using outdoor I–V and EL.

Materials screen (films ~1 mm, 40°C). MEPSOLARIS-1350 exhibited a markedly lower WVTR than MEPOX-441

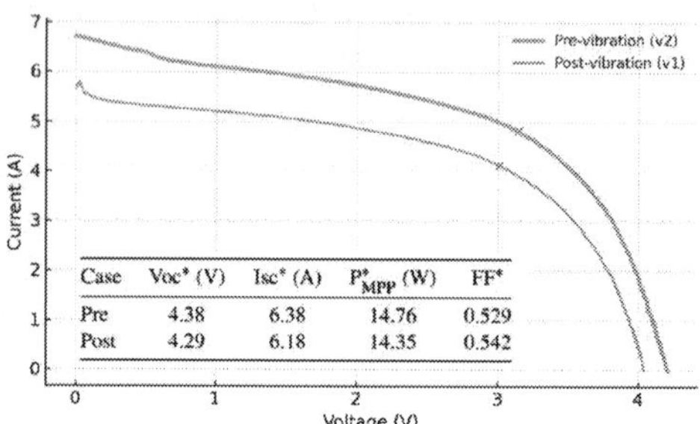

Case	Voc* (V)	Isc* (A)	P_{MPP}^{*} (W)	FF*
Pre	4.38	6.38	14.76	0.529
Post	4.29	6.18	14.35	0.542

Fig. 5: Outdoor I–V, pre (gold) vs post (blue); *as measured* (no STC). Crosses mark the MPP of each sweep.

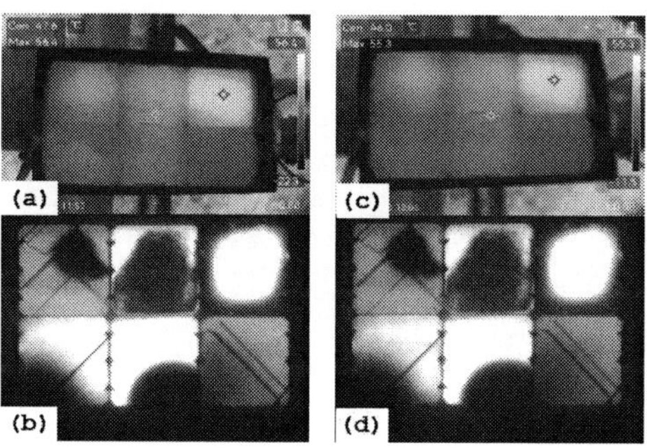

Fig. 6: Thermography (top row) and electroluminescence at 4 A (bottom row) acquired during I–V. Left: pre-vibration; right: post-vibration. Identical camera/current settings were used for pre/post EL.

(86.7 vs. 350.3 g m^{-2} d^{-1}, ~4× difference). MEPOX-441 showed a linear CTE of 48.2 ± 15.9 ppm K^{-1} (25–60°C) and tensile values typical of unfilled epoxies ($E \approx 0.438$ GPa, $\sigma_y \approx 1.59$ MPa).

Module response to vibration. After single-axis excitation (72.4 Hz, 0.68 g$_{\mathrm{rms}}$, 12 min, X axis), the STC-translated power (IEC 60891) was **97%** of baseline and EL at 4 A remained unchanged, indicating no electrically active cracking at the tested level.

Implications. Epoxy–fiberglass stacks are a viable glass-free route for VIPV prototypes. Barrier performance favors MS1350 over M441, while the positive CTE mismatch to c-Si suggests that laminate design (backing thickness/lay-up) and perimeter sealing or barrier coatings will be key for durability.

Next steps. (i) Replace or hybridize the matrix to improve moisture barrier (e.g., MS1350 + edge seals/coatings); (ii) extend to standard reliability sequences (damp-heat 85/85, thermal cycling, UV/optical stability) and to automotive-relevant random vibration; (iii) quantify adhesion/peel and interfacial aging; and (iv) scale to curved demonstrators with energy-yield assessment for VIPV.

Acknowledgments

This work was supported by the Chilean Solar Energy Research Center (SERC Chile) under Grant ANID/FONDAP/1523A0006, the HEUMA ING2030 Project 16ENI2-71940, and the Power Electronics and Electromobility Laboratory (POWEREMLAB). We also acknowledge the Master's Program in Solar Energy at the University of Antofagasta.

References

[1] S. Rodríguez-Romero, J. Rabanal-Arabach, C. A. Rojas, M. Trigo-Gonzalez, G. Mondaca-Cuevas, D. Arias,

F. Castro-Gallardo, and E. Fuentealba-Vidal, "Analysis of advanced nonisolated topologies for vehicle-integrated photovoltaic (vipv) systems in urban electric transport buses," *IEEE Journal of Photovoltaics*, pp. 1–7, 2025.

[2] F. Castro-Gallardo, J. Rabanal-Arabach, S. Rodríguez-Romero, D. Olivares, and E. Fuentealba, "Enhancing electric vehicle autonomy with solar energy: A case study of the "takai urban" in northern chile," *SiliconPV Conference Proceedings*, vol. 2, 2 2025. [Online]. Available: https://www.tib-op.org/ojs/index.php/siliconpv/article/view/1307

[3] S. Kim, M. Holz, S. Park, Y. Yoon, E. Cho, and J. Yi, "Future options for lightweight photovoltaic modules in electrical passenger cars," *Sustainability*, vol. 13, p. 2532, 2021, review; published 26 Feb 2021. [Online]. Available: https://doi.org/10.3390/su13052532

[4] G. Espitia-Mesa, E. Hernández-Pedraza, S. Molina-Tamayo, and R. Mejía-Gutiérrez, "Design, analysis, and modeling of curved photovoltaic surfaces using composite materials," *TecnoLógicas*, vol. 25, no. 53, p. e2171, May 2022. [Online]. Available: https://doi.org/10.22430/22565337.2171

[5] C. Peike, I. Hädrich, K.-A. Weiß, and I. Dürr, "Overview of PV module encapsulation materials," *Photovoltaics International*, no. 19, pp. 85–92, Mar. 2013.

[6] J. Rabanal-Arabach, "Development of a c-si photovoltaic module for desert climates," Ph.D. dissertation, Universität Konstanz, Konstanz, 2019.

[7] ASTM International, "Standard test methods for water vapor transmission of materials," ASTM International, West Conshohocken, PA, ASTM Standard E96/E96M-16, Apr. 2016, historical version. [Online]. Available: https://www.astm.org/e0096_e0096m-16.html

[8] ——, "Standard test method for linear thermal expansion of solid materials with a push-rod dilatometer," ASTM International, West Conshohocken, PA, ASTM Standard E228-22, Dec. 2022, active version. [Online]. Available: https://www.astm.org/e0228-22.html

[9] ——, "Standard test method for tensile properties of plastics," ASTM International, West Conshohocken, PA, ASTM Standard D638-14, Apr. 2014, active version. [Online]. Available: https://www.astm.org/d0638-14.html

[10] R. Kopecek, F. Buchholz, V. D. Mihailetchi, J. Libal, J. Lossen, N. Chen, H. Chu, C. Peter, T. Timofte, A. Halm, Y. Guo, X. Qu, X. Wu, J. Gao, and P. Dong, "Interdigitated back contact technology as final evolution for industrial crystalline single-junction silicon solar cell," *Solar*, vol. 3, pp. 1–14, 2023, open Access (CC BY). [Online]. Available: https://doi.org/10.3390/solar3010001

[11] I. E. C. 60904-1:2020, "Photovoltaic devices. part 1, measurement of photovoltaic current-voltage characteristics," Tech. Rep., 2020.

[12] I. E. C. 60891:2021, "Photovoltaic devices - procedures for temperature and irradiance corrections to measured i-v characteristics," Tech. Rep., 2021.

DESIGN, SIZING, AND SENSORISATION OF AN FPV POWER PLANT AT THE MONTE NOVO DAM, PORTUGAL

Dorivaldo Duarte*[1], Luis Fialho[2], Pedro Horta[1], Sara Pereira[1]

*Corresponding author: duarte@uevora.pt
[1] Renewable Energies Chair, Polo da Mitra da Universidade de Évora, Edifício Ário Lobo de Azevedo, 7000-083 Nossa Senhora da Tourega, Portugal.
[2] Eurac Research, Viale Druso (Drususallee) 1, 39100 Bolzano, Italy

Abstract: This study presents the design for implementation of a floating photovoltaic (FPV) system on the Monte Novo reservoir in Évora, a potable water supply resource. The installation integrates multiple flotation technologies and structural layouts, combined with a dense sensor network for real-time monitoring of environmental parameters, water quality, and energy performance. The work focuses on assessing the mutual impacts between the FPV system and the aquatic ecosystem, while defining robust protocols for safe operation and long-term reliability. In addition, the study explores hybridisation with the electrical grid to strengthen water treatment processes. By addressing technical performance, environmental interactions, and operational integration, the study provides evidence-based insights to guide future FPV projects in sensitive freshwater environments and contributes to advancing sustainable solutions for the water–energy nexus.

Keywords: Floating PV, Water quality, Environmental impact, Aquatic ecosystem, Sensorisation

1. Introduction

FPV systems have attracted significant attention as an innovative and sustainable solution for renewable energy generation. In recent years, FPV systems have experienced rapid growth, both in terms of installed capacity and technological advancements. According to the International Renewable Energy Agency (IRENA), the global installed capacity of floating solar systems surpassed 3.5GW in 2021, with projections indicating an increase to over 27GW by 2030, driven by their cost-effectiveness and efficiency in utilising surfaces that would otherwise remain underutilised [1]. This growth is further supported by advancements in floating structures.

The installation of FPV systems in water bodies designated for human consumption represents a significant advancement in terms of innovation and sustainability, particularly for Portugal, as it requires a high level of sensorisation to continuously monitor several parameters. The results generated will give an important contribution for the development of testing protocols and safety standards for the installation of FPV systems in potable water bodies.

Furthermore, careful integration with sensor systems allows for continuous monitoring of water quality, ensuring that potable water standards are maintained [2] [3].

Continuous sensing of the water properties is crucial to ensure the safety and quality of the potable water supply. Studies have shown that the installation of FPV systems can affect parameters such as temperature, turbidity, and oxygen levels, making real-time monitoring essential to prevent adverse effects on water quality. The integration of FPV systems with advanced sensor and monitoring systems allows its safe and sustainable integration in the water bodies, and can contribute to boost the deployment of this technology in worldwide [4] [5].

2. Methodology

The diagram presents the methodology for implementing a pilot FPV plant in freshwater reservoirs. The process includes reservoir selection considering uses and restrictions, obtaining environmental and water domain permits, system design and sizing (floats, modules, sensors, anchoring, and data acquisition), and finally, energy licensing and plant construction. This approach ensures the technical, environmental, and legal feasibility of the installation, optimising energy utilisation without compromising the reservoir's original function.

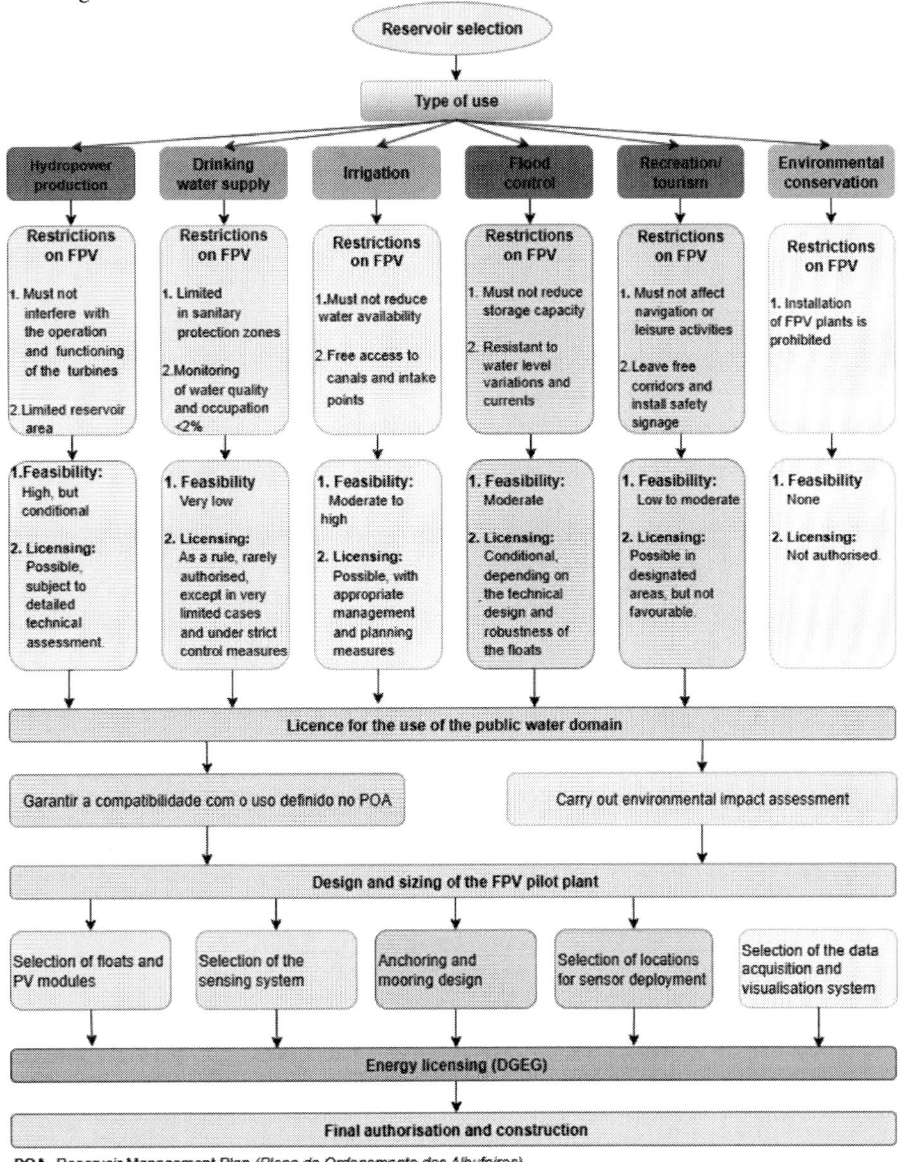

Figure 1. Methodology overview for implementing a pilot FPV plant

3. Description of the FPV system

3.1. Location and Characterisation of the Reservoir

The pilot system will be installed at the Monte Novo Dam (38.514, -7.712), a potable water reservoir whose primary uses include public water supply to the city of Évora, agricultural irrigation as part of the regional hydraulic management system, and flood control. Secondary uses, such as recreational activities and sport fishing, are also present but subject to restrictions. Due to its relative water level stability during the peak solar radiation period (spring and summer), an average depth exceeding 10 metres, and minimal interference with navigation or leisure activities, coupled with its proximity to existing electrical infrastructure, such as substations and medium-voltage lines, the site provides suitable conditions for the installation of the FPV pilot plant and its integration with the existing facilities [6] .

3.2. FPV system configuration

This FPV pilot plant was designed to systematically evaluate the performance of three distinct floating platform technologies across four structural configurations.

I. **System 1:** Features an East–West orientation, with modules arranged in a portrait layout and a fixed tilt between 12° and 15°.

II. **System 2:** Also follows an East–West orientation but utilises a landscape layout with a fixed tilt of 15°.

III. **System 3:** Comprises two variants:

   a) *Variant 1* is south facing, with modules in a landscape layout and an adjustable tilt ranging from 10° to 40°.

   b) *Variant 2* maintains an East–West orientation, landscape layout, and the same adjustable tilt range.

The selection of these configurations allows for a comprehensive assessment of the factors influencing FPV system performance. Variations in orientation and tilt enable the analysis of the effect of solar incidence angles on energy yield and the optimisation of module positioning. Simultaneously, the diversity of structural layouts facilitates the

evaluation of platform stability under dynamic environmental conditions, including wind and water movement. Furthermore, the pilot configuration provides the opportunity to study water surface utilisation, contributing to an understanding of the spatial efficiency of FPV systems while minimising potential ecological and recreational impacts.

By integrating both fixed and adjustable tilt systems, as well as multiple orientations and module arrangements, the pilot establishes a robust experimental framework. This approach supports the investigation of interactions between structural design, environmental conditions, and energy performance, providing critical information to guide the design, optimisation, and deployment of larger-scale FPV installations in similar reservoirs.

The FPV system has been designed with an installed capacity of approximately 200 kW, remaining within the limits for low-voltage energy injection in accordance with Decree-Law No. 15/2022 and Regulation No. 815/2023 [7] [8]. This limitation ensures compatibility with the existing electrical grid and simplifies the licensing and operation procedures of the system.

3.3. Sensorisation

The sensor network was designed to assess the performance of the FPV system, taking into account environmental variables and the conditions of the aquatic environment in which the system is installed. In addition, it enables the monitoring of the FPV system's impacts on the ecosystem, including local fauna and flora, as well as water quality.

I.   *Reservoir bank meteorological Station*

The installation of a meteorological station on the reservoir bank was designed to monitor environmental conditions, system performance, and impacts on the aquatic ecosystem. Solar radiation, wind, temperature, relative humidity, precipitation, and other meteorological parameters will be recorded using the sensors listed in **Table 1**.

Table 1. Set of sensors for the reservoir bank

Description	Qt.
Campbell Scientific CR310 Datalogger	1
Campbell NL241 Wi-Fi Transmitter	2
Solar Radiation Sensor	1
Gill WindSonic Wind Sensor	1
Campbell HyroVue10 Temperature and Relative Humidity Sensor	1
Lambrecht Precipitation Sensor	1
Campbell Present Weather Sensor	1

II.   FPV platform sensor network

The monitoring system is organised into five main categories of sensors: environmental, energy, subsurface, water quality, and operational. Environmental sensors measure variables such as air temperature and humidity, wind speed and direction, and solar radiation. Within the energy component, sensors measuring incoming and reflected solar radiation enable the calculation of albedo and the analysis of the surface energy balance. Subsurface monitoring is conducted using temperature sensors distributed at various depths in the water, allowing the assessment of thermal gradients. For water quality, multiparameter probes measure pH, conductivity, dissolved oxygen, and turbidity. Additionally, inclinometers monitor potential movements of the floating platforms, while automated systems ensure continuous and integrated data acquisition The complete list of sensors and equipment is presented in **Table 2.**

Table 2. FPV platform sensor network

Description	Qt.
Campbell Scientific CR1000X Datalogger	2
Solar Radiation Sensor	7
Pyranometer Mounting Support	7
Solar Radiation Sensor (for albedo)	2
Albedo Kit	1
Wind Sensor with GPS	1
Campbell HyroVue10 Temperature and Relative Humidity Sensor	1
Campbell CS241 Module Temperature Sensor	7
Campbell 109 Depth Temperature Profile Sensors	11
Eureka Water Quality Probe	1
Rion Inclinometer	4

III.   Upstream buoy sensor network relative to the FPV system

In addition to the meteorological and platform instrumentation, specific equipment was installed to characterise the thermal profile of the water column and assess water quality. This includes a Campbell Scientific CR1000X datalogger with a Campbell NL241 Wi-Fi transmitter for data acquisition and transmission, a set of 11 Campbell 109 temperature sensors at different depths, and an Eureka Manta+30a multiparameter probe for water quality monitoring. The complete list of equipment is provided in **Table 3**.

Table 3. Upstream buoy sensor network relative to the FPV system

Description	Qt.
Campbell Scientific CR1000X Datalogger	1
Campbell NL241 Wi-Fi Transmitter	1
Campbell 109 Depth Temperature Profile Sensors	11
Eureka Water Quality Probe	1

IV.   Meteorological station at the water intake

To complement the monitoring system, a Campbell Scientific CR310 datalogger was installed for data acquisition and management, along with a UWT NR7200 level sensor to measure water level variations in the reservoir. The list of equipment is summarised in **Table 4**.

Table 4. Meteorological station at the water intake

Description	Qt.
Campbell Scientific CR310 Datalogger	1
Level Sensor	1

4.   Results and Discussion

The selection of the reservoir represented the first fundamental step of this work, taking into account its geomorphological and environmental characteristics, as well as restrictions related to land and water use. This choice was made through an integrated approach, considering the specific requirements for water quality monitoring and ensuring that the installation FPV system would not compromise the multiple uses of the water resource.

Following this selection, an analysis of the hydrographic characteristics was carried out, along with a bathymetric survey. These data proved essential not only for the design of the mooring and anchoring system but also for assessing the stability of the FPV installation. The analysis ensured that even under scenarios of reduced water levels, down to their minimum values, there would be no risk of structural or operational damage to the system. Based on these results, the design of the FPV pilot plant was developed, including the selection of floater types, module configurations and orientations, and the specification of the necessary instrumentation. This set of equipment addresses both the requirements of water quality monitoring and the assessment of the system's energy performance. The sensor network was designed in conjunction with a data acquisition and visualisation platform, ensuring a continuous flow of information and enabling real-time analysis. **Figure 2** presents a synthesis of these developments.

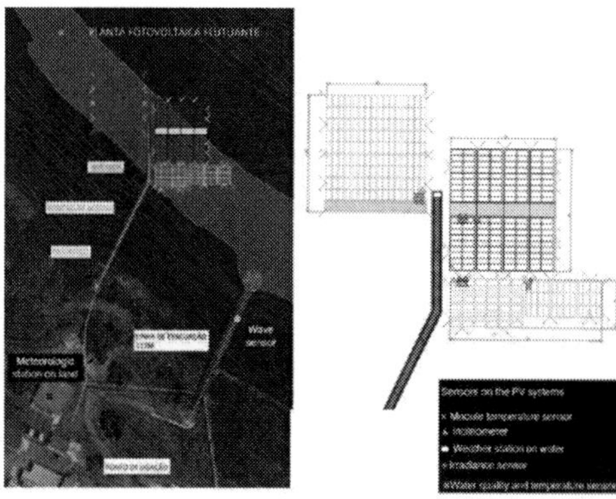

Figure 2. Configuration of the FPV pilot

In parallel with these technical developments, the licensing process was initiated, involving various local and national authorities, including municipalities, environmental conservation agencies, the bodies responsible for the National Agricultural Reserve and the National Ecological Reserve, as well as those with jurisdiction over the reservoir's water domain. It was found that no specific licensing framework currently exists for FPV systems,

and as such, the project was categorised as a conventional photovoltaic power plant. This classification required full compliance with all legal and regulatory requirements applicable to the surrounding environment, making the process more complex and time-consuming. Another important outcome was the preparation of the technical specifications document, which consolidated all the requirements for both the FPV system and the associated instrumentation. This document serves as a key tool to align technical specifications with monitoring needs and to ensure the performance guarantees of the pilot installation.

Regarding the monitoring strategy, the integrated measurement of environmental, hydrological, and operational variables will be crucial for ensuring both the energy efficiency and environmental sustainability of the FPV system. The measurement of incoming and reflected solar radiation will be fundamental for evaluating the performance of the photovoltaic panels and understanding the system's impact on the surface energy balance of the reservoir. Atmospheric parameters such as air temperature, humidity, and wind will influence not only the efficiency of the modules but also the local environmental conditions, including evaporation dynamics.

Furthermore, thermal monitoring at various depths in the water column will allow the identification of temperature gradients that will be essential for assessing potential environmental impacts, such as changes in thermal stratification caused by the floating system. These changes may, in turn, affect water quality, which will be assessed through measurements of pH, dissolved oxygen, and turbidity. These data will provide insight into the possible consequences of shading and surface coverage by the FPV system on aquatic ecosystems.

Finally, operational sensors, such as inclinometers and water level sensors, will play a key role in the early detection of structural movements and variations, ensuring the safety and stability of the floating platforms. The continuous integration and acquisition of all monitoring data will support more efficient and proactive management of the system, serving as a critical tool for optimising operation while minimising environmental impacts.

5. Conclusions

The implementation of FPV systems in water supply reservoirs presents significant challenges, as it requires balancing energy efficiency, water security, and environmental protection. Currently, no licensing framework exists specifically for FPV installations, making each project subject to rigorous evaluation. In this context, the proposed installation demands a robust sensor network to continuously monitor the interactions between the pilot FPV plant and the surrounding ecosystem, including environmental parameters and water quality.

The comprehensive instrumentation and monitoring distinguish this project from commercial FPV installations, providing highly reliable scientific data. This enables a detailed understanding of the impacts of FPV systems on supply reservoirs and supports the development of best practices for design, operation, and maintenance. Ultimately, the project establishes a solid foundation for future FPV developments, promoting the safe, efficient, and scientifically grounded integration of floating photovoltaic systems in sensitive environments.

6. Future works

The next steps involve launching the tender for the acquisition of the FPV systems, the instrumentation, and the data acquisition and visualisation system, followed by their installation and commissioning. Once deployed, the sensors will operate continuously, enabling permanent monitoring of both energy performance and water quality, and thus supporting the assessment of bidirectional interactions between the FPV system and the surrounding ecosystem. The collected data will provide the basis for calculating energy indicators such as the performance ratio (PR) and the levelised cost of energy (LCOE), as well as for evaluating potential environmental impacts. This integrated analysis will provide the foundation for the development of a best-practice manual and dedicated testing and commissioning protocols, thus contributing to the standardisation and optimisation of future FPV installations.

7. Acknowledgements

This research was partly funded by the PRR Mobilizing Agendas, project Alliance for Energy Transition (ATE) with Grant agreement ID C644914747-00000023.

8. References

[1] International Renewable Energy Agency (IRENA), «Floating Solar: A Guide to the Technology, Applications and Markets,» IRENA, Abu Dhabi, 2021.

[2] R. L. Pedroso de Lima, K. Paxinou, F. C. Boogaard, O. Akkerman e L. Fen-Yu, «In-Situ Water Quality Observations under a Large-Scale Floating Solar Farm Using Sensors and Underwater Drones, https://doi.org/10.3390/su13116421,» *Sustainability*, 2021.

[3] «Large-scale floating photovoltaic systems impact the water quality of deep sand extraction lakes in the Netherlands,» Deltares, 2024.

[4] S. Gadzanku, N. Lee e A. Dyreson, «Enabling Floating Solar Photovoltaic (FPV) Deployment,» National Renewable Energy Laboratory (NREL), 2022.

[5] canalsolar. [Online]. Available: https://canalsolar.com.br/en/solar-flutuante-crescer-significativamente-mundo-woodmac/.

[6] Agência Portuguesa do Ambiente (APA), «Barrahens de Portugal," Sistema Nacional de Informação Hídricas.,» [Online]. Available: https://snirh.apambiente.pt/index.php?idMain=1&idItem=1.3. [Consultato il giorno 05 09 2025].

[7] Diário da República, «Decreto-Lei n.º 15/2022, de 14 de janeiro».

[8] Diário da República, «Regulamento n.º 815/2023, de 27 de julho».

 UNIVERSITY OF ÉVORA
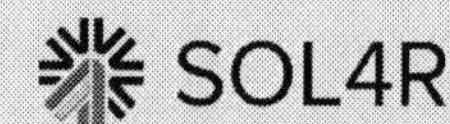 SOL4R

DESIGN, SIZING, AND SENSORISATION OF AN FPV POWER PLANT AT THE MONTE NOVO DAM, PORTUGAL

Dorivaldo Duarte[*,1], Luis Fialho[2], Pedro Horta[1], Sara Pereira[1]
*Corresponding author: duarte@uevora.pt
[1]Renewable Energies Chair, Polo da Mitra da Universidade de Évora, Edifício Ário Lobo de Azevedo, 7000-083 Nossa Senhora da Tourega, Portugal.
[2]Eurac Research, Viale Druso (Drususallee) 1, 39100 Bolzano, Italy

ABSTRACT

This study presents the design and implementation of a floating photovoltaic (FPV) system on the Monte Novo reservoir in Évora, a potable water supply resource. The installation integrates multiple flotation technologies and structural layouts, combined with a dense sensor network for real-time monitoring of environmental parameters, water quality, and energy performance. The work focuses on assessing the mutual impacts between the FPV system and the aquatic ecosystem, while defining robust protocols for safe operation and long-term reliability. In addition, the study explores hybridisation with the electrical grid to strengthen water treatment processes. By addressing technical performance, environmental interactions, and operational integration, the study provides evidence-based insights to guide future FPV projects in sensitive freshwater environments and contributes to advancing sustainable solutions for the water–energy nexus.

OBJECTIVE

- Design and sizing of a pilot FPV plant at Monte Novo reservoir.
- Compare floating technologies and module configurations (orientation, tilt, layout) for stability and energy efficiency.
- Implement an advanced sensor network to monitor:
  1. Meteorological conditions
  2. Energy performance
  3. Water quality
- Assess interactions with the aquatic ecosystem, ensuring environmental protection and drinking water safety.
- Develop operation and maintenance protocols for safe, reliable, and durable system performance.
- Integrate with the low-voltage grid for legal and operational compatibility.
- Produce scientific and technical knowledge to support future FPV standards, best practices, and testing protocols.

METHODOLOGY

Reservoir selection → Type of use

Hydropower production	Drinking water supply	Irrigation	Flood control	Recreational tourism	Environmental conservation
Restrictions: Limited reservoir area	Monitoring of water quality and occupation <2%	Free access to canals and intake points.	Resistant to water level variations and currents	Leave free corridors and install safety signage	Installation of FPV plants prohibited
Licensing: Possible, subject to technical assessment	Rarely authorized under strict control	Possible with proper manage-ment	Conditional, depending on float design and robustness	Possible in designated areas, but unfavour-able	Not authorised

Licence for the use of the public water domain

- Ensure compatibility with the use defined in the POA
- Carry out environmental impact assessment

Design and sizing of the FPV pilot plant

- Selection of floats and PV modules
- Selection of the sensing system
- Anchoring and mooring design
- Sensor location selection
- Selection of the SCADA

Energy licensing (DGEG)

Final authorisation and construction

POA - Reservoir Management Plan (Plano de Ordenamento de Albufeira)
DGEG - Directorate-General for Energy and Geology (Direção-Geral de Energia e Geologia)
SCADA - Supervisory Control and Data Acquisition

DESCRIPTION OF FPV SYSTEMS

- **Location:**
  - Monte Novo Dam, Évora (38.514, -7.712), drinking water reservoir used for public supply, irrigation, and flood control.
  - Stable water levels and >10 m depth make it ideal for FPV installation.

- **Installed capacity:**
  - 200 kW, compatible with low-voltage grid injection (DL 15/2022, Regulation 815/2023).

- **Floating platforms** (three technologies tested across four configurations):
  - System 1:
    - East–West, portrait, fixed tilt 12–15°
  - System 2:
    - East–West, landscape, fixed tilt 15°
  - System 3:
    - a. South-facing, landscape, adjustable tilt 10–40°
    - b. East–West, landscape, adjustable tilt 10–40°

RESULTS

Description	Qt.
Set of 11 Campbell 109 Temperature Profile Sensors:	
– 1 sensor with 5 m cable	
– 2 sensors with 10 m cables	
– 3 sensors with 15 m cables	
– 2 sensors with 20 m cables	
– 3 sensors with 25 m cables	1
Eureka Manta+30a Water Quality Probe	1

Description	Qt.
Class A" Solar Radiation Sensor EKO MS-80SH	1
Gill WindSonic Wind Sensor	1
Campbell HyroVue10 Temperature and Relative Humidity Sensor	1
Lambrecht 15189 Precipitation Sensor	1
Campbell CS125 Present Weather Sensor	1

Description	Qt.
"Class A" Solar Radiation Sensor EKO MS-80SH	7
Pyranometer Mounting Support	7
"Class A" Solar Radiation Sensor EKO MS-80SH (for albedo)	2
Albedo Kit	1
Gill GMX200 Wind Sensor with GPS	1
Campbell HyroVue10 Temperature and Relative Humidity Sensor	1
Campbell CS241 Module Temperature Sensor	7
Set of 11 Campbell 109 Temperature Profile Sensors:	
– 1 sensor with 5 m cable	
– 2 sensors with 10 m cables	
– 3 sensors with 15 m cables	
– 2 sensors with 20 m cables	
– 3 sensors with 25 m cables	1
Eureka Manta+30a Water Quality Probe	1
Rion HDA436T Inclinometer	4

Description	Qt.
UWT NR7200 Level Sensor	1

FUTURE WORKS

- Launch tender for FPV systems, instrumentation, and data acquisition platform.
- Install and commission the plant with continuous sensor monitoring.
- Monitor energy performance (PR, LCOE) and water quality.
- Assess interactions between FPV and the ecosystem.
- Use data to develop best-practice guidelines and testing protocols.
- Contribute to the standardisation and optimisation of future FPV projects.

CONCLUSIONS

- FPV deployment in water supply reservoirs requires balancing energy efficiency, water security, and environmental protection.
- The lack of a specific licensing framework demands rigorous project evaluations.
- The sensor network enables continuous monitoring phof water quality and environmental impacts.
- The project stands out from commercial FPV plants by generating highly reliable scientific data.
- Results support best practices for FPV design, operation, and maintenance.
- Contributes to the safe and efficient integration of FPV systems in sensitive environments.

ACKNOWLEDGEMENTS

This research was partly funded by the PRR Mobilizing Agendas, project Alliance for Energy Transition (ATE) with Grant agreement ID C644914747-00000023

 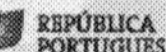 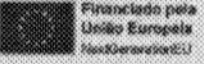

MOBILE E-BIKE SHARING SYSTEMS WITH INTEGRATED PHOTOVOLTAICS: ELECTRIC MOBILITY SOLUTIONS FOR LARGE EVENTS IN ÉVORA, PORTUGAL

Helena Oliveira [a], Paulo Carmo [a], José A. Silva [a], Luís Fialho [b], Paulo Infante [c], Pedro Horta [a]
a Renewable Energies Chair, University of Évora. Mitra Campus of the University of Évora, Edifício Ario Lobo de Azevedo, 7000-083 Nossa Senhora da Tourega, Portugal
b Eurac Research, Viale Druso (Drususallee) 1, 39100 Bolzano, Italy
c Department of Mathematics, University of Évora, Rua Romão Ramalho, 7000-671 Évora, Portugal
helena.oliveira@uevora.pt; paulo.carmo@uevora.pt; jose.silva@uevora.pt; luis.fialho@eurac.edu; pinfante@uevora.pt; phorta@uevora.pt

ABSTRACT: Mobile e-bike sharing stations integrated with photovoltaics are proposed for Évora to serve baseline urban demand and event-related surges while respecting heritage constraints. The system is powered primarily by photovoltaics, with optional grid-assist for resilience. We present a siting–sizing framework that (i) selects candidate locations via AHP and a p-median model based on origin–destination flows and travel times, and (ii) sizes PV and storage under two energy hypotheses: full-recharge of all e-bikes versus a usage-driven demand model (Wh/km × trip length × trips/bike). Using worst-month irradiance and aggregate conversion losses, a worked example shows that the full-recharge assumption yields higher capacities (≈6 kWp PV + 25 kWh storage per 10 bikes for event peaks), whereas the usage-driven model reduces sizing substantially while meeting service levels; both are reported to ensure robustness. This compact framework is directly applicable to heritage cities planning PV-micromobility for large events.
Keywords: Electric Mobility, Photovoltaic Energy, Smart City, Urban Planning

1 INTRODUCTION

This study proposes a practical and scalable solution for sustainable urban mobility in Évora, Portugal, through the implementation of mobile e-bike docking stations powered primarily by photovoltaic energy. These stations will be strategically distributed across the city and equipped with battery storage to enable 24-hour operation for both e-bike sharing and charging. The system will be supported by a digital monitoring application offering real-time data, user interface, and integrated security features.

The concept of mobile stations is particularly relevant given Évora's designation as the European Capital of Culture for 2027, which will attract large audiences to a historic urban environment recognized by UNESCO since 1986 [1]. The initiative aligns with Évora's smart city agenda and its participation in the EU-funded POCITYF project [2], which promotes climate-neutral innovation in heritage cities.

Portugal's National Strategy for Active Mobility sets ambitious targets for bicycle modal share in urban areas, 4% by 2025 and 10% by 2030 [3]. Évora already leads in electric public transport [4] and academic cycling initiatives [5], yet its transport sector remains the largest contributor to local GHG emissions (37.97%) [6]. This project aims to reduce emissions and foster long-term behavioral change by integrating clean energy and intelligent mobility infrastructure into the city's cultural and urban landscape.

The central region of the city of Évora (Figure 1) has a specific PV output of approximately 1652.0 kWh/kWp, as indicated by the data for annual and monthly average values of PV electricity (AC) supplied by a PV system and normalized to 1 kWp of installed capacity, from the Global Solar Atlas. This high output highlights the region's significant potential to harness solar energy, which can be effectively utilized to support sustainable mobility solutions. By leveraging this significant solar resource, Évora can improve its green infrastructure and contribute to reducing CO_2 emissions in the domestic transportation sector [7].

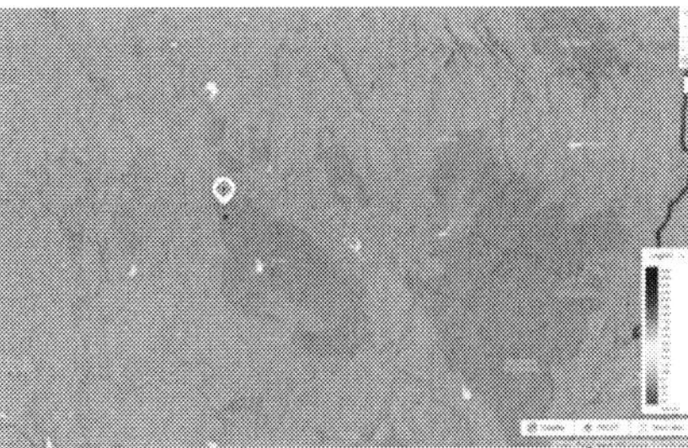

Figure 1: Specific photovoltaic power of Évora
Source: [7] (accessed: February 2025)

One of the objectives of this project is to gather recommendations for the implementation of a monitoring application that allows users to easily know the availability of e-bikes for rent, as well as available spaces for docking and charging, through an interactive map. This application should provide real-time monitoring of e-bikes, including location, battery status and availability.

The sharing stations will be strategically located to facilitate the daily routine of residents and users, integration with other existing means of public transport and the journey between different tourist attractions, events and nearby establishments.

2 RELATED WORKS

2.1 Integrated photovoltaic charging stations for electric micromobility

There are many examples of integrated photovoltaic charging stations for electric micromobility that inspire this work:

- An urban sharing platform in London, UK (2017), is a successful example of how data from a wide range of mobility measures, including e-bikes, e-cargo bikes, electric vehicle charging, smart parking and solar energy systems, can be combined and shared separately to inform policy decisions, generate financial savings and reduce CO_2 emissions [8].
- The SUNPOD CYCLO charging station, from the French company MOBENDI, is an example of a

modular and scalable option, with solar energy production and integrated storage batteries, i.e. 100% self-sufficient in electricity [9].

- Swiftmile, a Californian company, is a complete charging and parking solution for e-bikes, e-scooters and e-mopeds, featuring advanced fleet management technology and available with integrated solar panels [10].

In Portugal, there are successful examples of electric bike sharing, such as Gira - Lisbon's Bicycle Sharing System, but only a few stations with modular infrastructure have the potential for solar power [11]. In contrast, there are companies in Portugal that develop and distribute mobile stations for electric bike sharing, with integrated charging, digital management, and solar solutions [12], and some even combine solar and wind power to ensure full autonomy in an off the grid setup [13].

Unlike fixed stations, mobile units can be deployed in smaller towns, rural areas, or university campuses with lower initial investment. These stations offer a high degree of spatial flexibility, allowing municipalities to adapt infrastructure to seasonal demand, temporary events, or urban renovations. In heritage cities like Évora, where permanent installations may face regulatory or aesthetic constraints, mobile units provide a non-invasive alternative that can be relocated or reconfigured as needed, as demonstrated by Beam Global's BeamBike system, which operates fully off-grid (Figure 2) and is designed for rapid deployment and relocation [14].

Figure 2: BeamBike system
Source: [14] (accessed: September 2025)

Given that the technology for mobile e-bike sharing stations powered by solar energy is already available and proven, this study focuses on the strategic planning of station placement. The effectiveness of the system depends largely on the selection of locations that ensure accessibility, user engagement, and integration with existing urban infrastructure.

3 METHODS

3.1 Demand modelling

To support the strategic deployment of solar-powered e-bike sharing stations in Évora, a demand modeling framework was developed to simulate usage patterns under different urban conditions. This model aims to inform station sizing, energy requirements, and operational flexibility, particularly in a city characterized by seasonal tourism, cultural events, and heritage constraints.

- Baseline Scenario: Typical Urban Day

The baseline scenario represents a standard weekday in Évora, capturing regular commuting flows, student mobility, and local errands. Key parameters include:
- Temporal distribution of trips by hour (morning/evening peaks), distinguishing between weekdays and weekends.
- Trip length percentiles (p50/p90), used to estimate average and upper-bound energy consumption per trip.
- OD (Origin–Destination) profiles across nine strategic points, including residential zones (e.g., Horta das Laranjeiras), commercial hubs (Évora Plaza), university areas, and heritage sites.
- Event Scenario: High-Demand Conditions

To account for fluctuations during cultural, academic, or seasonal events, a second scenario was modeled using a multiplicative factor applied to trip volumes and temporal peaks. This scenario reflects:
- Increased demand during festivals, conferences, and tourism surges.
- Shifted usage patterns, with extended evening activity and higher turnover rates at central stations.
- Stress testing of station capacity and solar generation adequacy under peak conditions.
- Application of the Model
  The demand model supports:
- Station sizing: Estimating the number of bikes and charging docks required per location.
- Energy planning: Aligning solar generation profiles with usage peaks to optimize battery autonomy and reduce grid dependency.
- Operational logistics: Informing redistribution strategies, maintenance scheduling, and dynamic station placement (for mobile units).
- Origin–Destination Matrix

A simplified OD matrix was constructed to analyze trip flows between the nine proposed station sites. This matrix enables:
- Identification of high-demand corridors.
- Prioritization of intermodal integration zones.
- Validation of station placement based on real and projected mobility patterns.

3.2 Solar resource & system model[1]

To ensure autonomous operation of solar-powered e-bike sharing stations in Évora, a dimensioning model was developed based on local solar resource data, estimated daily energy demand per station, and system efficiency parameters. The goal is to guarantee energy availability even under worst-case conditions, such as low solar yield in winter and peak demand during urban events.

- Monthly Solar Yield ($Y[\frac{kWh}{kWp}.day]$)

According to PVGIS simulations for Évora [15], the average daily solar yield per installed kilowatt-peak (kWp) varies seasonally:
- Average 8.26 kWh/day in Summer.
- Average 4.51 kWh/day in Autumn.
- Average 2.62 kWh/day in Winter.
- Average 6.29 kWh/day in Spring.

These values reflect long-term averages and includes typical meteorological conditions, making it suitable for preliminary sizing.

---

[1] The system design follows applicable standards: EN 15194 (EPAC e-bikes), IEC 61215/61730 (PV modules), IEC 62109 (PV power converters), and IEC 62619/62133-2 (Li-ion stationary/portable batteries). Charging cabinets include thermal protection and ventilation; the EMS enforces SOC limits (20–90%) and rate control. Data handling complies with GDPR; the app/backend adopt privacy-by-design and standard cybersecurity controls.

- Estimated Daily Load per Station ($E_{load}[day]$)
  Based on demand modeling (Section 3.1), each station is expected to support:
  - Baseline load: ~2.5 kWh/day (charging 10 bikes with 250 Wh each)
  - Event peak load: up to 7.5–12.5 kWh/day (factor 3–5× increase)
- System Efficiency and Losses
  To account for real-world losses, a global system efficiency factor of 80–85% is applied, considering:
  - MPPT (Maximum Power Point Tracking) and inverter losses
  - Battery charge/discharge inefficiencies
  - Cable and environmental losses
  Thus, the effective solar yield becomes:
$$Y_{eff} = Y \times \eta_{sys}$$
- Robustness Criterion
  To ensure robustness, the system must satisfy:
  - Worst scenario: Winter ($Y \approx 2.62 \frac{kWh}{kWp}.day$)
  - Peak event load: up to 12.5 kWh/day
    Required installed capacity per station:
$$Required\ kWp = \frac{E_{load}}{Y_{eff}} = \frac{12.5}{2.62 \times 0.80} \approx 6.0\ kWp$$
  Battery sizing (2 days autonomy):
$$Battery\ capacity = 2 \times 12.5 = 25\ kWh$$
- Design Implications
  - Stations should be equipped with $\geq 6\ kWp$ solar panels and $\geq 25\ kWh$ battery storage to ensure full autonomy year-round.
  - Modular configurations allow scaling based on location-specific demand.
  - Hybrid systems (solar + wind) may be considered for enhanced resilience in low-radiation periods.

3.3 Energy sizing with two hypotheses (robustness check)

Let Y_m be the monthly specific PV yield (kWh/kWp·day) for Évora (worst case scenario value), and let η_{sys} be the aggregate system efficiency (MPPT/inverter/charge/distribution). The results are reported to $\eta_{sys} \in [0.80, 0.85]$.

H1: Full-recharge (upper bound).
Daily load assumes full recharge of N_b bikes with battery capacity C_b(kWh):
$$E_{load}^{H1} = N_b\,C_b \times f_{util},$$
with $f_{util} \leq 1$(fraction of capacity replenished daily; baseline $f_{util} = 1$for a conservative upper bound). Required PV and storage for autonomy of Ddays:
$$P_{PV}^{H1} = \frac{E_{load}^{H1}}{Y_m\,\eta_{sys}},\ E_{BESS}^{H1} = \frac{D\,E_{load}^{H1}}{DoD}.$$

H2: Usage-driven (demand model).
Daily load derives from travel demand:
$$E_{load}^{H2} = N_b \times c_{Wh/km} \times L_{trip} \times T_{per\,bike} \times (1 + \ell),$$
where $c_{Wh/km}$is the specific e-bike consumption, $L_{trip}$the average trip length, $T_{per\,bike}$trips/bike/day, and ℓaccounts for charging/distribution losses. Sizing:
$$P_{PV}^{H2} = \frac{E_{load}^{H2}}{Y_m\,\eta_{sys}},\ E_{BESS}^{H2} = \frac{D\,E_{load}^{H2}}{DoD}.$$

Worked example (10 bikes, worst case scenario sizing).
- Baseline (typical day): $c_{Wh/km} = 10$, $L_{trip} = 3$ km, $T_{per\,bike} = 2$, $\ell \approx 0.15$, $Y_m = 2.62$kWh/kWp·day, $\eta_{sys} = 0.80$, DoD = 80%, $D = 2$days.

- $E_{load}^{H2} \approx 0.71$kWh/day $\Rightarrow$ $P_{PV}^{H2} \approx 0.34$kWp; $E_{BESS}^{H2} \approx$ 1.8kWh useful (~2.2 kWh nominal).
- Event peak (×5 trips): $E_{load}^{H2} \approx 3.5$kWh/day $\Rightarrow P_{PV}^{H2} \approx$ 1.7kWp; $E_{BESS}^{H2} \approx 7.1$kWh useful (~8.9 kWh nominal).

For comparison, **H1** with full-recharge of 10×0.25 kWh/day under the same Y_m, η_{sys} yields $\approx$ **6 kWp PV** and **25 kWh** storage for 2-day autonomy in event conditions. Reporting **both** H1/H2 makes the design robust yet realistic and aligns with the "primarily PV" positioning.

The Table 1 below summarizes the results under worst-case PV yield conditions for Évora (Y_m = 2.62 kWh/kWp·day), system efficiency η_{sys} = 0.80, and depth of discharge DoD = 80%.

Table 1: Energy sizing results under H1 and H2 hypotheses

Scenario	Daily Load (kWh)	PV Required (kWp)	Storage Required (kWh useful)	Storage Nominal (~kWh)
H1: Full Recharge	2.50	1.19	6.25	7.81
H2: Baseline Demand	0.69	0.33	1.72	2.15
H2: Event Peak	3.45	1.65	8.62	10.78

3.4 Location optimisation

To ensure strategic placement of solar-powered mobile e-bike stations in Évora, a location optimisation framework was developed combining multi-criteria decision analysis (MCDA) and spatial allocation models. The goal is to balance operational efficiency, user accessibility, and urban constraints, particularly in heritage zones.

- Multi-Criteria Decision Analysis (MCDA)
  An Analytic Hierarchy Process (AHP) was applied to evaluate candidate locations based on the following criteria (Table 2):

Table 2: Multicriteria Decision Analysis

Criterion	Description
Demand density	Estimated trip volume from demand modeling (Section 3.1)
Intermodality	Proximity to bus stops, parking lots, and pedestrian zones
Solar exposure	Average insolation and shading conditions (from PVGIS/GSA)
Heritage constraints	Restrictions on permanent infrastructure in protected urban areas
Safety and vandalism risk	Historical data on theft, vandalism, and nighttime visibility
Visual impact	Integration with urban aesthetics and minimization of visual clutter

Criteria were weighted via AHP (Demand 0.30, Intermodality 0.25, Solar exposure 0.10, Heritage constraints 0.10, Safety/Vandalism 0.10, Visual impact 0.15). The pairwise matrix yielded a Consistency Ratio (CR)=0.05, below the 0.10 threshold, indicating acceptable internal consistency.

Location–allocation used a p-median model with K=8 facilities to minimize demand-weighted travel time from OD pairs; we solved it with OR-Tools CP-SAT to optimality (gap 0%). A sensitivity sweep K ∈ [6,10] is provided in the supplement.

Each criterion was weighted based on stakeholder input and urban planning priorities. The resulting composite score guided the ranking of the nine proposed locations.

- Spatial Allocation Model

To refine the station network, a p-median model was applied to minimize the weighted average distance between origin–destination flows and station locations. The model uses:

- OD matrix from Section 3.1
- Flow weights based on simulated trip volumes
- Constraints on station mobility and solar exposure

This approach ensures that stations are placed where they serve the highest demand with minimal detour, while respecting urbanistic and patrimonial limitations.

- Seed Network and Refinement

The initial set of nine strategic points, including Évora Plaza, University of Évora, Centro Histórico, and peripheral residential zones, served as a seed network. These locations were refined using the MCDA-AHP scores and flow-weighted spatial allocation, resulting in a robust and context-sensitive station layout.

The Estimated Shading classification was inferred based on the criteria of visual impact and patrimonial sensitivity, according to the weights defined in the AHP model. The logic applied was:

- Low shadow: points with low visual impact (≤ 0.55) and lower heritage sensitivity (≤ 0.85), indicating a lower risk of aesthetic or cultural interference.

- High shade: points with high visual impact (≥ 0.90) or high heritage sensitivity (≥ 0.90), requiring greater care in urban integration.

- Medium shade: intermediate cases, where the criteria indicate neither high risk nor absence of restrictions.

4 CASE STUDY: ÉVORA

4.1 Cycle path network and opportunities for sustainable electric mobility in Évora

The existing and planned cycle paths in the city of Évora, in addition to meeting adequate urban conditions, motivate the purpose of this study. Évora has 4 cycle paths in operation, implemented on the outskirts of the historic center, plus the Ecopista route that starts in the urban center and crosses the entire city towards the city of Arraiolos (± 25 km). Furthermore, the project includes connecting these cycle paths to the wall of the Historic Center and extending them to the Évora Industrial and Technological Park (PITE). It also includes the development of a Cycle Path along Avenida Dr. Francisco Barahona, between the Rossio roundabout and the train station [16].

The Historic Center has limited paid parking, with designated areas for residents, visitors, and people with reduced mobility. Parking lots in Évora could be strategic assets for this electric mobility project with e-bike sharing, especially if integrated with solar infrastructure, docking stations, and urban intermodality.

Parking lots outside the city walls, such as Porta da Lagoa and Avenida Túlio Espanca, offer better accessibility and physical space. Two parks, Av. Túlio Espanca and Rua Eng. Arantes e Oliveira, are being

equipped with photovoltaic systems for energy production as part of the European POCITYF project [17].

For the academic community and tourists, having bicycles at shared docking stations available with the ease of returning them after use at different points in the city often solves the problem of physical space in homes and accommodations. In addition, it is important to offer an e-bike in usable condition, with charging and green, safe and smart parking. This makes the option accessible to those who have difficulty driving on the terrain of the city, which is predominantly flat (Figure 3), but with gentle hills and elevations that require greater physical effort [18].

Figure 3: Topographic map of Évora
Source: [18] (accessed: January 2025)

4.2 Initial Investment Strategies for Solar-Powered E-Bike Sharing Stations in Évora

The initial investment required for installing solar-powered charging stations often represents a major barrier to large-scale implementation, particularly in cities with constrained public budgets and heritage-sensitive urban environments such as Évora.

To support the implementation of solar-powered e-bike sharing stations in Évora, the following table summarizes key financing alternatives, highlighting their mechanisms, benefits, and contextual relevance to the city's urban and heritage constraints (Table 3).

Table 3: Initial Investment Strategies for Solar-Powered E-Bike Sharing Stations in Évora

Financing Model	Description	Relevance to Évora
Public–Private Partnerships	Collaboration between local government and private sector for installation and maintenance, often via concession agreements.	Enables flexible deployment in heritage-sensitive areas; reduces municipal burden while ensuring service quality.
Green Financing Instruments	Includes tax incentives, low-interest loans, and dedicated credit lines for clean energy and mobility projects.	Aligns with Évora's sustainability goals and can support solar infrastructure in public parking areas (e.g., Água de Prata).
Public Sector Grants	Funding from municipal, regional, or EU programs (e.g., Horizon Europe, POCITYF) targeting renewable energy and smart mobility.	Can be leveraged for pilot stations near cultural hubs and university zones, especially during EU2027 events.

Financing Model	Description	Relevance to Évora
Crowdfunding & Donations	Community-based funding involving citizens, local businesses, and institutions to support station deployment.	Encourages civic engagement and ownership, particularly in residential areas like António Gedeão and Horta das Laranjeiras.
Corporate Sponsorship	Branding and co-investment by companies in exchange for visibility and social responsibility recognition.	Ideal for commercial zones like Évora Plaza; promotes private sector involvement in sustainable urban mobility.
Energy Cooperatives	Local energy communities invest in solar infrastructure and share benefits from energy generation and mobility services.	Could be explored in partnership with University of Évora and local stakeholders for long-term energy autonomy.

4.3 Maintenance and Operational Efficiency: Ensuring Long-Term System Performance in Évora

One of the key concerns in deploying solar-powered infrastructure for electric mobility, particularly in high-traffic urban areas such as charging stations, is ensuring sustained operational efficiency over time. In Évora, where heritage constraints and seasonal fluctuations in demand must be considered, maintenance strategies must be both technically robust and context sensitive:

a. **Preventive Maintenance and Remote:** Monitoring Modern technologies allow real-time monitoring of station performance, enabling early detection of faults and minimizing service disruptions. In Évora's historic center, where physical interventions must be minimal, remote diagnostics and predictive maintenance protocols are essential to preserve both infrastructure and urban aesthetics.

b. **Local Technical Training and Workforce Development:** To ensure sustained system availability, it is crucial to train local maintenance teams in solar and mobility technologies. This not only reduces downtime but also fosters local employment and strengthens Évora's technical capacity in renewable energy and sustainable transport, aligning with the city's long-term strategic goals.

c. **Long-Life Batteries and Modular Systems:** Using durable batteries and modular components (such as inverters and docking units) allows for phased upgrades and simplified replacements. In Évora, where flexibility is key due to frequent cultural events and spatial constraints, modularity supports rapid reconfiguration and ensures that the system evolves alongside technological advancements.

5   RESULTS

The study proposes prioritizing mobile stations within the Historic Center of Évora to ensure flexibility in the management of electric bike-sharing infrastructure, allowing for the relocation of facilities in response to temporary changes in the urban space resulting from major events. This approach respects the city's heritage and ensures the continuity of sustainable mobility services, even in contexts of high land use.

To ensure that the implementation of solar-powered e-bike sharing stations, with integrated batteries for uninterrupted docking, charging, rental, and monitoring, is compatible with the city's spatial and operational realities, the following locational criteria were considered essential:
- Historic Center prioritization: enabling relocation when major events require local adjustments.
- User-oriented planning: proximity to parking lots, schools, shops, markets, restaurants, and tourist attractions, supporting key traffic routes and ensuring pleasant, accessible journeys.
- Public transport integration: proximity to bus and train stations, stops, and taxi hubs, especially for events attracting large groups from nearby cities.
- Solar exposure optimization: preference for less shaded areas to maximize photovoltaic efficiency.

The AHP matrix was applied to the nine proposed station sites, generating a composite score for each location. These scores were then used to refine the initial seed network, prioritizing points with high demand density, strong intermodal connections, and favorable solar exposure, while respecting heritage constraints and minimizing visual impact.

In parallel, a p-median location-allocation model was implemented using the OD matrix from Section 3.1. This model minimizes the flow-weighted average distance between trip origins/destinations and station locations, ensuring operational efficiency and user accessibility.

The combination of MCDA and spatial optimization resulted in a robust, context-aware station layout, adaptable to seasonal variation and event-based demand. The mobile nature of the infrastructure allows for periodic reallocation based on updated demand profiles and urban dynamics.

From the nine candidate sites evaluated, eight were selected based on technical, urbanistic, and functional criteria. The selection of these eight points reflects a balance between spatial efficiency, heritage sensitivity and operational feasibility. The multicriteria approach allows for the technical justification of each inclusion and exclusion, aligning with the objectives of sustainable mobility and respect for the urban context of Évora. Table 4 presents the decision-making indexes:

Table 4: Summary Table:Strategic Point Evaluation

STRATEGIC POINT	AHP SCORE	ESTIMATED SHADING[2]	AVG. OD DISTANCE (M)	DECISION
António Gedeão	0.838	Low	1211.	Include
Évora Plaza	0.795	Low	2367.	Include
Porta de Aviz	0.863	High	1291.	Include

---

[2] Estimated Shading: inferred from visual impact and heritage sensitivity scores. Points with lower visual interference and reduced patrimonial constraints were classified as having low shading.

Água de Prata Parking Lot	0.89	High	1494.	Include
Horta das Laranjeiras	0.878	High	812.	Include
Giraldo Square	0.958	High	1033.	Include
Rodoviária do Alentejo	0.82	Low	1392.	Include
Évora Train Station	0.792	Low	1327.	Include
Fire service	0.73	Medium	1210.	Exclude

The resulting network is strategically balanced, encompassing high-traffic corridors, intermodal hubs, student residences, commercial zones, and green spaces, including the following points:

- António Gedeão University Residence (38.561199, -7.912974): A residential location with a large number of students. This station promotes daily e-bike use as an alternative to motorized transportation for the commuting of students, in addition to reducing pressure on local parking.
- Évora Plaza (38.548690, -7.905595): A commercial center with a large flow of visitors and workers. The presence of a station at this location favors short trips for shopping, leisure, and services, in addition to allowing integration with peripheral residential areas.
- Porta de Aviz (38.576884, -7.910092): A strategic entrance to the Historic Center, with the potential to serve as a transition point between heritage and modern areas. Electric mobility here helps reduce car traffic within the city walls.
- Água de Prata Parking Lot (38.576187, -7.914491): A park with solar infrastructure under development (POCITYF), ideal for installing green charging stations. It can function as an intermodal hub, especially during events or peak hours.
- Horta das Laranjeiras (38.567196, -7.907665): A green and recreational space, excellent for promoting the tourist and leisure use of e-bikes. The installation here reinforces the project's sustainable nature and expands access to low-density urban areas.
- Giraldo Square (38.570567, -7.908990): The symbolic and functional heart of the city. The presence of a station at this location ensures visibility, tourist engagement, and quick access to services, commerce, and heritage.
- Rodoviária do Alentejo, S.A. (38.567404, -7.917300): Bus terminal with high passenger turnover. Installing a station at this location favors intermodality and expands the reach of the shared system for those arriving from outside the city.
- Évora Train Station (38.560774, -7.907245): Railway entry point to the city. Integration with the e-bike system allows for quick travel to the historic center, universities, and shopping areas, promoting a fluid and sustainable mobility experience.

To assess the spatial coverage of the proposed e-bike system, we generated isochrones of 5, 10 and 15 minutes of travel time from a central location (38.5711, -7.9106, Serpa Pinto Street - Évora), using the OpenRouteService

(ORS) API with the cycling-electric profile. This profile accounts for the specific performance of e-bikes, including acceleration and average speeds on the road network. The resulting polygons represent the maximum area that can be reached within each time threshold, providing a realistic measure of accessibility that complements the set of eight candidate stations previously identified. Isochrone generation was implemented in R with the openrouteservice, sf and leaflet packages, and the approach is fully reproducible. Figure 4 illustrates the 5/10/15-minute isochrones, which will be used to benchmark system coverage in both baseline and event scenarios [19].

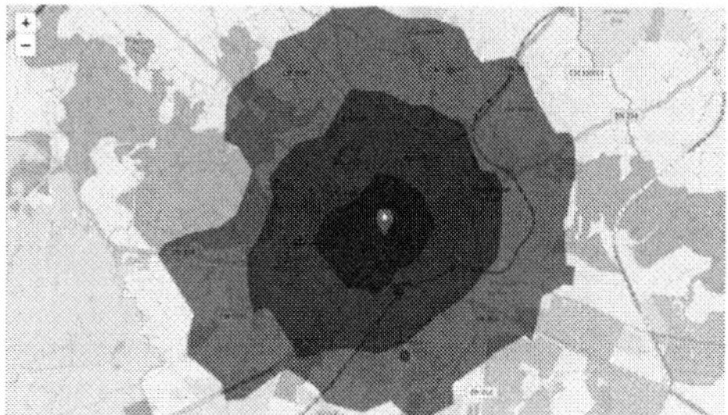

Figure 4: Isochrones of 5, 10 and 15 minutes for e-bike trips from the city centre (Serpa Pinto Street, Évora), generated with HeiGIT gGmbH, OpenRouteService[3]
Source: [19]; ORS, processed in R (openrouteservice, sf, leaflet packages) (accessed: September 2025)

Most of the eight selected candidate stations fall within the 10-minute isochrone, ensuring accessibility for daily commuting and intermodal trips, while the 15-minute coverage extends the system's reach to peripheral residential and leisure areas. This confirms that the proposed network provides adequate spatial coverage under both baseline and event scenarios.

To support the strategic deployment of solar-powered e-bike sharing stations in Évora, a demand simulation was conducted using synthetic data modeled in R. The results are presented in four visualizations (Figure 5a–5d) that inform key operational and locational decisions:

• Temporal Distribution of Trips Figure 5a illustrates the hourly distribution of trips across weekdays and weekends. Weekday demand shows pronounced peaks around 8:00 and 17:00, consistent with commuting patterns, while weekend usage is more evenly distributed throughout the day. These findings suggest that:
– Stations near residential and employment zones should prioritize early morning and late afternoon availability.
– Weekend demand may require broader coverage in leisure and tourism areas, with extended operational windows.

• Trip Length Percentiles Figure 5b presents the P50 and P90 percentiles of trip duration, estimated from a bimodal distribution modeled in R. The P50 value (~15 minutes) reflects typical intra-urban mobility, while the P90 (~30+ minutes) indicates outlier trips that may require higher battery autonomy or strategic redistribution. These metrics support:
– Sizing of battery capacity per station.

---

[3] HEIGIT - Heidelberg Institute for Geoinformation Technology. OpenRouteService (accessed: September 2025). From https://openrouteservice.org.

– Estimation of solar generation needs based on average energy consumption per trip.

• Origin–Destination Matrix Figure 5c shows the simulated OD flows between nine strategic points in Évora. The heatmap highlights asymmetric demand patterns, with certain nodes acting as major trip generators or attractors. This analysis informs:

– Prioritization of station placement in high-flow corridors.

– Identification of intermodal integration points (e.g., university ↔ historic center ↔ commercial zones).

– Dynamic reallocation strategies for mobile stations based on temporal and spatial demand.

• Estimated Travel Time Matrix Figure 5d presents the simulated travel times (in minutes) between the nine proposed station sites, calculated from geodesic distances and assuming an average e-bike speed of 15 km/h. This visualization complements the OD flow analysis by introducing a temporal dimension to spatial accessibility. Key insights include:

– Identification of time-efficient corridors, where short travel durations align with high trip volumes, reinforcing their suitability for station placement and redistribution logistics.

– Detection of peripheral nodes with longer travel times, which may require additional battery autonomy or serve as candidates for grid-assist fallback strategies.

– Support for dynamic routing and fleet balancing, especially during peak hours or event-driven demand shifts.

Together, these visualizations enhance the operational planning framework by linking spatial layout to real-world

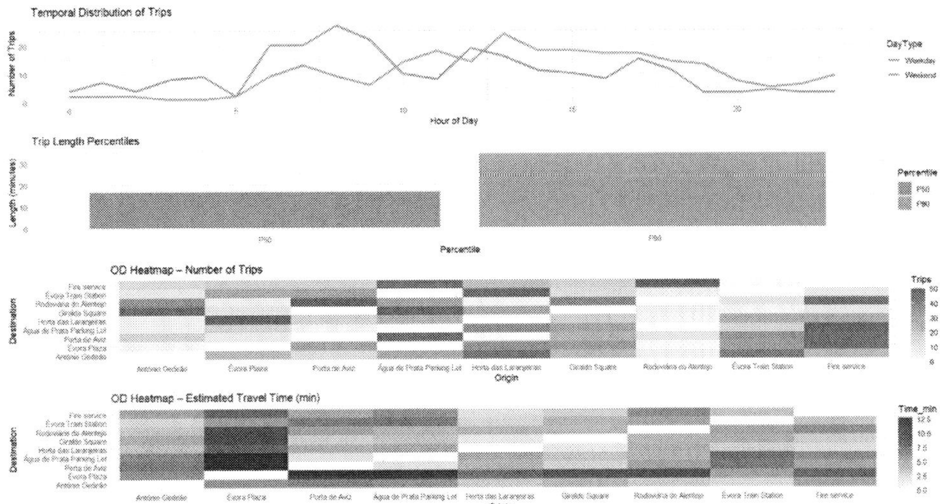

Figure 5: Demand modelling

travel behavior, ensuring that station deployment responds not only to demand intensity but also to temporal feasibility and urban dynamics.

From the nine candidate locations evaluated through the AHP matrix and spatial optimization, eight were selected for initial deployment. This decision reflects a balance between maximizing coverage and maintaining operational feasibility.

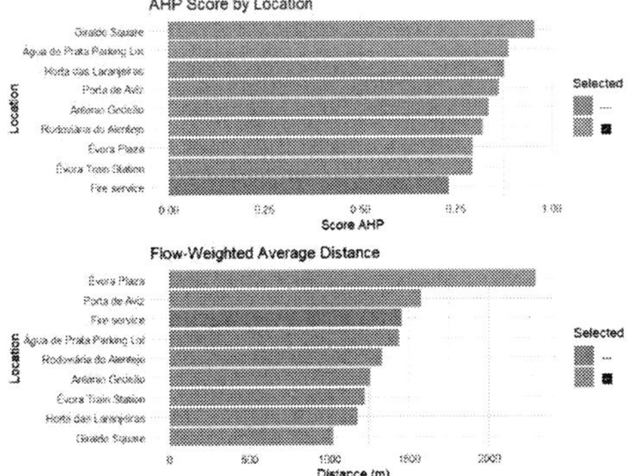

Figure 6: Station Selection Strategy

The exclusion of one site was based on its comparatively lower composite score and higher flow-weighted average distance, indicating reduced accessibility and strategic relevance within the current demand scenario (Figure 6).

The selection process prioritized locations that offer strong intermodal connectivity, favorable solar exposure, and proximity to high-demand corridors. The modular nature of the infrastructure allows for future inclusion or rotation of sites as demand patterns evolve, ensuring that the system remains responsive and scalable.

6 DISCUSSIONS

• **Trade-offs: "Primarily PV" vs. "Grid-Assist"**

The decision to operate stations primarily on photovoltaic energy reflects a commitment to full autonomy and carbon neutrality. However, this choice entails important trade-offs:

- Advantages of Primarily PV: Zero operational emissions and full energy independence; Simplified permitting in heritage zones (no grid connection or trenching); Symbolic value in showcasing clean energy leadership.
- Limitations: Vulnerability to seasonal variation and shading (especially in winter or dense urban areas);

Need for oversizing PV and battery systems to meet peak demand, increasing cost and footprint; Limited fallback options during extreme weather or prolonged overcast periods.

- Grid-Assist Alternative: Allows for smaller PV arrays and batteries, reducing upfront investment; Ensures uninterrupted service during low-generation periods; Enables smart charging strategies (e.g., grid charging during off-peak hours).

The choice between these models depends on site-specific constraints, policy priorities, and operational resilience goals. In Évora, where heritage preservation and visual impact are critical, a mobile, PV-exclusive model may be preferable, but hybrid configurations could be considered for high-demand or shaded locations.

- **Operational Dynamics During Events**

Cultural, academic, and tourism events in Évora introduce temporary spikes in mobility demand, which challenge the static assumptions of baseline station sizing. Key considerations include:

- Temporal reallocation: Mobile stations can be repositioned to event zones (e.g., festival venues, university campuses) to absorb demand surges.
- Energy stress: Higher trip volumes increase charging cycles, requiring robust battery autonomy or temporary energy support.
- User behavior shifts: Events may alter trip timing (e.g., extended evening use), duration, and origin–destination patterns.

Operational strategies should include:

- Predictive modeling: Using historical event calendars and demand simulations to anticipate peak loads.
- Flexible logistics: Rapid deployment protocols, mobile maintenance units, and real-time monitoring.
- Fallback planning: Optional grid-assist or mobile powerbanks to ensure continuity without compromising the PV-first principle.

These dynamics reinforce the value of modularity and mobility in station design, allowing the system to adapt to urban rhythms without permanent infrastructure.

7 CONCLUSIONS

The combined analysis of AHP criteria, shading estimation and flow-weighted average distance reveals a robust selection of strategic points for the implementation of e-bike stations in Évora.

Giraldo Square has the highest AHP score (0.958), standing out as the most balanced point between demand, intermodality and low equity interference. Its average distance (1033 m) reinforces the operational centrality.

Horta das Laranjeiras combines a high AHP score (0.878) with the shortest average distance (812 m), suggesting strong coverage potential with low travel cost.

Água de Prata Parking Lot and Porta de Aviz have high scores (≥ 0.86) and high shading, which requires attention to visual and heritage integration, but are compensated by good connectivity.

Évora Plaza, despite having the longest average distance (2367 m), was included due to its intermodal relevance and consistent demand, evidenced by the AHP score (0.795).

Fire Service, with the lowest AHP score (0.730) and average shading, was excluded from the final selection because it had lower relative performance in the combined criteria, despite its average distance being competitive

(1210 m).

The innovative contribution of this study lies in its strategic approach to integrating solar-powered mobility infrastructure within the urban and heritage context of Évora. By focusing on the deployment of mobile and modular e-bike sharing stations powered by renewable energy, the project addresses critical challenges related to sustainable transport, energy transition, and urban planning in medium-sized cities with historical constraints.

Rather than emphasizing technological novelty alone, the study prioritizes contextual feasibility, identifying optimal station locations based on accessibility, solar exposure, and urban dynamics. This includes the use of public parking areas with photovoltaic potential, intermodal hubs, and flexible deployment zones within the historic center, ensuring that mobility solutions remain adaptable to seasonal events and spatial limitations.

The proposed model contributes to the broader goals of climate adaptation and decarbonization by promoting low-emission transport and efficient land use. It also reinforces the importance of interoperability, local workforce training, and preventive maintenance as pillars for long-term operational sustainability.

Ultimately, this study offers a replicable framework for other heritage cities seeking to balance environmental goals with mobility innovation. It aligns with national and European strategies for smart cities, energy efficiency, and inclusive urban development, positioning Évora as a reference in the integration of clean energy and sustainable transport systems.

8 FUTURE WORK

The potential of Évora to lead innovative actions in sustainable urban mobility and renewable energy integration is considerable and deserves further exploration. Building on the design and methodology proposed in this study, which prioritizes flexible, solar-powered e-bike sharing stations adapted to heritage and urban constraints, several avenues for future research and implementation are identified.

1. Energy and Infrastructure Enhancements
- Energy efficiency optimization: Investigate passive cooling systems and smart energy management for solar charging stations, especially in high-exposure zones such as public parking areas and intermodal hubs.
- Fallback energy strategies: Evaluate the feasibility of auxiliary power sources (e.g., grid connection, mobile power banks) for extreme weather conditions or justify exclusive PV operation through oversizing and autonomy modeling.
- Battery management protocols: Define operational thresholds for state-of-charge (SOC), thermal safety, and charge/discharge cycles to ensure system reliability.

2. Environmental and Operational Impact
- Carbon mitigation assessment: Quantify the modal shift from fossil-fueled transport to electric micromobility, supported by solar infrastructure and behavioral incentives.
- Performance indicators: Develop KPIs such as trips per bike per day, solar kWh delivered, CO_2 avoided, station uptime, and Levelized Cost of Charge

(LCOC) to evaluate system efficiency and cost-effectiveness.
- Resilience and adaptability: Analyze how modular stations respond to seasonal demand, urban events, and spatial reconfiguration needs within the historic center.

3. Urban Integration and Safety
- Heritage-sensitive deployment: Explore mobile, non-invasive station designs with concealed cabling, low-profile solar pallets, and no ground perforation to comply with heritage preservation standards.
- Shading and solar losses: Conduct photometric sampling or develop seasonal shadow maps to assess real-world solar exposure and optimize station placement.
- Electrical and fire safety: Include a technical review of Li-ion charging risks, ventilation requirements, thermal cutoff mechanisms, and applicable IEC/EN standards.
- Cybersecurity and data governance: Address privacy and security concerns related to geolocation, user tracking, and GDPR compliance within the app and backend systems.

4. Smart City and Socioeconomic Integration
- Platform interoperability: Investigate integration with public transport, energy grids, and digital mobility services to enhance user experience and operational intelligence.
- Community and workforce engagement: Study the socioeconomic impacts of solar mobility, including local job creation, inclusive access, and contributions to low-carbon urban development.

9   ACKNOWLEDGEMENTS

This work was supported by the project "NGS - Pacto de Inovação - New Generation Storage" Agenda, funded by the Portuguese Recovery and Resilience Plan (PRR), with reference C644936001-00000045.

10   REFERENCES

[1] UNESCO National Commission. Accessed on January 25, 2025, from https://unescoportugal.mne.gov.pt/pt/temas/proteger-o-nosso-patrimonio-e-promover-a-criatividade/patrimonio-mundial-em-portugal.

[2] Évora 2027 - Official Website (2025). Accessed on January 25, 2025, from https://www.evora2027.com.

[3] RCM – Council of Ministers Resolution No. 131/2019, National Strategy for Active Mobility. Accessed on January 25, 2025, from https://dre.pt/dre/en/detail/resolution-of-the-council-of-ministers/131-2019-123666113.

[4] TREVO - Urban Transport Network of the City of Évora. News. Accessed on January 29, 2025, from https://www.trevo.com.pt/

[5] UéUbike. University of Evora. Accessed on January 25, 2025, from https://www.ubike.uevora.pt/.

[6] MEM+, Municipal Emissions Monitoring. Emissions by sector - Évora. Accessed on January 29, 2025, from https://memmais.tecnico.ulisboa.pt/

[7] Global Solar Atlas. Specific photovoltaic power of Évora. Accessed on February 06, 2025, from https://globalsolaratlas.info/map

[8] BABLE. An E-Bike Loan Scheme Supporting Low-Carbon Shared Mobility (2017). Accessed on January 31, 2025, from https://www.bable-smartcities.eu/explore/use-cases/use-case/an-e-bike-loan-scheme-supporting-low-carbon-shared-mobility.html

[9] MOBENDI. SUNPOD CYCLO - Station de recharge solaire pour vélos électriques. Accessed on February 06, 2025, from https://mobendi.com/notre-station-solaire-pour-velos-electriques/

[10] Swiftmile. Micromobility Charging Stations. Accessed on February 06, 2025, from https://swiftmile.com/

[11] Gira - Bicicletas de Lisboa. Lisbon Bicycle Sharing System. Accessed on September 15, 2025, from https://www.gira-bicicletasdelisboa.pt/

[12] NIDTEC - Technology Solutions. Charging station for electric bicycles. Accessed on September 15, 2025, from https://nidtec.pt/

[13] BICIWAY. BiciCharger Sun+Wind. Accessed on September 15, 2025, from https://www.biciway.com/pt

[14] Beam Global. BeamBike. Accessed on September 16, 2025, from https://beamforall.com/product/beambike/

[15] European Commission, Joint Research Centre. (n.d.). Photovoltaic Geographical Information System (PVGIS). Accessed on September 16, 2025, from https://joint-research-centre.ec.europa.eu/pvgis_en

[16] Cycle path. Cycle paths in Évora. Accessed on January 28, 2025, from https://www.ciclovia.pt/ciclovias/4alentejo/2evora/evora/evora.php

[17] Câmara Municipal de Évora. Where to park. Accessed on January 28, 2025, from https://www.cm-evora.pt

[18] Topographic map. Topographic map of Évora. Accessed on January 28, 2025, from https://pt-pt.topographic-map.com/map-kfwkl/%C3%89vora/?center=38.57078%2C-7.9093 https://globalsolaratlas.info/detail?c=38.542258,-7.896423,11&s=38.590696,-7.957193&m=site

[19] Oliveira, H., 2025. Isochrones of 5, 10 and 15 minutes for e-bike trips from the city centre (Serpa Pinto Street, Évora), generated with ORS. Accessed on September 22, 2025, from https://rpubs.com/Hluisa/isochrones-evora

THE SELF-CONSUMPTION POTENTIAL OF RAILWAY STATIONS: PORTUGAL AS A CASE STUDY

Margarida Luís, Miguel Centeno Brito
University of Lisbon, Faculty of Sciences, Lisbon, Portugal
fc54864@alunos.ciencias.ulisboa.pt, mcbrito@ciencias.ulisboa.pt

ABSTRACT: The European Union aims for climate neutrality by 2050. With transport being responsible for over one-third of carbon emissions, using transport infrastructure, such as rail, for renewable energy deployment can support decarbonisation while avoiding land-use conflicts. Solar Photovoltaics (PV) are particularly suited due to their availability, efficiency, and low maintenance. This study evaluates the solar potential of Portugal's railway infrastructure, with a focus on train station rooftops. It also examines the alignment between energy generation and consumption, exploring different PV system configurations to optimise the integration of renewable energy. The assessment of solar potential was based on estimates of physical and technical capacity, using tools such as Google Earth and PVGIS. Energy consumption at the railway stations does not match passenger flow, as it peaks during the night, and therefore does not coincide with PV generation hours. Adjusting PV system sizing at train stations to match their daytime energy demand can help minimise curtailment. If surplus generation persists, it can be managed through a collective self-consumption scheme or by integrating an energy storage system (ESS).
Keywords: Photovoltaic, Solar railways, Self-sufficiency, Self-consumption

1 INTRODUCTION

The European Climate Law sets the goal for the European Union (EU) to achieve climate neutrality by 2050 [1]. As the transport sector accounts for more than one-third of the CO_2 emissions from end-use sectors [2], decarbonisation is a pressing priority. Integrating renewable energy systems into the transport infrastructure offers a promising pathway, with rail emerging as a strong candidate given its existing reliance on electricity. Solar energy emerges as the most suitable renewable source due to the affordability, flexibility, and low maintenance of photovoltaic systems. While large-scale PV deployment is often linked to land-use conflicts, integrating PV into railway infrastructure offers a dual-use solution. This approach maximises space efficiency, adds value to an essential transport asset, and minimises additional environmental impacts.

Most studies on the solar potential of railways focus on geographical suitability and estimated energy output, often neglecting how the generated energy will actually be used [3], [4]. While they typically evaluate potential installed capacity and expected yield, few compare this generation to real energy consumption data [5], [6]. When such comparisons do occur, they are usually based on daily or monthly averages, which fail to reflect the hourly fluctuations in both energy demand and PV generation, overlooking the resulting supply-demand mismatch. This study addresses that gap by assessing the solar potential of the Portuguese railway network using real hourly energy consumption data, enabling a more comprehensive analysis of energy alignment.

This study assesses the physical and technical potential of integrating photovoltaic (PV) systems into railway infrastructure, more specifically, railway stations. Although traction substations and their respective consumption profiles were also analysed, they are the subject of a different publication. Focusing on mainland Portugal, this study evaluates various technical PV configurations on railway stations' rooftops. The estimated PV energy generation is then compared with railway station energy consumption to analyse the potential impacts on self-consumption and self-sufficiency across the national rail network.

2 METHODOLOGY

2.1 PV Configurations

The solar potential of the railway stations was assessed based on a diverse range of rooftop PV configurations that can be deployed on their rooftops to supply non-traction energy needs. Figure 1 shows the configurations analysed along with their respective specific installed capacities.

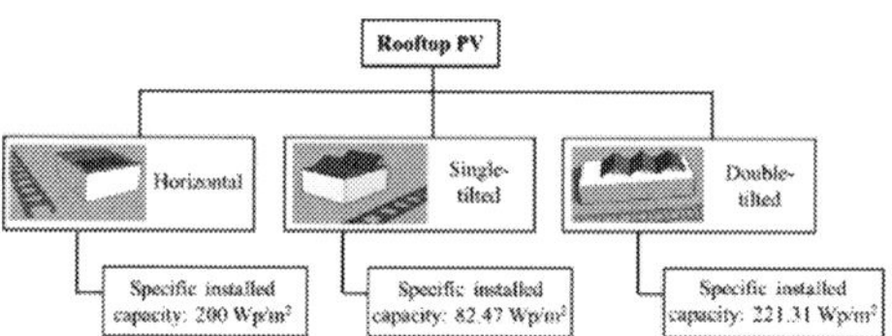

Figure 1: Technical PV configurations' schematics and respective specific installed capacities

The horizontal rooftop configuration consists of PV modules arranged co-planar with the roof of the train station. Assuming a 20% conversion efficiency, the specific installed capacity of this configuration is 200 W/m^2.

For the single-tilted and double-tilted configurations, the modules are south-facing with a 35° tilt, which is the optimal tilt angle for Portugal [7]. Using Equation 1, where D is the distance between modules, M is the module width (1 m), θ is the tilt angle (35°), and α is the solar elevation angle (28°) on the winter solstice day in Portugal [8], the minimum spacing between modules was calculated to be approximately 1.5 m. The specific installed capacity of the single tilted configuration is 82.47 W/m^2.

$$D = \frac{M \sin\theta}{\tan\alpha} \qquad (1)$$

The double-tilted rooftop configuration is comprised of PV modules forming a triangle, oriented East and West. In this configuration, each PV module occupies less rooftop area than in the single-tilted configuration, since they are not installed to avoid self-shadowing losses. The area that each of the modules occupies was calculated according to equation 4, where A is the area occupied by the module, M is the module's width (1 m), and H is the module's height. Each module occupies 0.9 m^2 of rooftop space, meaning that the specific installed capacity of this configuration is 221.31 W/m².

$$A = \sqrt{M^2 - H^2} \times M \qquad (2)$$

2.2 Case study: Portugal

As of 2024, the Portuguese railway network comprises 1,794 km of electrified tracks and 546 operating railway stations [9]. Given the impracticality of analysing the entire network, four representative railway lines were selected for this study: *Linha do Norte* (Line N), *Linha da Beira-Baixa* (Line BB), *Linha de Évora + Alentejo* (Line EA), and *Linha do Sul* (Line S). These lines provide broad geographical coverage, extending from north to south and east to west, while encompassing various types of rail services, including suburban, regional, and long-distance routes. This selection captures a diverse size and energy consumption range of railway stations, ensuring a representative assessment of the solar potential across the Portuguese railway system. The selected railway lines include a total of 196 train stations.

2.3 Geographical Potential

Geographical potential is mostly defined in literature as the incident irradiation on areas deemed suitable for PV deployment [10], [11], [12]. This study takes a different approach by defining geographical potential as the area deemed suitable for PV installation, rather than focusing on the solar irradiance received by that area.

The geographical potential of the railway stations pertains to their rooftop area. These areas were manually measured using satellite imagery and Google Earth's measuring tool [13]. Since the images are taken from a top-down perspective, the measurements are more accurate for stations with flat roofs than for those with sloped roofs.

2.4 Technical Potential

In the literature, technical potential is often defined as the portion of geographical potential that can be converted into electricity [10], [11], [14]. In this study, technical potential is divided into capacity potential and generation potential. The first regards the capacity (W_p) that is possible to install in the obtained geographical potential, and the second regards the amount of energy (kWh) that the capacity potential can effectively convert into electricity. The capacity potential refers to the maximum PV capacity that can be installed within the identified geographical potential, while the generation potential represents the amount of electricity that this installed capacity can realistically produce.

PV energy generation for the different technical configurations was estimated using PVGIS [15]. To automate this process, the *get_pvgis_hourly* function from the PVlib Python library was employed [16]. The energy output provided by the *get_pvgis_hourly* function is expressed in W/kWp. These values were then multiplied by the capacity potential of each technical PV configuration to determine the total energy generation (generation potential).

2.5 Energy Consumption Data

It is important to highlight the difference between traction and non-traction energy consumption in the railway system. Traction energy consumption covers the energy used to operate trains, including propulsion, lighting, air conditioning, and door mechanisms. Non-traction energy consumption refers to energy used by supporting infrastructure such as railway stations and maintenance centres. These two demand types differ significantly: traction loads are dynamic and subject to sudden peaks driven by train movement, while non-traction loads are more stable and predictable. This study focuses more strongly on the potential contribution of solar energy to meeting train station energy demands.

Non-traction energy consumption data for 2023 were supplied by Infraestruturas de Portugal. Originally recorded in 15-minute intervals, the data was aggregated into hourly intervals to match the PV energy production data and facilitate a consistent self-consumption analysis.

2.6 Self-Consumption Analysis

One of the main challenges of PV energy generation is its limited generation, being circumscribed to daylight hours. Similarly, energy consumption in the railway sector is variable and not evenly distributed throughout the day. To address these fluctuations, a self-consumption analysis was conducted to determine which of the proposed PV configurations best aligns with non-traction energy demands. Hourly PV generation data from the rooftop systems were matched with train station energy consumption. This hourly comparison allows the analysis to account for variations in both energy production and demand throughout the day. Self-sufficiency and self-consumption were obtained according to equations 3 and 4, where SS is self-sufficiency, SC is self-consumption, PV_C is the PV energy consumed, E_D is the energy demand of a given location, and PV_G is the PV energy generated. The analysis was carried out for each technical PV configuration and across multiple levels of installed capacity to assess performance under different deployment scenarios.

$$SS\ (\%) = \left(\frac{PV_C}{E_D}\right) \times 100 \qquad (3)$$

$$SC\ (\%) = \left(\frac{PV_C}{PV_G}\right) \times 100 \qquad (4)$$

3 RESULTS

3.1 Railway Stations' Solar Potential

The geographical potential of the railway stations in the selected railway lines amounts to 0.27 km². However, it is not evenly distributed throughout the 196 train stations, with 0.02 km² in Line BB, 0.15 km² in Line N, 0.02 km² in Line EA, and 0.08 km² in Line S. Regarding energy consumption data, it was only available for 84 train stations in the selected railway lines. The total geographical potential for the train stations with energy consumption data is 0.16 km², with 0.01 km² for Line BB, 0.12 km² for Line N, 0.02 km² for Line EA, and 0.01 km² for Line S. Line S has the biggest discrepancy between the actual rooftop area and the rooftop area of the train stations with energy consumption data. In comparison, the train stations along Line N are considerably larger than those on Line BB. Although Line N has only twice as many stations with available data, its total rooftop area is 11 times larger. The train stations on Line EA and Line S are similar in size, as both the number of stations and the total rooftop area are comparable.

Figure 2 shows the annual PV energy generation from rooftop systems at train stations, assuming 50% of the available rooftop area is used for PV installation. As expected, the double-tilted configuration yields the highest energy output across all railway lines, due to its higher installed capacity. Conversely, the single-tilted configuration, having the lowest specific installed capacity, produces the least energy. Despite having fewer train stations with available data, Line S generates significantly more energy than Line BB in both the horizontal and double-tilted configurations.

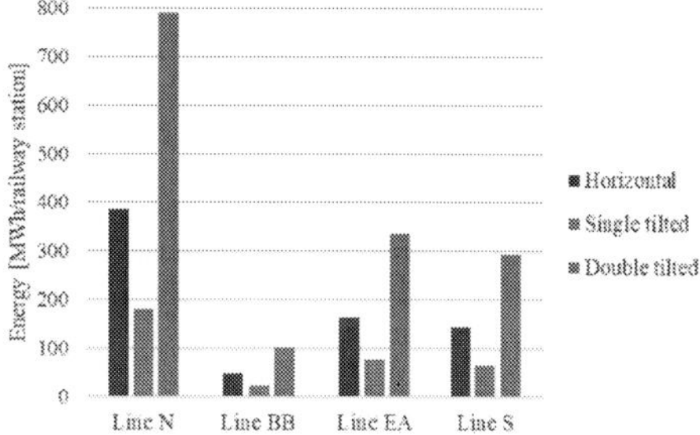

Figure 2: Annual PV generation of the railway stations in the selected railway lines when the PV system occupies 50% of their rooftop area

3.2 Self-consumption Analysis: Case Studies

To better understand how PV generation interacts with varying train station load profiles, two individual stations from different railway lines were discussed in detail. The selected stations are *Vila Franca de Xira* (VFX), located on Line N, and Pinhal Novo (PN), situated simultaneously in Line S and Line EA. VFX is located in the southernmost part of Line N and has a rooftop area of 589 m², while PN has a significantly larger rooftop with an area of 8,675 m² and is located on the westernmost part of Line S and the easternmost part of Line EA. Figure 3 presents the load profiles of these stations on June 3rd, 2023. PN stands out for its higher and more variable energy consumption, in contrast to VFX, which maintains an almost constant load throughout the day.

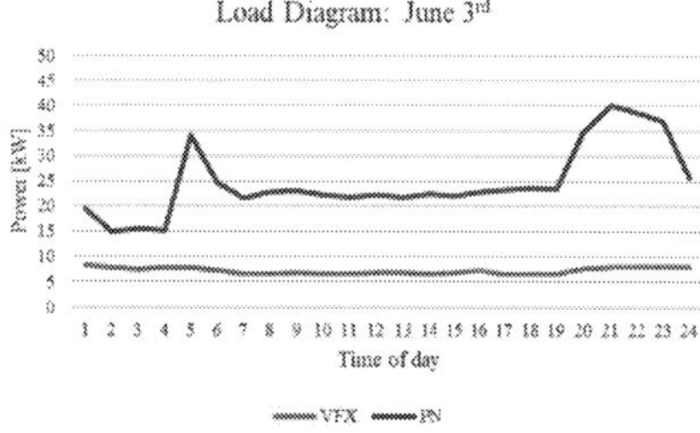

Figure 3: Load diagram of the railway stations VFX and PN, the case studies in the self-consumption analysis

Figure 4 illustrates the self-sufficiency and self-consumption rates of *Vila Franca de Xira* (VFX) as the rooftop occupancy increases, consequently increasing the installed capacity. The highest self-consumption rate, 100%, was achieved with the single-tilted configuration at 10% rooftop occupancy (4.86 kWp). Under the same conditions, the double-tilted configuration reached a self-consumption rate of 74%, with a slightly higher installed

capacity of 13 kWp. The lowest self-sufficiency rate, at just 10%, was also recorded for the single-tilted configuration at 10% rooftop occupancy. The balance point between the metrics for this train station is around 40%.

Given the station's consumption profile, the horizontal configuration offers the best alignment between PV generation and energy demand. At 10% rooftop occupancy (4.86 kWp), it achieves 97% self-consumption and 21% self-sufficiency. While the self-sufficiency rate is moderate, this configuration provides the most balanced performance between the two metrics. Under the same conditions, the double-tilted setup reaches 74% self-consumption and 34% self-sufficiency, whereas the single-tilted configuration achieves full (100%) self-consumption but only 10% self-sufficiency.

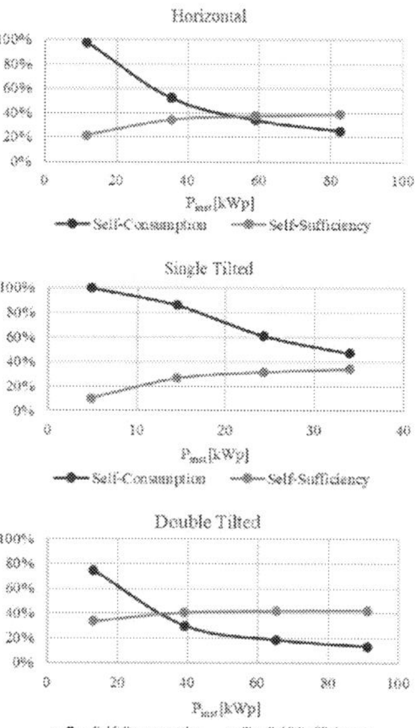

Figure 4: Self-sufficiency vs Self-consumption for the railway station VFX, located on Line N

In this scenario, if the goal is to maximise self-sufficiency, the double-tilted configuration with 50% rooftop occupancy emerges as the most suitable option. However, even at this level, it achieves only 42% self-sufficiency, accompanied by a low self-consumption rate of 19%. The data suggests that this system has reached its performance peak, self-sufficiency remains unchanged between 50% and 70% occupancy and increases by just 1% when rooftop use rises from 30% to 50%. Similarly, the horizontal and single-tilted configurations are nearing their saturation points, as evidenced by the minimal increases in self-sufficiency despite higher rooftop occupancy. This suggests that these PV systems are already producing as much energy as possible during daylight hours, while the remaining demand occurs at night, when solar generation is not available.

Figure 5 shows how self-consumption and self-sufficiency rates at the *Pinhal Novo* (PN) train station evolve with increasing rooftop occupancy and corresponding increases in installed capacity. The highest self-consumption rate is achieved with the single-tilted configuration at 10% rooftop occupancy, reaching 68%. In contrast, the lowest self-consumption occurs, consistently with other train stations, in the double-tilted configuration at 70% rooftop occupancy, yielding just 3%. The maximum self-sufficiency rate is 40%, attained by the double-tilted configuration at rooftop occupancies of 30%, 50%, and 70%, indicating a stagnation point beginning at 30% rooftop occupancy. The lowest self-sufficiency rate is 28% and coincides with the conditions that produce the highest self-consumption (single tilted configuration, 71.54 kWp of installed capacity).

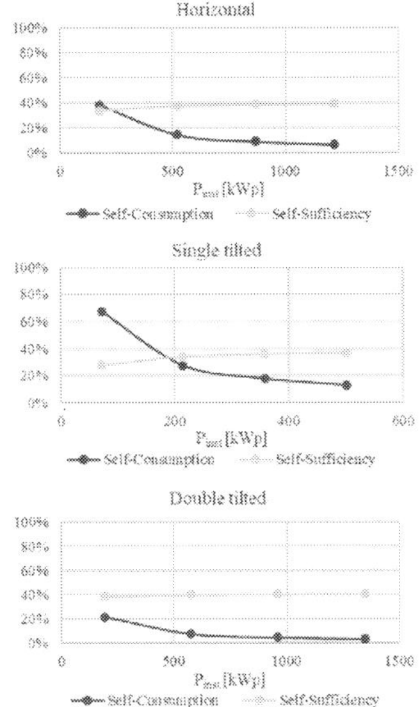

Figure 5: Self-sufficiency vs Self-consumption for the train station PN, located in Lines S and EA

At this railway station, the configuration and rooftop occupancy that best align PV generation with energy demand is the single-tilted setup at 10% rooftop occupancy, which yields the highest self-consumption. This configuration corresponds to an installed capacity of 72 kWp. Given that most of the station's energy demand occurs during nighttime hours, maximising self-consumption is the most effective way to utilise PV generation. However, 32% of the energy produced under this setup remains unused and must either be injected into the grid or curtailed.

3.3 Self-consumption analysis: Selected railway lines

Figure 6 shows the load profiles of train stations along the selected railway lines for a summer day. Line N stands out with the highest energy demand, while the other lines exhibit similar consumption patterns. Generally, energy use is slightly lower in the summer than in the winter. The demand across Lines BB, EA, and S is similar. All railway lines show lower demand during daylight hours, with noticeable peaks around 7 AM and 7 PM.

Figure 7 illustrates the self-sufficiency rate of the selected railway lines regarding the train stations' loads. When rooftop occupancy reaches 70%, self-sufficiency rates show little variation across different configurations within the same railway line. The highest self-sufficiency is recorded in Line N, where the double-tilted configuration at 70% rooftop coverage achieves a rate of 41%. Conversely, the lowest self-sufficiency is found in

Line BB, with the single-tilted configuration covering just 10% of the rooftop area, resulting in only 10% self-sufficiency.

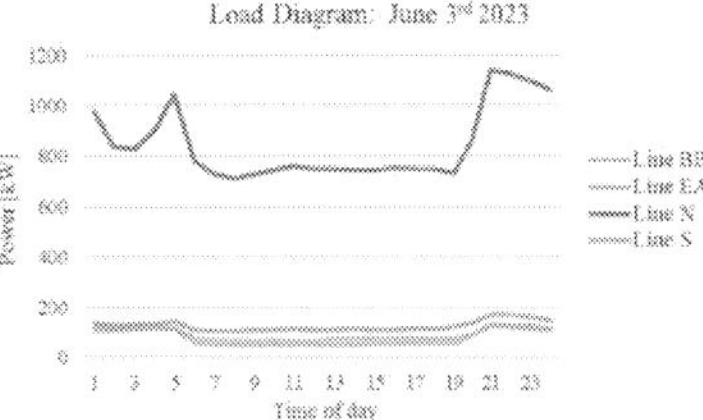

Figure 6: Load diagram of the railway stations located along the selected railway lines for June 3rd, 2023

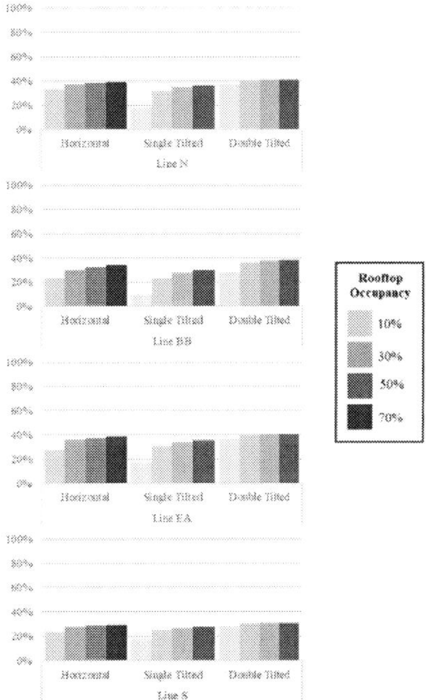

Figure 7: Evolution of the self-sufficiency rates at train stations of the selected railway lines as rooftop occupancy increases

Line S shows the smallest gains in self-sufficiency as rooftop occupancy increases, particularly with the double-tilted configuration. The most notable improvement occurs when rooftop coverage rises from 10% to 30% resulting in a 7% increase in self-sufficiency, significantly lower than the 13% to 14% gains observed on other lines for the same increase.

Beyond 30% rooftop occupancy, additional improvements in self-sufficiency become marginal across all configurations, with increases consistently under 5%. In some cases, such as the double-tilted configuration, self-sufficiency levels off entirely. This plateau effect is largely due to most energy occurring outside PV generation hours. Consequently, self-sufficiency in train stations tends to stabilise at around 40%, earlier than in traction substations, where physical space constraints, rather than time-of-use mismatches, limit the system size and performance.

Figure 8 shows the evolution of the self-consumption rates for the selected train stations as rooftop occupancy increases. Line S is the only line that does not reach 100% self-consumption at 10% rooftop occupancy, peaking instead at 94%. The highest self-consumption rate for the horizontal configuration is recorded in Line BB, also at 10% rooftop occupancy, reaching 80%. Likewise, the double-tilted configuration achieves its highest self-consumption in Line BB under the same conditions, at 72%. Overall, Line BB consistently exhibits the highest self-consumption rates across all configurations and occupancy levels.

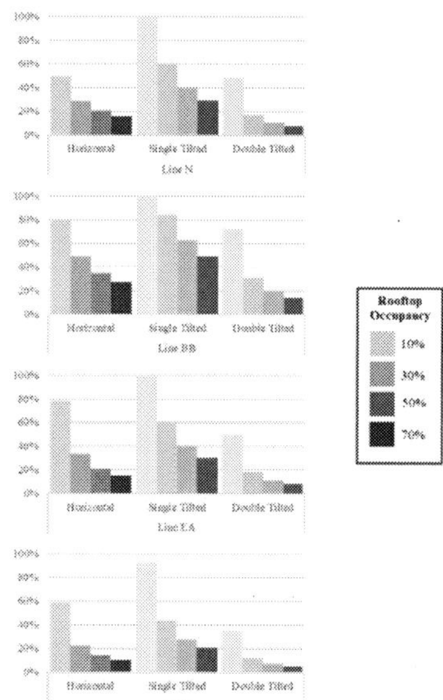

Figure 8: Evolution of the self-consumption rates at the train stations of the selected railway lines as rooftop occupancy increases

The largest increases in self-consumption generally occur when rooftop occupancy is reduced from 30% to 10% across all railway lines and configurations. The only exception is found in Line BB, where the single-tilted configuration shows the greatest increase when occupancy decreases from 50% to 30%.

4   DISCUSSION

Railway stations in Portugal exhibit their highest consumption at night, which suggests that station energy use is mostly due to lighting and largely independent of passenger traffic or train operations; as illustrated in Figure 4, energy demand at train stations drops during the morning rush hour (7 AM to 10 AM), despite high passenger flow. Similarly, in the evening, peak consumption occurs after the afternoon rush hour (5 PM to 7 PM) has ended. Some rural train stations barely have energy consumption during the day, only at night, presenting a total mismatch with PV energy generation.

Given the typical consumption profile of Portuguese train stations, characterised by high nighttime demand, achieving full self-sufficiency using only PV systems is unfeasible without the integration of energy storage

systems (ESS) and demand-side management (DSM) strategies. However, PV systems can still effectively meet daytime energy needs. Since ESS significantly increases overall system costs, a more practical approach is to optimise PV generation for daytime consumption, maximising self-consumption during sunlight hours. DSM strategies, such as shifting non-essential nighttime loads to the day, can further improve PV utilisation. In stations with very low daytime demand, analysing nearby energy loads could help absorb surplus PV production, reducing curtailment and enabling efficient grid injection.

5   CONCLUSIONS

This work explores the solar potential of the Portuguese railway network, with a focus on integrating photovoltaic (PV) energy into railway station operations and identifying strategies to mitigate the mismatch between energy generation and consumption. With renewable sources already accounting for 71% of Portugal's energy mix, the railway sector is already benefiting from a substantial share of clean traction energy.

Four railway lines out of the Portuguese railway system were analysed regarding the mismatch between energy consumption and PV energy generation. Three rooftop technical configurations were evaluated: horizontal, single-tilted, and double-tilted.

Train stations exhibit a great mismatch between PV generation and energy demand due to their predominantly nighttime consumption. Consequently, no railway line achieves more than 41% self-sufficiency, and self-consumption rates are relatively low. Only the single-tilted configuration reaches 100% self-consumption, and even then, not across all railway lines. In contrast, the horizontal and double-tilted configurations consistently perform worse, with self-consumption rates always below 80% for the smaller systems analysed. To address this imbalance, PV systems should be sized based on daytime demand, as they cannot supply energy during the night. Integrating ESS offers another solution, enabling excess daytime generation to be stored for later use. Additionally, implementing DSM strategies, such as shifting or reducing non-essential nighttime loads, can enhance energy efficiency and better align demand with PV availability.

The Portuguese railway system has significant solar potential, offering a path to greater renewable energy use and improved environmental sustainability. Future research should analyse real rooftop areas and consumption profiles of train stations and assess how nearby energy needs could reduce curtailment. A detailed economic analysis, including the role of storage systems, is essential, and exploring hybrid solutions with wind or hydropower could ensure energy availability during low solar production periods.

6   ACKNOWLEDGEMENTS

We thank Infraestruturas de Portugal (IP) for providing load demand data and for their valuable advice.

This work is supported by the Portuguese Fundação para a Ciência e Tecnologia, FCT, I.P./MCTES through national funds (PIDDAC): UID/50019/2025 and LA/P/0068/2020 https://doi.org/10.54499/LA/P/0068/202 0).

7   REFERENCES

[1]   'European Climate Law - European Commission'. Accessed: Jul. 31, 2025. [Online]. Available:

https://climate.ec.europa.eu/eu-action/european-climate-law_en

[2] 'Transport - Energy System', IEA. Accessed: Mar. 11, 2025. [Online]. Available: https://www.iea.org/energy-system/transport

[3] M. Herz, A. Sepanski, U. Hupach, B. Schönauer, and S. Ulrich, 'SOLAR FOR RAILWAYS - INVESTIGATION OF THE PV POTENTIAL ON THE GERMAN RAIL INFRASTRUCTURE'.

[4] F. Ding, J. Yang, and Z. Zhou, 'Economic profits and carbon reduction potential of photovoltaic power generation for China's high-speed railway infrastructure', *Renewable and Sustainable Energy Reviews*, vol. 178, p. 113272, May 2023, doi: 10.1016/j.rser.2023.113272.

[5] Z. Chen *et al.*, 'Using existing infrastructures of high-speed railways for photovoltaic electricity generation', *Resources, Conservation and Recycling*, vol. 178, p. 106091, Mar. 2022, doi: 10.1016/j.resconrec.2021.106091.

[6] L. Ji, Z. Yu, J. Ma, L. Jia, and F. Ning, 'The Potential of Photovoltaics to Power the Railway System in China', *Energies*, vol. 13, no. 15, p. 3844, Jul. 2020, doi: 10.3390/en13153844.

[7] M. Z. Jacobson and V. Jadhav, 'World estimates of PV optimal tilt angles and ratios of sunlight incident upon tilted and tracked PV panels relative to horizontal panels', *Solar Energy*, vol. 169, pp. 55–66, Jul. 2018, doi: 10.1016/j.solener.2018.04.030.

[8] 'OAL - Conjunções'. Accessed: May 30, 2025. [Online]. Available: https://oal.ul.pt/solsticio-de-inverno-2019/

[9] 'Rede Ferroviária | Infraestruturas de Portugal'. Accessed: Mar. 20, 2025. [Online]. Available: https://www.infraestruturasdeportugal.pt/pt-pt/infraestruturas/rede-ferroviaria

[10] Y. Zhang, J. Ren, Y. Pu, and P. Wang, 'Solar energy potential assessment: A framework to integrate geographic, technological, and economic indices for a potential analysis', *Renewable Energy*, vol. 149, pp. 577–586, Apr. 2020, doi: 10.1016/j.renene.2019.12.071.

[11] Monique Maria Hoogwijk, 'On the global and regional potential of renewable energy sources', Doctoral dissertation, 2004. [Online]. Available: https://np-net.pbworks.com/f/Hoogwijk+(2004)+Global+and+regional+potential+of+renewable+energy+sources+(Thesis+Utrecht).pdf

[12] S. Izquierdo, M. Rodrigues, and N. Fueyo, 'A method for estimating the geographical distribution of the available roof surface area for large-scale photovoltaic energy-potential evaluations', *Solar Energy*, vol. 82, no. 10, pp. 929–939, Oct. 2008, doi: 10.1016/j.solener.2008.03.007.

[13] 'Google Earth'. Accessed: Apr. 18, 2024. [Online]. Available: https://earth.google.com/web/@38.74537372,-9.19274542,80.09038843a,1243.56553885d,35y,0h,0t,0r/data=CgRCAggBOgMKATBCAggASg0I___ ______ARAA

[14] A. Gómez, M. Rodrigues, C. Montañés, C. Dopazo, and N. Fueyo, 'The potential for electricity generation from crop and forestry residues in Spain', *Biomass and Bioenergy*, vol. 34, no. 5, pp. 703–719, May 2010, doi: 10.1016/j.biombioe.2010.01.013.

[15] 'JRC Photovoltaic Geographical Information System (PVGIS) - European Commission'. Accessed: May 16, 2025. [Online]. Available: https://re.jrc.ec.europa.eu/pvg_tools/en/

[16] W. F. Holmgren, C. W. Hansen, and M. A. Mikofski, 'pvlib python: a python package for modeling solar energy systems', *JOSS*, vol. 3, no. 29, p. 884, Sep. 2018, doi: 10.21105/joss.00884.

PERFORMANCE ANALYSIS OF NON-ISOLATED DC-DC BOOST CONVERTER TOPOLOGIES IN VIPV SYSTEMS UNDER VARIABLE IRRADIANCE

Sebastían Rodríguez-Romero[1, 3, *], Jorge Rabanal-Arabach[1, 3], Mauricio Trigo-Gonzalez [1, 3], Gino Mondaca-Cuevas[1], Christian A. Rojas [2, 3], Alejandro Stowhas-Villa [2, 3], Fernando Castro-Gallardo[1, 3] and Edward Fuentealba-Vidal[1, 3]

[1] University of Antofagasta, Av. Angamos 601, 1270300 Antofagasta, Chile.
[2] Universidad Técnica Federico Santa María, Valparaíso 2390123, Chile.
[3] Solar Energy Research Center, Tupper 2007, 8370451 Santiago, Chile.

* Corresponding Author: sebastian.rodriguez@uantof.cl

ABSTRACT: The adoption of Vehicle-Integrated Photovoltaic (ViPV) systems into urban electric buses improves sustainability and reduces grid dependency in public transport. However, challenges such as variable irradiance and shading conditions limit their effectiveness. This study evaluates three advanced non-isolated DC-DC converter topologies (Boost Interleaved, Quadratic Boost, and Multi-Input/Single-Output) under MPPT control using the Perturb and Observe (P&O) algorithm. Simulations were conducted in Simulink using irradiance and temperature data collected in Antofagasta, Chile. The system assumed 600 PV cells forming a 350 V string connected to a 540 V DC-Link bus powered by a 50 kWh LiFePo4 battery bank. Key metrics analyzed include voltage gain, efficiency, stability, and current ripple under realistic urban conditions. Results demonstrate that Interleaved Boost exhibits high efficiency under uniform irradiance conditions, achieving stable current distribution with a low ripple of 2%. However, its performance is less robust during rapid irradiance changes. Quadratic Boost maintained a stable voltage gain in steady-state conditions and operated with a low duty cycle, reducing stress on switching components and enhancing long-term reliability. Nevertheless, it underperformed during abrupt transients due to the inherent complexity of its coupled stages, which impacted its ability to adapt to rapid system changes. The Multi-Input/Single-Output (MISO) topology effectively integrated multiple input sources and demonstrated strong performance under partial shading scenarios. However, its overall complexity and ripple management require optimization to improve efficiency in high irradiance conditions. These findings identify Interleaved Boost as the best option for stable conditions, while Quadratic Boost offers advantages in reducing component stress under steady-state operation. MISO emerges as a flexible alternative for scenarios with frequent shading. This research provides modeling insights for designing ViPV systems in urban electric buses, addressing the challenges of dynamic environments and improving sustainability in public transport.

Keywords: Vehicle-Integrated Photovoltaics (ViPV), DC-DC converters, MPPT, electric buses, partial shading, energy efficiency.

1 INTRODUCTION

The transportation sector contributes nearly 25% of global greenhouse gas (GHG) emissions [1], becoming one of the main drivers for the transition toward low-carbon technologies. Among renewable options, photovoltaic (PV) systems stand out due to their effectiveness in both grid-connected and off-grid applications, particularly in high-irradiance environments such as the Atacama Desert in northern Chile [2], [3], [4]. This region provides one of the most demanding natural laboratories for testing the performance and reliability of solar energy technologies.

Electric vehicles (EVs) represent a promising strategy to reduce fossil fuel dependency. However, challenges related to driving range and charging infrastructure remain [5]. In this context, Vehicle-Integrated Photovoltaics (ViPV) emerges as a complementary solution capable of delivering 10–30 km of daily range under favorable solar conditions [6], [7], while simultaneously reducing operating costs and carbon emissions. Yet, irradiance variability and partial shading in urban environments introduce significant uncertainties in converter operation and overall system efficiency [8], [7], [9], [10].

DC-DC converters are key to ensuring regulated energy transfer between PV arrays, batteries, and drivetrains [11]. However, comparative analyses of advanced non-isolated topologies under real irradiance conditions remain limited [12], [13]. This study addresses this gap by evaluating three high-gain non-isolated converters, namely Interleaved Boost, Quadratic Boost, and Multi-Input Single-Output (MISO), within a ViPV system designed for urban electric buses. The analysis employs real irradiance and temperature profiles collected in Antofagasta, Chile, to assess voltage regulation, efficiency, and input current ripple under dynamic operating conditions.

The main contribution of this work is to provide a comparative performance evaluation of advanced non-isolated DC-DC converters under real-world irradiance conditions, highlighting trade-offs in efficiency, stability, and current ripple. This offers design guidelines for

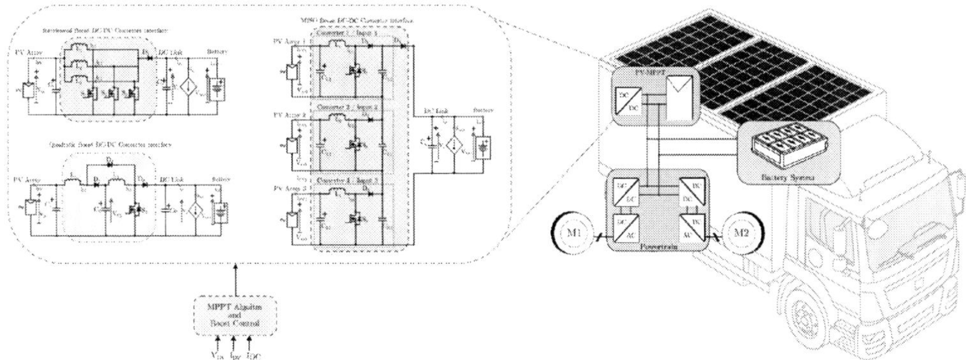

Fig. 1: Functional diagram of an integrated energy conversion and control system of ViPV powertrain systems.

selecting robust topologies in ViPV systems for urban electric transportation.

2 METHODOLOGY

2.1 PV System

The photovoltaic generator was modeled using experimental irradiance and temperature data obtained in the city of Antofagasta. A crystalline silicon reference cell mounted on the roof of a test vehicle provided the environmental inputs, which were implemented in Simulink using time-based lookup tables to replicate realistic operating conditions. The PV array consisted of 600 series-connected cells, delivering a nominal voltage of 350 V. This generator was coupled to a 540 V DC bus that supplied a 50 kWh $LiFePO_4$ battery bank. The storage system was represented by a $2RC$ equivalent circuit parameterized with experimental data and optimized through genetic algorithms, ensuring an accurate representation of voltage dynamics and state-of-charge evolution.

2.2 DC-DC Converters

Three non-isolated high-gain DC-DC converters were studied under identical operating conditions with a switching frequency of 10 kHz. The topologies considered were the Interleaved Boost converter, the Quadratic Boost converter, and the Multi-Input Single-Output (MISO) Boost converter. All of them were modeled in state-space representation and simulated in order to analyze their voltage gain, efficiency, and current ripple under dynamic solar conditions.

The electrical and simulation parameters used for the study are summarized in Table I. The component values were selected to maintain the inductor current ripple below 20% and to ensure settling times shorter than 100 ms, allowing consistent comparison across the three topologies.

Each converter was evaluated with a Maximum Power Point Tracking (MPPT) strategy based on the Perturb and Observe (P&O) algorithm. The algorithm flowchart is shown in Fig. 2, which illustrates the sequence of perturbation and decision steps to track the maximum power point. The control was implemented through a cascaded structure, where the outer voltage loop regulated the PV array voltage while the inner current loop controlled the inductor current. Propor-

Table I: Simulation Parameters.

Description	Symbol	Value
PV input	V_{PV}	350 V
Battery, output voltage	V_{batt}, V_o	540 V
Capacitors	C_1, C_2, C_3, C_o	200 μF
Inductors	L_1, L_2, L_3	2 mH
Output resistor	R_o	80-90 Ω
Switching frequency	f_{sw}	10 kHz
Max. Power	60 km/h	3.5 kW

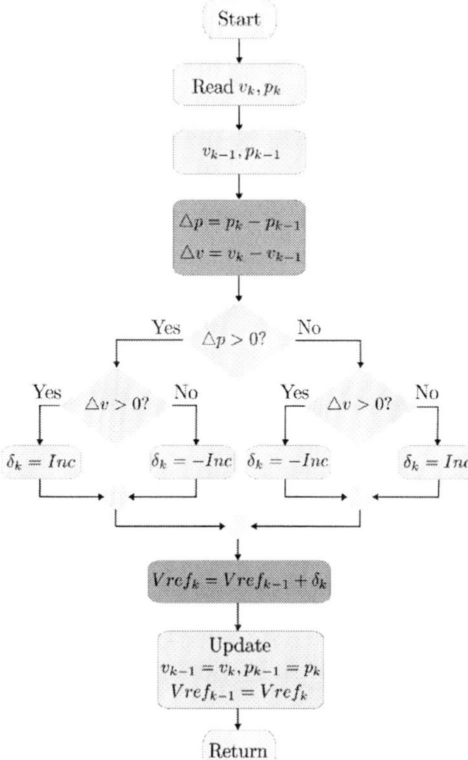

Fig. 2: Flowchart of the Perturb and Observe (P&O) MPPT algorithm

tional–integral controllers were applied to both loops in order to achieve stable tracking and adequate dynamic performance.

The control architectures of the Quadratic Boost, Interleaved Boost, and MISO Boost converters are illustrated in Fig. 3, highlighting their integration with the MPPT scheme. Furthermore, the performance of

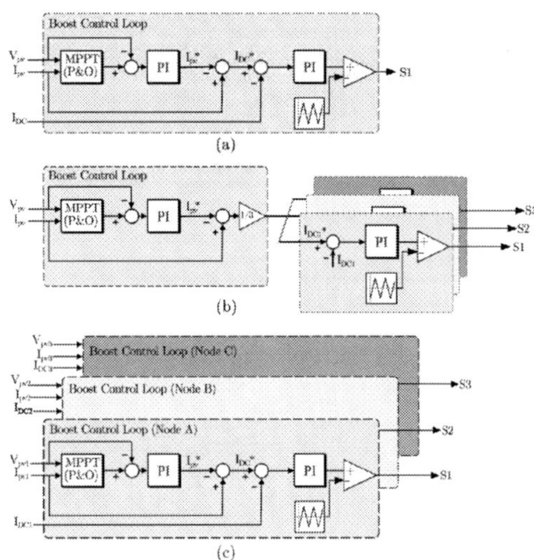

Fig. 3: MPPT control loop architectures for each converter topology: Quadratic (top), Interleaved (middle), and MISO (bottom).

the P&O algorithm under different irradiance profiles was analyzed to validate its use within the study. The results are presented in Fig. 4, where three scenarios are depicted: (a) operation under uniform irradiance of 1000 W/m² without shading, (b) a transition from 1000 W/m² to 500 W/m² corresponding to partial shading, and (c) a severe shading event with irradiance dropping from 1000 W/m² to below 100 W/m². This evaluation demonstrates the ability of the algorithm to maintain tracking across rapid irradiance changes, although oscillations around the maximum power point become more evident under shading.

3 RESULTS AND DISCUSSION

The three converter topologies delivered more than 3.2 kW with efficiencies higher than 98.4% under uniform high-irradiance conditions. Nevertheless, significant differences emerged when the system was subjected to variable and critical solar scenarios, which revealed the trade-offs between efficiency, current ripple, and voltage stability.

The Interleaved Boost converter exhibited strong steady-state performance and fast recovery during irradiance transients. These characteristics were achieved at the cost of elevated current peaks and increased thermal stress on the semiconductor devices, which may affect long-term reliability.

The Quadratic Boost converter reached the required voltage gain at relatively low duty cycles, reducing the stress on switching components. However, it was more sensitive to rapid irradiance variations, showing pronounced ripple in both duty cycle and current waveforms. This behavior indicates that, although suitable under stable conditions, its performance deteriorates significantly under dynamic scenarios.

The MISO Boost converter consistently maintained

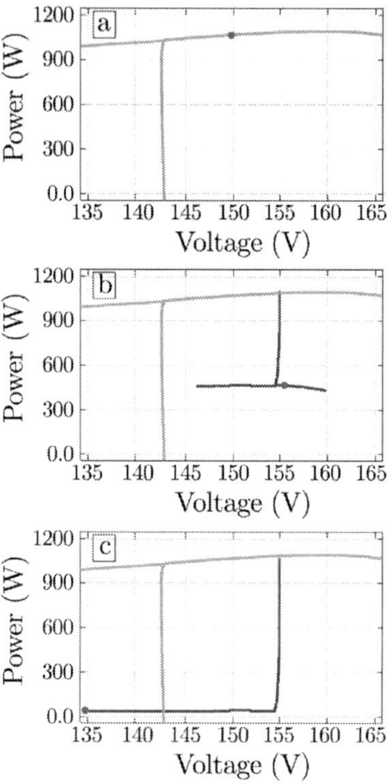

Fig. 4: MPPT algorithm response under different irradiance scenarios: (a) uniform irradiance of 1000 W/m², (b) transition from 1000 W/m² to 500 W/m² (partial shading), and (c) transition from 1000 W/m² to below 100 W/m² (severe shading).

voltage regulation and sustained efficiency across all operating conditions. Its ability to operate with low input current ripple, even during severe shading events where irradiance dropped below 100 W/m², demonstrated its robustness. This topology minimized the stress on components and ensured reliable energy transfer across the full operating range.

The comparative qualitative performance is summarized in Table II, which highlights voltage stability, efficiency, and input current ripple for each topology. According to the table, the Interleaved Boost provides medium efficiency and stability, the Quadratic Boost shows lower robustness under disturbances, and the MISO configuration achieves high efficiency with superior stability and minimal current ripple. These

Table II: Comparative qualitative performance of non-isolated DC-DC topologies under real irradiance

Criterion	Interleaved Boost	Quadratic Boost	MISO
Voltage stability	Medium	Low	High
Efficiency	Medium–High	Medium	High
Input current ripple	Medium	High	Low

results are further illustrated in Fig. 5, where the temporal responses of the converters are presented under different irradiance and temperature conditions.

Subfigures (a) to (g) depict the irradiance profiles, FET currents, output voltages, and output currents across two test intervals. The figure evidences that while the Interleaved Boost responds rapidly, it induces higher current peaks; the Quadratic Boost suffers from ripple amplification during transitions; and the MISO Boost maintains stable operation even under partial and severe shading.

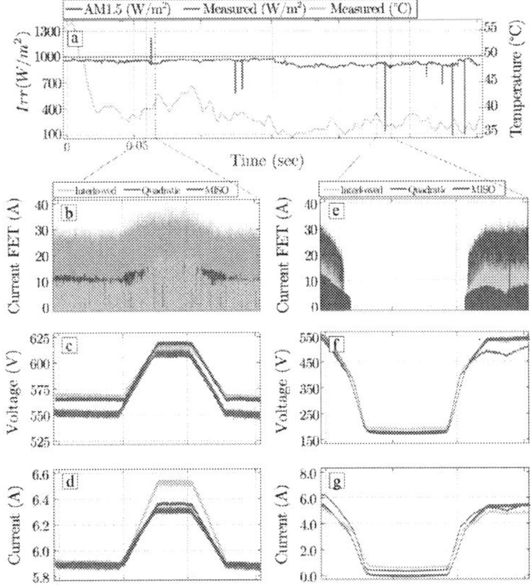

Fig. 5: Comparative performance of Interleaved, Quadratic, and MISO converters under variable irradiance and temperature conditions: (a) solar irradiance (AM1.5 and measured) and measured temperature; (b) FET current during the first interval; (c) output voltage during the first interval; (d) output current during the first interval; (e) FET current during the second interval; (f) output voltage during the second interval; (g) output current during the second interval.

4 CONCLUSIONS

This study analyzed the performance of three advanced non-isolated DC-DC converter topologies for Vehicle-Integrated Photovoltaic (ViPV) systems in urban electric buses, using real irradiance and temperature profiles collected in northern Chile. The Interleaved Boost, Quadratic Boost, and MISO Boost converters were simulated under identical conditions to assess their voltage stability, efficiency, and current ripple.

The results demonstrated that, although all converters achieved efficiencies above 98% under high irradiance, their behavior diverged under dynamic conditions. The Interleaved Boost exhibited rapid transient recovery but with elevated current peaks and thermal stress. The Quadratic Boost operated with reduced stress on switching devices due to low duty cycles, but its performance degraded during abrupt irradiance variations. In contrast, the MISO Boost consistently maintained stable output voltage, low input current ripple, and sustained efficiency even under severe shading events, making it the most robust and reliable

alternative for urban scenarios with highly variable solar conditions.

The main contribution of this work lies in providing a comparative evaluation of advanced non-isolated DC-DC converters under realistic irradiance variations, highlighting the trade-offs between efficiency, stability, and current ripple. These results establish technical guidelines for selecting suitable topologies in ViPV systems, particularly in environments characterized by rapid and frequent solar fluctuations.

Future research should focus on experimental validation of the converters and the integration of adaptive or predictive MPPT strategies to further enhance tracking accuracy and dynamic robustness. Such developments will strengthen the role of ViPV systems in reducing grid dependency and improving sustainability in public transportation.

ACKNOWLEDGMENTS

This work was supported by the Chilean Solar Energy Research Center (SERC Chile) under Grant ANID/FONDAP/1523A0006 and the Chilean National Agency for Research and Development (ANID) through the National Doctorate Program under Grant ANID/Subdirección de Capital Humano/Doctorado Nacional/2024-21241192. Special thanks to the Consortium of Engineering Faculties of the Antofagasta Region, the HEUMA ING2030 16ENI2-71940 Project for their unparalleled fundings, Power Electronics and Electromobility Laboratory (POWEREMLAB) and the Doctoral Program in Solar Energy of the Universidad de Antofagasta for their invaluable support and research environment.

References

[1] D. W. Cunningham, E. P. Carlson, J. S. Manser, and I. C. Kizilyalli, "Impacts of wide band gap power electronics on photovoltaic system design," *IEEE Journal of Photovoltaics*, vol. 10, pp. 213–218, 1 2020.

[2] J. D. Clarke, "Antiquity of aridity in the chilean atacama desert," *Geomorphology*, vol. 73, no. 1, pp. 101–114, 2006. [Online]. Available: https://www.sciencedirect.com/science/article/pii/S0169555X05002023

[3] A. Marzo, P. Ferrada, F. Beiza, P. Besson, J. Alonso-Montesinos, J. Ballestrín, R. Román, C. Portillo, R. Escobar, and E. Fuentealba, "Standard or local solar spectrum? implications for solar technologies studies in the atacama desert," *Renewable Energy*, vol. 127, pp. 871–882, 2018.

[4] J. Rabanal-Arabach, "Development of a c-si photovoltaic module for desert climates," Ph.D. dissertation, Universität Konstanz, Konstanz, 2019.

[5] D. R. E. Trejo, S. Taheri, J. L. Saavedra, P. Vázquez, C. H. D. Angelo, and J. A. Pecina-Sánchez, "Nonlinear control and internal stability analysis of series-connected boost dc/dc converters in pv systems with distributed mppt," *IEEE Journal of Photovoltaics*, vol. 11, pp. 504–512, 3 2021.

[6] M. Yamaguchi, K. Nakamura, R. Ozaki *et al.*, "Analysis for the potential of high-efficiency and low-cost vehicle-integrated photovoltaics," *Solar RRL*, vol. 7, no. 1, 2022.

[7] P. Hoth, A. Dannenberg, E. Lüpfert *et al.*, "Vehicle-integrated photovoltaics—a case study for berlin," *World Electric Vehicle Journal*, vol. 15, no. 3, p. 113, 2024.

[8] M. C. Brito, T. Santos, F. Moura, D. Pera, and J. Rocha, "Urban solar potential for vehicle integrated photovoltaics,"

Transportation Research Part D: Transport and Environment, vol. 94, p. 102810, 2021.

[9] L. S. José, R. González, R. Ortega, E. Gutiérrez *et al.*, "Performance evaluation of mppt algorithm of vipv systems in realistic urban routes using image processing," *Solar Energy Materials and Solar Cells*, vol. 276, p. 113061, 2024.

[10] S. Rodríguez-Romero, J. Rabanal-Arabach, C. A. Rojas, M. Trigo-Gonzalez, G. Mondaca-Cuevas, D. Arias, F. Castro-Gallardo, and E. Fuentealba-Vidal, "Analysis of advanced nonisolated topologies for vehicle-integrated photovoltaic (vipv) systems in urban electric transport buses," *IEEE Journal of Photovoltaics*, pp. 1–7, 2025.

[11] A. Asadi, M. S. Karimzadeh, X. Liang, M. S. Mahdavi, and G. B. Gharehpetian, "A novel control approach for a single-inductor multi-input single-output dc-dc boost converter for pv applications," *IEEE Access*, vol. 11, pp. 114753–114764, 2023.

[12] R. Daxini, K. S. Anderson, J. S. Stein, and M. Theristis, "Photovoltaic module spectral mismatch losses due to cell-level eqe variation," *IEEE Journal of Photovoltaics*, 2025.

[13] P. H. S. B. Loureiro and A. M. S. S. Andrade, "Single switch asymmetrical high step-up dc-dc converter based on differential connection," *IEEE Transactions on Power Electronics*, 2024.

3D INTEGRATED PHOTOVOLTAIC SURFACES FOR PORTABLE APPLICATIONS

Thomas M. Kraft*, Riikka Suhonen, Kaisa-Leena Väisänen, Kyösti Heikkinen, Antti Nurmesjärvi, and Mari Ylikunnari
VTT Technical Research Centre of Finland Ltd., Kaitoväylä 1, Oulu 90590, Finland
*thomas.kraft@vtt.fi

ABSTRACT: To enable the use of portable, and potentially wearable, 3D molded autonomous energy modules the applicability of high pressure injection overmolded flexible solar cells was investigated [1]. The goal was to find commercially available flexible amorphous Si photovoltaic (PV) modules, test their overmolding possibilities and to investigate overmolding materials of the PV as a baseline for future studies. The devices' electrical behavior was measured under different conditions and in an outdoor test environment. Based on processing and testing, the goal was to evaluate the manufacturing possibilities of a 3D integrable autonomous energy module for wearable plastic/composite equipment.
The investigation was divided into three sub-tasks: 1) material design, 2) PV device overmolding, and 3) testing. Regarding materials, commercial solar cells made of amorphous silicon were used in the project due to their easy availability, and two materials were tested for overmolding: polycarbonate (PC) and thermoplastic polyurethane (TPU). For the overmolding process, various parameters were evaluated, with the TPU being a more suitable material for the selected PV devices. Finally, the overmolded cells were tested under different lighting conditions, bending stress, accelerated ageing, and the effect of scratching and dirt on the cell's operation was studied.

Keywords: structural electronics, injection molding, flexible PV

1   AIM AND APPROACH

Traditional solar panels aren't always practical for off-grid electronics users' gear. What's needed are lightweight, attachable, and detachable modules that include a solar cell, battery, and fasteners. These modules can be quickly integrated into gear, making it easier to stay powered up without extra weight. They can also be carried in multiples, shared among users, and placed close to where the power is needed.

Current wearable solar solutions often involve sewing solar cells onto fabrics, which can't be detached or replaced easily. Pre-shaped, detachable modules offer better durability and protection against wear and tear. They ensure off-grid electronics users have reliable power without compromising mobility or equipment weight.
The criterion for selecting the solar cell was its commercial availability, flexibility, and thin structure. Three different power solar cells were used in the work: MPT3.6, MPT4.8, and MPT6, purchased from PowerFilm Inc (Table I).

Table I: Power, and voltage, and current values provided by the manufacturer.

Cell	Power [mW]	Operating Voltage [V]
MPT3.6	180	3.6
MPT4.8	240	4.8
MPT6	300	6.0

2   RESULTS

The requirements for the overmolding material were flexibility, and suitability to be injection overmolded. Based on these criteria, two materials were selected for molding: polycarbonate (PC) and thermoplastic polyurethane (TPU). An Engel victory 120 overmolding device was used in the work and done on either the illuminated or non-illuminated side of the solar cell.

The electrical performance of the solar cells was measured using the AM1.5 artificial sunlight measurement device, which provided a current-voltage curve. Based on the obtained curve, the measurement program calculated the maximum power of the solar cell. The artificial sunlight was restricted with steel meshes, reducing the incoming sunlight power (100 mW/cm²) to 1/3 (33 mW/cm²) and 1/9 (11 mW/cm²) of its original value. Further studies done at various different bending radii: 4.55 cm, 3.30 cm, and 2.80 cm and measured in different positions relative to the incoming light.

The overmolded cells were stressed in a weather cabinet under various accelerated conditions. There were four different stress tests:
• ISOS protocol for solar cells: 100 mW/cm² light, 50% humidity, 65°C temperature
• IEC protocol with standardized high temperature and humidity: 85% RH, 85°C
• IEC protocol with temperature cycling: -40°C to +85°C
• Mechanical stress: scratching the cell, scratching the overmolding material, contamination

2.1 Injection over-molding of PV modules

During the overmolding process, suitable process parameters for the materials and the solar cell were determined. Despite adjusting the parameters, all the cells broke during the PC overmolding process due to layer incompatibility and high processing temperature required for PC.

Figure 1: Flat overmolding of the PV module with TPU.

10.4229/EUPVSEC2025/4DV.1.55
020423-001

Figure 2: Curved TPU over-molding of the PV module.

Figure 3: Domed TPU over-molding of the PV module.

When molding with TPU, the solar cells withstood the overmolding process well, and moldings were made with three different molds: flat surface, curved surface, and dome-shaped surface (Figure 1, Figure 2, Figure 3). When molding into a curved shape, the cell easily detached from the overmolding material during mold removal. When molding into a dome shape, the cell did not stretch into the shape during molding, resulting in folds in the cell.

2.2 PV performance

By adjusting the illumination power of the simulated sunlight, various shaded conditions could be tested. Each overmolded solar cell was evaluated before and after overmolding, with parallel samples for accuracy. Weather cabinets simulated outdoor conditions, exposing cells to moisture and temperature changes.

Effect of Bending Radius

The angle of light significantly affects power output. As shown in Figure 4, for large cells like the MPT6, power drops by over 80% from 0° to 90°. Smaller bending radius and larger cell size further reduce power due to shading. For instance, MPT6's power dropped from 400 mW (flat at 1 SUN) to 50 mW with a 2.80 cm bending radius.

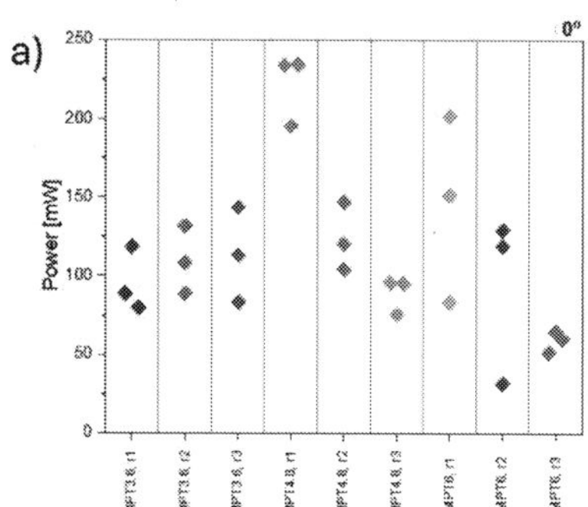

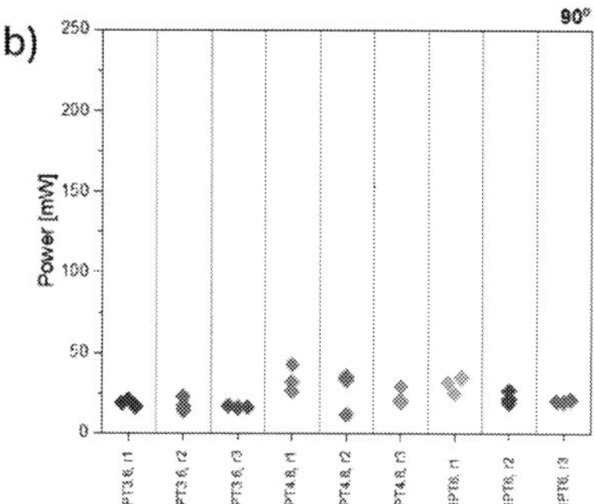

Figure 4. The effect of bending radius to cell performance. The bending radius used were r1 = 4.55 cm, r2 = 3.30 cm and r3 = 2.80 cm. At two angles of incident light a) 0° and b) 90°.

Effect of Overmolding

The performance of cells molded into flat or curved shapes remained unchanged, and the measured power values matched the manufacturer's specified values at 1SUN illumination (Figure 5). Additionally, the side of overmolding did not affect the cells' performance. Figure 5 shows the measured power values of MPT3.6 cells molded with a flat mold before and after overmolding.

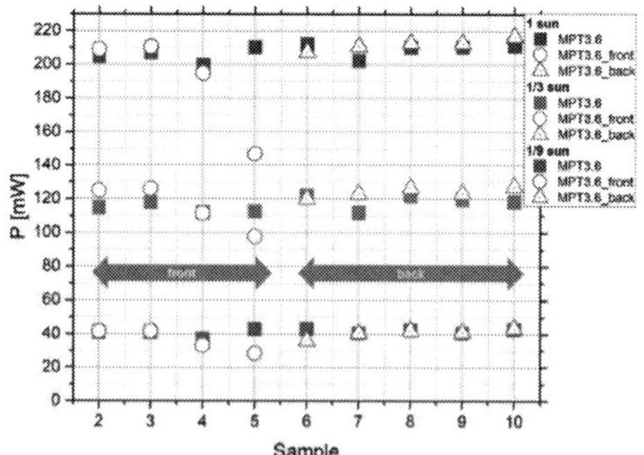

Figure 5: Cell performance before and after TPU over-molding measured at 1 sun, 1/3 sun and 1/9 light intensities. The filled symbols are power values before overmolding and "front" and "back" refer to the side of TPU overmolding.

Stress Tests of Overmolded Cells

Overmolded and non-overmolded cells were subjected to various accelerated conditions to assess their performance under stress. The cells were measured regularly outside the weather cabinet.

In Figure 6, the cell performance test of the overmolded and reference (no overmold) cells during ISOS-L-3 stability test is shown. After ~1500h of stress, the performance of reference cells starts to decrease which is mainly due to a decrease in voltage, caused by internal defects in the cell. Promisingly, the overmolded cells show stable performance even after 2500h of stress indicating that overmolding protects the flexible solar cells from degradation.

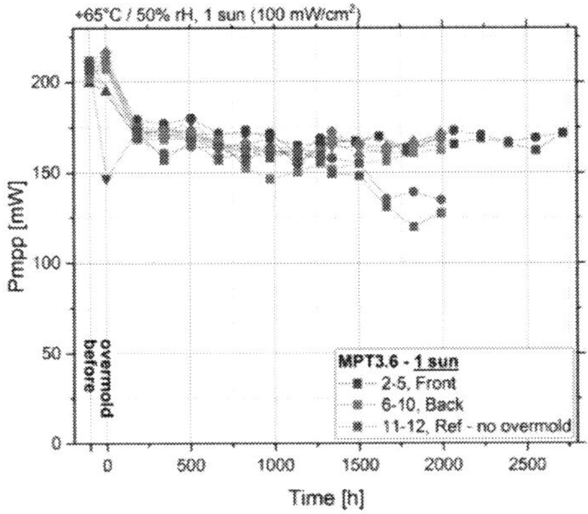

Figure 6. Performance of overmolded samples over time when stressed according the ISOS-L-3 stability test.

In the high temperature and humidity test, cells were kept at 85% humidity and 85°C temperature whereas in the temperature cycling test, cells were kept between -40°C and +85°C. As shown in Figure 7a, some variation in the cell performance was measured but with most of the cells, the output power was still > 90% of the original after 26 days of stressing. Whereas in the temperature cycling test, the performance did not change during cycling (Figure 7b). The overmolding material TPU became opaque (Figure 7c) but, surprisingly, this did not affect the electrical performance.

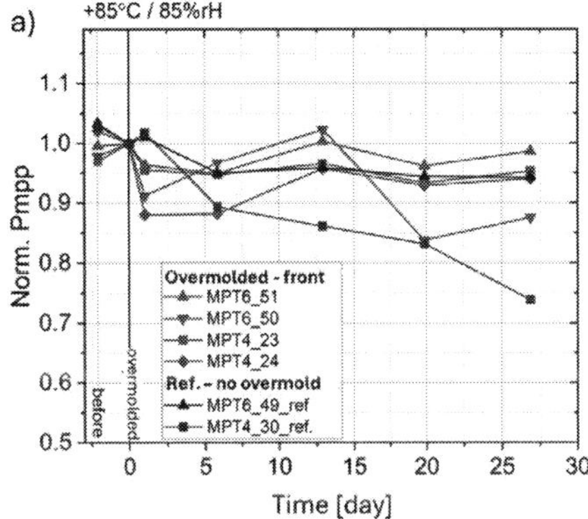

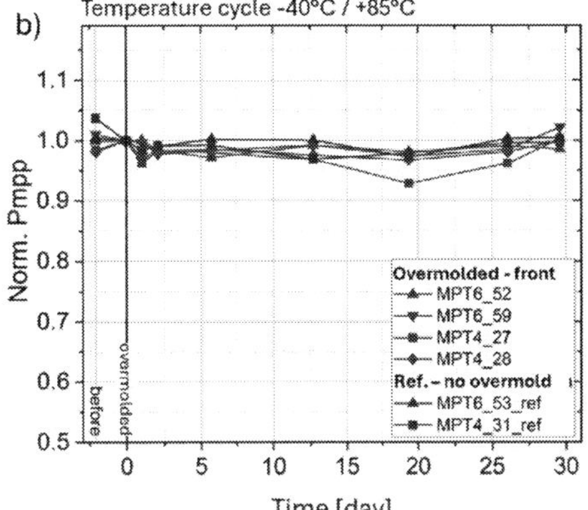

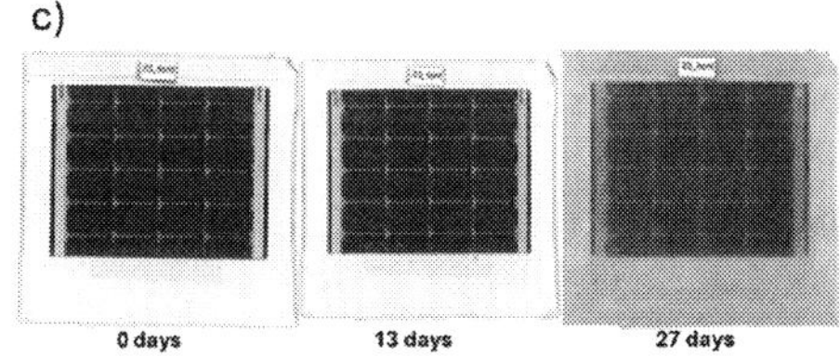

Figure 7. Cell performance during the IEC tests at a) +85°C and 85% rH and b) temperature cycling from -40°C to +85°C. In c) photographs of the overmolded samples after temperature cycling tests.

Mechanical Stress

Under mechanical stress, the surface of the cell was scratched with P60 sandpaper. When scratching the illuminated side of the front-molded TPU, the cell's electrical performance remained the same as the overmolded, non-scratched cell. Without the TPU protection, the cell stopped functioning when the illuminated side was scratched. The contamination of the cell surface was simulated by covering three cells (Table II) with a clear plastic film printed with partially covering patterns. Shadow A's coverage area was 37%, and Shadow B's coverage area was 56%, with the entirely black film covering 100%. Contamination significantly affects the current produced by the cell, thereby reducing the cell's power.

Table II: Power, voltage, and current of one MPT6 cell illuminated through covering films.

Film	Coverage	P [mW]	V [V]	I [mA]
Clear	0%	351	7	53
Shadow A	37%	157	7	24
Shadow B	56%	58	6	9
Black	100%	0	0	0

Outdoor Testing

The test site is located at VTT Oulu (N65.0564, E25.4580), where the temperature range during a one year period can fluctuate from −34.0 °C to +33.0 °C. The daylight duration varies from 3 hours 34 minutes in winter to 22 hours 3 minutes in summer. For this study, the testing period spans from 29 April 2025 to 28 July 2025 (Figure 8). The modules were fixed to a south facing stand and monitored with I-V sweeps every 30 minutes. Between I-V sweeps the modules were kept under a constant bias at maximum power point voltage of the previous I-V sweep. The test site also includes a weather station monitoring humidity, air pressure, wind speed and direction, precipitation, and solar irradiance.

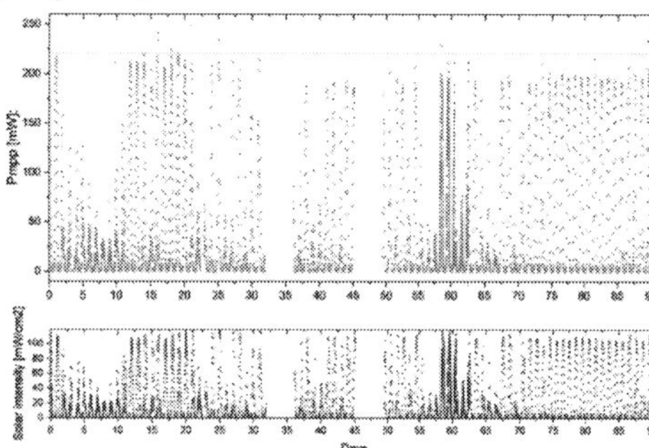

Figure 8: Outdoor Maximum Power Point (Pmpp) of over-molded PV modules (top) and corresponding measured solar intensity (bottom) over three months. Horizontal line at 220 mW corresponds to P_{MPP} measured with AM 1.5 prior to outdoor testing.

3 CONCLUSIONS

This study evaluated the suitability and primary considerations for integrated PV applications such as wearable devices and curved surfaces. It examined several key factors affecting performance after devices were injection overmolded with TPU.

The relationship between bending radius and cell area was explored, demonstrating that a smaller bending radius combined with a larger cell area leads to reduced power output. Additionally, it was found that the power output of the cell decreases by more than 80% when the illumination angle shifts from 0° to 90°.

Temperature and humidity effects were investigated, showing that overmolded cells possess strong resistance to accelerated stress environments; nonetheless, the overmolding material itself may undergo state changes when exposed to elevated temperature and relative humidity. Mechanical stress, such as scratching, was also considered: direct scratches on the cell surface result in performance failure, whereas scratches on the overmolded surface do not impact cell performance, highlighting the

importance of protecting the cell surface from mechanical damage. Finally, contamination was addressed, with results indicating that when 56% of the cell area is obstructed, only 15–17% of the original power is produced.

In summary, this study highlights the crucial factors influencing the performance of flexible solar cells, including irradiance, bending radius, angle of illumination, temperature, humidity, mechanical stress, and contamination. These findings emphasize the importance of optimizing both material selection and environmental protection to ensure reliable operation in real-world applications. Furthermore, TPU overmolding, both flat and curved, was suitable for the selected solar cells and that the overmolded modules performed well outdoors and showed little degradation.

4 AKNOWLEDGEMENTS

This research was funded by the Scientific Advisory Board for Defence (MATINE) and the CETPartnership (REFORM, CETP-2022-00348), the European Partnership under Joint Call 2022 for research proposals, co-funded by the European Commission (GA N°101069750) and with funding by Business Finland, decision number 2876/31/2023.

Further support provided by the Research Council of Finland (RCF), Printed intelligence infrastructure funding, decision 358621 and the RCF Flagship Programme, Photonics Research and Innovation (PREIN), decision number 346545.

5 REFERENCES

[1] Ylikunnari, "Aurinkokennoenergiamoduulit 3D-pintojen integrointiin". Valtioneuvoston hallintoyksikkö, Julkaisutuotanto, Helsinki 2024

3D Integrated Photovoltaic Surfaces For Portable Applications

Authors Thomas M. Kraft*, Riikka Suhonen, Kaisa-Leena Väisänen, Kyösti Heikkinen, Antti Nurmesjärvi, Mari Ylikunnari

Ambition

Development of 3D integrated photovoltaic (PV) surfaces for portable and potentially wearable applications [1]

- Focused on three main tasks:
  - mold cavity designs
  - solar cell overmolding process
  - testing and integration

Commercially available flexible amorphous silicon solar cells were used, and two materials, polycarbonate (PC) and thermoplastic polyurethane (TPU), were tested as overmolding materials.

Injection Over-Molded PV modules

Amorphous Si-PV modules were overmolded at VTT. Three mold cavities were designed for the study to investigate the effect of:

- TPU vs. PC
- curved stress
  - shapes: flat, curve, dome

Figure 1: Injection overmolding equipment at VTT

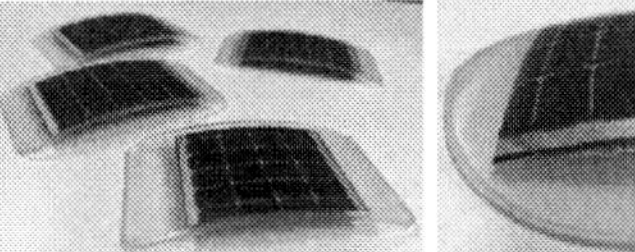
Figure 2: Injection overmolded PV modules from PowerFilm Inc. with TPU: (left) flat; (middle) curved; (right) domed forms.

When overmolding with TPU, the solar cells withstood the molding process well, however, all the modules were damaged during the PC overmolding process (due to elevated T and P in the mold cavity).

The performance of modules molded into flat or curved shapes remained unchanged, and the measured power values matched the manufacturer's specified values at 1SUN illumination. Domed forms had low yield.

Additionally, side of overmolding (front or back) did not affect the cells' performance. Figure 3 shows the measured power values of moldules molded with a flat mold before and after overmolding.

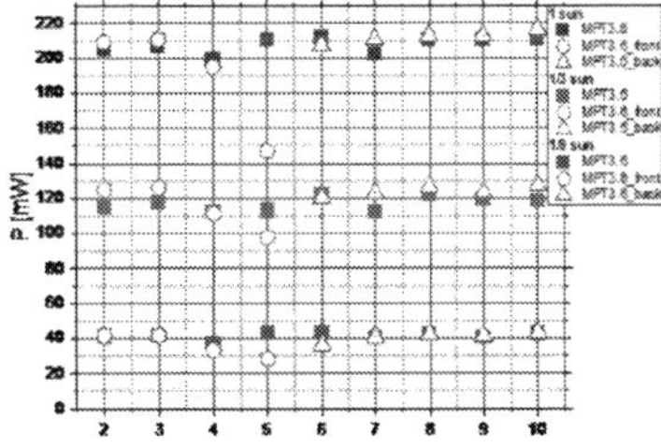
Figure 3: PV performance before (solid) and after (line) TPU overmolding flat form.

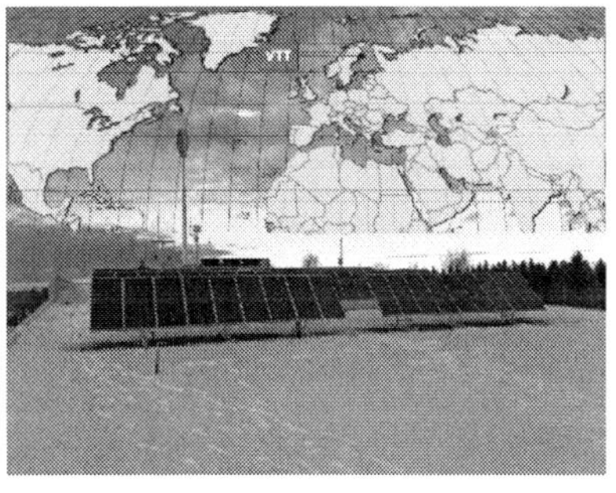
Figure 4: Outdoor PV test site in Oulu, Finland at VTT (left) and modules after 3 months outdoors (right).

Sub-Arctic Outdoor PV Testing

- Test site: VTT Oulu (N65.0564, E25.4580)
- Temperatures: −34.0 °C to +33.0 °C
  - Daylight: 3 h 34 min (winter) to 22 h 3 min (summer)

- I-V sweeps and correlating with humidity, air pressure, wind speed & direction, precipitation, solar irradiance. 29.04.25 to 28.07.25

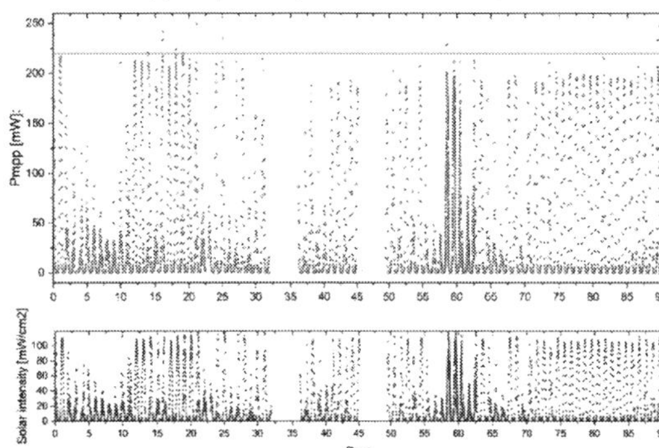
Figure 5: Outdoor Maximum Power Point (Pmpp) of over-molded PV modules (top) and corresponding measured solar intensity (bottom) over three months. Horizontal line at 220 mW corresponds to P_{MPP} measured with AM 1.5 prior to outdoor testing.

Conclusion

- **TPU overmolding was suitable for the selected solar cells.**
- **Overmolded modules performed well outdoors and showed little degradation.**
- **The performance of modules molded into flat or curved shapes remained unchanged**

Acknowledgements

This research was funded by the Scientific Advisory Board for Defence (MATINE) and the CETPartnership (REFORM, CETP-2022-00348), the European Partnership under Joint Call 2022 for research proposals, co-funded by the European Commission (GA N°101069750) and with funding by Business Finland, decision number 2876/31/2023.

Further support provided by the Research Council of Finland (RCF), Printed intelligence infrastructure funding, decision 358621 and the RCF Flagship Programme, Photonics Research and Innovation (PREIN), decision number 346545.

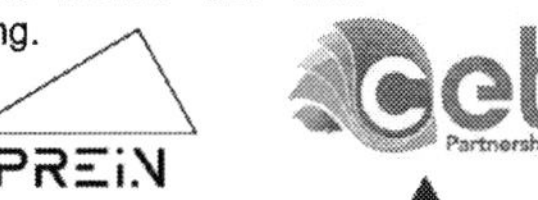

Contact: Thomas Kraft, PhD
Senior Scientist, Project Manager
Tel. +358 20 722 2070, thomas.kraft@vtt.fi
020424-001

beyond the obvious
www.vttresearch.com

[1] Ylikunnari, "Aurinkokennoenergiamoduulit 3D-pintojen integrointiin". Valtioneuvoston hallintoyksikkö, Julkaisutuotanto, Helsinki 2024

4DV.1
T4.6

Modelling of marine assembly logistics for an offshore floating photovoltaic (OFPV) plant subject to weather dependencies

Lu-Jan Huang, Simone Mancini, Minne de Jong

louis.huang@tno.nl

Full details in our recent journal paper:

METHODOLOGY

This study applies a **discrete-event simulation** approach (*TNO UWiSE*), modelling operations such as transit, loading, and installation as time-based events. Each task is governed by **weather thresholds** (e.g. wave limits), with delays logged when conditions exceed those limits. Some events must occur **consecutively without interruption**, requiring a continuous weather window. The model uses **multi-year hourly weather data** to capture uncertainty in installation outcomes.

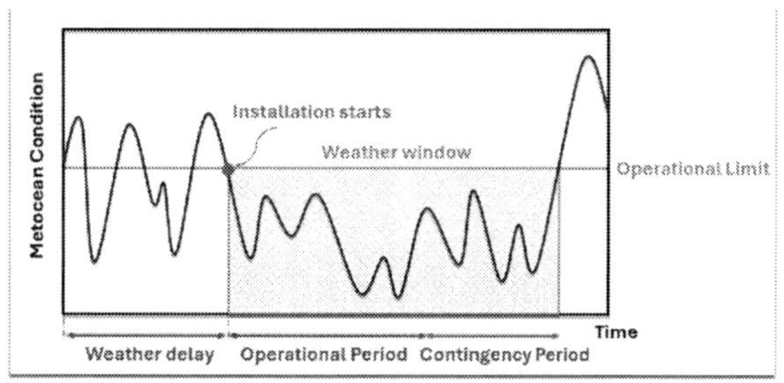

CASE STUDY: MODULAR OFPV

The 5 MWp OFPV plant consists of **54 triangular floating platforms** arranged into a large hexagonal array (left). Each platform (right) is based on a **truss-type prototype**, elevated ~10 m above sea level to withstand harsh wave conditions. Buoyancy and damping are provided by aluminum floats and gas cylinders, with **anchoring via 35 mooring lines and seabed anchors**.

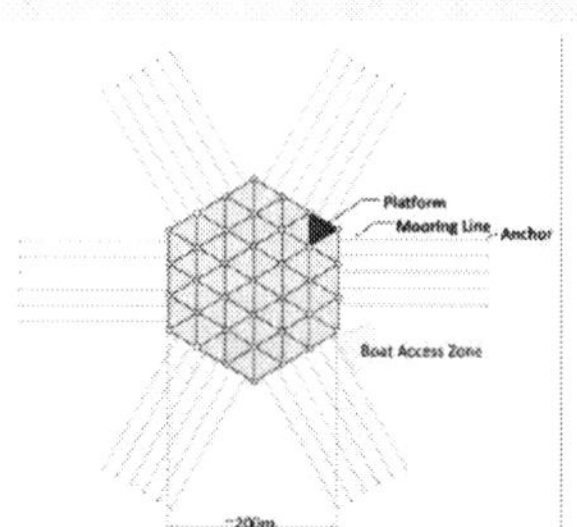

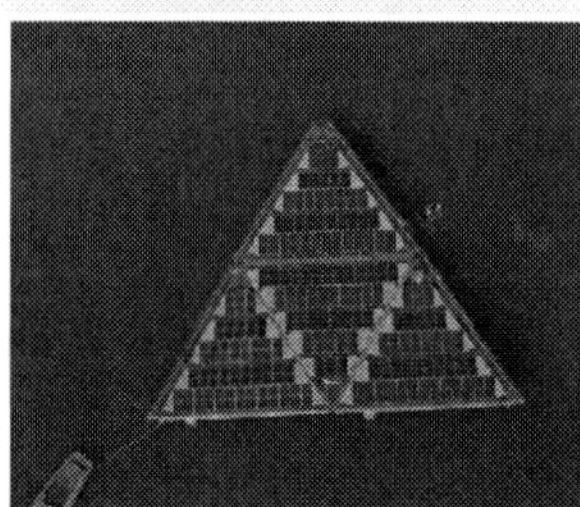

Reference: SolarDuck

MARINE ASSEMBLY LOGISTICS

Platforms are towed in **pre-assembled sets of six** using tugboats, then coupled offshore and secured with 35 mooring lines using a multicat vessel. All operations are modeled with vessel requirements, weather limits, and method statements defined per campaign.

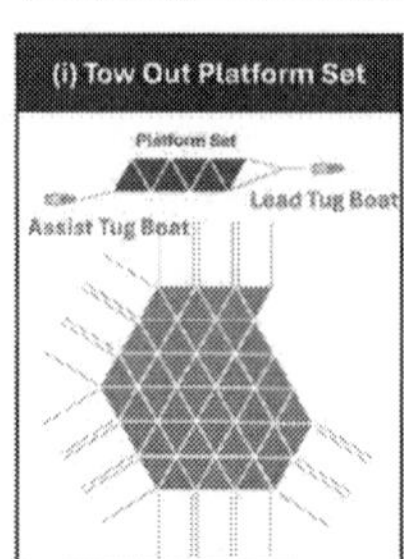

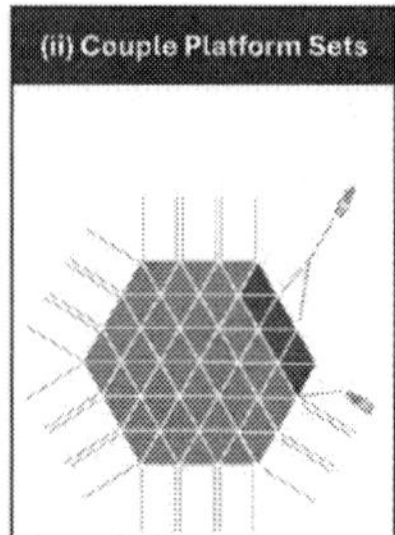

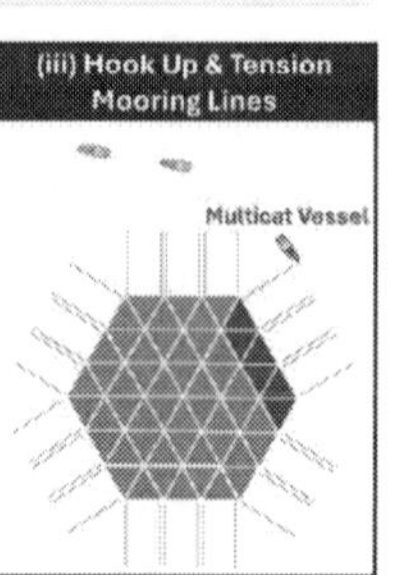

SCENARIOS

Three scenarios were modeled to assess how **weather risk** impacts installation planning. The key difference is whether a **continuous weather window** is enforced for interdependent steps. Comparison of scenarios shows how these policies affect timing and weather delay risks for critical operations.

Scenario	Risk Level	Risk Management Policy
1	High	No weather window is reserved to secure continuity between highly inter-dependent operational steps
2	Medium	Weather window of **Hs = 1.5 m with 50% margin** is reserved to reduce risks of discontinuity between highly inter-dependent operational steps.
3	Low	Weather window of **Hs = 1.0 m with 50% margin** is reserved to reduce risks of discontinuity between highly inter-dependent operational steps.

FINDINGS

- **Seasonal impact:** Installation during autumn/winter takes on average 160% longer than in spring/summer, driven by harsher wave conditions.
- **Risk policy impact:** Across all months, increasing policy strictness raises average duration from 70 days (high risk) to 130 days (low risk), due to added weather window requirements for interdependent tasks.
- **Anchor pre-laying** and **platform & mooring installation** account for >75% of all weather delays
- These campaigns are most sensitive to risk policies due to **task interdependencies** and tight weather thresholds.
- Mitigation should target these phases via faster operations, relaxed constraints, or modular methods that reduce weather exposure.

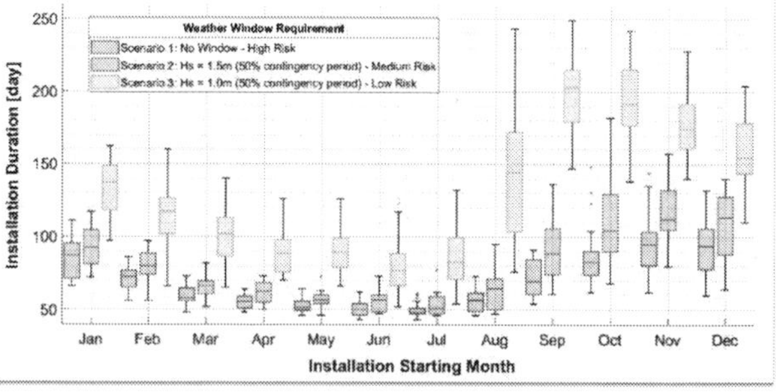

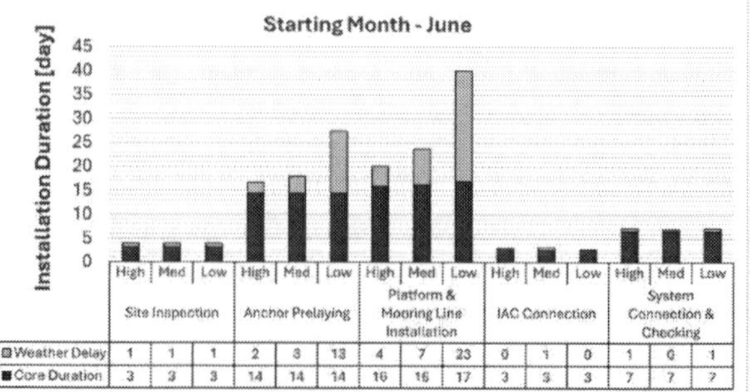

	High	Med	Low	High	Med	Low	High	Med	Low	High	Med	Low	High	Med	Low
	Site Inspection			Anchor Prelaying			Platform & Mooring Line Installation			IAC Connection			System Connection & Checking		
Weather Delay	1	1	1	2	3	13	4	7	23	0	1	0	1	0	1
Core Duration	3	3	3	14	14	14	16	16	17	3	3	3	7	7	7

This research was partially financed by the Netherlands Enterprise Agency within the DEI+ Merganser project.

Sizing Strategy for Green Hydrogen Production: Maximizing PV Utilization and Electrolyzer Efficiency

Carlos Meza[1,2], Mohammad Nabipour[1,2], Matthias Ebert[1]

[1]*Fraunhofer Center for Crystalline Silicon Photovoltaics CSP, Halle (Saale), Germany*
[2]*Hochschule Anhalt University of Applied Sciences, Köthen, Germany*

carlos.meza@hs-anhalt.de

Abstract

ABSTRACT: Green hydrogen production from solar photovoltaic (PV) power is central to decarbonization strategies. European regulations mandate a temporal correlation between renewable energy generation and electrolyzer operation, currently on a monthly basis. This paper presents a sizing methodology to determine the optimal power ratio between a PV plant and an electrolyzer to comply with these regulations. This sizing ratio is defined by the month with the lowest solar resource availability. A techno-economic analysis for a case study demonstrates that the ratio derived from this energy balance approach is closely aligned with the ratio that minimizes the Levelized Cost of Hydrogen (LCOH) under various electricity pricing scenarios. The methodology provides a robust framework for designing economically viable and compliant green hydrogen systems. Operational strategies involving real-time estimation algorithms are identified as a necessary next step for future work but are beyond the scope of this paper.

Keywords: Green Hydrogen, PV Sizing, Electrolyzer, LCOH, System Design

1 Introduction

Green hydrogen, produced via water electrolysis powered by renewable energy sources, is a key component in global efforts to decarbonize the industrial and transportation sectors[4], [5], [3]. The European Union has established a regulatory framework to ensure that hydrogen labeled as "green" genuinely contributes to reducing greenhouse gas emissions. A central requirement of this framework is the principle of temporal correlation, which mandates that the production of hydrogen is closely linked in time with the generation of the renewable electricity used to power it [6].

This correlation is assessed monthly, meaning that the total renewable energy generated within a calendar month must be equal to or greater than the energy consumed by the electrolyzer in that same month. This provision allows for some flexibility, enabling producers to use grid electricity to stabilize electrolyzer operation as long as the monthly energy balance is met.

The intermittent nature of solar photovoltaic (PV) power makes sizing photovoltaic hydrogen systems a complex task. An oversized photovoltaic plant can lead to significant power clipping during the summer months, while an undersized plant can require substan-

tial and costly electricity imports from the grid during winter months.

This work presents a sizing methodology for photovoltaic-based hydrogen production systems designed to meet the current monthly green hydrogen certification criteria. The objective is to define the power ratio between the PV plant and the electrolyzer in such a way that all the energy generated by the photovoltaic power is consumed by the electrolyzer on a monthly basis, thus preventing energy waste. This approach is then compared with an economic optimization that seeks to minimize the Levelized Cost of Hydrogen (LCOH) [2].

2 Methodology

The methodology is based on a simulation framework developed in Python that incorporates hourly weather data from a typical meteorological year (TMY) to estimate the PV power and hydrogen generation for a given site. Figure 1 shows a block diagram of the developed model. The proposed sizing strategy is based on meeting the monthly temporal correlation requirement stipulated by the EU regulations [6]. The core principle is to establish a monthly energy balance between the PV generation and the electrolyzer's consumption.

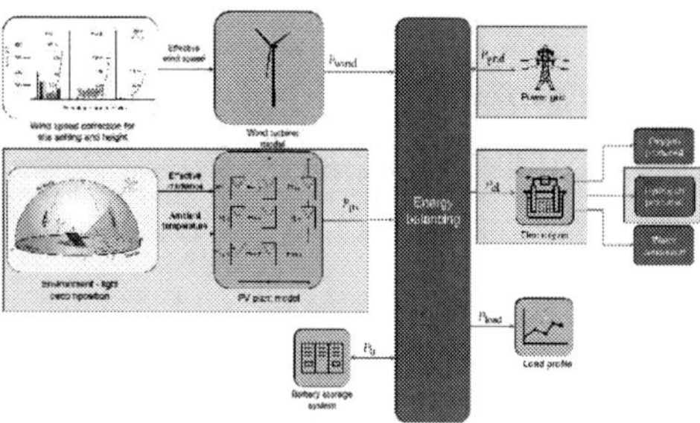

Figure 1: Scheme of the power to hydrogen system configuration (The gray box indicates the elements we focus on in this article.)

2.1 Sizing Based on Energy Balance

The temporal correlation for a given month, m, can be expressed as an integral equation where the total energy produced by the PV plant equals the total energy consumed by the electrolyzer:

$$\int_{t_m}^{t_m+T_m} P_{pv}(t)dt = \int_{t_m}^{t_m+T_m} P_{el}(t)dt = E_m \quad (1)$$

Here, $P_{pv}(t)$ is the PV power at time t, $P_{el}(t)$ is the power consumed by the electrolyzer at time t, and E_m is the total energy for month m. Notice that E_m is both the energy generated by the PV plant and the energy consumed by the electrolyzer in month m.

To avoid the detrimental effects of variable power operation on the electrolyzer, such as reduced efficiency and accelerated degradation, this methodology assumes that the electrolyzer operates at a constant optimal power level, P_{el}^*. Under this condition, the energy balance depends on the total operating hours of the electrolyzer each month, given that

$$\int_{t_m}^{t_m+T_m} P_{el}^*(t)dt = T_{m_{max}} P_{el}^* \quad (2)$$

The key sizing parameter is the ratio, $r_{pv/el}$, defined as the PV plant's nominal power at Standard Test Conditions (STC), P_{pv}^*, to the electrolyzer's nominal operating power, P_{el}^*:

$$r_{pv/el} = \frac{P_{pv}^*}{P_{el}^*} \quad (3)$$

This ratio can be calculated for each month by relating the monthly specific PV yield, Y_m (in kWh/kWp), to the maximum number of hours in that month, $T_{m_{max}}$:

$$r_{pv/el,m} = \frac{T_{m_{max}}}{Y_m} \quad (4)$$

This calculation results in 12 distinct values for $r_{pv/el}$, one for each month of the year. To ensure that PV energy is not curtailed in any month, the sizing strategy adopts the minimum of these 12 values as the definitive system ratio, $r_{pv/el}^*$:

$$r_{pv/el}^* = \min(r_{pv/el,1}, ..., r_{pv/el,12}) \quad (5)$$

This conservative approach guarantees that even in the month with the lowest solar irradiation (typically a winter month), all the generated PV energy can be consumed by the electrolyzer operating for all available hours. In all other months, the electrolyzer will operate for fewer than the maximum available hours to match the higher PV energy output.

2.2 Case study

The analysis was carried out for a case study located in Sombor, Serbia (latitude: 45.7° N, longitude: 19.7° E). We have used PVGIS TMY data for this location as input weather data for the model. Three different PV structures were analyzed, namely, fix-tilted, single-axis tracker and vertical. Additionally, the following assumptions were made:

- For the fix-tiled mounting structure: Azimuth: 180°.

- For the tracker and vertical PV, Azimuth angle 90°.

- Height above ground: 1 meter (standard for bifacial ground-mounted systems to enable rear-side irradiance capture).

- Mutual shading: Not considered; pitch between rows is assumed to be infinite to isolate the effect of tilt. This allows full irradiance to reach each row without shading losses, simplifying performance comparison.

- Albedo: 0.14 (typical for natural grassland or bare soil conditions in the Vojvodina region).

- Module type: Bifacial PV modules, with the following characteristics:

    - Bifaciality factor: 0.80 (i.e., the rear side produces 80% of what the front side does under the same irradiance).

    - Rated power at STC: 600 W

    - Module efficiency: 22.2 %

2.3 Utilization Factor

A key metric used in this document is the electrolyzer utilization factor shown in (6), which represents the ratio of electricity consumed by the electrolyzer to the total electricity produced by the PV system:

$$U_{el} = \frac{E_{el}}{E_{pv}} \quad (6)$$

A U_{el} below 0.5 indicates that the electrolyzer is significantly under-utilizing the available solar energy. In such configurations, the PV plant is either oversized or the electrolyzer is undersized, often resulting in excess energy being exported to the grid or curtailed. This behavior signals a shift away from a Power-to-Hydrogen (PtH) business model toward a more electricity-driven configuration, where grid sales dominate the revenue structure.

2.4 Techno-Economic Analysis

To evaluate the economic viability of the proposed sizing ratio, a techno-economic analysis was performed using the Levelized Cost of Hydrogen (LCOH) as the primary metric following the approaches of [2], [1] [7]. The LCOH calculation includes Capital Expenditures (CAPEX) for the PV plant (I_{pv}) and electrolyzer (I_{el}), Operational Expenditures (OPEX) of the PV plant (O_{pv}) and the electrolyzer (O_{el}), stack replacement costs (C_s), and costs related to grid interaction (C_{grid}), i.e.,

$$LCOH = \frac{I_{el} + I_{pv} + C_s + \sum_{y=1}^{N} (O_{el}(y) + O_{pv}(y) + C_g(y))}{m_{H2}} \tag{7}$$

where y is an specific year, N is total number of years used for the economical analysis and m_{H2} is the total hydrogen produced over the service lifetime of the PV-based green hydrogen plant. In this work, hydrogen production was estimated from the PV plant's energy output for a typical meteorological year, adjusted for PV degradation across the entire project lifetime.

The economic parameters used for the calculation of the LCOH are presented in the following table.

Parameter	Value	Unit
PV plant CAPEX (fixed tilt)	800	€/kW
PV plant CAPEX (single axis tracking)	1007	€/kW
PV plant OPEX (fixed tilt)	13.3	€/kW p.a.
PV plant OPEX (single axis tracking)	20	€/kW p.a.
PV inverter cost	75	€/kW
AEM electrolyzer CAPEX	1285	€/kW
AEM electrolyzer OPEX	2	% of CAPEX p.a.
Stack replacement cost	15	% of CAPEX
Water cost	0.005	€/L
Electricity sale price	0.06	€/kWh
Electricity purchase price	0.06	€/kWh
WACC (equal to discount rate)	6	%
Plant life	25	years

3 Results and discussion

The sizing methodology was applied using Typical Meteorological Year (TMY) data for the selected location.

First, the specific monthly PV yield (Y_m) was simulated for the three PV systems, i.e., fixed-tilt, single-axis tracker and vertical. Using (4), the required $r_{pv/el}$ for each month was calculated. Figure 2 shows the resulting Utilization Factor and LCOH vs. the sizing parameter ratio for the fixed-tilt, tracker and vertical structures, respectively.

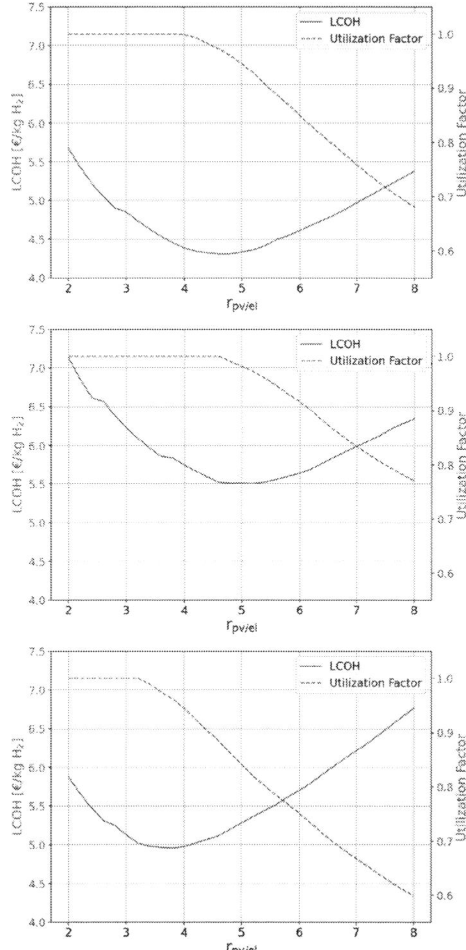

Figure 2: Variation of LCOH and electrolyzer utilization factor as a function of $r_{pv/el}$. The three subplots correspond to different PV system structures from top to bottom: fixed-tilt structure, vertical structure, and single-axis tracker.

The minimum ratio was determined to be approximately 4 for the fix-tilted structure. According to the methodology, this value is selected as $r_{pv/el}^*$ to ensure no PV energy is clipped throughout the year. The results show a clear U-shaped curve for the LCOH. As the ratio increases, the system becomes more self-sufficient, reducing the need for grid imports and thus lowering the LCOH. However, beyond an optimal point, the LCOH begins to rise again. This is because a very high $r_{pv/el}$ ratio implies a large investment in PV capacity (high CAPEX) that is not fully utilized, as the electrolyzer size remains fixed. The optimal $r_{pv/el}$ ratio that minimizes the LCOH is close to 4.6. This value is close to the 4 ratio determined by the energy balance methodology. This alignment demonstrates that sizing the system to avoid PV energy clipping based on a monthly balance is not only compliant with regulations but is also an economically sound strategy. The small difference between the energy-based ratio (4) and the cost-optimal ratio (4.6) indicates that a slight oversizing beyond the no-clipping limit provides a marginal economic benefit by further reducing reliance on grid electricity imports during less sunny periods.

4 Conclusion

This paper presented a sizing methodology for PV-hydrogen systems aimed at fulfilling the monthly temporal correlation requirements for green hydrogen certification in the EU. The methodology defines the PV-to-electrolyzer power ratio by ensuring that all PV energy generated in any given month can be fully utilized by the electrolyzer. This is achieved by selecting the minimum monthly ratio, which corresponds to the month with the highest solar energy yield.

A techno-economic analysis confirmed that the sizing ratio determined by this energy-balance approach is closely aligned with the ratio that minimizes the Levelized Cost of Hydrogen (LCOH) under different electricity market prices. The optimal economic ratio was found to be consistently around 4.6 for a fixed-tilt system, near the calculated no-curtailment ratio of 4 This finding validates the proposed method as a robust and practical tool for the initial design of economically viable and regulation-compliant green hydrogen projects.

It is important to highlight that this work focuses on a high-level sizing methodology. The actual operation of such a system requires dynamic strategies to manage the fluctuating PV power in real-time. Therefore, future work should focus on the development and integration of estimation and control algorithms to manage the energy flows between the PV plant, electrolyzer, and the grid on an operational basis. These aspects were considered out of the scope of the present paper.

Acknowledgments

This work was supported by the German Federal Ministry of Education and Research under the HyDS project (grant number 03SF0697B). We would like to thank our project partners at Leipziger Energiegesellschaft mbH & Co. KG, in particular Mr. Andriy Baranochnyk and Mr. Fabian Severing, as well as Dr. Klemens Ilse and Mr. Sebastian Schindler from Fraunhofer IMWS, for their valuable support.

References

[1] Abdin, Z., Khalilpour, K., Catchpole, K.: Projecting the levelized cost of large scale hydrogen storage for stationary applications. Energy Conversion and Management **270**, 116241 (2022). https://doi.org/10.1016/j.enconman.2022.116241, https://www.sciencedirect.com/science/article/pii/S0196890422010184

[2] Hönig, F., Rupakula, G.D., Duque-Gonzalez, D., Ebert, M., Blum, U.: Enhancing the levelized cost of hydrogen with the usage of the byproduct oxygen in a wastewater treatment plant. Energies **16**(12) (2023). https://doi.org/10.3390/en16124829

[3] Odenweller, A., Ueckerdt, F.: The green hydrogen ambition and implementation gap. Nature Energy **10**(1), 110–123 (2025). https://doi.org/10.1038/s41560-024-01684-7

[4] Oliveira, A.M., Beswick, R.R., Yan, Y.: A green hydrogen economy for a renewable energy society. Current Opinion in Chemical Engineering **33**, 100701 (2021). https://doi.org/10.1016/j.coche.2021.100701, https://www.sciencedirect.com/science/article/pii/S2211339821000332

[5] Squadrito, G., Maggio, G., Nicita, A.: The green hydrogen revolution. Renewable Energy **216**, 119041 (2023). https://doi.org/10.1016/j.renene.2023.119041, https://www.sciencedirect.com/science/article/pii/S0960148123009552

[6] Union, E.: Commission delegated regulation (eu) 2023/1184 of 10 february 2023 supplementing directive 2018/2001 of the european parliament and of the council by establishing a union methodology setting out detailed rules for the production of renewable fuels of non-biological origin. Official Journal **L 157**, 11–19 (2023-06-20)

[7] Wolf, N., Tanneberger, M.A., Höck, M.: Levelized cost of hydrogen production in northern africa and europe in 2050: A monte carlo simulation for germany, norway, spain, algeria, morocco, and egypt. International Journal of Hydrogen Energy **69**, 184–194 (2024). https://doi.org/10.1016/j.ijhydene.2024.04.319, https://www.sciencedirect.com/science/article/pii/S0360319924016318

Sizing Strategy for Green Hydrogen Production: Maximizing PV Utilization and Electrolyzer Efficiency

Carlos Meza[1,2], Mohammad Nabipour[1,2], Matthias Ebert[1]

[1] Fraunhofer Center for Crystalline Silicon Photovoltaics CSP, Walter-Hülse-Straße 1, 06120 Halle, Germany

[2] Anhalt University of Applied Sciences, Bernburger Str. 55, 06366 Köthen, Germany

Motivation and objectives

* Transition to green hydrogen using photovoltaic (PV) systems as a sustainable pathway to decarbonize energy-intensive processes.
* Strategy for sizing and operating PV water electrolysis systems based on a monthly correlation, compliant with European green hydrogen certification; focus on grid-connected solutions.
* Assessment of the impact of PV layouts on the levelized cost of hydrogen (LCOH) and the role of grid interactions in system performance.

Methodology

* According to European regulations, hydrogen produced by 31. December 2029, is to be produced in the same calendar month as the renewable electricity from the PPA or from a new storage facility directly connected to the renewable generator or electrolyser.
* The hydrogen produced is considered green, even if energy is exchanged with the electricity grid during the calendar month.
* Parameter $r_{pv/el}$: ratio between the nominal power (STC) of the PV system and the nominal power of the electrolyzer.

$$r_{pv/el} = \frac{PV\ capacity}{El\ capacity}$$

* The value of that maximizes the utilization of PV power while satisfying the energy balance condition for monthly time correlation depends on the monthly PV energy production and the number of available hours in each month.
* LCOH is used as an economic metric to compare different hydrogen production strategies.

$$LCOH = \frac{\sum Cost}{\sum Hydrogen\ production}$$

* To be economically attractive, green hydrogen must have costs compatible with those that potential off-takers are willing to pay. Maximizing hydrogen production while minimizing the cost of the system, means providing the lowest LCOH is crucial. Therefore, the optimal combination of sizes for PV-electrolyzer system is investigated to yield the lowest LCOH.
* A key metric used in this study is the electrolyzer utilization factor U_{EL}:

$$U_{EL} = \frac{Electricity\ consumed\ by\ electrolyzer}{Total\ electricity\ produced\ by\ PV}$$

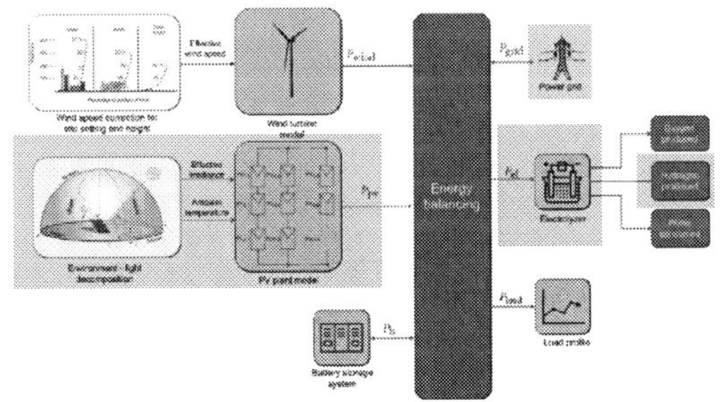

Figure 1: Scheme of the power to hydrogen system configuration (The gray box indicates the elements we focus on in this article.)

Case study

* Green hydrogen production in Sombor, Serbia by hourly simulations using PVGIS TMY data
* Electrolyzer size: 1000 kW, efficiency curve
* Bifacial PV modules (bifaciality factor = 0.8) and monofacial PV modules, nominal power at STC = 600 W

Results and discussion

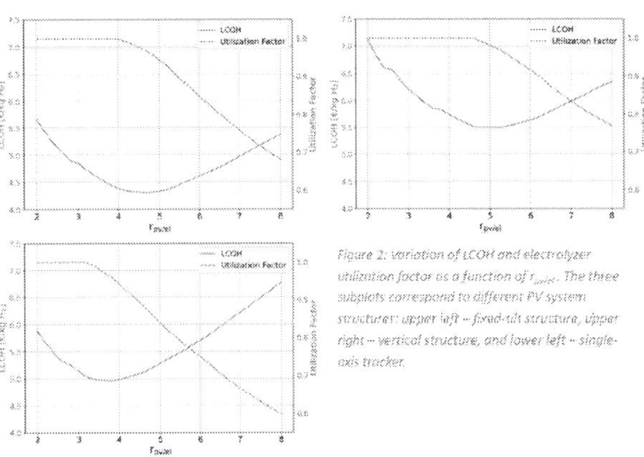

Figure 2: variation of LCOH and electrolyzer utilization factor as a function of $r_{pv/el}$. The three subplots correspond to different PV system structures: upper left – fixed-tilt structure, upper right – vertical structure, and lower left – single-axis tracker.

* The minimum U_{EL} ratio was determined to be approximately 4 for the fixed-tilt structure. According to the methodology, this value is selected as optimal $r_{pv/el}$ to ensure no PV energy is clipped throughout the year.
* As the ratio $r_{pv/el}$ increases, the system becomes more self-sufficient.
* Beyond an optimal point, the LCOH begins to rise again. This is because a very high $r_{pv/el}$ implies a large investment in PV capacity that is not fully utilized, as the electrolyzer size remains fixed.
* The optimal $r_{pv/el}$ for fixed-tilt structure that minimizes the LCOH is close to 4.6 which is close to the ratio determined by the energy balance methodology equal to 4.
* This alignment demonstrates that sizing the system to avoid PV energy clipping based on a monthly balance is not only compliant with regulations but is also an economically sound strategy.

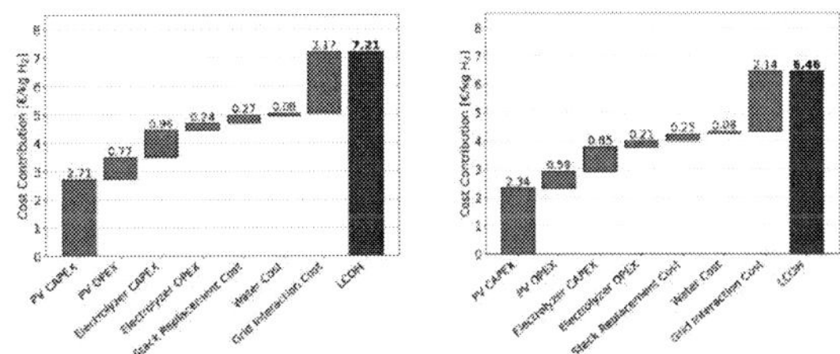

Figure 3: Cost components contributing to the LCOH for tracker structure with $r_{pv/el}$ = 3.6 (left) and for fixed-tilt structure with $r_{pv/el}$ = 4.6 (right). In this case, the PV system interacts with the grid in a monthly correlation with electricity sale price of 6 ¢/kWh and electricity purchase price of 10 ¢/kWh.

* Grid interaction cost impacts on LCOH with the cost contribution of 2.14 €/kg H_2 for fixed-tilt structure and 2.17 €/kg H_2 for single-axis tracker structure, and stands after the PV CAPEX cost.

Conclusions and outlook

* Proposes a sizing methodology for PV-hydrogen systems that meets current EU green hydrogen certification requirements.
* Techno-economic analysis shows by this energy-balance approach that sizing ratio ($r_{pv/el}$) closely matches the ratio that minimizes LCOH.
* Future work: develop and integrate estimation and control algorithms to manage PV-electrolyzer-grid energy flows during operation (out of scope of this study).

ACKNOWLEDGMENT

The work in the "HyDS" project is funded by the Federal Ministry of Education and Research (grant number: 03SF0697B). We thank the project partners of Leipziger Energiegesellschaft mbH & Co. KG, Mr. Andriy Baranochnyk and Mr. Fabian Severing as well as Dr. Klemens Ilse and Mr. Sebastian Schindler from Fraunhofer IMWS for supporting the work.

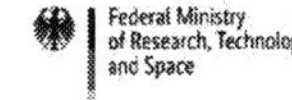

020427-001

RETROFITTING SHIPPING CONTAINERS INTO POSITIVE ENERGY BUS STATIONS WITH PHOTOVOLTAIC LVDC MICROGRIDS FOR SUSTAINABLE TRANSPORT IN RENEWABLE RESOURCE-RICH, HARSH ENVIRONMENTS

Mohammad Nazififard [1], Erwin Franquet [1], Ahmad Sedaghat [2], Mohammad Salem [3], Mohammad Farhat [4]
[1] Université Côte d'Azur, Polytech'Lab, France
[2] Dep. of Mechanical Engineering, College of Engineering, Australian University, West Mishref, Safat 13015, Kuwait [3]
Dep. of Civil Engineering, College of Engineering, Australian University, West Mishref, Safat 13015, Kuwait
[4] Dep. of Electrical and Electronics Engineering, College of Engineering, Australian University,
West Mishref, Safat 13015, Kuwait
mohammad.nazififard@univ-cotedazur.fr erwin.franquet@univ-cotedazur.fr a.sedaghat@au.edu.kw msalem@au.edu.kw
m.farhat@au.edu.kw

ABSTRACT: This study evaluates the performance of a stand-alone photovoltaic (PV) system designed to power a bus stop constructed from recycled shipping containers under Kuwait's hot and arid climate conditions. The design aims to reduce construction costs and promote environmental sustainability through the implementation of a positive energy building. The system operates independently from the municipal grid, with all generated energy stored in batteries to ensure complete energy autonomy. Energy consumption was simulated using DesignBuilder software, assuming an average occupancy of two people. The station's annual energy demand was estimated at approximately 3660.1 kWh. The PV system comprises four fixed 670 W panels, installed at a 29° tilt angle and oriented south to optimize solar energy capture. Energy storage is provided by a 36 V lead-acid battery bank with a total capacity of 3671 Ah. PVsyst simulation results indicate that the system can generate approximately 4494.82 kWh annually, with 3385.33 kWh delivered to the useful load—covering about 92.5% of the station's total energy demand. This demonstrates a high level of energy self-sufficiency and significantly reduces dependence on external power sources. However, around 895.75 kWh per year (19.27% of the generated energy) is lost, primarily due to storage limitations and a temporal mismatch between energy generation and consumption. This excess energy could be utilized for supplementary applications, such as charging electric vehicles. Installing EV charging stations near bus stops offers a practical and sustainable solution to enhance overall system efficiency and environmental benefits.
Keywords: Energy storage, EV charging, Renewable energy, clean transportation, Sustainable cities, Sustainable mobility, Photovoltaic charging station.

1 INTRODUCTION

Green environmental policies aimed at reducing carbon emissions from energy sources are currently being implemented worldwide. Cities play a critical role in mitigating energy consumption and carbon dioxide emissions. Accordingly, the European Council's 2030 Climate and Energy Framework sets a target to increase the share of renewable energy to at least 27% of total energy consumption [1]. Similarly, the United Nations' 2030 Agenda for Sustainable Development includes 17 Sustainable Development Goals (SDGs), two of which directly support energy efficiency and sustainable urbanization: SDG 7 (Affordable and Clean Energy) and SDG 11 (Sustainable Cities and Communities) [2] .

European Union (EU) member states have introduced several measures to reduce emissions from the energy sector. In December 2019, the European Union set a target to lower its net greenhouse gas emissions by a minimum of 55% by the year 2030, relative to 1990 levels, and to become climate-neutral by 2050 [3], [4]. The EU's updated development strategy includes actions to lower CO_2 emissions, transform transport and industrial sectors, reduce emissions from buildings, overhaul food production systems, and protect biodiversity [5].

At the international level, agreements such as the Kyoto Protocol, the Paris Agreement, and more recent initiatives like the Glasgow Climate Pact and the outcomes of COP28 emphasize the reduction of greenhouse gas emissions. These accords promote the transition to cleaner energy technologies and the development of sustainable transport systems to address the escalating climate crisis. Key challenges in promoting sustainable mobility include improving public transportation services, integrating urban planning, encouraging shared mobility, and promoting cycling. These efforts aim to reduce the growing reliance on private vehicles in cities worldwide [6], [7].

Public transportation, including buses, trains, and trams, is a vital component of sustainable urban mobility [8]. It plays a key role in reducing both traffic congestion and environmental pollution. Developing clean and efficient transit networks is essential for smart and sustainable urban planning [9]. However, urban sprawl has increased dependence on private vehicles [10]. Consequently, there is an urgent need to develop modern, clean, and intelligent public transit systems to achieve environmental and social sustainability goals.

The transportation sector is currently the fastest-growing contributor to energy consumption and greenhouse gas emissions [11]. Primary energy sources used in electricity generation and transport account for approximately 60% of global energy use. Integrating renewable energy sources into the transport sector presents a significant opportunity to transition to a low-carbon energy system [12] [13]. In cities such as Kuwait, where traffic congestion is severe, public transportation can reduce private vehicle use, alleviate traffic density, and improve the environment [14]. One promising strategy is to increase the share of renewable energy in the electricity mix [15]. Among renewable technologies, photovoltaic (PV) systems are considered one of the most viable options for achieving a carbon-neutral energy sector [16] [17]. PV applications have expanded significantly in urban environments, now supporting residential power and heating needs. Additional uses include street lighting, electric vehicle (EV) charging stations, digital signage, traffic signals, and solar-powered infrastructure.

However, not all urban areas are suitable for solar panel installations [18], [19]. Urban planners and policymakers must therefore assess local solar potential to implement effective PV-based solutions [20]. While rooftop and façade solar potential have been widely studied, exploring unconventional urban surfaces for PV deployment represents a new frontier in urban energy research. Future efforts should focus on expanding usable surface areas for solar energy systems. Ground-mounted PV (GPV), rooftop PV (RPV), and building-integrated PV (BIPV) have been extensively analyzed. The next step is to design solar-oriented infrastructure as part of holistic urban energy systems.

Bus stops, essential infrastructure in public transport systems, can benefit significantly from solar-powered technologies that enhance both service and quality of life. This supports broader smart city objectives. Traditional bus stops typically provide only basic shelter from weather conditions; however, their functionality can be expanded to include PV-powered amenities such as internet connectivity, device charging stations, digital advertising displays, and real-time information screens [21].

Improved lighting is another opportunity. Adequate illumination enhances passenger safety during nighttime hours [22]. While conventional bus stop lighting systems are typically grid-connected, solar-powered lighting is a viable alternative in areas with high solar exposure. Furthermore, weather-protected bus stop designs have been shown to increase public transport use by providing comfort and protection in adverse climates [23]. In extreme climates, enclosed bus stops have been proposed as a way to further promote public transport usage. When integrated with clean energy systems, such designs can reduce emissions by supplying power and heat sustainably [24]. Despite advances in geospatial tools and energy modeling, the effective integration of renewable energy into public infrastructure such as bus stops remains limited in many urban areas. This study aims to address this gap by evaluating solar-powered solutions specifically for bus stop infrastructure.

In response to growing energy demands in the transport sector and the need for sustainable urban systems, this study assesses the feasibility of converting recycled shipping containers into energy-positive bus stops in regions with high solar potential and harsh climates. These bus stops are designed to operate independently from the main grid by utilizing DC microgrids powered by photovoltaic systems [25], [26]. Prefabricated shipping containers offer several advantages, including reduced construction costs and rapid deployment of clean, smart infrastructure. The main objectives of this study are to:

- Assess the feasibility of using recycled shipping containers for constructing bus stops suitable for extreme weather conditions.
- Design a photovoltaic system and low-voltage DC (LVDC) infrastructure capable of supporting lighting, heating, mobile device charging, and EV charging.
- Analyze the solar potential of public spaces and identify optimal locations for implementation based on technical and climatic factors.

2 LITERATURE REVIEW

Sedaghat et al. [27] evaluated off-grid PV systems for cooling portable cabins in Kuwait's extreme heat,

achieving a 24.1% reduction in energy use and cutting CO_2 emissions by 129.4 kg over nine months. Similarly, Ding et al. [28] assessed solar-powered bus parking lots in Tianjin, China, integrating drone imaging and solar modeling tools. Their system could power 50% of the electric bus fleet and reduce CO_2, SO_2, and NO_x emissions.

AlKheder et al. [14], [29] investigated public transportation optimization in Kuwait, showing that increased bus use could reduce emissions by up to 46%, and numerical models improved bus scheduling to enhance efficiency and service quality.

Vossos et al. [30] examined DC distribution in U.S. homes with PV systems, showing energy savings of up to 14% with battery storage. Building on this, Chauhan et al. [31] demonstrated that DC microgrids reduce energy consumption and conversion losses compared to AC systems due to fewer conversion stages. Similarly, Gerber et al. [32] found DC systems in commercial buildings saved up to 18% energy under optimal conditions. Gelani et al. [33] further reported that DC systems outperform AC systems, especially during high load periods, due to improved converter performance.

In tropical regions, Dahiru and Tan [34] optimized grid-connected nanogrids combining renewables and storage, achieving high renewable supply and significant greenhouse gas reductions. Ammous et al. [35] highlighted the efficiency advantage of LVDC systems over conventional PV architectures, attributing gains to reduced conversion stages. Villacorta et al. [36] confirmed these benefits through an LVDC system at the Technical University of Ecuador, which lowered energy losses via DC-to-DC converters.

Alsaedi et al. [37] and Ammous et al. [38] independently reported LVDC systems offer 15–20% higher efficiency than AC systems in residential PV applications, emphasizing local consumption and fewer conversion steps as key factors. Finally, Ollas et al. [39] showed that DC distribution in a Swedish home reduced annual energy losses by 15.8% compared to AC systems with PV and battery storage, reinforcing the superior efficiency of DC systems.

Al-Thani et al. [40] provided a comprehensive review of renewable energy systems integrated with electric vehicle (EV) charging infrastructure in urban environments. Their work emphasizes the need to reduce emissions from combustion vehicles and improve urban air quality. The study shows that EV charging stations can operate either on-grid or off-grid using sources such as solar, wind, hydropower, and alternative carriers like hydrogen and ammonia. Supplementary energy storage, particularly batteries, is essential to manage fluctuations in renewable generation. The results indicate that integrating EVs with renewable energy sources can reduce carbon emissions, stabilize energy supply, and increase user adoption of green vehicles. However, the study also highlights challenges, including the need for advanced smart charging algorithms and improved storage systems.

Barman et al. [41] analyzed global charging infrastructure, energy storage technologies, smart grids, and industrial strategies to assess the role of renewable energy in EV charging. Their study reviewed international experiences with solar, wind, and hydropower as energy sources for EV charging. The findings underscore the importance of integrating smart charging with renewables to achieve sustainable transportation. This integration reduces costs and improves efficiency through load management and time-based tariffs. However, challenges remain, such as the need for infrastructure standardization, cybersecurity, and stronger governmental support through financial and educational incentives.

Cavalcante et al. [42] proposed a novel framework for using surplus solar energy from photovoltaic systems to charge EVs, introducing a decentralized energy exchange model between institutions and vehicle owners via blockchain technology. Their case study, conducted at an educational institution in Portugal, demonstrated that a 724 kW-peak PV system could charge more than 3,213 vehicles annually and generate over €45,000 in revenue. The system achieved a payback period of approximately two years and an internal rate of return of 61%, along with a 20% reduction in greenhouse gas emissions compared to conventional grid charging. Despite these benefits, the study identified challenges related to the scalability of blockchain, its energy consumption, the variability of solar energy, and the lack of regulatory frameworks for decentralized energy markets.

3 METHODOLOGY

3.1 Case study

This study evaluates the potential of converting a 20-foot SCF decommissioned shipping container into a photovoltaic-powered, positive-energy bus station in Kuwait through a series of systematic steps addressing both functional design and environmental considerations. First, the functional requirements of the bus station in Kuwait's hot and dry climate are determined, taking into account climatic challenges and passenger needs. The station must provide shelter for waiting passengers, offering adequate seating and protection from solar radiation as well as extreme hot and cold weather. To achieve this, structural modifications are made to the shipping container, including the installation of a window and a transparent door on the container side (Fig. 1-a). Additionally, to maintain interior comfort under Kuwait's extreme temperatures, an air conditioning system is installed. A model was developed to predict the energy performance of the bus station and validated with experimental data from a prototype. After validation, simulations were conducted under average passenger occupancy conditions to evaluate the station's net-zero energy performance and assess its feasibility at the city scale [44].

DesignBuilder software was used to model the station's energy load. The software estimates annual energy demand by accounting for the building's thermal characteristics, ventilation, lighting, and internal equipment. Energy consumption was simulated based on actual passenger occupancy data. Previous studies report an average occupancy of 1.8 passengers in the morning and 1.7 in the afternoon, indicating a relatively uniform distribution throughout the day. For modeling purposes, the average occupancy was rounded to two passengers to define a consistent daily usage pattern in DesignBuilder [29], [45].

This consumption scenario was used to simulate daily energy use, as shown in Figure 1-b. Based on this model, the station's total annual energy consumption was calculated to be 3,660.1 kWh. In the next step, the shipping container was converted into the bus station. An innovative photovoltaic low-voltage direct current (LVDC) microgrid system was designed and implemented to supply the required electricity.

The PV system consists of four 670W PV module installed on the container's roof. The PV panels are mounted at a tilt angle of 29° and oriented due to maximize solar radiation capture. The system is configured as a stand-alone unit, with no connection to the national electricity grid. All of the station's energy needs are supplied exclusively through solar power generation and on-site energy storage. The fabricated bus station is shown in Figure 1-c.

This study proposes an innovative sustainable solution for public transportation in Kuwait by transforming of decommissioned shipping containers into positive energy bus stations. A comparison between the energy consumption across different scenarios and the energy generation from the PV LVDC microgrid is performed to assess the bus station's potential for energy self-sufficiency and its ability to generate surplus energy for return to the grid (Fig. 2).

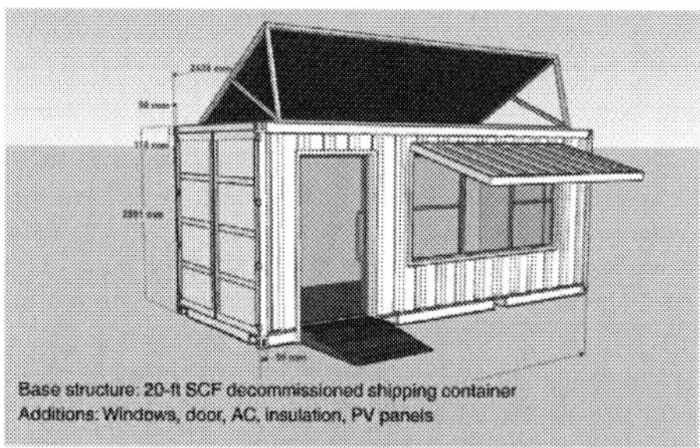

(a) Conceptual Design of Bus Station

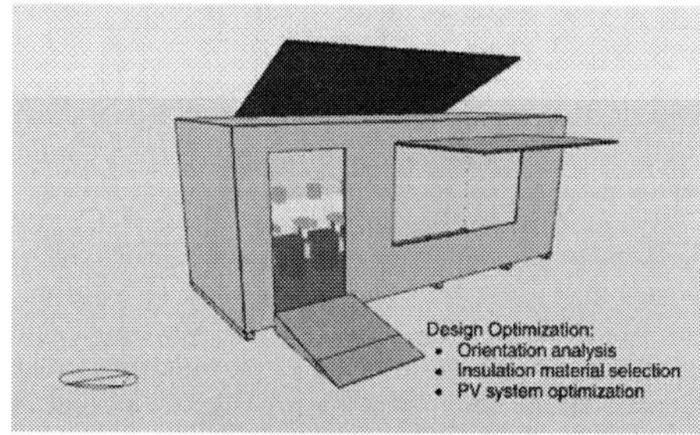

(b) Simulation & Optimization

(c) Prototype Development

Figure 1: (a) Schematic of a 20-foot solar-powered, ventilated bus station with PV panels installed on the roof; (b) model of the bus station used for energy simulations; (c) photograph of the constructed bus station.

3.2 Validation

According to ASHRAE Standard 55-2023, the appropriate indoor temperature range for light activities and typical clothing levels is generally between 20 °C and 26 °C. However, this range may vary slightly depending on clothing insulation and the metabolic rate of individuals [46]. Under summer conditions, thermal comfort is typically defined within a narrower range of 23 °C to 26 °C [47]. Additionally, the recommended relative humidity range for maintaining comfort is between 30% and 60% [48]. To improve simulation accuracy, real weather data were collected from a weather station installed at the bus stop. These data include parameters such as dry-bulb temperature, dew point temperature, relative humidity, wind speed and direction, total horizontal solar radiation, and other relevant variables [49]. This dataset replaced the default EPW (EnergyPlus Weather) file, which typically provides 10-year average values that may not accurately reflect site-specific conditions. Using real-time data significantly reduces simulation errors and aligns the output more closely with actual performance. Figure 2 presents the hourly energy consumption pattern of the bus stop from August 4 to 18, 2025. The simulation results for the base scenario (without occupants) are compared with measured data, providing a clear assessment of model performance under standard operating conditions. The results show strong agreement between the simulation and experimental data, validating the modeling approach.

Figure 3 further demonstrates this agreement by comparing simulated and measured thermal comfort conditions inside the bus stop during the same period. Figure 4 presents the hourly energy consumption patterns at the bus station between August 4 and August 18, 2025, comparing simulated results with measured data under the first occupancy scenario. This comparison offers insight into model performance under baseline operating conditions. The simulation results closely match the empirical data, validating the modeling approach. The simulation's accuracy was evaluated using various statistical performance indicators, as presented in Table I. A Mean Bias Error (MBE) of −0.0187 kWh and a Normalized MBE of −1.89% suggest a slight underestimation of energy consumption. The coefficient of determination (R^2) is 0.9507, indicating that the model accounts for about 95.07% of the variation in the observed data. Furthermore, the Coefficient of Variation of the Root Mean Square Error (CV(RMSE)) is 11.78%, which complies with the acceptable limits outlined in ASHRAE guidelines [50].

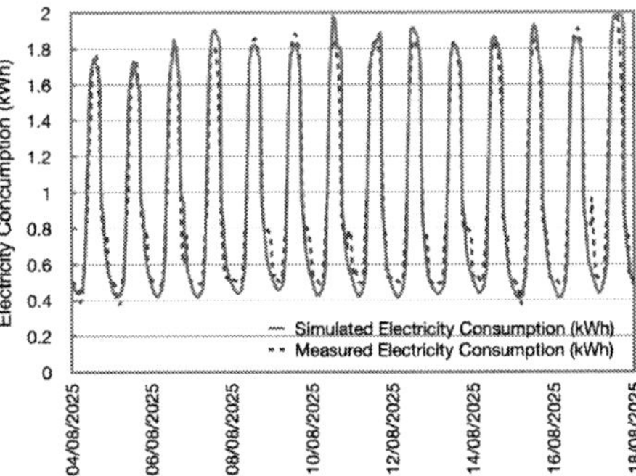

Figure 2: The hourly energy consumption patterns at the bus station from August 4 to August 18, 2025.

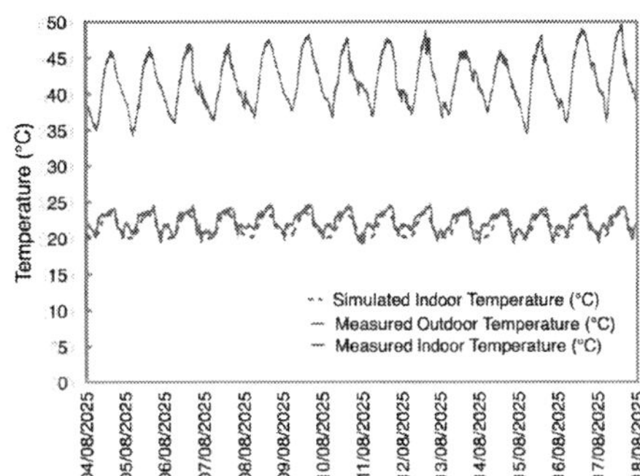

Figure 3: Comparison of simulated comfort temperatures and measured numbers.

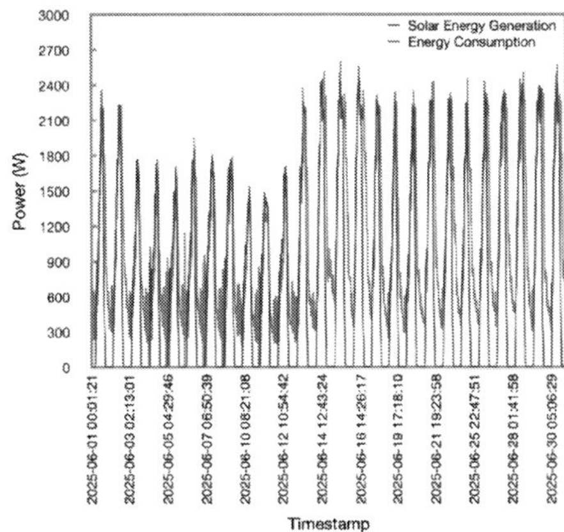

Figure 4: The hourly energy consumption patterns at the bus station from August 4 to August 18, 2025.

Table I: Model Evaluation Metrics

Metric	Value
R^2 Score	0.9629
Adjusted R^2	0.9627
MAE	0.0728
MSE	0.0102
RMSE	0.1012

4 RESULTS

The simulated consumption profile was exported as average power (kW) and imported into PVsyst, where it served as the user-defined load. The system's total annual energy consumption was estimated at 3,660.1 kWh. The PV system configuration includes four south-facing fixed PV modules rated at 670 W each, installed at a tilt angle of 29° to optimize year-round solar capture. Energy storage is provided by a 36 V lead-acid battery bank with a total capacity of 3,671 Ah. PVsyst simulation results indicate that the system can generate approximately 4,494.82 kWh per year. Of this, 3,385.33 kWh per year is delivered as useful energy to the load, covering approximately 92.49% of the bus stop's annual energy demand. This demonstrates a high degree of energy self-sufficiency and significantly reduces reliance on external power sources. However, not all generated energy is utilized. Approximately 895.75 kWh per year, or 19.27% of the available energy, is lost primarily due to battery storage limitations and temporal mismatches between energy generation and consumption. Additionally, 274.76 kWh per year of energy demand remains unmet, referred to as "Missing Energy," which indicates that auxiliary sources may be necessary to ensure continuous operation during peak demand periods.

Key performance indicators further validate system efficiency. The specific yield was calculated as 1,263 kWh/kWp/year, reflecting favorable performance under Kuwait's solar irradiance conditions [49]. The performance ratio (PR) was 61.42%, indicating good operational efficiency under real environmental conditions. Figure 5 presents the system's loss diagram, identifying various sources of energy loss. The most significant loss is due to unused energy (19.27%), followed by thermal losses (10.75%), which highlight the impact of Kuwait's high ambient temperatures. Other losses include inverter inefficiencies (4.05%), ohmic losses in cabling (1.60%), and module mismatch losses (2%). Battery performance, expressed as state of charge (SOC), is illustrated in Figure 6. The SOC profile reveals a seasonal pattern: during winter and early spring, energy production exceeds demand, resulting in fully charged batteries and an energy surplus. Conversely, during the summer months (June to September), high ambient temperatures reduce PV efficiency while demand increases due to cooling and ventilation loads. This leads to significant battery discharge and lower SOC levels, contributing to the recorded "Missing Energy" and highlighting a critical challenge in maintaining a stable energy supply during peak demand periods. Overall, the PVsyst simulations confirm that the standalone PV system is effective, achieving 92.49% energy self-sufficiency for the bus stop. However, two major challenges remain: performance degradation due to high temperatures and energy wastage caused by limited battery capacity. The analysis revealed that a significant portion of the energy generated, 895.75 kWh per year, remains unused because the batteries become fully charged, particularly during peak solar periods. This surplus energy offers an opportunity for alternative applications. One promising solution is to redirect the excess energy toward charging electric vehicles (EVs) [42], [41]. Given the bus stop's location, installing one or more EV charging stations near the PV array would be a practical and sustainable enhancement, further increasing the system's utility and environmental benefits. The results of this study align with previous research emphasizing the importance of utilizing renewable energy sources to minimize carbon emissions and enhance energy sustainability. Consistent with the findings of Al-Thani [40] and Barman [41], this study demonstrates that integrating energy storage systems with renewable sources can improve energy self-sufficiency and enable the use of surplus energy for charging electric vehicles. Similarly, Cavalcante [42] reported that surplus energy generated by photovoltaic systems provides significant economic and environmental benefits. In agreement with Jain and Bhullar [43], the findings highlight the need to optimize system performance and effectively manage energy storage to maintain overall efficiency and sustainability. Furthermore, the operational challenges identified in this study, including energy loss, limited battery capacity, and reduced photovoltaic performance under high temperatures, correspond to concerns raised in earlier research.

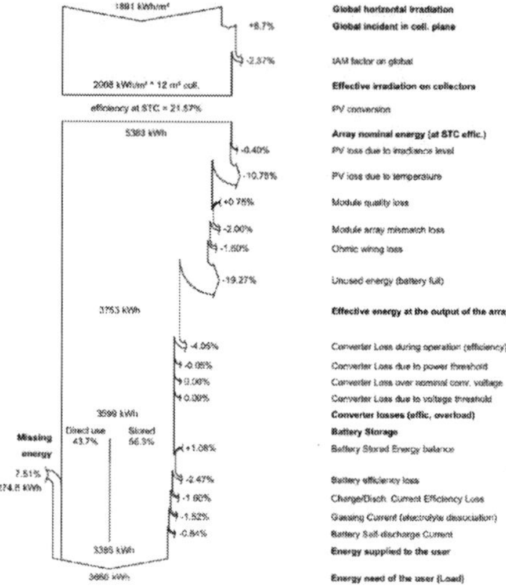

Figure 5: Energy loss diagram.

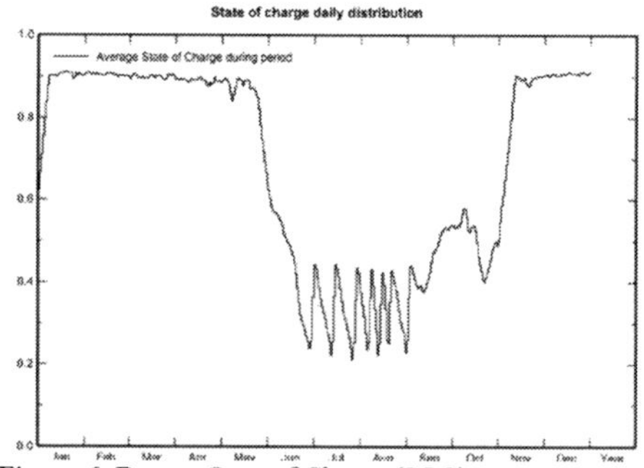

Figure 6: Battery State of Charge (SOC).

5 CONCLUTION

This study investigates the feasibility of converting a recycled shipping container into a positive energy bus stop suitable for the hot and arid climate of Kuwait. The station's energy demand was simulated using DesignBuilder software, based on actual passenger occupancy patterns. Subsequently, the performance of a stand-alone PV system was evaluated using PVsyst software. Simulation results indicate that the PV system can meet over 92% of the station's annual energy demand. However, approximately 895.8 kWh per year of the generated energy remains unused due to storage limitations and a mismatch between energy production and load demand.

Conversely, only 274.8 kWh per year of the load is left unmet, demonstrating the high efficiency and reliability of the system in stand-alone operation. These findings suggest that solar-powered bus stops offer a viable and sustainable solution for urban public transport infrastructure. In addition to meeting internal energy needs, the excess energy can be utilized for ancillary applications like charging electric vehicles, thereby contributing to the development of clean and integrated transportation systems.

Declaration of AI-assisted technologies in the writing process

The authors used AI-assisted English editing tools to improve readability and language, and they reviewed and revised the manuscript, taking full responsibility for the final version.

6 REFERENCES

[1] Eurostat, *Sustainable development in the European Union: Monitoring report on progress towards the SDGs in an EU context*. Publications office of the European Union, 2020.

[2] "SDGs: Sustainable Development Knowledge Platform. Available online: https://sustainabledevelopment.un.org/sdgs (accessed on 15 July 2024)."

[3] "EU's Plan for a Green Transition—Consilium. Available online: https://www.consilium.europa.eu/en/policies/green-deal/eu-plan-for-a-green-transition/ (accessed on 15 July 2025)."

[4] "A European Green Deal | European Commission. Available online: https://ec.europa.eu/info/strategy/priorities-2019-2024/european-green-deal_en (accessed on 15 July 2025)."

[5] G. Climate, "Decision-/CMA.3 Glasgow Climate Pact." [Online]. Available: https://www.ipcc.ch/report/ar6/wg1/.

[6] J. Vepsäläinen, K. Kivekäs, K. Otto, A. Lajunen, and K. Tammi, "Development and validation of energy demand uncertainty model for electric city buses," *Transp Res D Transp Environ*, vol. 63, pp. 347–361, Aug. 2018.

[7] M. Rupp, N. Handschuh, C. Rieke, and I. Kuperjans, "Contribution of country-specific electricity mix and charging time to environmental impact of battery electric vehicles: A case study of electric buses in Germany," *Appl Energy*, vol. 237, pp. 618–634, Mar. 2019.

[8] R. Goodspeed, T. Xie, T. R. Dillahunt, and J. Lustig, "An alternative to slow transit, drunk driving, and walking in bad weather: An exploratory study of ridesourcing mode choice and demand," *J Transp Geogr*, vol. 79, p. 102481, 2019.

[9] I. Lopez-Carreiro and A. Monzon, "Evaluating sustainability and innovation of mobility patterns in Spanish cities. Analysis by size and urban typology," *Sustain Cities Soc*, vol. 38, pp. 684–696, 2018.

[10] S. C. Kwan, R. Sutan, and J. H. Hashim, "Trip characteristics as the determinants of intention to shift to rail transport among private motor vehicle users in Kuala Lumpur, Malaysia," *Sustain Cities Soc*, vol. 36, pp. 319–326, 2018.

[11] R. Sims *et al.*, "IPCC Fifth Assessment Report (AR5)-Chapter 8: Transport," 2014.

[12] S. A. Sadat and M. Nazififard, "Introducing a Novel Hybrid Mobile Energy Storage System for Vulnerable Community Resilience Support," *Proceedings - 2020 6th International Conference on Electric Power and Energy Conversion Systems, EPECS 2020*, pp. 46–51, Oct. 2020.

[13] L. G. González, D. Cordero-Moreno, and J. L. Espinoza, "Public transportation with electric traction: Experiences and challenges in an Andean city," *Renewable and Sustainable Energy Reviews*, vol. 141, p. 110768, May 2021.

[14] S. AlKheder, "Promoting public transport as a strategy to reduce GHG emissions from private vehicles in Kuwait," *Environmental Challenges*, vol. 3, p. 100075, 2021.

[15] M. A. Green, "How did solar cells get so cheap?," *Joule*, vol. 3, no. 3, pp. 631–633, 2019.

[16] S. Zeynali and M. Nazififard, "Integrating Photovoltaic Systems into Urban Infrastructure: A Case Study of Tehran International Tower," *2024 11th Iranian Conference on Renewable Energy and Distribution Generation, ICREDG 2024*, 2024.

[17] M. Nazififard and E. Franquet, "Systematic analysis of roof-mounted photovoltaic systems for achieving net-zero energy in urban historic buildings in hot and arid climates: Potential and challenges," *Energy Build*, vol. 348, p. 116394, Dec. 2025.

[18] S. Ali Sadat, J. Faraji, M. Nazififard, and A. Ketabi, "The experimental analysis of dust deposition effect on solar photovoltaic panels in Iran's desert environment," *Sustainable Energy Technologies and Assessments*, vol. 47, Oct. 2021.

[19] M. Nazififard and N. Torabi, "Experimental Analysis of Dust Accumulation on the Panels of a Microgrid-Connected Photovlitaic System in an Arid Climate," *2023 13th Smart Grid Conference, SGC 2023*, 2023.

[20] T. Santos, N. Gomes, S. Freire, M. C. Brito, L. Santos, and J. A. Tenedório, "Applications of solar mapping in the urban environment," *Applied Geography*, vol. 51, pp. 48–57, 2014.

[21] T. Santos, K. Lobato, J. Rocha, and J. A. Tenedório, "Modeling Photovoltaic Potential for Bus Shelters on a City-Scale: A Case Study in Lisbon," *Applied Sciences*, vol. 10, no. 14, 2020.

[22] B. Kooi, "Security concerns at hot-spot bus stop locations," *Journal of Applied Security Research*, vol. 10, no. 3, pp. 277–307, 2015.

[23] Q. Miao, E. W. Welch, and P. S. Sriraj, "Extreme weather, public transport ridership and moderating effect of bus stop shelters," *J Transp Geogr*, vol. 74, pp. 125–133, 2019.

[24] D. A. Hensher, "Climate change, enhanced greenhouse gas emissions and passenger transport–What can we do to make a difference?," *Transp Res D Transp Environ*, vol. 13, no. 2, pp. 95–111, 2008.

[25] A. Imanloozadeh, M. Nazififard, and S. A. Sadat, "A new stochastic optimal smart residential energy hub management system for desert environment," *Int J Energy Res*, vol. 45, no. 13, pp. 18957–18980, Oct. 2021.

[26] A. Imanloozadeh, M. Nazififard, and H. Hashemi-Dezaki, "Optimal technoeconomic reliability-oriented design of islanded multicarrier microgrids with electrical and hydrogen energy storage systems considering emission concerns," *Energy Sci Eng*, vol. 12, no. 6, pp. 2702–2745, Jun. 2024.

[27] A. Sedaghat *et al.*, "Integrating solar PV systems for energy efficiency in portable cabins: A case study in Kuwait," *Solar Energy*, vol. 277, p. 112715, 2024.

[28]	X. Ding, Z. Zhang, W. Zhang, X. Yue, and Y. Zhang, "Evaluation of the energy-economic-environment potential of urban-scale photovoltaic bus parking lots: The case of Tianjin, China," *J Clean Prod*, vol. 425, p. 138983, 2023.

[29]	S. AlKheder, F. AlRukaibi, and A. Zaqzouq, "Optimal bus frequency for Kuwait public transportation company: A cost view," *Sustain Cities Soc*, vol. 41, pp. 312–319, 2018.

[30]	V. Vossos, K. Garbesi, and H. Shen, "Energy savings from direct-DC in U.S. residential buildings," *Energy Build*, vol. 68, no. PARTA, pp. 223–231, Jan. 2014.

[31]	R. Chauhan, F. Gonzalez-Longatt, B. S. Rajpurohit, and S. Singh, "DC Microgrid in Residential Building," 2018, pp. 367–387.

[32]	D. L. Gerber, V. Vossos, W. Feng, C. Marnay, B. Nordman, and R. Brown, "A simulation-based efficiency comparison of AC and DC power distribution networks in commercial buildings," *Appl Energy*, vol. 210, pp. 1167–1187, Jan. 2018,

[33]	H. E. Gelani, F. Dastgeer, K. Siraj, M. Nasir, K. A. K. Niazi, and Y. Yang, "Efficiency Comparison of AC and DC Distribution Networks for Modern Residential Localities," *Applied Sciences*, vol. 9, no. 3, 2019.

[34]	A. T. Dahiru and C. W. Tan, "Optimal sizing and techno-economic analysis of grid-connected nanogrid for tropical climates of the Savannah," *Sustain Cities Soc*, vol. 52, p. 101824, Jan. 2020.

[35]	A. Ammous, A. Assaedi, A. Alahdal, and K. Ammous, "Energy efficiency of a novel low voltage direct current supply for the future building," *Int J Energy Res*, vol. 45, May 2021.

[36]	A. Rios Villacorta, J. Guamán-Molina, F. Mayorga, and D. Taipe, "Platform of Intelligent Control of Indoor Lighting integrated into LVDC Distribution System: A Case Study in the Technical University of Ambato," *Technology and Economics of Smart Grids and Sustainable Energy*, vol. 7, p. 26, Jul. 2022.

[37]	A. Alsaedi, F. Alharbi, A. Alahdal, A. Alahmadi, A. Ammous, and K. Ammous, "Low Voltage Direct Current Supplies Concept for Residential Applications," *Energy Exploration & Exploitation*, vol. 40, p. 014459872110728, May 2022.

[38]	A. Ammous, A. Alsaedi, A. Alahmadi, F. Alharbi, and K. Ammous, "Efficiency Performances of LVDC Supplies for Residential Building," *Computer Systems Science and Engineering*, vol. 45, pp. 2171–2186, Nov. 2022.

[39]	P. Ollas, T. Thiringer, M. Persson, and C. Markusson, "Energy Loss Savings Using Direct Current Distribution in a Residential Building with Solar Photovoltaic and Battery Storage," *Energies (Basel)*, vol. 16, no. 3, 2023.

[40]	H. Al-Thani, M. Koç, R. J. Isaifan, and Y. Bicer, "A Review of the Integrated Renewable Energy Systems for Sustainable Urban Mobility," *Sustainability*, vol. 14, no. 17, 2022.

[41]	P. Barman *et al.*, "Renewable energy integration with electric vehicle technology: A review of the existing smart charging approaches," *Renewable and Sustainable Energy Reviews*, vol. 183, p. 113518, 2023.

[42]	I. Cavalcante *et al.*, "Electric Vehicles Charging Using Photovoltaic Energy Surplus: A Framework Based on Blockchain," *Energies (Basel)*, vol. 16, no. 6, 2023.

[43]	A. Jain and S. Bhullar, "Operating modes of grid integrated PV-solar based electric vehicle charging system- a comprehensive review," *e-Prime - Advances in Electrical Engineering, Electronics and Energy*, vol. 8, p. 100519, 2024.

[44]	M. Nazififard and S. Zeynali, "Analysis of Photovoltaic Panel Integration for Achieving Net-Zero Energy in French Residential Retrofits in a Mediterranean Climate," *E3S Web of Conferences*, vol. 545, p. 02006, Jul. 2024.

[45]	F. AlRukaibi and S. AlKheder, "Optimization of bus stop stations in Kuwait," *Sustain Cities Soc*, vol. 44, pp. 726–738, 2019.

[46]	"ASHRAE 55-2023".

[47]	M. Koheji, "On Cooling and Comfort: The Engineering of Thermal Spaces in Bahrain," *Engineering Studies*, vol. 17, no. 1, pp. 30–50, Jan. 2025.

[48]	Y. K. Kim, Y. Abdou, A. Abdou, and H. Altan, "Indoor Environmental Quality Assessment and Occupant Satisfaction: A Post-Occupancy Evaluation of a UAE University Office Building," *Buildings*, vol. 12, no. 7, 2022.

[49]	N. Ghareeb *et al.*, "Integrating experimental and theoretical approaches for enhanced machine learning modeling of solar radiation," *Engineering Science and Technology, an International Journal*, vol. 70, p. 102156, Oct. 2025.

[50]	R. and A.-C. E. (ASHRAE) American Society of Heating, "ASHRAE Guideline 14-2002: Measurement of Energy and Demand Savings," Jul. 2002.

COMPARATIVE STUDY OF SOLAR PV WATER PUMPING SYSTEMS IN INDIA: TRANSFORMING AGRICULTURE

Richa Parmar[1*], A. R. Saxena[2], Prashant Misra[1], Jai Prakash[1]
[1]National Institute of Solar Energy (NISE), Gurugram, India,
[2]National Institute of Technology (NIT), Delhi, India
Email: richa.parmar@nise.res.in

ABSTRACT: This paper discusses the design and testing of Solar PV Water Pumping Systems (SPVWPS) in India, highlighting the advantages of solar water pumps, technical challenges, and potential to improve crop yield with a strong focus on the positive impact of such systems on Indian farmers. Additionally, the paper explores different types of pumps, including helical, centrifugal, and reciprocating piston pumps, and provides detailed information of SPVWPS working principles as well as various components and performance characteristics. Furthermore, this paper provides insights into the test protocols for solar water pumps, specifically for Indian climatic conditions. The study concludes by evaluating the performance of various pump types and demonstrating how solar water pumps contribute to improving agricultural productivity and economic stability for Indian farmers.
Keywords: PV modules, Solar Water Pumping System, Pump Controllers, Battery, Storage, Irradiance.

1 INTRODUCTION

India's agricultural sector faces significant water scarcity, with farmers relying heavily on unreliable grid power or diesel-powered pumps [1]. Solar Photovoltaic (PV) water pumping systems offer a sustainable and cost-effective solution by harnessing abundant solar resources. SPVWPS are particularly suitable for remote and off grid locations, where conventional water pumping solutions are either unavailable or economically unviable. Recognizing their potential, Government of India has promoted solar water pumps through policies such as Pradhan Mantri Kisan Urja Suraksha evam Utthaan Mahabhiyan (PM-KUSUM) scheme [2]. More than 2,00,000 solar pumps have already been deployed nationwide, and the scheme targets 3 million installations by 2025. This large scale adoption is driven by declining PV costs, increasing subsidies with improved system efficiencies.

Global trends also highlight the competitiveness of SPVWPS technologies, showing the advances in module efficiency, pump controller technology and energy storage have made them viable even in regions with limited grid access [3], In India key challenges includes high upfront costs, lack of technical expertise and limited after sales support. However, with favourable policies, increasing subsidies, upskilling and the decreasing cost of solar panels, solar water pumps are becoming more accessible to farmers in India.

The present study evaluates the design, components and testing protocols of SPVWPS under Indian climatic conditions, comparative performance analysis of centrifugal, helical, and reciprocating piston pumps is conducted using standardized testing at National Institute of Solar Energy (NISE), with emphasis on efficiency, water output, seasonal variation and economic viability for agricultural applications.

2 METHODOLOGY

The performance evaluation of SPVWPS was conducted at National Institute of Solar Energy (NISE), Gurugram, India (28.26°N, 77.08°E). Based on five years of onsite data (2018-2023), the site records an average of approximately 300 sunny days annually. Peak solar irradiance values can reach up to 1000W/m², although such levels are typically sustained only for short durations and are more prominently observed during the winter season, reflecting the sesonal variabilty in solar resource availability.

2.1 System Components: The three major components used for SPVWPS are as follows:

2.1.1 Solar PV array with Module Mounting Structures (MMTS): Photovoltaic PV array converts solar energy into electrical energy (Figure 1). The most widely used panel types are monocrystalline and polycrystalline. Monocrystalline panels generally provide higher efficiency and longer life but are comparatively more expensive. Depending on pump size and irrigation requirements, the power output of PV arrays generally varies up to 9kWp.

2.1.2 Motor Pump Set: Pump sets used in solar water pumping systems are mainly classified into two categories: surface and submersible pumps. Surface pumps are installed on the ground surface and are suitable for lifting water from shallow sources (up to ~ 7m), whereas submersible pumps are placed in the borewell and are more appropriate for deeper water tables, typically ranging from 10m to over 150m, depending on irrigation demand and site conditions

Figure 1: PV Array for Solar Water Pumps

Furthermore, Solar water pumps are classified into dynamic and positive displacement types. Dynamic pumps, primarily centrifugal (axial flow or radial flow), are widely used for irrigation due to their ability to deliver large volumes of water at low to medium heads. Positive displacement pumps include rotary, helical rotor and reciprocating pumps as shown in Figure 2. In addition, various motor technologies such as Brushless DC (BLDC), Switched Reluctance (SRM), and AC Induction Motors are integrated with pumps to operate the system efficiently and enhance overall performance under varying operating conditions.

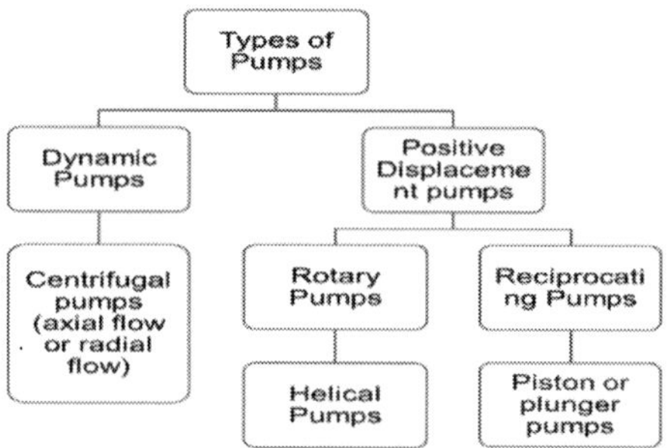

Figure 2: Types of Pumps

a) Centrifugal pumps: Centrifugal pumps are designed for continuous operation and are capable of delivering high flow rates, making them suitable for irrigation across larger-scale land holdings as shown in Figure 3. In this study, submersible type of centrifugal pump performance was evaluated under varying operating conditions. While centrifugal pumps offer advantages in terms of simplicity, cost-effectiveness, and ease of maintenance, their efficiency generally decreases when operating at higher heads or under low-flow conditions.

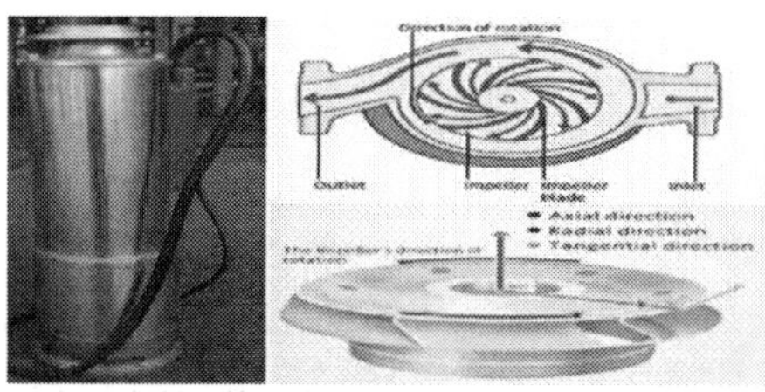

Figure 3: Centrifugal Solar Water Pump and Impeller mechanism

[1]**b) Helical rotor pumps:** Helical rotor pumps illustrated

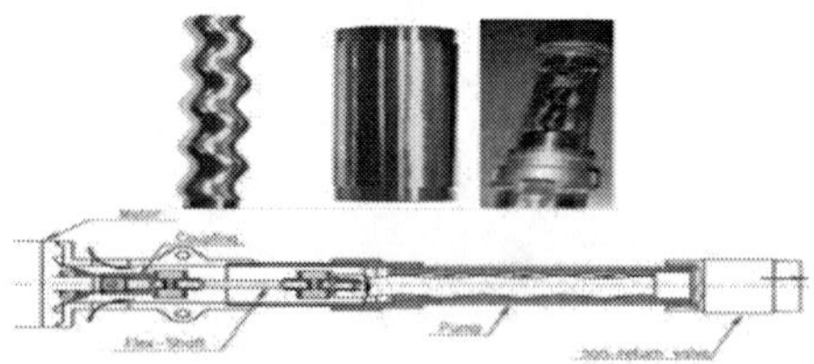

Figure 4: Helical Solar Water Pump and description of Screw gauge technology

[1] (adapted from Foster & Cota, 2013, ISES Solar World Congress, "Solar water pumping advances and comparative economics") and : Cross-section of typical helical rotor pump end (Foster & Cota, 2009)

in Figure 4, are a class of positive displacement pumps designed to deliver moderate flow rates under comparatively higher heads.

c) Reciprocating piston pumps: Reciprocating piston pumps constitute low-power solutions, generally available in capacities of 0.1 hp, 0.25 hp, and 0.5 hp, and are primarily suited for shallow well applications with total dynamic heads in the range of 5–35 m. Owing to their small capacity and portability, these pumps are predominantly utilized by small marginal farmers with landholdings of up to 1 acre, as well as for kitchen gardens and livestock watering. In certain configurations, a battery backup of up to 20 minutes is integrated, enabling continued operation during periods of low solar irradiance

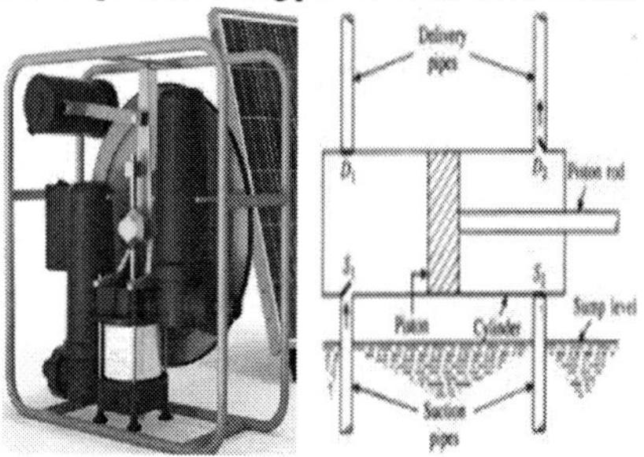

Figure 5: Reciprocating Piston Solar Pump

or at night, thereby enhancing system operational hours for small-scale users. A reciprocating piston pump shown in Figure 5.

2.1.3 Pump Controllers: Pump controllers are essential components that regulate energy flow and convert DC output from solar panels into AC suitable for driving the pump set. They optimize system performance by dynamically adjusting pump speed according to solar irradiance, ensuring efficient operation under variable sunlight conditions [4]. Key features of a pump controller include a Maximum Power Point Tracker (MPPT), which continuously extracts the maximum available power from the PV array; a Variable Frequency Drive (VFD), which modulates pump speed to match water demand and solar input; and, in many cases, a Remote Monitoring System (RMS), enabling real-time monitoring and control of pump operation as illustrated in Figure 6.

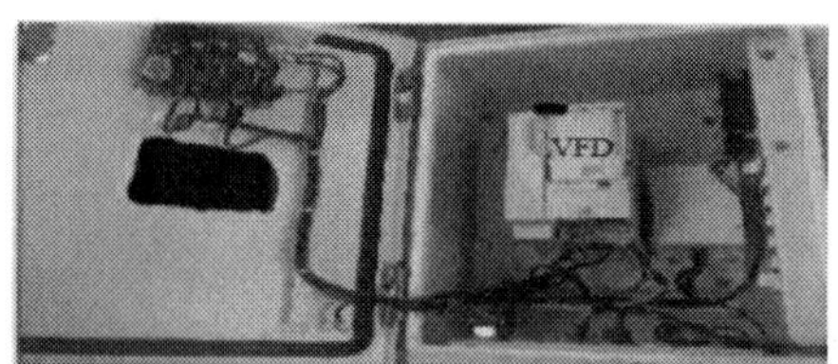

Figure 6: Solar PV Pump Controller with MPPT, VFD & RMS

2.2 Sizing Considerations: Proper sizing of a PV system for solar water pumping involves calculating the energy required to operate the pump for a specified duration [5].

A summarized description of the PV array requirements corresponding to different pump capacities and operating heads is given in Tables 1 and 2 as per Ministry of New and Renewable Energy (MNRE) updated SPVWPS F.No. 41/3/2018-SPV Division [2]. The pump capacity should be determined based on crop water requirements and end user demand, which are influenced by crop type, local climate, and irrigation practices. The system must be designed according to the available solar irradiance, which is typically 4–5 kWh/m²/day in most parts of India. In certain applications, water storage tanks and battery backups are incorporated to ensure uninterrupted operation during periods of low irradiance or after sunset [6].

Table 1: Technical Specifications of Solar Deep well (submersible) Pumping Systems with D.C. Motor Pump Set

Description	Model A	Model B	Model C	Model D	Model E	Model F
PV array (Wp)	1200	1800	3000	4800	6750	9000
Motor Pump-set capacity (hp)	1	2	3	5	7.5	10
Shut Off Head (meters)	45	45	100	150	150	150
Total Dynamic Head (TDH) (meters)	30	30	70	100	100	100
Water output * (Liters Per Day)	45600	68400	45000	50400	70875	94500

Table 2: Technical Specifications of Solar Deep well (submersible) Pumping Systems with A.C. Induction Motor Pump Set

Description	Model A	Model B	Model C	Model D	Model E	Model F
PV array (Wp)	1200	1800	3000	4800	6750	9000
Motor Pump-set capacity (hp)	1	2	3	5	7.5	10
Shut Off Head (meters)	45	45	100	150	150	150
Total Dynamic Head (TDH) (meters)	30	30	70	100	100	100
Water output * (Liters Per Day)	42000	63000	42000	43200	60750	81000

* Water output figures are on a clear sunny day with three times tracking of SPV panel, under the "Average Daily Solar Radiation" condition of 7.15 kWh/ sq.m. on the surface of PV array (i.e. coplanar with the PV Modules).

3 AIM AND APPROACH: TESTING OF SOLAR PV WATER PUMPING SYSTEMS

The primary objective of testing solar PV water pumping systems is to evaluate the performance and efficiency under different climatic conditions. This includes assessing energy conversion efficiency, water output, and overall system sustainability to ensure optimal design and functionality for agricultural and rural applications [7].

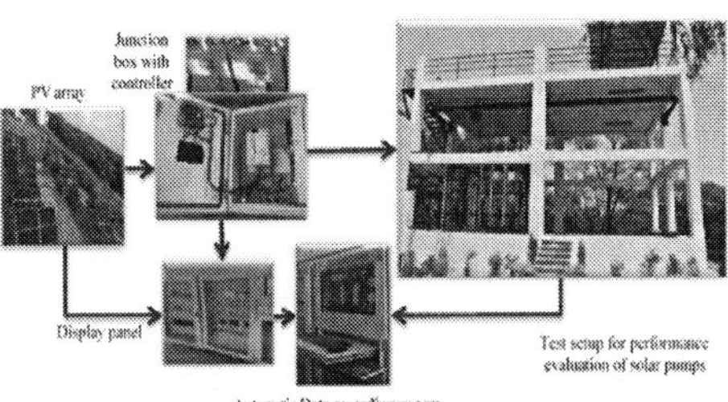

Figure 7 Solar Water Pump Test and R&D Facility at NISE (India)

3.1 *Experimental setup and site details:* All experiments were conducted at NISE test and R&D facility (Figure 7), which includes a 7-meter-deep sump well for water storage. The site is equipped with six test slots, slot details specified in Table 3, each fitted with a flow meter, pressure gauge, pressure sensor, and an automatic gate valve, facilitating controlled evaluation of different pump systems under different operating conditions (Outdoor Real time and simulated ideal conditions). A junction box with four terminals i.e. PV input, controller input, controller output, and pump output and connects the PV array to the pump system.

Table 3: Test Slot Specifications and Suitable Pump Capacities

Slot No.	Diameter	Suitable Pump Capacity
1	0.5 inch	< 1 hp
2	1 inch	0.5 hp – 2 hp
3	2 inch	3 hp – 7.5 hp
4	3 inch	7.5 hp – 10 hp
5	4 inch	10 hp – 25 hp
6	6 inch	25 hp – 50 hp

The PV array is also linked to a display panel to monitor array temperature and irradiance in real time. The display panel provides information on pump speed (RPM), water level, slip speed, and delivery pressures. Data acquisition is performed using a dedicated laboratory software connected to a laptop via Ethernet, which logs measurements at every 5 seconds interval. This setup allows precise monitoring and evaluation of system performance for different pump types and configurations. Details of laboratory instruments given in Table 4.

Table 4 Instruments used in the solar water pumping division at NISE

S.No.	Instrument	Make / Model	Function
1	Pyranometer	Kipp & Zonen / 163582	Measures solar irradiance
2	Solar Array Simulator	Chroma / 62150H-1000S	Enables precise control of voltage and current, simulating different environmental conditions such as solar radiation and temperature for accurate performance testing

S.No.	Instrument	Make / Model	Function
3	Power Analyzer	Yokogawa / WT1800	Measures electrical parameters including voltage, current, power, harmonics, and efficiency across system components
4	Pressure Gauge & Transmitter with Display	Yokogawa / EJA530E-JBS4N-012EL	Measures the head of pumps during operation
5	Electromagnetic Flow Meter	Yokogawa / S5W916138-AXG025	Measures water flow
6	Temperature Sensor	GCS / 15Bo57284	Measures the PV module surface temperature
7	Data Logging Software	Customized in LabView	Logs data at 5-second intervals
8	Digital Power Meter	Yokogawa / WT33E	Measures electrical parameters of the system

3.1.2 Testing Parameters: The performance of the solar PV water pumping systems was evaluated based on the following key parameters [7]:

- Pump performance metrics, including flow rate, total head, and energy consumption.
- System performance at variable heads, assessing pump output and efficiency under different total dynamic head (TDH) conditions to simulate real field conditions.

3.1.3 Data Collection: Continuous data on pump performance, PV panel efficiency, and weather conditions was collected over different operating conditions to assess long-term performance. Therefore, hot and cold profiles were designed to replicate real environmental conditions of an ideal summer day and ideal winter day.

The hot profile represents high solar irradiance and elevated module temperatures typically observed in peak summer day, leading to reduced PV module efficiency due to heat & thermal effects. Similarly, the cold profile corresponds to lower ambient temperatures and moderate irradiance levels typical of peak sunny winter day, resulting in higher module efficiency and stable power output. These profiles were incorporated into the DC programmable power supply to simulate realistic seasonal variations for performance evaluation, as illustrated in Figure 8.

Input data included irradiance, module temperature, and module efficiency, which were then fed to the pump controller. Water output measurements were recorded after the predefined head was established, ensuring consistency across all pump types and configurations.

4 RESULTS AND DISCUSSION

The performance of the tested SPVWPS was evaluated across centrifugal, helical rotor, and reciprocating piston pumps, considering under different operating conditions including variable total dynamic heads (TDH), seasonal irradiance variations in Hot & Cold Profile, and peak/off-peak sun hours.

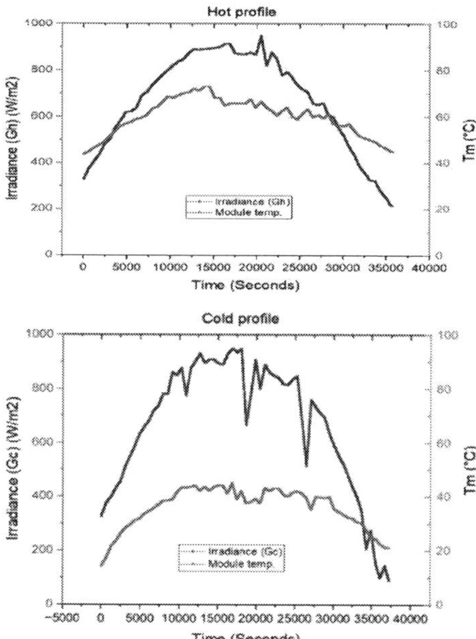

Figure 8: Hot profile and cold profile vs Irradiance graph

4.1 Pump Performance and Efficiency

4.1.1 Centrifugal Pumps: Submersible centrifugal pumps demonstrated robustness and delivered consistently high flow rates, making them suitable for large-scale irrigation applications. The 10 hp AC submersible pump tested at NISE, maintains high efficiencies across tested head levels, reflecting its robust electrical design. Among all measured heads, 100 meter head, i.e., the design head, distinctly stands out as the optimal operating point, balancing the system's WTW Eff. and hydraulic output for sustained, high-volume water delivery with minimal energy losses. The controller efficiency reaches 96.86% (Cold) and 96.61% (Hot), while the flow rate remains well-balanced under full-load conditions. Wire-to-water efficiency is highest at this head (100 m), at 53.97% (Hot) and 56.29% (Cold), indicating efficient energy transfer and system operation. And the average wire-to-water efficiency (WTW Eff.) was observed to be 49.32% under cold conditions and 46.11% under hot conditions. Water output decreases at higher total dynamic heads due to the inherent characteristics of centrifugal pumps, where increasing head results in higher system resistance and reduced flow rate. However, wire-to-water efficiency reaches its peak at the designed head (e.g., 100 m for the 10 HP pump), as this operating point represents the optimal balance between electrical input, hydraulic load, and pump performance, allowing maximum energy transfer from the PV array to the water. For instance, at a head of 150 m, the efficiency of a 10 hp pump was measured at 40.55% under cold conditions with a DC input power of 6.94 kW, and 31.23% under hot conditions at 6.20 kW DC power which is lowest as shown in Figure 9.

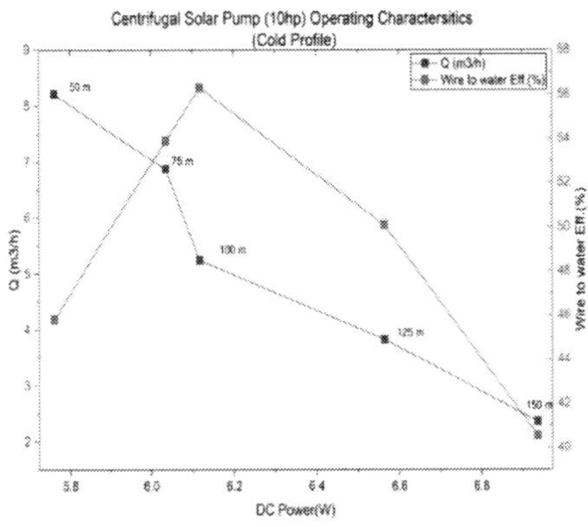

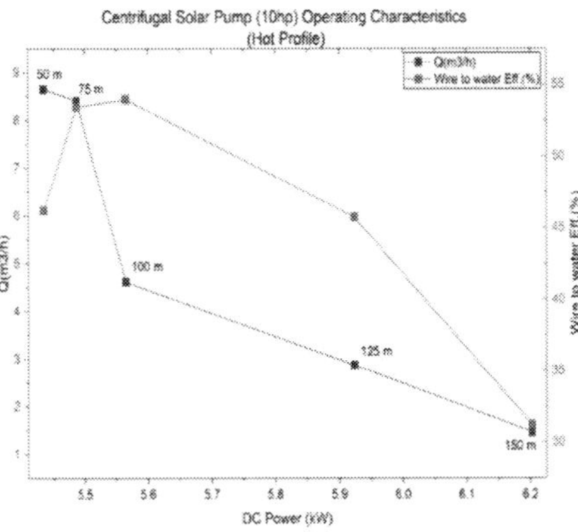

Figure 9: Hot profile and cold profile vs flow graph of 10hp Centrifugal Solar Water Pumps

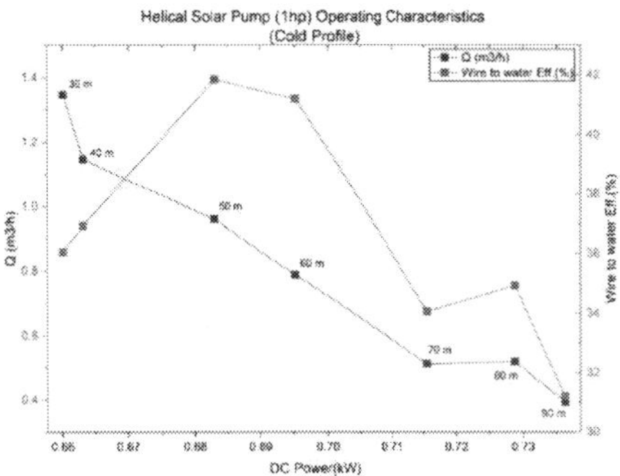

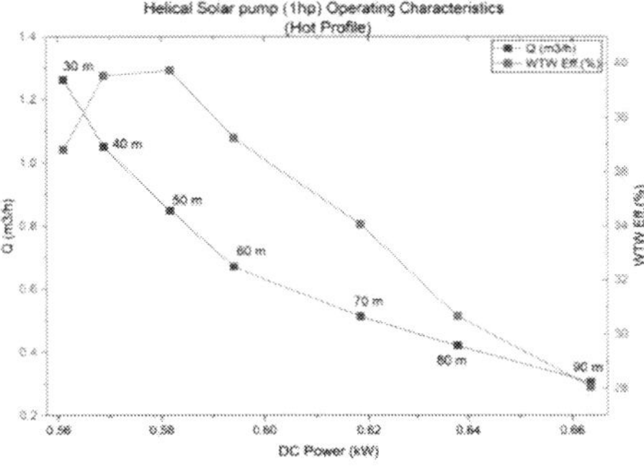

Figure 10: Hot profile and cold profile vs flow graph of 1hp Helical Solar Water Pumps

4.1.2 Helical Rotor Pumps: Positive displacement helical pumps delivered moderate flow rates at higher total dynamic heads ranging from 30 to 90 m. As shown in Figure 10, a 1 hp configuration maintained steady operation and demonstrated average efficiencies of 36.60% under cold conditions and 35.16% under hot conditions.

The performance evaluation of the 1 hp DC helical submersible pump across various heads under hot and cold profiles provides critical insights into how environmental conditions and system parameters influence overall efficiency and output. Notably, at 60 meters, the design head, both WTW eff. and hydraulic performance are optimized. The controller efficiency peaks at 95.65% (Cold) and 95.54% (Hot), indicating excellent power conversion under real operating conditions. Wire-to-water efficiency at design head (60 m) is 41.2% (Cold) and 37.25% (Hot), demonstrating effective energy transfer from the PV panel to the pump. At the maximum tested head of 90 m, efficiency was observed at 31.19% with a DC input power of 0.74 kW in cold conditions, and 28.07% at 0.66 kW in hot conditions.

4.1.3 Reciprocating Piston Pumps: Reciprocating piston pump performance evaluated under real-time outdoor conditions, demonstrated effective performance for low-head, shallow-well applications. In the present evaluation, compact 1 hp pump configurations were tested across a total dynamic head range of 30–90 m. These systems demonstrate suitability for applications involving clean water, with particular relevance to potable water supply, community-level distribution networks, and smallholder irrigation practices.

The pump characteristics shown in Figure 11 indicate high wire-to-water efficiency, with maximum efficiency of 62.22% observed at the design head of 33 m. At higher heads, such as 38 m, efficiency decreased slightly to 57.12%, reflecting the behavior of reciprocating pumps where increased hydraulic resistance reduces flow. Flow rates varied from 0.86 to 1.29 m³/h depending on the head. These results confirm that reciprocating piston pumps maintain efficient operation near the design head while offering a compact, low-power solution suitable for smallholder irrigation, kitchen gardens, and livestock watering..

4.2 Seasonal and Irradiance Effects: Hot and cold profiles, representing ideal summer (June) and winter (January) irradiance patterns, were used to evaluate system performance.

4.3 Variable Head Performance

- Testing at different Total Dynamic Head (TDH) values highlighted pump-specific characteristics: centrifugal pumps delivered maximum flow at design but saw reduced efficiency at non design heads.
- Data confirmed that selecting pump type according to required head and water volume is crucial for optimal performance and system efficiency.

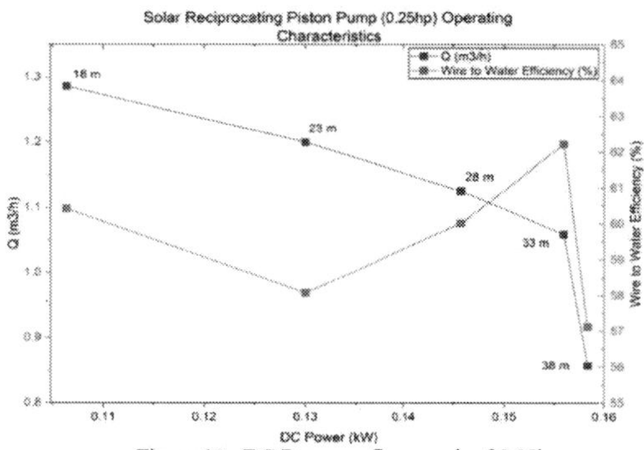

Figure 11: DC Power vs flow graph of 0.25hp Reciprocating Piston Solar Pump

5 CONCLUSION

The findings confirm that system performance is influenced by seasonal variations, with winter months yielding higher efficiency due to reduced thermal stress and improved PV module output. In hot profiles, the system consumes more DC power but delivers higher flow rates, that to reduced fluid resistance and improved pump dynamics. However, elevated temperatures tend to reduce voltage levels slightly, impacting overall energy conversion, also at higher head flow rate and water output drop significantly due to increased frictional and pressure losses, despite stable controller and MPPT efficiencies. The pump exhibits optimal performance at its designed head, with performance decrease at heads above or below this point. This analysis shows that choosing the right head is very important for getting the most water and best performance from a solar pump system.

The three evaluated pump technologies, centrifugal pumps were most effective for large-scale irrigation with moderate head requirements, while helical rotor pumps suitable for applications such as drinking water supply and community-level drinking water distribution. Reciprocating piston pumps emerged as a low-power (less than 1 hp) solution ideally suited for small marginal farmers, enabling efficient operation in shallow head ranges of 5–35 m.

Emerging reciprocating piston pump technologies currently under R&D exhibit promising potential for higher head applications, greater throughput capacity, and robust performance under low-irradiance conditions ($160W/m^2$). Such innovations represent a future pathway for advancing solar-based irrigation systems in India.

Overall, the results validate solar PV water pumps as technically robust, field-viable, and socio-economically impactful solutions for irrigation and drinking water needs, while highlighting opportunities for further integration, and policy-driven scaling.

References

1. Muralidhar K., & Rajasekar N., (2021), A review of various components of solar water-pumping system: Configuration, characteristics, and performance. International Transactions on Electrical Energy Systems, 31: e13002. https://doi.org/10.1002/2050-7038.13002.

2. Comprehensive guidelines for implementation of Pradhan Mantri Kisan Urja Suraksha Evam Utthaan Mahabhiyan (PM-KUSUM), Ministry of New and Renewable Energy (MNRE), 32/645/2017-SPV Division.

3. Rathore, P. K. S., Das, S. S., & Chauhan, D. S. (2018). Perspectives of solar photovoltaic water pumping for irrigation in India. Energy Strategy Reviews, 22, 385–395. https://doi.org/10.1016/j.esr.2018.10.009.

4. Gualteros, S., & Rousse, D. R. (2021). Solar water pumping systems: A tool to assist in sizing and optimization. Solar Energy, 225, 382–398. https://doi.org/10.1016/j.solener.2021.06.053.

5. Maity R., Sudhakar K., & Razak A. A. (2024), Agri-Solar Water Pumping design, energy, and environmental analysis: A comprehensive study in Tropical Humid climate. Heliyon, 10 (2024), e39604. https://doi.org/10.1016/j.heliyon.2024.e39604.

6. Ahmed N. M., Hassan A. M., Kassem M. A., Hegazi A. M., & Elsaadawi Y. F., (2023), Reliability and performance evaluation of a solar PV-powered underground water pumping system. Scientific Reports, 13:14174. https://doi.org/10.1038/s41598-023-41272-5.

7. Verma S., Mishra S., Chowdhury S., Gaur A., Mohapatra S., Soni A. & Verma P. (2021). Solar PV powered water pumping system – A review. Materials Today Proceedings, 46, 5601–5606. https://doi.org/10.1016/j.matpr.2020.09.434

8. Schüpbach, E., Muntwyler, U., Jost, M., Müller, A., & Urena, D. (2014). Introducing Solar Water Pumps to Female Farmers in India. European Photovoltaic Solar Energy Conference and Exhibition (EU PVSEC) 2014. https://doi.org/10.24451/arbor.7687.

9. Serbouh, Y., Benikhelef, T., Benazzouz, D., Chikh, M. a. A., Touil, S., Richa, A., & Mahmoudi, H. (2022). Performance optimization and reliability of solar pumping system designed for smart agriculture irrigation. Desalination and Water Treatment, 255, 4–12. https://doi.org/10.5004/dwt.2022.28316.

10. Dankoff, W., Foster, R., Cota, A., Lespin, E. (2022). Advances in Solar Powered Water Pumping: Providing for Energy Resiliency and Social Equity. In: Ghosh, A.K., Rixham, C. (eds) Proceedings of the American Solar Energy Society National Conference. ASES SOLAR 2022. Springer Proceedings in Energy. Springer, Cham. https://doi.org/10.1007/978-3-031-08786-8_3

PARTIAL LOAD EFFICIENCY OF PHOTOVOLTAICS IN DIRECT COUPLING TO HYDROGEN ELECTROLYSIS

M. Rennhofer[1], Ph. Mayer-Ullmann[1], D. Krainer[1,2], G. Ujvari[1], J. Lichtenberger[1], K. Kainz[1], V. Neussl[1,3]
[1]AIT Austrian Institute of Technology GmbH (AIT), Österreich
[2]TU Wien, Vienna University of Technology, Österreich
[3]Montanuniversität Leoben, Österreich
marcus.rennhofer@ait.ac.at

ABSTRACT: There are still many challenges to be overcome in order to achieve the goal of climate-neutral energy supply. On the one hand, there is a need for massive expansion of solar or wind energy and, on the other, further technological development in terms of performance, reliability and flexibility. Here, hydrogen (H2) can act as a central bridge between the volatile energy from sun or wind and the still dominant hydrocarbon-based energy system. Here we present two research initiatives (PH2ÖNIX and a mini-H2 technology demonstrator) investigating the use of photovoltaics and hydrogen production in direct DC coupling, one in a small set-up with research components and one with real components for industrial sites.

1 INTRODUCTION

In the PH2ÖNIX demonstrator, electricity from a nearby PV roof system (2x30 kWp) supplies two electrolysers, each 10 kW, PEM and the AEM technology, respectively. The hydrogen is stored in gas cylinders. A PEM fuel cell with 8 kW uses the stored hydrogen to generate electricity, thus completing the circuit of converting electricity from power to H2 into electricity (P2P). For the mini H2-technology demonstrator, 2 PV mini-modules with a total of 9 A and 4.8 V were directly connected to a small hydrogen electrolysis PEM cell with a nominal operating voltage of 4 V. Two topologies were investigated, one with high current (parallel modules) and one with high voltages (serial modules).

For the setups, different research questions were followed that investigate several components of the coupling of PV systems and H2 electrolysis systems. The paper focuses on PV self-consumption in real operation and the influence of direct system coupling on the efficiency levels and working points of the individual components, the partial load efficiencies and in particular, the influence of weather on the system working points.

While the direct DC coupling is not new, the approach here was to investigate systems of largely different power level to conclude on scaling factors. Further, for each system different modes of operation and diverse operation points allow to conclude on optimization potentials in design. Finally, PV-2-H2 scaling factors were investigated and are still under investigation. For PH2ÖNIX, a over dimensioning of PV power to H2 power is possible for investigating its impact on H2 production, ramp-up times and efficiencies. For the mini technology demonstrator different settings with low current and high voltage or high current low voltage were implemented and the impact on the H2 production was followed.

All this investigations are of relevance for of-grid PV-H2 systems. The system coupling without grid and direct DC might be in the minority of industrial application cases but it also brings in advantaged as minimum amount of technical components and investment and high reliability in operation. Understanding effects of mismatching electrical parameters as well as impact of weather is of high importance.

2 METHODOLOGY

2.1 Basic approach

The main aim of the studies was to investigate one typology of PV-H2 electrolysis coupling, which is special in the way that is has an absolute minimum of system components. The PH2ÖNIX project is investigating system scenarios for direct off-grid coupling of PV systems with water electrolysers, see Figure 1 the electrolysis of the research initiatives for hydrogen production exclusively draws electricity from a PV system. The variable energy is stored as hydrogen, but for PH2ÖNIX it is reenergized in times without generation via a fuel cell. Both systems have the same basic idea of coupling but at different system size, PH2ÖNIX with 60 KWp PV and 2x 10 kW electrolysis, the mini technology demonstrator 50 W PV with 36 W electrolysis. The approach was to investigate different operation modes in dependence of environmental conditions and conclude on system efficiency and longevity. In the following the system details for the two setups are given. They are also summarized in Table I.

2.2 Ph2önix – PV & Grid-Back-Up

In the PH2ÖNIX demonstrator at the AIT Seibersdorf campus, electricity from a nearby PV roof system (2x30 kWp) supplies two electrolyzers. Each electrolyzer has an electrical output of 10 kW. At night or late afternoon, a PEM fuel cell with 8 kW of electrical output uses the stored hydrogen.

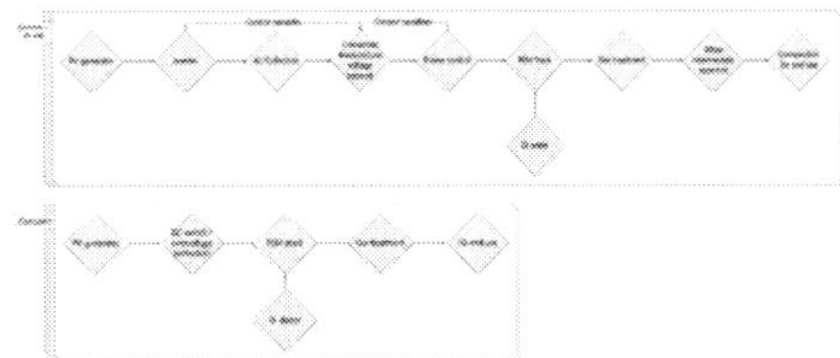

Figure 1: System diagrams for direct coupling types of PV-H2 electrolysis, (top) for PH2ÖNIX and (bottom) for the mini H2 demonstrator

10.4229/EUPVSEC2025/4DV.1.78

Table I: Standing waves ratio

Equipment	Technology Demonstrator	PH₂ÖNIX
PV-system	50 Wp	63kWp
H2-electrolysis	36 W	2 x 10 kW
Storage	none	bundle 30bar
Fuel Cell	none	8kW
Coupling type	direct DC	direct DC or AC local grid

2.3 Technology demonstrator - Only PV-coupling

For the Mini-H2 demonstrator, 2x6-cell PV mini modules were selected, with a total maximum of 9 A ISC and 3.8 V open-circuit voltage on a small fuel cell store hydrogen electrolysis PEM cell with a nominal 4 V operating voltage and a maximum of 9 A input voltage, directly DC coupled.

3   RESULTS

As exemplary results here the system electrical efficiency is shown for the H2 mini technology demonstrator in the case of serial PV modules (too high voltage, too low current) and parallel PV modules (too low voltage, too high current).

The Figure 2 shows some operating points of the coupled system (orange-black) as well as ideal characteristic curve (black) and the STC characteristic curve of the 2 x 6 cell modules. The operating points show voltages that are too high and currents that are too low for the electrolyser. The main factors are the start time of the electrolyser, the temperature of the water and the compensation of the currents that are too low by high.

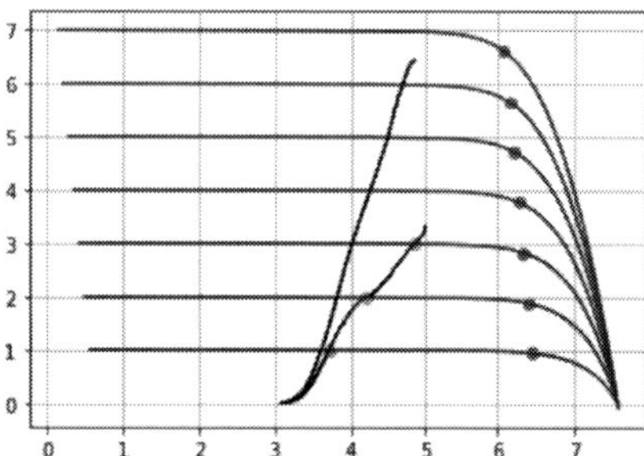

Figure 2: System efficiency dependency on operation conditions of the PV. Red points indicate joint operation point during heating up phase of the electrolyzer.

3.1 Partial load efficiencies

The influence of the position of the point where the systems are coupled at 1000 W relative to the MPP point of the PV shows clear when one makes the efficiency analysis of the used sunlight, see Figure 3. The pictures show the recorded proportions of sunlight at the respective irradiation. In Figure 3, top, for both modules in series (high voltages), and in Figure 3, bottom, for the scenario with the modules parallel (high currents).

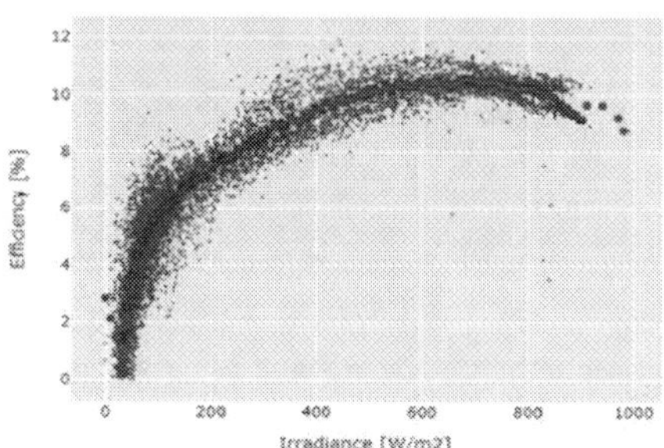

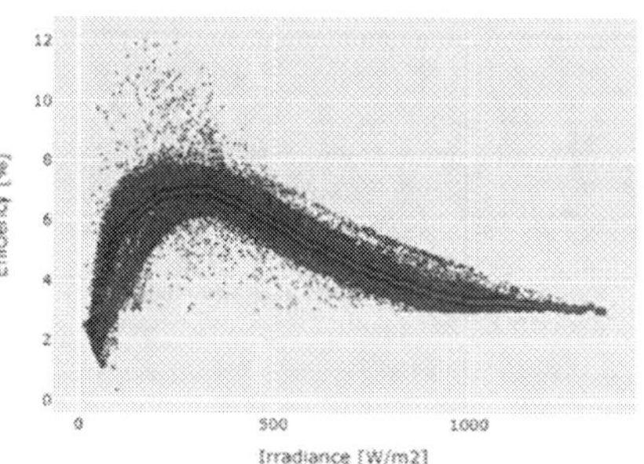

Figure 3: The influence of the position of the point where the systems at 1000 W regarding the efficiency analysis - absorbed shares of sunlight at the respective irradiation. Top: for both modules serial; Bottom: for both modules parallel

3.2 System behavior and degradation

While the efficiency of a PV module alone usually increases with the radiation, a clear maximum is pronounced for the coupled system. Figure 3 shows a significant decrease in efficiency above 700 W/m2, all working points are at voltages lower than the MPP voltage. For the parallel case, Figure 3, right, the maximum efficiency is smaller and the maximum is already about 300 W/m2. At 1000 W/m2 the system has almost no efficiency, all working points are higher than the MPP voltage.

For the serial connected modules, the hydrogen flow was investigated. Since all the working points are at voltages smaller than the MPP voltage, the relationship between irradiation and current is almost linear. The relationship between H2 flow of the electrolyser (H2 generation) and current is also linear, see Figure 4. The graph also shows that the H2 flow is temperature independent at constant voltage.

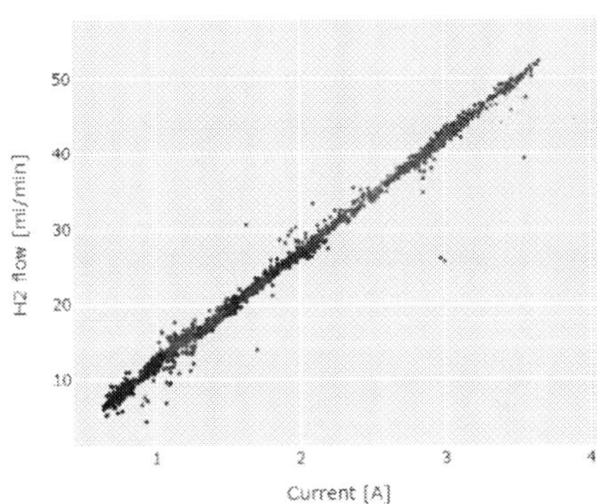

Figure 4: H2 flow of the electrolyser, the evaluation is shown for voltages of 4 V (nominal voltage).

Finally, an analysis was made to determine whether the non-optimal operating conditions affect the lifetime of the electrolyser. Figure 5 shows the related statistical analysis, showing all H2 flow values per month. It can be seen that there is a systematic decrease in the flow while the main cause is the system-coupling related high voltages larger than the nominal electrolysers voltage of 4V.

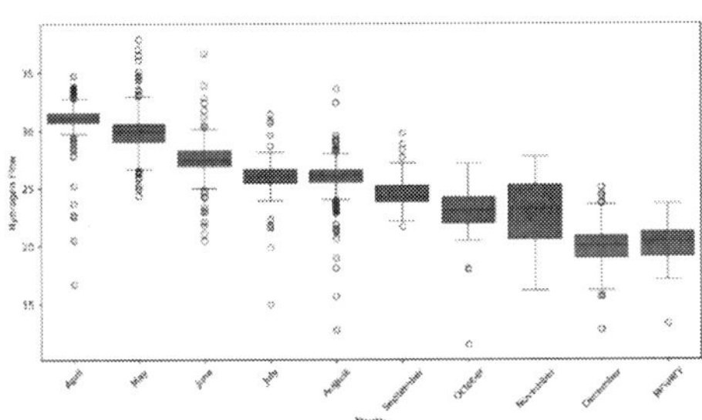

Figure 5: Statistical analysis of the aging of the system based on H2 flow values.

4 CONCLUSIONS

Concluding, two test systems for direct DC coupling of PV and H2-electric circuits were investigated, which differ in their system setup and size.

For the 50W system, the evaluations of the working points, system efficiencies and the time behavior of the H2 flow were evaluated and shown here. The analysis shows that although a directly coupled system is simple by number of components, but more know-how has to be put into the coordination and behavior of the working points. In detail, it was possible to deduce that:

- Directly coupled systems are functional and stable
- The choice of nominal voltages at STC for both systems is central to system efficiency
- Electrolysis systems allow working points outside the ideal characteristic

- The temperature influence on the functionality is very pronounced
- The hydrogen flow is approximately linear with the irradiation scalable
- The hydrogen flow decreases systematically through aging when high voltages are present.

MARCUS RENNHOFER[*1] // PHIL... KUBICEK[1] // GUSZTAV UJVARI[1] // JANINE Lichtenberger[1] // BERNHARD KUBICEK[1] // KONRAD KAINZ[1]

1 AIT Austrian Institute of Technology GmbH, Center for Energy, Photovoltaic Systems, EnergyBase Vienna.
2 Montanuniversität Leoben, Österreich
3 TU Wien, Vienna University of Technology

* marcus.rennhofer@ait.ac.at

PARTIAL LOAD EFFICIENCY OF PHOTOVOLTAICS IN DIRECT COUPLING TO HYDROGEN ELECTROLYSIS

GOALS and METHODS

For the goal of a climate-neutral energy supply, the massive expansion of solar or wind energy is needed. For reliability, storage & flexibility, hydrogen (H2) can act as a central bridge. The coupling was tested in two systems of different sizing.

Methodological approach

- In contrast to conventional concepts in which the electrolyzer is connected to the power grid, the electrolysis of the research initiatives for hydrogen production draws electricity exclusively from a PV system.
- Both system included crystalline PV and PEM electrolysis
- For PH$_2$ÖNIX, it is converted back into electricity via a fuel cell in times when there is no generation
- PV related and hydrogen related parameters were monitored and evaluated
- Main focus was put on partial load behavior far away of the optimal operation points

Ph2önix – PV & Grid-Back-Up

- In the PH2ÖNIX demonstrator at the AIT Seibersdorf campus, electricity from a nearby PV roof system (2x30 kWp) supplies two electrolyzers. Each electrolyzer has an electrical output of 10 kW. At night or late afternoon, a PEM fuel cell with 8 kW of electrical output uses the stored hydrogen

Technology demonstrator - Only PV-coupling

- For the Mini-H2 demonstrator, 2x6-cell PV mini modules were selected, with a total maximum of 9 A ISC and 3.8 V open-circuit voltage on a small fuel cell store hydrogen electrolysis PEM cell with a nominal 4 V operating voltage and a maximum of 9 A input voltage, directly DC coupled.

Technical Details

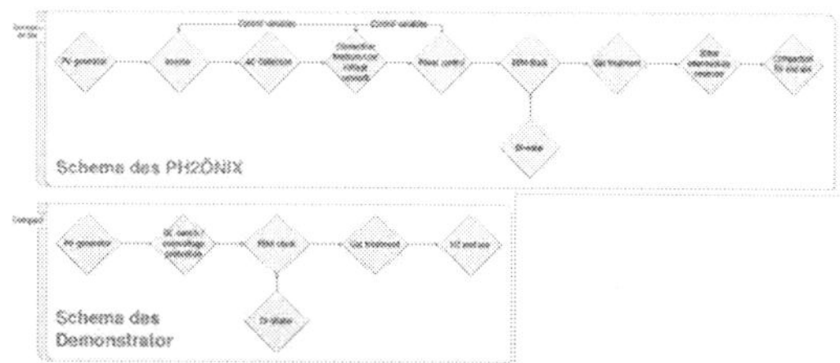

Schema des PH2ÖNIX

Schema des Demonstrator

Equipment	Technology demonstrator	PH2önix
PV-System	~50 Wp	63 kWp
H2-Elektrolyis	36 W	2 x 10 kWp
Storage	none	bundle storage at 30 bar
Fuel-cell	none	8 kWp
Coupling type	direct DC	direct DC or AC local grid

System set-up for the PH$_2$önix

- Construction of PH2ÖNIX with photovoltaic systems, electrolysers and reverse power generation at the AIT Seibersdorf campus.

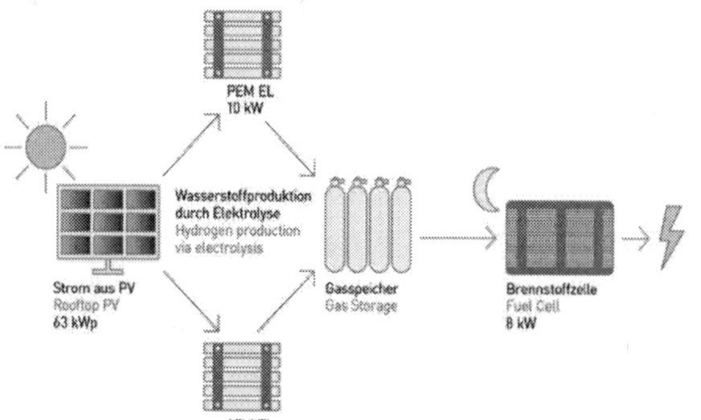

Joint Operation Points PV-electrolysis

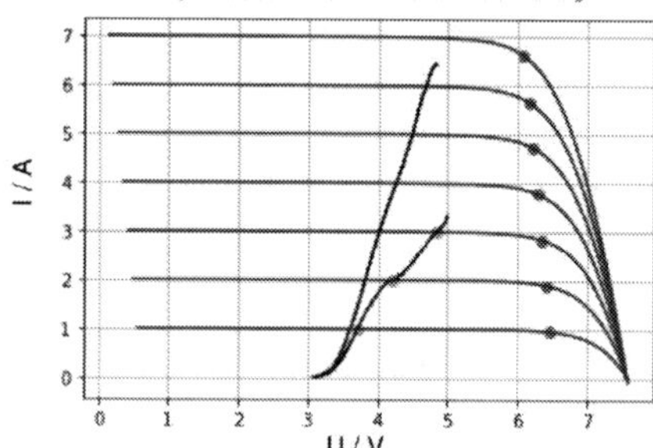

System efficiency depends on maintaining optimal operating points (MPP)

The figure shows some operating points of the coupled system (orange-black) as well as ideal characteristic curve (black) and the STC characteristic curve of the 2 x 6 cell modules. The operating points show voltages that are too high and currents that are too low for the electrolyser. The main factors are the start time of the electrolyser, the temperature of the water and the compensation of the currents that are too low by high voltages with the same PV output.

Coupling – Efficiency - Continuos Operation

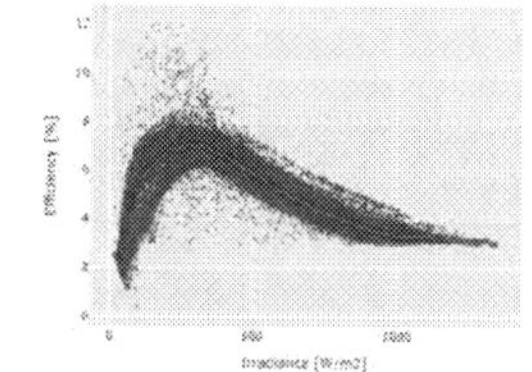
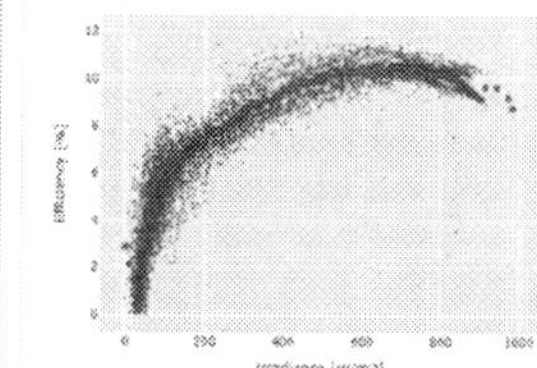

Coupling and Efficiency

Left: Efficiency analysis - recorded portions of sunlight during the respective irradiation for two modules in parallel. **Right:** Two Modules in series.

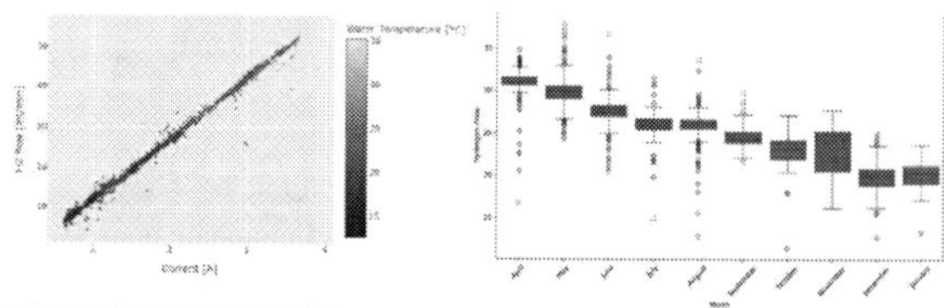

Continuos Operation and Aging

Left: H2 flow of the electrolyser. The evaluation is shown for voltages of 4 V (nominal voltage). The graph also shows that the H2 flux is temperature independent at constant voltage.

Right: Statistical analysis of the aging of the system using H2 flow values. The central cause of the decrease is the system coupling-related high voltages.

Goals Achieved & Conclusion

Two test systems for **direct DC coupling of PV and H2 electrolsysis** were presented, which differ in their system performance. The **operating efficiency and durability** depend fundamentally on the component design. It was researched in detail that:

- ✓ Directly coupled systems are functional and stable
- ✓ The choice of nominal voltages at STC for both systems is central to system efficiency
- ✓ Electrolysis systems allow operating points away from the ideal characteristic curve
- ✓ Hydrogen flow systematically decreases through aging when there are over voltages.

The research was supported by the PH2ÖNIX (KPC photovoltaic lighthouses of the BMK Austria).

PREDICTING SHADING LOSSES IN PHOTOVOLTAIC PLANTS: A NOVEL APPROACH

D. López Dalmau[1], H. Mirandona López[1], C. Javier Lopes Gomes[1], J. Tomàs Villalonga Palou[1], C. Rossa[1]
[1]Sunveon
calle del Musgo, 2, 1B, Madrid, Spain. 28023

ABSTRACT: Accurately estimating shadow impact on large-scale photovoltaic (PV) plants is challenging due to the computational demands of traditional methods. This study introduces the Sunveon Model, a novel, efficient approach for simulating shading and mismatch losses without requiring complex I-V curve calculations. The model uses a hybrid methodology, combining a 2D irradiance model with a 3D submodule-level shading model. Its key innovation is the use of a regression model, whose accuracy was validated against over 500,000 I-V curves, to directly predict a string's Maximum Power Point (MPP), significantly reducing computational time. It also quantifies mismatch losses with a new 'Mixed Fill Factor' that establishes a direct quadratic relationship between losses, shadow percentage, and irradiance. Validated against real-world data, the Sunveon Model proved more accurate than two industry-standard models, showing substantially lower errors. A key finding is that mismatch losses for standard cells are about 64% higher than for half-cell modules. In summary, the Sunveon Model offers a precise and efficient tool for large-scale PV analysis.

Keywords: Shading-induced losses, mismatch losses, computational efficiency, 3D shading model

1 INTRODUCTION

Accurately estimating the impact of shadows on photovoltaic generation is significantly constrained by the current scale of photovoltaic (PV) plants and the complexity of the terrain. This challenge is compounded by the excessive computational cost associated with calculating complete I-V curves, which restricts their application in precisely estimating energy production from large-scale PV plants. For example, on a conventional PC, a typical 50 MW plant (about 3,000 strings) can be simulated in 30 seconds for shading table generation (12×13 positions per string) plus 50 seconds for yield simulation. This has motivated most standard production models available on the market to simplify yield estimations, working with statistical approaches to simulate the impact of shadows on current PV plants[1], [2], [3], which can be hundreds of megawatts in size. These models typically simulate only a few representative strings within the plant, leading to over or underestimating shading effects due to common loss factors. This, in turn, affects accurate assessment of mismatch losses.

This study proposes a novel approach to simulate shading-induced losses in PV plants without the need to compute complete I-V curves, thereby significantly reducing computational costs. Additionally, it proposes a method to estimate the mismatch losses due to different shade patterns throughout the strings.

2 METHODOLOGY

2.1 How the Sunveon Model works

Using a dataset of over 500,000 I-V curves from different manufacturers and spanning various shading and irradiance conditions, we developed linear regressions to accurately predict losses for standard and half-cell modules. This approach eliminates the need to calculate new I-V curves for every simulation, capturing the electrical effects in all possible shading scenarios in an actual PV plant. The impact of series and shunt resistances was very low in all cases and could be considered negligible.

From one of the classical transposition models[4], [5], the model uses a distinct approach to more precisely estimate diffuse and reflected irradiance on both the front and rear sides of modules. It estimates the shading effects on diffuse irradiance caused by surrounding structures, considering the shading state of the terrain[6], [7]. To achieve that, the model follows these steps:

1. The process begins by defining the basic parameters of a 2D scenario (Fig.1). This includes the characteristics of the structure (e.g., type, dimensions, axis height, pitch between rows, transparency, module spacing, number of modules, width, bifaciality), terrain characteristics (slope, albedo), and the location's latitude. The scenario sets the positions of the axes of five simulated rows of structures (either fixed-tilt or tracking). A constant slope is set for these five rows, as well as the terrain limits, and their normal and directional vectors. Latitude is important as it influences the sign of the slope angle, especially for fixed structures.

2. Since the scenario's composition is affected by the sun's position (structure rotation, projected shadows), some of its geometry must be recalculated at each interval. This involves calculating the solar ray vector in the 2D scenario by transforming its coordinates from a global reference system to the local 2D system. The position of the collectors and their segments are then calculated, attributing an index to each. For fixed structures, segment positions are constant, but for trackers, positions are calculated based on structure rotation, which depends on sun position and tracking strategy. The model also determines if segments are shaded or not.

3. Once segment locations and indices are calculated, view factors between them are determined. This involves calculating factors towards adjacent row segments, ground segments, and finally, the sky. Reciprocity is

used to avoid unnecessary calculations. Obstructions between segments are also accounted for when calculating lengths and diagonals.

4. Possible incident irradiance values are calculated for each segment type (front, back, ground) and shading scenario (illuminated/shaded), breaking it down into direct, circumsolar diffuse, and horizontal diffuse components. Isotropic diffuse component is treated differently, with its value inherently incorporating shadow effects, eliminating the need to differentiate between shaded and illuminated states. The model calculates direct irradiance for each segment type, considering the solar ray's incidence angles. The classical transposition methods[4], [5] are then applied, by removing the effect of coefficients dependent on inclination or incidence angle (Fig.2).

5. The model combines a 2D irradiance model with a 3D shadow calculation model. The 2D model discretises surfaces like structures and the ground into segments to calculate irradiance exchange using view factors. It provides the incident irradiance for two states: illuminated and shaded. These results are then combined with the 3D model, which provides information on the number of shaded submodules within a string. This new approach streamlines the process by focusing on the binary illumination states and the specific proportion of shaded submodules (Fig.3 and Fig.4).

Following these steps, the incident irradiance on both the front and rear of the central simulated row is estimated under illumination and shading conditions. This calculation, which is assumed to be the valid result, provides a detailed characterisation of incident irradiance in partially shaded rows. This results in a characteristic incident irradiance for each binary state of the submodules, either shaded (active bypass diode) or illuminated (no active bypass diode)[8], resulting in a characteristic I-V curve for the array formed by half-cell (Fig.5) or standard (Fig.6) modules. The output of the 2D irradiance model is then combined with a 3D submodule-level shading model, where individual strings exhibit different shadow patterns, and consequently, varying proportions of affected submodules. This analysis accounts for two key factors related to shading. First, the shading state is not a total absence of light; it specifically includes the amount of diffuse irradiance reaching shaded cells. Second, we consider edge effects, such as the minimum shadow cast by the module's frame, which would affect the entire submodule.

The Fig 1. depicts the 2D scenario defined by the model in the step 1. As a representative case of the model, the Fig. 2 depicts the global irradiation along a sunny day obtained from the Perez transposition model (grey line), and for both illuminated and shaded parts of the string calculated by the Sunveon model (blue and orange lines). Fig. 3 and Fig. 4 depict two 3D scenarios with their corresponding shading factor (% of shaded submodules) at each string of a PV Layout. The Fig. 5 and Fig. 6 depict, respectively, an I-V curve used to obtain the regression models from half-cell and standard modules.

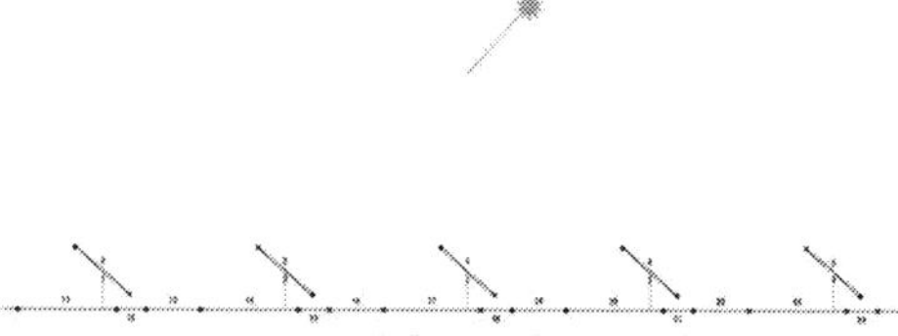

Figure 1: 2D scenario defined by the model

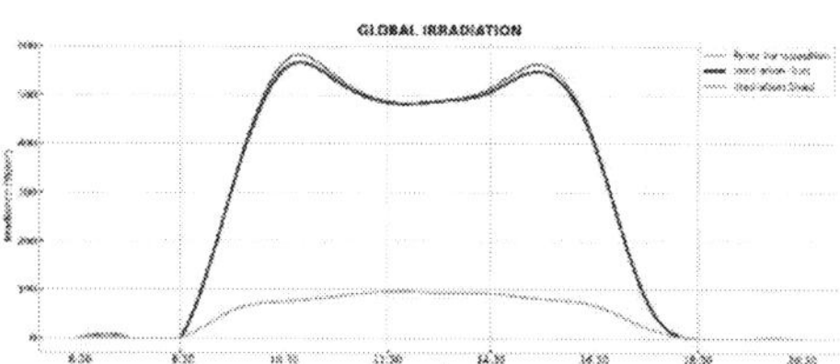

Figure 2: Global irradiation for illuminated and shades parts of a string, obtained from the Perez transposition model

Figure 3: 3D scenario depicting a front view of a PV plant illustrating the distribution of the shading factor. The darker the string's colour, the more shaded it is relative to the most illuminated string

Figure 4: 3D scenario depicting a diagonal view of a PV plant illustrating the distribution of the shading factor. The darker the string's colour, the more shaded it is relative to the most illuminated string

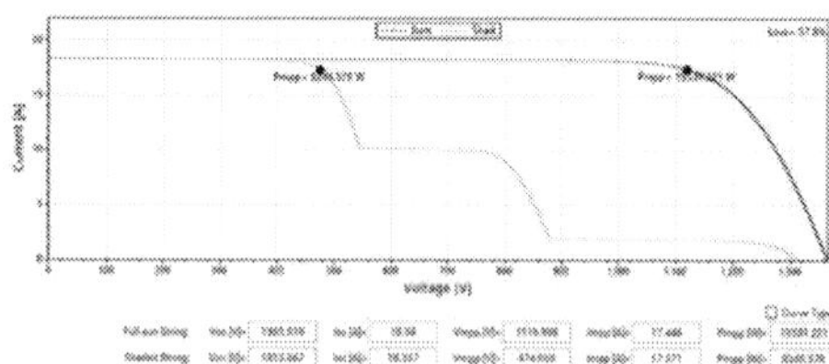

Figure 5: I-V curve of an illuminated and a shaded string of half-cell PV modules

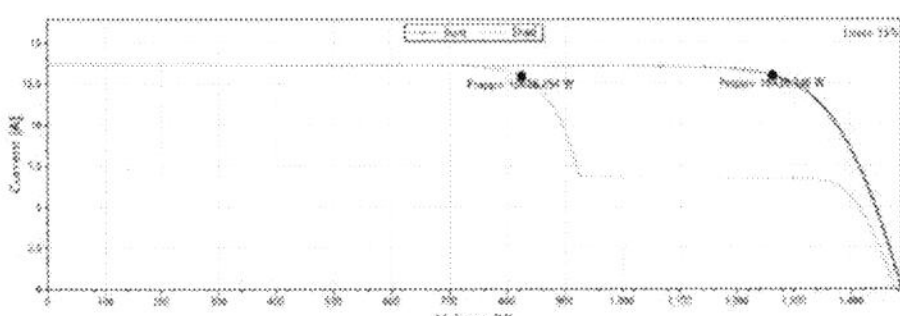

Figure 6: I-V curve of an illuminated and a shaded string of standard PV modules

The Sunveon Model is applicable to both standard and half-cell modules. It combines irradiance and shading models to estimate the Maximum Power Point (MPP) of each individual string within a solar plant, taking into account the mismatch losses induced by shadows. Unlike traditional methods, it doesn't require a full I-V curve calculation for every string. Instead, the regressions obtained from the over half a million I-V curves provide the necessary parameters to accurately estimate the energy production. We can extend the estimations to an entire PV plant by a precise calculation of input conditions for inverter MPPTs, allowing a granular production within any layout (Fig.7).

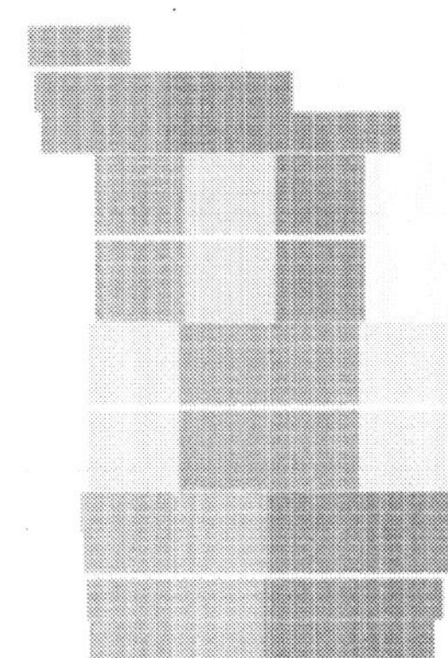

Figure 7: Electrical Layout (Power blocks) of a 70 MW$_p$ plant

It is worth commenting that the model in its complete version also includes other types of losses, such as IAM, soiling and thermal losses induced by the wind[9], but their detailed description is beyond the scope of this article. Here we opted to make a description only for the ways to obtain a more precise irradiance reaching the modules. In this case, here we consider the intrinsic mismatch losses between the modules as null[10], [11].

3 RESULTS AND DISCUSSION

3.1 Benchmark validation

The model was validated against over 500,000 I-V curves, which resulted from shading patterns observed in real PV layouts (from five different PV plants, ranging from approximately 5 to 150 MW$_p$) under diverse incident irradiance conditions. The same analysis was also conducted using two other shadow models often used in the industry. The I-V curves derived from these various shading patterns are considered the 'real losses,' and the performance of all three models (the two industry-standard models and the Sunveon Model) is plotted against these real losses for comparison.

The models are described below:
- Model 1: it reduces the beam component of the incident irradiance according to percentage of shaded submodules, then it computes the MPP power (P$_{MPP}$) of the string (single-diode model)[12], [13].
- Model 2: it computes the P$_{MPP}$ at illumination and shade conditions, then computes a new value that lies in-between both, depending on the shading factor[14].
- Sunveon Model: it uses a novel regression model with the following inputs: P$_{MPP}$ at illumination, proportion of shaded submodules in the string and proportion of incident diffuse irradiance. A specific model is developed both for standard and half-cell modules.

3.2 The reliability of the Sunveon Model

As a representative case, Fig. 8 and Fig. 9 summarise the comparison between simulated I-V curves of a single string under various shading patterns and irradiance conditions. The results from the Sunveon Model (yellow squares) are presented alongside those from two industry-standard models, Model 1 (red diamonds) and Model 2 (blue triangles), for both standard and half-cell modules. The findings from large-scale numerical tests are detailed in Table I (Standard modules) and Table II (Half-cell modules), located below their respective figures.

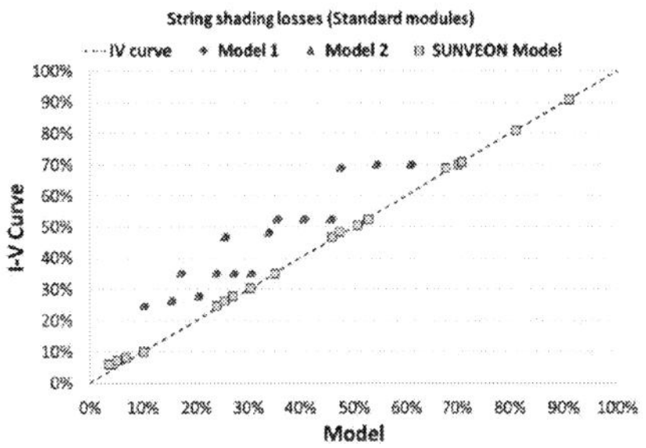

Figure 8: I-V Curve vs Shading loss models for Standard modules

Table I: Large-scale numerical testing (Standard modules)

	MAE [%]	STD [%]
Model 1	4.26	5.49
Model 2	6.48	4.76
Sunveon Model	0.79	1.53

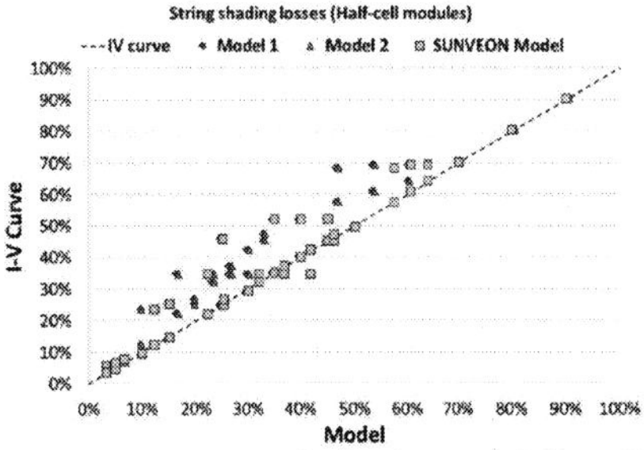

Figure 9: I-V Curve vs Shading loss models for Half-cell modules

Table II: Large-scale numerical testing (Half-cell modules)

	MAE [%]	STD [%]
Model 1	7.05	5.61
Model 2	6.99	5.62
Sunveon Model	1.36	2.28

The results from both Standard and Half-cell modules consistently demonstrate the superior accuracy and reliability of the Sunveon Model compared to Model 1 and Model 2, reflected both in their Mean Absolute Error (MAE) and Standard Deviation (STD). In both cases, the Sunveon Model aligns remarkably closely with the benchmark (the real I-V curve data), while the other models consistently underestimate losses, with their predictions typically falling above the diagonal when plotted against actual values. The following comments apply:

For Standard Modules:

- The Sunveon Model exhibits remarkably low error rates with an MAE of 0.79% and an STD of 1.53%. This precision is evident in its close alignment with the benchmark.

- Model 1 shows significantly higher errors with an MAE of 4.26% and an STD of 5.49%.

- Model 2 also presents elevated errors, with an MAE of 6.48% and an STD of 4.76%.

For standard modules, the Sunveon Model greatly outperforms the other models, with its MAE being approximately 5 to 8 times lower than that of the other two models and its STD approximately 3 times lower, indicating a far more precise and consistent prediction capability.

For Half-cell Modules:

- The Sunveon Model continues to show strong performance, with a MAE of 1.36% and a STD of 2.28%. While slightly higher than for standard modules, these values remain exceptionally low, confirming the model's robustness.

- Model 1 presents an MAE of 7.05% and an STD of 5.61%.

- Model 2 shows similar performance to Model 1, with an MAE of 6.99% and an STD of 5.62%.

A similar trend is observed in half-cell modules; though the Sunveon Model's errors are slightly higher (MAE 1.36%, deviation 2.28%), this is expected due to the more complex electrical topology of half-cell modules, consisting of six submodules arranged as two parallel strings of three submodules in series. Despite this, the estimation remains highly precise. Even in this more challenging scenario, the Sunveon Model maintains a substantially lower MAE (approximately 5 times lower)

and STD (about 2.5 times lower) compared to Model 1 and Model 2. The trend of Model 1 and Model 2 consistently underestimating losses persists, albeit with some points deviating further from the diagonal, indicating less precision than for standard modules.

3.3 Mismatch losses due to different shading patterns

Each string, with its respective illumination and/or shading pattern, has a unique electrical characteristic and, consequently, an associated Fill Factor (FF). The parallel connection between these strings subsequently leads to instantaneous mismatch losses[15]. Based on the Sunveon Model, we were able to derive a new mismatch loss model that is applicable for estimating these losses in parallel strings due to different shading patterns. We describe this model below, step by step:

- Firstly, it is established a unique series of n modules, and then, 10 random different shading patterns (from about 0.5% to about 90%) are applied for each irradiance value, ranging from 100 W/m² to 900 W/m², in increments of 50 W/m².

- Each of these simulation conditions (shade and irradiance) generates an electrical response, and consequently, an individual FF. To assign an appropriate weight to both illuminated and shaded areas, we considered the FF here as the ratio between the maximum power in shade and the product of V_{oc} and I_{sc} in illumination. To differentiate this from the original concept of FF, we have termed this relation the 'Mixed Fill Factor,' calculated as:

$$FF_{mix} = \frac{I_{\text{MPP,shd}} \, V_{\text{MPP,shd}}}{I_{\text{sc,illum}} \, V_{\text{oc,illum}}} \qquad (1)$$

where $I_{\text{MPP,shd}}$ and $V_{\text{MPP,shd}}$ are the current and voltage at the maximum power point in shading conditions and $I_{\text{sc,illum}}$ and $V_{\text{oc,illum}}$ are the short-circuit current and open-circuit voltage in illumination. It is worth commenting that the error in using the values in illumination rather than in shading conditions is no more than 3% in the worst cases.

- For each irradiance value, there are 10 different FF_{mix} values. The coefficient of variation of these values can now be calculated by the relation between the associated standard deviation and the mean value (Equation 2):

$$CV_{FF,mix} = \frac{\sigma_{FF_{mix}}}{FF_{mix}} \qquad (2)$$

- The ten strings combined in a single MPPT give rise to a characteristic I-V curve with its respective electrical patterns due to the different shades in each string. The ratio between the total power of this hypothetical shaded array and the sum of the individual power of each shaded string give rise to an electrical mismatch loss, i.e.:

$$EMM_{shd}(\%) = 1 - \frac{P_{total,array,shd}}{\sum_1^n P_{i,n\,string,shd}} \qquad (3)$$

- A relationship between $EMM_{shd}(\%)$ and

$CV_{FF,mix}$ is then established ($R^2>0.95$). Equation 4 allows to calculate the mismatch losses directly from the method described in section 2.1 – i.e. for parallel connections-, now without the need to calculate any I-V curve. The relationship is also seen in Fig. 10.

$$EMM_{shd}(\%) = 0.0076\, CV_{FF,mix}(\%)^2 + 0.2445\, CV_{FF,mix}(\%) \quad (4)$$

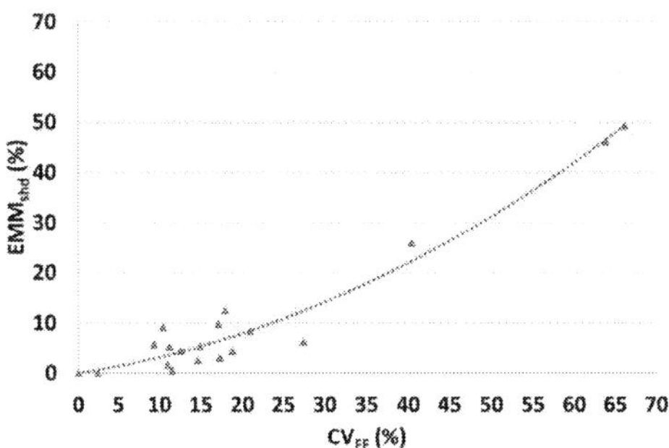

Figure 10: Relationship between the percentual values of Electrical Mismatch Losses (EMM_{shd}) and coefficient of variation of Mixed Fill Factor ($CV_{FF,mix}$)

Previous studies have also established a quadratic relationship for mismatch losses[11], [16], [17], [18], though mainly focused on series connections.

3.4 Mismatch losses for standard and half-cell modules

Mismatch losses between strings vary significantly depending on the shading conditions across different strings and also on the irradiance in the illuminated sections. One can intuitively infer that higher irradiances lead to greater mismatch losses, as the illumination gradient between shaded and illuminated areas becomes more pronounced. However, the precise magnitude of these losses is the key question. Equation 6 allows us to shed some light on these questions. Fig. 11 shows the mismatch losses for both standard and half-cell modules in a hypothetical case where n strings are connected in a single MPP, each one with its respective shading pattern. The losses are analysed for different shading patterns and subject to an in-illumination irradiance range of 100-1000 W/m². A direct comparison between both technologies shows that the standard modules are subject to about 64% more losses than the half-cell modules, or in other words, about two-thirds.

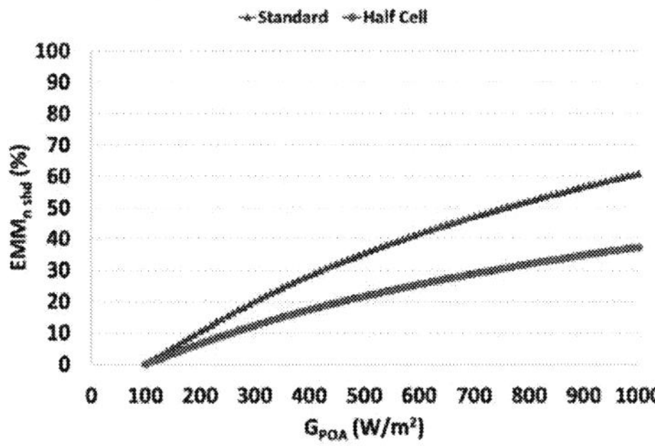

Figure 11: Mismatch losses vs in-illumination irradiance

over the PV panels

A quadratic relationship allows the estimation of mismatch losses for these cases, for different irradiance levels.

$$MML_G(\%) = a\, G_{POA}^2 + b\, G_{POA} - c \quad (6)$$

where G_{POA} is the plane-of-array irradiance. The values of each coefficient are shown in Table III.

Table III: Coefficients for mismatch losses estimations from shading casts and in-illumination irradiance

	Half-cell	Standard cell
a	-2.10⁻⁵	-4.10⁻⁵
b	0.067	0.111
c	-5.82	-9.84

It is worth noting that these models were developed specifically for parallel connections. Its accuracy for series connections remains to be verified.

3.5 From substrings to an entire PV plant

These estimates are calculated for the entire PV plant and accumulated over a full year. Figure 12 shows the maximum energy produced by each string over the year for the same 70 MWp PV plant as shown in Fig. 7. The output of each string is then proportionally compared to the highest-producing string, as indicated by the colour scheme. In this instance, the maximum energy accumulated by a single string is 51.4 MWh.

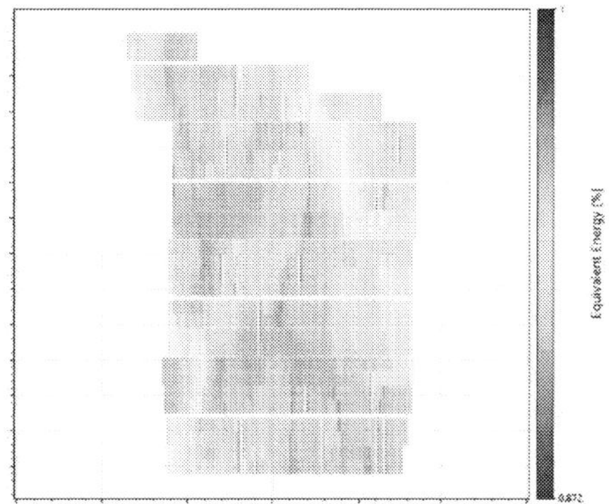

Figure 12: String maximum energy (accumulated) during a year for a 70 MW$_p$ PV plant. The colours show the equivalent energy proportional to the string that produces the most energy

Fig. 13 depicts the maximum accumulated energy yielded by the inverters for the same PV plant and period. The total energy delivered in this case is 11.8 GWh.

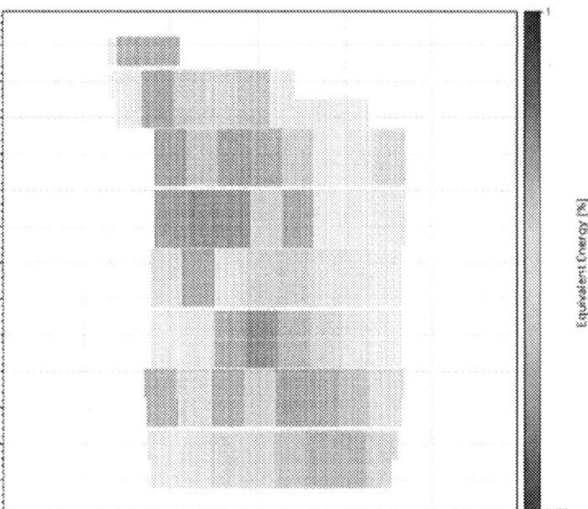

Figure 13: Inverter maximum energy (accumulated) during a year for a 70 MW$_p$ PV plant. The colours show the equivalent energy proportional to the inverter that produces the most energy

For this PV plant, the combined Shading and Yield simulations ran about 43% faster than those based on I-V curves (40 min vs. 70 min). The yearly analysis considered roughly 85 transposition clusters and was carried out with a 15-minute time step. An interpolated simulation with the Sunveon model took 2.67 minutes in total, including per-string Shading Tables (0.32 min) and yield calculations (2.35 min). From this breakdown, it can be inferred that Shading calculations alone require 37.65 minutes. When isolating the yield component, the Sunveon model runs approximately 93% faster than full I-V curve simulations (2.35 min vs. 32.35 min). Although the extent of this computational gain depends on plant size, it remains highly significant even for smaller systems—for instance, around 75% faster for a 5 MW plant.

4 CONCLUSIONS

The challenge of accurately and efficiently estimating shading and mismatch losses in large-scale photovoltaic (PV) plants is a significant constraint for current production models. Conventional methods, which often rely on computationally expensive full I-V curve calculations or ray-tracing, can be slow. Conversely, simplified approaches may lead to substantial over- or underestimations of shading effects.

This study proposes the Sunveon Model, a novel and more efficient approach. It employs a hybrid transposition methodology, combining a 2D irradiance model with a 3D submodule-level shading model to accurately characterise incident irradiance on both standard and half-cell modules. A key advantage is its ability to estimate a string's Maximum Power Point (MPP) without requiring full I-V curve calculations, thus significantly reducing computational costs (between 75% and 93% for the yield calculation). The model also establishes a new method for quantifying mismatch losses using a 'Mixed Fill Factor,' allowing these losses to be calculated directly from a quadratic relationship.

The model's superior performance was validated against over 500,000 real I-V curves from five PV plants. The Sunveon Model consistently aligned more closely with this benchmark data compared to two industry-standard models, which were shown to systematically over or underestimate losses. Although errors for half-cell modules were slightly higher due to their more complex electrical topology, the model's performance remained highly precise, confirming its robustness.

A clear quadratic relationship was established between mismatch losses and both the percentage of cast shadow and the in-illumination irradiance. These equations allow for the direct estimation of losses. Notably, the analysis revealed that mismatch losses for standard cell modules are about two-thirds higher than for half-cell modules. It is important to note that these models were developed and validated specifically for parallel connections, with accuracy for series connections still to be verified.

In summary, the Sunveon Model offers a highly precise and robust tool for large-scale PV plant analysis, providing a valuable and computationally efficient alternative to existing methods by accurately modelling shading-induced and mismatch losses.

5 ACKNOWLEDGEMENTS

C.R. is partially supported by Torres Quevedo Grant No. PTQ2023-013183, funded by the Agencia Estatal de Investigación from the Spanish Ministry of Science. Most of the data used is available on the NREL web page, and the authors would like to thank them for it.

6 REFERENCES

[1] H. Rezk *et al.*, 'A novel statistical performance evaluation of most modern optimization-based global MPPT techniques for partially shaded PV system', *Renewable and Sustainable Energy Reviews*, vol. 115, Nov. 2019, doi: 10.1016/j.rser.2019.109372.

[2] O. Tsafarakis and W. G. J. H. M. van Sark, 'A density-based time-series data analysis methodology for shadow detection in rooftop photovoltaic systems', *Progress in Photovoltaics: Research and Applications*, vol. 31, no. 5, pp. 506–523, May 2023, doi: 10.1002/pip.3654.

[3] A. G. Olabi *et al.*, 'Artificial neural networks applications in partially shaded PV systems', *Thermal Science and Engineering Progress*, vol. 37, Jan. 2023, doi: 10.1016/j.tsep.2022.101612.

[4] R. Perez, P. Ineichen, R. Seals, J. Michalsky, and R. Stewart, 'Modeling daylight availability and irradiance components from direct and global irradiance', *Solar Energy*, vol. 44, no. 5, pp. 271–289, 1990, doi: 10.1016/0038-092X(90)90055-H.

[5] J. E. Hay, 'Calculation of monthly mean solar radiation for horizontal and inclined surfaces', *Solar Energy*, vol. 23, no. 4, pp. 301–307, 1979, doi: 10.1016/0038-092X(79)90123-3.

[6] M. A. Anoma, D. Jacob, B. C. Bourne, J. A. Scholl, D. M. Riley, and C. W. Hansen, 'View Factor Model and Validation for Bifacial PV and Diffuse Shade on Single-Axis Trackers', in *IEEE 44th Photovoltaic Specialists Conference (PVSC)*, Washington D.C., 2017, pp. 1549–1554. doi: 10.1109/pvsc.2017.8366704.

[7] D. Tschopp, A. R. Jensen, J. Dragsted, P. Ohnewein, and S. Furbo, 'Measurement and modeling of diffuse irradiance masking on tilted planes for solar engineering applications', *Solar Energy*, vol. 231, no. January, pp. 365–378, 2022, doi: 10.1016/j.solener.2021.10.083.

[8] A. Mermoud and T. Lejeune, 'Partial shading on PV arrays: by-pass diode benefits analysis', in *25th European Photovoltaic Solar Energy Conference*, Sep. 2010.

[9] C. Rossa, 'Energy losses in photovoltaic generators due to wind patterns', *Nature Communications Engineering*, vol. 2, no. 66, pp. 1–9, Sep. 2023, doi: 10.1038/s44172-023-00119-7.

[10] L. L. Bucciarelli, 'Power loss in photovoltaic arrays due to mismatch in cell characteristics', *Solar Energy*, vol. 23, no. 1, pp. 277–288, 1979.

[11] C. Rossa, F. Martinez-Moreno, and E. Lorenzo, 'Experimental observations in mismatch losses in monofacial and bifacial PV generators', *Progress in Photovoltaics: Research and Applications*, vol. 29, no. 12, pp. 1223–1235, Dec. 2021, doi: 10.1002/pip.3447.

[12] PVsyst, 'PVsyst shading calculation model - linear losses'. Accessed: Jul. 31, 2025. [Online]. Available: https://www.pvsyst.com/help-pvsyst7/shadings_model.htm

[13] M. Oliosi, B. Wittmer, and A. Mermoud, 'Analysis of Electrical Shading Effects in PV Systems', in *38th European PV Solar Energy Conference*, Sep. 2021, p. 2021.

[14] F. Martínez-Moreno, J. Muñoz, and E. Lorenzo, 'Experimental model to estimate shading losses on PV arrays', *Solar Energy Materials and Solar Cells*, vol. 94, no. 12, pp. 2298–2303, 2010, doi: 10.1016/j.solmat.2010.07.029.

[15] P. R. Satpathy and R. Sharma, 'Reliability and losses investigation of photovoltaic power generators during partial shading', *Energy Convers Manag*, vol. 223, Nov. 2020, doi: 10.1016/j.enconman.2020.113480.

[16] C. H. Rossa, E. Lorenzo, and F. Martinez-Moreno, 'Observations in PV module operation voltage distribution aling a PV array. An in-deep look on mismatch losses', in *35th European Photovoltaic Solar Energy Conference and Exhibition*, Brussels, 2018, pp. 2051–2055. doi: 10.4229/35thEUPVSEC20182018-6DV.1.38.

[17] R. Evans, M. Boreland, and M. A. Green, 'A holistic review of mismatch loss: From manufacturing decision making to losses in fielded arrays', *Solar Energy Materials and Solar Cells*, vol. 174, pp. 214–224, Jan. 2018, doi: 10.1016/J.SOLMAT.2017.08.041.

[18] C. Deline, S. Ayala Pelaez, S. MacAlpine, and C. Olalla, 'Estimating and parameterizing mismatch power loss in bifacial photovoltaic systems', *Progress in Photovoltaics: Research and Applications*, vol. 28, no. 7, pp. 691–703, Jul. 2020, doi: 10.1002/pip.3259.

PREDICTING SHADING LOSSES IN PHOTOVOLTAIC PLANTS: A NOVEL APPROACH

D. López Dalmau, H. Mirandona López, C. Javier Lopes Gomes, J. Tomàs Villalonga Palou, C. Rossa*

Sunveon

Calle Musgo, 2, 1B, Madrid, Spain. 28023

*crossa@sunveon.com

Abstract

Accurately estimating shadow impact on large-scale photovoltaic (PV) plants is challenging due to the computational demands of traditional methods. This study introduces the Sunveon Model, a novel, efficient approach for simulating shading and mismatch losses without requiring complex I-V curve calculations. The model uses a hybrid methodology, combining a 2D irradiance model with a 3D submodule-level shading model. Its key innovation is the use of a regression model, based on over 500,000 I-V curves, to directly predict a string's Maximum Power Point (MPP), significantly reducing computational time. It also quantifies mismatch losses with a new 'Mixed Fill Factor' that establishes a direct quadratic relationship between losses, shadow percentage, and irradiance. Validated against real-world data, the Sunveon Model proved more accurate than two industry-standard models, showing substantially lower errors. A key finding is that mismatch losses for standard cells are about 70% higher than for half-cell modules. In summary, the Sunveon Model offers a precise and efficient tool for large-scale PV analysis.

Methodology

2D View factor Transposition

- Transposition model & view factors (front+rear).
- Accounts for terrain shadowing and diffuse shadings.
- Incident irradiance in 2 states: illumination + shade.

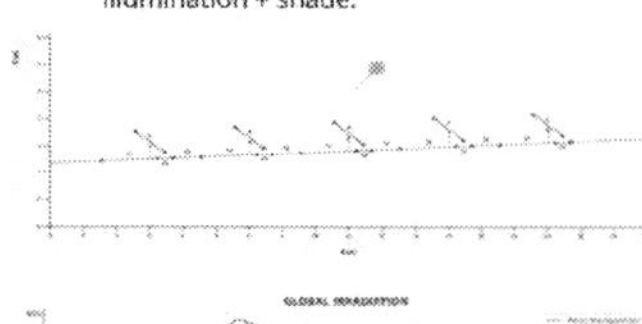
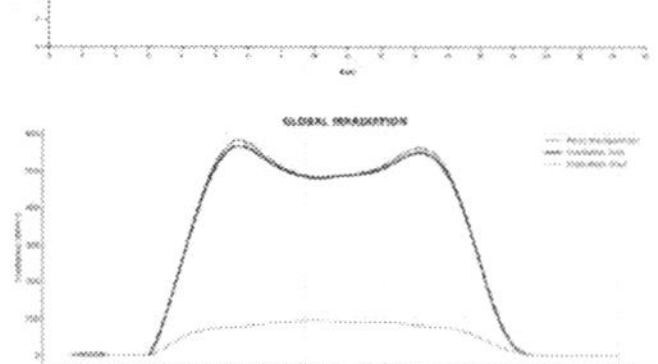

3D Shading Model

- 3D shadows: string level (% of submodules)

String Electrical Production (Sunveon Model)

- Regression model from I-V Curves
- High precision to estimate strings and arrays MPP

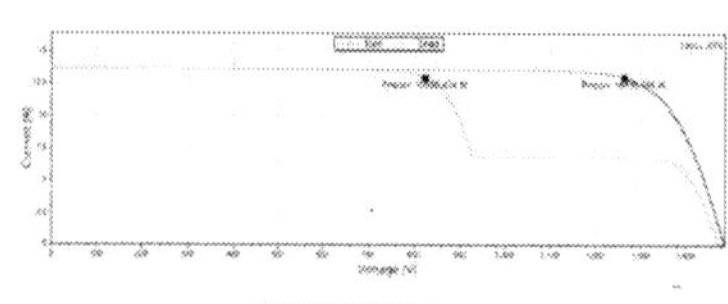

Standard Cell IV Curve

Half Cell IV Curve

Plant Production at inverter level

- Precise calculation of input conditions for inverter MPPTs
- Granular production data within the layout.
- "Mixed" fill factor: $FF_{mix} = \frac{I_{MPP,shd}\, V_{MPP,shd}}{I_{sc,illum}\, V_{oc,illum}}$
- Production according to PV plant Electrical Layout.

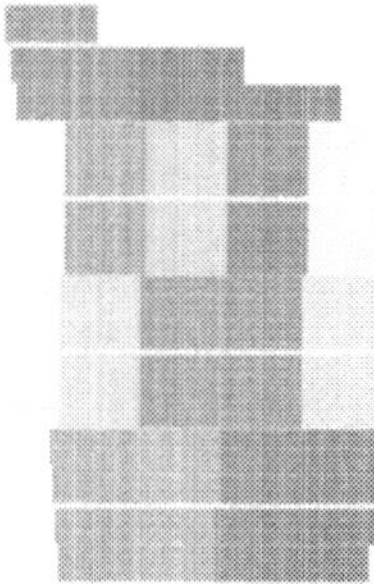

Results

String Losses estimation

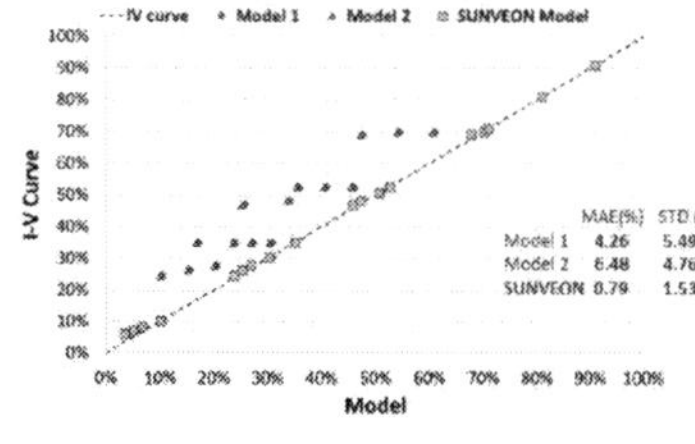

String shading losses [Standard modules]

	MAE (%)	STD (%)
Model 1	4.26	5.49
Model 2	6.48	4.76
SUNVEON	0.79	1.53

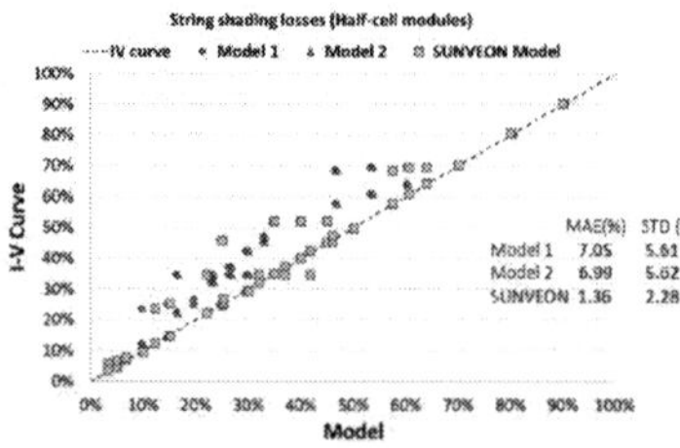

String shading losses (Half-cell modules)

	MAE (%)	STD (%)
Model 1	7.05	5.61
Model 2	6.99	5.62
SUNVEON	1.36	2.28

+

Array Mismatch Losses

$$EMM_{shd}(\%) = 1 - \frac{P_{total,array,shd}}{\sum_i^n P_{i,n\,string,shd}} \quad \text{VS} \quad CV_{FF,mix} = \frac{\sigma_{FF,mix}}{\overline{FF}_{mix}}$$

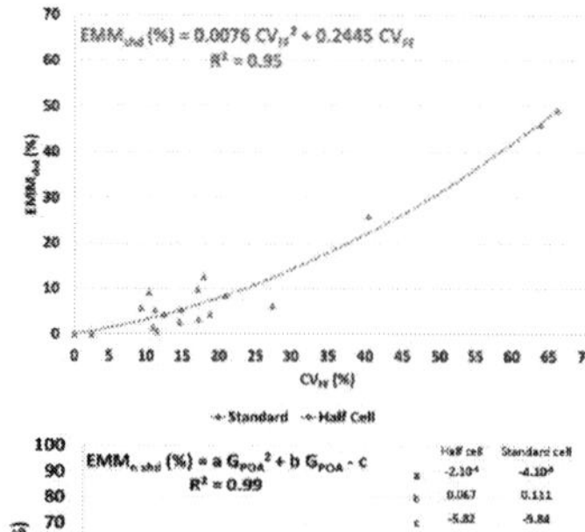

$$EMM_{shd}(\%) = 0.0076\, CV_{FF}^2 + 0.2445\, CV_{FF}$$
$$R^2 = 0.95$$

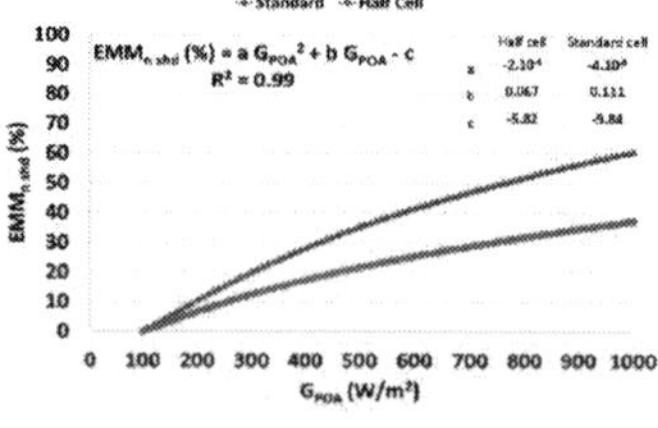

$$EMM_{n\,shd}(\%) = a\, G_{POA}^2 + b\, G_{POA} - c$$
$$R^2 = 0.99$$

	Half cell	Standard cell
a	$-2 \cdot 10^{4}$	$-4 \cdot 10^{4}$
b	0.067	0.111
c	-5.82	-5.84

=

Energy Production

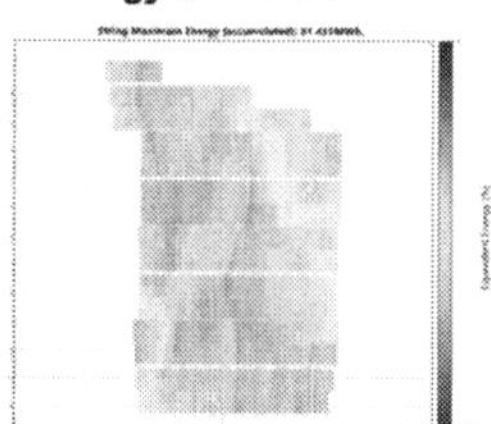

String level production per year

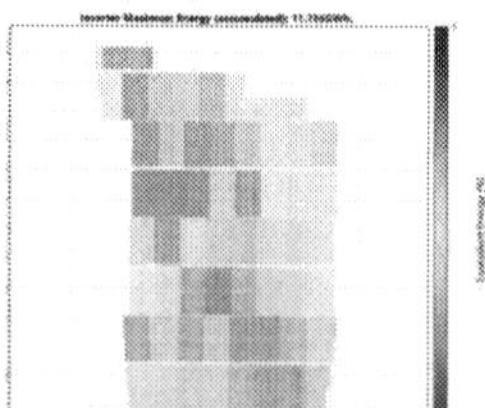

Inverter level production per year

Conclusions

- **New Model for Shading Losses**

The Sunveon Model is a novel, efficient tool that accurately estimates shading losses in large-scale PV plants. Unlike conventional methods that are slow or can be inaccurate, this model uses a hybrid approach to save computational time and provide precise results. Yield computation is between 75% faster for a 5 MW plant and up to 93% faster for a 70 MW plant compared to full I-V curve simulations.

- **Robustness of the Model**

The model's superior accuracy was proven by validating it against over 500,000 I-V curves. The Sunveon Model consistently performed better than the two other models.

- **Key Findings on Mismatch Losses**

The study established a direct, quadratic relationship between mismatch losses and the fill factor for parallel connections. It also found that standard cell modules have approximately 64% higher mismatch losses than half-cell modules, presenting a quadratic relationship with the irradiance.

Acknowledgements

MINISTERIO DE CIENCIA, INNOVACIÓN Y UNIVERSIDADES

AGENCIA ESTATAL DE INVESTIGACIÓN

NREL

SUNVEON

BACKTRACKING 3D: A NOVEL APPROACH TO CONVENTIONAL BACKTRACKING ALGORITHMS FOR IMPROVED PV PERFORMANCE IN COMPLEX TERRAINS

J. Tomás Villalonga Palou, D. López Dalmau, H. Mirandona López, C. Javier Lopes Gomes, C. Rossa
[1]SUNVEON
calle del Musgo, 2, 1B, Madrid, Spain. 28023

Backtracking strategies are widely used in photovoltaic (PV) plants to reduce shading, but they become ineffective on the irregular terrains typical of large-scale installations. Slope-aware approaches improve performance but rely on simplified terrain models, which fail to represent the diverse slopes of real PV layouts. As a result, current methods remain limited in mitigating shading losses, reducing irradiance capture, and lowering overall energy yield. To overcome these limitations, an innovative tracking strategy based on Machine Learning is proposed to optimize the performance of PV plants in complex terrains.

Keywords: backtracking strategies, irregular terrain, backtracking 3D, machine learning, shading losses

1 INTRODUCTION

Backtracking strategies are widely applied in tracking photovoltaic (PV) plants, to prevent mutual shadings between generators, especially during the early and late hours of the day[1]. In modern PV plants, which can cover areas as vast as a small city and reach installed powers in the gigawatt range[2], the inherent irregularity of the terrain makes conventional backtracking algorithms ineffective, as they fail to completely eliminate shading and consequently reduce the yield potential. In this sense, significant advancements have been made by incorporating slope-aware backtracking strategies[3], [4], [5], [6]. However, these tracking approaches assume a generalised terrain model, either flat or with a uniform slope, whereas real PV layouts are often installed in complex terrains made up of a wide variety of slopes, which limits the effectiveness of these methodologies in reducing the yield penalty due to near shadings. In this context, this work presents an innovative tracking strategy that accounts for the specificity of different zones within the plant site, based on a novel, multi-zonal clustering-based tracking strategy for photovoltaic plants in complex terrains (BT3D).

2 METHODOLOGY

2.1 The approach

The proposed methodology begins by dividing the plant site into distinct clusters, enabling a more granular and accurate representation of the landscape. This is achieved through machine learning techniques, specifically Ward's Hierarchical Clustering, which groups areas with similar terrain characteristics. The clustering is performed independently of the size or location of each zone within the plant—meaning that distant zones with comparable properties are treated similarly. This approach provides a precise characterization of the terrain, marking a significant departure from conventional methods that typically assume a uniform or gently sloping surface. Each cluster is assigned a specific transposition model (including bifaciality) and a coordinated tracker movement strategy, allowing for precise adaptation to local terrain slope and solar position. The rotation is determined by both the cross-axis slope of the terrain section and the representative axis tilt of the trackers in the

selected cluster, as illustrated in Fig. 1

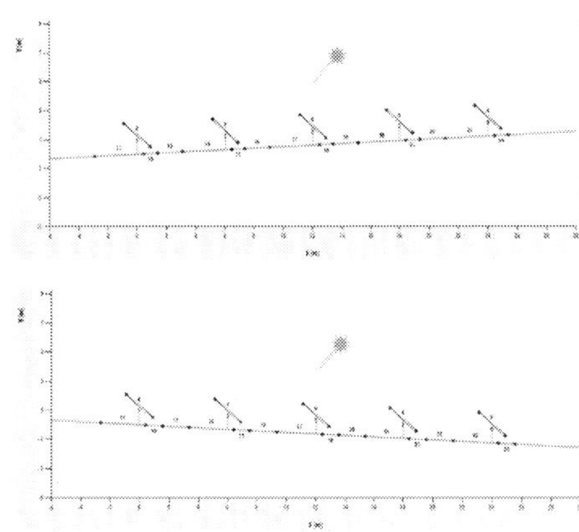

Figure 1: Cluster detail

This strategy optimizes tracker orientation according to the specific conditions of each zone, substantially reducing the negative impact of electrical shading on the PV plant's final energy yield. In addition, it improves irradiance capture and minimizes shading losses compared to conventional backtracking, which applies a single transposition model to the entire plant. In contrast, the proposed method assigns each cluster its own transposition value. This targeted approach is particularly relevant because it maximizes energy yield by adapting tracker orientation to local conditions, a key factor for efficient PV plant operation.

Under overcast conditions, the methodology further accounts for terrain heterogeneity at the cluster level. Within each cluster, the tracker rotation angle is optimized to maximize captured irradiance using Brent's method, a derivative-free numerical algorithm well suited for efficiently finding the optimal tilt. The search range spans from the standard tracking angle to the flat position (0°) and is adjusted by a slope-dependent margin, shown in equation 1:

$$\theta_{margin} = -\gamma \cdot \max(0, \cos\psi) \qquad (1)$$

10.4229/EUPVSEC2025/4DV.4.4
020434-001

where γ is the cross-axis slope angle and ψ is the angular difference between the solar azimuth and the slope aspect. This correction enables each cluster to progressively compensate for terrain slope when aligned with the solar vector. By allowing clusters to operate independently, the methodology contributes significantly to improving the overall energy yield of the plant.

2.2 Validation

The method is validated through simulations and compared with conventional backtracking, evaluating the increase in production in five real PV plants, located in Spain. Moreover, the predictability of the methodology, coupled with its significantly lower computational cost than other algorithms available in the market and literature (due to the group-based clustering behaviour), ensures compatibility with common simplifications in desktop software solutions, such as shading tables. The proposed approach offers a computationally efficient alternative to ray-tracing methods, which, while accurate, are computationally intensive (requiring 10,000 to 100,000 times more computing power) and impractical for conventional computers[7].

2.3 Brent's Algorithm

Brent's method [8] is a deterministic, derivative-free optimization algorithm designed to identify a local minimizer of a continuous function $f : [a, c] \rightarrow \mathbb{R}$ over a bounded interval $[a, c]$ known to contain at least one minimizer. The method achieves both efficiency and robustness by adaptively combining inverse quadratic interpolation (IQI) and golden-section search (GSS). At each iteration, three abscissae are maintained— x (the current best estimate), w (the second-best point), and v (the point before w)—which define a quadratic polynomial interpolating $(v, f(v))$, $(w, f(w))$, and $(x, f(x))$. The candidate minimizer x_p is obtained by solving $P'(q) = 0$, yielding the closed-form update:

$$x_p = x - \frac{(x-w)^2(f(x)-f(v))-(x-v)^2(f(x)-f(w))}{2[(x-w)(f(x)-f(v))-(x-v)(f(x)-f(w))]} \qquad (2)$$

This step is accepted only if xp lies strictly within $[a, c]$ and is numerically stable, ensuring meaningful progress. Otherwise, the method reverts to a GSS step, in which the next candidate is computed as:

$$x_g = x \pm \varphi(c - x), \varphi = \frac{\sqrt{5}-1}{2} \approx 0.618 \qquad (3)$$

This strategy shrinks the interval by a fixed ratio regardless of smoothness. After each new evaluation, the bracketing triplet (a, b, c) is updated to preserve the condition $a < b < c$ and $f(b) < min(f(a), f(c))$. Convergence is declared when the interval width satisfies $|c - a| < x_{tol}$ or when function values stagnate such that $|f(x\_new) - f(x)| < \varepsilon$. By blending the superlinear local convergence of IQI with the global reliability of GSS, Brent's method ensures robust minimization performance and is widely regarded as a standard in one-dimensional optimization.

2.4 Ward's Hierarchical Clustering Algorithm

Ward's method is an agglomerative hierarchical clustering [9] procedure that constructs a nested partition of a dataset by iteratively merging clusters. Unlike linkage criteria based on pairwise distances, Ward's method employs a minimum variance principle, selecting at each step the pair of clusters whose merger induces the smallest possible increase in the total within-cluster sum of squares. This criterion leads to compact and homogeneous clusters, making the method particularly suitable for exploratory data analysis.

Let clusters A and B contain nA and nB observations with centroids $\bar{x}_A$ and $\bar{x}_B$, respectively. The increase in the total within-cluster sum of squares resulting from their merger is:

$$\Delta(A, B) = \frac{nAnB}{nA+nB} \parallel \bar{x}_A - \bar{x}_B \parallel^2 \qquad (4)$$

where $\parallel \cdot \parallel^2$ denotes the squared Euclidean norm. At each iteration, the pair (A, B) that minimizes $\Delta(A, B)$ is selected for fusion.

Algorithmic procedure
1. **Initialization:** Each of the N observations forms a singleton cluster.
2. **Iteration:** For all candidate pairs(A, B), compute $\Delta(A, B)$ and identify the minimizing pair.
3. **Update:** Replace clusters A and B by their union, update centroids and distances, and decrease the cluster count by one.
4. **Termination and interpretation:** The process continues until the desired number of clusters k is obtained, where k is specified according to the analytical objectives.

3 RESULTS AND DISCUSSION

Fig. 2 shows the distribution of the clusters considered at one of the analysed plants, which has an installed capacity of 51 MW. For this specific plant, the number of clusters is equal to 40.

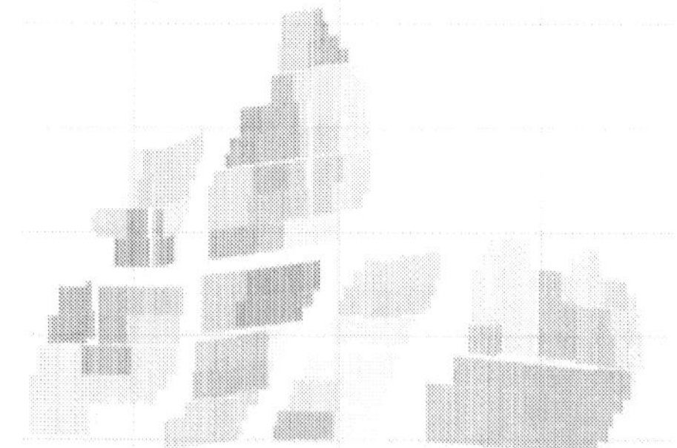

Figure 2: Multi-zonal cluster

Fig. 3 shows a heat map of the results for the same plant, comparing the 3D backtracking algorithm methodology (BT3D) with the traditional methodologies - standard tracking (ST) and conventional backtracking (BT) - during the early and late hours of the day, which are more prone to higher amounts of shading.

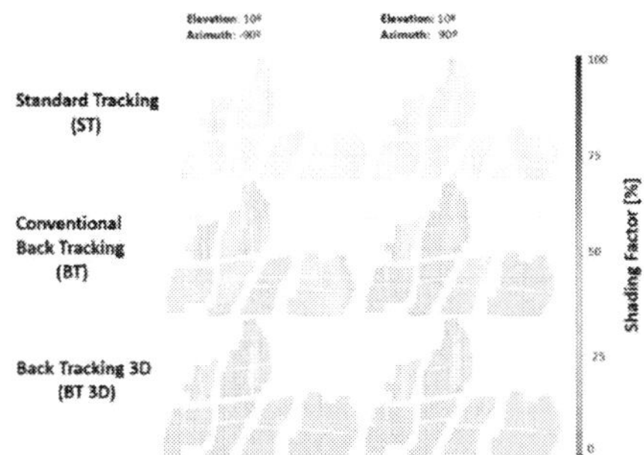

Figure 3: Shading factor heatmap

It should be noted that these specific results drawn from the analysed plant are equally representative of the other PV plants, without loss of generality. This is supported by the annual results for total energy accumulated by the strings, considering the different tracking strategies analyzed in Table I and Table II.

Table I: Strings total cumulative energy per plant. ST, BT and BT3D stands for standard tracking, conventional backtracking and backtracking 3D, respectively

| | | Total Cumulative Energy (Strings) per year [GWh] | | |
| | | Tracking Strategy | | |
Plant	P[MW_p]	ST	BT	BT3D
PV1	5.12	12.3	12.47	12.65
PV2	50.00	123.84	124.91	126.54
PV3	47.15	114.03	114.87	116.51
PV4	36.52	86.37	86.75	89.17

Table II: Comparison between standard strategies and the proposed strategy. ST, BT and BT3D stands for standard tracking, conventional backtracking and backtracking 3D, respectively

| | | Tracking Strategy Improvement | |
Plant	P[MW_p]	BT3D vs ST	BT3D vs BT
PV1	5.12	2.85%	1.44%
PV2	50.00	2.18%	1.30%
PV3	47.15	2.17%	1.43%
PV4	36.52	3.24%	2.79%

The results indicate that the total energy accumulated by the strings using the BT3D strategy improves consistently, with an average gain of approximately 2.6% compared to ST and 1.7% compared to BT across the analysed plants. This increase in production is mainly attributed to the lower incidence of shading, which reduces both direct irradiance losses and the number of submodules affected by partial shading. As a representative case, Fig. 4 depicts the climate-dependence gain applying the proposed methodology for PV4.

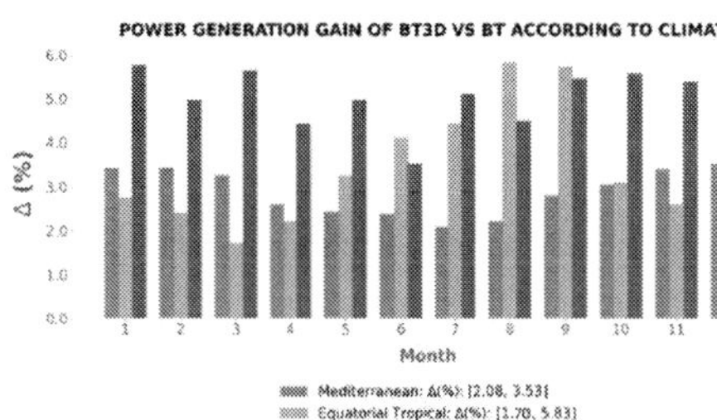

Figure 4: Climate-dependent power gain: BT3D vs BT

By analyzing the performance of the PV4 photovoltaic plant across diverse climates highlights the significant impact of geographical location on the energy output of the proposed algorithm. The results reveal substantial monthly gains in energy production, ranging from approximately 1.7% to 6%, depending on the climate. These improvements arise from the combination of detailed terrain modelling and the algorithm's ability to maximize captured irradiance under varying climate scenarios. This effect is further illustrated in the daily plots shown in Fig. 5, Fig. 6 and Fig. 7, which demonstrate the BT3D model's marked performance advantage over the BT model under specific weather conditions.

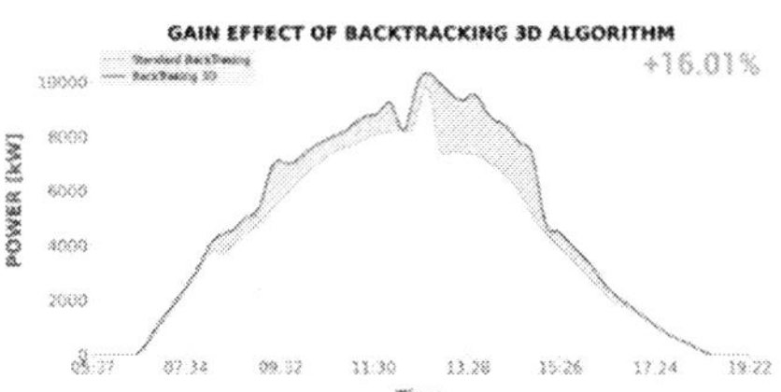

Figure 5: Typical overcast day – Equatorial tropical climate

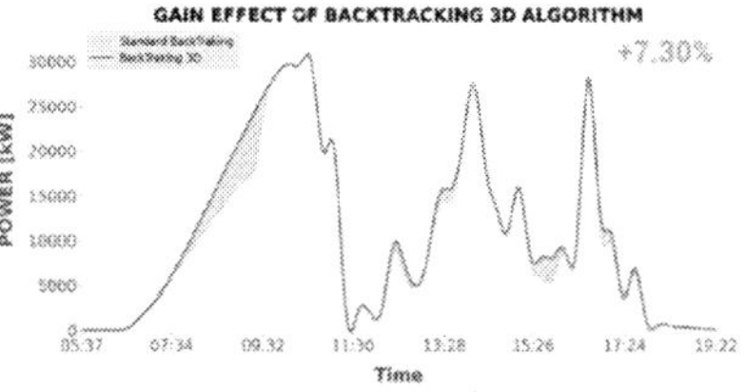

Figure 6: Typical clear to partialy cloudy day – Oceanic climate

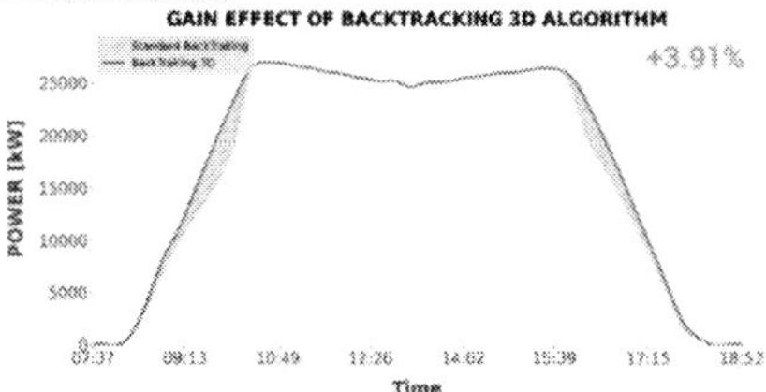

Figure 7: Typical sunny day – Mediterranean climate

4 CONCLUSIONS

The detailed terrain representation achieved through clustering improves the accuracy of incident irradiance calculations, resulting in a 1.7% increase in string production compared to conventional backtracking (BT) and a 2.6% increase compared to standard tracking (ST). This improvement is particularly relevant, as accurate irradiance estimation is essential for optimizing PV plant design and operation, especially in challenging terrains.

In addition, the BT3D model demonstrates substantial performance improvements over the BT model under specific climatic scenarios, with gains ranging from 1.7% compared to BT to 6% compared to ST.

The predictable tracker behavior within each cluster also makes the proposed methodology compatible with commonly used simplified shading solutions, such as Shading Tables. This compatibility enables efficient integration with existing design tools while reducing computational burden, thereby facilitating the practical implementation of the method in real-world PV plant design and assessment.

Furthermore, the proposed method offers a computationally efficient alternative to traditional ray-tracing techniques, requiring 10,000 to 100,000 times less computing power. This efficiency not only overcomes significant computational limitations but also broadens accessibility, making the approach suitable for a wider range of users and projects.

5 ACKNOWLEDGEMENTS

C.R. is partially supported by Torres Quevedo Grant No. PTQ2023-013183, funded by the Agencia Estatal de Investigación from the Spanish Ministry of Science. Most of the data used is available on the NREL web page, and the authors would like to thank them for it.

6 REFERENCES

[1] E. Lorenzo, L. Narvarte, and J. Muñoz, 'Tracking and back-tracking', *Progress in Photovoltaics: Research and Applications*, vol. 19, no. 6, pp. 747–753, Sep. 2011, doi: 10.1002/pip.1085.

[2] V. Shaw, 'World's largest solar plant goes online in China', PV Magazine. Accessed: Jan. 29, 2025. [Online]. Available: https://www.pv-magazine.com/2024/06/06/worlds-largest-solar-plant-goes-online-in-china-2/

[3] K. S. Anderson and A. R. Jensen, 'Shaded fraction and backtracking in single-axis trackers on rolling terrain', *Journal of Renewable and Sustainable Energy*, vol. 16, no. 2, Mar. 2024, doi: 10.1063/5.0202220.

[4] K. Anderson and M. Mikofski, 'Slope-Aware Backtracking for Single-Axis Trackers', Golden, CO, 2020. [Online]. Available: https://www.nrel.gov/docs/fy20osti/766 26.pdf.

[5] L. Perez *et al.*, 'Comparison of tracking algorithms for photovoltaic systems on irregular terrains', in *40th European Photovoltaic Solar Energy Conference and Exhibition (EU PVSEC)*, 2023, pp. 1–4. [Online]. Available: https://www.researchgate.net/publicatio n/374387385

[6] E. Cooper, K. Anderson, and D. Riley, 'Performance Improvements Through Advanced PV Backtracking on Uneven Terrain', *IEEE J Photovolt*, pp. 1–7, 2025, doi: 10.1109/JPHOTOV.2025.3558254.

[7] A. Asgharzadeh *et al.*, 'A Benchmark and Validation of Bifacial PV Irradiance Models', *Conference Record of the IEEE Photovoltaic Specialists Conference*, no. July, pp. 3281–3287, 2019, doi: 10.1109/PVSC40753.2019.8981272.

[8] R. P. Brent, *Algorithms for Minimization without Derivatives*, vol. 1. Englewood Cliffs, New Jersey: Prentice-Hall, 1973.

[9] J. H. Ward, 'Hierarchical Grouping to Optimize an Objective Function', *J Am Stat Assoc*, vol. 58, no. 301, pp. 236–244, Mar. 1963, doi: 10.1080/01621459.1963.10500845.

BACKTRACKING 3D: A NOVEL APPROACH TO CONVENTIONAL BACKTRACKING ALGORITHMS FOR IMPROVED PV PERFORMANCE IN COMPLEX TERRAINS

J. Tomàs Villalonga Palou, D. López Dalmau, H. Mirandona López, C. Javier Lopes Gomes, C. Rossa

Sunveon

Calle Musgo, 2, 1B, Madrid, Spain. 28023

*crossa@sunveon.com

Abstract

Backtracking strategies are widely used in photovoltaic (PV) plants to reduce shading, but they become ineffective on the irregular terrains typical of large-scale installations. Slope-aware approaches improve performance but rely on simplified terrain models, which fail to represent the diverse slopes of real PV layouts. As a result, current methods remain limited in mitigating shading losses, reducing irradiance capture, and lowering overall energy yield. To overcome these limitations, an innovative tracking strategy based on Machine Learning is proposed to optimize the performance of PV plants in complex terrains.

Methodology

Clustering Strategy

- Apply Ward's Hierarchical Clustering
- Input: Geometrical parameters of PV structures
- Output: Multi-zonal segmentation of uneven terrain

Tracker coordination

- Each cluster enables grouped tracker rotation
- Rotation adapts to:
  - Local terrain slope
  - Solar position

Transposition Modeling

- Assign cluster-specific transposition
- Includes bifacial effects

Performance Optimization

- Under overcast conditions, clusters rotate to maximize irradiance capture by using an efficient numerical search (Brent's method).

Figure 1: Multi-zonal cluster

Figure 2: Cluster detail

Figure 1 illustrates the proposed **terrain clustering** approach applied to a specific photovoltaic plant. Figure 2 shows how each **cluster** is assigned a **distinct solar transposition**, adapted to the local **cross-axis slope** and **axis tilt** conditions.

Results

Performance Comparison

- A heat map (Figure 3) compares three solar tracking methods: **3D backtracking (BT3D), standard tracking (ST), and conventional backtracking (BT).**
- The comparison focuses on performance during the early and late hours of the day when shading is most significant.
- Results for this plant are **representative of all other plants** analyzed, as supported by the annual energy data in Table I.

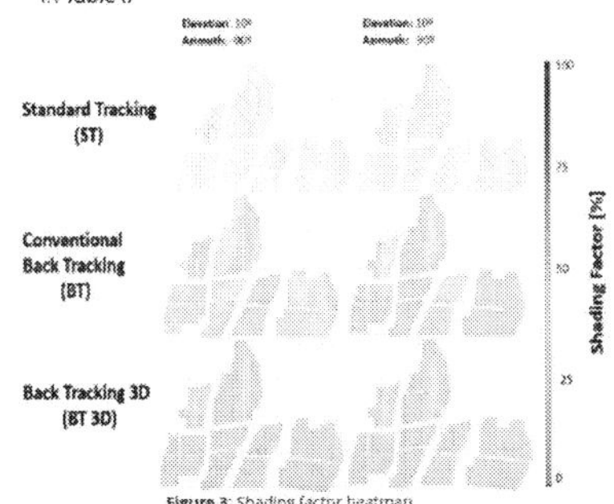

Figure 3: Shading factor heatmap

Tracking Strategy Improvement			
Plant	P [MW$_p$]	BT3D vs ST	BT3D vs BT
PV1	5.12	2.85%	1.44%
PV2	50.00	2.18%	1.30%
PV3	47.15	2.17%	1.43%
PV4	36.52	3.24%	2.79%

Table I: Comparison between standard strategies and the proposed strategy

Impact of Location and Climate

- Figure 4 illustrates how the PV4 plant's energy performance changes with geographic location and climate.
- The study used **Typical Meteorological Year (TMY)** datasets for **Mediterranean, equatorial tropical, and oceanic climates.**
- The original plant geometry was maintained to isolate the effect of climate on the proposed algorithm's performance.

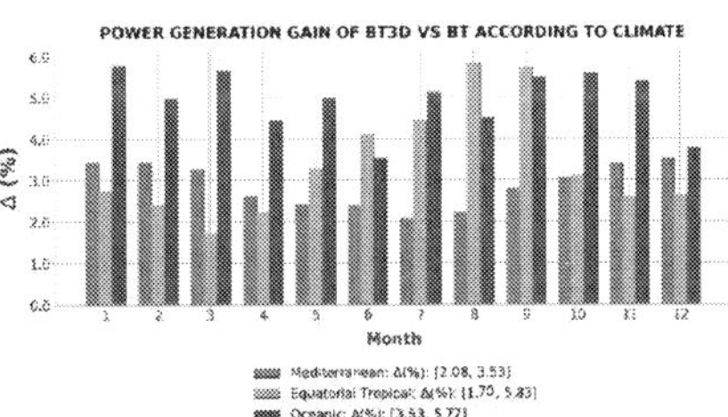

Figure 4: Climate-dependent power gain: BT3D vs BT

Energy Performance

- The proposed method shows significant monthly gains in energy production.
- This gain is due to the synergy between **terrain granularity** and **maximized irradiance.**
- Figures 5, 6, and 7 show that the **BT3D model** substantially outperforms the **BT model** on certain days and under specific weather conditions.

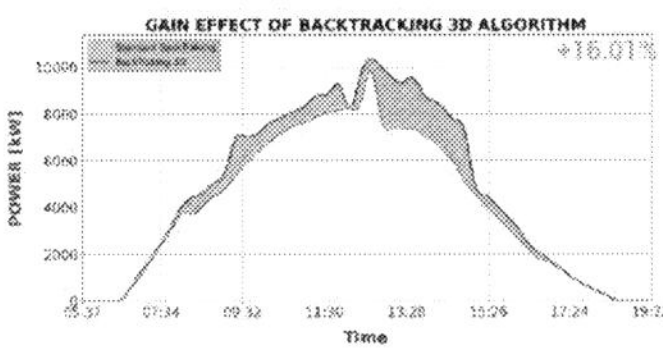

Figure 5: Typical overcast day – Equatorial tropical climate

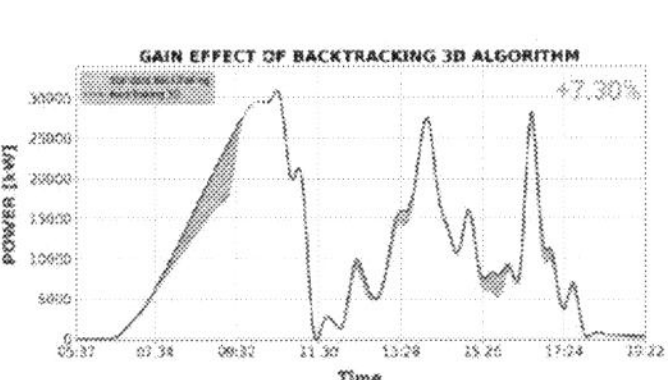

Figure 6: Typical clear to partially cloudy day – Oceanic climate

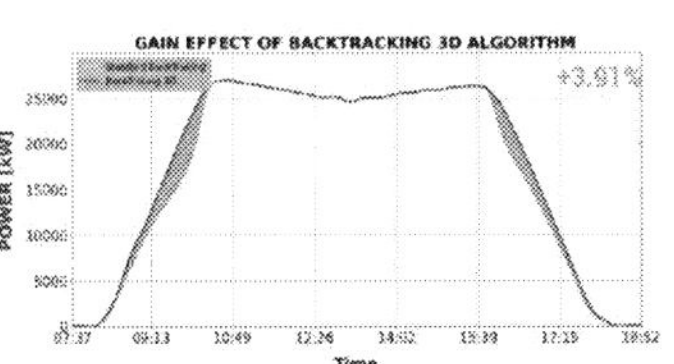

Figure 7: Typical sunny day – Mediterranean climate

Conclusions

- **Increased Production:** The new method, which uses terrain clustering, boosts electrical production by **1.7% over conventional backtracking (BT)** and **2.6% over standard tracking (ST).**
- **Efficient & Practical:** This approach is compatible with existing tools like **Shading Tables**, making it easy to integrate into current design workflows without a heavy computational burden.
- **Computational Power:** It is highly efficient, requiring **10,000 to 100,000 times less computing power** than traditional ray-tracing methods, making it widely accessible.

Acknowledgements

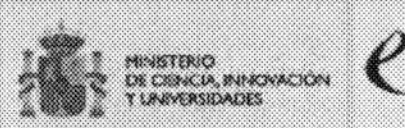

SUNVEON

Evaluation of Front Eave Load Caused by Snow Accumulation on Photovoltaic Array

Tadanori Tanahashi[1], Takahiro Chiba[2], Satoru Adachi[3], Hayato Arakawa[3], Yuki Tsuno[1], Kazuaki Ikeda[1], and Takashi Oozeki[1]

[1] National Institute of Advanced Industrial Science and Technology (AIST), Japan
[2] Hokkaido University of Science, Japan
[3] National Research Institute for Earth Science and Disaster Resilience (NIED), Japan

Background and Motivation

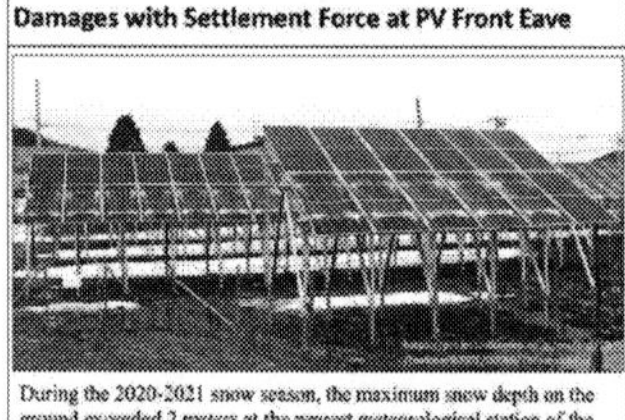
Damages with Settlement Force at PV Front Eave

During the 2020-2021 snow season, the maximum snow depth on the ground exceeded 2 meters at the nearest meteorological station of the Japan Meteorological Agency (JMA).

Snow Settling at Front Eave of PV Array

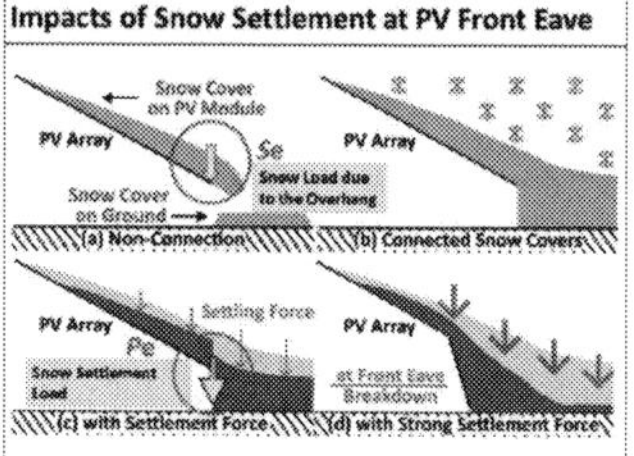
Impacts of Snow Settlement at PV Front Eave

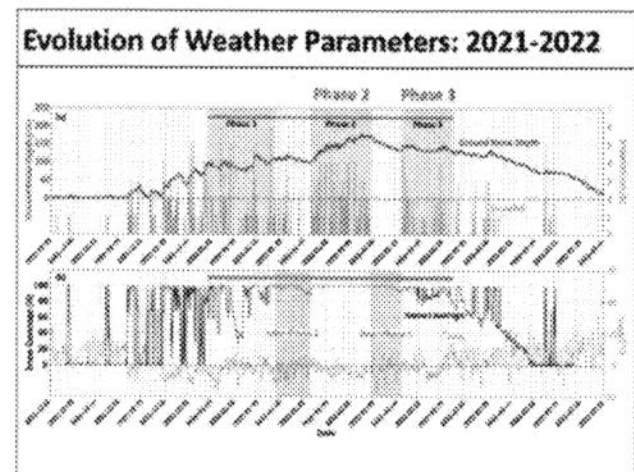
Evolution of Weather Parameters: 2021-2022

Summary

Evolution of Daily Max $P'_{e\text{-EMP}}$, Daily S_e, and $T_{mod\text{-att}}$

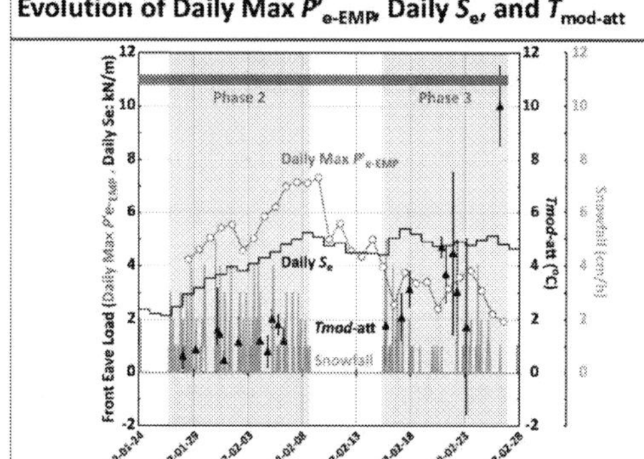

In snowy high-latitude and high-altitude regions, photovoltaic (PV) systems often experience heavy snow accumulation on their modules, which can cause significant damage to both the modules and their mounting structures. Such damage is largely attributed to the heavy snow load on the front eave of the PV array. This load increases due to (1) snow overhang at the front eave (Se), (2) settlement forces generated by the connection between the snow on the modules and the snow accumulated on the ground (Pe), and not only (3) the direct snow load on the PV modules themselves. To date, the loads from direct snow accumulation on modules and snow overhang (Se) have been addressed, and corresponding structural safety test procedures (IEC 61215 and IEC 62938) have been established as international standards. However, the additional load on the front eave caused by settlement of merged snow (Pe) has not been accurately evaluated. Furthermore, the relative strength of Se and Pe has remained undetermined.

In this study, we estimated the linear load at the front eave ($P'e$) and Se during one snow season in a heavy-snow region and found that the intensity of $P'e$ greatly exceeded the load caused by snow overhang on the PV array (see the respective intensities during phase 2 in the left figure). This finding suggests that the structural safety requirements for snow load specified in the current IEC 62938 standard may be insufficient to mitigate the heavy snow loads observed in snowy high-latitude and high-altitude regions.

We also observed a distinctive evolution of snow loads in the front eave region [see the respective intensities during phase 3 in the left figure], which decreased due to heating of the PV modules. We expect that the heating of PV modules could serve as a potential measure to mitigate heavy snow loads in existing PV arrays installed in these areas.

Results

[Panel 01] Experimental Setup

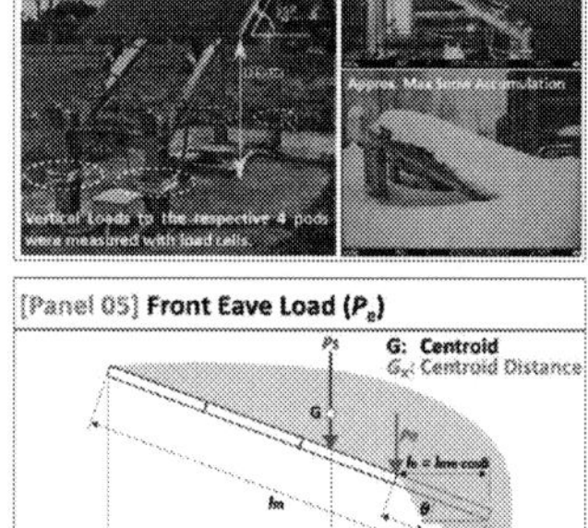

[Panel 02] Snow Load due to the Overhang

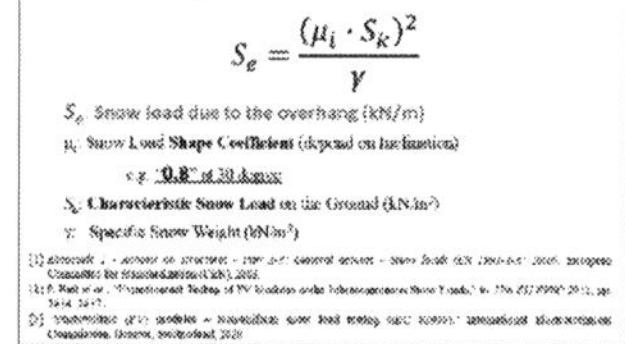

IEC 62938: 2020 Photovoltaic (PV) modules – Non-uniform snow load testing

$$S_e = \frac{(\mu_i \cdot S_k)^2}{\gamma}$$

S_e: Snow load due to the overhang (kN/m)
μ_i: Snow Load Shape Coefficient (depend on inclination)
   e.g. "0.8" at 30 degree
S_k: Characteristic Snow Load on the Ground (kN/m²)
γ: Specific Snow Weight (kN/m³)

[Panel 03] Estimation of Daily Se

$$Daily\ S_e = \frac{(\mu_i \cdot Daily\ S_k)^2}{\gamma}$$

[Panel 04] Daily Trends on Snow Load

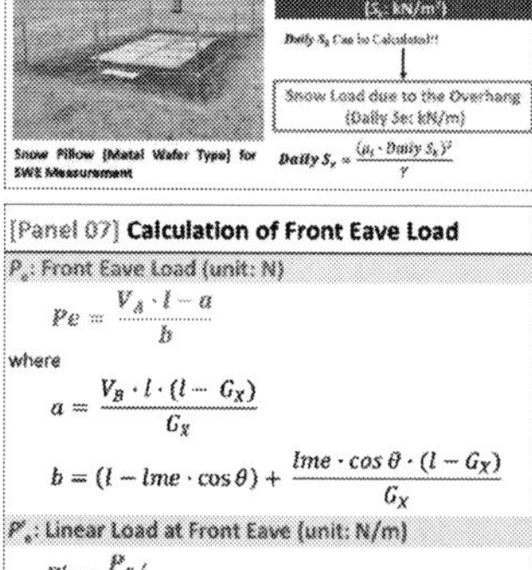

[Panel 05] Front Eave Load (P_e)

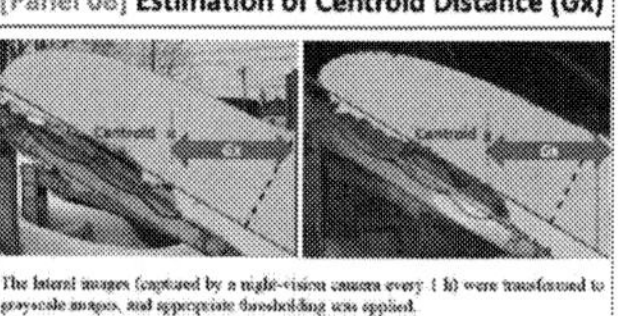

P_e: Front Eave Load (unit: N) resulting from Own Weight and Settlement Force

[Panel 06] Linear Load at Front Eave (P'_e)

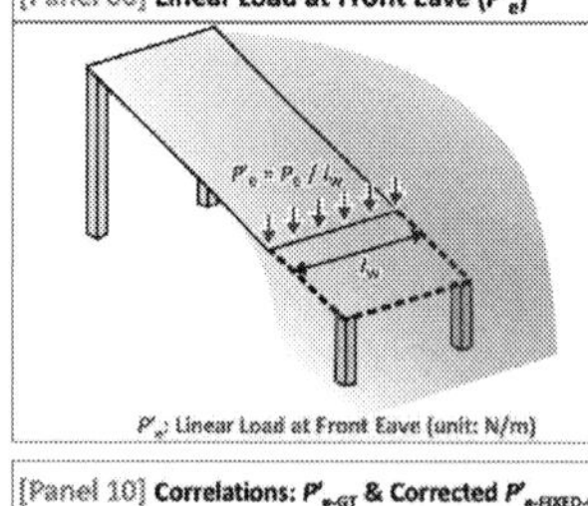

P'_e: Linear Load at Front Eave (unit: N/m)

[Panel 07] Calculation of Front Eave Load

P_e: Front Eave Load (unit: N)

$$Pe = \frac{V_A \cdot l - a}{b}$$

where

$$a = \frac{V_B \cdot l \cdot (l - G_X)}{G_X}$$

$$b = (l - lme \cdot \cos\theta) + \frac{lme \cdot \cos\theta \cdot (l - G_X)}{G_X}$$

P'_e: Linear Load at Front Eave (unit: N/m)

$$P'_e = \frac{P_e}{l_w}$$

[Panel 08] Estimation of Centroid Distance (Gx)

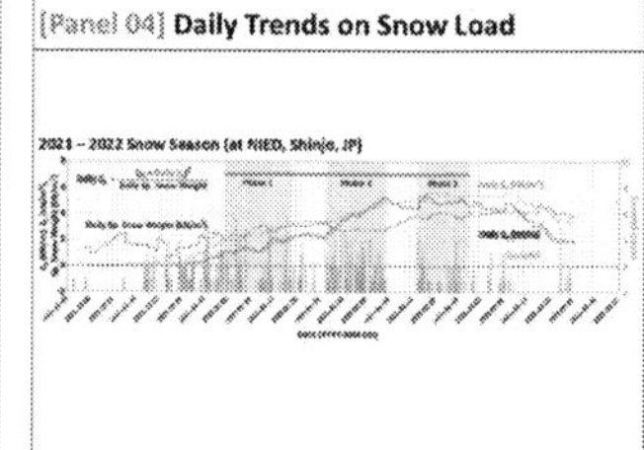

The thermal images (captured by a night-vision camera every 1 h) were transformed to grayscale images, and appropriate thresholding was applied.

Then, using the "Alsnake" package integrated into ImageJ software, the area of accumulated snow on the PV modules was extracted (Blue filled area), and the centroid of the snow accumulation (Red cross mark) was determined.

Centroid Distance (Gx) indicates the distance between the centroid and the bottom edge of PV modules.

[Panel 09] Evolution of $P'_{e\text{-GT}}$ and $P'_{e\text{-FIXED-GX}}$

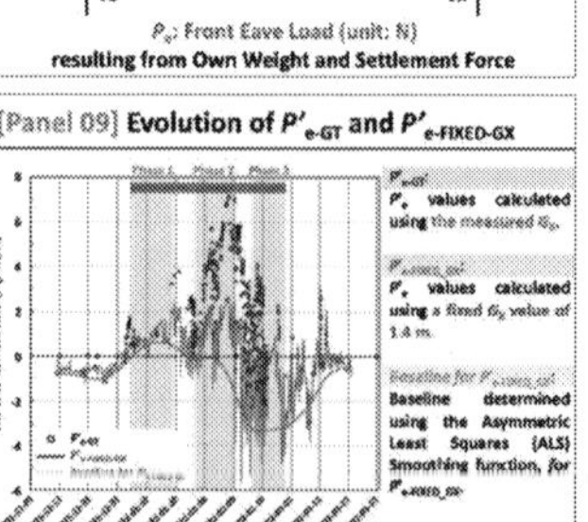

P'_e values calculated using the measured G_x.

$P'_{e\text{-FIXED-GX}}$: values calculated using a fixed G_x value of 1.4 m.

Baseline for $P'_{e\text{-FIXED-GX}}$: Baseline determined using the Asymmetric Least Squares (ALS) Smoothing function, for $P'_{e\text{-FIXED-GX}}$.

[Panel 10] Correlations: $P'_{e\text{-GT}}$ & Corrected $P'_{e\text{-FIXED-GX}}$

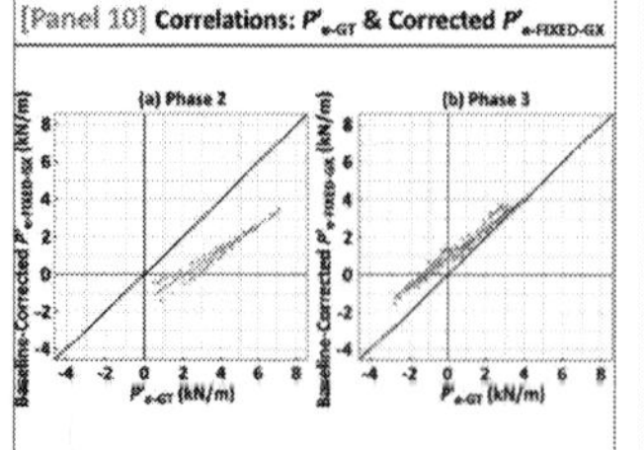

[Panel 11] Evolution of $P'_{e\text{-GT}}$ and $P'_{e\text{-EMP}}$

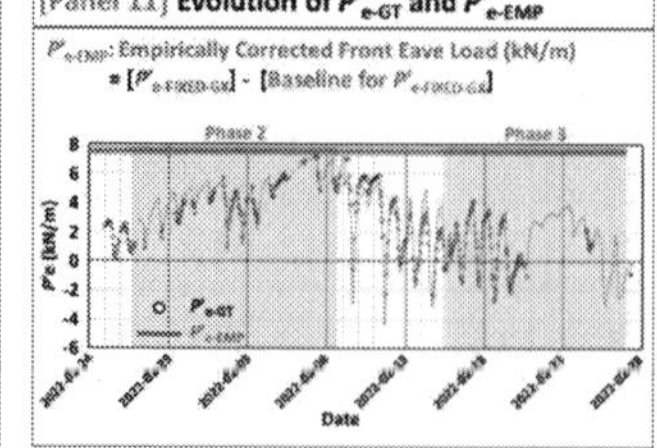

$P'_{e\text{-EMP}}$: Empirically Corrected Front Eave Load (kN/m)
= [$P'_{e\text{-FIXED-GX}}$] - [Baseline for $P'_{e\text{-FIXED-GX}}$]

[Panel 12] T_{mod} Evolution with Panel Heating

$$T_{mod\text{-}obs} = \alpha \cdot exp(-\beta \cdot t) + T_{mod\text{-}att}$$

$T_{mod\text{-}obs}$: Observed Module Temperature
$T_{mod\text{-}att}$: Attained Module Temperature

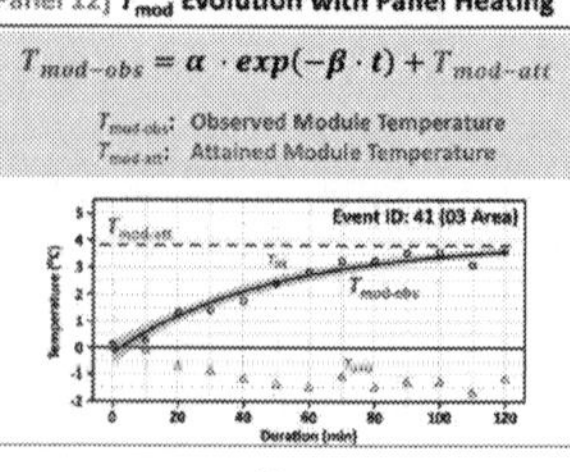

This work was supported in part by the "AIST Program for Promoting Technologies Invented by Industries in Disaster Areas in Tohoku (Seeds Support Program)".

EXPERIMENTAL SET-UP FOR VALIDATION OF MAXIMUM POWER POINT TRACKING ALGORITHMS FOR PHOTOVOLTAIC ARRAYS

Laura Sanchez[1], Gorka Torre[1], Jesus Sanchez[2], Alexander Maiz[2], Alain Sanchez-Ruiz[2], Josu Jugo[1] and Eneko Ortega[1,3]

[1] Electricity and Electronics Department, University of the Basque Country UPV/EHU, 48940, Leioa, Spain
[2] Department of Electronic Technology, University of the Basque Country UPV/EHU, 01006, Vitoria-Gasteiz, Spain
[3] Technological Institute of Microelectronics, University of the Basque Country UPV/EHU, 48013, Bilbao, Spain
eneko.ortegam@ehu.eus

ABSTRACT: The implementation of maximum power point tracking (MPPT) algorithms is essential for improving the performance ratio of photovoltaic (PV) systems. These algorithms optimize the energy generated by solar modules, ensuring maximum efficiency. Maximizing energy production becomes particularly important in sub-optimal conditions, such as partial shading, defects, and variable or diffuse irradiance. MPPT also mitigates the effects of mismatches between modules. This study developes a functional setup for testing and validating various MPPT algorithms. This setup will be developed in both a MATLAB-Simulink simulation environment and a laboratory setting and will be evaluated with two common MPPT algorithms: Perturb & Observe and Incremental Conductance under several scenarios, including changes in illumination, partial shading, and defects in the PV modules, such as variations in series and shunt resistance.
Keywords: photovoltaic systems, maximum power point tracking

1 INTRODUCTION

The growth of photovoltaic (PV) solar energy is increasing sharply during the last years, with a growth of more than 500 GW of installed PV capacity during 2024 [1]. Efficiency and performance of PV systems are growing in parallel. Performance is usually measured in terms of performance ratio (PR) [2], where performance losses, even for modern and well monitored PV systems can be up to 15 % [3]. Performance of PV systems may be affected by several causes such as high temperatures [4], shading of the PV modules [5], defects on the PV modules [6] or by system losses or inefficiencies.

PV arrays, composed by a variable number of PV modules connected in series and parallel, are in turn connected to an electronic circuit following different architectures as shown in [7]. When the PV modules feeds a DC bus, the used electronic circuit is a DC-DC converter. To ensure that the PV system is working at its maximum power, DC-DC converters can include maximum power point tracking (MPPT) algorithms. MPPT algorithms fix the PV modules operating current and voltage trough the control of the duty cycle of the DC-DC converter to ensure that the PV system power output is maximum.

The maximum power point (MPP) of the PV system depends on varying temperature and solar irradiation conditions. Recent studies have shown that solar irradiation conditions show high variability, of more than a 60% within the same day, being difficult to forecast [8], [9]. The use of an MPPT significantly improves the PR of a PV system by optimizing the use of the energy generated by the modules. The MPPT dynamically adjusts the voltage-current ratio so that the modules always operate at their MPP. This reduces electrical losses by preventing the PV modules from operating outside their optimal point, maximizing energy production even in suboptimal scenarios such as partial shading, presence of defects or diffuse and varying irradiance. The incorporation of this technology also mitigates the impact of mismatches between modules, improving overall system efficiency [10].

Several MPPT algorithms have been proposed by different authors to continuously recalculate the MPP of the PV system and obtain the maximum output power under varying operating conditions. Among the best known is the Perturb and Observe (P&O) algorithm, which is simple and effective under stable conditions, but it can exhibit oscillations under rapid changes in irradiance. The Incremental Conductance (IncCond), on the other hand is particularly useful in scenarios of varying irradiance. Recently, more sophisticated and accurate MPPT algorithms have been proposed based on Fuzzy Logic, optimization techniques or artificial neural networks [11], [12], reporting higher accuracies in achieving MPP with lower convergence times. However, they also require higher computational requirements, which may make it difficult to implement low-cost devices such as microcontrollers.

In this context, the aim of this work is to build a functional set-up in a simulation environment in MATLAB-Simulink, to deploy and validate different MPPT algorithms. The set-up will be validated with P&O and IncCond algorithms using a single PV module and a DC-DC Boost converter. The developed set-up will be used for the development and validation of new MPPT algorithms and for educational purposes.

2 DESCRIPTION OF THE SYSTEM

The basic diagram of the implemented system is shown in Fig.1. The system is composed by a PV system connected to a resistive load through a DC-DC Boost converter (to increase the output voltage). This resistive load represents the consumption of a load demanding the power generated by the PV system. The ratio between the input and output voltage in a Boost DC-DC converter is given by Eq. 1, where D is the duty cycle of the converter.

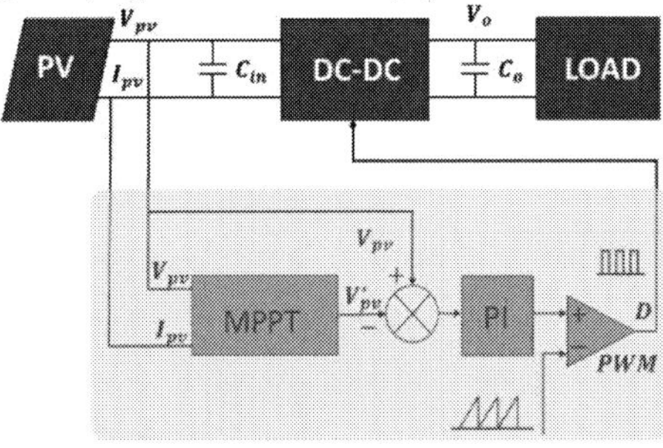

Figure 1: Schematic diagram of the implemented system

$$V_{out} = \frac{V_{PV}}{1-D} \qquad (1)$$

The PV module operates at a working point, generating a current I_{pv} and a voltage V_{pv}. The MPPT algorithm controls the operating point by shifting it to the point where the output power of the PV module is at its maximum. For that I_{pv} and V_{pv} are measured and following different algorithms (P&O or IncCond) the MPPT algorithm determines the reference voltage $V_{pv}*$ that maximizes the power generated by the PV module. This value is compared with the actual voltage V_{pv}, generating an error signal that is minimized by a proportional-integral (PI) controller. The PI controller adjusts the duty cycle D, modulated by a pulse width modulation (PWM) signal, to control the DC-DC converter and maximize the power output. In fact, what is controlled by the DC-DC converter is its equivalent input impedance, adapting it to the dynamic resistance of the module at its MPP. This is done by modifying the duty cycle D that relates the input and output impedance of the converter, that is, the load impedance and the one seen by the module, as shown in Eq. 2.

$$R_{opt} = \frac{V_{MPP}}{I_{MPP}} = Z_{OUT}(1-D)^2 \qquad (2)$$

The MPPT algorithm adjusts D dynamically as a function of the varying irradiance and temperature conditions, aiming to have the module operating at its MPP permanently.

The first algorithm to be implemented, P&O, is one of the simplest and most widespread MPPT techniques. It consists of periodically changing the PV module voltage in small increments proportional to the slope of the dP/dV curve, according to Eq. 3 and Eq. 4, where k is the current time instant, and observing the change in the generated power.

$$Vpv(k+1) = Vpv(k) \pm \Delta Vpv(k+1) \qquad (3)$$

$$\Delta Vpv(k+1) = \Delta Vpm(k) \pm K \frac{P(k)-P(k-1)}{V(k)-V(k-1)} \qquad (4)$$

If the power increases, the direction of the perturbation is maintained; if it decreases, the direction is reversed to approach the MPP. This process is repeated continuously, adjusting the voltage to maximize PV modules output power. Although simple and easy to implement, it can generate oscillations around the optimum point under stable conditions and respond slowly to rapid changes in irradiance or temperature.

The IncCond, unlike the P&O method, relies on calculating the derivative of power with respect to voltage (dP/dV). At the MPP, this derivative is zero. The algorithm computes the incremental conductance ($\Delta I/\Delta V$) and compares it to the instantaneous conductance (I/V). When both are equal, the system is operating at the MPP; if not, the voltage is adjusted in the appropriate direction to reach it. This method offers greater accuracy under rapidly changing irradiance conditions, although it is more complex to implement than P&O.

3 SIMULATION

Firstly, the proposed system has been implemented and validated on a simulation environment. For that, the model shown in Fig. 2 has been developed in MATLAB-Simulink.

The implemented model consists of a user-defined PV module connected to a DC-DC boost converter controlled by a PWM signal. The PV module used for the simulations was a commercial PV module of 120 cells and 3 bypass diodes with Isc = 14.26 A and Voc = 47.06 V .

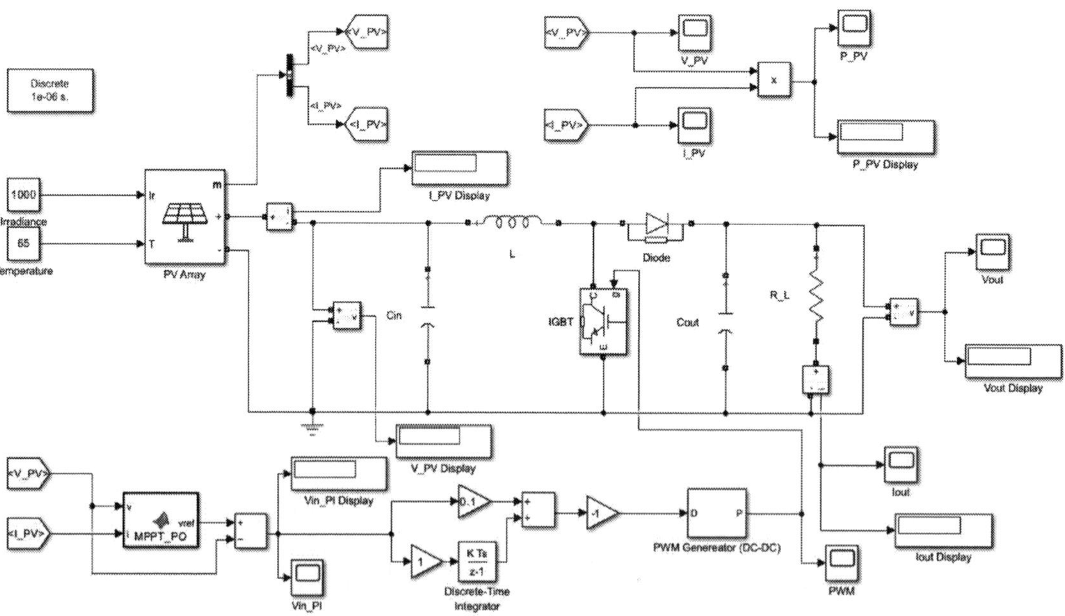

Figure 2: System model diagram developed in MATLAB-Simulink.

Cin is a 150 µF capacitor connected between the PV string and the DC-DC converter to emulate the intrinsic capacitance of the PV modules as a consequence of the quick dynamic behavior of the system. The DC-DC boost converter has an inductor of 622 mH, a capacitor of 140 µF , a diode and a MOSFET as active switch with internal freewheeling diode. The boost converter is controlled by a PWM signal whose switching frequency is 20 kHz. The PWM signal is generated using a MPPT algorithm and a PI controller.

The developed system has been simulated and validated using both the MPPT P&O and IncCond algorithms, under different conditions. Four different scenarios are presented below. First, when the PV module is operating correctly and does not present any type of fault or degradation. For the purpose of the simulation, the following parameters were defined: Rsh = 228.42 Ω and Rs = 0.0016 Ω per PV module cell. Secondly, three different failure types were simulated: increment of series resistance (Rs) to 0.3Ω in one PV cell, decrease in shunt resistance (Rsh) to 0.2Ω and partial shadow on one PVcell (Iph = 6A activating the corresponding bypass diode. Fig. 3 shows the I-V curves of the PV module at 800W/m2 irradiation for a module without failure (blue), PVmodule with series resistance failure (orange), shunt resistance failure (green) and partial shadow (red). Fig. 4 shows the power-voltage (P-V) of the PV modules. For the case of partial shadow, with one bypass diode active, it can be observed that the P-V curve exhibits two local maxima, which complicates the performance of MPPT algorithms.

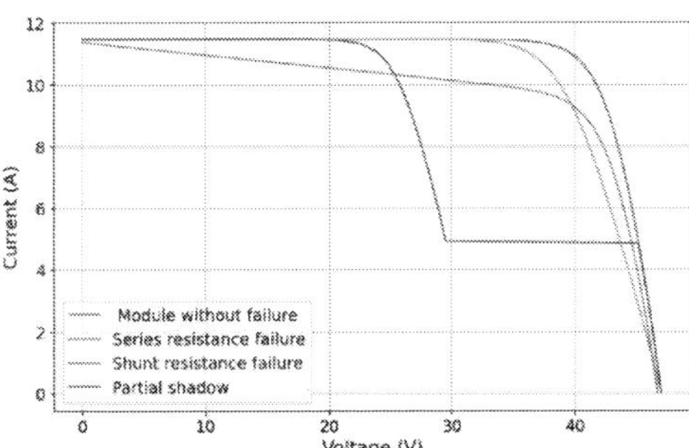

Figure 3: I-V curve of the PV modules operating without any failure, with an increment in series resistance, decrement in shunt resistance and shadow on a single PV cell (1 bypass diode activated).

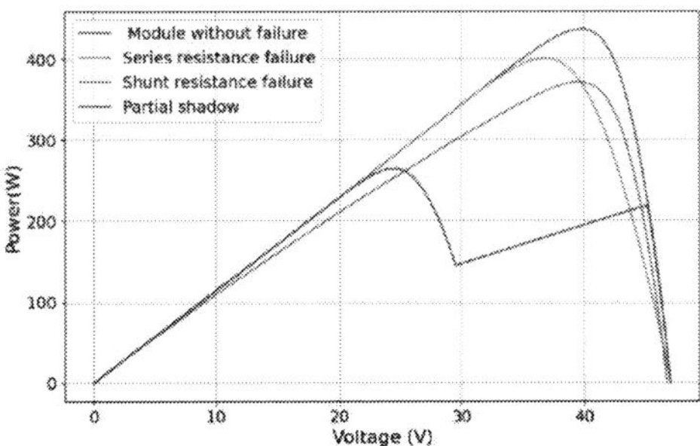

Figure 4: P-V curve of the PV modules operating without any failure, with an increment in series resistance, decrement in shunt resistance and shadow on a single PV cell (1 bypass diode activated).

For each case, the developed system has been simulated for different irradiance values. the irradiance is initially set to 800 W/m2 and later changed to 1000 W/m2 and 600 W/m2 respectively. The cell temperature is 65°C and remains constant throughout the simulation. For all simulations, the initial operating point of the PV module was set close to the MPP.

Fig. 5 shows the first simulation, using the MATLAB-Simulink model, with a PV module without any failure. As it can be seen, both MPPT algorithms present good performance, with very similar MPP values for the P&O and IncCond algorithm.

For PV modules with faults increasing Rs or decreasing Rsh, the maximum power output of a PV module decreases significantly when faults affecting the series resistance (Rs) or shunt resistance (Rsh) occur. An increase in Rs causes a greater drop in internal voltage as current flows, which reduces the voltage at the module terminals and, therefore, the power delivered. On the other hand, a decrease in Rsh allows part of the generated current to be diverted through non-useful paths (leakage currents), which reduces the current available at the load point. Both effects distort the I-V curve of the module and move its operating point away from the theoretical MPP, decreasing the efficiency of the system.

However, both MPPT algorithms proposed in this study are able to achieve the MPP of the new I-V curve of the PV module, obtaining slightly superior values for InCond algorithm in the case of Rs. Specially during non-constant irradiance periods (Fig. 6 and Fig. 7). This effect can be explained by the greater adaptability of the IncCond algorithm to variable conditions.

Similar experiments with partial shadows are being evaluated, achieving results equivalent to the previous ones.

4 LABORATORY IMPLEMENTATION

After validating the MPPT algorithms and the control system in a simulation environment, an experimental system is being developed to test the developed algorithms on a laboratory. For that, a PV module will be installed outdoor and connected to the DC-DC Boost converter shown in Fig.8.

The Boost DC-DC converter has been built using FDA38N30 MOSFET switched semiconductor, with an inherent freewheeling diode. External diode is STTH15R06. Equivalent inductance has been split in two toroidal inductors connected in series. The converter is sized to be able to work with 250 V input or output maximum voltage, and maximum 15 A current. Voltage and current measurements have been adapted to full-scale of the ADCs used in the microcontroller.

Ongoing work is focused on implementing the MPPT algorithms and the PI controller on an ESP32 microcontroller.

The developed system and algorithms will be validated in several scenarios, such as illumination changes, partial shadows or even defects on the PV module such as variations in series and shunt resistance.

5 CONCLUSIONS

A simulation set-up for the deployment and validation of MPPT algorithms has been developed and tested. The set-up consist of a simulation model developed on MATLAB-Simulink. A PI controller and P&O and

IncCond MPPT algorithms have been evaluated obtaining good results for different PV modules failures. A laboratory set-up with a PV-module, a Boost DC-DC converter and an ESP32 microcontroller is being developed to test the algorithms on an experimental set-up. The set-up will be used for the development and validation of new MPPT algorithms and for educational purposes.

6 ACKNOWLEDGEMENTS

The European Union's Horizon Europe programme is acknowledged for financial support through the SUPERNOVA project (Grant Agreement No 101146883).

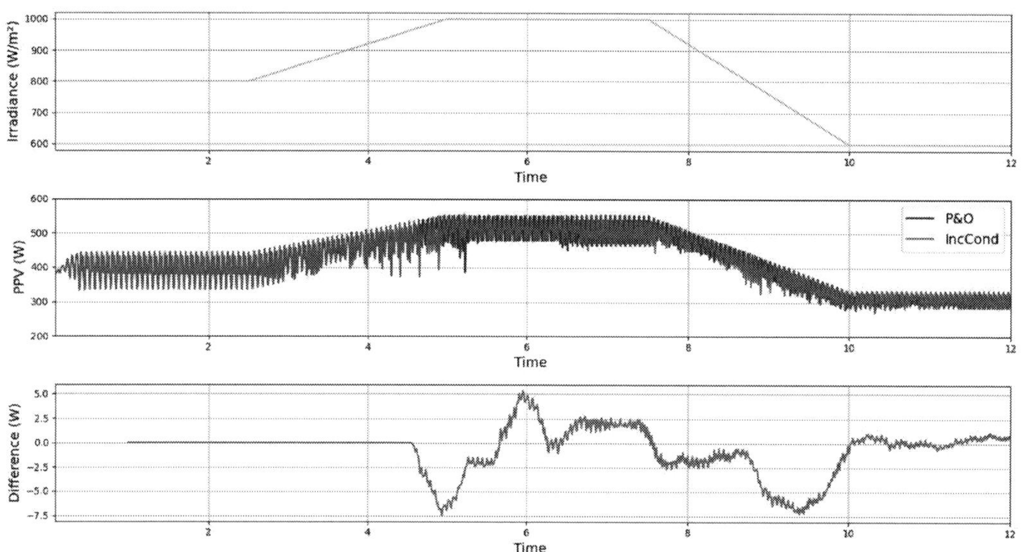

Figure 5: P&O and IncCond MPPT algorithms under variable irradiance conditions for PV modules withouth defects. Figure shows irradiance variations (top), MPPT algorithms achieved MPPT (middle) and power difference (P&O - IncCond).

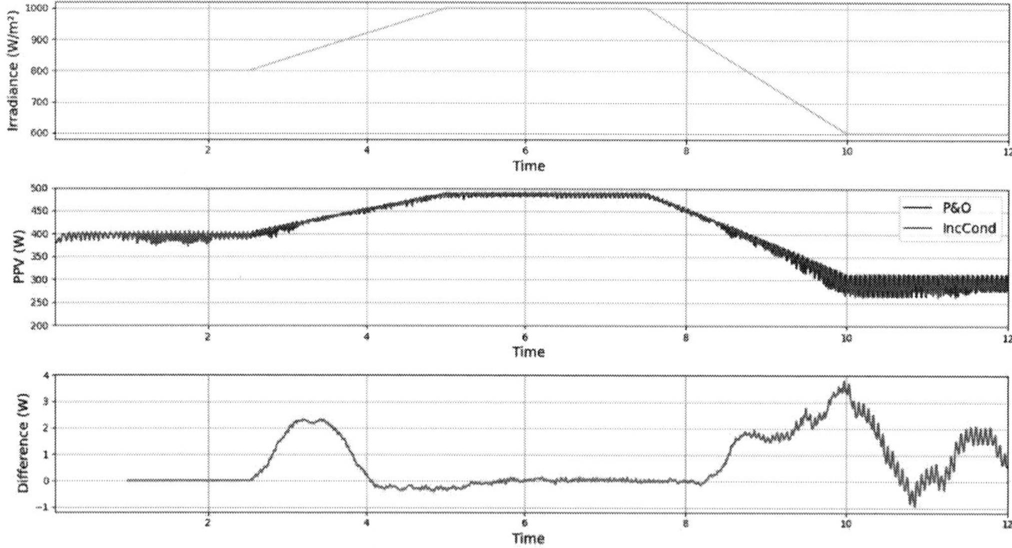

Figure 6: P&O and IncCond MPPT algorithms under variable irradiance conditions for PV modules with Rs increment. Figure shows irradiance variations (top), MPPT algorithms achieved MPPT (middle) and power difference(P&O - IncCond).

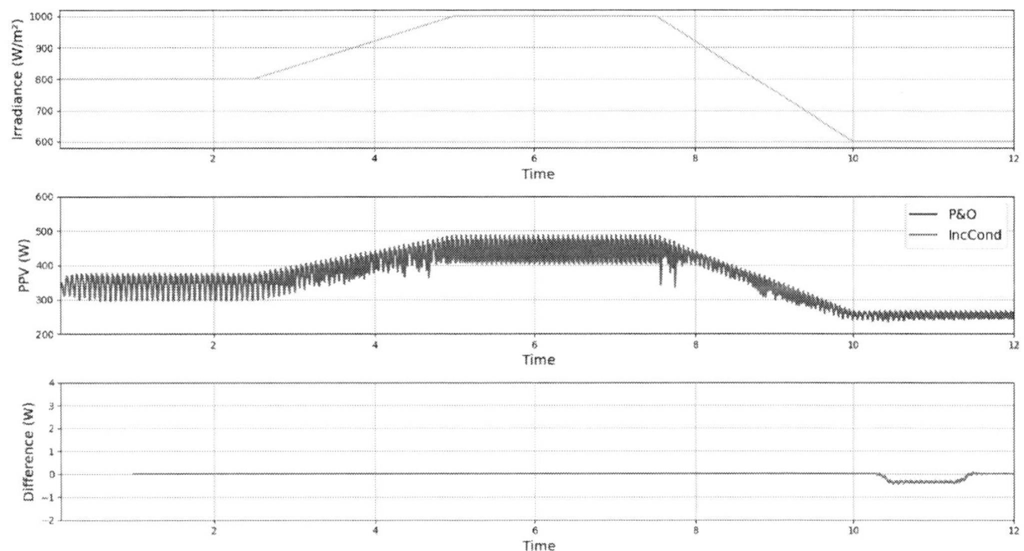

Figure 7: P&O and IncCond MPPT algorithms under variable irradiance conditions for PV modules with Rsh decrement. Figure shows irradiance variations (top), MPPT algorithms achieved MPPT (middle) and power difference(P&O - IncCond).

Figure 8: DC-DC Boost converter.

7 REFERENCES

[1] A. Jager-Waldau, Snapshot of photovoltaics - February 2024. EPJ Photovoltaics, vol. 15, p. 21, 2024.

[2] G. Blaesser, PV system measurements and monitoring the European experience. Solar Energy Materials, vol. 47, pp. 167-176, 1997.

[3] A. Louwen, S. Lindig, G. Chowdhury and D. Moser, Climate-and Technology-Dependent Performance Loss Rates in a Large Commercial Photovoltaic Monitoring Dataset. Solar RRL, vol. 8, p. 2300653, 2024.

[4] K. Hasan, S.B. Yousuf, M.S.H.K. Tushar, B.K. Das, P. Das and M.S. Islam, Effects of different environmental and operational factors on the PV performance: A comprehensive review. Energy Science and Engineering, vol. 10(2), p. 656-675, 2022.

[5] R.K. Pachauri, O.P. Mahela, A. Sharma, J. Bai, Y.K. Chauhan, B. Khan and H.H. Alhelou, Impact of partial shading on various PV array configurations and different modeling approaches: A comprehensive review. IEEE Access, vol. 8, p. 181375-181403, 2020.

[6] E. Ortega, G. Aranguren, M.J. Saenz, R. Gutierrez and J.C. Jimeno, Study of Photovoltaic Systems Monitoring Methods, in 44th IEEE Photovoltaic Specialist Conference (IEEE PVSC), 2017.

[7] H. Kim, G. Yu, J. Kim and S. Choi, PV String-Level Isolated DC–DC Power Optimizer with Wide Voltage Range, Energies, vol. 14(7), p. 1889, 2021.

[8] E. Ortega, S. Suarez, J.C. Jimeno, J.R. Gutierrez, V. Fano, A. Otaegi and S. Rodriguez-Conde, An statistical model for the short-term albedo estimation applied to PV bifacial modules, Renewable Energy, vol. 221, p. 119777, 2024.

[9] C.A. Gueymard, Cloud and albedo enhancement impacts on solar irradiance using high-frequency measurements from thermopile and photodiode radiometers. Part 1: Impacts on global horizontal irradiance, Solar Energy, vol. 153, pp. 755-765, 2017.

[10] C. Nataraj, G. Karthikeyan, G.J. Bharathi and S. Duraikannan, Comparative analysis of direct coupling and MPPT control in standalone PV systems for solar energy optimization to meet sustainable building energy demands, Scientific Reports, vol. 14(1), p. 22924, 2024.

[11] R. Sorensen and L. Mihet-Popa, Comparative Evaluation of Traditional and Advanced Algorithms for Photovoltaic Systems in Partial Shading Conditions, Solar, vol. 4(4), pp. 572-594, 2024.

[12] M. Derbeli, C. Napole, O. Barambones, J. Sanchez, I. Calvo and P. Fernández-Bustamante, Maximum power point tracking techniques for photovoltaic panel: A review and experimental applications, Energies, vol. 14(22), p. 7806, 2021.

Experimental set-up for Validation of Maximum Power Point Tracking Algorithms for Photovoltaic Arrays

UPV EHU

Laura Sanchez[1], **Gorka Torre**[1], **Jesus Sanchez**[2], **Alexander Maiz**[2], **Alain Sanchez-Ruiz**[2], **Josu Jugo**[1] and **Eneko Ortega**[*,1,3]

*eneko.ortegam@ehu.eus

[1] Electricity and Electronics Department, UPV/EHU, 48940, Leioa, Spain

[2] Department of Electronic Technology, UPV/EHU, 01006, Vitoria-Gasteiz, Spain

[3] Technological Institute of Microelectronics, UPV/EHU, 48013, Bilbao, Spain

INTRODUCTION

- To maximize energy output, PV systems use DC-DC or DC-AC converters with MPPT algorithms, which adjust voltage and current to ensure operation at maximum power.
- MPPT algorithms: from simple ones like P&O or CondInc to advanced methods using Fuzzy Logic or neural networks.

AIM

Build a functional set-up in a simulation environment in MATLAB-Simulink, to deploy and validate different MPPT algorithms.

DESCRIPTION OF THE SYSTEM

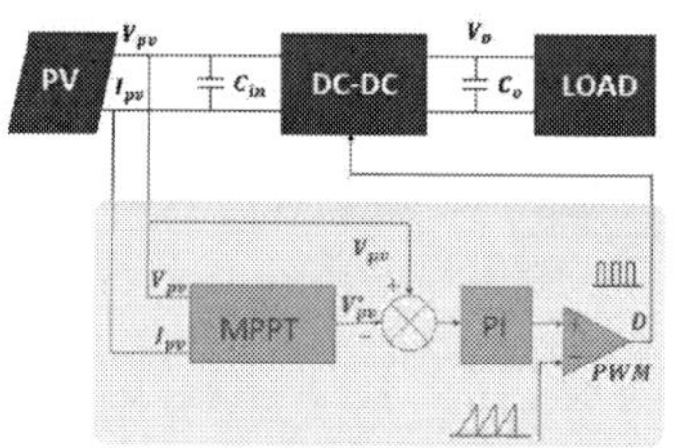

The system is composed by: PV system, resistive load and DC-DC Boost converter.

$$V_{out} = \frac{V_{pv}}{1-D} \quad (1)$$

The PI controller adjusts the duty cycle D, by a PWM signal, to control the DC-DC converter and maximize the power output.

The MPPT algorithm adjusts D to have the module operating at its MPP permanently.

P&O: periodically changes the PV module voltage in small increments proportional to the slope of the dP/dV curve and observing the change in the generated power. If the power increases, the direction of the perturbation is maintained; if it decreases, the direction is reversed to approach the MPP.

IncCond: calculates the derivative of power with respect to voltage (dP/dV)

SIMULATION AND LABORATORY IMPLEMENTATION

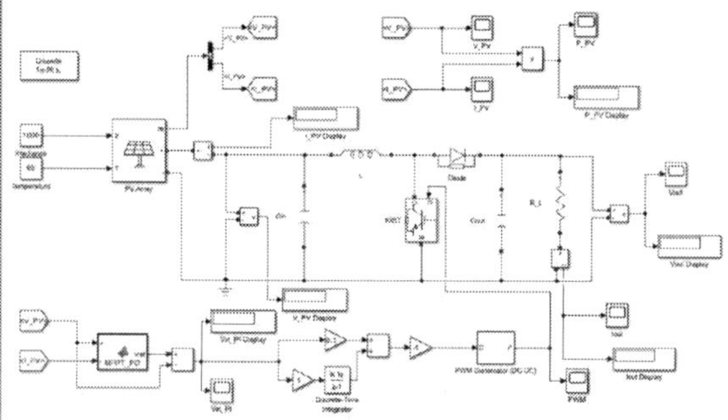

Simulation of P&O and CondInc MPPT algorithms:

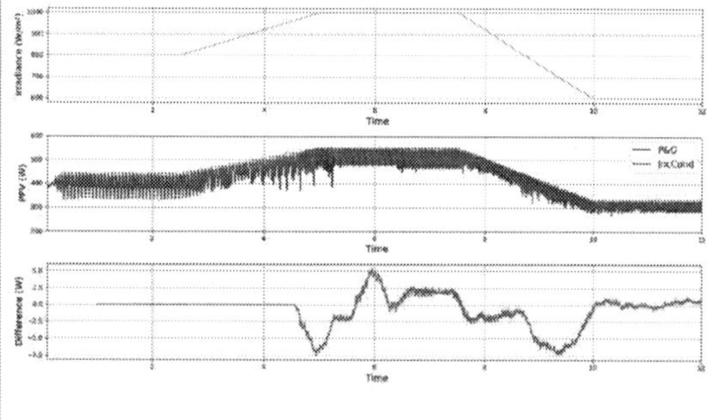

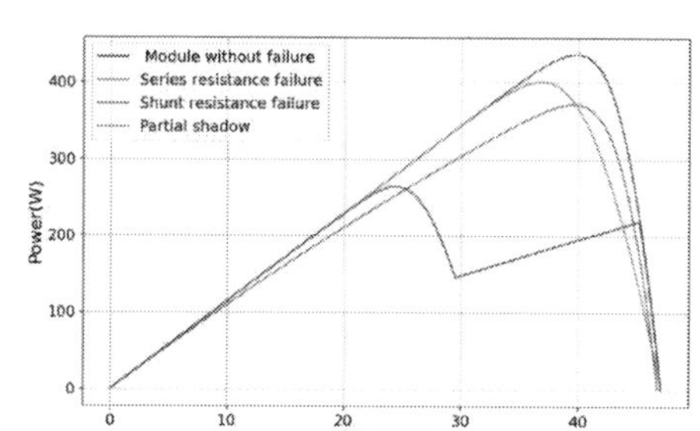

P-V curve of the PV modules under different operating conditions.

DC-DC Boost converter:

ACKNOWLEDGEMENTS

The European Union's Horizon Europe programme is acknowledged for financial support through the SUPERNOVA project (Grant Agreement No 101146883).

CONCLUSIONS

A simulation set-up for the deployment and validation of MPPT algorithms has been developed and tested. The set-up consist of a simulation model developed on MATLAB-Simulink. A PI controller and P&O and IncCond MPPT algorithms have been evaluated obtaining good results for different PV modules failures.

SIZING PHOTOVOLTAIC SELF-CONSUMPTION SYSTEMS THROUGH MISMATCH INDEX AND PROFITABILITY ANALYSIS

Kiane Alves e Silva, Luis Miguel Carrasco, Eduardo Lorenzo
Instituto de Energía Solar, Universidad Politécnica de Madrid
kiane.asilva@alumnos.upm.es, luismiguel.carrasco@upm.es, antonio.lorenzo@upm.es

ABSTRACT: This paper presents a methodology for evaluating and sizing photovoltaic self-consumption systems through a combined technical and economic approach. The analysis relies on hourly energy balance simulation and introduces the Mismatch Index (MI) to quantify the temporal alignment between energy availability and demand, enabling a more precise assessment of self-consumption performance. The financial analysis includes four indicators: Payback Period, Net Present Value, Internal Rate of Return, and Levelized Cost of Energy. The methodology has been applied to a real residential case using historical hourly data on consumption, irradiance, and electricity tariffs in Spain. As a result, the tool indicated a system size that achieves both technical alignment with demand and favorable economic outcomes. The proposed approach serves as a practical decision-support tool for residential PV system design, aligning energy behavior with realistic financial expectations.
Keywords: Photovoltaic systems; Self-consumption systems; Techno-economic analysis; Energy balance

1 INTRODUCTION

The increasing demand for sustainable energy solutions has made photovoltaic (PV) self-consumption systems an attractive option for residential, commercial, and institutional users. These systems offer several benefits, including environmental sustainability [1], savings on energy bills [2] and, in some cases, tax advantages [3]. However, their adoption is tied to their economic feasibility. While environmental concerns and energy independence are relevant motivators, financial returns are one of the main deciding factors in whether users choose to invest in a PV system or not [4].

According to the NREL technical report [5], for small-scale systems, the most commonly used economic indicators are those that are easy to understand by end users and directly tied to financial outcomes, highlighting Payback period (PBP), Monthly bill savings (MBS), and Net Present Value (NPV). Together, they represent investment recovery time, monthly cost reduction, and long-term economic value. However, in academic literature, particularly in techno-economic studies and comparative analyses of PV systems, Internal Rate of Return (IRR) and Levelized Cost of Energy (LCOE) are widely adopted due to their ability to standardize performance and compare different system configurations on equal terms [6], [7], [8], [9].

These financial considerations include not only the reduction of electricity bills and protection against rising energy prices, but also the stability and predictability of long-term savings. However, delivering these benefits requires more than just technical efficiency. The system must be property sized to match the user's specific consumption needs. A temporal mismatch between energy production and demand can significantly reduce self-consumption rates, diminishing overall returns.

Therefore, aligning energy generation with actual consumption behavior is as important as minimizing costs and maximizing output. By addressing both the financial expectations and the functional needs of the user can increase the viability of PV self-consumption systems.

Traditional performance indicators, such as self-consumption and self-sufficiency ratios, are commonly used to evaluate the effectiveness of PV systems [10]. These metrics provide valuable insights into how much of the generated energy is consumed locally and how

independent the user is from the grid, respectively [11]. However, they do not account for the temporal alignment between energy generation and demand. This means that even a system with a high self-consumption rate may perform poorly from an economic perspective if most of the energy consumed does not coincide with periods of peak generation, especially under variable electricity tariffs. Studies in Spain show that load profile variations have a greater impact on system size and profitability than solar resource or electricity tariff [12].

Therefore, this paper presents a new metric, namely Mismatch Index (MI), designed to evaluate how well the distribution of energy availability aligns with the user's hourly consumption profile. Based on the Gini Coefficient [13] and Lorenz Curve [14], widely used in economics to measure social income inequality, the MI quantifies the temporal disparity between available energy and energy demand.

The MI was originally introduced in a previous study [15] as a metric to quantify the temporal mismatch between PV energy generation, based on irradiance data, and user consumption. While this initial work revealed the potential of adapting the Gini Coefficient and Lorenz Curve for PV applications, it had a limitation in scope: it did not consider how the addition of a storage system can affect the mismatch between energy availability and demand.

In this study, the MI has been adapted to include the effect of energy storage. This allows us to evaluate how different combinations of PV and battery sizes impact the alignment between generation and consumption. As a result, the index becomes more suitable for the design of real self-consumption systems, especially when combined with economic analysis.

The use of these two analyses allows identifying configurations that not only deliver financial returns but also align closely with the user's real energy behavior. In this way, the proposed approach promotes the development of PV self-consumption systems that are not just economically feasible, but also functionally optimized.

To support this methodology, a computational tool has been developed, integrating mathematical models of on-grid PV systems with energy storage, detailed meteorological data, and real hourly energy consumption profiles. The tool performs an energy balance analysis to achieve an optimal match between the distribution of energy availability and consumption. In addition to numerical outputs, it provides graphical visualizations to assist in decision-making during system sizing. These include: i) an isometric plot showing the calculated MI values for various combinations of PV and battery capacities, and ii) profitability curves that illustrate the relationship between system sizing and financial performance.

2 METHODOLOGY

The proposed methodology is applied to a typical on-grid PV self-consumption system with energy storage. The system is composed of a PV generator, an energy storage unit (battery), a load, and a connection to the grid. A schematic diagram of the system is shown in Figure 1 illustrating the energy flows between generation, storage, load, and grid exchange. The blue arrows indicate the energy outputs from the self-consumption system (PV generation and battery discharge).

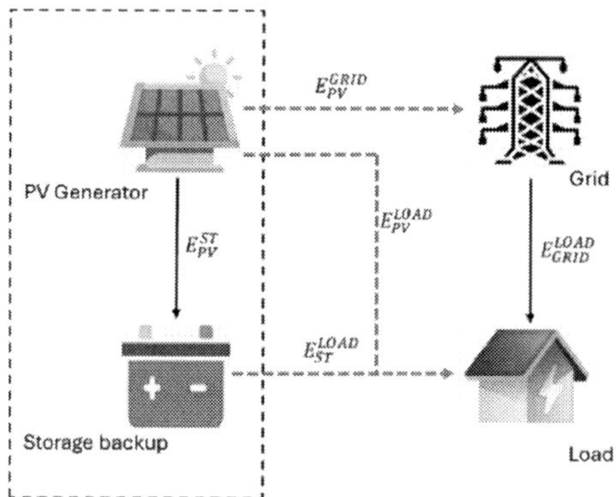

Figure 1 – Schematic of a generic PV self-consumption system with storage system.

The energy produced by the PV generator (E_{PV}) is first used to supply the demand (E_{PV}^{LOAD}). If there is surplus energy, it is stored in the battery (E_{PV}^{ST}) for later use. The battery's State of Charge (SOC) indicates the amount of energy currently stored, as a percentage of its total capacity. If the SOC is less than 100%, it charges when there is surplus energy and discharges when PV generation is not enough to meet the load demand (E_{ST}^{LOAD}). When the load is met and the battery is full, excess energy is sent to the grid (E_{PV}^{GRID}). If both PV and battery cannot meet the demand, energy is taken from the grid (E_{GRID}^{LOAD}).

A computational simulation tool has been developed to model this behavior using hourly data over one year. It calculates the energy balance for different PV and battery sizes, using real consumption profiles and typical meteorological year (TMY) data. The energy balance model used in this simulation has been introduced in a previous work [15], which details the interactions between PV generation, battery storage, and grid exchange under self-consumption conditions.

However, in the present study, the modeling framework is extended with three new elements:

- The use of the concept of System Energy Output (SEO), which is defined as the sum of the energy output from the PV generator and the battery.

- The application of the Mismatch Index (MI) to evaluate temporal alignment between energy availability and consumption.
- The integration of a profitability analysis to evaluate the economic performance of different system configurations.

A schematic representation of the methodological workflow is shown in Figure 2. The process begins with the integration of two main input datasets to simulate the hourly PV production – the hourly energy consumption profile and the hourly meteorological data (temperature and effective irradiation). Then, dynamic energy simulations are performed across multiple combinations of PV generator size (C_{PV}) and battery capacity (C_{ST}), defined as equation (1) and (2), respectively.

$$C_{PV} = \frac{E_{PV}}{E^{LOAD}} \tag{1}$$

$$C_{ST} = E_{ST} \times \frac{N_y}{E^{LOAD}} \tag{2}$$

where E_{PV} is the annual PV energy produced, E^{LOAD} is the annual demand of energy, E_{ST} is the energy storage capacity, and N_y is the number of days in the year.

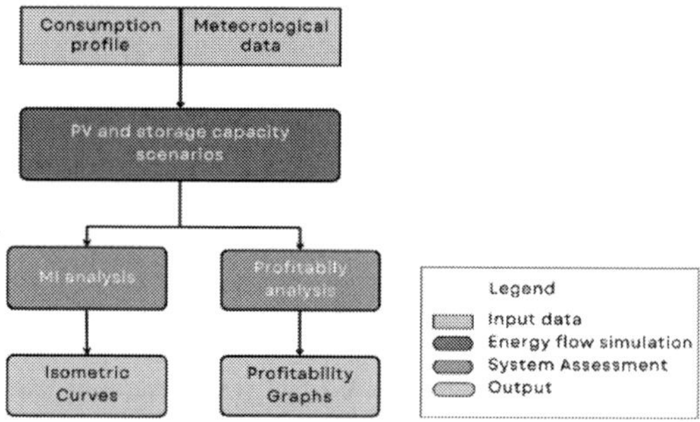

Figure 2 - Methodology flowchart.

Each simulation produces a different energy balance, which is then used to perform the MI and viability analysis.

2.1 Mismatch Analysis

To evaluate how well energy availability aligns with consumption over time, this study uses the MI, a temporal performance indicator based on the Lorenz curve and the Gini coefficient. Originally used to assess inequality in social economic inequality, these tools are adapted here to compare the distribution of energy availability with the distribution of user energy consumption.

In this analysis, the metric used to represent energy availability is the System Energy Output (SEO), defined as the total amount of energy made available by the system at each time step. The SEO includes all energy that passes through the self-consumption system: energy consumed directly from PV, energy exported to the grid, and energy discharged from the battery - that is, the energy flows represented by the dashed blue arrows in Figure 1. The SEO is defined as equation (3) and assumes an ideal system, with no losses considered.

$$SEO = E_{PV}^{Load} + E_{PV}^{Grid} + E_{ST}^{Load} \tag{3}$$

The SEO reflects all useful energy flows in from the

PV system and serves as the reference distribution against which consumption is compared.

The MI is calculated by constructing a Lorenz curve that compares the cumulative distribution of energy consumption to that of the selected metric. To plot the Lorenz curve, the data has been sorted in ascending order of SEO, so that the relative cumulative distribution of each variable is represented.

An illustrative curve is shown in Figure 3. In this case, the hourly cumulative data over one year is sorted in increasing order of SEO. The cumulative share of consumption is plotted on the x-axis, while the cumulative share of SEO is plotted on the y-axis. A perfect alignment between the two distributions would result in a 45° diagonal line (red dashed line), and any deviation from this line represents temporal mismatch (gray area).

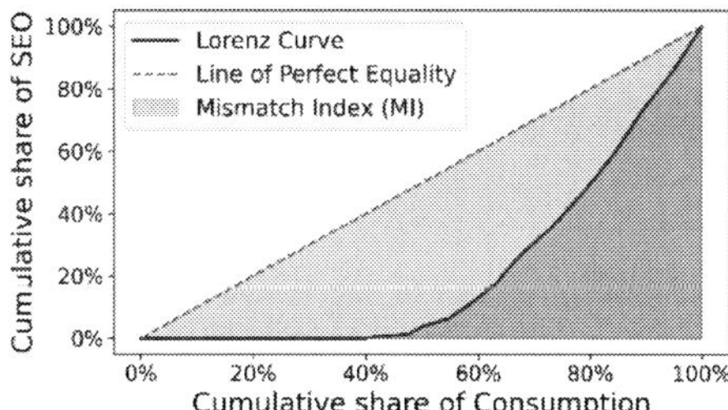

Figure 3 - Example of a Lorenz curve of SEO versus consumption.

Mathematically, the MI is defined as the normalized area between the Lorenz curve and the line of equality, represented as the gray area, and is calculated as presented in equation (4) [16].

$$MI = 1 - \sum_{k=1}^{N} (X_k - X_{k-1}) \cdot Y_k + Y_{k-1} \qquad (4)$$

where X_k is the cumulative share of energy consumption, Y_k is the cumulative share of SEO, and N is the number of time steps (8,760 for one year of hourly data).

MI values range from 0 (perfect temporal alignment) to 1 (maximum mismatch). A low MI indicates that energy is available when it is needed, while a high MI suggests that SEO and demand occur at different times.

Although the MI is applied here using SEO, the same method can be used with other PV system metrics, such as PV generation, effective irradiation, or energy cost, depending on the objective of the analysis. This flexibility makes the MI a powerful tool to support design decisions and improve system performance, especially in contexts where both energy and cost profiles vary significantly over time.

2.2 Profitability Analysis

In addition to the technical evaluation, the simulation tool includes an economic analysis to assess the financial performance of each simulated configuration.

In this study, we adopt a comprehensive approach by evaluating the economic performance of each configuration using the following four indicators: NPV, PBP, IRR, and LCOE.

The PBP (in years) estimates the time required to recover the initial investment (C_0) – also known as CAPEX – through accumulated savings [17] considering

the project lifetime (LT), also expressed in years. In its simplest form, it is defined as equation (5).

$$PBP = \frac{C_0}{B - C} \qquad (5)$$

where B is the annual financial benefit resulting from the PV system, including both the savings from self-consumed energy (based on the electricity import tariff) and revenues from excess energy exported to the grid (based on electricity export tariff). C represents the annual operational and maintenance costs (OPEX)

While PBP does not account for the time value of money, the NPV quantifies the profitability of an investment by bringing all projected future revenues and costs to present value using a discount rate and computing the net difference over the system's lifetime (LT) [9]. It is calculated as the difference between the present value of expected benefits and operational costs [18], as expressed in equation (6).

$$NPV = -C_0 + \sum_{t=1}^{LT} \frac{B_t - C_t}{(1 + r)^t} \qquad (6)$$

where B_t and C_t correspond to the benefits and OPEX in year t, respectively, and r is the discount rate.

Based on the NPV it is possible to calculate the IRR, since it is the discount rate (r) at which the NPV equals zero after the lifetime project [6], as expressed in equation (7)

$$0 = -C_0 + \sum_{t=1}^{LT} \frac{B_t - C_t}{(1 + IRR)^t} \qquad (7)$$

Lastly, the LCOE expresses the total cost of producing each kWh of energy over the system's lifetime, discounted to present value. Traditionally, LCOE calculation follows the ratio between the total discounted system costs and the total energy output [19], as presented in equation (8). This indicator provides an estimate of the cost of the generated energy, allowing the assessment of whether the system attains grid parity.

$$LCOE_{PV} = \frac{C_0 + \sum_{t=1}^{LT} C_t \times (1+r)^{-t}}{E_{PV}} \qquad (8)$$

3   RESULTS AND DISCUSSIONS

The base case analyzed in this study corresponds to a real residential household located in La Coruña (43.63° N, -7.74° W), in northern Spain, to which the proposed tool has been applied. The annual consumption for 2022 has been 2,989 kWh [20], and the annual effective irradiance has been 1.25 MWh/m² [21]. Figure 4 shows the normalized values of the average hourly profile of energy consumption and the effective irradiation of the site over a 24-hour day period. Both energy consumption and effective irradiation have been normalized individually with respect to its total annual value, allowing for a direct comparison of their temporal patterns.

The PV generation profile was estimated on [21] based on typical module characteristics and local irradiance conditions, assuming a 30° tilt angle and 0° azimuth orientation. The base case considers a nominal capacity (P_n) of 6 kWp to match the annual energy demand ($C_{PV} = 1$), and a battery capacity (C_{bat}) of 8.19 kWh, equivalent to the average daily demand ($C_{ST} = 1$).

This base case serves as the reference for all subsequent simulations and results discussed throughout the paper.

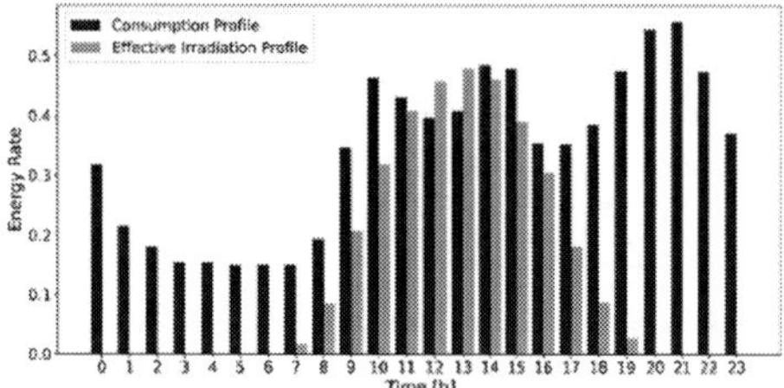

Figure 4 – Normalized average hourly consumption and irradiation profiles for the base case. Data obtained from [20] and [21], respectively. Each profile normalized to its own annual total.

3.1 Mismatch Results

The energy balance has been simulated with C_{PV} and C_{ST} ranging from 0 to 1, as fractions relative to the base case. To ensure accurate modeling of PV generation, the following technical assumptions have been considered: a Nominal Operating Cell Temperature (NOCT) of 41 °C and a power temperature coefficient of −0.26%/°C, both referring to the PV module; inverter efficiency of 98%; and overall system losses estimated at 15%, accounting for soiling, cabling, mismatching, and other typical effects.

The MI has been applied to each simulated configuration using the outputs from the energy balance. Figure 5 presents the resulting MI isometric curves over the range of C_{PV} and C_{ST} values. As expected, configurations with limited PV capacity or no storage have shown higher mismatch values, indicating reduced temporal alignment between availability and demand. The introduction of storage has significantly improved MI in most cases, particularly when combined with moderate PV generation levels.

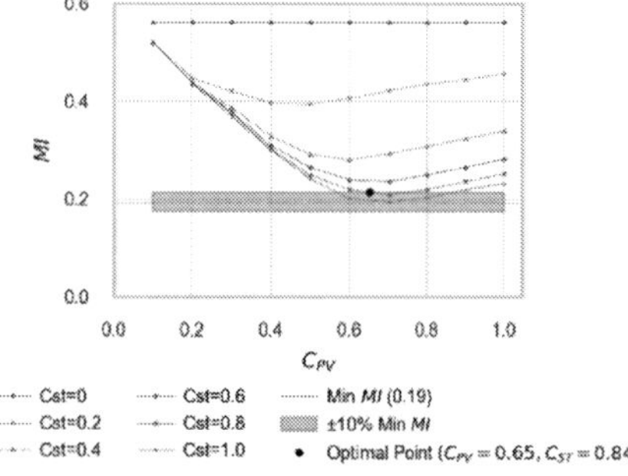

Figure 5 – Mismatch Index (MI) as a function of PV capacity (C_{PV}) for different storage capacities (C_{ST}).

According to the visual results presented in Figure 5, the minimum MI obtained is 0.19, which occurs when $C_{PV} = 0.7$ and $C_{ST} = 1.0$. Since designing a system based strictly on a single reference point may not be practical, a tolerance range instead accommodates configurations with similarly good performance. To support practical system design, a sensitivity range of ±10% around the minimum MI value (0.19) has been considered as an acceptable tolerance band for configurations with comparable MI-performance, represented in Figure 5 by the green shaded area.

Within this range, the smallest storage system that satisfies the tolerance criterion corresponds to $C_{ST} = 0.84$. For this storage size, the minimum PV capacity within the acceptable area is found at $C_{PV} = 0.65$. Therefore, this configuration can be considered the most suitable option from the perspective of this analysis.

3.2 Economic Results

For the financial evaluation, PVPC tariffs (*Precio Voluntario para el Pequeño Consumidor* in spanish) have been used for both energy imports and surplus exports. PVPC is the regulated time-of-use tariff structure applied in the Spanish electricity market for residential and small consumers, reflecting hourly wholesale market prices [22]. Hourly tariff data were obtained from the *Spanish Electricity System Operator Information Platform* (ESIOS) [23], which provides historical data on electricity purchase prices from the grid as well as compensation rates for surplus energy exported by self-consumption systems.

It is important to note that, under the current Spanish self-consumption regulation, there is a restriction on the economic compensation for surplus energy exported to the grid: the monthly compensation cannot exceed the billed amount for energy imported from the grid during the same billing period [24]. As a result, oversized systems or those with low self-consumption ratios may experience a reduction in economic benefits.

The financial simulations have been carried out considering a system lifetime of 10 years and a discount rate of 8% per year, consistent with typical assumptions for small-scale residential investments. An annual tariff growth of 8% has been applied to both buying and selling energy tariffs, combining expected inflation and market spread. PV system degradation has been modeled as a linear reduction of 0.5% per year in energy output.

CAPEX has been estimated based on recent market surveys. These data have been used to define PV and lithium-battery cost function according to system size, reflecting realistic price trends in the Spanish residential sector. Equation (9) shows the PV cost function where P_n is the PV capacity [kWp], and equation (10) refers to storage cost function where C_{bat} is the storage capacity [kWh]. Both equations were extracted using mathematical regression from current market studies.

$$CAPEX_{PV} = 2.577 \cdot (P_n)^{-0.303} \cdot P_n \qquad (9)$$

$$CAPEX_{ST} = 45.0389 \cdot (e^{0.0798 \cdot C_{bat}} - 1) \qquad (10)$$

The initial OPEX has been set at 2% of the total CAPEX and is assumed to increase annually by 2%, accounting for inflation and gradual maintenance adjustments over the system's lifetime.

Table 1 summarizes the main economic assumption used in the financial analysis.

Figure 6(a) shows that the shortest PBP values, around 6 years, occur for larger systems – since higher PV capacities generate more energy and therefore greater economic benefits. The inclusion of storage slightly improves the PBP, as storing energy for self-consumption is generally more profitable than selling the surplus to the grid. However, the relatively high cost of batteries limits this benefit, so that the impact on payback remains. In contrast, smaller systems present longer PBP values, which can reach up to 11 years. In these cases, the reduced PV capacity limits energy generation, keeping the system highly dependent on the grid and resulting in lower economic benefits. Consequently, investment recovery is slower and less attractive compared to larger configurations , but still corresponds to roughly half of the estimated system lifetime

Table 1 – Summary of economic assumptions used in the analysis.

Parameter	Value
System lifetime (LT)	20 years
Discount rate (r)	8% per year
Tariff annual growth	8 % per year
PV degradation	0.5% per year
CAPEX	$CAPEX_{PV} + CAPEX_{ST}$
Initial OPEX	2% of CAPEX
OPEX growth	2% per year
Tariff type	PVPC

Regarding NPV, the results in Figure 6(b) indicate economic viability in all scenarios, remaining positive throughout. Systems with $C_{PV} > 0.5$ show an average NPV of €4,673, reaching values above €6,000 in the most favorable cases. Although storage contributes to performance improvement, higher PV generation drives the financial return, consistent with the PBP trends.

The IRR results – Figure 6(c) – confirm the economic feasibility already indicated by the NPV, with values ranging from a minimum of 10% up to 18%. Since the lowest value remains above the 8% discount rate, all scenarios can be considered financially viable. Configurations with $C_{PV} > 0.5$ and $C_{ST} \geq 0.3$ show a slowdown in IRR growth, stabilizing around an average of 17.7%.

Finally, Figure 6(d) presents the LCOE$_{PV}$ results, which vary between €0.22 and €0.10/kWh, with an average of €0.13/kWh. Compared to the average electricity tariff in Spain of €0.21/kWh in 2022 [25], the PV system shows competitiveness. However, although market tariffs may fluctuate and even fall below the LCOE in certain periods, this indicator shows the stability of energy costs over the entire project lifetime, reinforcing the role of PV as a reliable long-term investment.

3.3 Techno-Economic Evaluation

Based on technical evaluations, a $C_{PV} = 0.65$ and $C_{ST} = 0.84$ configurations has been selected as it is the smallest system within the tolerance band relative to the minimun MI (0.19), as ilustrated in Figure 5. It represents a technically well-aligned system size, which can contribute to reducing investment costs.

A summary of the final techno-economical results for this system size are presented in Table 2. The system requires an initial investment of €3,610 and generates a net return of €16,474 over its lifetime, where net return corresponds to the difference between total benefits (€21,838) and the combined costs of CAPEX and OPEX (€5,364). When discounted to present value, this profit corresponds to an NPV of €4,516. The payback period of 6.6 years indicates that the investment is recovered well before the end of the 20-year project lifetime. This means that the system not only returns the initial capital within a safe margin, but also generates several years of net economic benefit during its operational horizon.

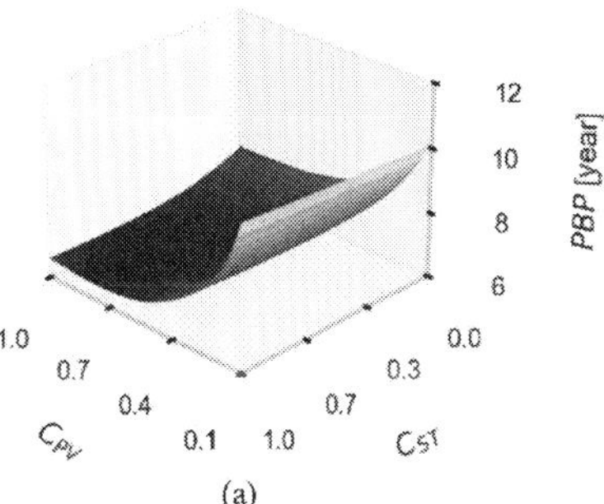

(a)

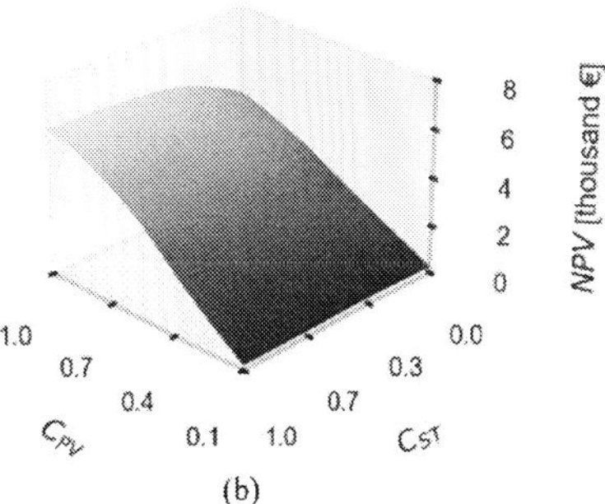

(b)

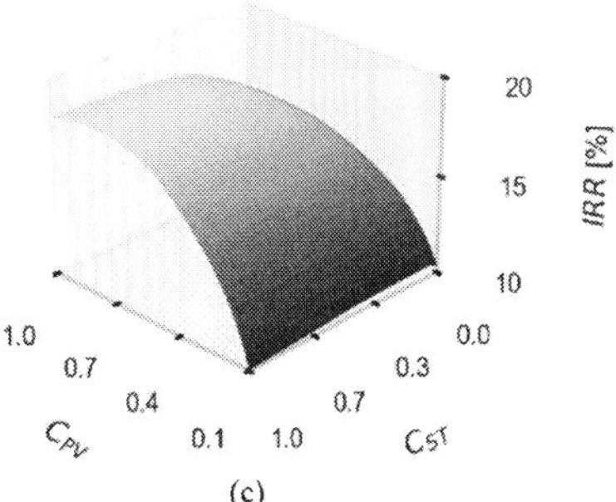

(c)

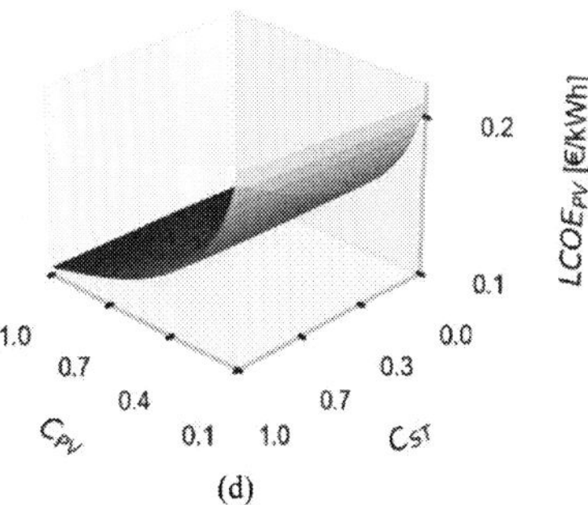

(d)

Figure 6 – Economic performance indicators for different PV and battery sizes (C_{PV} and C_{ST}, respectively): a) Payback Period (PBP); b) Net Present Value (NPV); c) Internal Rate of Return (IRR); d) Levelized Cost of Energy of the self-consumption system (LCOE$_{PV}$)

In addition, the IRR reaches 18%, a value that largely surpasses the assumed discount rate of 8% and confirms the profitability of the investment. LCOE$_{PV}$ results in €0.12/kWh, placing the cost of self-generated electricity in a competitive range compared to market tariffs and ensuring stability over the project lifetime.

Table 2 – Summary of simulated results for the smallest system within the MI tolerance band

Parameter	Value
PV generator	3.90 kWp
Battery storage	6.55 kWh
MI	0.21
CAPEX	€ 3,610
OPEX	€ 1,754
Benefits	€ 21,838
PBP	6.6 years
NPV	€ 4,516
IRR	18%
LCOE	0.12 €/kWh

4 CONCLUSIONS

This study presents a methodology for evaluating and sizing PV self-consumption systems by combining technical performance and economic indicators based on hourly energy flow simulations. The simulation result shows that it is possible to identify configurations that offer a strong balance between energy availability and financial return.

The MI has been introduced and applied to the SEO to assess the temporal alignment between energy availability and demand. This approach captures not only how much energy is produced, but also when it is available relative to consumption. MI plays a key role in providing us with information about the performance of a self-consumption system and its dependence on the electricity grid. .

The economic evaluation included four economic indicators – PBP, NPV, IRR, and LCOE. These metrics togheter provide a comprehensive overview of financial performance, highlithing how different system sizes influence return on investment.

The methodology has been applied to a real case study using historic hourly data for energy demand, environmental inputs and electricity tariffs. Among the simulated scenarios, the optimized system ($C_{PV} = 0.65$ and $C_{ST} = 0.84$) has been identified as both technically efficient and economically viable, generating a net economic benefit more than three times higher than the associated costs, over its lifetime, equivalent to €4,516 NPV. The economic viability is supported by a PBP of 6.6 years, which ensures cost recovery well before the end of the 20-year lifetime. The IRR reaches 18%, more than double the assumed discount rate, thus confirming a strong profitability margin. In addition, LCOE$_{PV}$ of 0.12 €/kWh highlighting its competitiveness and long-term stability.

This practical example reinforces the potential of the tool as a decision-support resource for designing well-balanced and cost-effective residential PV self-consumption systems. With the results obtained from the tool, users can evaluate which configuration best fits their needs and constraints – whether prioritizing faster payback, higher long-term net benefits, greater annual returns, or stable generation costs.

Future work may explore the inclusion of demand-side management strategies, different tariff structures, as well as extending the methodology to other user profiles or climates. Overall, the approach showed here can support more informed and technically grounded decisions for sizing effective and cost-efficient PV systems.

5 ACKNOWLEDGEMENTS

This work has been possible thanks to the Project IND2022/AMB-23718 funded by Comunidad de Madrid and to the Project LIFE21-CET-ENERCOM-JALON funded by the European Union. Views and opinions expressed are, however, those of the author(s) only and do not necessarily reflect those of the European Union or CINEA. Neither the European Union nor the granting authority can be held responsible for them

REFERENCES

[1] I. Montero, MT. Miranda, F. Barrena, F. J. Sepúlveda, and J. I. Arranz, "Analysis of photovoltaic self-consumption systems for hospitals in southwestern Europe," *Energy Build*, vol. 269, p. 112254, Aug. 2022, doi: 10.1016/j.enbuild.2022.112254.

[2] J. M. Roldán Fernández, M. Burgos Payán, and J. M. Riquelme Santos, "Profitability of household photovoltaic self-consumption in Spain," *J Clean Prod*, vol. 279, p. 123439, Jan. 2021, doi: 10.1016/J.JCLEPRO.2020.123439.

[3] I. D'Adamo, M. Gastaldi, and P. Morone, "Solar collective self-consumption: Economic analysis of a policy mix," *Ecological Economics*, vol. 199, p. 107480, Sep. 2022, doi: 10.1016/j.ecolecon.2022.107480.

[4] V. Rai, D. C. Reeves, and R. Margolis, "Overcoming barriers and uncertainties in the adoption of residential solar PV," *Renew Energy*, vol. 89, pp. 498–505, Apr. 2016, doi: 10.1016/J.RENENE.2015.11.080.

[5] E. Drury, P. Denholm, and R. Margolis, "The Impact of Different Economic Performance Metrics on the Perceived Value of Solar Photovoltaics - NREL/TP-6A20-52197," Oct. 2011. Accessed: Jul. 03, 2025. [Online]. Available: https://docs.nrel.gov/docs/fy12osti/52197.pdf

[6] I. B. Carrêlo, R. H. Almeida, L. Narvarte, F. Martinez-Moreno, and L. M. Carrasco, "Comparative analysis of the economic feasibility of five large-power photovoltaic irrigation systems in the Mediterranean region," *Renew Energy*, vol. 145, pp. 2671–2682, Jan. 2020, doi: 10.1016/J.RENENE.2019.08.030.

[7] G. Liu, M. Li, B. Zhou, Y. Chen, and S. Liao, "General indicator for techno-economic assessment of renewable energy resources," 2018, *Elsevier*. [Online]. Available: https://www.sciencedirect.com/science/article/pii/S0196890417311068

[8] S. Quoilin, K. Kavvadias, A. Mercier, I. Pappone, and A. Zucker, "Quantifying self-consumption linked to solar home battery systems: Statistical analysis and economic assessment q," 2016, doi: 10.1016/j.apenergy.2016.08.077.

[9] C. H. Villar, D. Neves, and C. A. Silva, "Solar PV self-consumption: An analysis of influencing indicators in the Portuguese context," *Energy*

Strategy Reviews, vol. 18, pp. 224–234, Dec. 2017, doi: 10.1016/J.ESR.2017.10.001.

[10] A. Ciocia *et al.*, "Self-Consumption and Self-Sufficiency in Photovoltaic Systems: Effect of Grid Limitation and Storage Installation," *Energies 2021, Vol. 14, Page 1591*, vol. 14, no. 6, p. 1591, Mar. 2021, doi: 10.3390/EN14061591.

[11] R. Luthander, J. Widén, D. Nilsson, and J. Palm, "Photovoltaic self-consumption in buildings: A review," *Appl Energy*, vol. 142, pp. 80–94, Mar. 2015, doi: 10.1016/J.APENERGY.2014.12.028.

[12] B. Domenech, G. Calleja, and J. Olivella, "Residential Photovoltaic Profitability with Storage under the New Spanish Regulation: A Multi-Scenario Analysis," 2021, doi: 10.3390/en14071987.

[13] C. Gini, "On the measurement of concentration and variability of characters," *Metron - International Journal of Statistics*, vol. LXIII, no. 1, pp. 1–38, 2005.

[14] T. Sitthiyot and K. Holasut, "A simple method for estimating the Lorenz curve," *Humanit Soc Sci Commun*, vol. 8, no. 1, p. 268, Nov. 2021, doi: 10.1057/s41599-021-00948-x.

[15] K. A. Silva, L. M. Carrasco, and A. L. Mata, "ENERGY FLOW ALGORITHM TO THE OPTIMIZATION OF ON-GRID PV BUILDINGS WITH OR WITHOUT BACKUP STORAGE," in *EU PVSEC 2023*, Lisboa, 2023. doi: 10.4229/EUPVSEC2023/4BV.4.24.

[16] S. Karam and M. S. Ryerson, "Operating at the individual level: A review of literature and a research agenda to support needs-forward models of transport resource allocation," *Transp Res Interdiscip Perspect*, vol. 21, p. 100887, Sep. 2023, doi: 10.1016/J.TRIP.2023.100887.

[17] I. H. Ibrik and S. Cruz, "Techno-economic assessment of on-grid solar PV system in Palestine," *Cogent Eng*, vol. 7, no. 1, Jan. 2020, doi: 10.1080/23311916.2020.1727131.

[18] Q. Tushar, G. Zhang, F. Giustozzi, M. A. Bhuiyan, L. Hou, and S. Navaratnam, "An integrated financial and environmental evaluation framework to optimize residential photovoltaic solar systems in Australia from recession uncertainties," *J Environ Manage*, vol. 346, p. 119002, Nov. 2023, doi: 10.1016/J.JENVMAN.2023.119002.

[19] P. Kästel and B. Gilroy-Scott, "Economics of pooling small local electricity prosumers—LCOE & self-consumption," *Renewable and Sustainable Energy Reviews*, vol. 51, pp. 718–729, Nov. 2015, doi: 10.1016/J.RSER.2015.06.057.

[20] "E-distribuición Redes Digitales, S.L."

[21] Universidad Politécnica de Madrid, "SISIFO: An online simulator of PV systems," 2023, v3.2. Accessed: Jul. 31, 2023. [Online]. Available: https://www.sisifo.info/es/default

[22] "Precio Voluntario para el Pequeño Consumidor (PVPC)." Accessed: Jul. 07, 2025. [Online]. Available: https://www.miteco.gob.es/es/energia/energia-electrica/electricidad/contratacion-suministro/precio-voluntario.html

[23] "Análisis | ESIOS electricidad · datos · transparencia." Accessed: Dec. 05, 2024. [Online]. Available: https://www.esios.ree.es/es/analisis/1739?compare_indicators=1001&vis=1&start_date=23-02-2024T00%3A00&end_date=23-02-2024T23%3A55&compare_start_date=22-02-2024T00%3A00&groupby=hour&zoom=6&latlng=39.99395569397331%2C-3.021240234375

[24] Government of Spain, *Real Decreto 244/2019*. Spain: Boletín Oficial del Estado, 2019, pp. 35674–35719. Accessed: Dec. 05, 2024. [Online]. Available: https://www.boe.es/buscar/doc.php?id=BOE-A-2019-5089

[25] "EUPD Research Reveals Top European Residential Solar Markets and Most Impacting Installers Amidst Booming Market Growth – EUPD Group." Accessed: Jul. 21, 2025. [Online]. Available: https://eupd-group.com/eupd-research-reveals-top-european-residential-solar-markets-and-most-impacting-installers-amidst-booming-market-growth/

SIZING PHOTOVOLTAIC SELF-CONSUMPTION SYSTEMS THROUGH MISMATCH INDEX AND PROFITABILITY ANALYSIS

Kiane Alves e Silva, Luis Miguel Carrasco, Eduardo Lorenzo

Instituto de Energía Solar – Universidad Politécnica de Madrid, Madrid Spain

kiane.asilva@alumnos.upm.es, luismiguel.carrasco@upm.es, antonio.lorenzo@upm.es

ABSTRACT

Context

The transition to clean energy has boosted the adoption of residential PV self-consumption systems. These systems contribute to reduce electricity bills, provide long-term energy price stability, and align with sustainability goals. However, system design is often based only on annual energy balance, ignoring the hourly match between PV generation and demand – a mismatch that reduces both self-consumption and profitability.

Objective

To develop a decision-support approach that identifies PV systems with storage configurations which are technically well-aligned with user demand and economically viable over their lifetime.

Challenge

Conventional indicators (self-consumption ratio, self-sufficiency) do not capture the temporal alignment between generation and demand. As a result, even technically efficient systems may underperform economically.

Contribution

- Introduces the Mismatch Index (MI) to evaluate hourly alignment between availability and demand.
- Integrates MI with profitability metrics (PBP, NPV, IRR, LCOE).
- Validates the approach with a real residential case study in Spain, demonstrating both technical and economic benefits.

Key Definitions

E_X^Y: Energy flow from source x to destination y

$$SEO = E_{PV}^{LOAD} + E_{PV}^{GRID} + E_{ST}^{LOAD}$$

$$C_{PV} = \frac{Annual\ PV\ production}{Annual\ energy\ demand}$$

$$C_{ST} = \frac{Energy\ Storage\ capacity}{Average\ daily\ demand}$$

METHODOLOGY

1 Hourly simulations of Energy Balanced

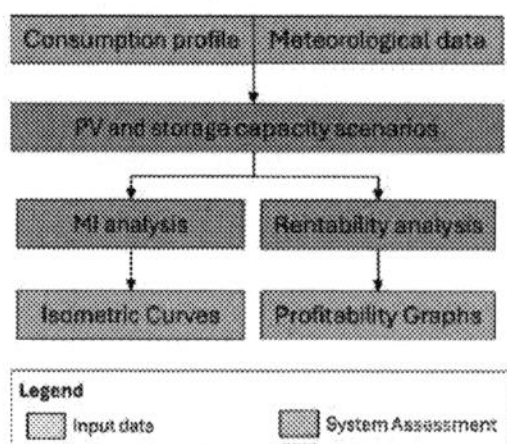

2 Representation of the PV Self-Consumption System

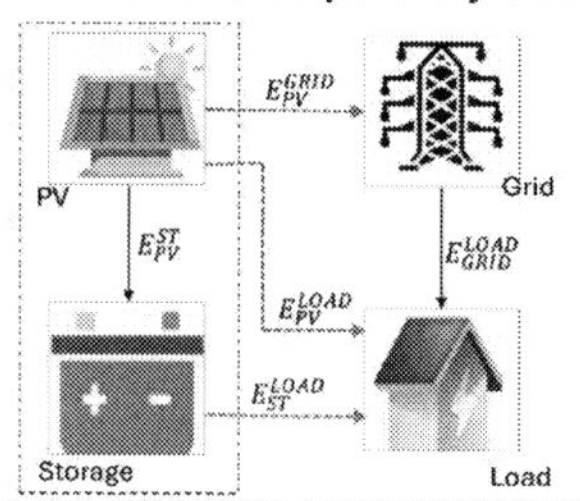

3 Mismatch Index (MI)

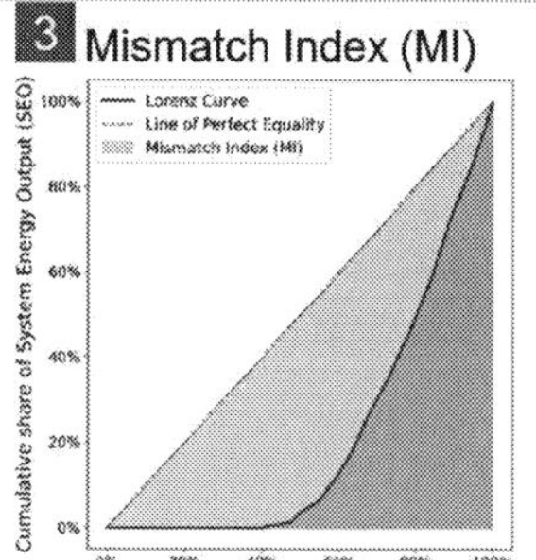

CASE STUDY

Methodology applied to a residential household in La Coruña, Spain:

$Annual\ Demand = 2.99\ MWh$
$Annual\ irradiance = 1.25\ MWh/m^2$

$PV\ system\ (C_{PV} = 1) = 6\ kWp$
$Storage\ Capacity\ (C_{ST} = 1) = 8.19\ kWh$

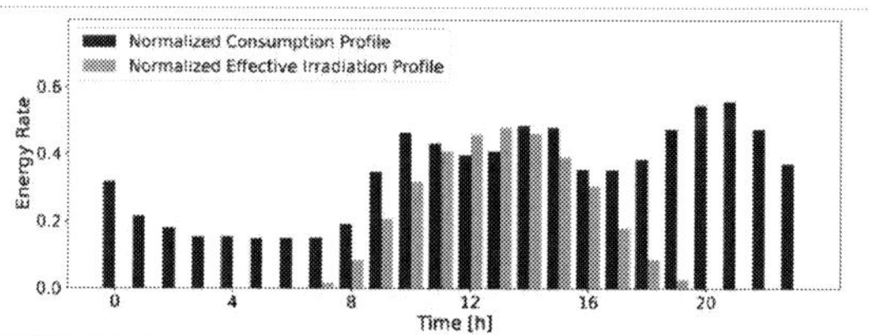

RESULTS

1 Temporal Alignment between Energy Generation and Demand (MI Analysis)

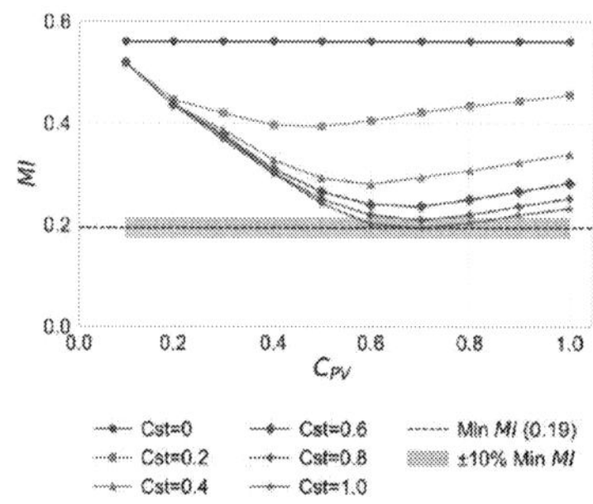

2 Economic Performance and Profitability Indicators (PBP, NPV, IRR, LCOE)

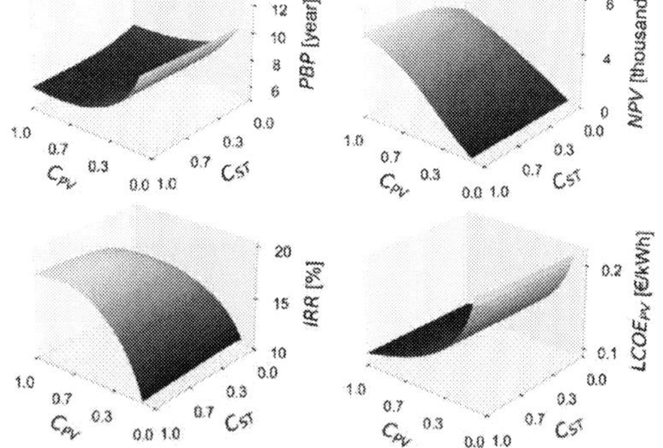

3 System Selection Based on Techno-Economic Criteria (20-years scenario)

The smallest configuration within the MI tolerance band (0.19 ± 10%) have been selected for detailed evaluation:

$PV\ system\ (C_{PV} = 0.65) \rightarrow 3.90\ kWp$
$Storage\ system\ (C_{ST} = 0.8) \rightarrow 6.55 kWh$
$MI = 0.21$

Parameter	Description	Value
CAPEX	Initial cost	€ 3,610
OPEX	Operation and maintenance cost	€ 1,754
Benefits	Savings and revenues	€ 21,838
PBP	Time to recover the initial investment	6.6 years
NPV	Present value of benefits minus costs	€ 4,516
IRR	Discount rate at which NPV = 0	18%
LCOE	Discounted cost per kWh produced	0.12 €/kWh

CONCLUSION

The proposed methodology combined temporal alignment (MI) and economic assessment to ensure reliable PV system sizing that are consistent with user demand while remaining financially viable.

This work has been possible thanks to the Project IND2022/AMB-23718 funded by the Comunidad de Madrid

020440-001

This work has received funding from the European Union under grant agreement No 101076395

METHODOLOGY FOR THE DESIGN OF OFF-GRID PHOTOVOLTAIC SYSTEMS FOR RESIDENTIAL ELECTRIC VEHICLE IN SHARED TRANSPORTATION SERVICES

David Leonardo Rodríguez Salazar, Johann Alexander Hernández Mora
Laboratorio de Investigación en Fuentes Alternativas de Energía (LIFAE), Faculty of Engineering, Universidad Distrital Francisco José de Caldas, Bogotá 110231, Colombia
rsdavidl@udistrital.edu.co, jahernandezm@udistrital.edu.co

ABSTRACT: The growing adoption of electric vehicles (EVs) in dense urban centers such as Bogotá, Colombia poses critical challenges for energy supply, particularly in shared transport schemes with intensive vehicle use. This paper presents a structured methodology to design and validate an off-grid photovoltaic (PV) system for residential EV charging, integrating probabilistic demand modeling and system simulation. A Monte Carlo approach was applied to capture stochastic variability in daily EV consumption, yielding critical percentiles such as P95 (77.4 kWh/day), used as a robust baseline for system sizing. The PV system was dimensioned considering solar resource availability, storage capacity, and conversion efficiencies, with a final configuration of 44 PV modules, a battery bank of 1,500 Ah at 48 V, and an 8 kW inverter. Validation in PV*SOL software confirmed an average daily generation of 74.8 kWh, with a performance ratio of 84.23 %. This value is approximately 3.4 % below the P95 demand. The results demonstrate the feasibility of deploying autonomous PV-based charging infrastructures for EVs in Bogotá, ensuring reliability even under adverse solar conditions and supporting the transition toward sustainable mobility in Latin American cities.
Keywords: Off-grid photovoltaic system, Electric vehicle charging, Monte Carlo simulation, Shared transportation, Bogotá

1 INTRODUCTION

As cities advance toward a greater penetration of electric mobility, the energy demand associated with electric vehicle (EV) charging acquires critical relevance. In dense urban environments such as Bogotá, where shared mobility services represent a growing share of the vehicle fleet, there is a pressing need for decentralized and sustainable energy solutions that enhance reliability while alleviating the burden on the conventional grid.

In parallel, recent developments in digital tools and simulation techniques enable the optimization of renewable energy system sizing. Monte Carlo simulation has proven to be a valuable resource for capturing the stochastic variability of electricity demand in both residential and industrial applications. Its application in the field of electric mobility allows for the estimation of critical consumption scenarios, represented by percentiles such as P95, which ensure system robustness.

Similarly, the deployment of stand-alone photovoltaic systems has shown to be a viable alternative to strengthening charging infrastructure in areas with limited grid availability [1]. When properly sized and evaluated under reliability and cost-efficiency criteria, these systems can meet the daily EV demand even under adverse conditions of solar radiation or high usage requirements.

This paper proposes a structured methodology in three stages: (1) probabilistic modeling of EV energy demand through Monte Carlo simulation, (2) sizing of a stand-alone photovoltaic system with storage and energy conversion components, and (3) performance validation through software analysis. The objective is to provide a replicable methodological framework that contributes to the consolidation of sustainable personal charging infrastructures in Bogotá and other cities facing similar mobility and energy challenges.

2 METHODOLOGY

The proposed methodology is developed in three integrated stages, enabling the progression from probabilistic demand modeling to the validation of a stand-alone photovoltaic system. To illustrate this process, a flow diagram (Figure 1) is included, summarizing the main phases: data collection, Monte Carlo simulation, system sizing, and software-based validation. This framework provides a clear overview of the sequence of steps and the iterative interactions between stages, ensuring that the final design achieves both robustness and efficiency.

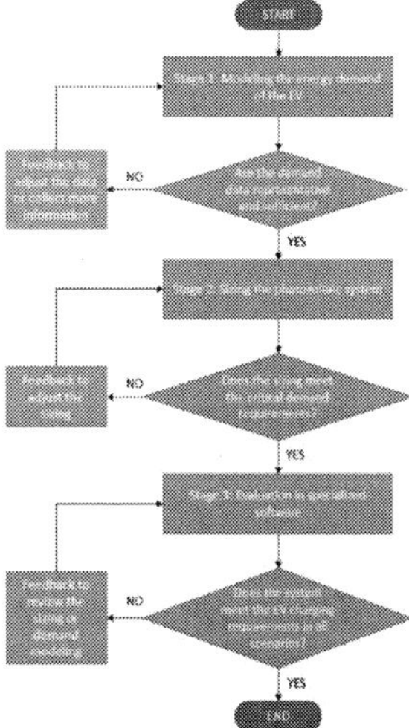

Figure 1. Methodology for an Off-Grid Photovoltaic System for Charging Residential EVs Used in Shared Transportation.

2.1 Energy demand estimation

The daily consumption of an EV can depend on random variables such as traveled distance, energy efficiency (kWh/km), and the use of auxiliary systems. To represent this variability, the Monte Carlo method is employed, as applied in energy studies such as [2], where it is used to assess the reliability of renewable-based systems. In that context, Monte Carlo simulation plays a crucial role in modeling probabilistic failure states and analyzing network capacity through power flow studies. Similarly, [3] applies Monte Carlo methods to demand estimation in charging stations, where random scenarios of connected vehicles and their state of charge are modeled to analyze the impact on the power grid, even under the integration of photovoltaic generation.

Accordingly, considering the variables mentioned above, the daily demanded energy is proposed to be modeled as:

$$E_d = \frac{D \cdot \eta_{EV} \cdot (1 + \alpha)}{\eta_{ch} \cdot \eta_{bat} \cdot \eta_{inv}}$$

Where D is the daily traveled distance [km], η_{EV} is the EV efficiency [kWh/km], α is the auxiliary consumption factor, and η_{ch}, η_{bat}, η_{inv} represent the efficiencies of the charge controller, battery, and inverter, respectively.

For this study, the following probability distributions were considered:

- Daily distance (D): Based on a survey of 20 shared-mobility drivers, a truncated normal distribution with a mean of 230 km/day was estimated. For the purposes of this study, two standard deviations were considered: 50 km for EV X and 30 km for EV Y. This selection is justified because the traveled distance exhibits a symmetric behavior around a mean, but with natural limits (negative or excessively high values are unrealistic under typical urban use). Hence, a truncated normal distribution is suitable to capture both daily variability and the restriction of values outside the realistic range.

- Energy efficiency (η_{EV}): The energy efficiency of electric vehicles depends on factors such as vehicle weight, driving conditions, and the technology of the battery and powertrain. Based on specialized literature such as [4], a bounded range of specific consumption can be established (0.13–0.23 kWh/km). However, these studies do not provide sufficient data to estimate a normal distribution with robust parameters. Nevertheless, a more representative or modal value of 0.15 kWh/km has been identified under urban operating conditions, as proposed in [5]. Under these circumstances, a triangular distribution was adopted, as it allows capturing the highest probability of occurrence around the modal value while also reflecting uncertainty toward the extreme values of the range.

- Auxiliar factor (α): The energy consumption associated with EV auxiliary systems (air conditioning, ventilation, lighting, signaling, among others) depends on traffic and environmental conditions. International studies such as [6] have shown that, at low speeds, in congested traffic, or under extreme weather, auxiliaries can double the effective energy consumption and drastically reduce driving range, whereas at higher speeds their relative impact decreases due to aerodynamic drag dominance. In the Colombian context, an experimental study in Bogotá [7], based on the model of Fiori [8], considered a fixed auxiliary consumption of 700 W, equivalent to approximately 18% of the total EV consumption under urban conditions (≈35 Wh/km additional). Based on this evidence, a triangular distribution in the range 0.1–0.2, with a mode at 0.15, was adopted as the

statistical representation of the auxiliary factor (α). This choice captures the higher probability of moderate consumption in typical Bogotá conditions, while reflecting the uncertainty and variability associated with dense traffic and adverse weather scenarios.

- Efficiency values (η_{ch}, η_{bat}, η_{inv}): To represent the losses in the charging and discharging chain, the product of partial efficiencies in series (controller/charger, battery, and inverter) was modeled. Empirical values from applied literature were adopted: battery efficiency (η_{bat}) = 0.90 [7], inverter efficiency (η_{inv}) = 0.98, and charge controller efficiency (η_{ch}) = 0.91 [9].

Consequently, 10,000 iterations of the Monte Carlo simulation were performed, obtaining daily demand distributions and critical percentiles (P50, P80, P95). These values are used in the next stage of system sizing.

2.2 Photovoltaic System Sizing

The system sizing is based on the energy demand estimated at the P95 percentile, following the methodology for stand-alone systems proposed in [9]. This procedure aims to ensure reliability under scenarios of maximum consumption demand. The process comprises the following stages:

- Solar resource assessment: The solar contribution is determined from the incident solar radiation characteristics of Bogotá. For this study, the geographical location corresponding to coordinates 4.61280100, -74.14294276 was considered as the reference point representing the specific case study site. The values of solar radiation obtained are presented in Table I of chapter 3, which allow estimating the required energy input for system sizing in the most unfavorable month.

- Peak power: The nominal power of the PV modules required to cover the daily energy demand under the least favorable solar conditions in Bogotá is calculated using the following equation:

$$P_{GEN} = 1.2 \cdot \frac{E_d}{HRS}$$

Where, E_d is the daily energy demand (resulting from the Monte Carlo simulation), and HRS represents the solar radiation hours (the value in hours equivalent to the incident solar radiation). On the other hand, the series configuration of the photovoltaic modules is defined by the following equation:

$$N_S = \frac{V_{oc-reg}}{V_{oc}}$$

Where, V_{oc-reg} is the maximum open-circuit voltage regulated by the charge controller, and V_{oc} is the open-circuit voltage of the selected photovoltaic module.

For the parallel configuration of the photovoltaic modules, the following equation is used:

$$N_P = \frac{P_{GEN}}{P_m \cdot N_S}$$

Where P_m is the panel power rating (as provided by the manufacturer).

Finally, the total number of panels is given by:

$$N_T = N_P \cdot N_S$$

- Battery capacity: The sizing of the battery bank is carried out under the criterion that it must be capable of supplying at least half a day of autonomy. This ensures coverage during periods when the photovoltaic modules do not generate sufficient energy, as well as during nighttime hours when shared transportation services are also in operation. For safety considerations, an additional 20% margin is included. Accordingly, the usable capacity of the battery bank is defined as:

$$C_u = \frac{1.2 \cdot E_d \cdot A}{V_n} \ [Ah]$$

Where A is the maximum number of consecutive days during which the installation will be able to meet the energy demand under unfavorable conditions, and V_n is the nominal voltage of the installation. It should be noted that E_d must be expressed in Wh. Once the usable capacity is defined, the nominal capacity of the battery bank is determined as:

$$C_n = \frac{C_u}{PD_{máx}} \ [Ah]$$

Where $PD_{máx}$ is the maximum allowable depth of discharge, established at 0.7.

- Charge controller: The selection of the charge controller is defined according to the following equation:

$$I_{reg} = 1.25 \cdot \sum_{i=1}^{n} I_{sci}$$

Where I_{sci} is the short-circuit current multiplied by the number of strings connected in parallel.

- Inverter: The sizing of the inverter must be based on the maximum power (kW) rather than the daily energy consumption (kWh). It is identified that the peak power required by the critical load—in this case, the internal EV charger—is in the range of 6–8 kW, according to slow-charging specifications for EVs.

With the above considerations, the general schematic of the photovoltaic system components is presented in Figure 2.

2.3 Evaluation of the Defined Photovoltaic System

The preliminary configuration is validated using PV*SOL software, with the objective of verifying that the proposed design meets the estimated energy demand at the P95 percentile under Bogotá's specific solar radiation and climatic conditions. However, PV*SOL does not provide a predefined topology for EVs in stand-alone systems. Therefore, the analysis is based on the general topology of an autonomous PV system, as shown in Figure 3.

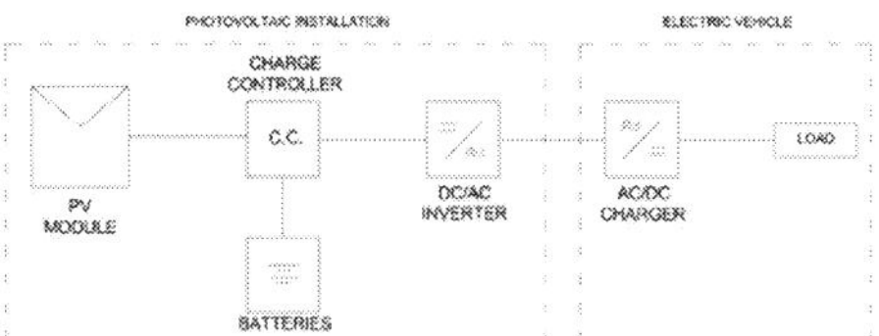

Figure 2. General diagram of an Off-Grid Photovoltaic System for charging residential EVs used in shared transportation.

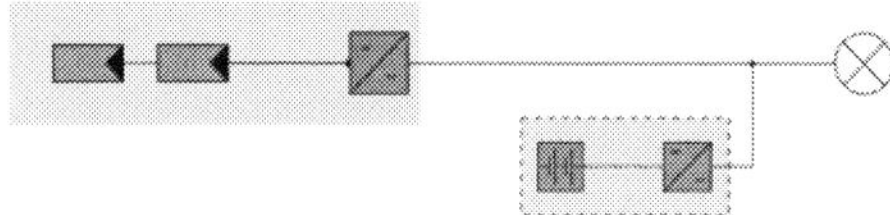

Figure 3. Topology in PV*SOL for a stand-alone system.

Although the theoretical scheme of the stand-alone system proposed in Figure 2 follows a DC-coupled topology—where a charge controller regulates the energy flow from the solar panels to the batteries—for the simulation in PV*SOL, it is necessary to adapt this design to the AC-coupled model (see Figure 3) employed by the software.

In this model, both the PV array and the battery bank are connected to a common AC bus through their respective inverters (a dedicated inverter for the PV modules and a bidirectional inverter/charger for the batteries).

This approach is conceptually different but functionally equivalent for evaluating the energy balance, system autonomy, and battery state of charge, which are the main objectives of the simulation. The overall system efficiency in PV*SOL accounts for the conversion losses of these inverters, providing results that are representative of real-world operation. In this way, the system is ensured to meet the robustness and reliability requirements prior to its actual implementation.

3 CASE STUDY: BOGOTÁ, COLOMBIA

The analysis focuses on Bogotá, Colombia, a city located at 2,640 m above sea level, with an average annual temperature of 13.6 °C, ranging between 4 °C and 21 °C. These climatic conditions are essential for applying temperature corrections to the photovoltaic modules.

Regarding the city's solar potential, the following table presents the estimated average values of solar radiation, based on different databases and analyzed over the twelve months of the year within a three-year period (2022–2024).

In terms of mobility, Bogotá shows a growing adoption of EVs in the private segment, although their presence in shared transport and remunerated services— such as electric taxis [10]— has gained relevance in recent years. Private EV usage has also begun to integrate into these schemes, as suggested by the Uber platform in [11], which adds value to this study by proposing a methodology to size stand-alone photovoltaic systems.

For the analysis, two random EV scenarios were defined, modeled under an intensive ride-sharing scheme with daily travel distances of approximately 230 km/day, emulating continuous usage patterns typical of collaborative services. This approach enables the estimation of EV energy consumption in high-turnover urban contexts. The technical parameters applied are based on surveys conducted with local EV users and manufacturer specifications.

Table I: Average Solar Radiation in Bogotá, Colombia

Month	Solar Radiation (KWh/m²-day)		
	PVWATS	METEONORM	Average
Jan	6.22	5.00	5.61
Feb	5.53	4.86	5.19
Mar	4.77	4.65	4.71
Apr	4.16	5.10	4.63
May	4.07	5.19	4.63
Jun	4.07	5.17	4.62
Jul	4.25	4.94	4.59
Aug	4.57	4.84	4.70
Sep	4.82	4.67	4.74
Oct	4.97	4.45	4.71
Nov	5.02	4.53	4.78
Dec	5.63	5.06	5.35
Average	4.84	4.87	4.86

4 RESULTS AND DISCUSSION

4.1 Energy demand

The Monte Carlo simulation enabled the estimation of the daily charging demand of an EV operating under a ride-sharing scheme, considering an average travel distance of 230 km/day and the study parameters defined in Section 2.1.

Figure 4 presents the probability histogram of the daily energy demand, highlighting the relevant percentiles for the sizing of the photovoltaic system.

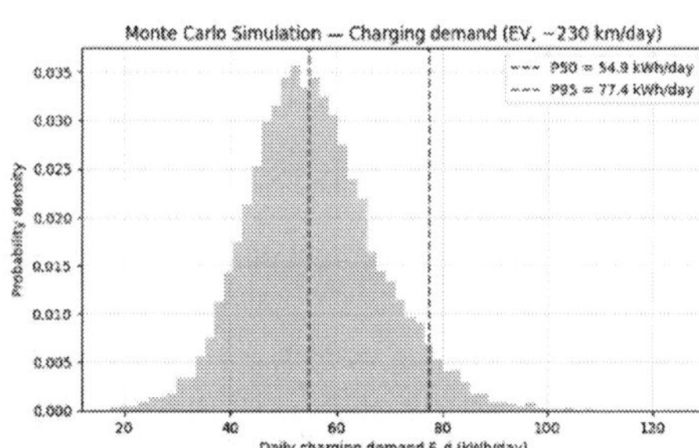

Figure 4. Monte Carlo simulation results to estimate the energy demand required for the EV.

The main statistical results obtained are summarized in the Table II.

Table II: Statistical Results of the Monte Carlo Simulation.

Indicator	Value [kWh/day]
Mean	55.7
Median (P50)	54.9
Standard Deviation	12.3
Percentile 80 (P80)	54.9
Percentile 95 (P95)	77.4

According to the distribution, the mean and the median are very close (55.7 and 54.9 kWh/day, respectively), indicating an approximately symmetric distribution around the central value. However, the presence of a right-hand tail reflects days with significantly higher consumption, reaching values of up to ~108 kWh/day in extreme scenarios.

In particular:

- P50 (54.9 kWh/day) represents the typical energy demand scenario.

- P80 (65.2 kWh/day) defines a more demanding scenario, with 80% reliability coverage.

- P95 (77.4 kWh/day) corresponds to a critical high-demand scenario, which is used for robust PV system sizing, since designing for this value ensures coverage of 95% of possible cases.

The variability in daily demand reflects the influence of factors such as travel distance, driving style, and vehicle efficiency, which justifies the use of probabilistic simulations to achieve a more realistic sizing of the energy system.

4.2 Photovoltaic System Sizing

Based on the average solar radiation values presented in Table I, and considering a daily energy demand of 77.4 kWh/day, the ratio between available solar radiation and energy demand is applied to identify the most unfavorable month in terms of solar resource. This month is then used as the reference for system sizing. The results of this ratio are presented in Table III.

Table III: Most unfavorable month for solar resource in Bogotá, Colombia.

Month	Solar Radiation (HRS)	Energy demand (E_d)	Ratio HRS/E_d
Jan	5.61	77.4	0.0725
Feb	5.19	77.4	0.0671
Mar	4.71	77.4	0.0608
Apr	4.63	77.4	0.0598
May	4.63	77.4	0.0598
Jun	4.62	77.4	0.0597
Jul	4.59	77.4	0.0593
Aug	4.70	77.4	0.0608
Sep	4.74	77.4	0.0613
Oct	4.71	77.4	0.0609
Nov	4.78	77.4	0.0617
Dec	5.35	77.4	0.0691

Accordingly, under the conditions of the most unfavorable month (July), the required peak power is calculated as:

$$P_{GEN} = 1.2 \cdot \frac{77.4\,kWh}{4.59\,h} = 20.235\,kW$$

Considering the use of EcoGreen photovoltaic modules rated at 550 Wp (Model EGE-550W-144M(M10)), with an open-circuit voltage V_{oc} de 49.68 V y and estimating a regulated open-circuit voltage V_{oc-reg} de 450 V, the required number of modules in series is obtained as:

$$N_S = \frac{450\,V}{49.68\,V} = 9.06 \approx 9$$

With the above, the distribution of photovoltaic modules in parallel is given by:

$$N_P = \frac{20.235}{(9 \cdot 0.550)} = 4.08 \approx 4$$

Thus, the total number of photovoltaic modules is calculated as:

$$N_T = 4 \cdot 9 = 36$$

However, 36 modules rated at 550 Wp yield only 19.8 kWp, which falls below the required P_{GEN}. Therefore, in order to ensure a sufficiently robust photovoltaic system configuration, the value was rounded up to 44 modules, arranged as four parallel strings of nine modules in series, plus one parallel string of eight modules in series.

$$N_T \approx 44$$

For the battery bank sizing, the usable capacity is defined as:

$$C_u = \frac{1.2 \cdot 77,400 \cdot 0.5}{48} = 967.5 \ [Ah]$$

The nominal capacity of the battery bank is then defined as:

$$C_n = \frac{967.5}{0.7} = 1,382.1429 \ [Ah]$$

If Maxpower 250-12 batteries are considered, the following configuration is required:

- Connection of four batteries in series to establish the system nominal voltage of 48 V.
- Connection of six parallel strings to attain a total capacity of 1,500 Ah.

To define the charge controller and the inverter for the proposed photovoltaic system, the following temperature correction for the selected photovoltaic module is considered.

The data required for these corrections are presented below:

- Tmin = 4 °C.

- Tmax = 21 °C.

- NOCT EGE-550W-144M(M10) = 45 °C.

- Voc EGE-550W-144M(M10) = 49.68 V.

- Isc EGE-550W-144M(M10) = 14.01 A.

- Temperature Coefficient of Isc EGE-550W-144M(M10) = 0.048 %/°C.

- Temperature Coefficient of Voc EGE-550W-144M(M10) = -0.28 %/°C.

- Temperature Coefficient of Pmax EGE-550W-144M(M10) = -0.35 %/°C.

- Pmax STC EGE-550W-144M(M10) = 550 W.

- G average for the study area = 1,197.79 W/m².

Thus, the temperature delta for the photovoltaic cell must first be defined. To this end, the cell temperature under site-specific conditions is determined and then subtracted from the standard test condition (STC) reference value of 25 °C.

$$T_{C_{amb}} = T_{amb} + \frac{NOCT - 20}{800} G_{avg}$$

- Case 1: Minimum temperature

$$T_{C_{amb}} = 4\,°C + \frac{45\,°C - 20\,°C}{800\ W/m^2} 1,197.79\ W/m^2$$
$$T_{C_{amb}} = 41.43\,°C$$

$$\Delta T_{min} = 41.43\,°C - 25\,°C = 16.43\,°C$$

- Case 2: Maximum temperature

$$T_{C_{amb}} = 21\,°C + \frac{45\,°C - 20\,°C}{800\ W/m^2} 1,197.79\ W/m^2$$
$$T_{C_{amb}} = 58.43\,°C$$

$$\Delta T_{max} = 58.43\,°C - 25\,°C = 33.43\,°C$$

Subsequently, the values of Isc, Voc, and Pmax are corrected for each temperature condition, also considering the adjustment for the average available irradiance. The general equations are as follows:

$$Isc_{Gavg} = \frac{G_{avg}}{G_{STC}} * Isc_{STC}$$

$$\Delta I = \Delta T * \text{temperature coefficient of Isc of PV module}$$

$$Isc_{new} = Isc_{Gavg} \pm \Delta I$$

$$Voc_{Gavg} \cong Voc_{STC}$$

$$\Delta V = \Delta T * \text{temperature coefficient of Voc of PV module}$$

$$Voc_{new} = Voc_{STC} \pm \Delta V$$

$$Pmax_{Gavg} = \frac{G_{avg}}{G_{STC}} * Pmax_{STC}$$

$$\Delta P = \Delta T * \text{temperature coefficient of Pmax of PV module}$$

$$Pmax_{new} = Pmax_{Gavg} \pm \Delta P$$

Consequently:

- Case 1.1: Isc correction for Tmin and G average:

$$Isc_{Gavg} = \frac{1,197.79\ W/m^2}{1,000\ W/m^2} * 14.01\ A = 16.78\ A$$

$$\Delta I = 16.43\,°C * 0.048\ \%/°C = 0.789\%$$

$$Isc_{new} = 16.78\ A + 0.789\% = 16.91\ A$$

- Case 1.2: Voc correction for Tmin and G average:

$$Voc_{Gavg} \cong 49.68\ V$$

$$\Delta V = 16.43\ °C * -0.28\%/°C = -4.6\%$$

$$Voc_{new} = 49.68\ V - 4.6\% = 47.39\ V$$

- Case 1.3: Pmax correction for Tmin and G average:

$$Pmax_{Gnew} = \frac{1{,}197.79\ W/m^2}{1{,}000\ W/m^2} * 550\ W = 658.78\ W$$

$$\Delta P = 16.43\ °C * -0.35\%/°C = -5.75\%$$

$$Pmax_{new} = 658.78\ W - 5.75\% = 620.89\ W$$

- Case 2.1: Isc correction for Tmax and G average:

$$Isc_{Gavg} = \frac{1{,}197.79\ W/m^2}{1{,}000\ W/m^2} * 14.01\ A = 16.78\ A$$

$$\Delta I = 33.43\ °C * 0.048\ \%/°C = 1.605\%$$

$$Isc_{new} = 16.78\ A + 1.605\% = 17.05\ A$$

- Case 2.2: Voc correction for Tmax and G average:

$$Voc_{Gavg} \cong 49.68\ V$$

$$\Delta V = 33.43\ °C * -0.28\%/°C = -9.36\%$$

$$Voc_{new} = 49.68\ V - 9.36\% = 45.03\ V$$

- Case 2.3: Pmax correction for Tmax and G average:

$$Pmax_{Gavg} = \frac{1{,}197.79\ W/m^2}{1{,}000\ W/m^2} * 550\ W = 658.78\ W$$

$$\Delta P = 33.43\ °C * -0.35\%/°C = -11.70\%$$

$$Pmax_{new} = 658.78\ W - 11.70\% = 581.7\ W$$

Based on the above, the selection of the charge controller is therefore conditioned by:

$$I_{reg} = 1.25 \cdot 5 \cdot 17.05\ A = 106.5625\ A$$

However, due to the five parallel strings, it is considered appropriate to use two controllers of the Victron SmartSolar MPPT RS 450/200-MC4 model, enabling the connection of four strings of nine modules in series with a maximum Voc of 426.51 V, and one string of eight modules in series with a Voc of 379.12 V.

Finally, to ensure the operation of the stand-alone photovoltaic system designed for EV charging, the Victron Energy MultiPlus-II 48/10000/140 inverter was selected. This unit, with an output power of 8 kW (10 kVA), is sized to meet the maximum demand of the EV onboard charger (estimated at 7.4 kW), thereby guaranteeing stable operation even during transient demand peaks. Its native integration with the previously selected Victron MPPT controllers allows for unified system management, maximizing energy efficiency and enabling remote monitoring.

All parameters corrected for temperature remain within the limits defined for both the charge controller and the inverter.

Based on the above, under the theoretical scheme of the dimensioned photovoltaic system, the daily energy production is:

$$E_{theo\ day} = HRS_{avg} \cdot N_T \cdot P_{máx\_mod}$$
$$E_{theo\ day} = 4.86\ h \cdot 44 \cdot 0.550\ kWp$$
$$E_{theo\ day} = 117.612\ kWh/day$$

4.3 Photovoltaic System Modeling in PV*SOL Software

To contrast the theoretical performance of the proposed photovoltaic installation with a practical scenario, the system was simulated in PV*SOL under the scheme presented in Figure 3. The objective was to determine the actual value of the energy generated by the system, which, according to the software, amounts to 27,112 kWh/year, equivalent to 74.78 kWh/day.

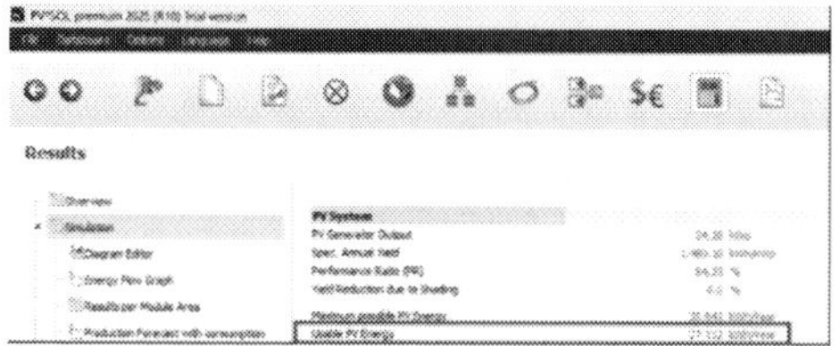

Figure 5. Results of the Simulation of the Stand-alone Photovoltaic System in PV*SOL Software.

The comparison between the theoretical results and the PV*SOL simulation reveals a significant difference in the energy generated by the photovoltaic system. In the theoretical model, without considering system losses, the estimated daily production was 117.612 kWh/day. In contrast, the PV*SOL simulation, which accounts for losses due to orientation, shading, temperature, component efficiency, wiring, and other real operating factors, reduced production to 74.8 kWh/day, representing approximately 36% less than the theoretical estimate.

The Performance Ratio (PR) of 84.23% obtained in PV*SOL is consistent with real values observed in photovoltaic installations under similar conditions, thereby validating the practical adjustment against the idealized calculation.

When comparing generation with the estimated demand:

- The theoretically designed system would comfortably cover the P95 percentile (77.4 kWh/day), with a margin of 52%.

- However, in the realistic PV*SOL scenario, the average daily generation of 74.8 kWh/day falls 3.4% short of the P95 demand, although it sufficiently covers the P50 (54.9 kWh/day) and P80 (65.2 kWh/day) percentiles.

This implies that the system, as currently sized, would reliably cover 80% of days; nevertheless, under critical P95 scenarios, energy deficits could occur, requiring either additional storage capacity (larger battery bank) or backup from an auxiliary source (e.g., grid or generator).

Thus, the PV*SOL simulation allows for a more accurate adjustment of performance expectations and highlights the importance of considering real operational losses in system sizing. If the objective is to ensure P95 coverage, the following measures are recommended:

- Moderate increase in the installed PV module capacity.

- Optimization of tilt and orientation configuration.

- Expansion of storage capacity to cover days with insufficient generation.

5 CONCLUSIONS

- The Monte Carlo simulation enabled the capture of part of the stochastic variability in electric vehicle (EV) demand under ride-sharing schemes, providing critical values (P50, P80, and P95) that strengthen the energy sizing process.

- The P95 percentile (77.4 kWh/day) was consolidated as the reference scenario for designing a robust photovoltaic (PV) system, ensuring 95% coverage of consumption situations for ride-sharing trips averaging 230 km/day.

- The comparison between the theoretical model (117.6 kWh/day) and the PV*SOL simulation (74.8 kWh/day) highlighted the importance of accounting for real-world losses associated with shading, orientation, component efficiency, and operational conditions.

- The Performance Ratio of 84.23% validated in PV*SOL demonstrates that the designed system is technically feasible and capable of meeting the critical EV demand, contributing to reduced dependence on the conventional grid.

- The installation of the system requires approximately 114 m² of available area, which represents a limitation in Bogotá, where households with this amount of space are typically located in multi-unit residential properties (condominiums). This restricts access for individual households to stand-alone systems of this scale.

- Given the spatial limitation, it is pertinent to consider grid-connected alternatives, which allow for surplus sharing, reduce the individual area requirement, and leverage existing electrical infrastructure as backup.

- The proposed methodology is replicable in other Latin American cities facing similar challenges in mobility and energy, contributing to the consolidation of sustainable and decentralized charging infrastructure solutions.

6 REFERENCES

[1] A. Villamarín Jácome, M. Saltos, and J. Echever, "Dimensionamiento Óptimo de Sistemas Fotovoltaicos y Baterías en Entornos Residenciales para Reducir la Dependencia de la Infraestructura Eléctrica Centralizada," *Revista Técnica "energía,"* vol. 21, no. 2, pp. 60–68, Jan. 2025, doi: 10.37116/revistaenergia.v21.n2.2025.685.

[2] A. C. Angulo Hurtado, " Análisis de la Penetración de Energías Renovables en la confiabilidad de los sistemas eléctricos utilizando simulación de Montecarlo," Artículos profesionales de alto nivel, Pontifica Universidad Católica del Ecuador, Esmeraldas - Ecuador, 2024.

[3] J. Lascano, L. Chiza, R. Saraguro, C. Quinatoa, and J. Tapia, "Estimación de la Demanda de una Estación de Carga para Vehículos Eléctricos Mediante la Aplicación de Métodos Probabilísticos," *Revista Técnica "energía,"* vol. 20, no. 1, pp. 52–64, Jul. 2023, doi: 10.37116/revistaenergia.v20.n1.2023.569.

[4] International Energy Agency, "Global EV Outlook 2024 Moving towards increased affordability," Apr. 2024.

[5] I. Sanz Arnaiz, "Análisis de la evolución y el impacto de los vehículos eléctricos en la economía europea," Trabajo final de grado, Universidad Pontificia Comillas Madrid, Madrid, 2015.

[6] I. Evtimov, R. Ivanov, and M. Sapundjiev, "Energy consumption of auxiliary systems of electric cars," *MATEC Web of Conferences*, vol. 133, p. 06002, Nov. 2017, doi: 10.1051/matecconf/201713306002.

[7] S. Torres Franco, M. M. Suárez Pradilla, I. C. Durán Tovar, and A. R. Marulanda Guerra, "Evaluation of the energy consumption of an electric vehicle in the city of Bogotá," *Revista de la Escuela Colombiana de Ingeniería*, vol. 120, 2020.

[8] C. Fiori, K. Ahn, and H. A. Rakha, "Power-based electric vehicle energy consumption model: Model development and validation," *Appl Energy*, vol. 168, pp. 257–268, Apr. 2016, doi: 10.1016/j.apenergy.2016.01.097.

[9] P. Pineda, "Guía de dimensionado simple de una instalación solar fotovoltaica Off-Grid," 2023.

[10] E. Mayorga Rincón, "Esta es la nueva flota de taxis eléctricos que llegó a Bogotá: se caracterizan porque su color no es amarillo como los convencionales," *El Tiempo*, Aug. 06, 2025.

[11] Uber Colombia, "Comfort Electric de Uber: Vehículos 100% eléctricos en Bogotá," Uber Newsroom.

Methodology for the Design of Off-Grid Photovoltaic Systems for Residential Electric Vehicle in Shared Transportation Services

David Leonardo Rodríguez and Johann Alexander Hernández

LIFAE, Faculty of Engineering, Universidad Distrital Francisco José de Caldas, Bogotá, Colombia.

Abstract

The increasing adoption of electric vehicles (EVs) in Bogotá poses significant energy challenges, particularly under shared transportation schemes. This study proposes a methodology for the design and validation of an off-grid photovoltaic (PV) charging system for residential EVs, integrating probabilistic demand modeling and simulation in PV*SOL. The methodology combines Monte Carlo simulations (10,000 iterations) with technical dimensioning of PV arrays, battery storage, and power electronics. The designed system, consisting of 44 PV modules, a 1,500 Ah battery bank (48 V), and 8 kW inverter, achieved an average simulated generation of 74.8 kWh/day, which is approximately 3.4 % below the critical demand level of 77.4 kWh/day (P95). The results confirm the technical feasibility of off-grid PV charging infrastructures to support sustainable mobility in urban contexts.

Methodology

The proposed methodology integrates probabilistic demand modeling with technical sizing and simulation of an off-grid photovoltaic system for residential EV charging. It is developed in three integrated stages that allow transitioning from demand modeling to the validation of the PV system. To illustrate this process, a flowchart (Figure 1) is included, summarizing the main phases: data collection, Monte Carlo simulation, system sizing, and software-based validation. This scheme provides a clear overview of the sequential steps and the iterative interactions between stages, ensuring robustness and efficiency in the final design.

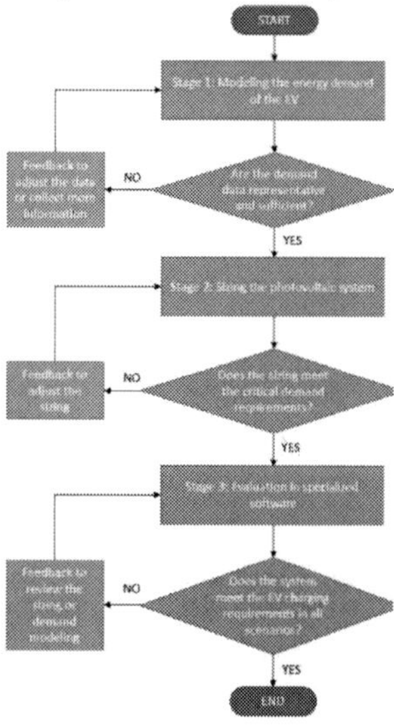

Figure. 1. Methodology for an Off-Grid Photovoltaic System for Charging Residential EVs Used in Shared Transportation.

Step 1. Energy Demand Estimation:

Daily EV charging demand was modeled through Monte Carlo simulations (10,000 iterations), based on urban driving profiles under shared-use conditions. Representative statistical percentiles (P50, P80, P95) were extracted to account for variability in vehicle usage.

The estimated daily charging energy E_d was calculated as:

$$E_d = \frac{D \cdot \eta_{EV} \cdot (1 + \alpha)}{\eta_{ch} \cdot \eta_{bat} \cdot \eta_{inv}}$$

Where D is the daily driving distance [km], η_{EV} is the EV efficiency [kWh/km], α is the auxiliary systems consumption factor, and $\eta_{ch}, \eta_{bat}, \eta_{inv}$ are the efficiencies of the charge controller, battery, and inverter, respectively.

This formulation was extended using Monte Carlo simulation to generate a distribution of daily demand values, which were then used for system dimensioning.

Step 2. System Sizing:

The PV array, battery bank, charge controller and inverter capacity were dimensioned according to the P95 demand value (77.4 kWh/day), ensuring 95% supply reliability.

Step 3. Simulation and Validation:

The system was validated in PV*SOL using Bogotá's solar resource conditions. The effective performance ratio (PR) were obtained from the simulation.

Results

Energy Demand Estimation

Results showed an average of 55.7 kWh/day, with a typical scenario at P50 = 54.9 kWh/day, a more demanding case at P80 = 65.2 kWh/day, and a critical high-demand case at P95 = 77.4 kWh/day. Extreme situations reached up to ~108 kWh/day. For design purposes, the P95 value was selected to ensure 95% supply reliability.

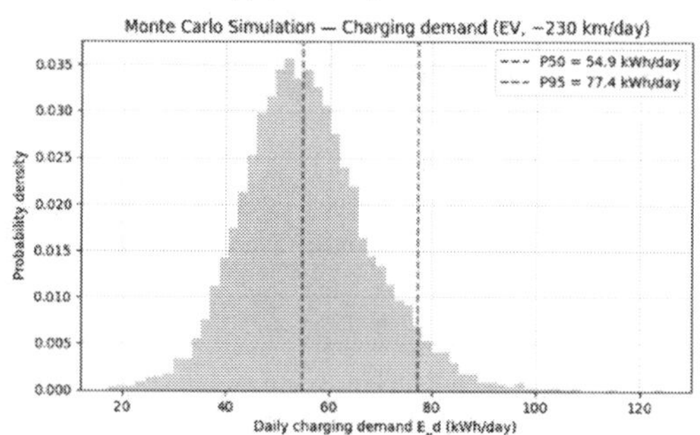

Figure. 2. Monte Carlo simulation results to estimate the energy demand required for the EV.

PV Sizing

The system was dimensioned using the P95 demand (77.4 kWh/day) to ensure 95% supply reliability. This resulted in a required peak power of 20.235 kWp, covered by 44 EcoGreen 550 Wp modules (≈24.2 kWp). The storage system consists of a 48 V, 1,500 Ah battery bank (Maxpower 250-12) arranged in 4S6P, providing sufficient autonomy. Charge regulation is achieved with two Victron SmartSolar MPPT 450/200 controllers, while a Victron MultiPlus-II 10 kVA inverter ensures stable operation of the EV charger (7.4 kW).

Simulation Output

- Theoretical PV generation: 117.6 kWh/day
- PV*SOL simulation output: 74.8 kWh/day
- Performance Ratio simulation output: 84.23%

The system configuration reliably meets P50 and P80 demand and nearly covers P95. Minor shortfalls are expected during low-solar months, mitigable through hybridization or demand management.

Summary

- Probabilistic modeling via Monte Carlo allowed incorporating demand uncertainty, ensuring a robust sizing approach under variable EV usage.
- The system configuration adequately meets average and high-demand scenarios (P50, P80). However, it fails to fully cover the P95 demand, exposing a limitation under peak consumption conditions.
- The achieved PR of 84.23% demonstrates the technical feasibility of the system under Bogotá's solar resource.
- The main constraint lies in the required installation area (~114 m²), which is rarely available in individual households, particularly in multifamily housing units.
- Considering these spatial and demand-coverage limitations, grid-connected or hybrid PV systems emerge as more viable alternatives. The methodology remains transferable to evaluate PV-based EV charging infrastructures in other urban contexts with similar energy and mobility challenges.

PERFORMANCE EVALUATION OF INSTALLED BIFACIAL PV MODULES: TOWARDS THE GROUND ALBEDO ENHANCEMENT

Dounia Dahlioui[1*], Steve Schading[1], Ingar Alvaro Høye[2], Tore Sandnes Vehus[1]
[1]University of Agder, Department of Engineering Sciences, 4879 Grimstad, Norway
[2]Solkraft Sør AS, 4532 Øyslebø, Norway
*e-mail of corresponding author: dounia.dahlioui@uia.no

ABSTRACT: The growing deployment of bifacial photovoltaic (bPV) modules in large-scale utility PV power plants is driven by their potential to achieve higher energy output with minimal additional cost. The present study evaluates the performance of bPV modules installed in Grimstad, Norway, by analyzing their specific yield and assessing the impact of reflector integration on energy gains. A detailed review of ground reflectors used to enhance albedo and, consequently, bPV performance is presented. Reflectors were tested under real outdoor conditions to determine their effectiveness in improving bPV output. The installed system demonstrated substantial performance under Nordic conditions, achieving an annual specific yield of approximately 1282 kWh/kWp. The study evaluated two reflector types: white reflectors showed superior stability and consistent power gains, whereas semi-mirrored reflectors provided variable performance due to mismatch effects from uneven rear-side illumination. Experimental results indicated limited gains of 0.86-1.14% under optimal configurations, with some approaches yielding negative performance for semi-mirrored reflectors. These findings suggest that reflector implementation may not be economically viable for standard bPV installations until significant cost reductions are achieved. The study highlights the importance of experimental validation over simulation-based predictions, as optical interactions between reflective materials and atmospheric conditions may not be accurately captured by simulations. Future research should focus on utilizing larger areas for installation and exploring elevated configurations to fully validate the potential of reflector-enhanced bPV systems, while emphasizing their rentability.

Keywords: Bifacial photovoltaic, Nordic, energy yield, albedo, ground reflectors.

1 INTRODUCTION

The adoption of bifacial solar modules in large-scale utility PV power plants has grown, driven by the potential for increased energy output with minimal additional cost. An energy yield of 1300 kWh/kWp per year has been found for bifacial PV installed in low latitude areas [1], while 1000 kWh/kWp was calculated in high latitude locations such as Sweden [2]. However, a study in Norway reported 1342 kWh/kWp, though the authors noted this is exceptionally high for Norwegian PV installations [3].

Figure 1 shows the expected world market share on bifacial PV with an increase from less than 20% in 2019 to 70% in 2030 [4]. However, according to literature [5] two major limits exist when considering bifacial PV operation in high-latitude locations. First, there is a scarcity of confirmed field data particular to these places, limiting the ability to accurately evaluate and assess these systems. Second, present simulation methods for bPV systems do not provide enough accuracy to capture specific issues of high latitudes. According to TÜV Rheinland [6], many key factors influence the performance and energy output of bifacial PV modules. The energy gain is impacted by location and installation parameters, including ground albedo, tilt angle, mounting height, structural design, and row spacing, which play a role in shading and sunlight exposure.

The enhancement of ground albedo through the integration of reflectors with bifacial PV has been studied as a possible solution since decades [7]. Authors of [8] highlighted pioneering research on ground reflectors designed to enhance the reflected energy captured by the rear side of bifacial photovoltaic systems, including studies dating back to 1985.

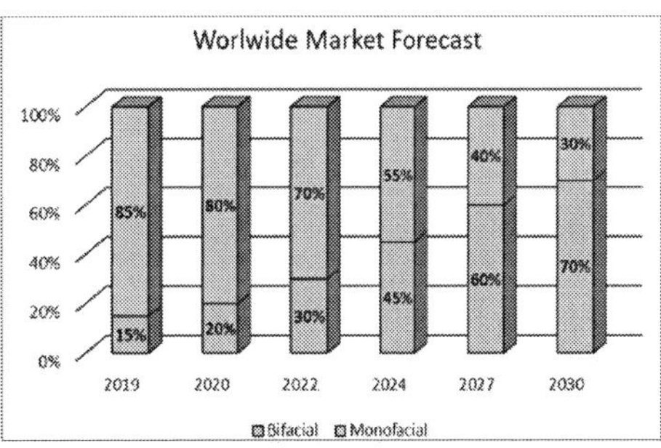

Figure 1: Prediction of the bifacial world market for the different cell technologies [4].

Based on the conducted literature detailed in appendix 1, reflector materials can be classified into three optical categories based on their scattering behavior [9] as shown in Fig. 2. Diffuse reflectors like white paint [10], [11] and gravel [1], [12] provide uniform rear-side illumination with minimal angle dependence. For specular reflectors like aluminum [13] and mirrors [14] that can create concentrated hotspots but may cause non-uniform irradiance patterns. Finally, glossy reflectors such as photopaper [9] and white tiles [15] represent an intermediate category with medium angle dependence, combining predominantly directional reflection with some diffuse scattering due to their smooth but slightly textured surfaces. The distribution of papers per reflectors type is presented in Figure 3, with 73% of research efforts focusing on diffuse reflectors. Ground reflectors show significant variation in performance gains, as detailed in Appendix 1. The gains are raning from 2.8% increases in bifacial performance as found for white tarps [16] to 59% energy increase compared to monofacial systems using diffuse reflectors [11]. It should be noted that most reported gains compare bifacial systems with monofacial PV, explaining their large amplitude. For fair comparison, the reference should be bifacial PV systems with different reflectors under identical exposure conditions

The objective of this study is to evaluate bPV module performance in Nordic climates, where field performance data remains limited, through specific yield analysis. The study also investigates energy gains achieved with different reflective ground surfaces to assess their effectiveness in enhancing bifacial PV performance.

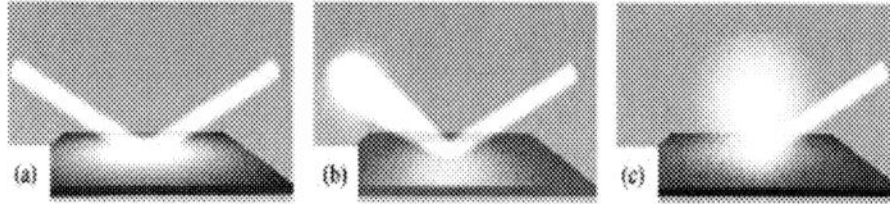

Figure 2: Schematic of a (a) diffuse, (b) glossy, and (c) specular reflector (light incident from the right) [9].

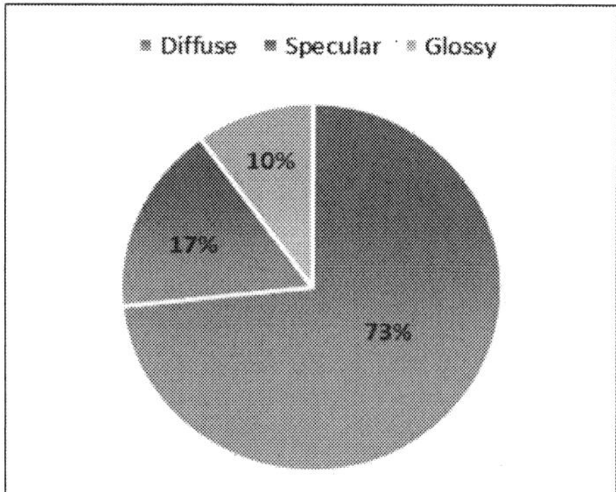

Figure 3: Distribution of published works by reflector types as reported in 18 papers (See Appendix 1).

2 EXPERIMENTAL APPROACHES

2.1 Study site and experimental Setup

Three bifacial PV modules, shown in Fig 4, have been installed on the rooftop of a building at the University of Agder's Grimstad campus in Norway (58.3345°N, 8.5755°E). The location falls under the Cfb climate classification according to the Köppen-Geiger system, characterized by mild temperatures, frequent rainfall (approximately 1,119 mm annually), and an average temperature of 9.7 °C. Each module is a 555 Wp N-type bifacial monocrystalline silicon half-cell with a double-glass design. The modules are equipped with microinverters, allowing real-time monitoring of individual energy production. The PV array is installed with a south-facing orientation at a 40° tilt angle.

2.2 Ground reflectors installation

Based on the results obtained from outdoor measurements of reflection properties, a selection of reflectors has been made. Among the tested materials, the white plates demonstrated the highest spectral albedo within the wavelength range of 300 nm to 1100 nm, with an albedo factor of approximately 0.7. In contrast, the semi-mirrored material exhibited the lowest spectral albedo, with a factor of 0.25. For comparison purposes, we selected white and semi-mirrored plates for installation.

These reflectors were installed beneath the PV panels to study the performance of the bPV system in an optimized configuaion. The nearby meteorological station provides measurements of Global Horizontal Irradiance (GHI) via Kipp & Zonen CMP11 pyranometers. Additionally, irradiance data is available from an albedometer, which consists of two Kipp & Zonen CMP11 pyranometers mounted to measure both upward and downward-facing irradiance. Missing albedo and GHI data were sourced from the NASA Power database [17], while cloud opacity data were obtained from Solcast [18].

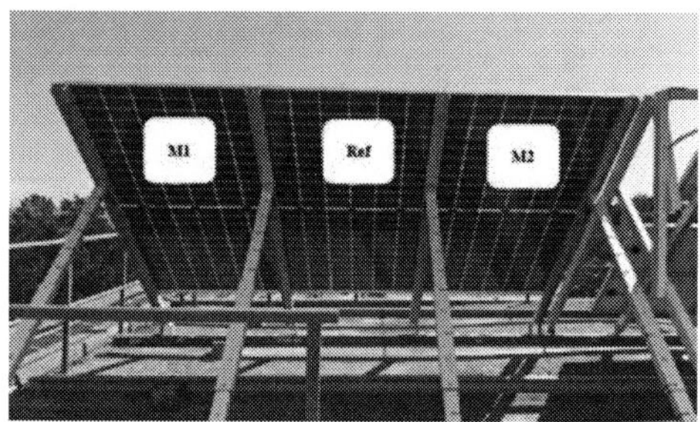

Figure 4: Modules M1 and M2 will be equipped with ground reflectors, while the reference module will remain without reflectors.

After the simultaneous exposure and due to space limitations, to avoid interference with the reference module, each reflector was exposed individually for one month as shown in Fig. 5. However, this sequential approach may introduce variability due to different irradiance conditions during each test period.

Figure 5: Bifacial PV with corresponding reflectors. (a) Simultaneous exposure, (b) Individual exposure.

3 RESULTS AND DISCUSSIONS

3.1 Yield assessment

Figure 6 shows the specific yield calculated based on the recorded production for the entire PV demonstrator presented with the corresponding global horizontal irradiance (GHI) and albedo. The bifacial PV demonstrates good seasonal performance with a total yield of 1183.25 kWh/kWp over 337 days of monitoring. Considering the average daily yield of 3.51 kWh/kWp, the estimated annual specific yield is around 1281.56 kWh/kWp. Peak performance occurs during spring and summer months (May-July) with daily yields frequently exceeding 7 kWh/kWp and reaching a maximum of 8.02 kWh/kWp. Winter months (December-January) show expected lower yields averaging below 1 kWh/kWp due to reduced daylight hours and solar irradiance. Wintertime is characterized by snow conditions which are clearly visible on the albedo values that reached 0.68 for example on 2nd January 2025 where the recorded snow depth was 18 cm according to [19].

The overall correlation between energy yield and irradiance is high. However, some days, such as 17th February and 14th March 2025, show a high energy yield compared to the relatively low received irradiance. The daily average of GHI is calculated as the mean of hourly values, which may underestimate the results. These periods correspond mainly to missing data from our weather station, which were supplemented with data from weather databases.

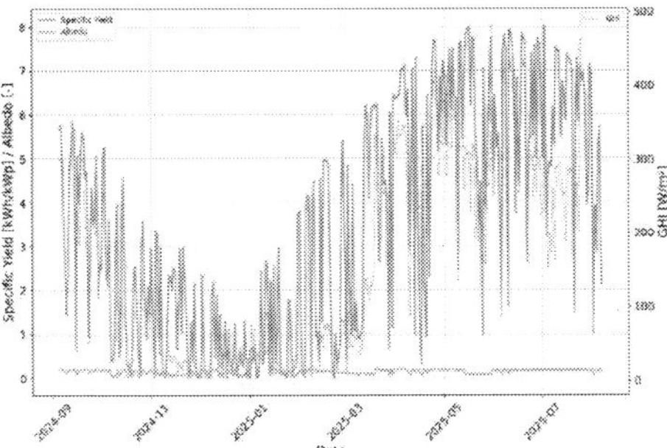

Figure 6: Daily specific yield for the period from 05 September 2024 to 07 August 2025, with the corresponding GHI and albedo.

3.2 Comparison of reflectors performance

To minimize the impact of rapidly changing irradiance conditions, such as during sunrise or sunset, we focused on 11:00, 13:00, and 15:00 hours for meaningful comparisons in power gain as shown in Fig. 7.

Based on the comprehensive almost one-year dataset, both white and semi-mirrored reflectors demonstrate positive mean performance throughout the day. White reflector provides superior consistency and reliability with peak performance at 13H (1.03% mean gain) and moderate variability manifested by a standard deviation interval of 1.41-2.36% while achieving maximum gains up to 20.74%. Semi-mirrored reflector showed mean performance between 0.71 and 1.09% gains with notably higher median values at 11H and 13H (0.71% and 0.91% respectively), lower overall variability and a maximum gain reaching 13%.

Daily negative gains in power production have been observed throughout the monitoring period for both reflector types, with semi-mirrored reflectors showing a higher frequency of negative values. The hypothesis for this unconventional result is that cross-interference between reflectors is affecting the reference panel measurements. Since both reflector systems were installed beneath adjacent bifacial PV panels with limited spacing, the reflected irradiance from the test reflectors is likely reaching the reference panel. This additional illumination of the reference panel may alter its performance baseline, causing the calculated gains to appear reduced or even negative.

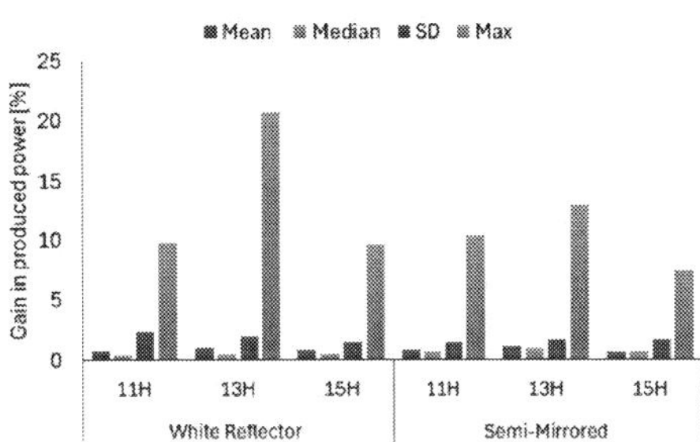

Figure 7: Average gain in produced power at times of the day during almost one year of monitoring for white and semi-mirrored plates.

It should be noted that [20] recommends that the reflective material should extend the module's width two times and four times the module's length to ensure that as much of the irradiance incident on the panel's rear surface is reflected off the foil. As the available installation area has limited space, this recommendation could not be implemented in the present work.

The semi-mirrored reflector, having higher reflectivity, generates more intense and directionally scattered reflected light, resulting in greater stray light effects on the corresponding PV module and more frequent negative gain calculations. To validate this hypothesis and obtain accurate reflector performance data, the following figure presents results from individual reflector exposure tests with increased spatial separation to prevent cross-interference effects.

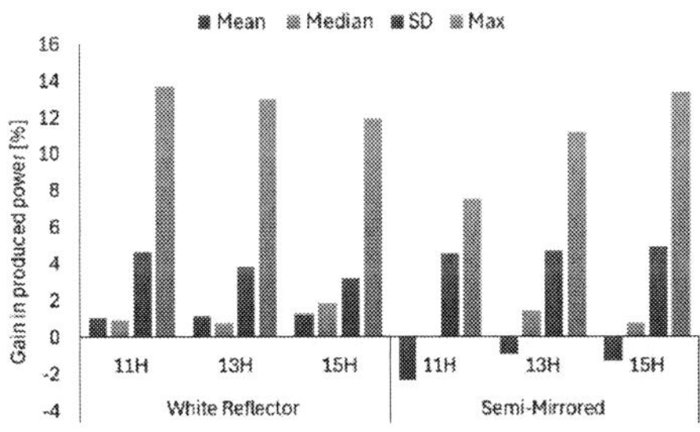

Figure 8: Bifacial gain enhancement from white reflectors and semi-mirrored at different times of the day for 1 month field study (Individual exposure).

Based data shown in Fig. 8, noticeable negative mean gain values are obtained for semi-mirrored reflector compared to white reflectors. It has been noticed that most of negative values in gain correspond to days with high irradiance and clear sky conditions. The system shows negative performance (-30 to -62W) during high irradiance conditions and clear sky where the cloud opacity was very low as shown in Fig. 9.

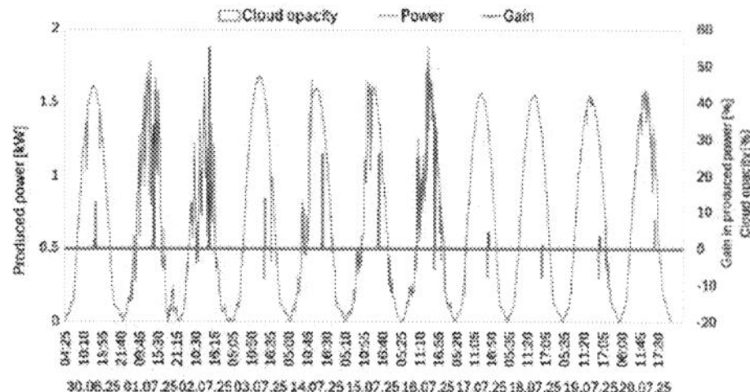

Figure 9: Produced power for entire system with corresponding gain from semi-mirrored reflector per PV module.

Figure 9 reveals that positive gains occur predominantly during cloudy conditions, as observed on July 15th where the coud opacity reached 26% [21]. Under diffuse lighting conditions, the semi-mirrored reflector effectively captures scattered light, enhancing rear-side illumination. Conversely, clear sky conditions may generate thermal effects that negate the optical benefits of the reflector. Therefore, using a thermal camera FLUKE Ti400, a series of thermal inspections has been conducted on sunny days where the temperatures of the module with semi-mirrored reflectors and the reference one did not exceed 38°C. No anomalies have been detected regarding the thermal effects. The study by [22] reveals that the ground albedo of concrete surfaces remains relatively stable, while the albedo of high-reflective surfaces can vary significantly on sunny days. This variation is attributed to the incident-angle dependence of ground reflections, particularly for reflectors with specular or mirror-like properties, which can result in mismatch loss in PV modules. Similarly, [23] investigates the behavior of both diffuse and specular reflectors. The study found that mirrors redirect more incoming irradiance, but only in specific reflection directions. Diffuse reflectors are more versatile as they redirect light with fewer angular restrictions, minimizing shading and maximizing light capture. In contrast, surfaces with diffuse reflections tend to maintain a stable albedo throughout the day

The white reflector demonstrated consistent positive performance throughout both daily cycles and the entire monitoring period. Variability was observed, particularly manifested by high standard deviation in morning measurements. However, the white reflector maintained optical benefits by enhancing both diffuse and direct irradiance reflection. Table 2 presents the overall gain for both simultaneous and individual exposure scenarios.

The slight gains observed suggest that reflector implementation may not be recommended for standard bifacial PV installations, consistent with other authors who advise against ground albedo enhancements until substantial cost reductions are realized [16]. However, significant improvements may be achievable with elevated panel configurations as recommended by [24], representing a promising direction for future work.

Table 1: Overall gain for simultaneous and individual exposure of reflectors.

Reflectors	White [%]	Semi-Mirrored [%]
Simultaneous	0.86	0.89
Individual	1.14	-1.56

4 SENSITIVITY ANALYSIS

The production modeling of 40 kWp of bifacial PV was conducted by SAM (Solar Advisor Model), considering the weather conditions of Grimstad. The installation consists of three subarrays, each containing one string, with two strings connected in parallel and oriented south. Each string has 18 PV modules of 555 W and 1 row, so a total of 4 rows is installed at a height of 0.5 from ground. The weather file has been obtained from the National Solar Radiation Database (NSRDB). For a typical GCR of 0.3, a height of 0.5 m as the experimental installation height, the parametric analysis of the energy yield to tilt angle and albedo is then carried out using SAM simulations. The number of possible run simulations is the product of the number of possible values for each factor, so a total of 25 runs. It should be noted that the albedo valued imputed based on the results of the experimental study conducted for the white and semi-mirrored plates.

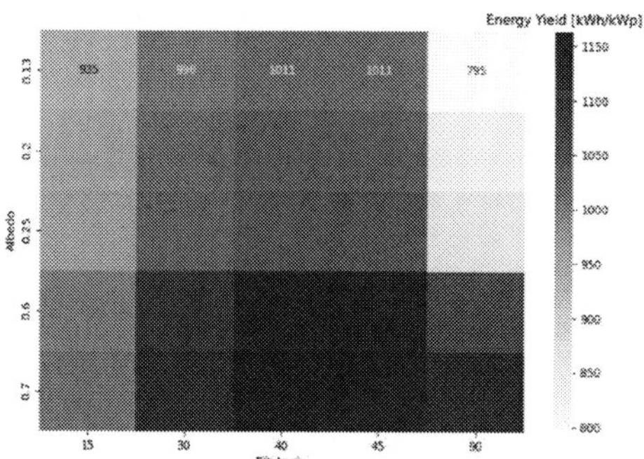

Figure 10: Results of 25 simulations for five different albedo values on the ground and four different tilt angles of PV modules shown in terms of annual specific performance for a fixed GCR.

The results of 25 simulations are presented in Fig. 10, showing annual energy yield versus tilt angle for different ground albedo values. The simulation results demonstrate a clear positive correlation between tilt angle and energy yield, with the exception of the 90° vertical configuration. Maximum energy yields of 1148 kWh/kWp and 1163 kWh/kWp were achieved at 40° and 45° tilt angles respectively, using the highest albedo value of 0.7. In contrast, the minimum energy yield of 795 kWh/kWp occurred with the lowest albedo of 0.13 and a vertical configuration.

While simulations consistently predict that higher albedo surfaces improve bifacial PV performance, the experimental results reveal important limitations of modeling software. Despite the semi-mirrored reflector having high reflectivity, it produced negative performance impacts under clear sky conditions; an effect not captured by standard simulation tools. This discrepancy highlights a gap between theoretical predictions and real-world performance, emphasizing that reflector material properties beyond simple albedo values significantly influence bifacial PV systems.

5 CONCLUSIONS

This study demonstrates that bifacial PV systems in Nordic conditions achieve substantial annual energy yields of 1281.56 kWh/kWp, confirming their viability in high-latitude environments. The experimental evaluation of ground reflectors under real outdoor conditions revealed distinct performance characteristics between reflector types. White reflectors demonstrated superior stability and consistent power gains, while semi-mirrored reflectors showed variable performance, likely due to mismatch loss that negatively impacted their reliability under the tested configurations.

The limited gains observed (0.86-1.14%) suggest that reflector implementation may not be economically justified for standard bifacial PV installations until substantial cost reductions are achieved. The potential for exploiting greater reflector surface areas, particularly with elevated modules, offers significant opportunities for improving bifacial PV performance.

This work highlights as well the critical importance of experimental validation over simulation-based predictions, as the complex optical interactions between reflective materials and varying atmospheric conditions cannot be accurately captured through modeling alone. Future investigations should focus on spatial adjustments and elevated configurations to fully realize the potential of reflector-enhanced bifacial PV systems.

6 ACKNOWLEDGEMENTS

This work has been funded partially by Forskningsmobilisering Agder in Norway and the Research Council of Norway in the framework of FME Solar (No 350244). The authors thank Prof. Anne Gerd Imenes from University of Agder for her valuable contribution to this work.

7 REFERENCES

[1] D. L. Dias, G. A. Rampinelli, G. N. Garrido, J. A. Tejero, M. S. de Cardona Ortín, and L. E. Bremermann, "Performance assessment of bifacial and monofacial PV systems on different types of soils in a low-latitude site," *Renew Energy*, vol. 246, Jun. 2025, doi: 10.1016/j.renene.2025.122868.

[2] E. Molin, B. Stridh, A. Molin, and E. Wackelgard, "Experimental yield study of bifacial PV modules in nordic conditions," *IEEE J Photovolt*, vol. 8, no. 6, pp. 1457–1463, Nov. 2018, doi: 10.1109/JPHOTOV.2018.2865168.

[3] H. N. Riise et al., "Performance analysis of a BAPV bifacial system in Norway," in *Conference Record of the IEEE Photovoltaic Specialists Conference*, Institute of Electrical and Electronics Engineers Inc., Jun. 2021, pp. 1304–1308. doi: 10.1109/PVSC43889.2021.9518963.

[4] P. K. Sahu, J. N. Roy, and C. Chakraborty, "Performance assessment of a bifacial PV system using a new energy estimation model," *Solar Energy*, vol. 262, Sep. 2023, doi: 10.1016/j.solener.2023.111818.

[5] B. D. Dimd, A. S. Garcia, and M. Bellmann, "Empirical analysis of bifacial photovoltaic modules in high-latitude regions: Performance insights from a field laboratory in Norway," *Energy Convers Manag*, vol. 325, Feb. 2025, doi: 10.1016/j.enconman.2024.119396.

[6] V. Rodrigues, "Measurement and validation of bifacial modules' power output," 2019. Accessed: Feb. 04, 2025. [Online]. Available: https://www.pv-magazine.com/wp-content/uploads/2019/04/Vitor-Rodrigues-Presentation.pdf

[7] A. Luque, E. Lorenzo, G. Sala, and S. Lopez-Romero, "DIFFUSING REFLECTORS FOR BIFACIAL PHOTOVOLTAIC PANELS," 1984.

[8] R. Guerrero-Lemus, R. Vega, T. Kim, A. Kimm, and L. E. Shephard, "Bifacial solar photovoltaics - A technology review," Jul. 01, 2016, *Elsevier Ltd.* doi: 10.1016/j.rser.2016.03.041.

[9] S. S. Pal, F. H. C. Van Loenhout, J. Westerhof, and R. Saive, "Understanding and Benchmarking Ground Reflectors for Bifacial Photovoltaic Yield Enhancement," *IEEE J Photovolt*, vol. 14, no. 1, pp. 160–169, Jan. 2024, doi: 10.1109/JPHOTOV.2023.3319592.

[10] A. Basak, S. Chakraborty, and A. K. Behura, "Tilt angle optimization for bifacial PV module: Balancing direct and reflected irradiance on white painted ground surfaces," *Appl Energy*, vol. 377, Jan. 2025, doi: 10.1016/j.apenergy.2024.124525.

[11] A. Luque, E. Lorenzo, G. Sala, and S. Lopez-Romero, "DIFFUSING REFLECTORS FOR BIFACIAL PHOTOVOLTAIC PANELS," 1984.

[12] N. Riedel-Lyngskar et al., "Spectral Albedo in Bifacial Photovoltaic Modeling: What can be learned from Onsite Measurements?," in *Conference Record of the IEEE Photovoltaic Specialists Conference*, Institute of Electrical and Electronics Engineers Inc., Jun. 2021, pp. 942–949. doi: 10.1109/PVSC43889.2021.9519085.

[13] K. Ganesan, D. P. Winston, S. Sugumar, and S. Jegan, "Performance analysis of n-type PERT bifacial solar PV module under diverse albedo conditions," *Solar Energy*, vol. 252, pp. 81–90, Mar. 2023, doi: 10.1016/j.solener.2023.01.020.

[14] P. Ooshaksaraei, K. Sopian, R. Zulkifli, M. A. Alghoul, and S. H. Zaidi, "Characterization of a bifacial photovoltaic panel integrated with external diffuse and semimirror type reflectors," *International Journal of Photoenergy*, vol. 2013, 2013, doi: 10.1155/2013/465837.

[15] M. Alam, M. S. Gul, and T. Muneer, "Performance analysis and comparison between bifacial and monofacial solar photovoltaic at various ground albedo conditions," *Renewable Energy Focus*, vol. 44, pp. 295–316, Mar. 2023, doi: 10.1016/j.ref.2023.01.005.

[16] N. Riedel-Lyngskær, P. B. Poulsen, M. L. Jakobsen, P. Nørgaard, and J. Vedde, "Value of bifacial photovoltaics used with highly reflective ground materials on single-axis trackers and fixed-tilt systems: A danish case study," *IET Renewable Power Generation*, vol. 14, no. 19, pp. 3946–3953, Dec. 2020, doi: 10.1049/iet-rpg.2020.0580.

[17] "NASA POWER | Data Access Viewer (DAV)." Accessed: Aug. 19, 2025. [Online]. Available: https://power.larc.nasa.gov/data-access-viewer/

[18] "Solcast API Toolkit." Accessed: Aug. 18, 2025. [Online]. Available: https://toolkit.solcast.com.au/

[19] "SeeNorway." Accessed: Aug. 13, 2025. [Online]. Available: https://www.senorge.no/

[20] A. Garrod, S. Neda Hussain, M. H. Intwala, A. Poudhar, S. Manikandan, and A. Ghosh, "Electrical and thermal performance of bifacial photovoltaics under varying albedo conditions at

temperate climate (UK)," *Heliyon*, vol. 10, no. 13, Jul. 2024, doi: 10.1016/j.heliyon.2024.e34147.

[21] F. W. Watt and P. A. Campbell, "The effects of solar insolation and cloud opacity on the optimum array size for a direct-coupled solar pumping system," *Renew Energy*, vol. 228, Jul. 2024, doi: 10.1016/j.renene.2024.120594.

[22] B. Sun, L. Lu, Y. Yuan, and P. Ocłoń, "Development and validation of a concise and anisotropic irradiance model for bifacial photovoltaic modules," *Renew Energy*, vol. 209, pp. 442–452, Jun. 2023, doi: 10.1016/j.renene.2023.04.012.

[23] S. Pal and R. Saive, "Output Enhancement of Bifacial Solar Modules under Diffuse and Specular Albedo," in *Conference Record of the IEEE Photovoltaic Specialists Conference*, Institute of Electrical and Electronics Engineers Inc., Jun. 2021, pp. 1159–1162. doi: 10.1109/PVSC43889.2021.9519093.

[24] U. A. Yusufoglu *et al.*, "Simulation of energy production by bifacial modules with revision of ground reflection," in *Energy Procedia*, Elsevier Ltd, 2014, pp. 389–395. doi: 10.1016/j.egypro.2014.08.111.

[25] P. Ooshaksaraei, K. Sopian, R. Zulkifli, M. A. Alghoul, and S. H. Zaidi, "Characterization of a bifacial photovoltaic panel integrated with external diffuse and semimirror type reflectors," *International Journal of Photoenergy*, vol. 2013, 2013, doi: 10.1155/2013/465837.

[26] N. Riedel-Lyngskaer *et al.*, "The effect of spectral albedo in bifacial photovoltaic performance," 2021, doi: 10.11583/DTU.14695437.v1.

[27] D. S. Braga, L. L. Kazmerski, D. A. Cassini, V. Camatta, and A. S. A. C. Diniz, "Performance of bifacial PV modules under different operating conditions in the State of Minas Gerais, Brazil," *Renewable Energy and Environmental Sustainability*, vol. 8, p. 23, 2023, doi: 10.1051/rees/2023021.

[28] T. Kaewnukultorn, S. B. Sepúlveda-Mora, R. Purnell, and S. Hegedus, "Electrical and Financial Impacts of Inverter Clipping on Oversized Bifacial Photovoltaic Systems," *Energies (Basel)*, vol. 17, no. 22, Nov. 2024, doi: 10.3390/en17225658.

[29] D. Fontani *et al.*, "Field optimization for bifacial modules," *Opt Mater (Amst)*, vol. 138, Apr. 2023, doi: 10.1016/j.optmat.2023.113715.

[30] E. Mouhib, P. M. Rodrigo, L. Micheli, E. F. Fernández, and F. Almonacid, "Quantifying the rear and front long-term spectral impact on bifacial photovoltaic modules," *Solar Energy*, vol. 247, pp. 202–213, Nov. 2022, doi: 10.1016/j.solener.2022.10.035.

[31] M. R. Lewis, S. Ovaitt, B. McDanold, C. Deline, and K. Hinzer, "Artificial ground reflector size and position effects on energy yield and economics of single-axis-tracked bifacial photovoltaics," *Progress in Photovoltaics: Research and Applications*, Oct. 2024, doi: 10.1002/pip.3811.

[32] J. Westerhof *et al.*, "Impact of grass retroreflection on bifacial solar panel electricity yield in agrivoltaics," *J Photonics Energy*, vol. 15, no. 03, Jan. 2025, doi: 10.1117/1.JPE.15.032702.

8 APPENDICES

APPENDIX 1: Summary of published works on ground reflectors for bPV performance enhancement.

Ref	Height [m]	Albedo [-]	Reflectors	Findings	Outperformance
[11]	1.55	-	White-painted ground	The use of high reflectivity of acrylic paint in white-painted planes in bifacial panels significantly increased energy collection.	White painted ground
[25]	0.115*	-	Semi-mirror White-painted	The study utilized an extended semimirror and a white-painted diffuse reflector for rear surface reflection, achieving maximum power generation at 30° and 10°, with 20% and 15% output power enhancements.	Semi-mirror
[2]	0.15	0.85 0.05	Snow Tar paper	Investigating higher albedo on sunny days with snow for bifacial east-west modules yielded a 48% increase in specific yield of 7.57 kWh/kWp compared to tar paper.	Snow
[16]	1.56	0.22 0.6	Grass White tarp	Using a white tarp provides a 2.8% bifacial increase. Bifacial systems with white tarp have a lower LCOE (0.1-0.4 EUR/MWh) compared to those without.	-
[26]	1.5	-	Green grass Dry grass Gravel Snow	Spectral gains are highest for bifacial systems, with 25% for green grass, 15% for dry grass, and 5% for gravel. Tracked systems show lower gains due to larger sky view factors.	Green grass
[27]	NA	0.50 0.20	White polymeric layer Natural ground cover	The Três Marias and Itaguara Solar Plants utilized a white polymeric layer, resulting in a 3.5% and 5.14% increase in bifacial gain respectively.	White polymeric layer
[28]	Elevated panels	0.1 0.35 0.7	Black Gravel White ground	The white ground in winter leads to the highest bifacial gain (13.1%) and daily DC efficiency (22.2%) due to the combination of high reflectivity with low solar angle.	White ground
[10]	0	-	White paint	This study highlights the critical role of tilt angle and ground reflectance when using white paint in maximizing energy output from bPV modules.	White paint
[15]	1	0.30–0.35 0.5–0.6 0.7–0.8 0.10–0.15	Concrete White pebbles White tiles Soil	The annual rear irradiance gains analysis revealed that white pebbles and tiles have the highest gain range (>30% gain), followed by soil surface and concrete.	White pebbles White tiles
[20]	0.50	0.21 0.90	Grass Reflective material	The experiments showed that bPV panel efficiency is lowest under direct irradiance and highest under diffuse light, with higher efficiency using reflective materials.	-
[13]	0.94	0.39 0.53 0.28 0.31 0.20	White paint Aluminum Sand Cement Grass	Aluminum surfaces produced more albedo, bifacial gain, and output power. The average bifacial gain is 21.4%. White paint coatings yield better results, with an average bifacial gain of 18.9%.	-
[29]	2.96	-	Retro-Reflective (RR) materials	RR materials are most effective at noon, optimizing the field, resulting in over 10% improved maximum power compared to traditional PV modules with only front-side cells.	-
[24]	0 0.5 2	0.2 0.5	Ground	The study reveals that bifacial modules perform better in diffuse irradiance regions, and higher ground installations are beneficial for all locations, with enhanced benefits in direct light region.	-

[30]	1	0.334	Light soil	In terms of bifacial spectral energy gains, white sand is the most convenient among the ground types studied in this work.	-
		0.414	White sand		
		0.140	Green grass		
		0.391	Concrete slab		
[31]	1.5	0.7	High-density polyethylene geomembrane material (HDPE)	Tests showed reflector configurations can increase daily energy yield by up to 6.2%, with optimal placement directly underneath the module due to optimized rear irradiance increase.	-
[22]	1	0.54	Aluminum foil	Ground reflections' incident-angle dependence significantly affects ground-reflected irradiance modeling, with specular or mirror-like reflections causing mismatch loss in PV modules.	-
		0.15	Concrete ground		
[32]	0.25	-	Grass	The study found that assuming diffuse grass can overestimate solar panel yield by up to 10.5%. Simulations suggest that long grass contributes minimally to yield, with short grass being more beneficial.	-
[9]	1	-	Mirror	The study compares simulated albedo-dependent short-circuit current density of bPV, highlighting that a good reflector should redirect more light, reduce mismatch, and be robust to changing sun positions.	White paper
			White paper		
			Photopaper		

Panel separation from the reflector (parallel to the PV module).

FIELD-BASED EVALUATION OF SMALL-SCALE PHOTOVOLTAIC SYSTEMS: COMPLIANCE AND INSTALLATION PRACTICES IN FINLAND

Juho Ylipaino[1, 2], Aki Kortetmäki[1, 2], Marko Ylinen[3], Kari Kallioharju[1, 2], Juha Koskela[2]
[1] Tampere University of Applied Sciences, Tampere, Finland
[2] Tampere University, Tampere, Finland
[3] Satakunta University of Applied Sciences, Pori, Finland

ABSTRACT: This study evaluates the compliance of small-scale photovoltaic (PV) installations in Finland, focusing on 60 small-scale systems primarily installed between 2022 and 2024. The inspected systems were mainly located in detached houses, with participation based on voluntary recruitment. Using a systematic, field-based inspection methodology, the study examines adherence to standards throughout the installation process, including system design, installation practices, commissioning inspections, and documentation. Beyond identifying deficiencies, the analysis investigates installers' practices and interpretations of regulatory requirements. The findings reveal substantial variability in compliance, with only a small fraction of systems meeting all mandatory requirements. Common deficiencies include incomplete or missing commissioning inspection reports, inadequate system labeling, and deviations in safety-critical practices such as equipotential bonding. These issues emphasize the need for clearer guidance, enhanced installer training, and stricter oversight to ensure consistent adherence to standards. By offering a detailed evaluation of compliance challenges and highlighting examples of best practices, this study contributes to the development of safer, more reliable PV systems. It provides valuable insights for regulators, installers, and property owners, emphasizing the importance of standardization and professional expertise in supporting the successful adoption of PV technologies.
Keywords: Photovoltaic systems, Compliance, Installation practices, Safety and quality, Standards

1 INTRODUCTION

The installation of small-scale photovoltaic (PV) systems has increased rapidly in Finland in recent years, supported by falling component prices, favorable policy measures, and growing interest in self-generated renewable electricity [13]. While PV technology offers clear environmental and economic benefits, ensuring electrical safety and long-term reliability requires that systems are designed, installed, and commissioned in full compliance with binding standards and regulations.

All electrical installations in Finland, including PV systems, must comply with the Finnish Electrical Safety Act [4]. To fill enforcement of the Act, the national electrical safety authority maintains a mandatory list of standards, known as *Luettelo S10* [5]. Compliance with the standards on this list ensures that all statutory requirements are met. For PV systems, the list includes the SFS 6000 standard series, which applies to electrical installations up to 1000 V AC and 1500 V DC [6]. These standards are based on the European harmonization document CENELEC HD 60364 and the international IEC 60364 standards. In January 2023, Luettelo S10 was updated to include SFS-EN 62446-1:2016 + A1:2018, the Finnish adoption of EN 62446-1:2016, harmonized with IEC 62446-1:2016 [7], [8]. This standard specifies requirements for system documentation, commissioning tests, and inspection of grid-connected PV systems, thereby promoting consistent safety practices and regulatory compliance across all PV system installations.

In Finland, small-scale PV systems may be installed by any licensed electrical contractor [4]. There is no mandatory PV-specific certification, which can lead to differences in installers' knowledge of PV system's consistent application in practice. Contractor's supervisor of electrical works plays a central role in ensuring installation quality and safety. Their duties include guiding and managing the work, ensuring the competence of employees, instructing them in safety matters, and providing the necessary tools and working conditions [9]. They are responsible for ensuring that the Electrical Safety Act is complied with, that the condition of electrical installations meets statutory requirements before commissioning or handover, and that personnel performing the work possess adequate skills and receive sufficient instructions for their tasks [9]. The knowledge of the supervisor of electrical work and the extent and quality of supervision can vary in practice, potentially contributing to differences in compliance across installations.

Despite these binding requirements, previous investigation in Finland has shown considerable variation in installation quality, especially in commissioning inspections, documentation, and general installation practices [10]–[14]. Similar findings have been reported internationally, with faulty installations, deviations from manufacturer instructions, and inconsistent application of standards identified as recurring issues [15]–[17]. Earlier Finnish studies have mainly relied on self-reported information from contractors or customers, which may not fully reflect actual conditions. Systematic, on-site inspections enable a more accurate assessment of compliance by allowing direct verification of both technical implementation and documentation. They also provide insight into the practical effects of recent updates to national standards, such as the 2022 revision of SFS 6000, which became binding for installations in January 2023 after the update of the mandatory standard list [7], including the strong recommendation against unnecessary DC isolators and the requirement for non-combustible mounting surfaces.

This study addresses the lack of field-based compliance data by inspecting 60 small-scale PV systems primarily installed between 2022 and 2024 in Finland. The objective is to evaluate adherence to the Finnish Electrical Safety Act and relevant national and international standards, identify common deficiencies, and assess whether recent changes to the SFS 6000 standard are reflected in installation practices. The findings provide an evidence-based basis for improving PV installation quality through targeted training, clearer guidance, and effective application of standard requirements.

10.4229/EUPVSEC2025/4DV.4.17
020444-001

2 METHODOLOGY

This section describes the methodology used to investigate the compliance and safety of small-scale PV systems. The study involved the inspection of 60 small-scale PV systems using a standardized procedure. Figure 1 provides an overview of the full process from participant recruitment to data analysis. After an open call for participation, property owners submitted background information, based on which suitable sites were selected. On-site inspections were conducted using a predefined survey form, and the collected data were subsequently analyzed to assess compliance with applicable legislation and standards.

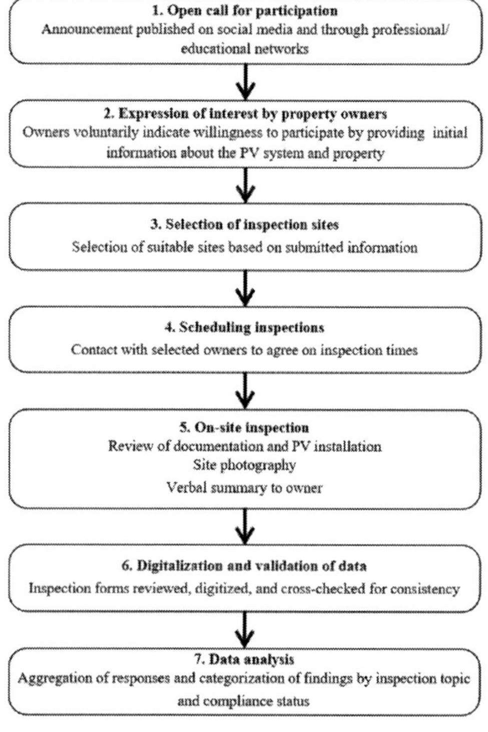

Figure 1: Process of site-recruitment, inspection, and data handling

2.1 Recruitment and selection of PV systems

The PV systems included in this study were selected on a voluntary basis. Property owners were invited to participate through open calls published on social media platforms and via professional and educational networks. The selection process was non-random and did not aim to create a statistically representative sample of all small-scale PV systems in Finland. Instead, the objective was to collect a diverse range of installations for a qualitative assessment of safety and compliance.

Interested participants signed up for the study by filling out a questionnaire about the property and PV system. Based on these responses, a selection of sites was made to represent the study group. For each selected site, a visit was scheduled, during which a standardized inspection was carried out and the available documentation was reviewed. No compensation was provided for participation, and each property owner gave informed consent for the site visit and data collection. The gathered data was anonymized for analysis and reporting purposes.

2.2 Characteristics of inspected PV systems

The inspected systems represented typical small-scale PV installations in Finland. The majority were commissioned in 2022 or 2023, allowing for an assessment of compliance with the latest applicable standards. Almost all were located in detached houses and connected with the common 3x25 A supply size. System sizes were most often between 6 and 10 kWp, which aligns with household self-consumption needs. In terms of technology, string inverters dominated, while microinverters and optimizers were used only occasionally. Across the 60 sites, installations have been carried out by 38 different electrical contractors, highlighting a fragmented installer base despite the relatively small market.

Table I presents an overview of key technical and procurement-related characteristics of the systems.

Table I: Technical and procurement-related characteristics of the inspected systems

Parameter	Distribution
Number of inspected systems	60
Installation year	2023 or later: 34 (57 %) 2022: 23 (38%) 2021 or earlier: 3 (5%)
PV system type	String inverter: 56 systems (93%) Microinverter: 3 systems (5%) String inverter with optimizer: 1 (2%)
Connection size	3x25 A: 50 sites (83%) 3x35 A: 9 sites (15%) 3x50 A: 1 site (2%)
Property type	Detached Houses: 57 (95%) Agricultural Buildings: 3 (5%)
PV system size (panel power)	Below 3 kWp: 1 (2%) 3-5 kWp: 15 (25%) 6-10 kWp: 39 (65%) 11-15 kWp: 1 (2%) Over 15 kWp: 3 (5%) Unknown: 1 (2%)
Number of panel strings	1 string: 32 (53%) 2 strings: 22 (37%) Over 2 strings: 3 (5%) No strings (micros): 3 (5%)
Number of electrical contractors	38 contractors across 60 systems

2.3 Inspection protocol

The data presented in this study were collected through a field survey of 60 small-scale PV systems. The systems were located primarily in detached houses in the Satakunta and Pirkanmaa regions and were selected on a voluntary basis through open calls via social media and professional networks. Each inspection followed a systematic protocol using a dedicated survey form developed for the research. The form was designed to assess compliance with the Finnish Electrical Safety Act (1135/2016), and relevant standards, including SFS 6000 and SFS-EN 62446-1. The inspection was structured into nine thematic sections, which are listed in Table II.

Table II: Thematic sections of the inspection form

Section	Evaluation topic
0	General information on the PV system
1	Commissioning inspection and inspection report
2	System labeling and documentation
3	Electrical protection (e.g., overcurrent, shock protection)
4	Means of disconnection (AC and DC sides)
5	Selection and installation of electrical equipment
6	Cabling and routing
7	Equipotential bonding
8	Mechanical installation

During each site visit, the inspector first reviewed available documentation with the property owner. This was followed by a detailed inspection of the physical installation, with all findings recorded using the survey form. Each inspection concluded with a verbal summary of the findings and a later written summary report, including key observations and photographs.

Each inspected item was assessed for compliance with applicable legislation and mandatory standards. If deviations were identified, they were classified using a predefined scale. Minor deficiencies referred to deficiencies that had little or no immediate impact on safety but indicated non-compliance with formal requirements. Major deficiencies included cases where safety could be compromised or where legally mandated elements were missing altogether.

After each inspection, the completed forms were reviewed and digitized for analysis. Quantitative responses were analyzed according to predefined categories, and qualitative observations were transcribed. To ensure consistency, a review process was conducted to check for missing or inconsistent entries before compiling the data for further analysis.

All inspections were carried out with the explicit consent of the property owners. Participants were informed of the scope and purpose of the study, and no personal identifying information was published. Photographs taken during site visits were used solely for documentation and reporting purposes and were anonymized in all project materials.

3 RESULTS

The evaluation of 60 small-scale PV systems revealed significant variability in compliance with mandatory installation and safety standards. None of inspected systems were fully compliant, while 40 % exhibited minor deficiencies, and 60 % showed significant deficiencies in at least one area. The most frequent and severe deficiencies were observed in commissioning inspections and related documentation, system labelling, and certain protection arrangements. Missing or inadequate documentation and deviations in the selection and installation of equipment were also common findings.

Positive observations were also made. Many systems demonstrated good adherence to basic wiring practices, and recent installations more often placed inverters in non-combustible environments, improving fire safety. In addition, avoidance of unnecessary DC isolators has become more common in newer systems, reflecting

evolving best practices. These trends were broadly similar in systems installed both before and after the 2023 update to national standards, although some recent improvements were noted in specific aspects of installation quality.

Next, the results are presented in detail under eight individual evaluation topics (sections 1-8).

3.1 Commissioning inspection and inspection report

None of the inspected systems had a commissioning inspection report that fully complied with the legal and standard requirements. In a total of ten sites (17%), the commissioning inspection report for the PV system was either unavailable or had not been handed over to the property owner. Therefore, the relative results presented in this section are based on the 50 sites where the commissioning inspection report was available. Among these, AC-side measurements were carried out in 49 sites (98%), and DC-side measurements in 40 sites (80%). However, both AC and DC measurement results were included in the report in only 39 sites (65%).

Among the sites where AC-side measurements had been performed, only 25% of the commissioning inspection reports met the content requirements specified in standard SFS 6000-6 for AC-side inspections. The most common deficiencies were the absence of phase sequence verification and failure to conduct functional tests. Of the sites with DC-side inspections provided, the requirements set out in standard SFS-EN 62446-1 were fully met in only 20% of the reports. In 72% of the sites (with DC-side inspections provided), the measurement results were not compared to the prevailing conditions at the time of measurement. Measurement results cannot be considered reliable unless they are assessed against the actual conditions during the measurement.

Table III summarizes the key findings related to the commissioning inspection and the associated documentation.

Table III: Summary of findings related to the commissioning inspection and inspection report (n = 60)

Indicator	Number of systems	Share (%)
Inspection report provided	50	83%
AC-side measurements provided	49	98% [1]
Complete AC-side measurements	12	25% [2]
DC-side measurements provided	39	78% [1]
Complete DC-side measurements	8	20% [3]
Summary:		
Fully compliant	8	13%
Minor deficiencies	24	40%
Major deficiencies	28	47%

[1] Value refers to sites with inspection report provided
[2] Value refers to sites with AC-measurements provided
[3] Value refers to sites with DC-measurements provided

3.2 System labeling and documentation

Standards governing PV installations set requirements for both system labeling and the provision of documentation to end users. The assessment revealed that while some basic labeling was typically in place, many systems lacked key safety-related markings, such as clear instructions for disconnection before maintenance. Label durability and readability were generally acceptable, though occasional issues were noted.

Documentation was often incomplete. Although basic system and installer information was commonly available, more detailed technical documents—such as component datasheets, wiring diagrams, and maintenance instructions—were frequently missing. In several cases, no documentation had been provided at all.

Overall, none of the systems reviewed fully met the labeling and documentation requirements. Most had minor deficiencies, while a significant number exhibited more serious deficiencies. Table IV summarizes the key findings concerning labeling and documentation.

Table IV: Summary of findings related to labeling and documentation (n = 60)

Indicator	Number of systems	Share (%)
Labeling:		
Required warning-labeling at distribution boards	54	90%
Required inverter disconnection instruction labeling	22	36%
Warning labels at DC-side components	44	73%
Compliant string cable labeling	23	38%
Documentation:		
Inverter datasheet provided	35	58%
Solar panel datasheet provided	27	45%
Mounting system datasheet provided	10	17%
Operating and maintenance instructions provided	20	33%
System specific wiring diagram provided	7	12%
Any document provided	5	8%
Summary:		
Fully compliant	0	0%
Minor deficiencies	38	63%
Major deficiencies	22	37%

3.3 Electrical protection

All inspected systems were equipped with appropriate protection measures against overcurrent and electric shock. On the AC side, overcurrent protection and automatic disconnection of supply were implemented consistently across all systems in accordance with applicable standards. No deficiencies were identified in these protections.

On the DC side, overcurrent protection was also implemented as required in all but one system. In that specific case, multiple panel strings were connected in parallel, which would have required separate string-specific overcurrent protection. However, this protection was missing. Despite this single shortcoming, all systems were assessed to have adequate protection against electric shock.

3.4 Means of disconnection

The assessment showed that AC-side disconnection was implemented appropriately in almost all sites, with only isolated deviations such as a missing disconnection switch or restricted access for the grid operator. This high compliance level is likely influenced by the requirements set by distribution system operators, who typically demand reliable AC isolation as part of the grid connection process, in addition to the national standards mandating it.

DC-side isolation was examined in systems without microinverters (57 sites). In line with the latest edition of SFS 6000 (published in 2022, binding from 2023), separate DC isolators should be avoided unless specifically required for maintenance or safety purposes. The updated requirement aims to reduce unnecessary components that could introduce additional failure points or increase maintenance needs. Most systems (approx. 80%) relied on the inverter's internal DC switch in combination with disconnectable plug connectors. A smaller share used external DC switches, some of which were considered redundant. In one case, there was no capability to perform DC isolation at all, as neither switches nor plug connectors were available. Overall, both AC and DC isolation methods generally met the standard requirements, though minor deviations and questionable design choices were observed in a limited number of systems.

Table V summarizes the key findings regarding means of disconnection on both the AC and DC sides.

Table V: Summary of findings on AC and DC side disconnection methods (n = 60)

Indicator	Number of systems	Share (%)
AC-side:		
Required AC-side isolator installed	59	98%
Lockable and DSO-accessible AC-side isolator	58	97%
DC side:		
Disconnection with inverter's internal DC-switch and disconnectable plug connectors	45	79% [1]
Disconnection with separate DC-isolator (before 2023)	9	36% [2]
Disconnection with separate DC-isolator (2023 or after)	3	9% [3]
DC isolators considered redundant (before 2023)	3	12% [2]
DC isolators considered redundant (2023 or after)	1	3% [3]
No compliant disconnection	1	2% [1]
Summary:		
Fully compliant	53	88%
Minor deficiencies	5	8%
Major deficiencies	2	3%

[1] Value refers to systems with string inverter configurations (n = 57).
[2] Value refers to systems with string inverter configurations installed before 2023 (n = 25).
[3] Values refers to systems with string inverter configurations installed 2023 or after (n = 32).

3.5 Selection and installation of electrical equipment

The assessment reviewed how appropriately system components had been selected and installed, with a particular focus on dimensioning, compatibility, and compliance with relevant standards and manufacturer instructions.

Most systems met the requirements, but various types of deficiencies were identified. In some cases, string voltages or currents exceeded inverter specifications, or component ratings were not fully adequate. Connector compatibility, especially among DC-side disconnectable plug connectors (commonly referred to as MC4), was often difficult to verify after installation. However, in several systems visible mismatches were observed, where connectors from different manufacturers had been joined together in contradiction to standard requirements

Installation practices around the inverter varied. While many inverters were properly mounted and had adequate clearance, some were installed on combustible surfaces or lacked the free space specified by the manufacturer. Although inverter manufacturers had already required non-combustible mounting surfaces in their installation instructions, this requirement was only later added to the updated SFS 6000 standard. This update is also reflected in the results, which are divided in Table VI between systems installed before and after 2023.

Table VI: Summary of findings related to selection and installation of electrical equipment (n = 60)

Indicator	Number of systems	Share (%)
Matched disconnectable plug connectors (MC4)	10	17%
Mismatched disconnectable plug connectors (MC4)	7	12%
Disconnectable plug connectors (MC4) compatibility unverifiable	43	72%
Inverter installed on non-combustible surface (before 2023)	14	53% [1]
Inverter installed on non-combustible surface (2023 or after)	2	6% [2]
Adequate inverter clearance	40	67%
Summary:		
Fully compliant	40	67%
Minor deficiencies	17	28%
Major deficiencies	3	5%

[1] Value refers to systems installed before 2023 (n = 26)
[2] Value refers to systems installed 2023 or after (n = 34)

3.6 Cabling and routing
This section reviewed whether AC and DC cables were selected in accordance with applicable standards and manufacturer instructions, and how mechanical protection along the cable routes was implemented.

Cable types and conductor sizes were generally appropriate for the application. On the AC side, standard installation cables with typical conductor diameters were commonly used, and most systems met the relevant requirements. DC-side cabling was also mostly implemented using suitable cable types and installation methods.

Mechanical protection of cables and cable routes varied. In a number of systems, observations included insufficient physical shielding, loose fastening, or exposed cable routes, particularly on rooftops and at structural penetrations. Minor deficiencies were relatively common, and a smaller number of systems showed more significant issues related to potential damage to cable insulation. Similar types of deficiencies were also noted in AC-side cabling, such as unprotected wall penetrations. The findings indicate variability in how mechanical protection was addressed across the assessed systems.

More detailed numerical results are not presented for this section, as installation practices and the related risks are difficult to compare directly against standard requirements or manufacturer instructions.

3.7 Equipotential bonding
The assessment reviewed whether potential equalization was implemented in accordance with applicable standards and inverter manufacturer requirements. In systems where specific equalization measures were required, most installations followed the instructions given. In microinverter-based systems (3 sites), where equalization was not required, implementation practices varied.

The extent and quality of the equalization could be confirmed in a portion of the sites. In many cases, rooftop accessibility limited verification, especially regarding connections to mounting structures and module frames. Where assessments were possible, implementation was generally appropriate, although some deficiencies were observed in the connections or coverage of bonded parts.

An overview of the findings is presented in Table VII.

Table VII: Summary of findings related to equipotential bonding (n = 60)

Indicator	Number of systems	Share (%)
Potential equalization required (by standard or manufacturer)	57	95%
System connected to potential equalization	52	87%
Connections made appropriately	29	56% [1]
All required parts connected	18	35% [1]
Summary:		
Fully compliant	37	62%
Minor deficiencies	14	23%
Major deficiencies	9	15%

[1] Values refer to systems with potential equalization implemented (n = 52).

3.8 Mechanical installation
This section examined the mechanical aspects of PV system installation, including module placement on the roof, mounting system attachments, shading conditions, and cable fastening between modules.

Most systems were installed with consistent distances between the array and roof edges. The positioning of arrays generally avoided significant external shading, though some minor shading from nearby structures was observed in a few cases.

Mounting systems and panel attachments were typically implemented using standard installation methods. Cable fastening between modules varied in quality, with deficiencies observed in a notable share of the systems. In several cases, the fastening solutions used could have been more robust or better suited to outdoor conditions.

4 DISCUSSION

The inspection results confirm earlier findings on the prevalence of deficiencies in commissioning inspections and system documentation. In many cases, the commissioning inspection report was incomplete or missing, despite the requirement in the Finnish Electrical Safety Act (1135/2016) to perform and document the inspection. These deficiencies appear to be linked to limited knowledge of PV-specific requirements and insufficient ability to interpret test results. Without adequate competence, installers may struggle to prepare reports in accordance with SFS 6000-6 and SFS-EN 62446-1. In Finland, small-scale PV systems can be installed by any electrical contractor under the supervision of a qualified supervisor of electrical works, but PV-specific training is not mandatory. Improving the quality and completeness of commissioning inspections therefore requires targeted training on PV-related risks and test procedures, combined with effective supervision by the supervisor of electrical works.

System documentation was also generally poor. While basic system and installer details were usually available, many legally required items—such as wiring diagrams, datasheets, and operating and maintenance instructions—were missing. These deficiencies are common in small-scale electrical work, particularly when no separate designer is involved. As many of these documents are normally prepared during a design phase, their absence suggests that design and installation are often handled by the same contractor without dedicated design resources. One potential improvement would be to integrate the SFS-EN 62446-1 documentation requirements into building permit or grid-connection procedures. Several distribution system operators already require commissioning inspection reports as part of the connection process; extending this requirement to the full documentation package could strengthen compliance.

Some technical aspects showed consistently high levels of compliance. Electrical protection on both AC and DC sides was generally implemented correctly, with only one serious DC-side deficiency—missing string-specific overcurrent protection in a parallel configuration. This isolated case demonstrates that even uncommon errors can have significant safety implications and may remain undetected without systematic inspections. AC-side disconnection arrangements were almost universally compliant, which can be explained by the requirements set by DSOs, who typically demand reliable AC isolation as a condition for grid connection. However, a small number of questionable design choices were observed, such as redundant DC isolators or the absence of DC-side disconnection, that may reduce the system's fire safety or safety during maintenance operations

By contrast, mechanical protection of cable routes and compliance with inverter manufacturer installation instructions were less consistent. Frequent deficiencies included unprotected penetrations through walls or roofs and loosely fastened rooftop cables, increasing the risk of insulation damage over time. Panel placement was generally in line with good practice, but fastening of inter-module cables was in some cases insufficiently robust for long-term outdoor conditions. As these tasks represent relatively basic installation work, such deficiencies may reflect installer attitudes, oversight, or limited awareness of requirements rather than technical complexity.

Certain parts of the inspection process were subject to verification limitations. In many systems, the compatibility of DC-side disconnectable plug connectors could not be confirmed because manufacturer markings were no longer visible after installation. Similarly, the assessment of equipotential bonding was sometimes constrained by limited rooftop access, preventing full verification of connections to module frames or mounting structures. These limitations introduce some uncertainty into the reported compliance rates in these areas.

There are also signs of improvement over time. For example, installing inverters on non-combustible surfaces have become more common since this requirement was incorporated into the national SFS 6000 standard. This indicates that transferring manufacturer recommendations into binding national standards can have a measurable positive effect on installation quality. Likewise, the updated requirement to avoid unnecessary DC isolators is reflected in the lower share of such devices among systems installed in 2023 or later. While redundant isolators were still found in a small number of newer installations, their declining prevalence suggests that the revised guidance is beginning to influence practices. However, persistent non-compliance with other requirements, such as adequate inverter clearance, shows that standards and manufacturer guidelines alone are not sufficient without effective training, supervision, and enforcement.

The results of this study are well aligned with those of an earlier investigation conducted in Finland [11], which also identified frequent deficiencies in commissioning inspections, documentation, and installation practices. The overall picture is therefore very similar, indicating that the challenges observed are not isolated cases but recurring patterns in small-scale PV installations. Compared to the earlier investigation, however, the present work provides a more detailed basis for analysis, as the systematic inspection protocol and broader set of evaluation topics enable a closer examination of specific problems and areas in need of improvement.

It is important to note that the inspected PV systems were recruited on a voluntary basis and were mainly located in detached houses. The sample is not statistically representative of all small-scale PV installations in Finland, and results should therefore be interpreted as indicative of common compliance patterns rather than precise population-wide estimates. Nevertheless, voluntary recruitment allowed for a wide range of installation types, contractors, and commissioning years, providing valuable qualitative insight into recurring strengths and weaknesses in current practices.

Future research could focus on installations where a PV-related fire or near-miss incident has occurred. Comparing such cases with the compliance patterns identified in this study would allow for a more accurate assessment of the real-world safety implications of the observed deficiencies. This evidence could support the prioritization of regulatory updates, targeted training programs, and inspection practices in areas presenting the greatest actual risk.

5 CONCLUSION

This study conducted systematic on-site inspections of 60 small-scale photovoltaic systems installed in Finland primarily between 2022 and 2024 to assess compliance with the Finnish Electrical Safety Act and mandatory national and international standards. The evaluation covered all main aspects of PV installations, including commissioning inspections, documentation, labeling, electrical protection, means of disconnection, equipment selection and installation, cabling, equipotential bonding, and mechanical installation.

None of the inspected systems met all mandatory requirements, and all exhibited either minor or significant deficiencies. The most common issues were incomplete or missing commissioning inspection reports, inadequate documentation, and deficiencies in labeling. In contrast, electrical protection and AC-side disconnection were generally implemented correctly, and several installation practices have shown measurable improvement over time, such as wider adoption of non-combustible mounting surfaces for inverters and fewer unnecessary DC isolators in newer systems.

As the inspected systems were selected through voluntary participation and were mainly located in detached houses, the sample does not statistically represent all small-scale PV systems in Finland. The results should therefore be considered indicative of general compliance patterns rather than precise estimates for the entire installation base. Nevertheless, the study provides valuable insight into recurring strengths and weaknesses, as well as the visibility of recent national standard changes in practical installation work.

The results underline that standard updates can have a clear and positive effect on installation quality when requirements are specific and binding. However, persistent deficiencies in commissioning inspections, documentation, and certain installation details indicate that updated requirements alone are not sufficient. Improving compliance will require targeted training and education for installers, with emphasis on PV-specific risks, test procedures, and documentation obligations, supported by effective supervision from qualified supervisors of electrical work. Requiring commissioning inspection reports and related documentation as a condition for grid connection or building permit approval by authorities and DSOs could also strengthen compliance in practice. Strengthening both competence and oversight will contribute to safer, more reliable, and longer-lasting PV systems in Finland. Similar challenges and improvement needs have also been observed internationally, making the findings relevant beyond the Finnish context.

6 ACKNOWLEDGMENT

The authors would like to acknowledge the support of the Finnish Centre for Electrical Safety and Energy Efficiency (STEK).

7 DECLARATION OF GENERATIVE AI AND AI-ASSISTED TECHNOLOGIES IN THE WRITING PROCESS

During the preparation of this work the authors used ChatGPT-5 to improve readability and language. After using this tool, the authors reviewed and edited the content as needed and take full responsibility for the content of the publication.

8 REFERENCES

[1] Statistics Finland, "Altogether 95 per cent of Finland's electricity production was based on fossil-free energy in 2024." Accessed: Aug. 14, 2025. [Online]. Available: https://stat.fi/en/publication/cm1kktw8ualm207vwnzpsmpc8

[2] European Commission, "European Solar Charter," Brussels, 2024. Accessed: Aug. 14, 2025. [Online]. Available: https://energy.ec.europa.eu/topics/renewable-energy/solar-energy/european-solar-charter_en

[3] J. Ahola, "National Survey Report of PV Power Applications in Finland 2019," 2019. Accessed: Aug. 14, 2025. [Online]. Available: https://iea-pvps.org/wp-content/uploads/2020/09/NSR_Finland_2019.pdf

[4] *Electrical Safety Act 1135/2016*. 2016. [Online]. Available: https://www.finlex.fi/fi/laki/alkup/2016/20161135

[5] "Luettelo S10." Tukes, 2023. Accessed: Jan. 27, 2025. [Online]. Available: https://tukes.fi/teollisuus/standardit

[6] *SFS 6000-standard series: Low Voltage Electrical Installations*, 2022.

[7] Finnish Safety and Chemicals Agency (Tukes), "Luettelo S10 on päivitetty." Accessed: Jan. 13, 2025. [Online]. Available: https://tukes.fi/-/luettelo-s10-on-paivitetty

[8] *SFS-EN 62446-1: Photovoltaic (PV) systems – Requirements for testing, documentation and maintenance – Part 1: Grid connected systems – Documentation, commissioning tests and inspection*, 2016.

[9] Finnish Safety and Chemicals Agency (Tukes), "Duties of Supervisors of Electrical Works." Accessed: Aug. 14, 2025. [Online]. Available: https://tukes.fi/en/electricity/electrical-works-and-contracting/duties-of-supervisors-of-electrical-works

[10] J. Ylipaino, K. Kallioharju, A. Kortetmäki, M. Ylinen, and J. Koskela, "Ensuring Compliance in the Installation of Residential Photovoltaic Systems: A Study of Standards and Practices in Finland," in *2025 21st International Conference on the European Energy Market (EEM)*, May 2025, pp. 1–5. doi: 10.1109/EEM64765.2025.11050297.

[11] S. Hatakka, E. Iivonen, and J. Välimaa, "Aurinkosähköjärjestelmien asennustyön vaatimustenmukaisuus," Turvallisuus- ja kemikaalivirasto, 2022. Accessed: Jan. 13, 2025. [Online]. Available: https://tukes.fi/-/aurinkosahkojarjestelmien-asennuksissa-tehdaan-paljon-virheita

[12] A. Rasinkoski, "Aurinkosähkön paloriskit ja sammutusturvallisuus," 2020. Accessed: Aug. 14, 2025. [Online]. Available: https://www.motiva.fi/ratkaisut/uusiutuva_energia/aurinkosahko/aurinkosahkon_paloturvallisuus/aurinkosahkon_paloturvallisuus_-projekti_2020-2021

[13] M. Pulkkinen, "Aurinkosähköjärjestelmien asentaminen, havaitut virheet sekä koulutus," 2023. Accessed: Aug. 14, 2025. [Online]. Available: https://lutpub.lut.fi/handle/10024/166708

[14] A. Kortetmäki, M. Ylinen, and J. Ylipaino, "Omatuotannon vaikutus pienkiinteistön sähköverkkoon," Tampereen ammattikorkeakoulu, publication, 2023. Accessed: Aug. 14, 2025. [Online]. Available: http://www.theseus.fi/handle/10024/804597

[15] M. Gradecka and Y. Lethbridge, "Fire and Solar PV Systems - Investigations and Evidence," BRE National Solar Centre, May 2018. Accessed: Aug. 14, 2025. [Online]. Available: https://assets.publishing.service.gov.uk/media/5c90a30840f0b633ff9a3537/Fires_and_solar_PV_systems-Investigations_Evidence_Issue_2.9.pdf

[16] L. Sloof-Hoek *et al.*, "Eindrapport Verbeteren monitoring en voorschriften brandveiligheid (BI)PV," TNO, Sept. 2025. Accessed: Aug. 14, 2025. [Online]. Available: https://www.tno.nl/en/newsroom/2024/11/building-fires-solar-panels-first-study/

[17] "Assessing Fire Risks in Photovoltaic Systems and Developing Safety Concepts for Risk Minimization," TÜV Rheinland Energie und Umwelt GmbH, 2018. Accessed: Aug. 14, 2025. [Online]. Available: https://www.ise.fraunhofer.de/en/research-projects/pv-brandschutz.html

THE IMPACT OF VIRTUAL NET-METERING ALLOCATION ON SELF-CONSUMPTION RATIOS IN MULTI-DWELLING BUILDING PHOTOVOLTAIC SYSTEMS

Aki Kortetmäki[1, 2], Juho Ylipaino[1, 2], Kari Kallioharju[1, 2], Juha Koskela[2], Pertti Järventausta[2]
[1]Tampere University of Applied Sciences
Kuntokatu 3, 33520 Tampere
[2]Tampere University
Korkeakoulunkatu 7, 33720 Tampere

ABSTRACT: Collective self-consumption (CSC) in multi-dwelling buildings (MDBs) became feasible in Finland following EU regulations through the Credit Calculation Model (CCM) with virtual net-metering integrated into the national Datahub system. This study evaluates self-consumption ratios (SCR) under three metering configurations—common-area consumption (CC), CCM, and behind-the-meter (BM)—using hourly consumption data (2019–2021) from 32 MDBs (14–168 apartments, built 1960s–2020s) in Pirkanmaa region. PV production was simulated with PVGIS-SARAH3 for 10–60 kWp systems at south, 45° east, and 45° west orientations (18° tilt). The goal was to quantify SCR gains from adopting CCM and to compare BM and CCM to guide simulations when only aggregated building-level data are available. CCM increased SCR by approximately 30% for 20–60 kWp systems compared with CC. BM–CCM differences averaged 6 to 9% (range 0 to 19.5%) for 20–60 kWp systems. West-oriented arrays achieved slightly higher SCR due to better load alignment. These findings provide quantitative tools for DSOs, housing companies, and PV designers to improve SCR estimation and PV project viability in MDBs. While results are based on Pirkanmaa, they offer guidance for broader contexts until higher-resolution metering and flexible loads are incorporated in future studies.
Keywords: Photovoltaic, Self-Consumption, Multi-dwelling buildings, Energy communities

1 INTRODUCTION

Collective renewable energy use across Europe now enables consumers to participate actively in local energy generation and sharing under EU directives promoting energy communities and collective self-consumption [1], [2]. Finland incorporated these concepts into its regulatory framework by defining groups of active customers and local energy communities in 2021, and by adding the definition of Citizen Energy Communities in 2023 [3], [4].

To operationalize collective self-consumption (CSC) in multi-dwelling buildings (MDBs), Finland introduced the Credit Calculation Model (CCM), known in Finnish as "hyvityslaskenta", in 2021 and subsequently integrated it into the national centralized data exchange system, Datahub [5]. CCM enables virtual net-metering, where photovoltaic (PV) production exceeding common-area consumption (CC)—such as corridor lighting, elevators, and ventilation—is redistributed on an hourly basis (or in 15-minute intervals where advanced smart metering is available) among shareholders according to a predefined sharing coefficient.

Before CCM was introduced, PV generation in MDBs could only offset CC—even when the surplus energy was consumed within the same building—and any excess was credited as sold energy. CCM thus represents a major step forward by allowing surplus production to be allocated to apartments. A third approach involves a single collective electricity contract with secondary apartment-level meters. In this so-called behind-the-meter (BM) system, the self-consumption ratio (SCR) is typically highest, as surplus energy is recorded only when PV production exceeds the total aggregated load during the metering period. However, Finland's Electricity Market Act grants residents the right to opt out of BM arrangements, making BM less common in housing-company structures and more typical in rental properties [6]. Figure 1 illustrates these metering configurations in MDBs, including separate CC meter (1), apartment-level meters (2), and separate BM meter in case of collective electricity contract (3).

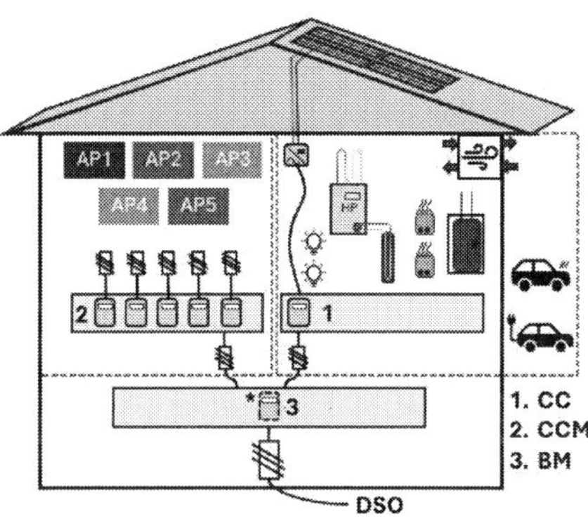

Figure 1: Metering arrangements in Finnish multi-dwelling buildings. BM is used only when a collective electricity contract is in place.

Internationally, extensive research has focused on optimizing PV self-consumption and sizing strategies under various sharing schemes and energy community models. For example, in Nordic countries, Berg et al. [7] studied how two static sharing keys affect cost distribution in a residential energy community in Norway. Similar studies in Spain [8], [9], France [10], and Austria [11] have examined both static and dynamic sharing coefficients under different energy community setups.

Our previous work also reported the effects on SCR of four different static sharing schemes, namely area-based allocation, equal allocation, ownership shares in the housing companies, and apartment floor area [12]. In Finland, allocation in MDBs is usually based on apartment ownership shares in the housing company, reflecting typical investment structures. Although hourly or quarter-hourly consumption data exist for optimal PV system size design, privacy rules often restrict DSOs to providing only aggregated building-level data or, in some cases, only common-area consumption data. Consequently, simulations of SCR can be performed for BM and CC cases but remain less accurate for CCM, where individual consumption profiles are unavailable.

Our earlier work on CCM's impact on SCR involved only two relatively large housing companies (114 and 224 apartments) and two PV system sizes, offering valuable but limited insight [13]. A broader, more diverse dataset is needed to understand how allocation methods and metering configurations affect SCR under real-world conditions.

This study addresses that gap by analyzing anonymized apartment-level hourly consumption data from 32 MDBs in the Pirkanmaa region, combined with PV production simulations for multiple system sizes and orientations. Using apartment floor area as a proxy for ownership shares—supported by prior findings from Ylipaino et al. [12], which show negligible SCR differences between area-based and ownership-based allocation—this work quantifies SCR under CCM and compares results to BM and CC cases. The findings provide practical guidance for stakeholders designing PV systems for MDBs, particularly under regulatory and data-access constraints.

2   METHODOLOGY

2.1 Data set

Data for this study were obtained from 32 multi-dwelling buildings (MDBs) located in the Pirkanmaa region of Finland. These buildings, constructed between the 1960s and 2020s, represent a diverse range of residential properties and include 14 to 168 apartments per property. Although the apartments are owned by a rental housing company, each apartment retains its own electricity meter, and residents pay for electricity based on their individual consumption.

Hourly electricity consumption data were collected for the period 2019–2021 for each apartment, together with common-area consumption. To ensure privacy, an anonymization process was conducted jointly with the property owner and the local DSO. Through this process, apartment-level consumption data were linked to each apartment's floor area and the property address without exposing identifiable personal information. This linkage enabled the aggregation of apartment consumption with common-area consumption for each building and the calculation of sharing coefficients based on apartment floor area. Figure 2 presents the total annual consumption of each building, showing both common-area consumption and total aggregated consumption.

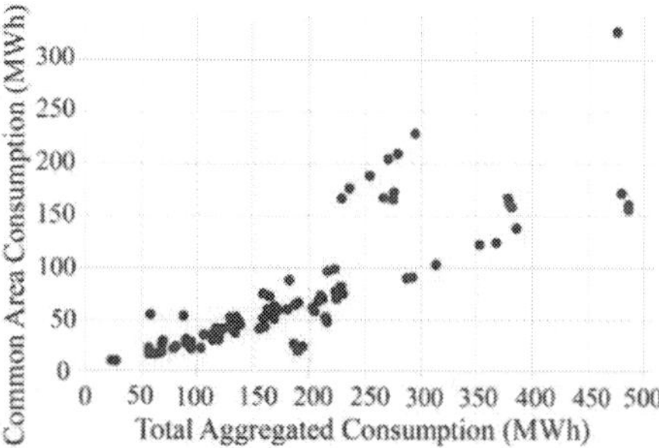

Figure 2: Annual common-area consumption in relation to total aggregated consumption in the building (n=32).

Hourly PV production was simulated using PVGIS for a range of system sizes (10, 20, 30, 40, 50, and 60 kWp) and orientations (south, 45° west, and 45° east), assuming a typical 18° roof tilt. The PVGIS-SARAH3 solar radiation database was employed [14].

2.2 Calculation models

The SCR was calculated for each property using three metering solutions—CC, CCM, and BM. Calculations were performed separately for each study year to capture annual variability, and all data handling, cleaning, and calculations were conducted in R.

In the first phase, surplus energy was calculated for common-area consumption. Annual surplus energy for the CC configuration was determined as shown in Equation 1.

$$S_{CC} = \sum_{\substack{t=1 \\ E_{PV}(t) > C_{CC}(t)}}^{a} E_{PV}(t) - C_{CC}(t) \tag{1}$$

where a is the number of hours in a year, E_{PV} is the PV energy production at time t, and C_{CC} is the common-area consumption at time t. Surplus energy occurs at time t when PV production exceeds C_{CC}.

For the CCM configuration with virtual net-metering, the share of production exceeding C_{CC} was distributed among shareholders n according to the sharing coefficient, which were based on each apartment's floor area relative to the building's total living area. Surplus energy S_{CCM} was then calculated using Equation 2.

$$S_{CCM} = \sum_{t=1}^{a} \sum_{n=1}^{N} S_n(t,n) \Leftrightarrow$$
$$\sum_{\substack{t=1 \\ k(n) \cdot S_{CC}(t) > C_n(n,t)}}^{a} \sum_{n=1}^{N} k(n) \cdot S_{CC}(t) - C_n(n,t) \tag{2}$$

Where N is the total number of shareholders, S_n is the surplus energy of shareholder n, and C_n is the consumption of shareholder n. Surplus energy occurs at time t when the amount of shared energy allocated to a shareholder exceeds that shareholder's consumption.

Surplus energy under the BM configuration was calculated using Equation 3.

$$S_{BM} = \sum_{\substack{t=1 \\ E_{PV}(t) > C_B(t)}}^{a} E_{PV}(t) - C_B(t) \tag{3}$$

Where C_B is the total aggregated consumption of the building.

After determining hourly surplus energy, the self-consumption ratio (SCR) for each metering scenario was calculated using Equation 4.

$$SCR = \sum_{t=1}^{a} \frac{E_{PV}(t) - S(t)}{E_{PV}(t)} \cdot 100\% \tag{4}$$

Where S represents surplus energy for the CC, BM, or CCM configuration. Finally, the difference in SCR between BM and CCM configurations was calculated for each building and year, as this difference represents a key outcome for improving SCR simulations when only aggregated consumption data are available.

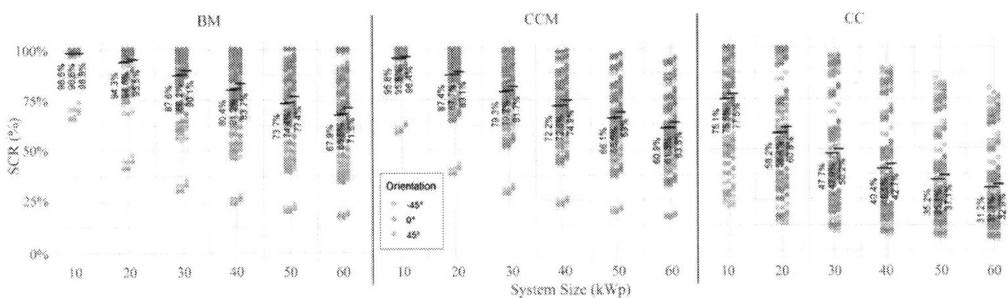

Figure 3: Results for SCR with BM, CCM, and CC configurations.

3   RESULTS

SCR were calculated for each building, each study year, each PV system size, and each metering configuration. Figures were first prepared to present these combinations individually. Figure 3 shows the SCR of each building for the study years using BM, CCM, and CC. For each configuration and system size, red points on the left represent systems oriented 45° east (south-east), green points in the middle represent south oriented systems, and blue points on the right represent systems oriented 45° west (south-west).

Across these configurations, substantial variation in SCR is observed between different buildings. A consistent trend emerges in which west-oriented systems show slightly higher SCR values. This reflects a better alignment with consumption profiles, though it is also partly attributable to the lower overall energy production of west-oriented systems compared with south-oriented systems.

As the differences between metering methods were a primary focus of this study, Figures 4 and 5 present the SCR differences for each individual point shown earlier, together with average values. Figure 4 illustrates the difference between CC and CCM configurations, while Figure 5 shows the difference between CCM and BM.

On average, adopting CCM in a building increased SCR by approximately 30% for system sizes between 20 kWp and 60 kWp across all orientations compared with the CC configuration. For 10 kWp systems, the increase ranged from 18.9% to 20.7%, depending on orientation.

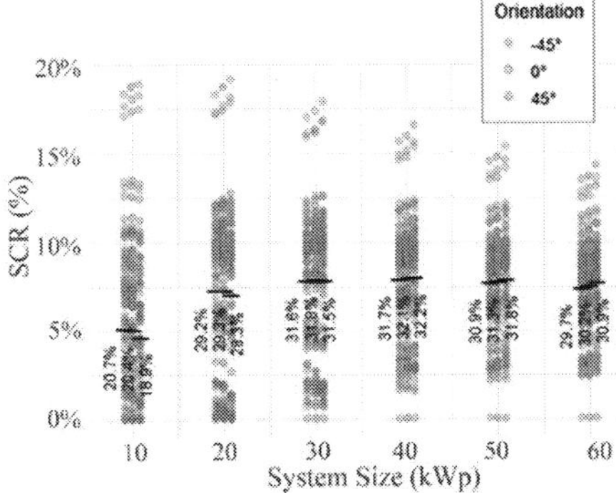

Figure 4: Difference in SCR between CC and CCM configurations.

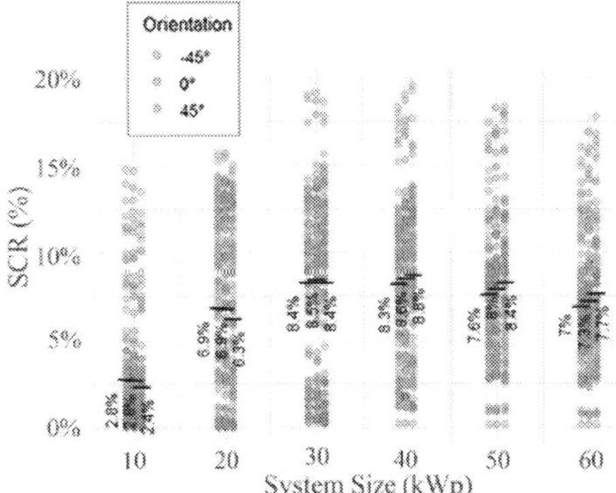

Figure 5: Difference in SCR between BM and CCM configurations.

When comparing average values between CCM and BM, clear differences were also observed. This occurred because some individual apartments did not consume their allocated share of production—even when total building consumption exceeded PV production—which caused SCR values under CCM to remain slightly lower. For 10 kWp systems, the difference between CCM and BM averaged 2.4–2.8%, reflecting the generally high SCR across all configurations at this small system size. For 20–60 kWp systems, the difference varied between 6.3% and 8.8% on average across orientations. However, high variability was present among buildings, with differences ranging from 0% up to 19.5%.

4   DISCUSSION

This study extends existing knowledge on self-consumption ratios (SCR) by incorporating a large and diverse dataset of multi-dwelling buildings (MDBs) and PV system configurations. In the first phase of analysis, real data–based calculations demonstrated how adopting the Credit Calculation Model (CCM) in MDBs has significantly increased viability through higher SCR compared with earlier situations where only common-area consumption (CC) was utilized. Although CCM has been available for several years, information dissemination to shareholders and housing companies has progressed gradually. These results provide quantitative evidence for professionals and stakeholders to communicate the benefits of CCM adoption. However, the wide range of differences between buildings and system sizes underscores the need for case-specific calculations to produce accurate SCR estimates.

The second major finding of this study concerns the difference in SCR between BM and CCM configurations. This comparison is critical for simulations where only aggregated building-level consumption data are available—data that inherently represent BM conditions. The results presented here offer a stronger empirical basis than our previous studies, which were limited to two large MDBs (114 and 224 apartments) with PV systems of 34 kWp and 59.3 kWp, respectively, oriented 71.3° east. While earlier work reported SCR differences of 5–15% [13], our new study—covering 32 buildings—revealed differences ranging from 0% to 19.5%. The variation suggests that PV size relative to total consumption, apartment numbers, occupancy behavior, and common-area load characteristics all influence how closely CCM-based SCR approaches BM results. These factors merit further exploration in future research.

Orientation and system size effects were also examined. On average, west-oriented systems achieved slightly higher SCR than comparable east-oriented systems, likely reflecting better temporal alignment with evening consumption patterns. However, this topic warrants dedicated studies to fully assess the profitability and performance trade-offs of orientation under different metering configurations and sensitivity parameters.

This study focused on SCR variation between different metering configurations. Nevertheless, while SCR is one of the main parameters in assessing the viability of PV systems, other factors also influence the overall feasibility of different setups. For example, orientation affects not only total production and alignment with consumption but also the average electricity market prices during production hours. Furthermore, as this study concentrated only on SCR differences between CCM and BM, it should be noted that collective electricity contracts may provide additional economic benefits through reduced DSO fees and potentially more favorable agreements with energy providers due to larger aggregated demand [13].

Several limitations should be considered when applying these findings. All studied buildings were located in Pirkanmaa, Finland, and owned by the same rental housing company. Consumption characteristics and PV production patterns may differ in other regions, climates, or ownership models such as limited liability housing companies, which are common in Finland. In addition, this study did not analyze differences arising from variation between buildings and apartments or from different electricity contract types. Nevertheless, because the CCM–BM difference is largely driven by probabilistic occupancy effects, and given the wide variation already observed, these results offer a robust basis for estimating SCR in PV simulations for MDBs in other contexts.

This study used hourly consumption data, consistent with current SCR calculation practices. However, Finland is rolling out new smart meters capable of 15-minute intervals, which could influence the difference between BM and CCM. Shorter interval would require individual apartments to match their allocated production more precisely within each interval, potentially increasing the CCM–BM gap observed here. Future studies should revisit these comparisons using higher-resolution metering data.

In this study, the sharing coefficient was based on apartment floor area, providing a close approximation of the typical situation in which coefficients are assigned according to ownership shares. However, there are no strict regulations on how the coefficient must be defined among customers, so in some cases it may differ—potentially influencing the SCR gap between CCM and BM configurations. In several European countries, studies have also explored dynamic coefficient strategies, particularly in larger and more complex energy communities, to identify methods for maximizing the total SCR within the community while simultaneously narrowing the gap between CCM and BM [8], [9], [10], [11].

5   CONCLUSION

The main motivation of this study was to improve understanding of the SCR gap between two metering methods—CCM and BM—because in practice, only aggregated building-level consumption data (representing BM conditions) are often available. At the same time, we evaluated the increase in SCR compared with the recent situation in Finnish MDBs, in which only common-area consumption (CC) was considered.

A key finding is that adopting CCM increases SCR by approximately 30% for medium-to-large PV systems (20–60 kWp) compared with the earlier situation where only CC was utilized. For the smallest 10 kWp systems, the average change was about 19–21%, primarily because SCR was already high under both metering configurations.

To support SCR simulations for CCM in MDBs using aggregated consumption data, we found that the difference between BM and CCM configurations averaged 6–9% for 20–60 kWp systems, with values ranging from 0% to 19.5% across all studied buildings, orientations, and years. For smaller 10 kWp systems, the difference was only 2–3% on average.

These results provide numerical tools for DSOs, housing companies, and PV designers to improve SCR estimation and PV project profitability assessments in MDBs. The findings are based on Pirkanmaa region buildings owned by a single rental housing company and on hourly consumption data, which should be considered as limitations. Nevertheless, they offer valuable insights for broader contexts until more advanced tools become available.

Future research could examine the effect of 15-minute metering intervals as new smart meters are rolled out, since stricter alignment between consumption and shared production may influence the CCM–BM gap. In addition, the transition from 60-minute to 15-minute market time units and imbalance settlement periods may affect customer consumption profiles as well as the value of self-consumed and surplus energy across different time periods. Flexible loads—such as EV charging and battery storage—also represent promising avenues for increasing total SCR in MDBs when optimized for self-consumption, and these were not yet included in the buildings analyzed in this study.

Given the wide range of results observed, future studies should replicate this analysis in other regions or ownership models to provide broader validation and to examine the parameters influencing SCR variability. As this study did not address overall economic feasibility or optimal PV system design, subsequent work could incorporate economic optimization to better link SCR performance parameters with financial viability.

6 ACKNOWLEDGMENT

The authors gratefully acknowledge the support of STEK – The Association for Electrical Technology and Energy Efficiency, Tampereen Energia Sähköverkko Oy (distribution system operator), and Tampereen Vuokratalosäätiö sr. Their contributions were essential to the successful completion of this study.

7 DECLARATION OF GENERATIVE AI AND AI-ASSISTED TECHNOLOGIES IN THE WRITING PROCESS

During the preparation of this work the authors used ChatGPT-5 to improve readability and language. After using this tool, the authors reviewed and edited the content as needed and take full responsibility for the content of the publication.

8 REFERENCES

[1] Directive (EU) 2018/2001 of the European Parliament and of the Council of 11 December 2018 on the promotion of the use of energy from renewable sources. 2018. [Online]. Available: http://data.europa.eu/eli/dir/2018/2001/oj/eng

[2] Directive (EU) 2019/944 of the European Parliament and of the Council of 5 June 2019 on common rules for the internal market for electricity and amending Directive 2012/27/EU (recast) (Text with EEA relevance.), amended by Directive (EU) 2023/2413. 2019. [Online]. Available: http://data.europa.eu/eli/dir/2019/944/oj/eng

[3] Valtioneuvoston asetus sähköntoimitusten selvityksestä ja mittauksesta 767/2021. Oikeusministeriö. [Online]. Available: https://finlex.fi/fi/laki/alkup/2021/20210767

[4] Laki sähkö- ja maakaasumarkkinoiden valvonnasta annetun lain muuttamisesta 499/2023. Oikeusministeriö, Edita Publishing Oy. [Online]. Available: https://www.finlex.fi/fi/laki/alkup/2023/20230499

[5] Fingrid, 'Datahub'. [Online]. Available: https://www.fingrid.fi/en/electricity-market/datahub/

[6] Sähkömarkkinalaki 588/2013. Oikeusministeriö, Edita Lakitieto Oy. [Online]. Available: https://www.finlex.fi/fi/laki/ajantasa/2013/2013058 8

[7] K. Berg, R. Rana, H. Taxt, and M. F. Dynge, 'Economic assessment and grid impact of different sharing keys in collective self-consumption', in 2024 IEEE PES Innovative Smart Grid Technologies Europe (ISGT EUROPE), Dubrovnik, Croatia: IEEE, Oct. 2024, pp. 1–5. doi: 10.1109/ISGTEUROPE62998.2024.10863813.

[8] A. J. Gil Mena, V. F. Nasimba Medina, A. Bouakkaz, and S. Haddad, 'Analysis and optimisation of collective self-consumption in residential buildings in Spain', Energy Build., vol. 283, p. 112812, Mar. 2023, doi: 10.1016/j.enbuild.2023.112812.

[9] E. Llera-Sastresa, J. Á. Gimeno, J. L. Osorio-Tejada, and P. Portillo-Tarragona, 'Effect of Sharing Schemes on the Collective Energy Self-Consumption Feasibility', Energies, vol. 16, no. 18, p. 6564, Sept. 2023, doi: 10.3390/en16186564.

[10] A. D. Mustika, R. Rigo-Mariani, V. Debusschere, and A. Pachurka, 'A two-stage management strategy for the optimal operation and billing in an energy community with collective self-consumption', Appl. Energy, vol. 310, p. 118484, Mar. 2022, doi: 10.1016/j.apenergy.2021.118484.

[11] A. Eisner, C. Neumann, and H. Manner, 'Exploring sharing coefficients in energy communities: A simulation-based study', Energy Build., vol. 297, p. 113447, Oct. 2023, doi: 10.1016/j.enbuild.2023.113447.

[12] J. Ylipaino, A. Kortetmäki, K. Kallioharju, J. Koskela, and P. Järventausta, 'Evaluating Allocation Methods for Collective Selfconsumption in Nordic Multi-Dwelling Buildings', in 2025 21st International Conference on the European Energy Market (EEM), Lisbon, Portugal: IEEE, May 2025, pp. 1–6. doi: 10.1109/EEM64765.2025.11050109.

[13] A. Kortetmäki, J. Ylipaino, J. Koskela, K. Kallioharju, and P. Järventausta, 'The Impact of Metering Methods on Collective Self-Consumption: Insights from Multi-Dwelling Buildings in Finland', 2024. doi: 10.2139/ssrn.4782201.

[14] EU Science Hub, 'Photovoltaic Geographical Information System (PVGIS)'. [Online]. Available: https://joint-research-centre.ec.europa.eu/photovoltaic-geographical-information-system-pvgis_en

IAM MODELS AND PHOTOVOLTAIC ENERGY YIELD SIMULATIONS

Felipe Ríos-Ledesma, Laura Barrutia, Javier Ledesma, Luis Narvarte and Eduardo Lorenzo
Instituto de Energía Solar, Universidad Politécnica de Madrid, Nikola Tesla s/n, Madrid, 28031, España
felipe.rios.ledesma@upm.es, laura.barrutia@upm.es, javier.ledesma@upm.es, luis.narvarte@upm.es,
antonio.lorenzo@upm.es

ABSTRACT: The Incidence Angle Modifier (IAM) in photovoltaic (PV) modules is a relationship between the incident ray on a surface and the normal to this module surface, which causes optical losses in PV modules and consequently in PV systems. There are different directional models that describe the behavior for different angles of incidence with an assigned normalized value. These models have been implemented in SISIFO, an open and free PV simulation software developed by the IES-UPM. A simulation exercise, extended to static and tracked PV arrays, has been carried out with the aim of understanding the impact of the IAM losses and the compatibility between the different models. To quantify the losses associated with IAM, spectral effects and the presence of soiling in the locations are ignored but they could be seamlessly incorporated into the current simulation tool. The annual IAM losses calculated with the different models allow us to find correspondences between the models studied in the impact of the annual losses on global irradiance and its components. Using these values, the annual IAM losses calculated with the different models are between 1 to 3.5% in static systems and less than 1% in tracking systems.
Keywords: IAM, Correction Factor, PV Simulation, open-source.

1 Introduction

The Photovoltaic (PV) modules suffer optical losses when the sun's rays are not incident perpendicular to the plane of the arrays (POA), mainly due to increased reflections. To avoid this, most commercial PV modules today employ anti-reflective (AR) coatings [1] to improve the performance of PV modules with high angles of incidence (AOI), in the range of 60 to 90°. These optical losses depend on the position, tilt and orientation of the module, as well as factors inherent to the geographical location of the PV system: latitude, longitude and climatic conditions.

The Incidence Angle Modifier (IAM), refers to additional optical losses that occur when the angle between the incidence light on a surface and the normal to the surface, θ, is not zero. The angular losses associated with IAM can be, in clean PV modules, due to reflection caused by changes in the optical properties as they pass through the PV module materials, while in dirty modules, volumetric properties of the dust are involved, leading to additional losses [2]. This work focuses on the implementation of photovoltaic modules under optimal cleanliness conditions within the simulations. The spectral effects associated with the photovoltaic modules have been deliberately eliminated [3] to simplify the calculations and achieve greater clarity and ease in the final estimation of the performance of the PV system under study. This methodology makes it possible to reduce the complexity of the parameters involved and to obtain more direct comparative results with respect to the ideal performance of the PV module.

Existing directional models for the calculation of reflection losses have been predominantly applied in the context of optimising photovoltaic performance under standard test conditions (STC), where accurate characterisation of the incidence angle dependence of optical losses is particularly relevant. These detailed models, which vary in complexity and applicability, are summarised in Table 1. Additional information can be found on this table regarding their mathematical formulation, underlying assumptions, and the specific fitting parameters on which their correct implementation ultimately depends.

Table I: IAM models

Names	IAM model
ASHRAE (1996) [4]	$1 - b_0\left(\dfrac{1}{\cos\theta}\right)$
Air-glass (1996) [5]	$\dfrac{1 - \dfrac{1}{2}\left[\dfrac{\sin^2(\theta_T - \theta)}{\sin^2(\theta_T + \theta)} + \dfrac{\tan^2(\theta_T - \theta)}{\tan^2(\theta_T + \theta)}\right]}{1 - \left(\dfrac{n_1 - n_2}{n_1 + n_2}\right)^2}$
Martín Ruiz (2001) [6], [7]	$1 - \dfrac{\exp\left(-\dfrac{\cos\theta}{a_r}\right) - \exp\left(-\dfrac{1}{a_r}\right)}{1 - \exp\left(-\dfrac{1}{a_r}\right)}$
Sandia (2004) [8]	$a_0 + a_1\theta + a_2\theta^2 + a_3\theta^3 + a_4\theta^4 + a_5\theta^5$
Physical (2006) [9]	$\dfrac{1 - \dfrac{1}{2}\left[\dfrac{\sin^2(\theta_T - \theta)}{\sin^2(\theta_T + \theta)} + \dfrac{\tan^2(\theta_T - \theta)}{\tan^2(\theta_T + \theta)}\right]}{1 - \left(\dfrac{n_1 - n_2}{n_1 + n_2}\right)^2}\dfrac{\exp\left(-\dfrac{KL}{\cos\theta_T}\right)}{\exp(-KL)}$
Eye-sensitivity (2024) [10]	$1 - \Gamma^{(\theta - 90°)}$

Manufacturers often provide experimental IAM data through PAN files (with extension .PAN) for different angles of incidence, which allows comparative studies to be carried out. In addition, Figure 1 shows the IAM curve for ten different PV commercial modules with AR coating, whose experimental data have been provided by the manufacturers and extracted from the PVsyst software [11]. Differences depending on the type of PV module technology can be observed. These discrepancies might be considered, since they directly affect the optical reflection losses and, consequently, the overall energy yield of the PV system.

These IAM experimental results, which are essential for the parameterisation and accurate simulation of photovoltaic systems, make it possible to adjust the models of optical losses per angle of incidence and optimise the expected performance according to the constructive characteristics of the modules. Thus, the use of manufacturer-specific data, validated and hosted in tools, is vital to ensure that PV simulations reflect real-world conditions and provide reliable estimates of performance under different solar incidence conditions.

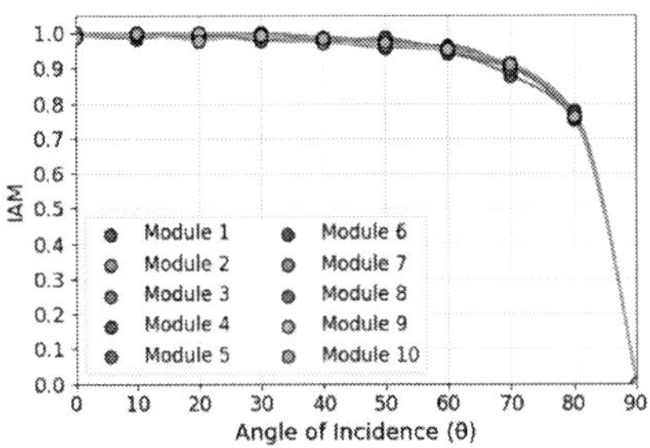

Figure 1: IAM values for different PV commercial modules with AR layers.

2 Correction factors for irradiance components

The calculation of the effective irradiance should be obtained with the lower uncertainty as possible. To reduce this uncertainty, both the effective irradiance corrected by the angle of incidence (G_{Front}^{AOI}) on the front surface of a photovoltaic module and the contribution of different solar components with their corresponding correction factors must be considered. Adjusted terms include direct solar irradiance (B_{Front}) together with circumsolar diffuse irradiance (D_{Front}^{CIR}), which are corrected by the factor $F_{B,Front} = IAM(\theta)$, reflecting the impact of the angle of incidence on the transmittance and reflection of the front glass. Diffuse isotropic diffuse irradiance (D_{Front}^{ISO}) is corrected by $F_{D,Front}$, while the diffuse component of the bright horizon (D_{Front}^{HB}) is associated with the factor $F_{HB,Front}$. In addition, the radiation reflected by the ground (R_{Front}) is considered by means of the factor $F_{R,\,Front}$. See Figure 2.

This formulation allows detailed and accurate modelling of the optical losses that affect the module's energy performance under real operating conditions, considering how the optical properties vary with solar geometry and module characteristics. Similar models are implemented and validated in simulation software such as PVsyst, and are based on the methodologies detailed in studies such as those by [8], which highlights the importance of incorporating angular corrections.

The consideration of these components and their correction factors is essential for a rigorous analysis in optimisation studies of photovoltaic systems, the design of new technologies and the evaluation of the field performance of PV systems. Specifically, these factors represent the sensitivity of each irradiance component to changes in angle of incidence and their effect on useful energy absorption, which directly influences loss modelling and the simulation of expected annual energy production.

$$G_{Front}^{AOI} = F_{B,Front}\left(B_{Front} + D_{Front}^{CIR}\right) + F_{D,Front}D_{Front}^{ISO} + F_{HB,Front}D_{Front}^{HB} + F_{R,Front}R_{Front}$$

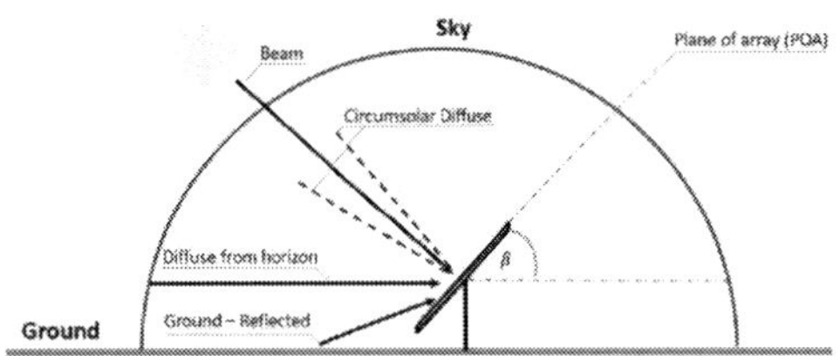

Figure 2: Components of irradiance in plane of array, POA.

The correction factors are applied to the equation that considers the solar resource components. In this work, we have corrected the directional component with the Martin-Ruiz IAM model recommended by the standard IEC-61853 [12]. This model is widely used because it fits a single experimental parameter ar.

To calculate the values of F_D, F_{HB} and F_R, the procedure for calculating the integral as proposed by [13]. Sweeping with typical ar values for widely studied PV modules.

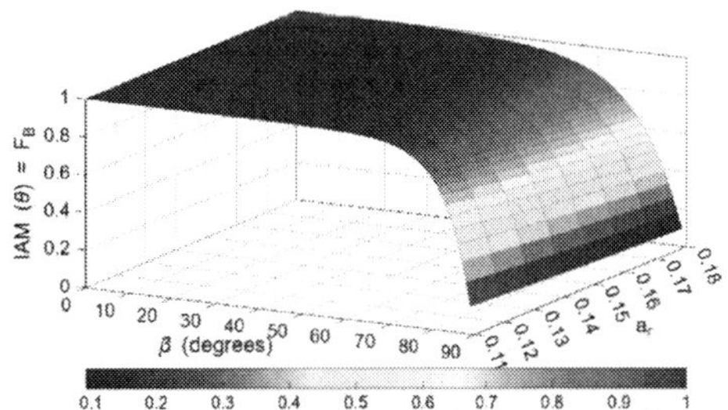

Figure 3: Correction factors F_B for Martin-Ruiz model

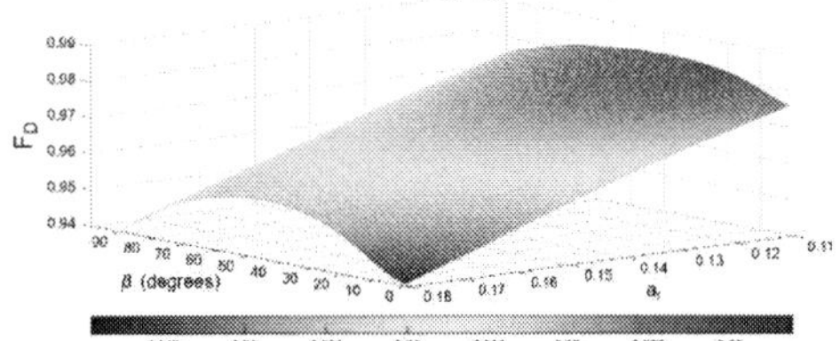

Figure 4: Correction factors F_D in sky for Martin-Ruiz model

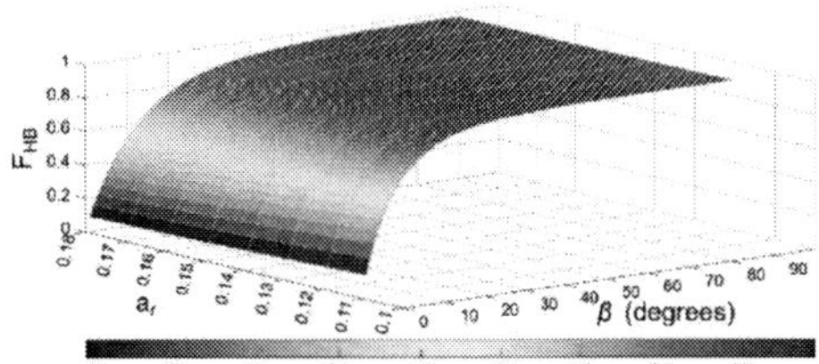

Figure 5: Correction factors F_{HB} in horizon for Martin-Ruiz mode

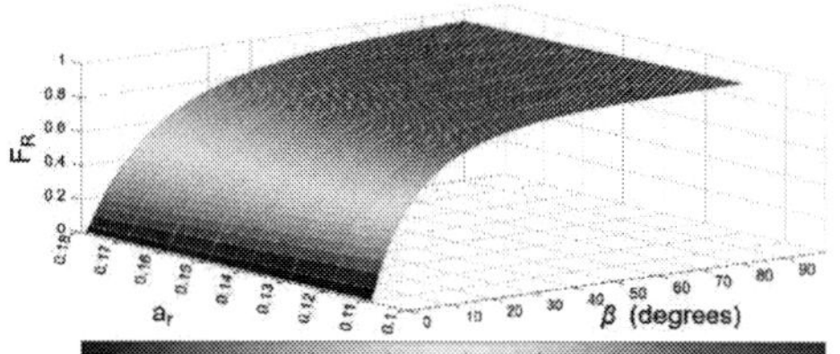

Figure 6: Correction factors F_R in ground-reflected for Martin-Ruiz model

These correction maps are available as metadata associated to previously defined matrices. As a result, the computational cost is significantly reduced, optimizing simulation time and allowing the available resources to be concentrated on the most relevant physical processes.

3 Implementation in SISIFO

The use of photovoltaic simulation software is a growing stage today with the emergence of simulation tools such as PVsyst and System Advisor Model (SAM) [11], [14]. The simulation stage is essential to analyse and optimise photovoltaic systems to estimate energy production with low uncertainty. In the case of this work, we have implemented the angular correction models for the study of IAM in SISIFO software (a free simulation tool developed at IES-UPM and freely available at www.sisifo.info) with the latest update—v3.3 (sisifoweb r503, sisifosvc r122, sisifomatlab r115)—the correction factors described in Section 2 have been implemented. It is available to simulate, under *Options – IAM model*, both for the front and rear face in bifacial modules in multirow PV arrays [15].

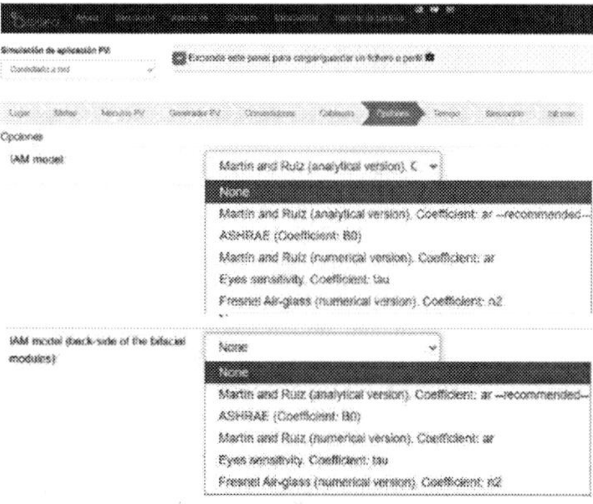

Figure 7: Drop-down menu in SISIFO to use IAM models on front and back side of a PV module.

4 Simulations Results and correspondences between the models

Annual Angular Losses (AAL) is defined as the difference between the global incident irradiance that would be obtained if no IAM losses were considered and the effective global irradiance after applying these angular factors, evaluated over a calendar year [10]. This parameter quantifies the cumulative energy reduction due to the angular dependence of the optical transmittance in the PV module and is a key value in the accurate modelling of the annual performance of PV systems when using simulation software.

$$AAL = \frac{\int_{year}[G - G^{AL}]\, dt}{\int_{year} G\, dt} \cong \frac{\sum_{year}[G - G^{AL}]}{\sum_{year} G}$$

The models have been implemented in the software SISIFO for static structures and for horizontal single-axis trackers. Thanks to this implementation, it has been possible to simulate a practical case that allows to quantify the difference between both static and with tracking on a horizontal axis system.

As a concrete example, the solar photovoltaic plant analysed in this work corresponds to a plant located in Chile, considering the following climatic characteristics.

Table II: Solar Climate Characteristics of PV Plant

Case study of a PV plant	
Latitude (°)	-24
Global horizontal irradiance (kWh/m²)	2680
Ratio D(0)/G(0)	0.14
Ground reflectivity	0.3
Tilt (°)	20
Ground coverage ratio (Static)	0.6
Ground coverage ratio (Tracking)	0.4

The results for each simulation are shown in Figure 8, showing a clear trend in the maximum annual overall loss values for each case with each IAM model parameter to be used to simulate.

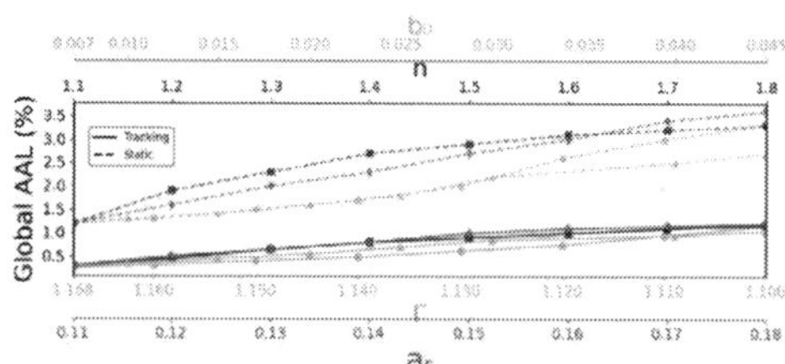

Figure 8: Annual Angular Losses Simulation Exercise for two different configurations (tracking and static).

The equivalence between parameters of each model in terms of annual yield is very important for simulation in PV software. This equivalence has been explored by other authors considering only the ASHRAE model and the physical model [16].

5 Conclusions

The angular correction factors implemented in SISIFO significantly improves the effective irradiance calculation and reduces the uncertainty in the simulation of PV systems, providing a robust and accurate tool for energy yield analysis. Available as open-source software, SISIFO facilitates access and transparency, allowing the research and professional community to perform reliable and reproducible simulations, contributing to the advancement and optimisation of PV projects.

The study of different IAM models and its implementation in this software has made possible to perform simulations with low uncertainty anywhere in the world where PV performance is to be studied.

In this work, annual losses due to IAM in static PV systems typically range from 1% to 3.5%. These losses are significantly reduced in systems with solar tracking, where they typically remain below 1% due to better constant orientation of the module with respect to the sun. The reduction of angular losses through tracking contributes significantly to the improvement of the efficiency and annual energy yield of the PV system.

Acknowledgements

This work was supported by the Spanish State Research Agency through the project MORE-N (Proyectos de I + D + i Generación de Conocimiento 2023), with grants PID2023-148369OB-C41 and PREP2023-001767 funded by MICIU/AEI/10.13039/501100011033 and by ESF+.

References

[1] A. M. Law, L. O. Jones, and J. M. Walls, "The performance and durability of Anti-reflection coatings for solar module cover glass – a review," Sep. 01, 2023, *Elsevier Ltd.* doi: 10.1016/j.solener.2023.06.009.

[2] B. Guo and W. Javed, "Effect of incidence angle on PV soiling loss," *Solar Energy*, vol. 269, Feb. 2024, doi: 10.1016/j.solener.2023.112298.

[3] W. Sang et al., "Spectral correction of photovoltaic module electrical properties," *Renew Energy*, vol. 237, Dec. 2024, doi: 10.1016/j.renene.2024.121907.

[4] A. F. Souka and H. H. Safwat, "Determination of the Optimum Orientations for the Double-Exposure, Flat-Plate Collector and Its Reflectors," *Solar Energy*, vol. 10, pp. 170–174, 1966, doi: https://doi.org/10.1016/0038-092X(66)90004-1.

[5] R. Preu, G. Kleiss, K. Bucher, R. Preu, G. Kleiss, and K. Reiche, K-Bucher, "PV-Module Reflexion Losses: Measurement, Simulation and Influence on Energy Yield and Performance Ratio," Nice: 13th European Photovoltaic Solar Energy Conference, 1995. [Online]. Available: https://www.researchgate.net/publication/28269 5694

[6] N. Martin and J. M. Ruiz, "Calculation of the PV modules angular losses under field conditions by means of an analytical model," *Solar Energy Materials & Solar Cells*, vol. 70, pp. 25–38, 2001, doi: https://doi.org/10.1016/S0927-0248(00)00408-6.

[7] N. Martin and J. M. Ruiz, "Corrigendum to 'Calculation of the PV modules angular losses under field conditions by means of an analytical model' [Sol. Energy Mater. Sol. Cells 70 (1) (2001) 25–38] (S0927024800004086) (10.1016/S0927-0248(00)00408-6)," Mar. 01, 2013, *Elsevier B.V.* doi: 10.1016/j.solmat.2012.11.002.

[8] D. L. King, W. E. Boyson, and J. A. Kratochvill, "Photovoltaic Array Performance Model," Alburquerque, NM, 2004. [Online]. Available: http://www.ntis.gov/help/ordermethods.asp?loc= 7-4-0#online

[9] W. De Soto, S. A. Klein, and W. A. Beckman, "Improvement and validation of a model for photovoltaic array performance," *Solar Energy*, vol. 80, no. 1, pp. 78–88, 2006, doi: 10.1016/j.solener.2005.06.010.

[10] A. Goncalves, D. Rativa, and L. A. Gomez-Malagon, "Model-Based Assessment of the Incident Angle Modifier on the Annual Angular Losses and Gain of PV Modules in Tracking Systems," *IEEE J Photovolt*, vol. 14, no. 1, pp. 185–193, Jan. 2024, doi: 10.1109/JPHOTOV.2023.3323802.

[11] "PVsyst SA. (2025). PVsyst Photovoltaic System Software (Version 7.4) [Software]. https://www.pvsyst.com/."

[12] "IEC-61853-2, 'Photovoltaic (PV) module performance testing and energy rating-Part 2: Spectral response, incidence angle and module operating temperature measurements,'" Switzerland, 2012.

[13] B. Marion, "Numerical method for angle-of-incidence correction factors for diffuse radiation incident photovoltaic modules," *Solar Energy*, vol. 147, pp. 344–348, 2017, doi: 10.1016/j.solener.2017.03.027.

[14] "National Renewable Energy Laboratory. (2025). System Advisor Model (SAM) (Version 2025.6.30) [Software]. https://sam.nrel.gov/."

[15] J. R. Ledesma, E. Lorenzo, and L. Narvarte, "Single-Axis Tracking and Bifacial Gain on Sloping Terrain," *Progress in Photovoltaics: Research and Applications*, 2024, doi: 10.1002/pip.3847.

[16] Fatehi JH and Sauer KJ, "Modeling the Incidence Angle Dependence of Photovoltaic Modules in PVsyst," Denver: IEEE 40th Photovoltaic Specialist Conference, PVSC, 2014, pp. 1335–1338.

IAM MODELS AND PHOTOVOLTAIC ENERGY YIELD SIMULATIONS

INSTITUTO DE ENERGÍA SOLAR

POLITÉCNICA

4DV.4.19

Felipe Ríos-Ledesma, Laura Barrutia, Javier Ledesma, Luis Narvarte and Eduardo Lorenzo

Instituto de Energía Solar, Universidad Politécnica de Madrid, Nikola Tesla s/n, Madrid, 28031, España

felipe.rios.ledesma@upm.es, laura.barrutia@upm.es, javier.ledesma@upm.es, luis.narvarte@upm.es, antonio.lorenzo@upm.es

IAM Models

ASHRAE
$$1 - b_0\left(\frac{1}{\cos\theta}\right)$$

Air-glass
$$\frac{1 - \frac{1}{2}\left[\frac{\sin^2(\theta_T - \theta)}{\sin^2(\theta_T + \theta)} + \frac{\tan^2(\theta_T - \theta)}{\tan^2(\theta_T + \theta)}\right]}{1 - \left(\frac{n_1 - n_2}{n_1 + n_2}\right)^2}$$

Martín-Ruíz
$$1 - \frac{\exp\left(-\frac{\cos\theta}{a_r}\right) - \exp\left(-\frac{1}{a_r}\right)}{1 - \exp\left(-\frac{1}{a_r}\right)}$$

Sandia
$$a_0 + a_1\theta + a_2\theta^2 + a_3\theta^3 + a_4\theta^4 + a_5\theta^5$$

Physical
$$\frac{1 - \frac{1}{2}\left[\frac{\sin^2(\theta_T - \theta)}{\sin^2(\theta_T + \theta)} + \frac{\tan^2(\theta_T - \theta)}{\tan^2(\theta_T + \theta)}\right]}{1 - \left(\frac{n_1 - n_2}{n_1 + n_2}\right)^2} \cdot \frac{\exp\left(-\frac{KL}{\cos\theta_T}\right)}{\exp(-KL)}$$

Eye sensitivity
$$1 - \Gamma^{(\theta - 90°)}$$

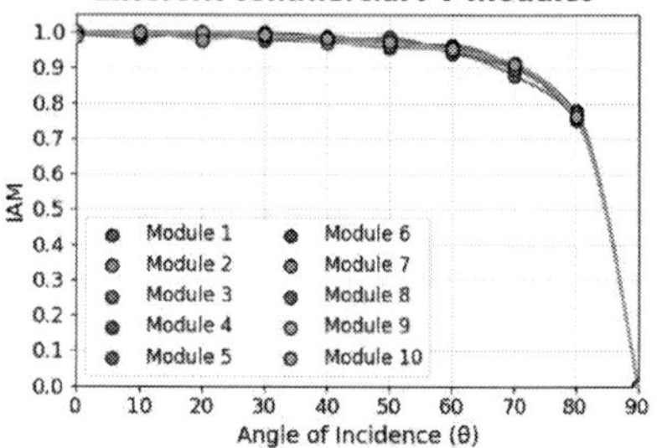

Behaviour of the IAM curve for different commercial PV modules

Correction Factors applied to SISIFO photovoltaic simulation software https://sisifo.info

To reduce the uncertainty in the calculation of the global to effective irradiance step.

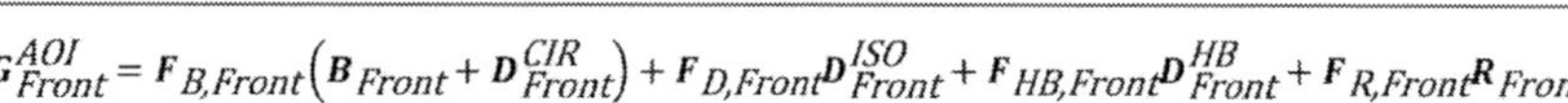

$$G_{Front}^{AOI} = F_{B,Front}\left(B_{Front} + D_{Front}^{CIR}\right) + F_{D,Front}D_{Front}^{ISO} + F_{HB,Front}D_{Front}^{HB} + F_{R,Front}R_{Front}$$

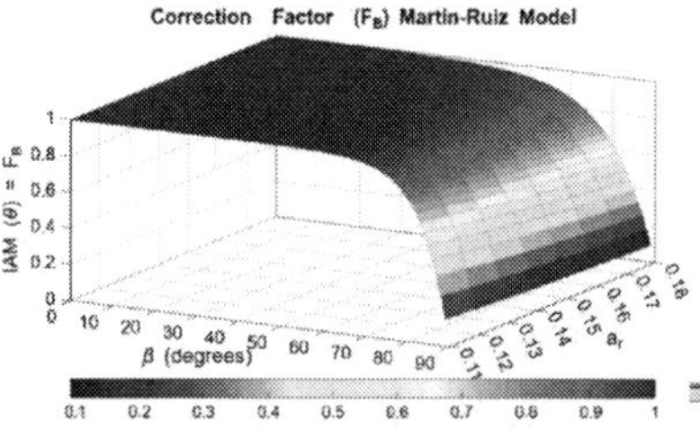

Correction Factor (F_B) Martín-Ruiz Model

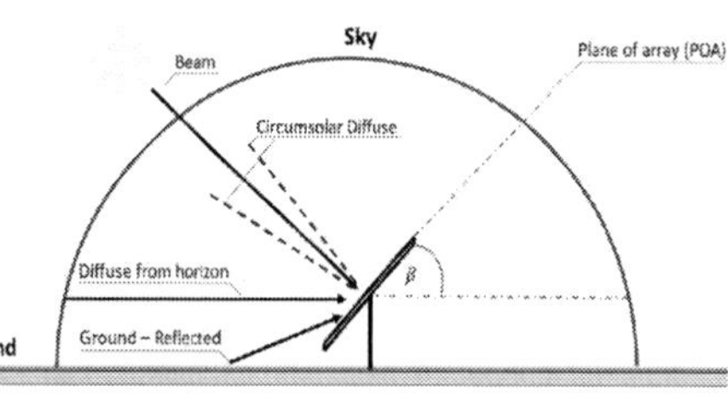

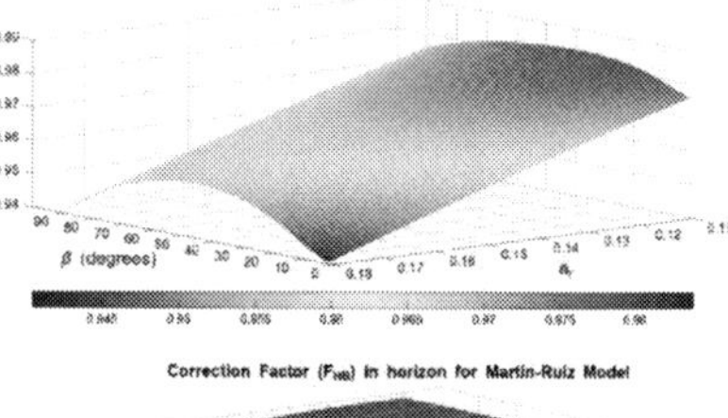

Correction Factor (F_0) in sky for Martin-Ruiz Model

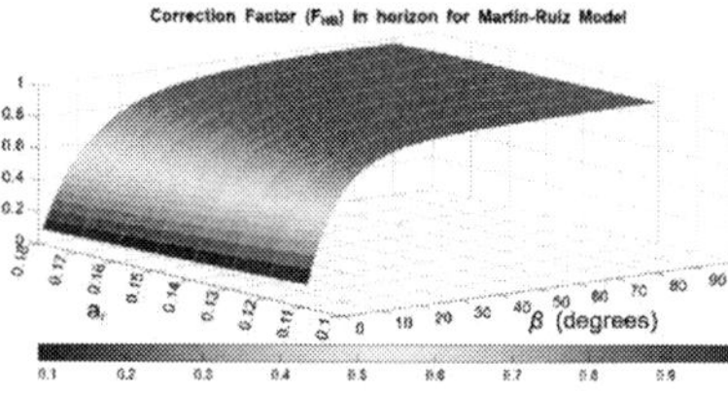

Correction Factor (F_{HB}) in horizon for Martin-Ruiz Model

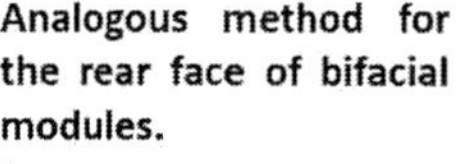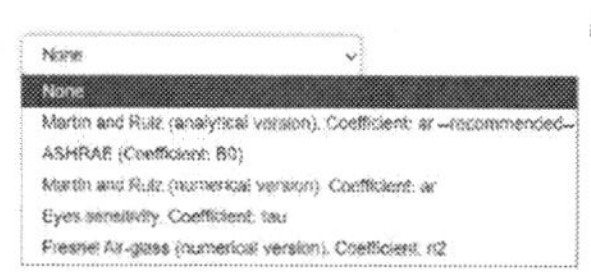

Analogous method for the rear face of bifacial modules.

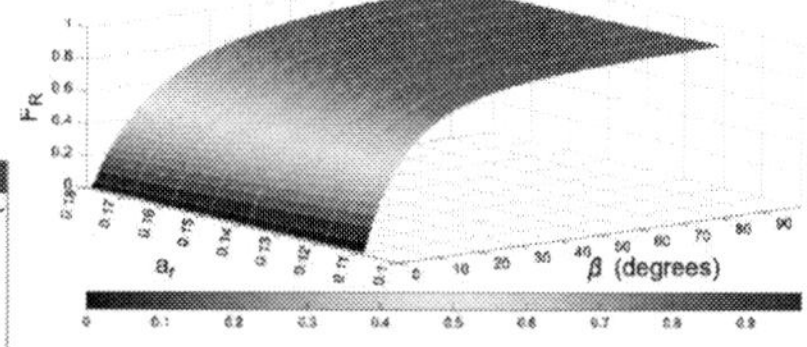

Correction Factor (F_R) in ground-reflected for Martin-Ruiz Model

Results for a case study of a Photovoltaic System

Annual angular losses (AAL) due to IAM in static PV System and with tracking system in Chile.

Estimating real yearly energy yields and performance.

Allow us to find correspondences between the models.

$$AAL = \frac{\int_{year}[G - G^{AL}]\,dt}{\int_{year} G\,dt} \cong \frac{\sum_{year}[G - G^{AL}]}{\sum_{year} G}$$

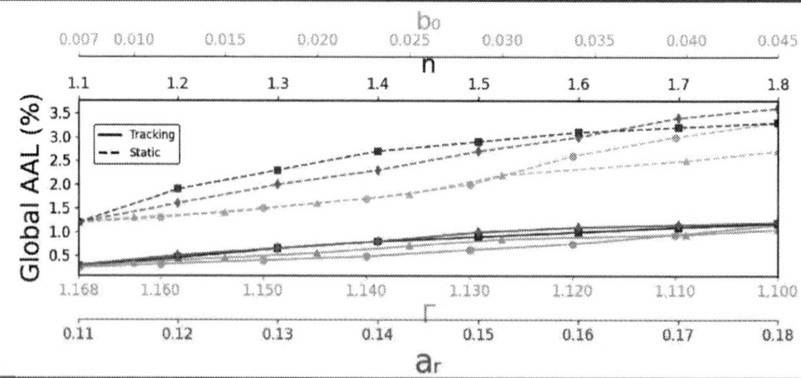

Conclusion

The annual IAM losses are between 1 and 3.5 % for static PV systems, which improve with tracking that is kept close to 1%.

The correction factors implemented in SISIFO reduce uncertainty and provide a valuable tool for PV simulations with OPEN software.

Grants PID2023-148369OB-C41 and PREP2023-001767 funded by MICIU/AEI/10.13039/501100011033 and by ESF+

020447-001

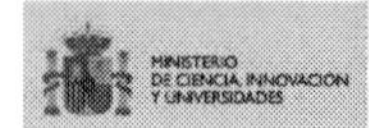

ESTIMATING FUTURE SOILING LOSSES USING CLIMATE MODELS

Gerardo Guerra[1], Pau Mercade Ruiz[1], Gaetana Anamiati[1], Lars Landberg[2]
[1]GreenPowerMonitor a DNV company, Gran Via de les Corts Catalanes, 130, Barcelona, Spain; Email: gerardo.guerra@dnv.com,
pau.mercade@dnv.com, gaetana.anamiati@dnv.com
[2]DNV Denmark, Tuborg Parkvej 8, Hellerup, Denmark; Email: lars.landberg@dnv.com

1. WHAT?

Perform an evaluation of future soiling losses for the 2021–2050 climate normal period [1] across 11 sites representative of the PV Köppen-Geiger climate zones [2]. The study will be based on the Kimber methodology [3] and precipitation data generated by a selection of CMIP6 model variants under the SSP245 and SSP585 scenarios [4].

3. HOW?

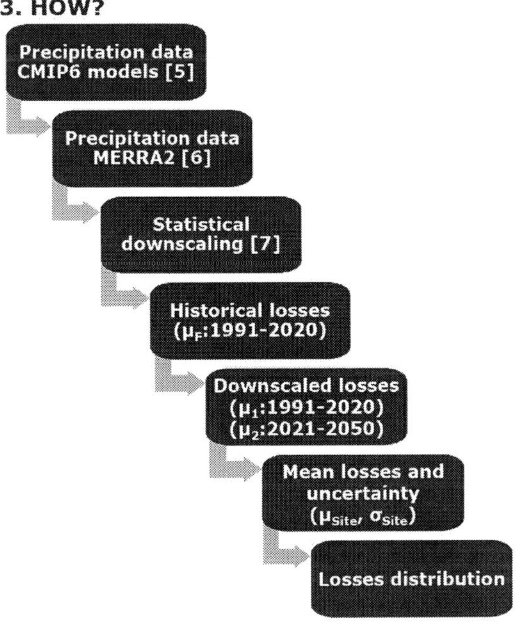

Fig 1. Estimation future losses

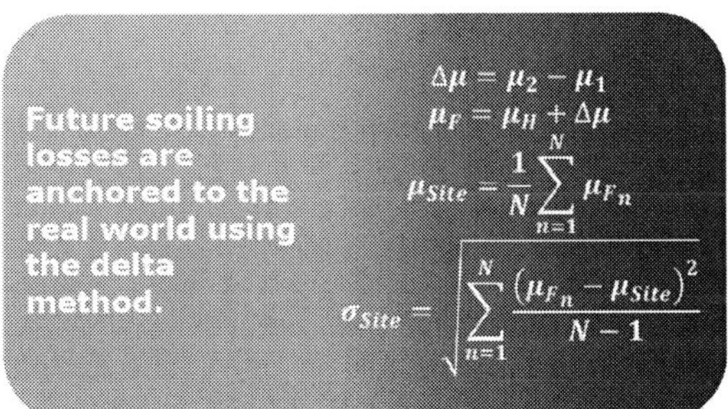

$$\Delta\mu = \mu_2 - \mu_1$$
$$\mu_F = \mu_H + \Delta\mu$$
$$\mu_{Site} = \frac{1}{N}\sum_{n=1}^{N}\mu_{F_n}$$
$$\sigma_{Site} = \sqrt{\sum_{n=1}^{N}\frac{(\mu_{F_n} - \mu_{Site})^2}{N-1}}$$

2. WHY?

As climate change may alter precipitation patterns, reliance on historical data for planning purposes becomes increasingly uncertain. Consequently, estimating future soiling losses using climate projections is essential for informed decision-making.

4. RESULTS

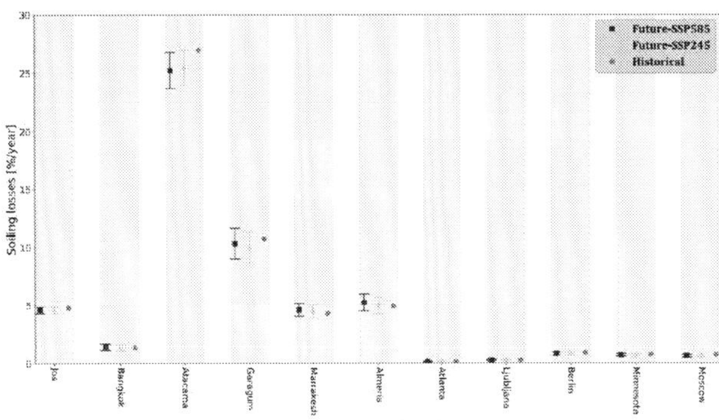

Fig 2. Test sites soiling losses.

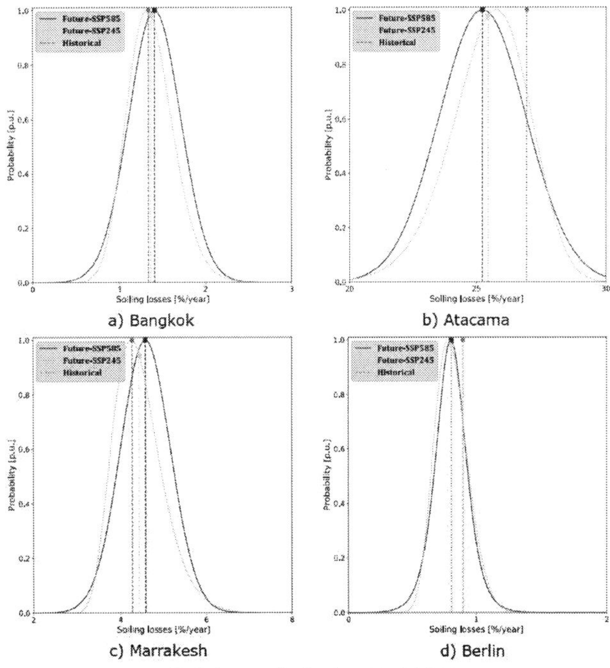

Fig 3. Losses distribution sample sites

5. CONCLUSIONS

* Average soiling losses are projected to remain stable at most sites, but high-emission scenarios introduce greater uncertainty.
* The use of historical baselines for statistical downscaling may not fully capture evolving climate trends.
* The exclusion of precipitation intensity overlooks potential operational risks such as flooding or mechanical stress on PV infrastructure.

6. REFERENCES

[1] World Meteorological Organization. (2017). WMO Guidelines on the Calculation of Climate Normals.
[2] Ascencio-Vásquez, J. Breci, K., & Topič, M. (2019). Methodology of Köppen-Geiger-Photovoltaic climate classification and implications to worldwide mapping of PV system performance. *Solar Energy*, 191, 672-685.
[3] Kimber, A., Mitchell, L., Nogradi, S., & Wenger, H. (2006). The Effect of Soiling on Large Grid-Connected Photovoltaic Systems in California and the Southwest Region of the United States. In *2006 IEEE 4th World Conference on Photovoltaic Energy Conference* (Vol. 2, pp. 2391-2395).
[4] O'Neill, B. C., Tebaldi, C., van Vuuren, D. P., Eyring, V., Friedlingstein, P., Hurtt, G., Knutti, R., Kriegler, E., Lamarque, J.-F., Lowe, J., Meehl, G. A., Moss, R., Riahl, K., & Sanderson, B. M. (2016). The Scenario Model Intercomparison Project (ScenarioMIP) for CMIP6. *Geoscientific Model Development*, 9(9), 3461-3482.
[5] Google cloud CMIP6
[6] NASA Power API
[7] Gudmundsson, L., Bremnes, J. B., Haugen, J. E., & Engen-Skaugen, T. (2012). Technical Note: Downscaling RCM precipitation to the station scale using statistical transformations – a comparison of methods. *Hydrology and Earth System Sciences*, 16(9), 3383-3390.

MAXIMUM POWER POINT TRACKING METHOD FOR GRID-CONNECTED PV SYSTEMS USING MAXIMUM POWER LINE

Hyoung-Kyu Yang, Seok Won Kim, Dongmyoung Joo, Yong-Su Noh, and Jin-Hong Kim
Korea Electronics Technology Institute (KETI) / Power System Research Center
14502, Bucheon, South Korea

ABSTRACT: In order to maximize energy production from a photovoltaic (PV) system, maximum power point tracking (MPPT) methods should rapidly track the maximum power point (MPP). This paper proposes an efficient MPPT method for grid-connected PV systems that can rapidly track the MPP while avoiding the power oscillations around the MPP. To achieve these, the proposed method employs output power control instead of PV array voltage control used in the conventional MPPT methods. The reference for the output power of PV systems is set to the maximum power line, which is the locus of MPPs under various irradiances at a given temperature. The proposed MPPT method forces the operating point of a PV array to rapidly converge to the MPP without the power oscillations. The simulation results clearly demonstrate that the proposed method can achieve a higher tracking efficiency than the conventional methods. Therefore, the proposed method helps foster the penetration level of PV generation in a cost-effective way.
Keywords: Maximum power line, maximum power point tracking, output power control, photovoltaic system.

1 INTRODUCTION

Photovoltaic (PV) generation has been playing a very important role in achieving high penetration levels of renewable energy because of its technical advances and enhanced economic viability during the last decade [1]–[3]. Generating more energy while reducing the production cost is inevitable so that the levelized cost of PV generation should be further reduced [4], [5]. To extract the maximum energy from the sun, a PV system should rapidly track the maximum power point (MPP), and the power oscillations should be avoided around the MPP.

Hence, a large number of maximum power point tracking (MPPT) methods have been proposed [6]–[24]. The perturbation and observation (P&O) method in [6]–[11], which has been widely used in the industry because of low cost and easy implementation, tracks the MPP by perturbing the PV array voltage (v_{pv}) with a fixed voltage step size and observing whether the power increases or not. A large v_{pv} step size can rapidly track the MPP, but cause the large power oscillations around the MPP. On the contrary, a small v_{pv} step size can avoid the power oscillations, but a slow tracking speed is inevitable. Thus, difficulties arise in determining the proper v_{pv} step size.

To overcome this, the variable step-size incremental conductance (VSSINC) method was suggested in [12]–[14]. The VSSINC method adjusts the v_{pv} step size by using the scaling factor depending on the gradient of the power-voltage (P-V) curve of a PV array. Thus, the VSSINC method can achieve a faster tracking speed while alleviating the power oscillations around the MPP. However, the VSSINC method is limited to improve the tracking speed because it should wait for the next perturbation step to check whether the power increases or not.

In [15]–[17], artificial-intelligence-based MPPT methods were suggested to decide the proper v_{pv} step size. However, the huge computational burden is inevitable, requiring more expensive processor. The model-predictive-control-based MPPT methods were reported in [18] and [19]. However, their performance is critically dependent on the converter topology and is very sensitive to converter parameter variations. The fuzzy-logic-based MPPT methods in [20] and [21] do not need to model the converter, but the closed-loop stability and performance issues are not guaranteed for various kinds of models. The authors of [22] suggested a direct MPPT method that tracks the MPP by estimating the ripples of the instantaneous PV array power and voltage. However, it was designed for single-phase inverters only, and the trade-off problem between the tracking speed and the power oscillations around the MPP still remains.

This paper proposes an efficient MPPT method for grid-connected PV systems that can rapidly track the MPP while avoiding the power oscillations around the MPP, thereby achieving a higher tracking efficiency. In the proposed method, output power control is employed instead of v_{pv} control used in the P&O and VSSINC methods. The proposed method does not perturb v_{pv}, but sets the reference for the output power as the maximum power line (MPL), which is the locus of MPPs with various irradiance conditions at a given temperature. The efficacy of the proposed MPPT method is investigated under various irradiance conditions using a PSIM software.

2 PROPOSED MPPT METHOD FOR PV SYSTEMS

2.1 PV Array Modeling

Fig. 1 shows a PV array represented as the single-diode equivalent circuit [25]–[27]. The ideal PV model consists of a current source and a diode in parallel. I_{ph} is the photocurrent generated by the incident light and I_D is the diode current. The equivalent series and parallel resistances, R_s and R_p, represent the contact resistance and leakage current in the practical PV model, respectively.

The current-voltage (I-V) characteristic of a PV array can be expressed as:

$$I = I_{ph} - I_D - \frac{V + R_s I}{R_p}. \qquad (1)$$

I_{ph} is a function of the irradiance and temperature as in:

$$I_{ph} = \left[I_{ph,n} + K_I \left(T - T_n \right) \right] \frac{G}{G_n} \qquad (2)$$

where G and G_n are the actual and nominal irradiances in W/m^2, respectively; T and T_n are the actual and nominal temperatures in K, respectively; K_I is the temperature coefficient of the short-circuit current, and $I_{ph.n}$ is the nominal photocurrent at the standard test condition (STC), which indicates that $G_n = 1000$ W/m^2 and $T_n = 298.15$ K (25 °C).

I_D is given by:

$$I_D = I_0 \left[\exp\left(\frac{V + R_s I}{V_t a} \right) - 1 \right] \qquad (3)$$

where

$$I_0 = I_{0,n} \left(\frac{T}{T_n} \right)^3 \exp\left[\frac{q E_g}{ak} \left(\frac{1}{T_n} - \frac{1}{T} \right) \right] \qquad (4)$$

and

$$V_t = \frac{N_s k T}{q} \qquad (5)$$

where I_0 is the saturation current, V_t is the thermal voltage, a is the diode ideality constant, $I_{0,n}$ is the nominal saturation current, q is the electron charge (1.602×10^{-19} C), E_g is bandgap energy (1.12 eV for the polycrystalline Si), k is the Boltzmann constant (1.380×10^{-23} J/K), and N_s is the number of cells connected in series. Fig. 2 shows the typical I-V (dotted) and P-V curves (solid) of a PV array.

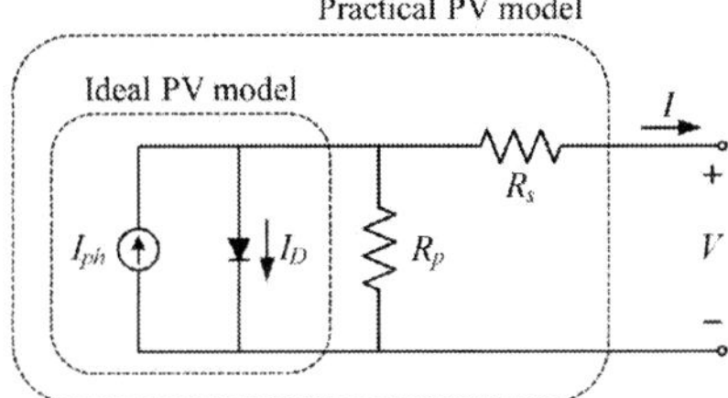

Figure 1: Single-diode equivalent circuit of a PV array.

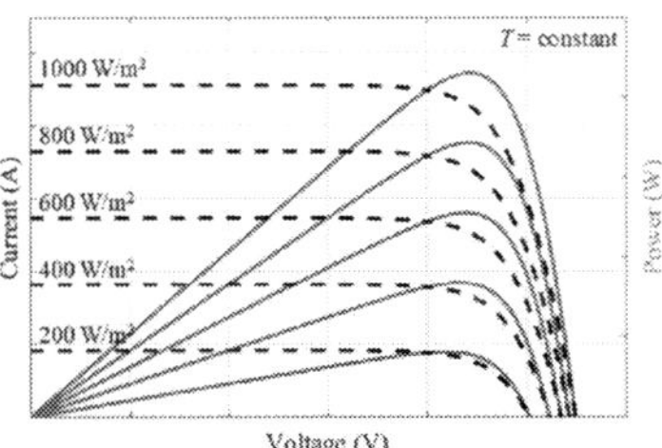

Figure 2: I-V and P-V curves of a PV array.

2.2 Derivation of the Maximum Power Line

The MPL is the locus of MPPs with various irradiances at a given temperature. The MPL can be obtained empirically. Alternatively, the MPL can be derived as follows. It can be assumed that R_s is very small and R_p is very large. Thus, these parameters can be neglected to obtain the simplified ideal model [28], [29]. Then, (1) can be simplified as:

$$I = I_{ph} - I_0 \left[\exp\left(\frac{V}{V_t a} \right) - 1 \right]. \qquad (6)$$

In the P-V curve, dP/dV can be represented as:

$$\frac{dP}{dV} = \frac{d}{dV}(VI) = I + V \frac{dI}{dV}, \qquad (7)$$

dP/dV at the MPP becomes 0 and thus the current at the MPP thus (I_{mpp}) can be obtained as:

$$I_{mpp} = -V_{mpp} \left. \frac{dI}{dV} \right|_{V=V_{mpp}, I=I_{mpp}} \qquad (8)$$

where V_{mpp} is the voltage at the MPP.
dI/dV at the MPP in (8) can be obtained from (6).

$$\left. \frac{dI}{dV} \right|_{V=V_{mpp}, I=I_{mpp}} = -\frac{I_0}{V_t a} \exp\left(\frac{V_{mpp}}{V_t a} \right). \qquad (9)$$

Finally, the power at the MPP (P_{mpp}) can be obtained from (8) and (9), as in:

$$P_{mpp} = V_{mpp} I_{mpp} = \frac{I_0}{V_t a} V_{mpp}^2 \exp\left(\frac{V_{mpp}}{V_t a} \right) \qquad (10)$$

As shown in (10), P_{mpp} is a function of V_{mpp} and V_t. In addition, P_{mpp} is not dependent on the solar irradiance. Fig. 3 shows a family of P-V curves for the irradiances from 200 W/m^2 to 1000 W/m^2 and the locus of P_{mpp} (MPL) obtained from the parameters of a PV cell in Table I.

Table I: Parameters of a PV Cell

Parameter	Symbol	Value
Nominal photocurrent	$I_{ph.n}$	3.80 A
Nominal saturation current	$I_{0,n}$	$2.16 \cdot 10^{-8}$ A
Thermal voltage	V_t	0.0257 V
Diode ideality constant	A	43.2
Temperature coefficient of short-circuit current	K_I	0.0024 A/K

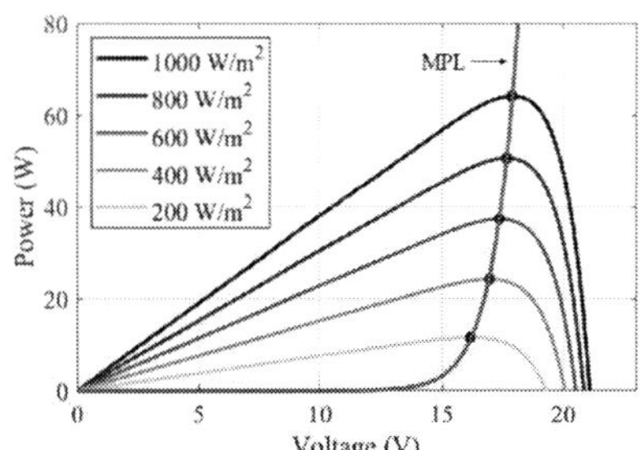

Figure 3: P-V curves and MPL at $T = 25$ °C.

2.2 Operating Principle of the Proposed MPPT Method

MPPT methods aim to track the MPP of the P-V curve whenever the irradiance changes. Fig. 4 shows the typical configuration of the single-stage grid-connected PV system. The power inverter, which can be either single- or three-phase depending on the grid type, is used to connect a PV array to the power grid. The MPPT controller generates I_g^* to maximize the PV array power (P_{pv}), by measuring v_{pv} and the PV array current (i_{pv}). The DC-link capacitor is connected in parallel to the PV array to store P_{pv} while stabilizing v_{pv}.

Fig. 5 shows the main difference between the P&O method and proposed method. The proposed method regulates the power injected to the grid (P_g) while the P&O method regulates v_{pv}. This implies that the P&O method sets the reference for v_{pv} (v_{pv}^*), whereas the proposed method sets the reference for P_g (P_g^*). In addition, the P&O method requires v_{pv} and i_{pv}, whereas the proposed method requires only v_{pv}. The P&O method perturbs v_{pv}^* by the voltage step size to track the MPP. Then, the P&O method should wait for the predefined time step (T_s) between the consecutive steps to observe whether P_{pv} increases or not. This inevitably slows the tracking speed. In addition, even around the MPP, the P&O method keeps perturbing v_{pv} with a fixed step size and thus P_{pv} keeps oscillating, causing the power losses. Further, while the irradiance is changing, the P&O method might repeat consecutive confusions because P_{pv} is changed not by v_{pv} perturbation but by the irradiance change. This forces the operating point to deviate from the MPP, thereby further delaying the convergence and causing more power losses.

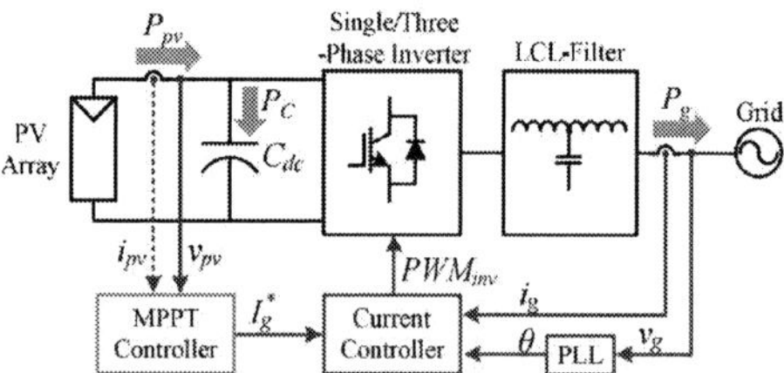

P_g, P_C: Power flowing into the grid and DC-link capacitor
P_{pv}, v_{pv}, i_{pv}: PV array power, voltage, and current
v_g, i_g: Grid voltage and current I_g^*: Reference for i_g
PLL: Phase-locked loop θ: Phase angle
PWM_{inv}: Pulse-width modulation C_{dc}: DC-link capacitance

Figure 4: Single-stage grid-connected PV system.

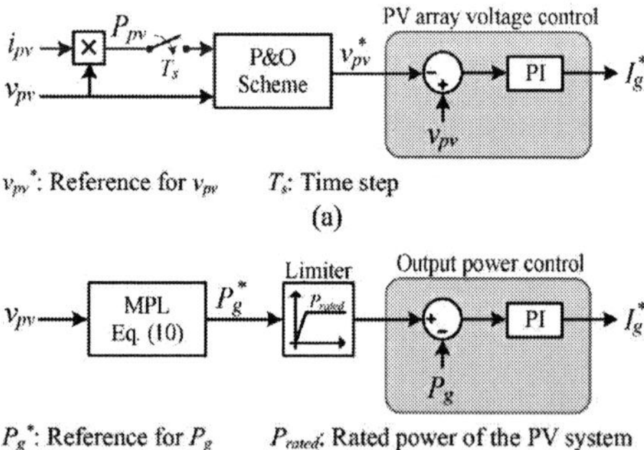

v_{pv}^*: Reference for v_{pv} T_s: Time step
(a)

P_g^*: Reference for P_g P_{rated}: Rated power of the PV system
(b)

Figure 5: MPPT control structure (a) P&O method and (b) Proposed method.

To rapidly track the MPPs while avoiding the oscillations around the MPP, the proposed method regulates P_g instead of v_{pv}. Because P_g is calculated by the measured v_g and i_g, the proposed method does not need to measure i_{pv}. P_g^* is set to the MPL in (10) by inserting v_{pv}

into V_{mpp}. To avoid the overcurrent in the PV system, P_g^* is limited by the rated power (P_{rated}). To generate I_g^*, a proportional-integral controller is used.

Assuming no loss in the single/three-phase inverter, the relationship between P_{pv} and P_g in Fig. 4 can be expressed as:

$$P_C = C_{dc} v_{pv} \frac{dv_{pv}}{dt} = P_{pv} - P_g \qquad (11)$$

where P_C is the power flowing into the DC-link capacitor and C_{dc} is the DC-link capacitance.

Fig. 6 shows the typical MPL (red line) and P-V curve (black line) at an irradiance. The MPL is limited by P_{rated} to prevent damage to the hardware. We will show how the proposed method can rapidly track the MPP without oscillations around the MPP when an irradiance remains. The MPL and P-V curve intersect at the MPP. The P-V curve is divided into two parts: left-hand side (LHS) of the MPP, where the P-V curve is larger than MPL, and right-hand side (RHS) of the MPP, where the P-V curve is smaller than MPL.

Let us choose an initial operating point of v_{pv} at the LHS of the P-V curve. In this section, P_{pv} is larger than the MPL and thus dv_{pv}/dt becomes positive according to (11). As a result, v_{pv} increases. The increase rate of v_{pv} depends on P_{pv} – P_g. The increase in v_{pv} results in the increase in P_{pv} and P_g. In the LHS, P_{pv} is larger than P_g. Consequently, v_{pv} keeps increasing until v_{pv} reaches the MPP. At the MPP, P_{pv} equals P_g. v_{pv} does not move further because dv_{pv}/dt becomes zero.

Now let us choose an initial operating point of v_{pv} at the RHS of the P-V curve, where P_{pv} is smaller than the MPL. In this section, dv_{pv}/dt becomes negative and thus v_{pv} decreases. As a result, P_{pv} increases and P_g decreases. In the RHS, P_{pv} is smaller than P_g. Consequently, v_{pv} keeps decreasing until v_{pv} reaches the MPP. At the MPP, P_{pv} equals P_g and thus v_{pv} remains. Note that the proposed method does not wait for T_s used in the P&O method to determine the tracking direction. That is why the proposed method rapidly tracks the MPP without oscillations around the MPP.

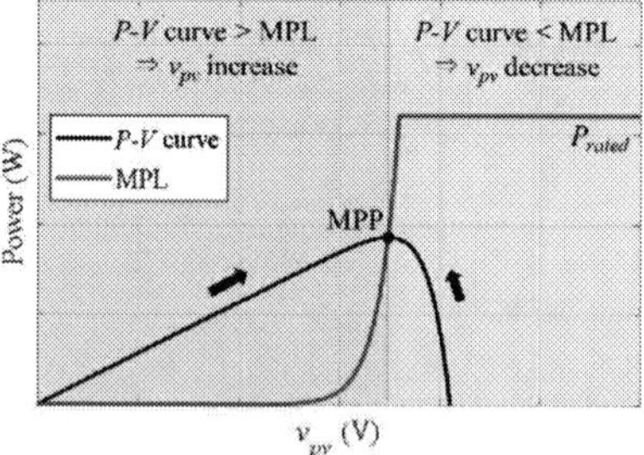

Figure 6: Operating principle of the proposed method.

3 SIMULATION RESULTS

This section investigates the performance of the MPPT methods based on a PSIM software. Table II shows the parameters of the PV system used in this paper. The performance of the proposed MPPT method is compared to the conventional MPPT methods: P&O method in [6]–[11] and VSSINC method in [12]–[14]. In this paper, the v_{pv} step size in the P&O method is set to 3 V. The v_{pv} step-size limit and scaling factor in the VSSINC method is set to 6 V and 0.2, respectively. T_s is set to 0.1 s in the P&O and VSSINC methods.

The key index of the comparison is the rise time (τ_{rise}), which indicates how rapidly MPPT methods track the MPP when the irradiance remains. In this paper, τ_{rise} is defined as the time for P_{pv} to reach 90% of the available maximum power (P_{max}), as in [30]. In addition, the tracking efficiency (η_{mppt}) indicates how much energy can be extracted from the sun during a time interval. As in [31], η_{mppt} is defined by:

$$\eta_{mppt} = \frac{\int_0^t P_{pv}(\tau)\,d\tau}{\int_0^t P_{max}(\tau)\,d\tau} \times 100 \ . \tag{12}$$

The performance of the MPPT methods is compared in the condition that the initial operating point is at the LHS or RHS of the MPP.

Table II: Parameters of the PV System

Parameter	Symbol	Value
PV array rated power	P_{rated}	10 kW
PV array MPP voltage	V_{mpp}	467 V
PV array MPP current	I_{mpp}	21.5 A
PV array open-circuit voltage	V_{oc}	548 V
PV array short-circuit current	I_{sc}	22.8 A
DC-link capacitor	C_{dc}	4.2 mF
LCL-filter	L_i, C_f, L_g	1 mH; 3.3 μF; 0.57 mH
Switching frequency	f_{sw}	10 kHz
Grid nominal voltage	V_g	190 V$_{rms}$
Grid nominal frequency	f_g	60 Hz

3.1 *Case I*: Initial operating point at the LHS of the MPP

Fig. 7 illustrates the results for *Case I* with the operating point on the left side of the *P-V* curve under the STC at 1000 W/m² and 25 °C. The initial operating point is located on the left side of the *P-V* curve and the MPPT methods start to control at 1 s. Then, the operating point in all methods converges to the MPP along with the *P-V* curve (see Fig. 7(c)). As shown in Fig. 7(a), τ_{rise} in the proposed method is 0.02 s while τ_{rise} in the P&O and VSSINC methods are 2.92 s and 1.91 s, respectively. In addition, η_{mppt} in the P&O, VSSINC, and proposed methods are 86.97%, 91.29%, and 99.80%, respectively. This is because the proposed method can instantaneously track the MPP with the significant increase rate in v_{pv}, which has the maximum value of 5415 V/s. In contrast, the P&O and VSSINC methods track the MPP with T_s of 0.1 s, which causes the maximum value of the increase rate in v_{pv} to be 30 V/s and 60 V/s, respectively. That is why the proposed method provides much faster performance in tracking the MPP than the conventional methods. In addition, the VSSINC and proposed methods cause no oscillations around the MPP, whereas the P&O method causes the power oscillations. Therefore, the P&O method generates less energy than the VSSINC and proposed methods.

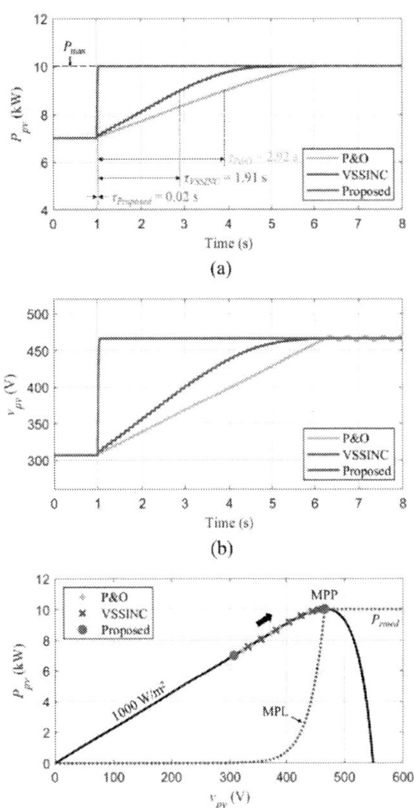

Figure 7: Results for *Case I*. (a) P_{pv}. (b) v_{pv}. (c) P_{pv}-v_{pv} locus.

3.2 *Case II*: Initial operating point at the RHS of the MPP

Fig. 8 illustrates the results for *Case II* with the operating point on the right side of the *P-V* curve under the STC at 1000 W/m² and 25 °C. The initial operating point is on the open-circuit point and the MPPT methods start to control at 1 s. Then, the operating point in all methods converges to the MPP along with the *P-V* curve (see Fig. 8(c)). As shown in Fig. 8(a), τ_{rise} in the proposed method is 0.03 s while τ_{rise} in the P&O and VSSINC methods are 1.40 s and 0.70 s, respectively. In addition, η_{mppt} in the P&O, VSSINC, and proposed methods are 77.22%, 89.23%, and 99.07%, respectively. This is because the proposed method can instantaneously track the MPP with the significant decrease rate in v_{pv}, which has the maximum value of −4345 V/s. In contrast, the P&O and VSSINC methods track the MPP with T_s of 0.1 s, which causes the maximum value of the decrease rate in v_{pv} to be −30 V/s and −60 V/s, respectively. That is why the proposed method provides much faster performance in tracking the MPP than the conventional methods. In addition, there is no oscillations around the MPP in the VSSINC and proposed methods as in *Case I*. Therefore, the proposed method generates significantly a larger amount energy with a faster tracking speed than the conventional methods.

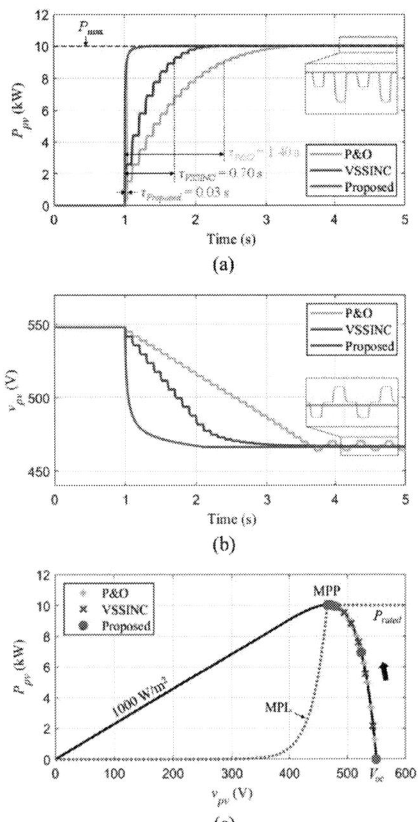

Figure 8: Results for *Case II*. (a) P_{pv}. (b) v_{pv}. (c) P_{pv}-v_{pv} locus.

4 CONCLUSIONS

This paper proposes an efficient MPPT method for grid-connected PV systems that uses output power control instead of PV array voltage control widely used in the conventional MPPT methods. The proposed method sets the output power reference as the MPL, thereby rapidly tracking the MPP while avoiding the oscillations around the MPP. The simulation results evidently demonstrate that the proposed method rapidly tracks the MPP, thereby achieving higher tracking efficiency. Further, no power oscillations are observed around the MPP in the steady-state. Hence, the proposed method helps provide a promising solution to foster the high penetration level of PV generation.

ACKNOWLEDGEMENT

This work was supported by Korea Institute of Energy Technology Evaluation and Planning(KETEP) grant funded by the Korea government(MOTIE)(RS-2023-00233148, Development of grid-forming topology and inverter core technology for grid access to distributed energy resources)

REFERENCES

[1] S. Kouro, J. I. Leon, D. Vinnikov, and L. G. Franquelo, "Grid-connected photovoltaic systems: an overview of recent research and emerging PV converter technology," *IEEE Ind. Electron. Mag.*, vol. 9, no. 1, pp. 47–61, Mar. 2015.

[2] E. Romero-Cadaval, B. Francois, M. Malinowski, and Q.-C. Zhong, "Grid-connected photovoltaic plants: an alternative energy source, replacing conventional sources," *IEEE Ind. Electron. Mag.*, vol. 9, no. 1, pp. 18–32, Mar. 2015.

[3] T. Stetz, J. von Appen, F. Niedermeyer, G. Scheibner, R. Sikora, and M. Braun, "Twilight of the grids: the impact of distributed solar on Germany's energy transition," *IEEE Power Energy Mag.*, vol. 13, no. 2, pp. 50–61, Mar./Apr. 2015.

[4] E. Koutroulis and F. Blaabjerg, "Design optimization of transformerless grid-connected PV inverters including reliability," *IEEE Trans. Power Electron.*, vol. 28, no. 1, pp. 325–335, Jan. 2013.

[5] Y. Yang, E. Koutroulis, A. Sangwongwanich, and F. Blaabjerg, "Pursuing photovoltaic cost-effectiveness: absolute active power control offers hope in single-phase PV systems," *IEEE Ind. Appl. Mag.*, vol. 23, no. 5, pp. 40–49, Sep./Oct. 2017.

[6] Y. H. Lim and D. C. Hamill, "Simple maximum power point tracker for photovoltaic arrays," *Electron. Lett.*, vol. 36, no. 11, pp. 997–999, May 2000.

[7] E. Koutroulis, K. Kalaitzakis, and N. C. Voulgaris, "Development of a microcontroller-based, photovoltaic maximum power point tracking control system," *IEEE Trans. Power Electron.*, vol. 16, no. 1, pp. 46–54, Jan. 2001.

[8] N. Femia, G. Petrone, G. Spagnuolo, and M. Vitelli, "Optimization of perturb and observe maximum power point tracking method," *IEEE Trans. Power Electron.*, vol. 20, no. 4, pp. 963–973, Jul. 2005.

[9] N. Kasa, T. Iida, L. Chen, "Flyback inverter controlled by sensorless current MPPT for photovoltaic power system," *IEEE Trans. Ind. Electron.*, vol. 52, no. 4, pp. 1145–1152, Aug. 2005.

[10] M. A. Elgendy, B. Zahawi, and D. J. Atkinson, "Assessment of perturb and observe MPPT algorithm implementation techniques for PV pumping applications," *IEEE Trans. Sustain. Energy*, vol. 3, no. 1, pp. 21–33, Jan. 2012.

[11] M. A. Elgendy, B. Zahawi, and D. J. Atkinson, "Operating characteristics of the P&O algorithm at high perturbation frequencies for standalone PV systems," *IEEE Trans. Energy Convers.*, vol. 30, no. 1, pp. 189–198, Mar. 2015.

[12] F. Liu, S. Duan, F. Liu, B. Liu, Y. Kang, "A variable step size INC MPPT method for PV systems," *IEEE Trans. Ind. Electron.*, vol. 55, no. 7, pp. 2622–2628, Jul. 2008.

[13] J. M. Enrique, J. M. Andújar, and M. A. Bohórquez, "A reliable, fast and low cost maximum power point tracker for photovoltaic applications," *Solar Energy*, vol. 84, no. 1, pp. 79–89, Jan. 2010.

[14] Q. Mei, M. Shan, L. Liu, and J. M. Guerrero, "A novel improved variable step-size incremental-resistance MPPT method for PV systems," *IEEE Trans. Ind. Electron.*, vol. 58, no. 6, pp. 2427–2434, Jun. 2011.

[15] N. Chettibi, A. Mellit, G. Sulligoi, and A. M. Pavan, "Adaptive neural network-based control of a hybrid AC/DC microgrid," *IEEE Trans. Smart Grid*, vol. 9, no. 3, pp. 1667–1679, May 2018.

[16] K. Yan, Y. Du, and Z. Ren, "MPPT perturbation optimization of photovoltaic power systems based on solar irradiance data classification," *IEEE Trans. Sustain. Energy*, vol. 10, no. 2, pp. 514–521, Apr. 2019.

[17] N. Kumar, B. Singh, B. K. Panigrahi, and L. Xu, "Leaky-least-logarithmic-absolute-difference-based control algorithm and learning-based InC MPPT technique for grid-integrated PV system," *IEEE Trans. Ind. Electron.*, vol. 66, no. 11, pp. 9003–9012, Nov. 2019.

[18] A. Lashab, D. Sera, J. M. Guerrero, L. Mathe, and A. Bouzid, "Discrete model-predictive-control-based maximum power point tracking for PV systems: overview and evaluation," *IEEE Trans. Power Electron.*, vol. 33, no. 8, pp. 7273–7287, Aug. 2018.

[19] A. Lashab, D. Sera, and J. M. Guerrero, "A dual-discrete model predictive control-based MPPT for PV systems," *IEEE Trans. Power Electron.*, vol. 34, no. 10, pp. 9686–9697, Oct. 2019.

[20] T. H. Kwan and X. Wu, "Maximum power point tracking using a variable antecedent fuzzy logic controller," *Solar Energy*, vol. 137, pp. 189–200, Nov. 2016.

[21] Y.-T. Chen, Y.-C. Jhang, and R.-H. Liang, "A fuzzy-logic based auto-scaling variable step-size MPPT method for PV systems," *Solar Energy*, vol. 126, pp. 53–63, Mar. 2016.

[22] F. E. Aamri, H. Maker, D. Sera, S. V. Spataru, J. M. Guerrero, and A. Mouhsen, "A direct maximum power point tracking method for single-phase grid-connected PV inverters," *IEEE Trans. Power Electron.*, vol. 33, no. 10, pp. 8961–8971, Oct. 2018.

[23] T. Esram and P. L. Chapman, "Comparison of photovoltaic array maximum power point tracking techniques," *IEEE Trans. Energy Convers.*, vol. 22, no. 2, pp. 439–449, Jun. 2007.

[24] B. Subudhi and R. Pradhan, "A comparative study on maximum power point tracking techniques for photovoltaic power systems," *IEEE Trans. Sustain. Energy*, vol. 4, no. 1, pp. 89–98, Jan. 2013.

[25] M. G. Villalva, J. R. Gazoli, and E. R. Filho, "Comprehensive approach to modeling and simulation of photovoltaic arrays," *IEEE Trans. Power Electron.*, vol. 24, no. 5, pp. 1198–1208, May 2009.

[26] E. I. Batzelis, G. E. Kampitsis, S. A. Papathanassiou, and S. N. Manias, "Direct MPP calculation in terms of the single-diode PV model parameters," *IEEE Trans. Energy Convers.*, vol. 30, no. 1, pp. 226–236, Mar. 2015.

[27] E. I. Batzelis and S. A. Papathanassiou, "A method for the analytical extraction of the single-diode PV model parameters," *IEEE Trans. Sustain. Energy*, vol. 7, no. 2, pp. 504–512, Apr. 2016.

[28] E. Saloux, A. Teyssedou, and M. Sorin, "Explicit model of photovoltaic panels to determine voltages and currents at the maximum power point," *Solar Energy*, vol. 85, no. 5, pp. 713–722, May 2011.

[29] Y. Mahmoud, W. Xiao, and H. H. Zeineldin, "A simple approach to modeling and simulation of photovoltaic modules," *IEEE Trans. Sustain. Energy*, vol. 3, no. 1, pp. 185–186, Jan. 2012.

[30] S. L. Brunton, C. W. Rowley, S. R. Kulkarni, and C. Clarkson, "Maximum power point tracking for photovoltaic optimization using ripple-based extremum seeking control," *IEEE Trans. Power Electron.*, vol. 25, no. 10, pp. 2531–2540, Oct. 2010.

[31] H. A. Sher, A. F. Murtaza, A. Noman, K. E. Addoweesh, K. Al-Haddad, and M. Chiaberge, "A new sensorless hybrid MPPT algorithm based on fractional short-circuit current measurement and P&O MPPT," *IEEE Trans. Sustain. Energy*, vol. 6, no. 4, pp. 1426–1434, Oct. 2015.

Maximum Power Point Tracking Method for Grid-Connected Photovoltaic Systems Using Maximum Power Line

Hyoung-Kyu Yang, Seok Won Kim, Dongmyoung Joo, Yong-Su Noh, and Jin-Hong Kim

Korea Electronics Technology Institute (KETI)

I. Introduction

❖ MPPT needs to be improved to extract maximum energy from the sun

- It should rapidly track the maximum power point (MPP)

- It should avoid the power oscillations around the MPP

❖ This study proposes an efficient MPPT method for PV systems

- The proposed MPPT method applies the output power controller with the maximum power line (MPL) to solve the issue.

II. Proposed MPPT Method for PV Systems

❖ Maximum power line (MPL) of PV array

- MPL is the locus of MPPs with various irradiance conditions at a given temperature

- MPL used in this study is derived from a single-diode equivalent circuit model

- Note that Eq. (1) is not dependent on solar irradiance

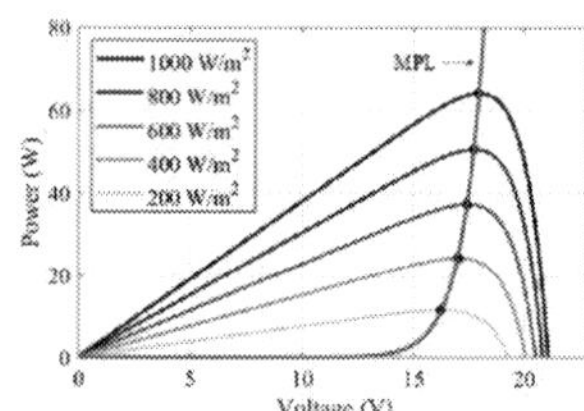

$$P_{mpp} = V_{mpp} I_{mpp} = \frac{I_0}{V_t a} V_{mpp}^2 \exp\left(\frac{V_{mpp}}{V_t a}\right) \cdots (1)$$

- P_{mpp} : Power at the MPP
- V_{mpp} : Voltage at the MPP
- I_0 : Saturation current
- V_t : Thermal voltage
- a : Diode ideality constant

< Fig. 1. P-V curves and MPL >

❖ Operating principle of proposed MPPT method

- The proposed method regulates P_g instead of v_{pv}

- The reference of P_g (P_g^*) is set to MPL in Eq. (1)

- To avoid the overcurrent of PV system, P_g^* is limited by the rated power

- Then, the operating point of PV array converges to MPP by Eq. (2)

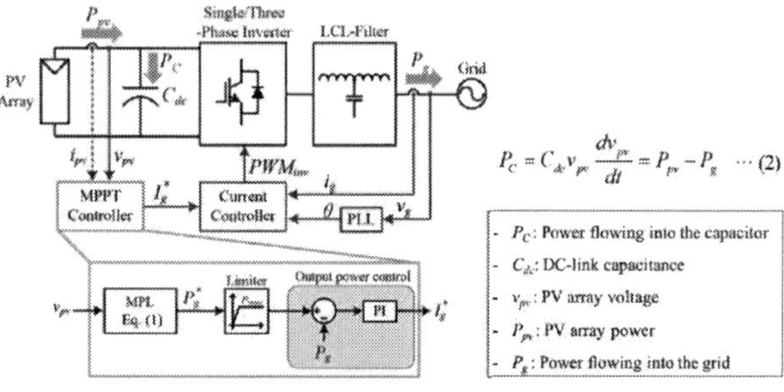

$$P_C = C_{dc} v_{pv} \frac{dv_{pv}}{dt} = P_{pv} - P_g \cdots (2)$$

- P_C : Power flowing into the capacitor
- C_{dc} : DC-link capacitance
- v_{pv} : PV array voltage
- P_{pv} : PV array power
- P_g : Power flowing into the grid

< Fig. 2. Single-stage PV system and MPPT controller >

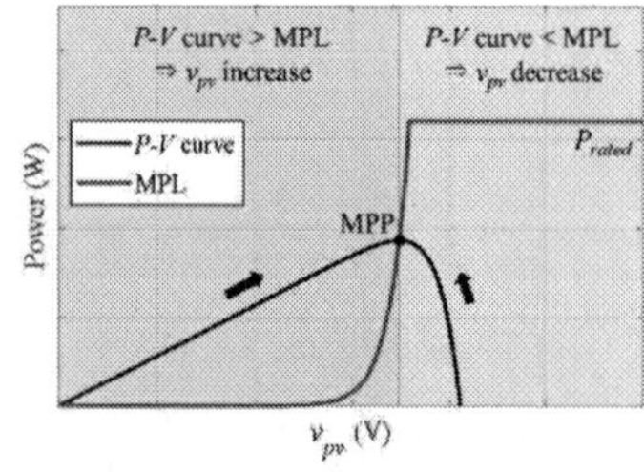

< Fig. 3. Operating principle of the proposed method >

III. Simulation Results

❖ Simulation conditions

- The performance of the proposed MPPT method is compared to the conventional P&O and VSSINC methods

- The test is conducted under irradiance 1000 W/m² and temperature 25 °C

- The rise time (τ_{rise}) is defined as the time for P_{pv} to reach 90% of the available maximum power (P_{max})

< Table 1. Parameters of the PV system >

Parameter	Symbol	Value
PV array rated power	P_{rated}	10 kW
PV array MPP voltage	V_{mpp}	467 V
PV array MPP current	I_{mpp}	21.5 A
PV array open-circuit voltage	V_{oc}	548 V
PV array short-circuit current	I_{sc}	22.8 A
DC-link capacitor	C_{dc}	4.2 mF
LCL-filter	L_i, C_f, L_g	1 mH; 3.3 μF; 0.57 mH
Switching frequency	f_{sw}	10 kHz
Grid nominal voltage	V_g	190 V_{rms}
Grid nominal frequency	f_g	60 Hz

❖ Case Studies

- *Case I* : Initial operating point at the left hand side of MPP

- *Case II* : Initial operating point at the right hand side of MPP

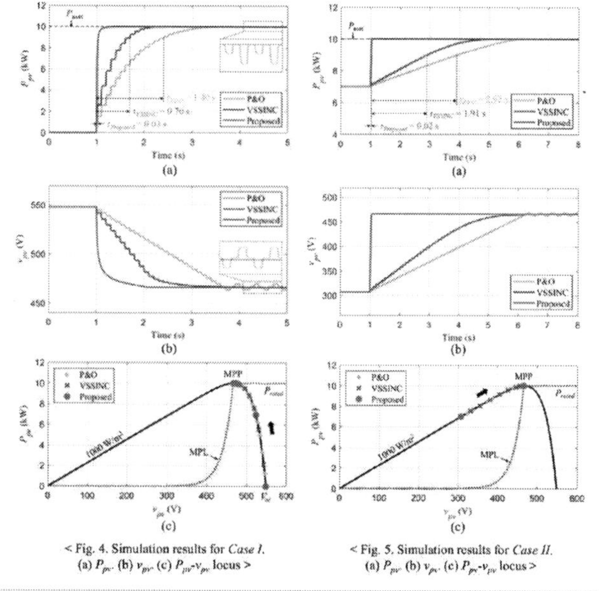

< Fig. 4. Simulation results for *Case I*. (a) P_{pv}. (b) v_{pv}. (c) P_{pv}-v_{pv} locus >

< Fig. 5. Simulation results for *Case II*. (a) P_{pv}. (b) v_{pv}. (c) P_{pv}-v_{pv} locus >

IV. Conclusion

❖ This study proposes the efficient MPPT method for PV systems that uses output power control

❖ The proposed method can rapidly tracking the MPP while avoiding the oscillations around the MPP

Acknowledgement

❖ This work was supported by Korea Institute of Energy Technology Evaluation and Planning(KETEP) grant funded by the Korea government(MOTIE)(RS-2023-00233148, Development of grid-forming topology and inverter core technology for grid access to distributed energy resources)

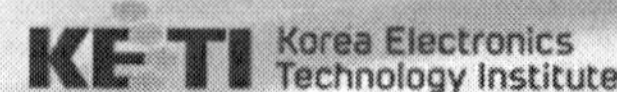

EU PVSEC

020450-001

KETI Korea Electronics Technology Institute

MODELLING, IMPLEMENTATION AND VALIDATION OF SOLAR TRACKING ALGORITHMS IN HORIZONTAL SINGLE AXIS TRACKERS

Nuria López, Mathis Pasquier, Nicholas Riedel-Lyngskær, Peter B. Poulsen and Sergiu V. Spataru
Technical University of Denmark (DTU), Department of Electrical and Photonics Engineering
Roskilde, Sjælland, 4000, Denmark

ABSTRACT: The increasing adoption of Horizontal Single-Axis Tracker (HSAT) systems in utility-scale solar farms has driven interest in tracking algorithms that optimize captured solar insolation. HSAT tracking algorithms calculate the optimal tracker angle to maximize incident solar irradiance at any given moment. However, many proposed algorithms lack experimental validation due to practical constraints and the proprietary nature of commercial HSAT controllers, and existing studies often neglect real-system implementation challenges. This work investigates the implementation of widely used tracking algorithms in HSAT systems, analyzing both simulated and measured plane-of-array (POA) irradiance and DC power production. A real-time HSAT model is proposed, incorporating tracker dynamics, including motor response time, rotational speed, and delays, as well as energy consumption. The model enables a realistic evaluation of tracker behavior and energy performance, highlighting discrepancies between idealized simulations and field measurements.

1 INTRODUCTION

New utility-scale PV plants are increasingly being equipped with trackers to maximize energy production, and the adoption of bifacial PV modules is also rising rapidly [1]. Trackers are devices designed to orient solar panels toward the optimal position of the sun, thus maximizing energy production. There are two main types of solar trackers: Single-Axis Trackers (SAT), which provide one degree of freedom, and Dual-Axis Trackers, which offer two degrees of freedom for greater adaptability to the sun's movement [2]. Single-axis trackers can have their axis of rotation oriented horizontally or at an incline. This study focuses on Horizontal Single-Axis Tracking (HSAT), where the axis of rotation is typically aligned along a north–south direction [3].

HSAT systems use motors and gear trains for precise movements. The optimal tracker tilt angle at any point in time is determined by a tracking algorithm, typically *Astronomical Tracking*, which minimizes the angle of incidence (AOI) between the solar panels and the sun's direct beam to maximize plane-of-array (POA) irradiance [4]. However, this method does not account for diffuse irradiance, which can be significant on cloudy days. Alternative algorithms, such as *Brute Force Search* and the *CENER Model*, attempt to maximize diffuse irradiance [5,6]. Most tracker manufacturers also have their own diffuse tracking algorithms, but these are proprietary.

Building on this context, the proposed HSAT model enables a direct comparison between real-field tracker performance and the predictions of implemented tracking algorithms, highlighting dynamic behaviors that are not fully captured by conventional models. By incorporating tracker dynamics, energy consumption, and additional measured parameters, the complete HSAT model provides more realistic simulations of tracker operation. This enhanced framework allows for improved evaluation of tracking strategies and their associated energy gains, supporting the development of more efficient and robust tracking algorithms for utility-scale solar plants.

2 OBJECTIVES

The primary objective of this work is to characterize the real operation of an HSAT and to develop a comprehensive HSAT model that goes beyond traditional energy production simulations by explicitly accounting for tracker dynamics and energy consumption. The model captures key operational characteristics such as motor response time, movement delays, and rotational speed, as well as the electrical energy required for tracking. This allows for a more realistic representation of the physical behavior of the tracker and its associated energy demands, and can be used to optimized new tracker designs and control.

Building on this model, the study aims to create a testing platform for the real-time implementation and evaluation of different tracking algorithms under real operating conditions. The platform integrates the HSAT model with field measurements from a full-scale PV tracker system, enabling side-by-side benchmarking of standard Astronomical Tracking against alternative diffuse tracking algorithms proposed in the literature.

A key goal is to validate the HSAT model and the testing platform by comparing the simulated results with sensor-based field measurements of irradiance, power output and tracker energy consumption. This comparison helps identify discrepancies between expected and actual performance, quantifies losses not captured by idealized models, and provides a robust framework for optimizing tracking algorithms under varying weather and operating conditions.

3 METHODOLOGY

Figure 1 illustrates the main inputs and outputs of the HSAT model following the *Astronomical Tracking* algorithm. The model had already been implemented; however, the tracker dynamics had not yet been included. During this study, these dynamics were analyzed and incorporated into the model, as shown in the red box labeled Tracker Control Unit (TCU).

The main outputs of the model are the optimal tracking angle θalgo in this case following the *Astronomical Tracking* algorithm, the front and rear plane of array irradiance GPOA and RPOA and the energy produced by the tracker (PDC).

The model was developed based on and validated at the Risø PV plant, previously described [7], which is equipped with eight Soltec SF7 HSATs, 295 Wp monofacial and bifacial module, and retrofitted with custom TCU's. Each HSAT operates with an independent TCU, as shown in Figure 2 allowing for side-by-side control and operation. The target angle is calculated through Python, and the command is transmitted from the central Network Control Unit (NCU) to each TCU. The TCU, an electronic device, applies voltage to the motor to rotate the tracker accordingly.

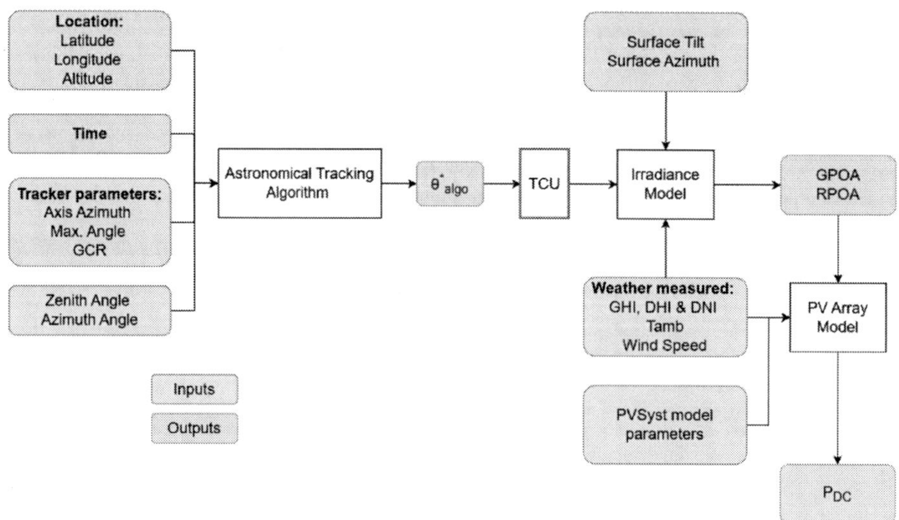

Figure 1:HSAT model following the Astronomical Tracking algorithm.

The solar irradiance components (DNI, DHI, GHI) used by the diffused tracking algorithm, are measured by a meteorological station located 250 m from the PV plant.

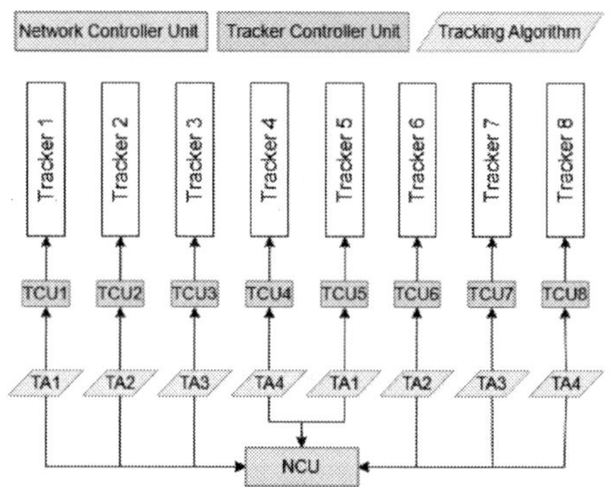

Figure 2: Overview of Trackers, TCUs, and Central NCU in Risø.

To measure and evaluate the actual captured insolation versus the model-simulated values, we deployed a few front plane-of-array (GPOA) sensors and one rear irradiance (RPOA) sensor on selected trackers during the summer of 2024, as illustrated in Figure 3.

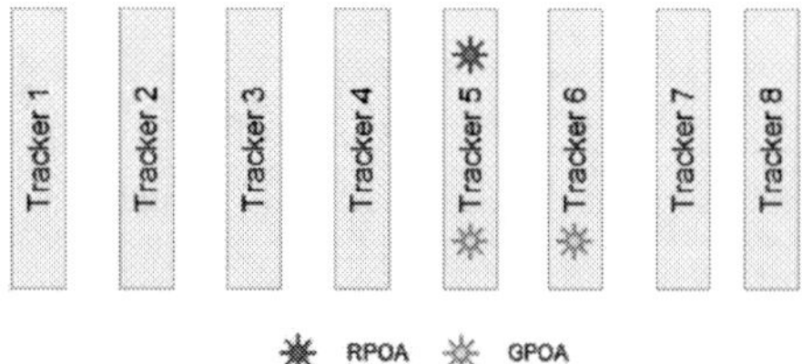

Figure 3: Placement of front and rear plane of array sensors on the HSATs.

Reference cells were used for this purpose, and the analysis focused on data from Tracker 5 and Tracker 6, which had fully operational sensors. Although additional reference cells have been installed on the remaining trackers, insufficient data were available for inclusion in this study.

3.1 Characterization of the trackers

The tracker dynamics were analyzed by evaluating the current and target angles in detail. On the 23rd of July, between 09:00 and 11:00, the tracker angles setpoints (denoted Target Angles) were manually controlled though the NCU/TCU to intentionally induce movements and observe the system's response, which was measured tracker tilt angle (denoted Current Angle) every 10 seconds, as shown in Figure 4. Two key performance indicators were defined: response time and delay.

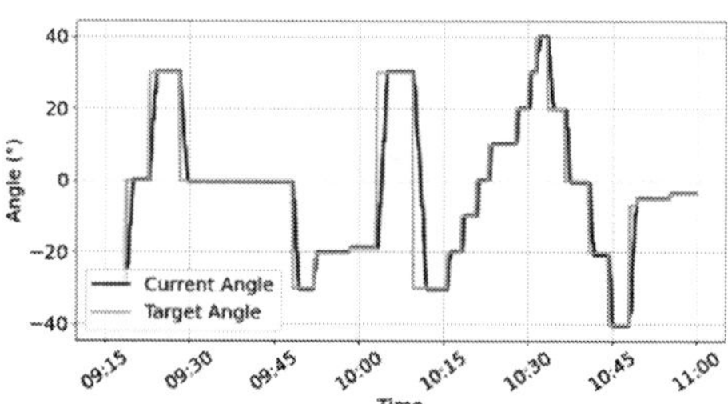

Figure 4: Current and Target Angles of Tracker 5 on the 23rd of July.

The **response time** represents the duration required for the motor to rotate the tracker from its initial position to the new target position, measured in seconds.
Because this time depends on the angular displacement, it was normalized by the response time and expressed as the Rotational Speed (RS), defined in Equation 1, in °/s.

$$RS = \frac{TargetAngle - CurrentAngle}{ResponseTime} \qquad (1)$$

The **delay** quantifies the time lag between the instant the target angle changes t_o and the moment the current angle starts deviating by more than a small threshold t_{delay}.
It is calculated in seconds, as shown in Equation 2, and represents the tracker's dead time before motion begins.

$$Delay = t_{delay} - t_o \qquad (2)$$

The tracker energy consumption ($E_{tracker}$) in Wh is calculated from the motor runtime (t_{motor}), motor voltage (V_{motor}), and motor current (I_{motor}), shown in Equation 3. The motor operates at a constant drive voltage of 24 V for all trackers.

$$E_{tracker} = V_{motor} \cdot I_{motor} \cdot \frac{t_{motor}}{3600} \qquad (3)$$

The tracker behavior was analyzed by comparing motor current with wind speed and direction to identify any correlations with wind conditions.

3.2 Improved HSAT Model and Validation

The HSAT model employs several *pvlib* implementations [8] to simulate system performance.
Optimal tracking angles are calculated using *pvlib.tracking.singleaxis*, module temperature is estimated with *pvlib.temperature*, and module electrical performance is modeled using *pvlib.pvsystem*. Plane-of-array (POA) irradiance, including bifacial effects, is obtained using *pvlib.bifacial.infinite_sheds*. Meteorological inputs (irradiance, temperature, and wind data) are sourced from on-site measurements retrieved from a dedicated database.
The DC power of each tracker (P_{DC}) is calculated using Equation 4 in W, where $P_{DC,module}^{max}$ represents the module's maximum DC power as a function of module parameters, cell temperature, and total effective irradiance. Since each tracker consists of four strings, the module-level output is scaled by a factor of four to obtain the total tracker DC production.

$$P_{DC} = P_{DC,module}^{max} \cdot N_{mod,series} \cdot 4 \qquad (4)$$

4 RESULTS

4.1 Rotational Speed and Delays

Figure 5 shows the rotational speed values recorded on 23rd July for Tracker 5, with an average rotational speed of 0.33°/s.
The speed remained relatively stable throughout the measurement period, indicating predictable and consistent tracker response behavior. This average rotational speed was used as a key input in the HSAT model to realistically simulate the dynamic behavior of the trackers, including response times and delays.

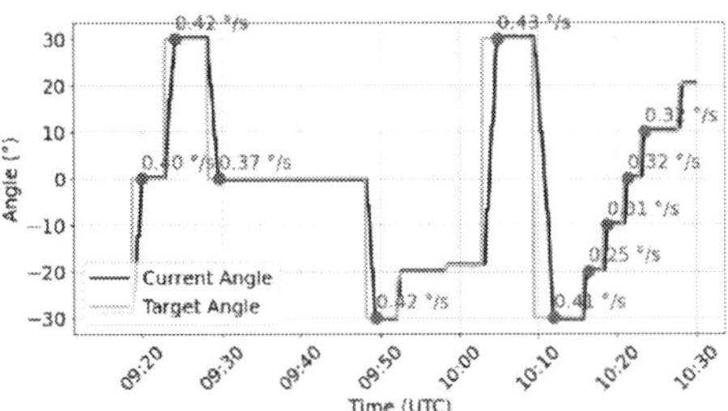

Figure 5: Rotational speeds, current angles, and target angles over the two-hour period.

Incorporating measured rotational speed ensures that the model closely reflects actual motor performance and tracker movements, providing a more accurate evaluation of tracking strategies. To better understand the distribution of tracker movements, Figure 6 presents a histogram of the recorded rotational speeds, showing that most values fall between 0.3 and 0.5 °/s highlighting the frequency at which different speeds occurred during the measurement period.

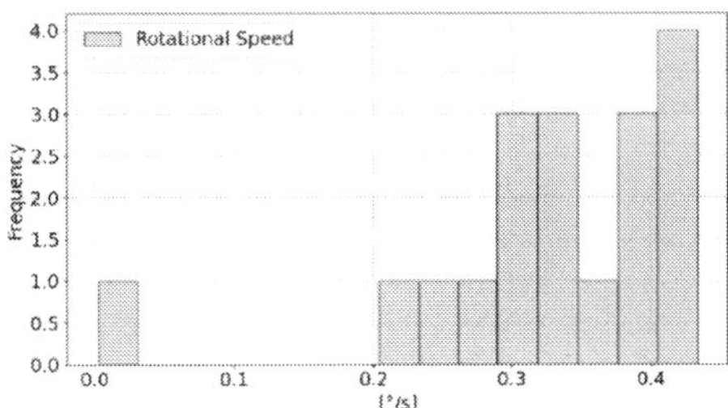

Figure 6: Histogram showing the distribution of rotational speeds measured during the two-hour period.

Figure 7 shows the distribution of the measured delays, with most values around 10 s, corresponding to the data timestamp resolution. The same values were observed for both trackers, even though the frequency is not the same. These delay measurements highlight the typical time lag between a target angle change and the actual tracker response, which should be considered in future HSAT model implementations to improve simulation realism.

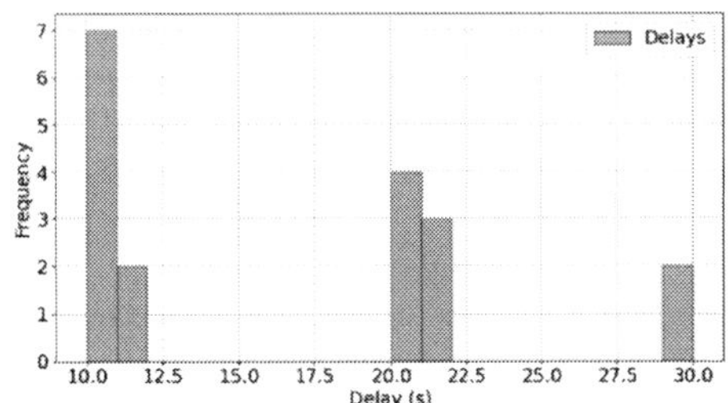

Figure 7: Histogram showing the distribution of delays during the two-hour period.

4.2 Energy consumption of the trackers

For characterizing the energy consumption of the trackers, the tracker average motor current was measured and reported by the TCUs, from different months and random days within the same month were analyzed. The consumption was also evaluated as a function of wind speed and wind direction, but no correlations were observed. Overall, the energy consumption of the trackers follows the same pattern across all analyzed days, as shown in Figure 8.

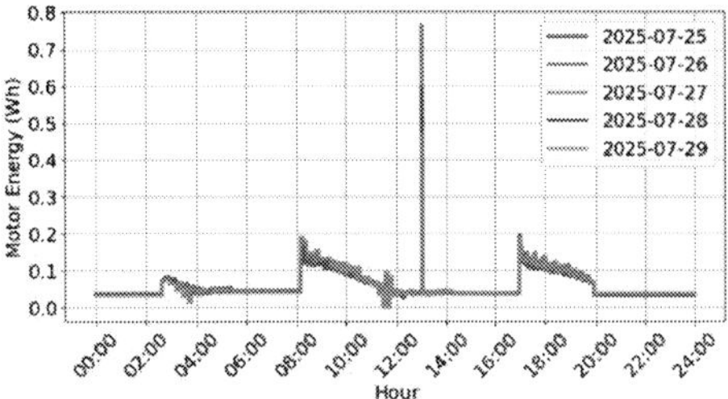

Figure 8: Motor energy consumption for four consecutive days in July.

4.3 Improved HSAT Model and Validation

To ensure the validity of comparing simulated values from the HSAT model with actual field data, the simulated tracking angles must match the measured angles. Figure 9 shows the measured angles of Tracker 5, which align with the simulated angles, as both use the *Astronomical Tracking* algorithm.

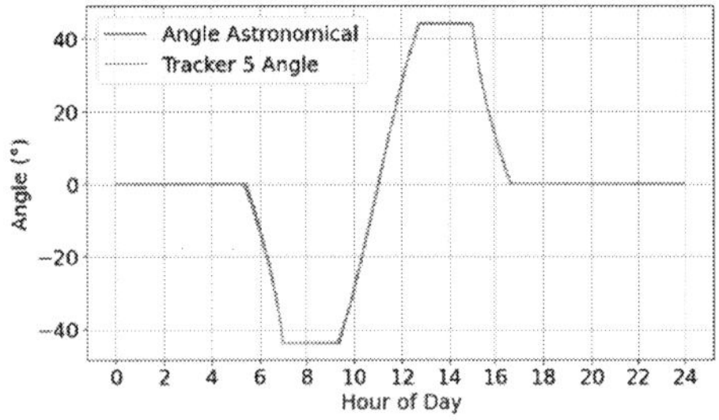

Figure 9: Simulated Astronomical Tracking Angles (blue line) and Actual Tracking Angles for Tracker 5 (orange line).

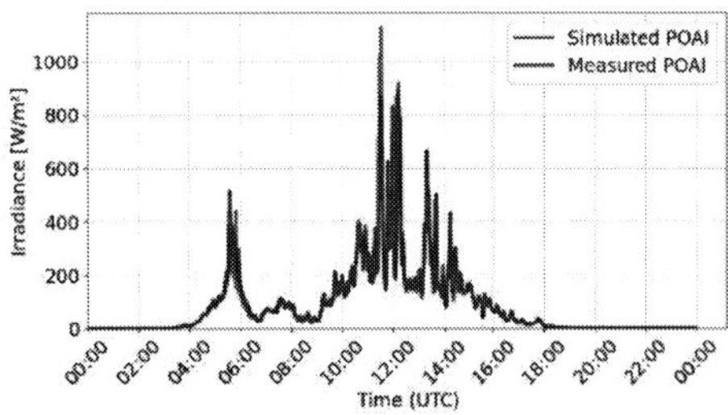

Figure 10: Comparison of simulated and measured POA irradiance for August 3rd.

The HSAT model was used to simulate POA irradiance (GPOA), which was then compared with field measurements. Figure 10 presents the results for a representative day. Similar trends were observed across several other days, with measured values consistently lower than simulated ones. This discrepancy reflects the idealized assumptions in the model, including the use of an isotropic sky model and the lack of operational losses

such as shading, soiling, temperature effects, and electrical inefficiencies.

The DC production of the trackers was also simulated using the HSAT model and compared with measured production data. The simulated production was slightly higher than the measured values, largely due to the overestimation of POA irradiance and the absence of real-world tracker losses in the model. These results, shown in Figure 11, highlight the importance of incorporating operational losses and realistic irradiance assumptions to improve the accuracy of performance predictions.

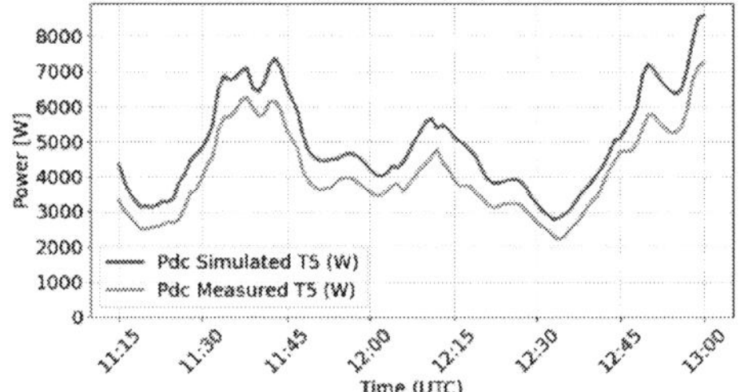

Figure 11: Comparison of simulated and measured tracker production over the two-hour period on July 23rd.

5. CONCLUSIONS AND FUTURE WORK

The analysis of the tracker system revealed several important insights. First, the energy consumption of the trackers remains largely constant across different days. This indicates that the motor operation and drive system behave consistently under normal conditionsand no significant influence from environmental factors such as wind speed or direction was observed.

Second, the POA irradiance simulated using the HSAT model was consistently slightly higher than the field measurements. This discrepancy arises from the modelling assumptions inherent in the simulation, such as the use of an isotropic sky model, idealized tracker alignment, and neglect of localized losses. These simplifications lead to a modest overestimation of the irradiance incident on the modules.

Finally, the DC energy production of the trackers was found to be lower than the simulated estimates. This reduction is primarily attributed to real-world effects not fully captured by the model, including inter-row shading, soiling of the module surfaces, elevated cell temperatures, and electrical losses within the module and system. These factors collectively reduce the effective energy output of the trackers compared to the idealized simulation, highlighting the importance of incorporating real-world performance factors when evaluating PV system behavior.

As future work, the HSAT model should be enhanced to incorporate all measured delays and rotational speeds, enabling a more realistic simulation of tracker dynamics and energy performance. Additionally, alternative diffuse tracking algorithms should be implemented and evaluated, using *Astronomical Tracking* as a reference. While Astronomical Tracking provides optimal performance under clear-sky conditions, it does not account for diffuse irradiance, which can lead to suboptimal energy capture on cloudy days. Diffuse tracking strategies, by contrast, incorporate real-time weather data such as solar irradiance, cloud cover, and atmospheric conditions to dynamically adjust the tracker angle for maximum energy yield. Ultimately, a full HSAT testing platform will be developed, which was the initial goal of this work.

[1] IEA PVPS, "Trends in Photovoltaic Applications 2024," International Energy Agency Photovoltaic Power Systems Programme (IEA PVPS), 2024. [Online]. Available: https://iea-pvps.org/wp-content/uploads/2024/10/IEA-PVPS-Task-1-Trends-Report-2024.pdf

[2] Solar Photovoltaic Energy, "Technology roadmap," Technical Report, IEA, 2014.

[3] M. S. A. Emon and M. Hasanuzzaman, "Solar thermal energy conversion." in *Technologies for Solar Thermal Energy*, Section 2.9.5: Single axis tracking, ScienceDirect, 2022.

[4] W. F. Marion and A. P. Dobos, "Rotation angle for the optimum tracking of one-axis trackers," Tech. Rep., National Renewable Energy Lab. (NREL), Golden, CO, USA, 2013.

[5] I. Muñoz, A. Guinda, G. Olivares, S. Díaz, A. M. Gracia-Amillo, and L. Casajús, "Evaluation of Horizontal Single-Axis Solar Tracker Algorithms in Terms of Energy Production and Operational Performance," *Solar RRL*, vol. 8, no. 1, p. 2300507, 2024.

[6] K. R. McIntosh, M. D. Abbott, and B. A. Sudbury, "The optimal tilt angle of monofacial and bifacial modules on single-axis trackers," *IEEE Journal of Photovoltaics*, vol. 12, no. 1, pp. 397–405, 2021.

[7] N. Riedel, A. C. de Aguilar Protti, M. L. Jakobsen, H. C. Pedersen, S. Thorsteinsson, P. B. Poulsen, A. A. Santamaria Lancia, G. A. dos Reis Benatto, G. Demurtas, F. Arrighi, D. Berrian, J. Libal, D. Barnard, and J. Vedde, "The Outdoor Bifacial Test Facility at Technical University of Denmark," in *Bifacial PV Workshop, BifiPV 2019*, 16–17 Sep. 2019, 2019.

[8] The pvlib Community, "pvlib Python User Guide," Accessed: Jan. 28, 2025. [Online]. Available: https://pvlib-python.readthedocs.io/en/stable/user_guide/index.html

42nd European Photovoltaic Solar Energy Conference and Exhibition

Instrumentation to Evaluate Single-Axis Tracker Operation and Irradiance Transposition Calculations

Anton Driesse
PV Performance Labs, Freiburg, Germany
anton.driesse@pvperformancelabs.com

Maddalena Bruno
Fraunhofer ISE, Freiburg, Germany
maddalena.bruno@ise.fraunhofer.de

Two Challenges

Clouds don't just reduce the available solar energy, they make everything much more **complicated**! It is hard to predict where and when they will appear, but even when they're already there, it's hard to know where to turn—if you're a single-axis tracker, that is.

To maximize power output, a single-axis tracker should in general be positioned so that its PV modules receive the **highest irradiance**. There are practical constraints why sometimes another position should be used, but the knowledge of the optimal position is still crucial.

In single-axis tracker systems, an algorithm decides what the position should be, and the manufacturer of the system usually claims it has the **best algorithm**.

The challenges:

1. How to **evaluate** their algorithms?
2. How to make your algorithm **even better**?

One Solution **

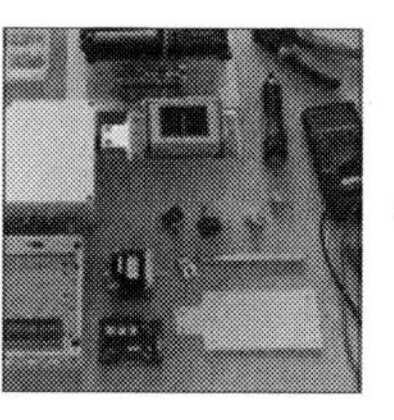

The POA-scan makes one rotation in only 2 seconds, while taking 400 POA irradiance measurements in all directions.

1. The maximum G_{POA} gives the optimal rotation angle, and the G_{POA} value measured at the PV tracker angle tells you how close a PV tracker controller came to that maximum.

2. PV tracker controllers use transposition models to estimate the irradiance at various angles and then identify the optimal one. Each POA-scan rotation provides unprecedented 400 validation points for fine-tuning transposition models.

Sample Tracking Algorithm Observations *

Using measured G_{POA} at all tracker angles, we can evaluate three tracking options

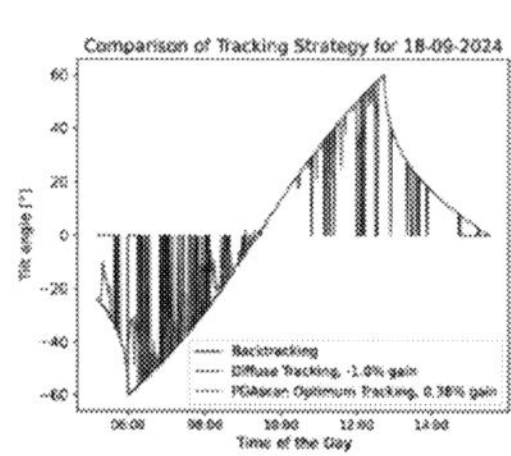

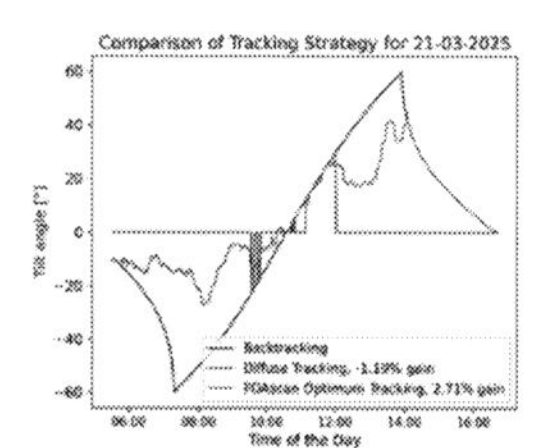

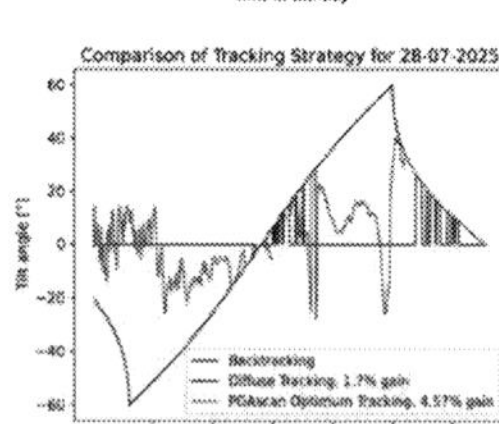

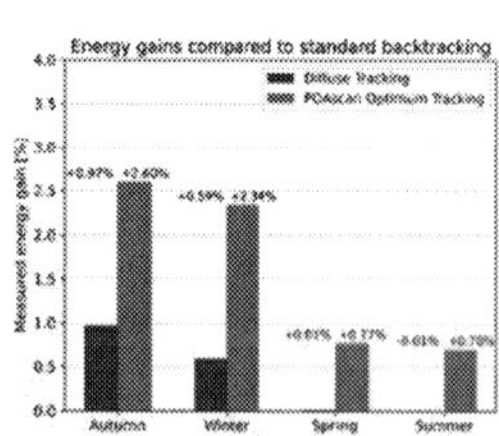

Compared to standard backtracking, moving to a horizontal position when the diffuse ratio (DHI/GHI) is high (blue) produces more energy in autumn and winter. But the POA-scan optimal angle measurements (red) show that further gains are possible with smarter algorithms during all four seasons (near Freiburg, Germany).

Sample Transposition Model Observations

A sunny afternoon, following a cloudy morning: sun azimuth 270 °, elevation 31°

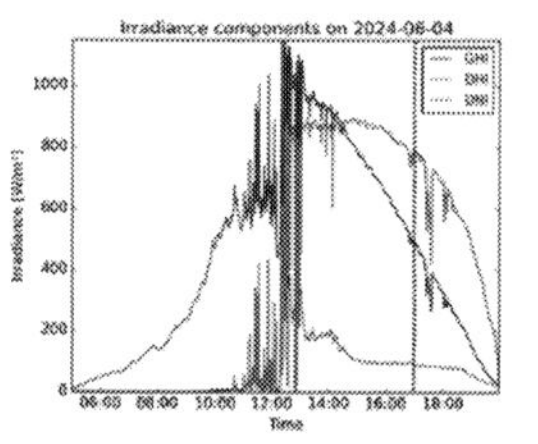

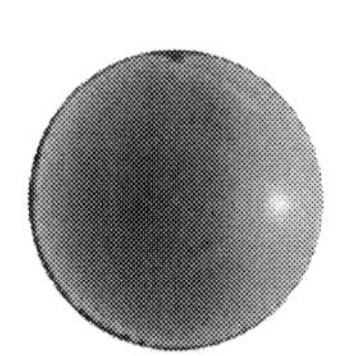

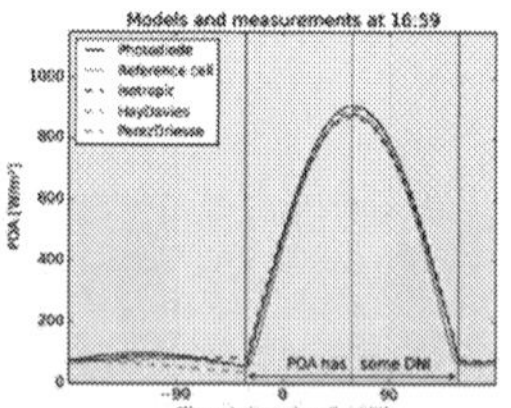

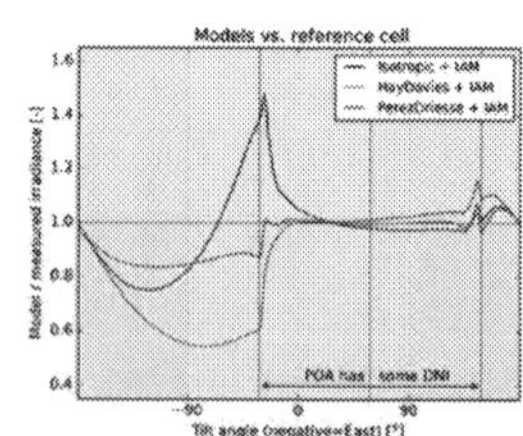

All three models under-predict tilted irradiance at the optimal tracker tilt angle. Over the full range of tilt angles, the Perez-Driesse model achieves the smallest relative error most of the time by capturing both horizon and circumsolar brightening of the non-isotropic sky, as seen in the sky image (at Fraunhofer ISE).

* Results from the DeepTrack Project ©Fraunhofer ISE.
M. Bruno et al., *"Field Insights on Optimizing Diffuse Light Tracking Performance"*,
IEA PVPS Task 13 Bifacial Workshop, Rome, 2024. [Online]. Pat. pending EP25173731.1

** The POA-scan instrument is designed and built by PV Performance Labs.
PV Performance Labs provides a range of services in support of PV system R&D and operations including planning, measurements, simulation and analysis.

920452-001

PERFORMANCE ASSESSMENT OF VEHICLE-INTEGRATED PHOTOVOLTAIC MODULE DESIGNS UNDER DYNAMIC SHADING CONDITIONS

R. Moruno, L. San José, R. Núñez, R. Herrero, I. Antón
Instituto de Energía Solar-Universidad Politécnica de Madrid (IES-UPM), Madrid, Spain
Av. Complutense, 30, Moncloa - Aravaca, 28040 Madrid

ABSTRACT: This paper investigates the impact of module architecture, cell orientation and interconnection on the performance of vehicle-integrated photovoltaic (VIPV) systems under dynamic shading. High-frequency image acquisition and electrical simulations were conducted using realistic shading scenarios recorded from a vehicle's trajectory. Eight configurations, combining cell orientation, interconnection topology, and module partitioning, were analyzed through IV curve simulations and P&O-based MPPT evaluation. Results show that total cross-tied (TCT) connections consistently outperform series connections, while mini-modules offer marginal yield improvements. The energy losses due to different reasons were classified and quantified, finding mismatch losses between 12 and 8%. Findings highlight that shading patterns are evenly distributed across the PV surface, leading to similar MPPT behavior across modules, with high algorithm efficiencies at reasonable perturbation periods (95% with 100 ms perturbation periods). These insights provide a foundation for optimizing VIPV system design under realistic operating conditions.
Keywords: Vehicle-integrated photovoltaics, dynamic shading, MPPT, PV architecture, energy yield.

1 INTRODUCTION

Vehicle-integrated photovoltaics (VIPV) can significantly extend the driving range of electric vehicles, reduce grid demand, and lower operating costs. Unlike conventional PV modules, however, VIPV must operate under highly dynamic and irregular shading conditions. Previous research [1] has shown that increasing the number of bypass diodes and dividing the PV area into smaller modules with individual converters [2] may mitigate shading effects. Nevertheless, it remains unclear how these strategies perform under realistic dynamic vehicle shading.

To address this gap, a high-frequency image acquisition setup and electrical simulation framework were implemented, making use of a methodology previously developed and validated by researchers from IES-UPM [3], who also collaborated on this work. This work intends to evaluate different module configurations, focusing on energy yield and an ideal converter's MPPT behavior under realistic driving conditions.

2 METHODS

2.1 High-frequency image acquisition

The experimental setup employed a high-speed camera (240 fps) fixed to a vehicle roof (**Fig. 1**), capturing shading patterns projected on a calibrated white surface during a 17-minute urban route in Madrid (**Fig. 2**). Image frames were geometrically corrected, binarized using the Otsu method [4], and divided into grids representing different PV module architectures (**Fig. 3**). The proportion of shaded and illuminated pixels in each grid element was used to derive cell-level irradiance. Diffuse light was considered to affect the entire surface uniformly for simplification. A 0.75 Sky View Factor was assumed, as it represents a reasonable value for moderately building-dense urban areas [5]. The direct beam was considered to affect only the illuminated areas, affected by the cosine of the angle of incidence and the Incidence Angle Modifier (IAM). IAM was calculated using the physical model indicated in [6].

Figure 1: Image-acquisition setup. The camera is fixed to a mast attached by a suction cup to the vehicle's roof. The white plank was magnetized.

The video was recorded on a location in the proximity of the Moncloa Campus (Madrid, Spain) on a spring morning (23rd May 2025, 9:58 am) with a Global Horizontal Irradiance (GHI) of 360 W/m^2, with a duration of 17:20 minutes. The ambient temperature was 11°C, based on sensors located in the vicinity. The vehicle took a number of turns and directions, without a dominant orientation during the route.

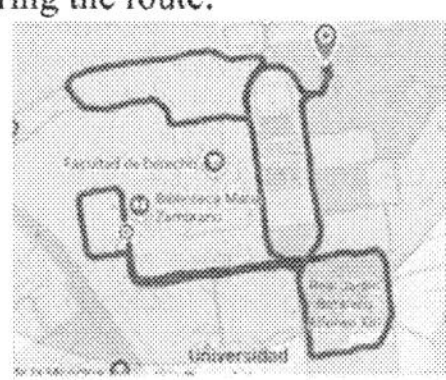

Figure 2: Trajectory of the recorded route, with an extension of approximately 5.6 km.

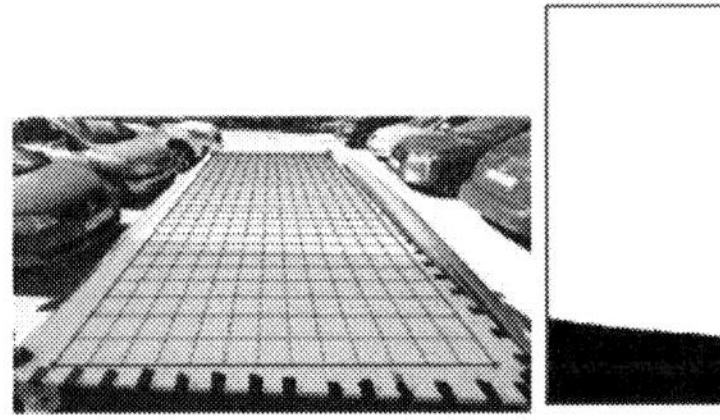

Figure 3: (Left). Frame recorded by the camera, with the grid representing the simulated module. (Right) Black and white binarization of the extracted area, after geometric transformations.

2.2 Electrical simulation

Eight configurations were simulated, combining:

- **Cell orientation:** vertical / horizontal
- **Interconnection:** series / TCT
- **Layout:** single large module (SLM) / six mini-modules (6MM)

A total of 216 shingled silicon cells (141 W, 0.8 m²) were modeled. Illumination matrices were fed into a PVMismatch-based [7] script to generate IV curves (240 per second). The number of bypass diodes of the global PV surface is provided on **Table I**.

Table I: Number of bypass diodes

	SLM	6MM
Series-H	6	12
Series-V	12	36
TCT-H	6	12
TCT-V	12	36

2.3 MPPT simulation

A perturb and observe (P&O) [8] MPPT algorithm was applied on every case, sweeping across a range of the algorithm parameters: perturbation size and period. The basic operating principle of this algorithm consists on applying a variation (perturbation size) in the tension that polarizes the module with a certain periodicity (perturbation period). It incorporates a memory so it can measure the power variation between iterations, deciding the direction of the next perturbation (positive or negative) to try to increment power output. Efficiency trends were evaluated to assess the expected performance of realistic converters compared to idealized conditions.

3 RESULTS

3.1 Energy Yield

Shadows were found to reduce energy yield (EY) by 21% and SVF by 3%. Due to the changing angle of incidence, IAM losses amount to 7.5%, whereas curvature and temperature had nearly negligible effects, almost cancelling each other (-0.29% for curvature and +0.14% for temperature). Thermal effects actually improved energy yield thanks to the low ambient temperature and strong convective conditions on a moving vehicle. The maximum EY that a module could reach in those conditions was 68%. The gap between 68% and the actual EY corresponds to mismatch losses (**Fig. 4**). The EY on each case can be found on **Table II**.

Table II: Energy Yield of every configuration

	SLM EY [%]	6MM EY [%]
Series-H	56.1%	55.8%
Series-V	56.8%	57.3%
TCT-H	59.9%	60.1%
TCT-V	60.0%	60.4%

These results indicate that TCT interconnections outperform series connections by 3–4% in terms of EY. Vertical series configuration performs better than horizontal series due to the higher number of bypass diodes. The partition of the surface into Mini-modules showed only marginal improvements (<1%) in maximum available energy but maintained voltages below the 60 V safety threshold for EV auxiliary devices [9].

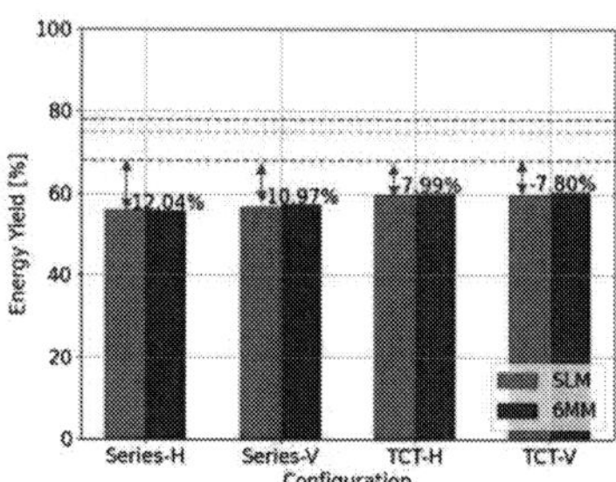

Figure 4: Maximum possible energy yield of each case of study, prior to the DC-DC converter. They are expressed as a percentage of the EY of the same module under the same GHI, which amounts to 13.68 Wh. The percentages indicate the mismatch losses of the average of both layouts (SLM and 6MM). The green dashed line represents the shading losses (-21%), the yellow one represents the SVF losses (-3%) and the turquoise one represents the IAM losses (-7.5%).

3.2 Shading Distribution

Shading was uniformly distributed across the PV surface, with an average shading factor of ~24% (**Fig. 5**). Slight deviations on MM5 and MM6 were caused by systematic artifacts (e.g., temporary camera shading).

The uniform shading can be explained by moving shadows: the same shadow moves from the front part of the PV surface to the back, as the vehicle moves forwards. This way, the same shadow covers frontal and rear modules, but at different instants, leaving similar IV curves across the Mini-Modules with a certain delay, depending on the vehicle's movement.

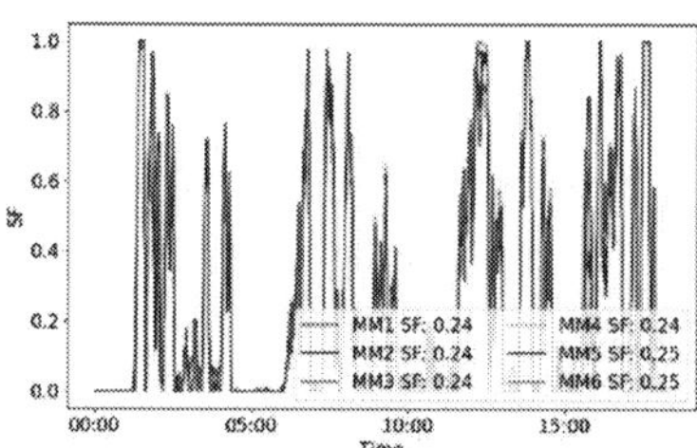

Figure 5: Temporal evolution of SF over each of the 6 Mini-Modules during the entire route. The legend indicates the average value on each case.

3.3 MPPT algorithm evaluation

Here, the P&O algorithm is evaluated on each collection of simulated IV curves. Several simulations are conducted on each case, each one with a certain value of step size and perturbation period. This analysis intends to explore efficiency trends related to the module's design parameters to provide an insight on the performance of a regular MPPT algorithm's efficiency.

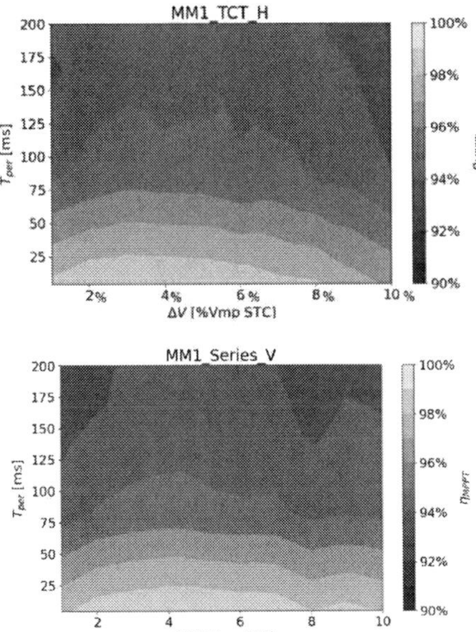

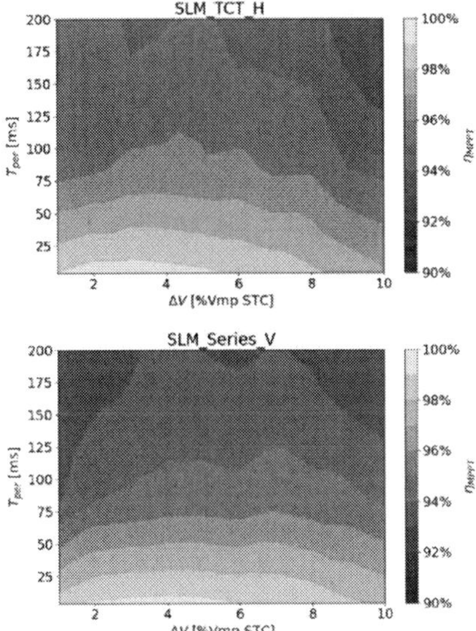

Figure 6: P&O efficiency heat map of the MM1 submodule. The X axis represents the perturbation size, expressed as a percentage of the maximum power voltage in Standard Test Conditions V_{MPSTC}. The Y axis represents the perturbation period. **Top)** TCT connection and horizontal cell orientation. **Bottom)** Series connection and Vertical cell orientation.

As they share similar shading profiles, according to the results described on the previous section, the performance of sub-modules with the same cell orientation and interconnection are almost identical. So, the findings obtained on one of them can be extrapolated to the rest. 98-99% efficiencies can be achieved when the perturbation period matches the timelapse between frames (**Fig. 6**), as that is the temporal resolution limit for these simulations. However, when more realistic perturbation periods are considered (100 ms) [10], these efficiencies drop down to 95-96%. It must be noted that this method does consider an ideal converter, without incorporating the dynamic effects due to the inner electronic components (capacitors, inductors, etc.), thus significantly impacting settling times.

TCT cell interconnection seems to be slightly more affected by perturbation size and series connection by perturbation period. This can be explained by the IV curves' shape. As TCT IV curves are steeper (higher currents, lower voltages), a similar perturbation produces larger current variations, affecting power extraction. Similar behavior is found in the Single Large Module configuration (**Fig. 7**), reaching matching efficiency trends with the MM case. This means that the efficiency of the MPPT algorithm is almost independent of the layout, but strongly dependent on algorithm parameters (step size and perturbation period).

Figure 7: P&O efficiency heat map of the SLM case. The X axis represents the perturbation size, expressed as a percentage of V_{MPSTC}. The Y axis represents the perturbation period. **Top)** TCT connection and horizontal cell orientation. **Bottom)** Series connection and Vertical cell orientation.

4 CONCLUSIONS

This study demonstrates that mini-module partitioning offers limited energy yield benefits but may be valuable for compliance with EV auxiliary voltage limits. TCT connections consistently deliver better performance compared to series connections, although potential ohmic losses should be considered. The vertical cell disposition is preferable to the horizontal one in the series connection case, as it allows implementing a higher number of bypass diodes, improving performance under partial shading. However, with TCT connection, energy yield is almost unaffected by cell orientation, as current can flow more freely.

Average shading factor over the module, even with a low sun elevation (~20°) reached an average value of 24%. Combined with angle of incidence losses, it explains the low energy output compared to unshaded conditions. In addition, these shadows presented a uniform distribution over the studied surface. The moving shadows induce similar IV curves on the different sub-modules, although with a temporal delay.

This similarity in shading profiles upon each sub-module explains the matching MPPT algorithm efficiency trends among them. While in all cases high efficiencies can be obtained with low perturbation periods, equal to the recorded video fps rate, the algorithm still retains around 95-96% efficiency with higher, more realistic periods. The single large module behaves in a similar way, which combined with the similar energy yield, indicates that the potential gains of using the module partition strategy with various DC/DC converters are reduced.

All in all, further research including accurate thermal behavior models, realistic converter behavior and different MPPT algorithms might result in alternate findings.

5 ACKNOWLEDGEMENTS

The authors gratefully acknowledge the DETEC-PV project, Grant PID2021-128853OB-I00, funded by MCIN/AEI/10.13039/501100011033 and "ERDF A way of making Europe."

R. Moruno thanks his grant "PID2021-128853OB-I00" funded by MCIN/AEI/ 10.13039/501100011033 and by "ERDF A way of making Europe".

6 REFERENCES

[1] J. Macías, R. Herrero, R. Núñez, and I. Antón, "On the effect of cell interconnection in Vehicle Integrated Photovoltaics: modelling energy under different scenarios," in *2021 IEEE 48th Photovoltaic Specialists Conference (PVSC)*, June 2021, pp. 1336–1339. doi: 10.1109/PVSC43889.2021.9518935.

[2] "Submodule Integrated Distributed Maximum Power Point Tracking for Solar Photovoltaic Applications | IEEE Journals & Magazine | IEEE Xplore." Accessed: Sept. 01, 2025. [Online]. Available: https://ieeexplore.ieee.org/abstract/document/6339082

[3] L. San José, R. Moruno, R. Núñez, R. Herrero, J. Macías, and I. Antón, "Performance evaluation of MPPT algorithm of VIPV systems in realistic urban routes using image processing," *Solar Energy Materials and Solar Cells*, vol. 276, p. 113061, Oct. 2024, doi: 10.1016/j.solmat.2024.113061.

[4] P. Puneet and N. Garg, "Binarization Techniques used for Grey Scale Images," *IJCA*, vol. 71, no. 1, pp. 8–11, June 2013, doi: 10.5120/12320-8533.

[5] K. Araki, Y. Ota, A. Nagaoka, and K. Nishioka, "3D Solar Irradiance Model for Non-Uniform Shading Environments Using Shading (Aperture) Matrix Enhanced by Local Coordinate System," *Energies*, vol. 16, no. 11, p. 4414, May 2023, doi: 10.3390/en16114414.

[6] W. De Soto, S. A. Klein, and W. A. Beckman, "Improvement and validation of a model for photovoltaic array performance," *Solar Energy*, vol. 80, no. 1, pp. 78–88, Jan. 2006, doi: 10.1016/j.solener.2005.06.010.

[7] "Quantification of System-Level Mismatch Losses using PVMismatch | IEEE Conference Publication | IEEE Xplore." Accessed: June 30, 2025. [Online]. Available: https://ieeexplore.ieee.org/abstract/document/8548107

[8] V. A. Martinez Lopez, U. Žindžiūtė, H. Ziar, M. Zeman, and O. Isabella, "Study on the Effect of Irradiance Variability on the Efficiency of the Perturb-and-Observe Maximum Power Point Tracking Algorithm," *Energies*, vol. 15, no. 20, p. 7562, Oct. 2022, doi: 10.3390/en15207562.

[9] "ISO 6469-3:2021," ISO. Accessed: July 28, 2025. [Online]. Available: https://www.iso.org/es/contents/data/standard/08/17/81746.html

[10] Y. Levron and D. Shmilovitz, "Maximum Power Point Tracking Employing Sliding Mode Control," *IEEE Trans. Circuits Syst. I*, vol. 60, no. 3, pp. 724–732, Mar. 2013, doi: 10.1109/TCSI.2012.2215760.

EUPVSEC 2025

Vehicle Integrated Photovoltaics module architecture optimization under dynamic shading

Ricardo Moruno Lobato, R. Núñez, R. Herrero, L. San José, and I. Antón

Instituto de Energía Solar, Universidad Politécnica de Madrid, Madrid (SPAIN)

020454-001

Motivation

INSTITUTO DE ENERGÍA SOLAR

VIPV: Urban Dynamic Shading

Impact of shading on VIPV

1. Module's architecture mismatch losses
2. Shading distribution
3. DC/DC converters efficiency

POLITÉCNICA

020454-002

Objectives

1. Optimize module design parameters

2. Study shading pattern distribution

3. MPPT VIPV parameter tuning

020454-003

Methodology

INSTITUTO DE ENERGÍA SOLAR

IV Curves simulations

240 fps

1. RECORD VIDEO

2. SELECT AREA

3. IMAGE PROCESSING

4. CONFIGURATION

5. IV CURVE SIMULATION

Layout
– SLM OR 6MM

6. SIMULATE MPPT ALGORITHM

[1] L. San José et al. *Solar Energy Materials and Solar Cells*, [276], p. 113061 (2024)

POLITÉCNICA

Methodology

IV Curves simulations

240 fps

1. RECORD VIDEO **2. SELECT AREA** **3. IMAGE PROCESSING** **4. CONFIGURATION**

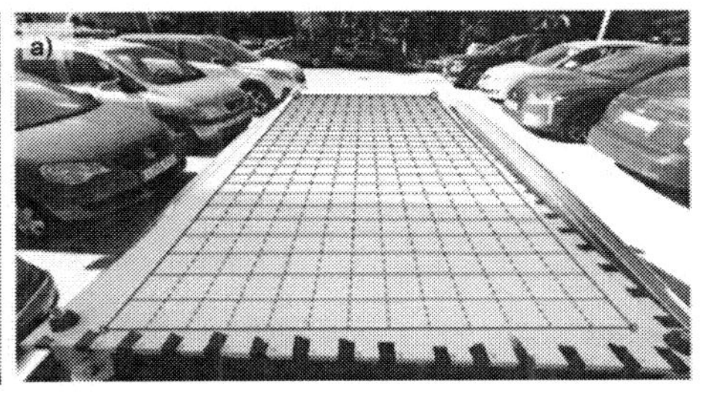

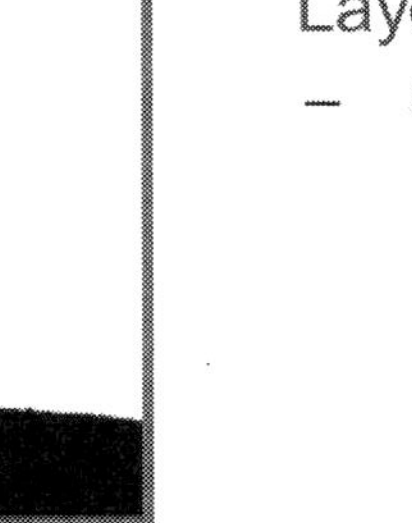

Layout
- SLM **OR** 6MM

[1] L. San José et al. *Solar Energy Materials and Solar Cells*, [276], p. 113061 (2024)

Methodology

INSTITUTO DE ENERGÍA SOLAR

IV Curves simulations

240 fps

1. RECORD VIDEO **2. SELECT AREA** **3. IMAGE PROCESSING** **4. CONFIGURATION**

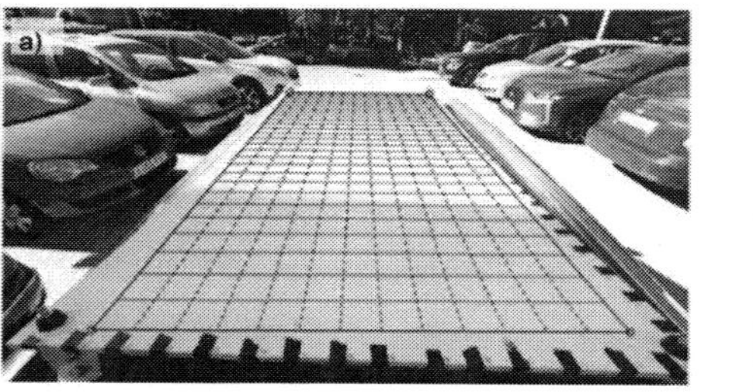

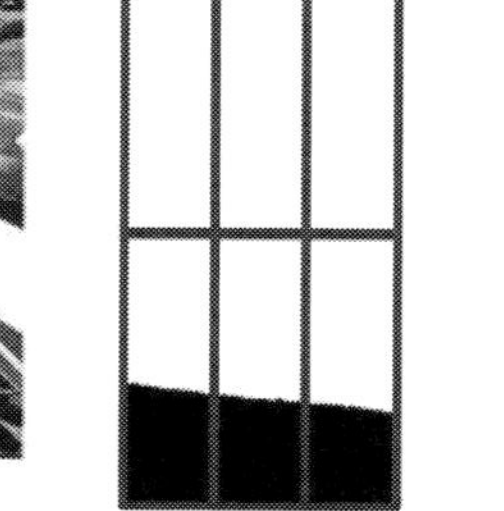

Layout
- SLM OR 6MM

[1] L. San José et al. *Solar Energy Materials and Solar Cells,* [276], p. 113061 (2024)

POLITÉCNICA

Methodology

IV Curves simulations

240 fps

1. RECORD VIDEO **2. SELECT AREA** **3. IMAGE PROCESSING** **4. CONFIGURATION**

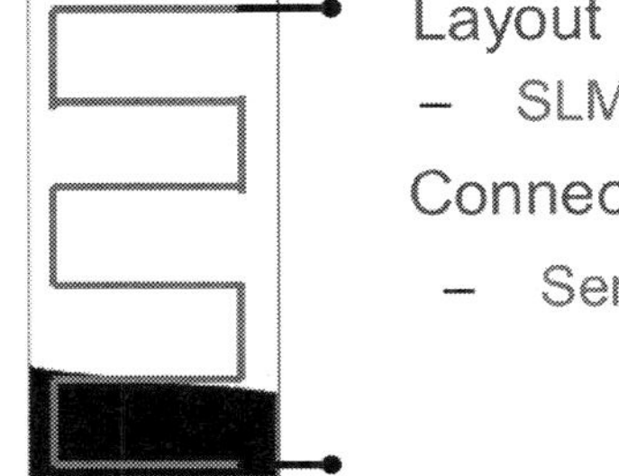

Layout
– SLM OR 6MM

Connection
– Series OR TCT

[1] L. San José et al. *Solar Energy Materials and Solar Cells*, [276], p. 113061 (2024)

POLITÉCNICA

020454-007

Methodology

INSTITUTO DE ENERGÍA SOLAR

IV Curves simulations

240 fps

1. RECORD VIDEO

2. SELECT AREA

3. IMAGE PROCESSING

4. CONFIGURATION

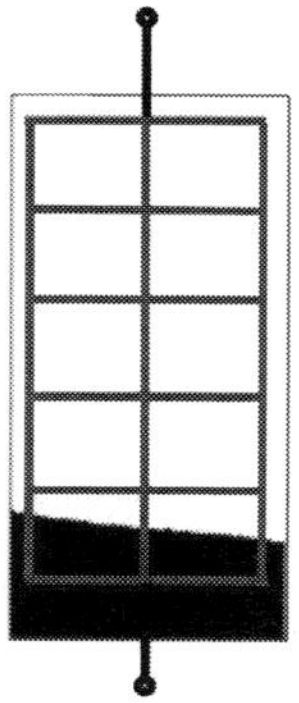

Layout
- SLM OR 6MM

Connection
- Series OR TCT

[1] L. San José et al. *Solar Energy Materials and Solar Cells,* [276], p. 113061 (2024)

POLITÉCNICA

020454-008

Methodology

INSTITUTO DE ENERGÍA SOLAR

IV Curves simulations

240 fps

1. RECORD VIDEO   **2. SELECT AREA**   **3. IMAGE PROCESSING**   **4. CONFIGURATION**

Layout
- SLM OR 6MM

Connection
- Series OR TCT

Cell Orientation
- V OR H

[1] L. San José et al. *Solar Energy Materials and Solar Cells*, [276], p. 113061 (2024)

020454-009

Methodology

INSTITUTO DE ENERGÍA SOLAR

IV Curves simulations

240 fps

1. RECORD VIDEO   **2. SELECT AREA**   **3. IMAGE PROCESSING**   **4. CONFIGURATION**

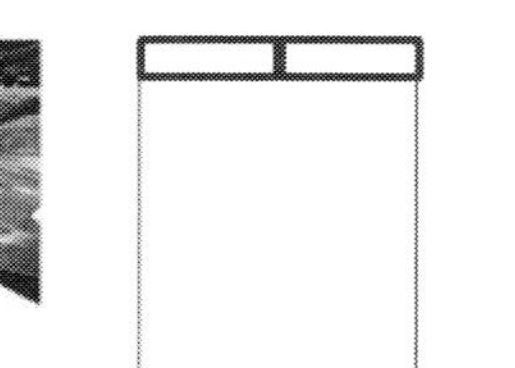

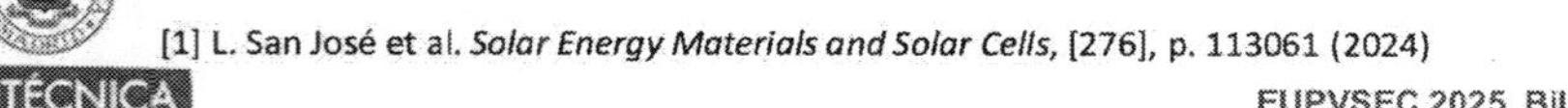

Layout
- SLM OR 6MM

Connection
- Series OR TCT

Cell Orientation
- V OR H

[1] L. San José et al. *Solar Energy Materials and Solar Cells*, [276], p. 113061 (2024)

POLITÉCNICA

020454-010

Methodology

IV Curves simulations

240 fps

1. RECORD VIDEO **2. SELECT AREA** **3. IMAGE PROCESSING** **4. CONFIGURATION** **5. IV CURVE SIMULATION**

Layout
- SLM OR 6MM

Connection
- Series OR TCT

Cell Orientation
- V OR H

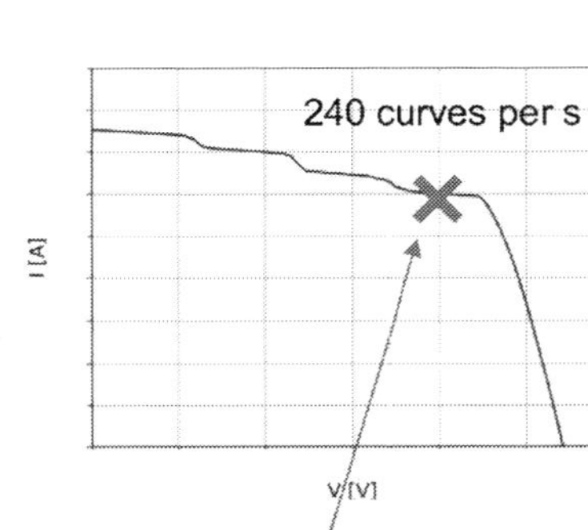

6. SIMULATE MPPT ALGORITHM

[1] L. San José et al. *Solar Energy Materials and Solar Cells*, [276], p. 113061 (2024)

POLITÉCNICA

Case of study

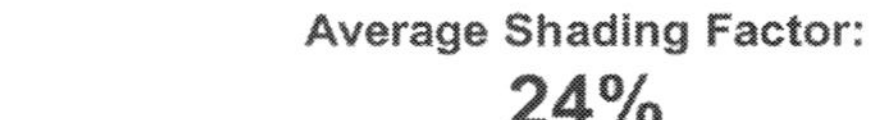

Route

- Extension: **~5.6 km**

- Time: **Spring morning (9:58 am)**

- Duration: **17:20 min**

- Conditions: **Clear sky**

  - **GHI** = 360 W/m^2

  - **Elevation** = 22 °

  - **Azimuth** = 81°

No predominant direction

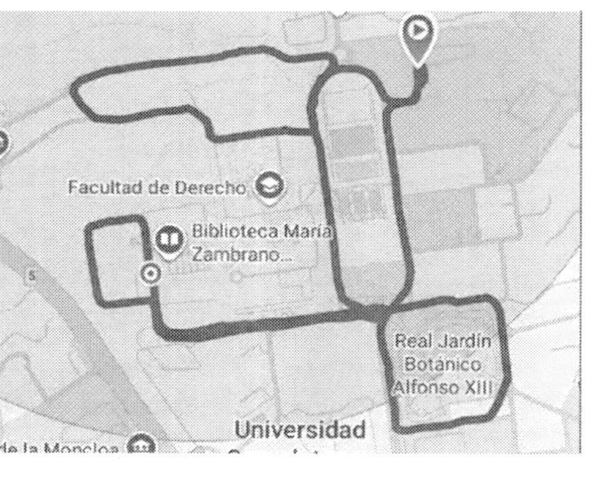

Average Shading Factor:
24%

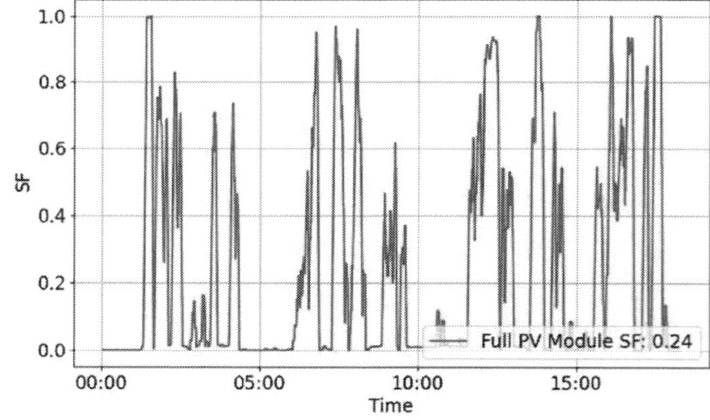

020454-012

Case of study

INSTITUTO DE ENERGÍA SOLAR

Module

- PV active surface: **0.8 m²**
- Cells: **216 shingle silicon cells (10.5 x 3.5 cm)**

Layout:
- Single Large Module (SLM)
- 6 Mini Modules (6 MM)

Connection:
- TCT
- Series

Orientation:
- Vertical (V)
- Horizontal (H)

SLM -Series -V

12x18 (V)

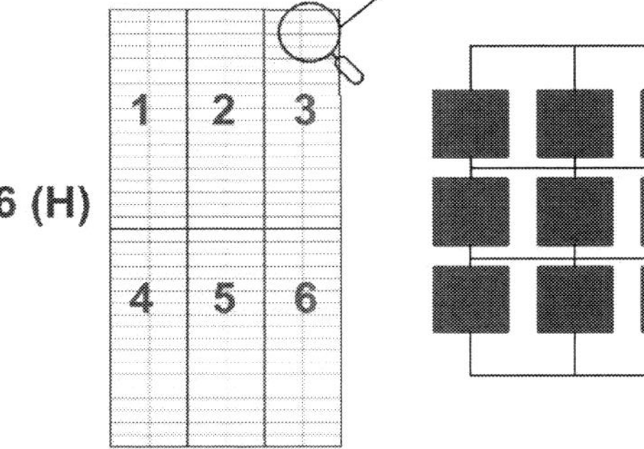

6MM-TCT -H

36x6 (H)

SLM

$P_{MP} = 141$ W

Configuration	Bypass diodes
SLM-Series-V	12
SLM-Series-H	6
SLM-TCT-V	12
SLM-TCT-H	6

6MM

$P_{MP\_MM} = 23.5$ W

$P_{MP\_GLOBAL} = 141$ W

Configuration	Bypass diodes (MM)	Bypass diodes (Global)
6MM-Series-V	6	36
6MM-Series-H	2	12
6MM-TCT-V	6	36
6MM-TCT-H	2	12

POLITÉCNICA

020454-013

Results: PV System Energy Yield Comparison

1. Optimize module design parameters

Examine maximum available
energy in entire route,
**PRIOR TO THE DC/DC
CONVERTER**

$$E_{max} = \int P_{MP}\, dt$$

SF: -21%

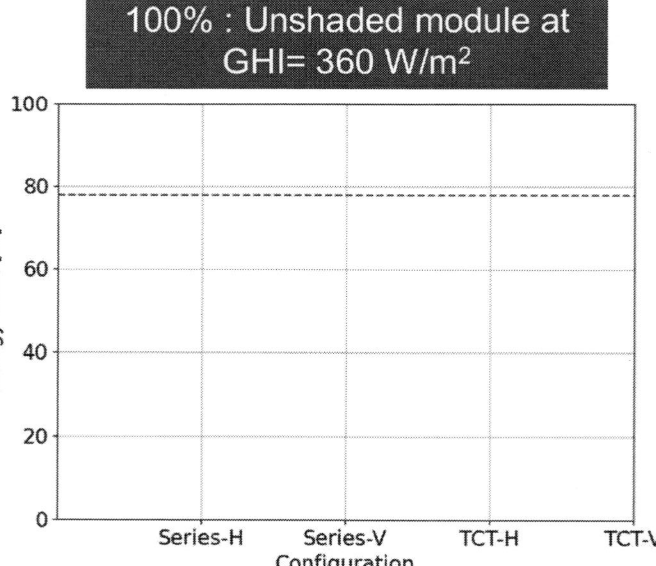

020454-014

Results: PV System Energy Yield Comparison

1. Optimize module design parameters

Examine maximum available energy in entire route, **PRIOR TO THE DC/DC CONVERTER**

$$E_{max} = \int P_{MP}\, dt$$

SF: **-21%**

SVF: -3%

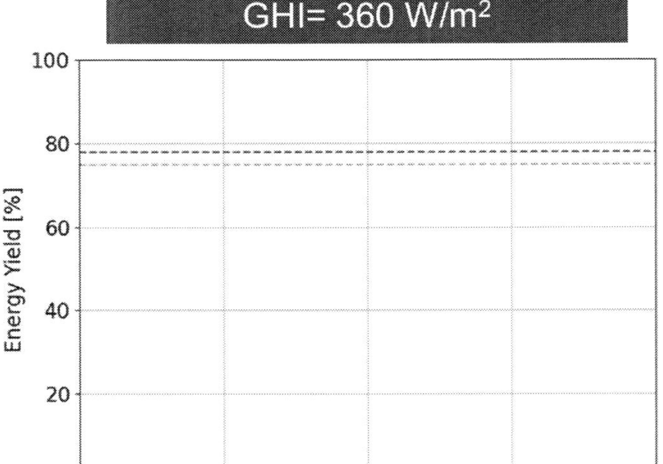

020454-015

Results: PV System Energy Yield Comparison

1. Optimize module design parameters

Examine maximum available
energy in entire route,
**PRIOR TO THE DC/DC
CONVERTER**

$$E_{max} = \int P_{MP}\, dt$$

SF: -21%

SVF: -3%

IAM: -7.5%

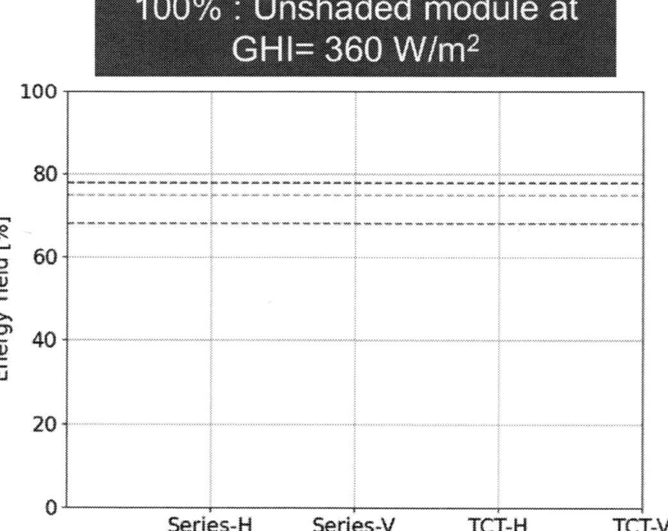

Results: PV System Energy Yield Comparison

1. Optimize module design parameters

Examine maximum available energy in entire route,
PRIOR TO THE DC/DC CONVERTER

$$E_{max} = \int P_{MP}\, dt$$

SF: -21%

SVF: -3%

IAM: -7.5%

Curvature: -0.29%

T:+0.14%

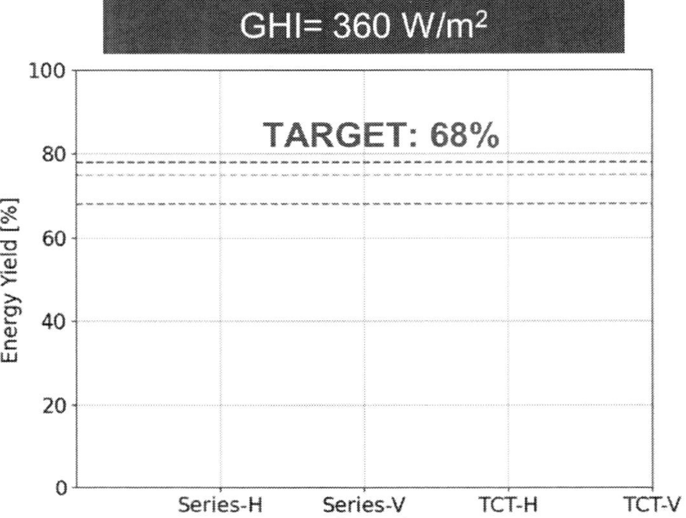

Results: PV System Energy Yield Comparison

1. Optimize module design parameters

Examine maximum available
energy in entire route,
**PRIOR TO THE DC/DC
CONVERTER**

$$E_{max} = \int P_{MP}\, dt$$

SF: -21%

SVF: -3%

IAM: **-7.5%**

**Curvature:
-0.29%**

T:+0.14%

– TCT outperforms series by ~3-4%.

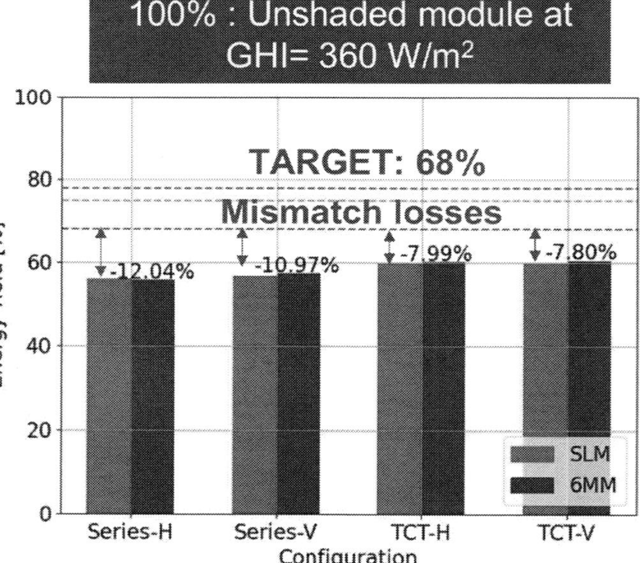

POLITÉCNICA

18

020454-018

Results: PV System Energy Yield Comparison

INSTITUTO
DE ENERGÍA
SOLAR

1. Optimize module design parameters

Examine maximum available
energy in entire route,
**PRIOR TO THE DC/DC
CONVERTER**

$$E_{max} = \int P_{MP}\, dt$$

SF: -21%

SVF: -3%

IAM: -7.5%

**Curvature:
-0.29%**

T:+0.14%

– TCT outperforms series by ~3-4%.

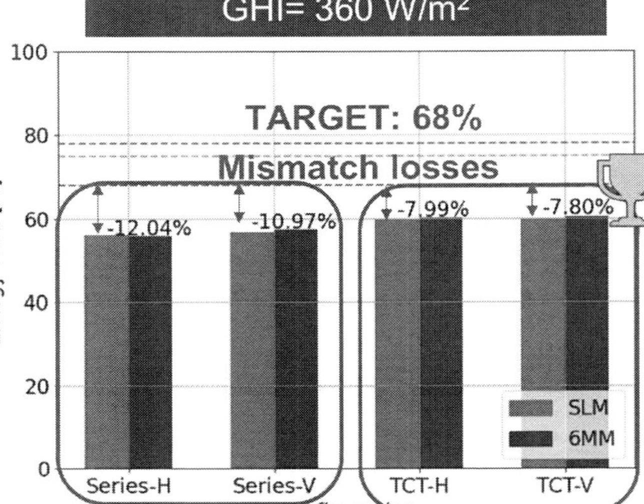

020454-019

Results: PV System Energy Yield Comparison

1. Optimize module design parameters

Examine maximum available
energy in entire route,
**PRIOR TO THE DC/DC
CONVERTER**

$$E_{max} = \int P_{MP}\, dt$$

SF: -21%
SVF: -3%
IAM: -7.5%
**Curvature:
-0.29%**
T:+0.14%

– TCT outperforms series by ~3-4%.

– Series-V outperforms Series-H by ~1%.

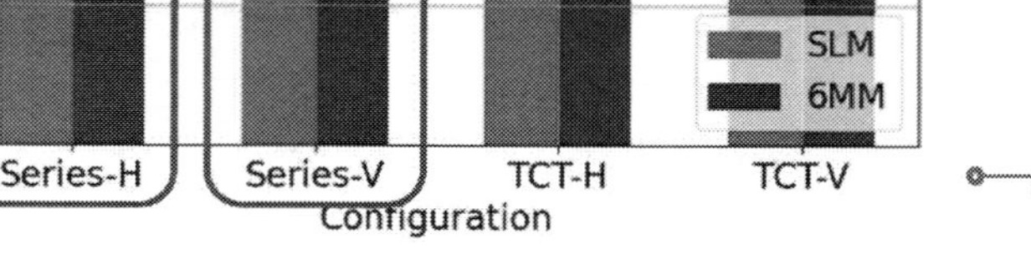

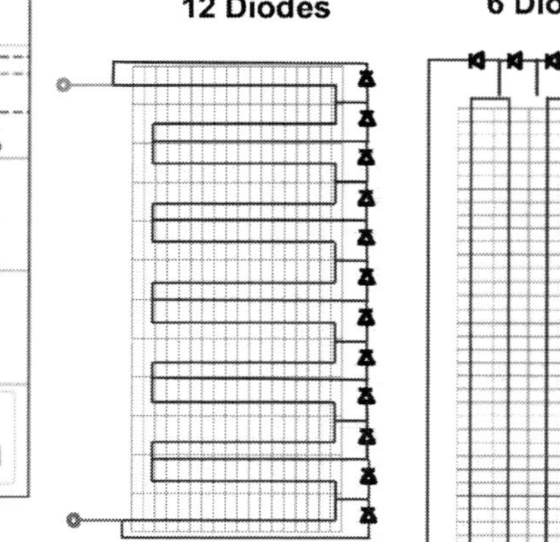

Results: PV System Energy Yield Comparison

1. Optimize module design parameters

Examine maximum available energy in entire route, **PRIOR TO THE DC/DC CONVERTER**

$$E_{max} = \int P_{MP}\ dt$$

SF: -21%

SVF: -3%

IAM: -7.5%

Curvature: -0.29%

T:+0.14%

– TCT outperforms series by ~3-4%.

– Series-V outperforms Series-H by ~1%.

– Small variation of available energy with 6MM vs 1 SLM (<1%).

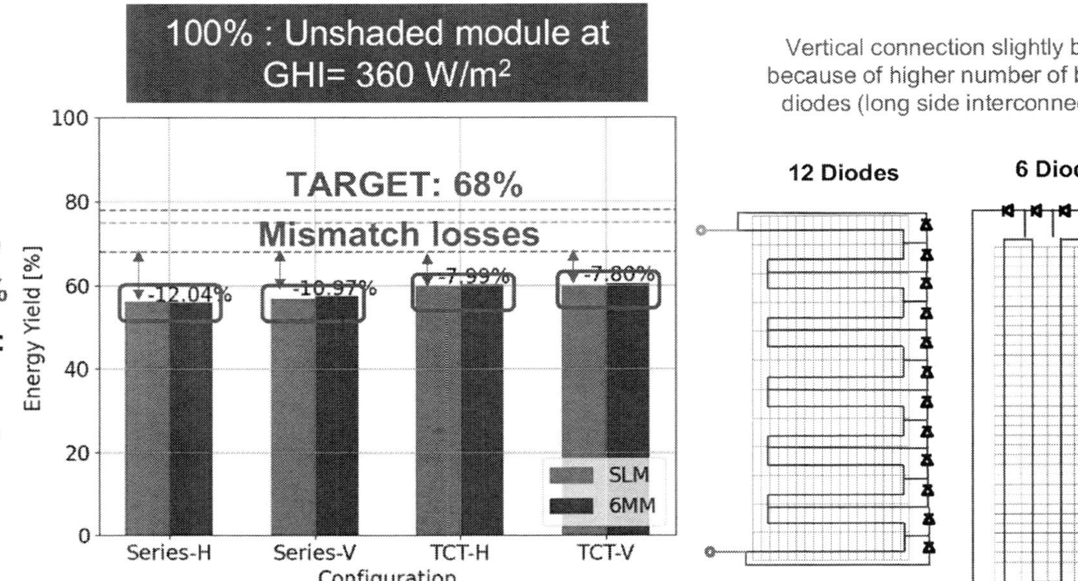

Vertical connection slightly better because of higher number of bypass diodes (long side interconnection)

Results : Sub-module Energy Yield Analysis

2. Study shading pattern distribution

Sub-Module Energy Yield indicates presence of shadows

Small variation of available energy across all modules: similar shading patterns across the surface

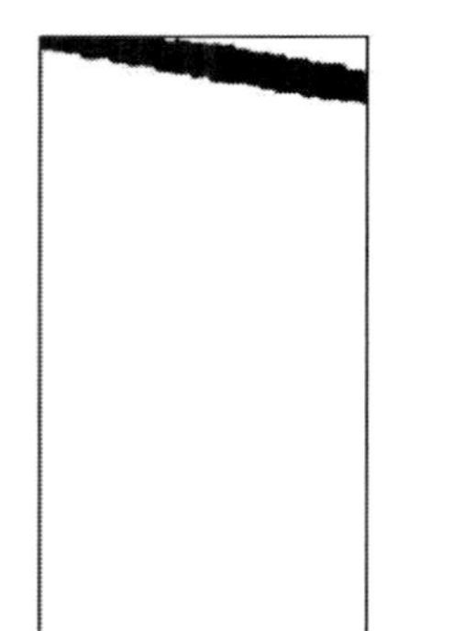

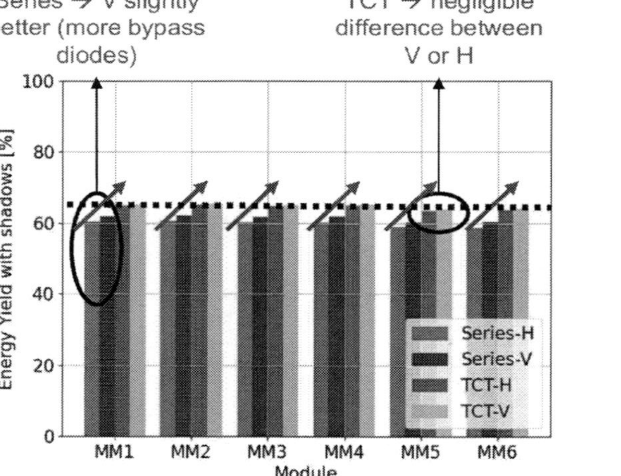

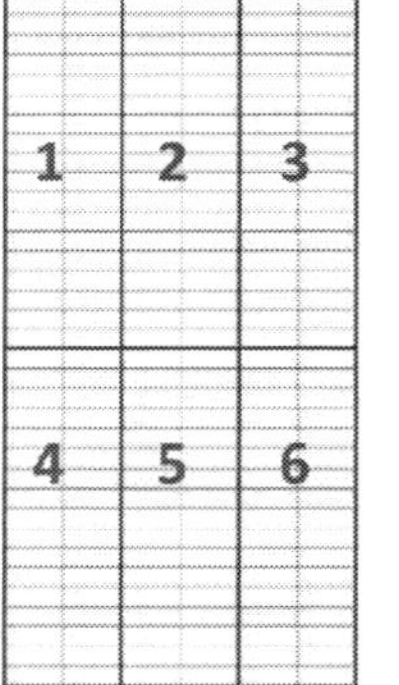

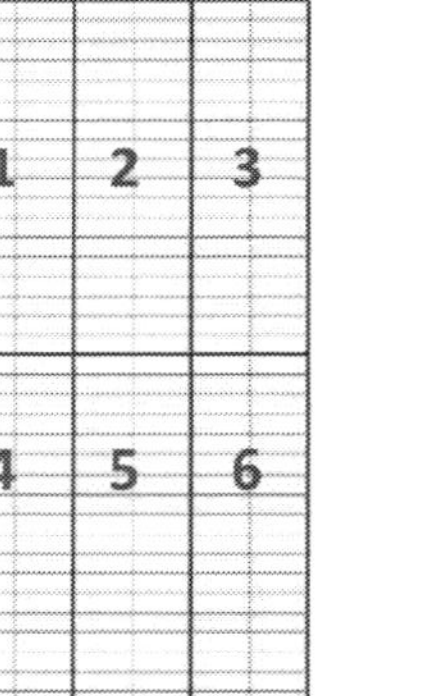

020454-022

RESULTS: P&O sensitivity analysis

3. MPPT VIPV parameter tuning

$$\eta_{MPPT} = \frac{\int P_{MPPT}\, dt}{\int P_{MAX}\, dt} \;[2]$$

TCT → Diagonal trend, sensitive to step size because IV curve shape

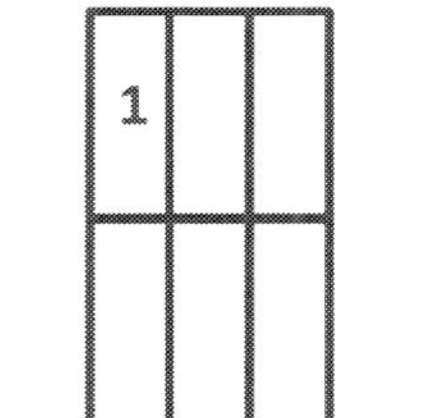

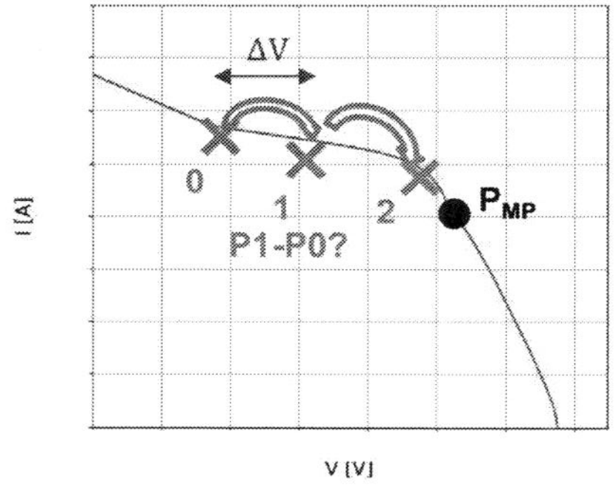

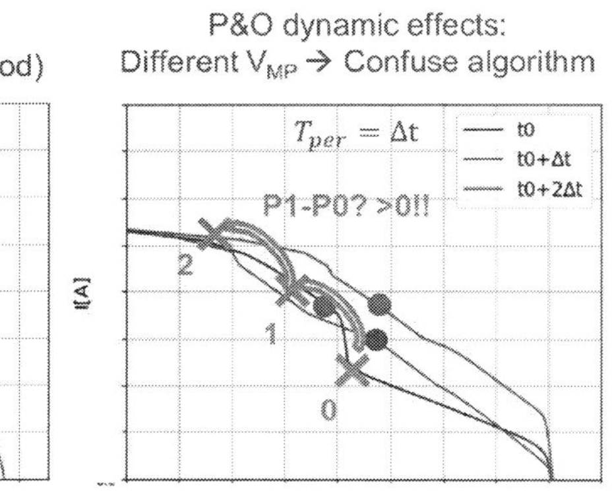

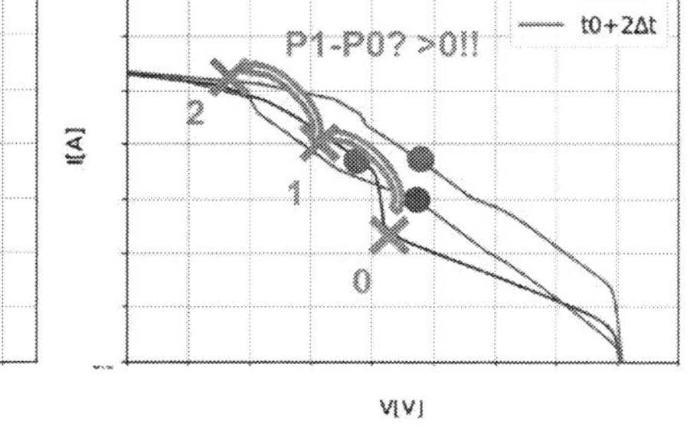

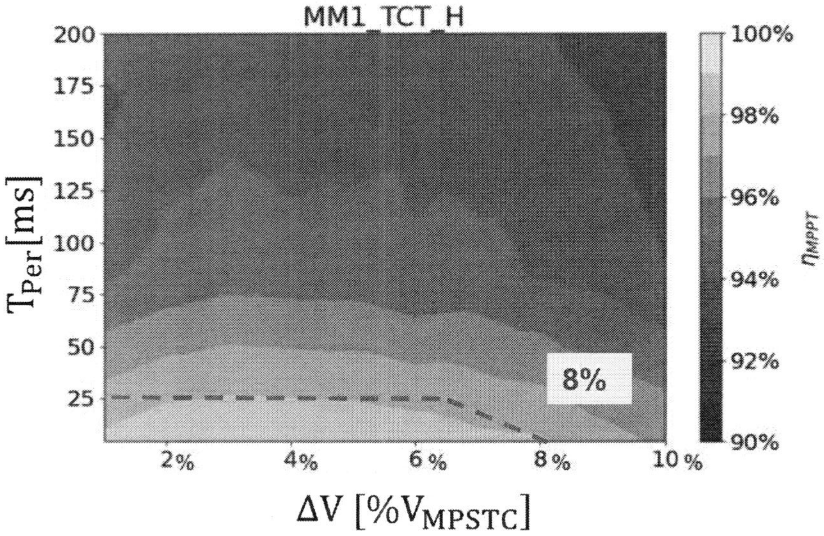

[2] "EVS-EN 50530:2010," EVS.

RESULTS: P&O sensitivity analysis

3. MPPT VIPV parameter tuning

$$\eta_{MPPT} = \frac{\int P_{MPPT}\, dt}{\int P_{MAX}\, dt} \quad [2]$$

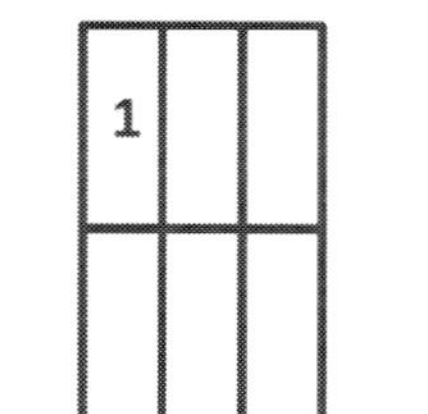

Series → Horizontal trend, sensitive to perturbation period

P&O algorithm tuning
(step size and perturbation period)

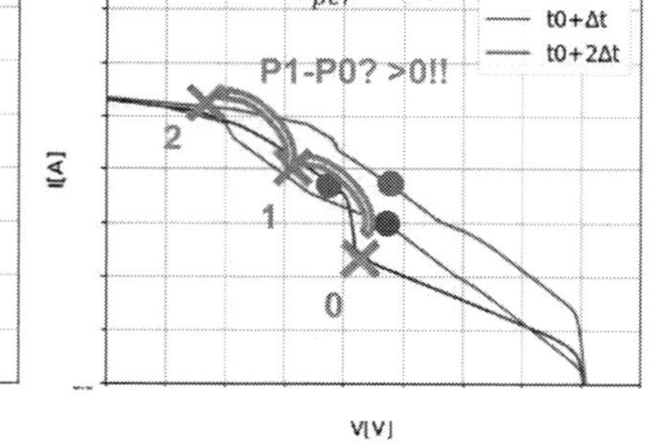

[2] "EVS-EN 50530:2010," EVS.

RESULTS: P&O sensitivity analysis

3. MPPT VIPV parameter tuning

$$\eta_{MPPT} = \frac{\int P_{MPPT}\, dt}{\int P_{MAX}\, dt} \quad [2]$$

Realistic P&O
period: ~100 ms [3]

Very similar η among all sub-modules

Low period eff:
98-99%

[2] "EVS-EN 50530:2010," EVS.
[3] Y. Levron et al. *IEEE Trans. Circuits Syst. I*, vol. 60, no. 3, pp. 724–732 (2013).

POLITÉCNICA

RESULTS: P&O sensitivity analysis

INSTITUTO
DE ENERGÍA
SOLAR

3. MPPT VIPV parameter tuning

$$\eta_{MPPT} = \frac{\int P_{MPPT}\, dt}{\int P_{MAX}\, dt} \; [2]$$

Realistic P&O
period: ~100 ms [3]

Very similar η among all sub-modules

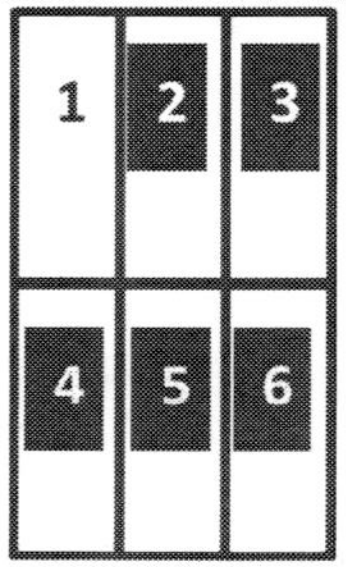

1	2	3
4	5	6

Low period eff:
98-99%

Realistic period eff:
95-96%

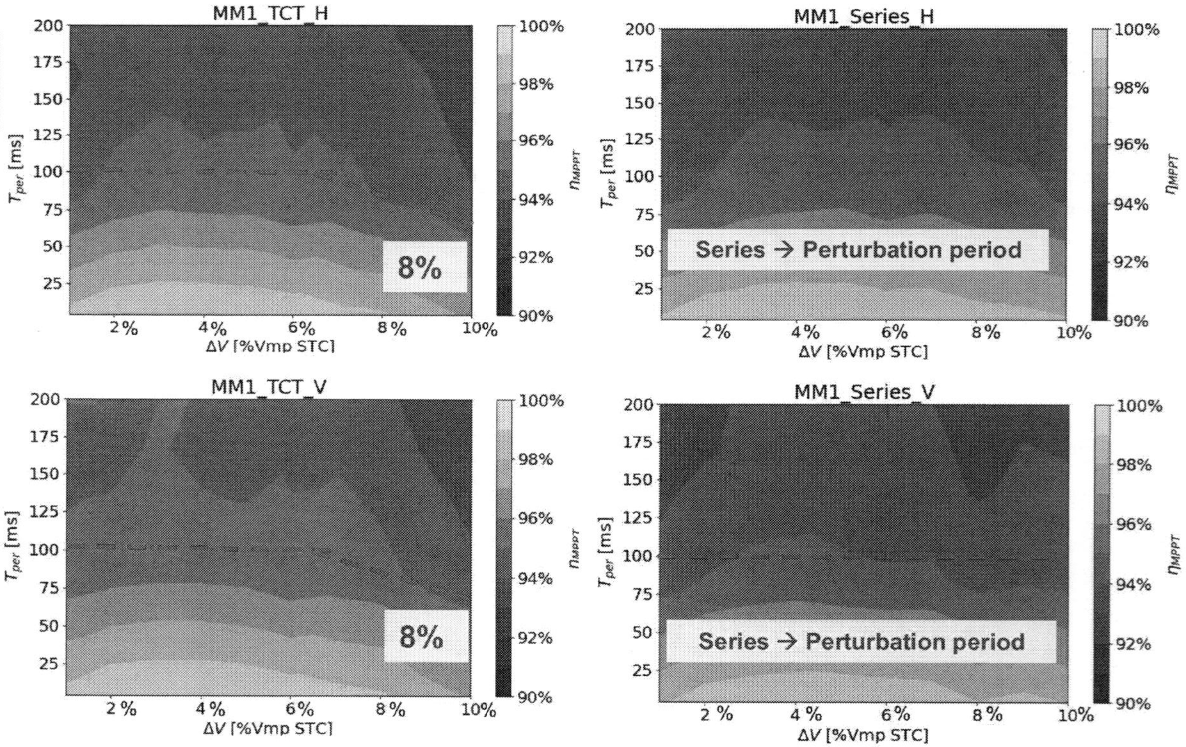

[2] "EVS-EN 50530:2010," EVS.

[3] Y. Levron et al. *IEEE Trans. Circuits Syst. I*, vol. 60, no. 3, pp. 724–732 (2013).

POLITÉCNICA

RESULTS: P&O sensitivity analysis

3. MPPT VIPV parameter tuning

$$\eta_{MPPT} = \frac{\int P_{MPPT}\, dt}{\int P_{MAX}\, dt} \quad [2]$$

Realistic P&O period: ~100 ms [3]

SLM

Same trends, similar efficiencies: 98-99% with 4.16 ms

[2] "EVS-EN 50530:2010," EVS.

[3] Y. Levron et al. *IEEE Trans. Circuits Syst. I*, vol. 60, no. 3, pp. 724–732 (2013).

RESULTS: P&O sensitivity analysis

INSTITUTO DE ENERGÍA SOLAR

3. MPPT VIPV parameter tuning

$$\eta_{MPPT} = \frac{\int P_{MPPT}\, dt}{\int P_{MAX}\, dt} \quad [2]$$

Realistic P&O period: ~100 ms [3]

SLM

Same trends, similar efficiencies:
98-99% with 4.16 ms
95-96% with 100 ms

[2] "EVS-EN 50530:2010," EVS.

[3] Y. Levron et al. *IEEE Trans. Circuits Syst. I*, vol. 60, no. 3, pp. 724–732 (2013).

POLITÉCNICA

Conclusions

- Mini-Module strategy provides **marginal Energy Yield** improvement, prior to DC/DC **(<1%)**.

- **Similar shading across all the roof**, but at different instants due to the **vehicle's movement**.

- **TCT** is the most productive connection, **independent** from cell orientation.

- **Series** connection performs **better** with **vertical** connection, due to the higher number of **bypass diodes**.

- **Almost identical efficiencies** with SLM or 6MM, very **similar trends**:

  - **98-99%** efficiency with lowest perturbation period possible (**4.16 ms**). However, might not be feasible.
  - **95-96 %** efficiency with realistic perturbation periods (**100 ms**).
  - **MPPT** efficiency strongly depends on MPPT parameters, not on module's architecture.

- Further studies are required to **validate** the Distributed MPPT strategy (better temperature, other surfaces, etc.). **Energy cost** of implementing various DC/DC converters should be considered.

020454-029

Thank you for your attention

Ricardo Moruno

r.moruno@upm.es

Happy to take your questions

We gratefully acknowledge the DETEC-PV project, Grant PID2021-128853OB-I00, funded by MCIN/AEI/10.13039/501100011033 and "ERDF A way of making Europe"

R. Moruno thanks his grant "PID2021-128853OB-I00" funded by MCIN/AEI/ 10.13039/501100011033 and by "ERDF A way of making Europe".

INSTITUTO
DE ENERGÍA
SOLAR
Innovation in photovoltaics since 1979

INFLUENCE OF DIFFERENT DRIVING PATTERNS AND ELECTRICAL DESIGNS ON VIPV PERFORMANCE

Judy Jalkh[1], Christian Doppler[1], Philip Caluori[1], Manuel Ruf[2]
Virtual Vehicle GmbH[1], Robert Bosch GmbH[2]
[1]Inffeldgasse 21A, 8010 Graz, +433168738821, judy.jalkh@v2c2.at

ABSTRACT: This study evaluates the potential performance of Vehicle-Integrated Photovoltaics (VIPV) under varying driving and parking patterns across European locations, including Athens, Paris, and Helsinki. By analyzing distinct dynamic driver usage scenarios such as commuting, long-distance travel, short trips, and average yearly driving behaviors, this research provides a comprehensive understanding of usage patterns on VIPV efficiency. The target is to design a one single VIPV-system capable of covering the monthly electric vehicle HVAC (Heating Ventilation & Air Conditioning) energy requirements, for as many observed scenarios as possible. As a result, a PV size of 1.64m² was selected, sufficient to widely cover the regarded HVAC demands, especially with short-distance and commuter drive profiles. The study also examines the energy optimization during partial shading conditions by studying different electrical architectures, like varying bypass diodes and Maximum Power Point Trackers (MPPTs). This analysis shows that both the intensity and pattern of shading influence the optimal electrical configuration, with high-intensity shading favoring a configuration with 35 bypass diodes for a 1.64m² PV area. Overall, these findings demonstrate substantial variability in VIPV performance depending on geographic location, driving behavior, and system design, providing key insights for optimizing VIPV systems across diverse use cases.
Keywords: VIPV, partial shading, driving behavior, bypass diode, MPPT

1 INTRODUCTION

Recent studies have examined VIPV for commercial vehicles in Europe [1] and passenger cars in Germany, Spain, and California [2], but often under idealized conditions and without considering diverse usage patterns or parking environments. These gaps limit understanding of how VIPV performs in real-world contexts.

This work addresses this by analyzing VIPV across three European climates (Athens, Paris, and Helsinki) using four driver types (short, long, average, commuter) and three parking conditions (street, garage, shaded).

The study is conducted within the EFFEREST project [3], which develops user-centric control systems for electric vehicles. The TOGG electric vehicle (EV) serves as a demonstrator, where VIPV integration on the roof is simulated under diverse driving and climate scenarios. A key benchmark is whether VIPV can cover part of the vehicle's HVAC energy demand, linking solar generation directly to passenger comfort, an aspect often missing in previous analyses.

Optimized electric configuration under partial shading is also analyzed in terms of bypass diode (BPD) layouts and MPPT methods, building on findings that optimized BPDs can retain up to 69.2% of output under shading [4] and that advanced MPPT improves response to fluctuating irradiance [5]. A measurement campaign on bypass diodes was carried out to visualize and validate the effects of shading patterns on power output.

By combining climate, usage, parking, and system design, this study offers a more realistic assessment of VIPV, showing which driver–city combinations benefit most and supporting the broader adoption of solar-integrated EVs for reduced emissions and greater energy independence.

2 DRIVING PATTERNS

2.1 Exemplary reference week

BOSCH created exemplary driving weeks to represent real-world vehicle usage by combining internal, public, and purchased data. Four reference driving scenarios were defined: Short Distance Drive (SD), Long Distance Drive (LD), Average Drive (Avg), and Commute (Comm). These were mapped to three climatic regions: Helsinki (cold), Paris (average), and Athens (hot). The exemplary weeks were generated by enriching one year of real driving data (start/stop times, distance, GPS, velocity) with stochastic parking data (street, garage, shaded), charging models, and regional climate conditions. From this combination, a representative week was selected for each driving type and city using a least-squares method, ensuring that weekly patterns matched annual statistics as closely as possible. It was assumed that passenger cars in private European use with one year of driving reflect lifetime behavior if no major socio-economic changes occur. The final dataset includes GPS traces, velocity profiles, and parking types. For example, the short distance driver exemplary week is shown in Figure 1. Table I differentiates between the driver types in terms of parking type and monthly mileage.

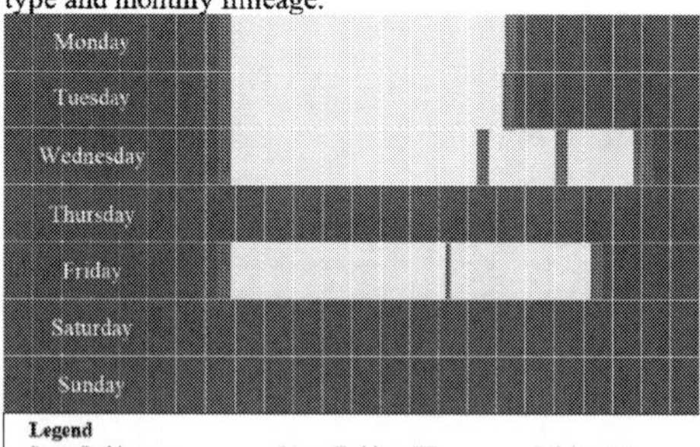

Figure 1: Exemplary week for short distance driver

Table I: Parameters of the four driver types

	Avg	SD	LD	Comm
Garage Parking	Yes	Yes	No	No
Street Parking [days/week]	3	4	7	7
Monthly Mileage [km]	~800	~300	~2600	~1250

2.2 SIC simulations

The in-house tool Solar Irradiance Calculator (SIC) has been used, which calculates dynamically the irradiation according to the changing driving profile of the moving TOGG EV. The model relies on several inputs to calculate the irradiance.

The main input is the weather data, namely GHI (Global Horizontal Irradiance), DNI (Direct Normal Irradiance), DHI (Diffuse Horizontal Irradiance), and the Temperature. This data is downloaded from the NSRDB database [6] for 365 days with 15 min interval for the year 2019 for the three studied cities. The "average" monthly day was elaborated for a more effective process to scale results.

The second input is the driving and parking cycle. The cycle is the 24-hr Bosch exemplary week for each city and driver type as discussed in the previous section. For simplification, the PV zone on the TOGG EV roof is assumed with a tilt of $0°$.

Next, the SIC calculates the experienced shade on the entire roof. The irradiance already includes shadows from the clouds in the DHI. A Random Shading Generator (RSG) was developed to simulate irregular shading effects from environmental obstacles such as trees and buildings. Its purpose is to randomly vary the shading percentage across the cycle while ensuring that the overall average shading for the entire cycle meets a specified target. It is made up of two parameters, the shading factor and the number of sections. The shading factor is a value between 0 and 1, where 0 represents complete shade and 1 represents no shade. The number of sections represent time discretization. A reduced number of sections results in increased section dimensions, causing the vehicle to remain under the same shading level for longer periods. The "exemplary week" cycles are made up of four different periods: driving, street parking, shaded parking, and garage parking. During driving, the RSG driving is used with a shading factor of 0.6 and 120 sections. During street parking, the shading factor is increased to 0.8 while the number of sections is reduced to 60. This is because, during driving, the vehicle's higher velocity causes the shadows cast on its roof to shift more rapidly. In contrast, when the vehicle is stationary, shadow transitions occur at a much slower rate. Furthermore, the shading factor during driving is generally lower, as the vehicle frequently operates in closer proximity to buildings, other vehicles, and large trucks, resulting in more pronounced and transient shading compared to when it is parked in open areas. During shaded parking, the DHI irradiance is used, and finally during garage parking the irradiance is 0.

An example is portrayed in Figure 2. The "Final Export" is the final output of the SIC to the simulation model discussed in section 3.1. To interpret the figure, it is essential to first focus on the parking conditions, as the final output depends on this information to determine the appropriate irradiance profile. From time 0 until ~8:30, the vehicle is parked in a garage, resulting in an irradiance value of 0. Between roughly 08:30 and 09:00, there is a short driving period during which the RSG driving irradiance profile is applied. The vehicle is then parked in a shaded location, so the diffuse irradiance is used. At ~11:00, a 30-minute driving period occurs, during which the RSG driving irradiance is again applied. Finally, the vehicle returns home and is parked in the garage, where the irradiance value returns to 0.

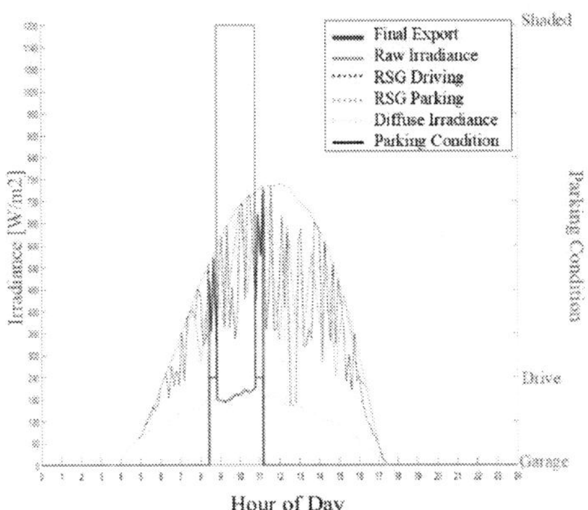

Figure 2: Different irradiance profiles [W/m²] and parking conditions for the Average driver on Friday in Athens

Simulations for the 4 driving scenarios, the 3 cities, 12 months, 7 days a week were performed resulting in 1008 irradiance outputs in W/m².

At this point the SIC only calculates the environmental parameters acting on the vehicle to output the irradiance. The PV characteristics are then used to calculate the PV power. These include a PV area of 1.64m², PV cell efficiency of 23%, and a PE efficiency of 95%.

2.3 HVAC calculations

The required HVAC energy is calculated for each driver type, month, exemplary day of week, and city. The goal of this work is to cover all the required HVAC energy demand via PV. A pre-calculation led to the following required energy quantities mainly based on environmental temperature: 3 kWh/100km for hot (30 °C) and cold (0 °C), 0 kWh/100km for normal temperatures (15 °C), and 7 kWh/100km for very cold temperatures (-10 °C).

As a next step, the average frequency of temperature categories had to be identified. Therefore, daily temperature data was sourced from online meteorological databases which include recorded maximum, average, and minimum temperatures for each day [7]. The classification of thermal conditions is based on these values: Hot days are defined as days where the maximum temperature exceeds 25 °C, with the maximum temperature serving as an upper boundary indicator. Cold days are defined as days where the mean temperature ranges between −5 °C and 5 °C, as the minimum temperature dataset predominantly reflects nighttime temperatures, whereas the simulations are focused on daytime operating conditions. Very cold days are those with a mean temperature below −5 °C. The number of normal days per month is determined as the remainder of the total days in the month after subtracting the counts of hot, cold, and very cold days. Table II summarizes the number of days per year in each temperature category for the three cities.

Table II: Number of days for each temperature category

	Hot	Cold	Very cold	Normal
Athens	151	5	0	209
Paris	67	31	0	267
Helsinki	10	156	20	179

Finally, monthly HVAC energy requirements are computed assuming operation only during driving. For each temperature category (hot, cold, very cold, and normal), the energy is obtained by multiplying percentage of days in each temperature category, the monthly driven distance, and the corresponding HVAC energy consumption per 100 km.

2.4 Results

In this section, the HVAC requirements and the produced PV energy are compared to understand the benefits of VIPV for each driver type and city.

Figure 3 summarizes in which months the PV production fully covers the HVAC requirements for all driver types and cities. For Athens, PV production is higher throughout the year, allowing it to satisfy HVAC demand for more months compared to Paris and Helsinki. For all cities, short distance and commuter drivers see similar coverage, with the prior gaining a few extra months in Athens and Paris, despite having a garage while the commuter parks on the street. Similarly, long distance and average drivers have comparable coverage, with the long distance driver slightly ahead, even though the average driver has a garage. This shows that having a garage does not necessarily reduce the benefits of PV. Driven distance is a key factor: the short distance driver covers only ~300 km/month and parks on the street during peak sunlight, whereas the average driver, with ~800 km/month and less street parking, experiences less PV contribution. The long distance driver, despite always parking on the street, has higher HVAC demand due to ~2600 km/month. In Helsinki, PV meets HVAC requirements from May to early October for all driver types, with short-distance and commuter drivers benefiting additionally in April.

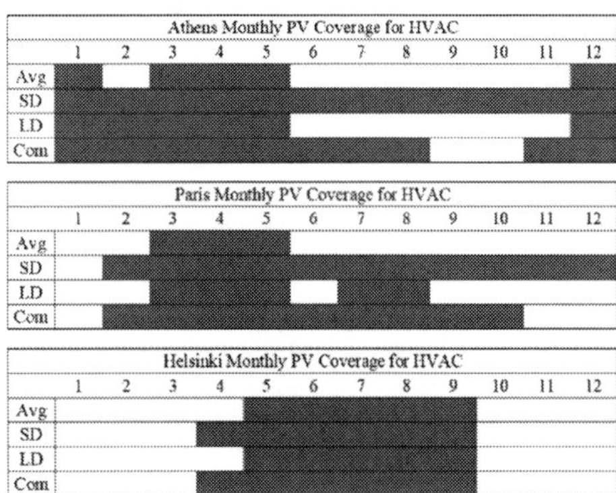

Figure 3: Months where PV output satisfies HVAC requirements (in blue)

In Table III, the yearly PV production and HVAC consumption energy values are presented. The short distance and commuter drivers in Athens and Paris have a surplus of PV energy that can be used for satisfying mileage (Red). Thus, one can conclude that VIPV is very beneficial for people driving a lower mileage living in southern regions of Europe.

Table III: Yearly PV output and HVAC requirements [kWh]

Cities	[kWh]	Avg	SD	LD	Comm
Athens	PV	78	152	313	356
	HVAC	127	49	397	199
Paris	PV	52	144	234	254
	HVAC	86	31	271	127
Helsinki	PV	45	123	196	219
	HVAC	167	76	553	259

In conclusion, VIPV performance depends on both garage availability and driven distance, which governs HVAC energy demand. Optimal utilization occurs for households with a garage under short distance driving and daytime street parking, whereas households without a garage benefit most from a commuter driving pattern with limited long trips.

3 ELECTRICAL ARCHITECTURES FOR PARTIAL SHADING

This section focuses on the effects of partial shading. The first sub-section focuses on finding the optimal bypass diode configuration to limit partial shading losses, while the second sub-section compares the behavior of two MPPT types under partial shading.

3.1 Simulation model

The simulation model is made in MATLAB/Simulink. The PV-cell technology modelled is based on the Maxeon Ne3 Cell [8]. Table IV lists all the parameters used to match the IV- and PV-curves between model and datasheet. The total PV area is made up of 15 by 7 PV cells, totaling 105 cells with 1.64m^2.

Table IV: PV cell simulation parameters

PV Cell Parameters	
Length [mm]	125
Width [mm]	125
Area [m^2]	0.015625
Voc [V]	0.7264
Isc [A]	6.123
Vmp [V]	0.61
Imp [A]	5.7
Pmax [W]	3.47
Efficiency [%]	22.3
N	1.05
Rs [Ω]	0.006
Rsh [Ω]	7

Next, the electrical circuit was studied. Therefore, BPDs and MPPTs are investigated.

3.2 BPD Simulations

BPDs are used to increase power output in shaded scenarios. Due to the limited available area on a vehicle roof, its precise design is crucial, to maximize PV power. To study which BPD configuration behaves best under partial shading, the PV simulation model discussed previously in section 3.1 were used The PV cells were connected in series to reach a higher voltage better aligning with the voltage levels of the EV battery.

As for the varying parameters, these include the Shading Factor (SF), the Shading Pattern (SP), and the Electrical Configuration (EC). The SF indicates the shadows light intensity, where 0 means no light and 1 is no shadow. E.g. SF lower than 0.3 refer to intense shading. A range of 0 to 0.8 was investigated.

The shaded area itself is represented by the SP, which is the shading pattern, namely the location of the shadow on the roof. Five SPs are considered: diagonal beam, 20% random area shading, 60% random area shading, half-roof shading, and quarter-roof shading. The diagonal beam SP simulates a streetlight pole shadow extending from the front right to the back left of the roof. Each random SP includes three scenarios to assess shadow placement effects, while the half-roof and quarter-roof SPs each include four scenarios corresponding to shadows on different roof sections (front, back, left, right). Figure 4 portrays the different SPs on the TOGG roof, with the grey cells indicating shaded areas and the white cells representing unshaded ones. The small black arrow marks the front of the roof.

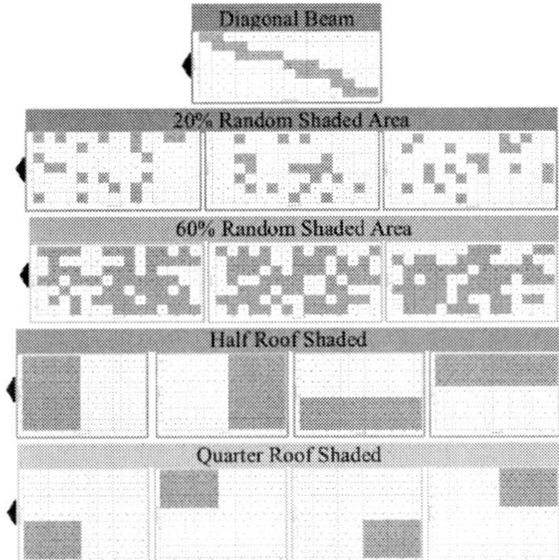

Figure 4: Shading patters on the TOGG roof

Finally, the electric configuration portrays the number of cells per BPD and thus the total number of BPDs. Table V shows the three scenarios used.

Table V: BPD simulation electric configuration scenarios

EC	1	2	3
Number of cells per BPD	3	7	15
Numbers of BPDs	35	15	7
Number of modules	35	15	7
Module dimensions [m²]	0.047	0.11	0.23

For example, Figure 5 shows the SP front half-roof shaded combined with the 35 BPDs EC. Each dashed section refers to a module that is bypassed by 1 BPD.

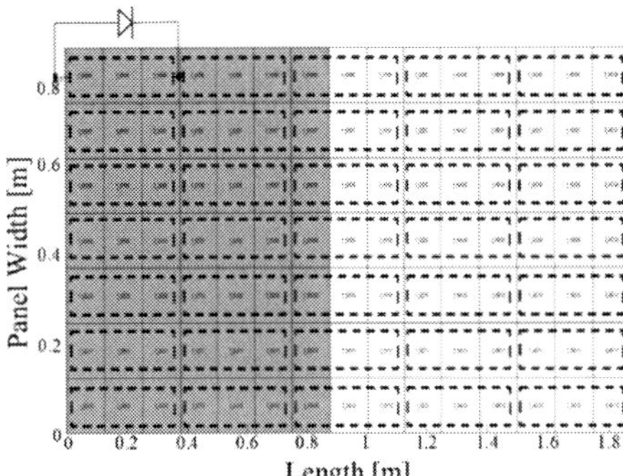

Figure 5: Front half-roof shading patter with 35 BPDs electric configuration

For each SP and SF, the three ECs were compared in terms of maximum power reached. Results indicate that under high-intensity shading (SF ≤ 0.3), ECs with 35 BPDs generally achieve higher power output. However, in half-roof shading scenarios, the 15 BPDs configuration performs better for front and rear shading, while the 7 BPDs configuration performs better for left and right shading. This is because with the half-roof shading, the orientation of the PV modules with respect to the shading location determines the EC preference. On the other hand, for lower intensity shading (SF >= 0.5), the EC does not matter.

For quarter-roof and 60% random shading patterns, SF has little influence on EC configuration preference. The 35 BPDs configuration consistently delivers the highest power, except at SF = 0.8 under all quarter-roof shading scenarios. In the 60% random shading cases, all scenarios produce similar power outputs, showing no clear EC preference regardless of SF, likely due to the extensive shading coverage across the roof.

The influence of shading patterns is evident when comparing the scenarios in Figure 6. Although each pattern (20% area shaded scenarios 1 and 2, any quarter-roof scenario, and the diagonal beam) covers 20% of the PV roof area, their power outputs vary for SF<0.5, demonstrating that shading distribution is as significant as the total shaded area. Nonetheless, all patterns consistently favor the 35 BPDs configuration under high intensity shading conditions.

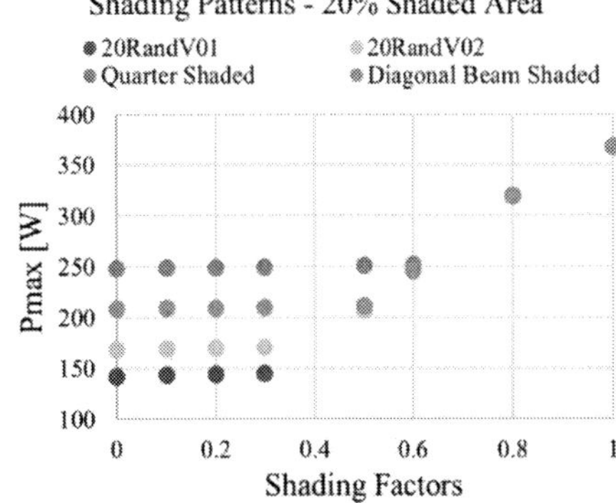

Figure 6: Maximum power reached [W] in terms of SF for four shading patterns with 20% shaded area

3.3 BPD Measurement Campaign

To analyze the behavior of PV systems under real-world conditions, a measurement campaign was conducted focusing on partial shading effects on a PV string. Electrical characteristics, including IV- and PV-curves for different ECs, were recorded under various shading scenarios. The results were used to calibrate and refine the simulation model, ensuring a realistic representation of partial shading and its impact on system performance.

The test setup is shown in Figure 7 and includes light sources, infrared camera, PV-cells and bypass diodes. Not visible in the figure are the adjustable load and voltmeter, which were used to derive the IV curves. Pyranometers from EKO INSTRUMENTS, ML-02 [9] were used to measure the irradiance. The PV cells used were Copper Indium Gallium Selenide (CIGS) half cells from ISC-Konstanz with a size of 160x160mm. The BPDs used were of the type Schottky-Diode STPS1545D. The Virtual Vehicle inhouse system "DataBeam" was used for data collection. An infrared camera was used for temperature visualization.

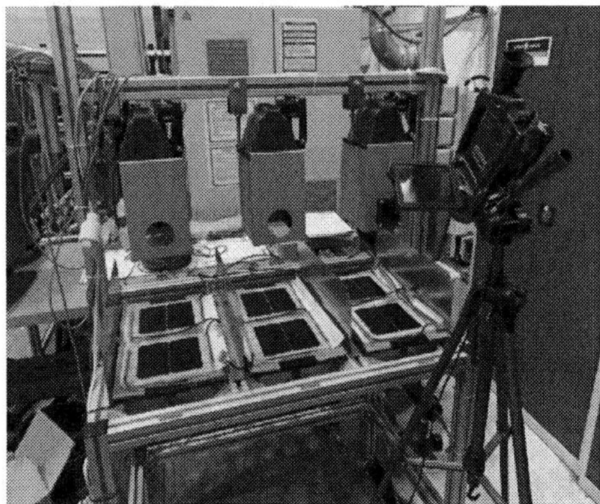

Figure 7: Test setup of measurement campaign, including light sources, infrared camera, PV-cells, bypass diodes

Figure 8 presents a schematic representation of the setup, highlighting the adjustable load, voltmeter, PV cells and their names. It also illustrates the four electrical configurations tested: no bypass diodes (EC-A), and configurations with 6 (EC-B), 3 (EC-C), and 2 (EC-D) bypass diodes.

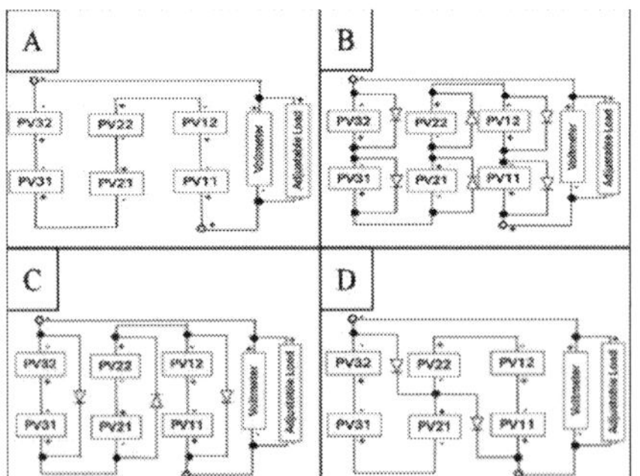

Figure 8: Measurement campaign setup with no bypass diodes, 6, 3, and 2 bypass diodes (A, B, C, and D respectively)

Table VI shows the average irradiance experienced on each of the PV cells at ~60°C, which is assumed as the steady state temperature.

Table VI: Average irradiance [W/m²] on each PV cell

PV Cell	Irradiance [W/m²]
PV32	381
PV31	318
PV22	386
PV21	383
PV12	323
PV11	264

Different SPs and BPD configurations were tested. The shaded cells in these experiments were directly covered above their surface and therefore experienced zero irradiance. The first set of results is presented in Figure 9, showing the variation in output power across different EC and SP combinations. Shadowed cells are indicated by grayed-out PV labels in the lower part of the figure. For a fixed EC and varying SP, the results show that with no BPDs (EC-A), the power drop is already drastic with just 1 shaded cell. The power barely decreases with additional shaded cells. The highest power output can be achieved , as expected, when 6 BPDs (EC-B) are used. For EC-C or EC-D, identical power is observed at one and two shaded cell scenarios. This is because the BPD is already activated with conducts after the first shaded cell, bypassing the whole protected substring, so further shading within that substring does not further reduce output.

Although EC-B generally delivers the highest power output, EC-C slightly outperforms EC-B in the case of 2 shaded cells. This occurs because, within this shaded region, EC-B incorporates 2 BPDs in series, whereas EC-C only has one. The additional diode in EC-B increases resistance, resulting in reduced power.

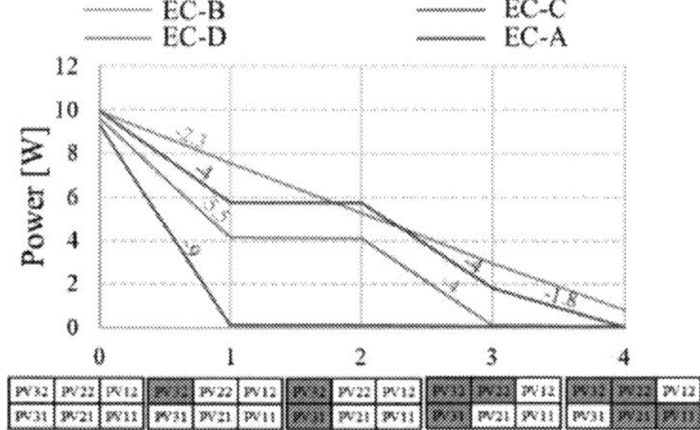

Figure 9: Power drop [W] for each SP and electric configuration

As a next step, the influence of the EC is investigated. Table VII compares the 3 EC cases previously shown in Figure 8 with 2 PV cells constantly shaded. With 1 cell per BPD (EC-B), the power is the same regardless of which cells are shaded. With more cells per BPD, the power depends on the SP and thus the number of strings affected. Case 2 vs case 3 with 2 cells/BPD (EC-C) is probably due to the distribution of the irradiance, even though the average is the same (Table VII).

Table VII: The average irradiance [W/m²] and power [W] for each electric configuration

Case	Shaded Cells	Avg Irr [W/m²]	Power [W]		
			EC-B	EC-C	EC-D
1	32 & 31	339	5.3	5.8	4.1
2	22 & 31	338	5.3	1.8	-
3	32 & 12	338	5.4	2.3	-
4	22 & 21	321	-	-	0.15

The results indicate that output power is governed by the fraction of strings affected by shading. Increasing the number of BPDs reduces this fraction. For instance, shading a single cell in a 1-cell-per-BPD configuration impacts only 1/6 of the strings, whereas in a 2-cells-per-BPD configuration, the same shading affects 1/3 of the strings, resulting in a greater power loss.

In general, it is valid that the more BPDs are used, the higher the power output of the whole system is. Configuration B in Figure 8 has the highest output, Configuration C still works well with only slightly lower power reduction but with significant less BPD used, hence this should be the favorite for future investigations.

3.4 MPPT comparisons

A second very big influence on the PV performance is made by the controller, the MPPT. It is used to set the modules to the voltage level with highest power output.

A previous study, which is a basis for this work was done with a so-called Perturbance and Observation (P&O) MPPT [10]. Due to slow stabilization times, also other possibilities like Particle Swarm Optimization (PSO) were investigated throughout this work.

For better understanding and optimizing power output under partial shading, this study includes the comparison of the P&O with the PSO MPPT. The P&O perturbs the voltage and then observes if the power response is positive or negative. Under partial shading, it can get stuck on the local instead of the global maximum power point (MPP) which leads to power loss. The PSO is bio-inspired (bird flocks/ fish swarms) and each particle is aware of its personal and global best. Under partial shading, it iteratively converges towards the global MPP.

To compare both MPPTs, a simulation model was set up with the PV model mentioned in section 3.1. The simulations include varying the SF (0.2, 0.5, and 0.8), the SP (mentioned in section 3.2), and the MPPT type. The following simulation parameters were used: an input irradiance of 1000 W/m2, a simulation time of 5 seconds, an MPPT time sample of 0.01 seconds, and an EC of 35 PV modules with 3 cells per BPD.

The results, as seen in Figure 10, show that the PSO MPPT reaches a higher maximum power than the P&O MPPT. In some cases, the added benefit (orange) is more pronounced than in others, but there is no clear trend. Due to the more favorable behavior of the PSO under partial shading, it will be integrated and used in future works.

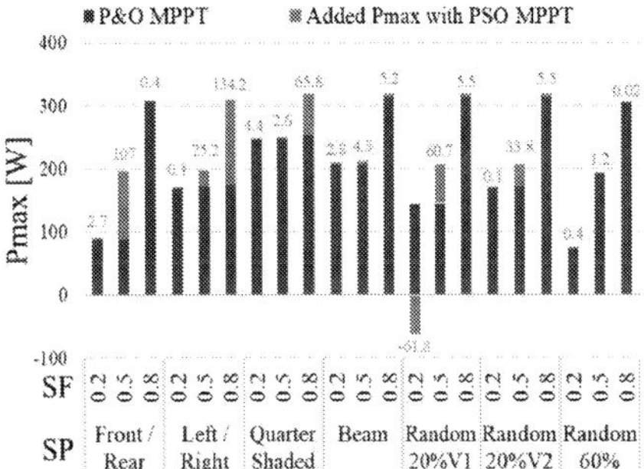

Figure 10: Maximum power [W] reached for the P&O and PSO MPPTs

4 CONCLUSIONS

In conclusion, four driving scenarios were analyzed for Athens, Paris, and Helsinki. PV energy production and HVAC coverage depend on both driven distance and parking location. Short trips with daytime street parking allow households, even with garages, to maximize VIPV benefits. For Short Distance and Commuter driving profiles, a PV area of 1.64m² is sufficient to fully cover the monthly HVAC energy demand in southern (Athens) and central (Paris) Europe. For Long Distance driving profiles, PV can supply the full HVAC demand for approximately half of the year. The lowest coverage occurs under Average Driving profiles due to the combination of infrequent street parking and high monthly mileage. In northern Europe (Helsinki), all driving profiles achieve full HVAC coverage from May to September, with Short Distance and Commuter drivers extending this coverage into April.

As for partial shading, the number of cells bypassed is important primarily with high intensity shading. The reached power is not only affected by the size of the shaded area, but also the distribution and location of the shadow. For a PV area of 1.64m² with a cell efficiency of 22.3%, a relatively low number of bypass diodes (~10) is sufficient under mild shading conditions, where the shaded cells receive 50 to 80% of their nominal irradiance. Under severe shading, with irradiance levels below 30% of the nominal value, a higher number of bypass diodes is required to maintain power output (~35 BPDs). Moreover, the PSO MPPT is better suited for partial shading than the P&O MPPT, even though there is no clear trend with respect to shading pattern or factor.

5 REFERENCES

[1] Kutter, C., Alanis, L.E., Neuhaus, D.H. and Heinrich, M. (2021) Yield Potential of Vehicle Integrated Photovoltaics on Commercial Trucks and Vans. 38*th European PV Solar Energy Conference and Exhibition* 2021, Online, 6-10 September 2021, 1412-1420. https://doi.org/10.4229/EUPVSEC20212021-6DO.8.2

[2] M. Heinrich, C. Kutter, F. Basler, M. Mittag, L. Alanis, D. Eberlein, A. Schmid, C. Reise, T. Kroyer,

D. H. Neuhaus and H. Wirth, "Potential and Challenges of Vehicle Integrated Photovoltaics for Passenger Cars," in *European Photovoltaic Solar Energy Conference and Exhibition (EU PVSEC)*, 2020.

[3] (n.d.). EFFEREST. https://efferest-project.eu/

[4] Klasen, N., Lux, F., Weber, J., Roessler, T., & Kraft, A. (2022). A Comprehensive Study of Module Layouts for Silicon Solar Cells Under Partial Shading. *IEEE Journal of Photovoltaics*, *12*(2), 546–556. https://doi.org/10.1109/jphotov.2022.3144635

[5] Abdulellah Aifan G. Alsulami, Abdullah Ali Alhussainy, Allehyani, A., Alturki, Y. A., Alghamdi, S. M., Alruwaili, M., & Alharthi, Y. Z. (2024). A comparison of several maximum power point tracking algorithms for a photovoltaic power system. *Frontiers in Energy Research*, *12*. https://doi.org/10.3389/fenrg.2024.1413252

[6] (n.d.). NSRDB. https://nsrdb.nrel.gov/

[7] *Weather data documentation*. (2025, July 2). Visual Crossing. https://www.visualcrossing.com/resources/documentation/weather-data/weather-data-documentation/

[8] Mateja, K., Skarka, W., & Drygała, A. (2022). Efficiency Decreases in a Laminated Solar Cell Developed for a UAV. *Materials*, *15*(24), 8774. https://doi.org/10.3390/ma15248774

[9] (n.d.). Solar Measurement and Environmental solutions | EKO Instruments. https://eko-instruments.com/

[10] Jalkh, J., Doppler, C., Spudat, C., Sammer, P., & Michelic, F. (2024). Energy harvesting potential for 3 EVs equipped with PV for the area of Graz in Austria. *Solar Energy Materials and Solar Cells*, *277*, 113116. https://doi.org/10.1016/j.solmat.2024.113116

6   ACKNOWLEDGEMENTS

This work was conducted in the EFFEREST project that has received funding from the European Union's Horizon Europe research and innovation programme under Grant Agreement No. 101138266. Views and opinions expressed are however those of the author(s) only and do not necessarily reflect those of the European Union or European Climate, Infrastructure and Environment Executive Agency (CINEA). Neither the European Union nor the granting authority can be held responsible for them. The publication was written at Virtual Vehicle Research GmbH in Graz and partially funded within the COMET K2 Competence Centers for Excellent Technologies by the Austrian Federal Ministry for Innovation, Mobility and Infrastructure (BMIMI), Austrian Federal Ministry for Economy, Energy and Tourism (BMWET), the Province of Styria (Dept. 12) and the Styrian Business Promotion Agency (SFG). The Austrian Research Promotion Agency (FFG) has been authorised for the programme management.

The authors would like to acknowledge ISC Konstanz for supplying their CIGS PV cells used is this study's measurement campaign.

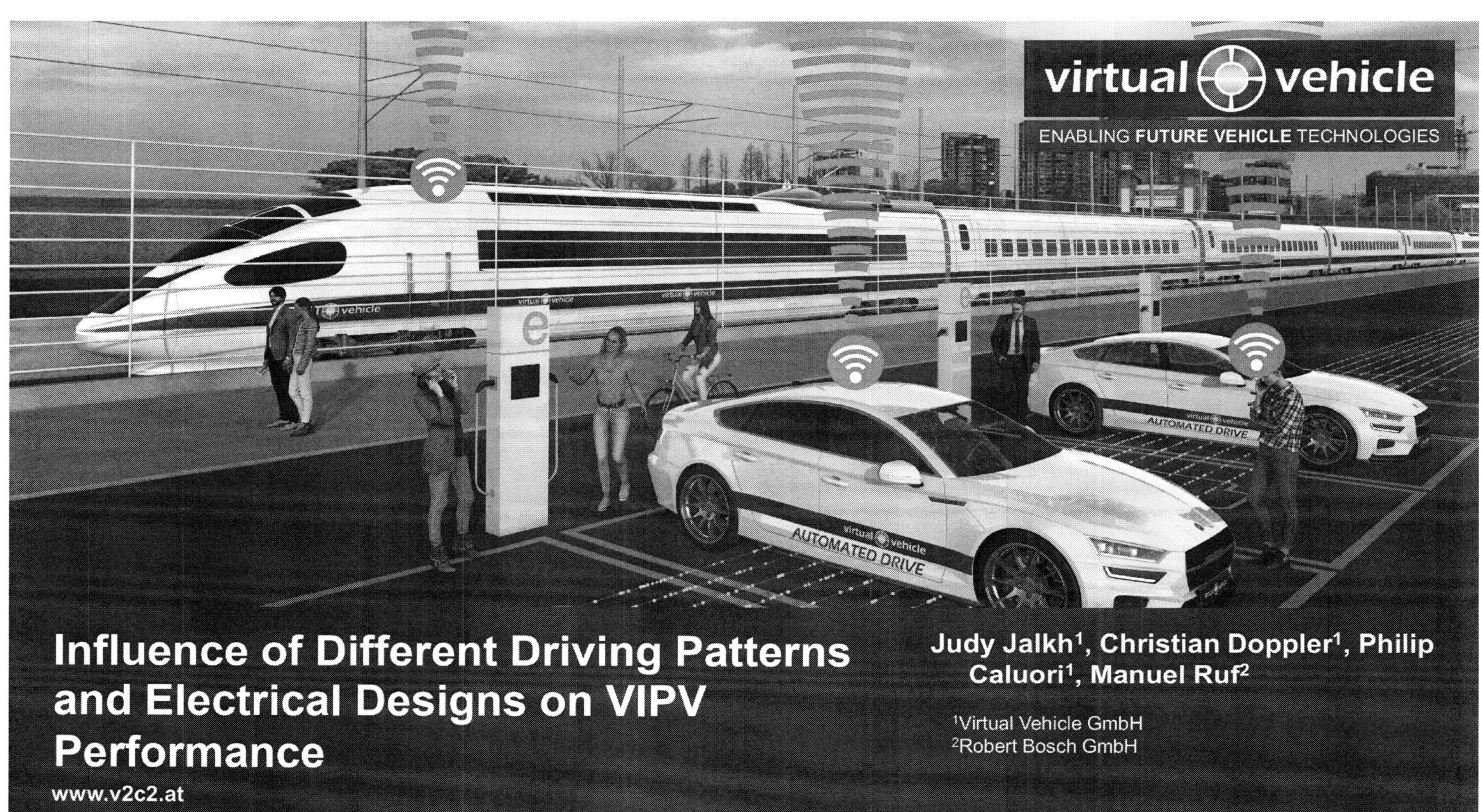

Influence of Different Driving Patterns and Electrical Designs on VIPV Performance

www.v2c2.at

Judy Jalkh[1], Christian Doppler[1], Philip Caluori[1], Manuel Ruf[2]

[1]Virtual Vehicle GmbH
[2]Robert Bosch GmbH

Outline

A. Introduction

B. Driving and Parking scenarios
1. Exemplary Reference Week
2. Solar Irradiance Calculator (SIC) simulations
3. HVAC Calculation
4. Results

C. Electrical architecture for partial shading
1. Simulation Model
2. Bypass diode (BPD) configurations and Results
3. BPD Measurement Campaign
4. MPPT comparisons

D. Conclusion

020456-002

Introduction

- The **EFFEREST** project aims to boost energy efficiency in electric vehicles by developing user-centric control systems that optimize both powertrain and cabin comfort.

- It uses the TOGG electric vehicle as a demonstrator, including simulation scenarios with vehicle-integrated photovoltaics (VIPV) on the roof.

- The goal is investigating VIPV success wrt:
    1. The effect of driving and parking patterns across different geographical locations
    2. The influence of the electric configurations on partial shading

Exemplary Reference Week

- Preselection of of 4 distinct vehicle usage-profiles [Short – Long – Average Distance Driver – Commuter].

- According to daily and annual mileage and driving pattern identification from vehicles monitored for ~1 year.

- Enrichment of base journals with vehicle simulation model including stochastic parking data, charging models, and climatic data from regions [Cold: Helsinki / Average: Paris / Hot: Athens].

- Extraction of an exemplary week for each usage-profile with least-square deviation of most important indicators from a weekly extrapolation to actual annual values.

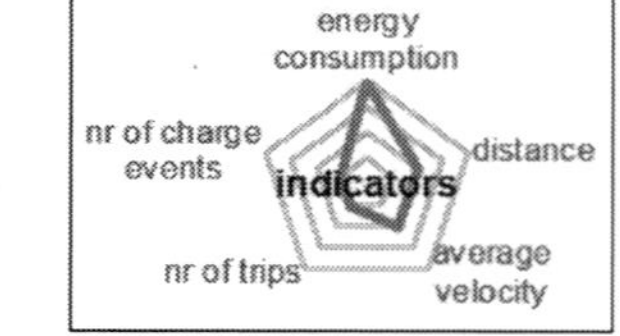

	Driver Type			
	Average Mileage (Avg)	Short Distance (SD)	Long Distance (LD)	Commuter (Com)
Garage Parking	Yes	Yes	No	No
Street Parking [days/week]	3	4	7	7
Monthly mileage [km]	~800	~300	~2600	~1250

Visualization of exemplary week for Short Distance Driver

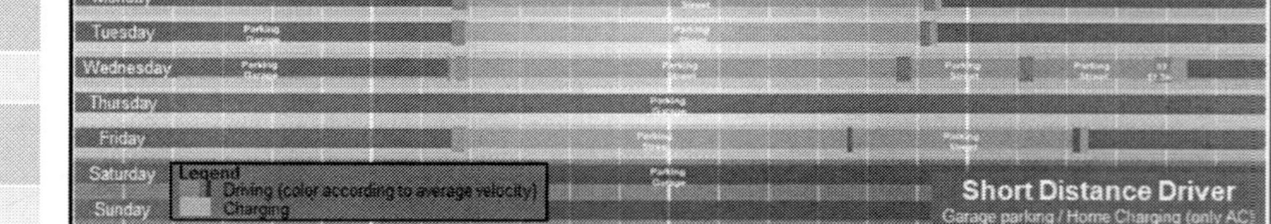

Which type of driver benefits the most from VIPV?

From Bosch

25/09/2025

SIC Simulations

Weather	Cycles	Shading	PV characteristics	Output

Weather
- GHI, DNI, DHI and Temperature
- **3 cities:** Athens, Paris, Helsinki
- Data for 365 days with 15 min interval for year 2019
- Calculation of **Monthly Average** weather conditions

from NSRDB: National Solar Radiation Database https://nsrdb.nrel.gov/

Cycles
- **Bosch Exemplary weeks** in 24-hr cycles joining parking and driving.
- Cycles include **4 driver types:** Long, short, commuter, average

Shading
- Random Shading Generator (RSG) is used.
- **When driving:** RSG with higher frequency.
- **When parking:**
  - Garage → irradiance = 0.
  - Shaded → only DHI considered.
  - Street → RSG lower frequency.

No Partial Shading at this point

PV characteristics
- Area of PV roof is 1.64 m².
- PV efficiency is 23%.
- PE efficiency is 95%.

Output
- **24-hr irradiance profiles** [W/m²] for 3 cities x 4 driver types x12 months x different vehicle zones (roof, doors, hood, trunk)
- In .m format

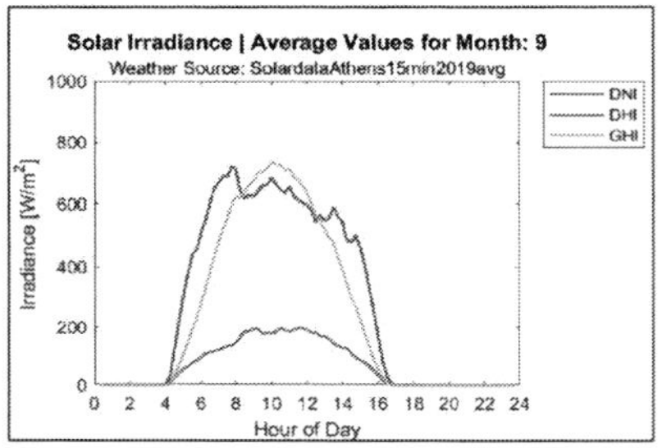

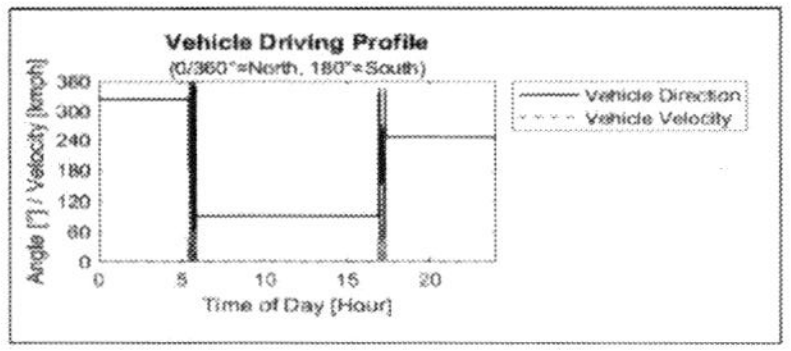

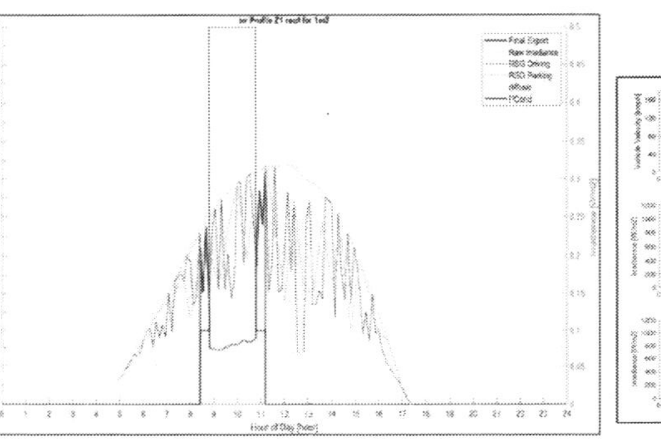

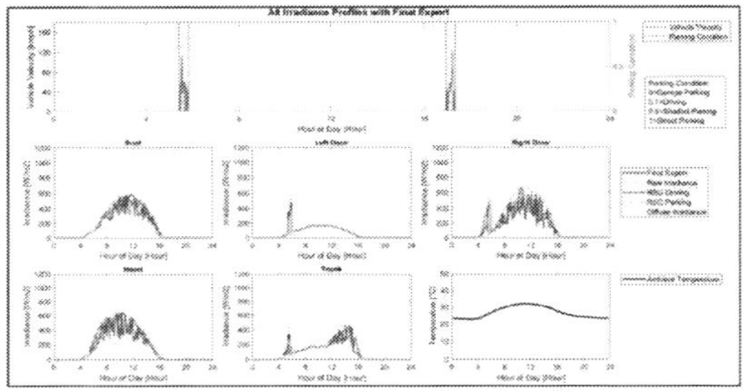

020456-005

HVAC Calculations

virtual vehicle

HVAC energy consumption values

- From EFFEREST proposal

Distribution of Temperature Conditions

- Number of Hot/Cold/Normal/Very Cold days per month
- Using real temperature data for 2023 from online sources[1]

Monthly Driven Distance

- HVAC only used when driving

Result

- Example for Short Distance Driver in Athens

	HVAC/ThMgt EFFEREST [kWh/100km]
Hot / 30°	3
Normal / 15°	0
Cold / 0°	3
Very Cold / -10°	7

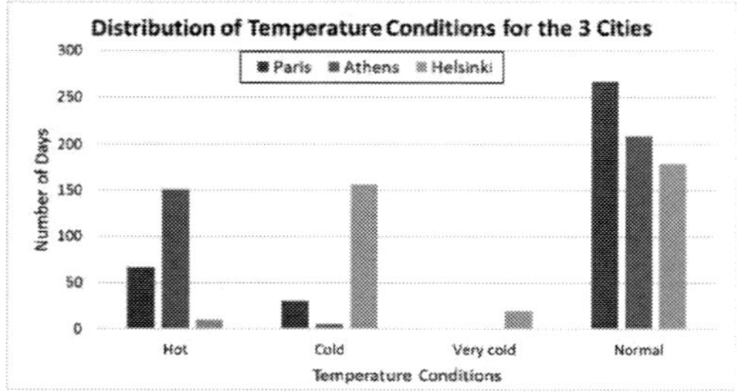

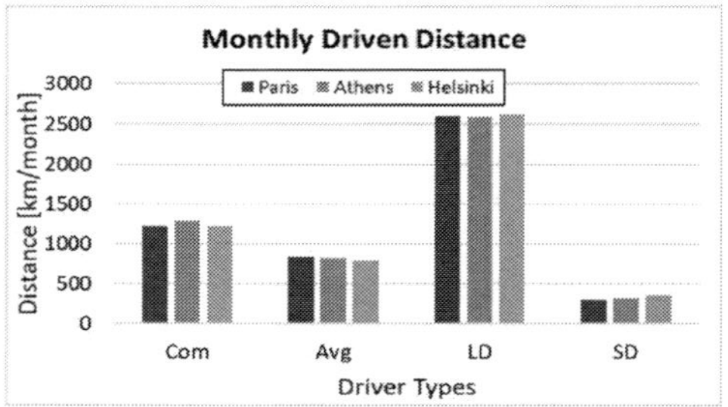

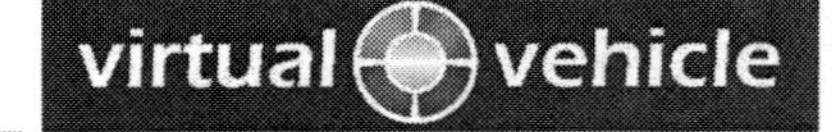

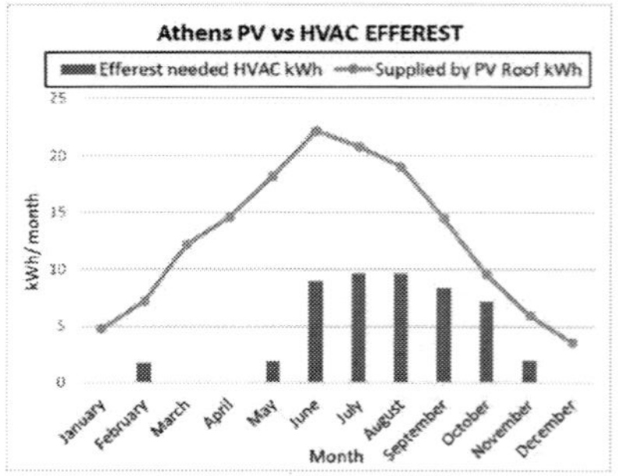

[1] https://www.visualcrossing.com/resources/documentation/weather-data/weather-data-documentation/

Results

Athens Monthly PV Coverage for HVAC

Month	1	2	3	4	5	6	7	8	9	10	11	12
Avg												
SD												
LD												
Com												

Paris Monthly PV Coverage for HVAC

Month	1	2	3	4	5	6	7	8	9	10	11	12
Avg												
SD												
LD												
Com												

Helsinki Monthly PV Coverage for HVAC

Month	1	2	3	4	5	6	7	8	9	10	11	12
Avg												
SD												
LD												
Com												

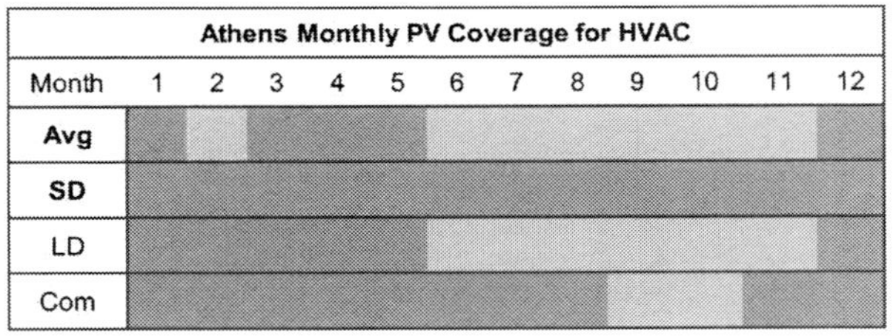

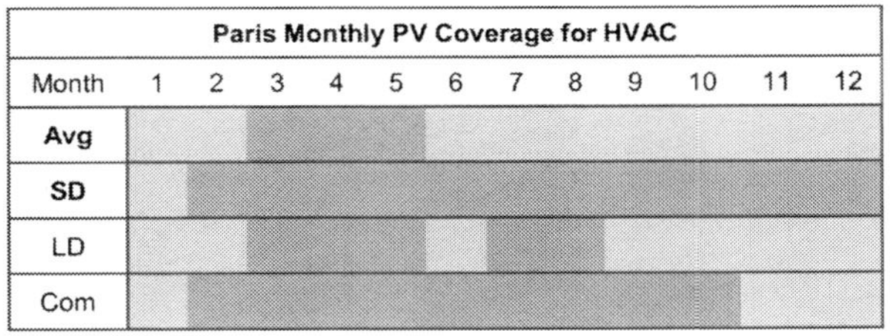

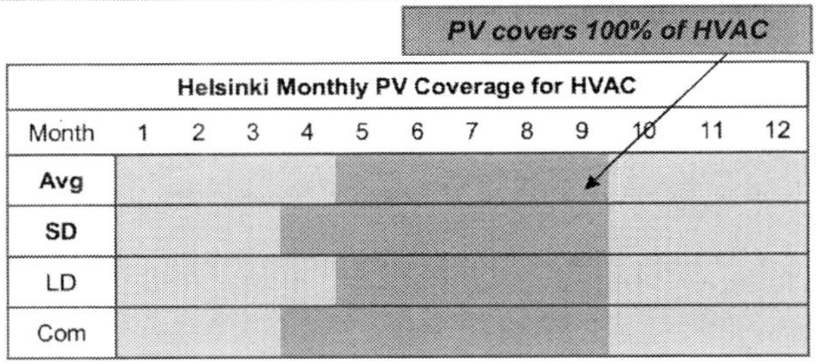

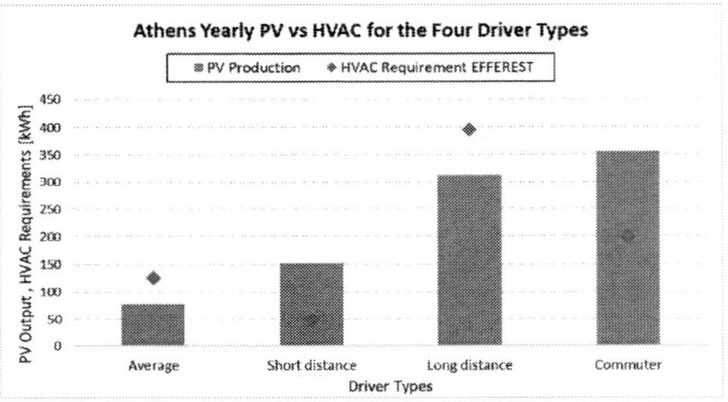

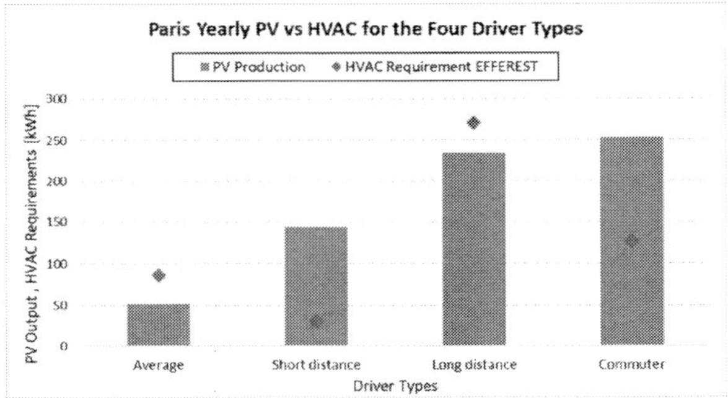

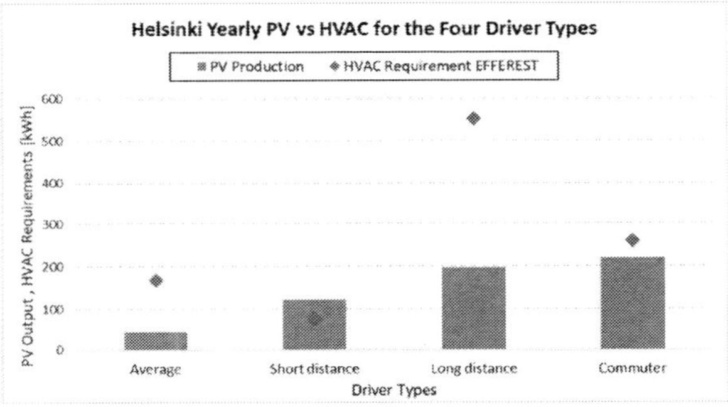

Conclusions:
- Both **garage presence** and **monthly driven distance** affect results.
- PV Surplus for commuter and SD driver can be used for mileage.

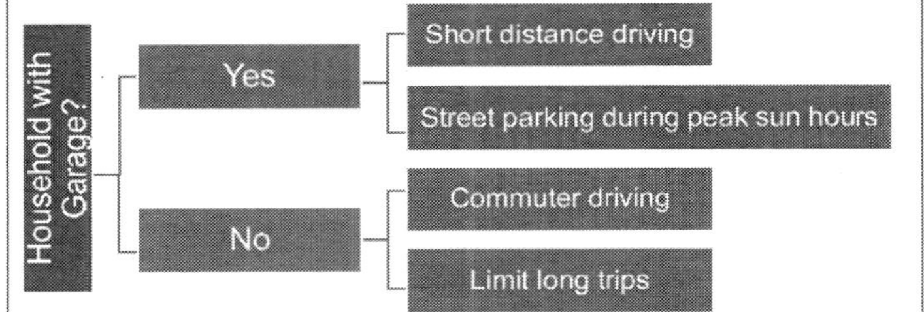

020456-007

Simulation Model

virtual vehicle

PV Cell Model

- PV technology: Maxeon Ne3 Cell[2]
- To include roof integration, the laminated version was chosen.

	PV Cell
Number of Cells	1
Cells Series	1
Cells Parallel	1
Cell Length [mm]	125
Cell Width [mm]	125
Cell Area [m2]	0.015625
Voc [V]	0.7264
Isc [A]	6.123
Vmp [V]	0.61
Imp [A]	5.7
Pmax [W]	3.47
Efficiency [%]	22.3
N (Quality Factor)	1.05
Rs [Ω]	0.006
Rsh [Ω]	7

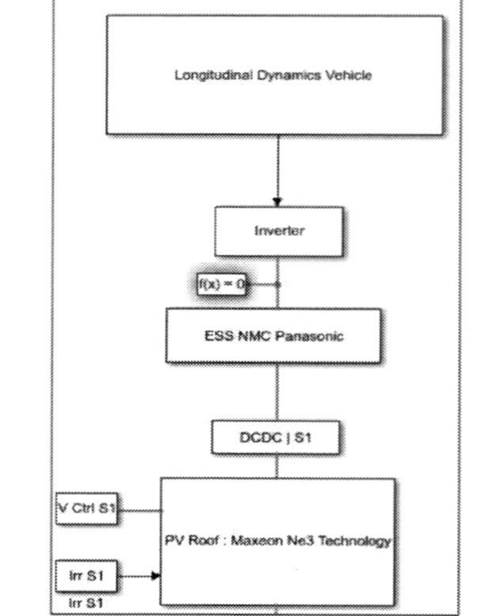

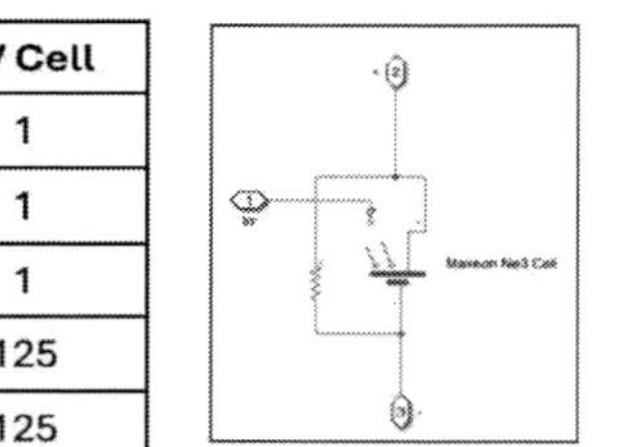

Matching simulated and datasheet curves

TOGG VIPV Model

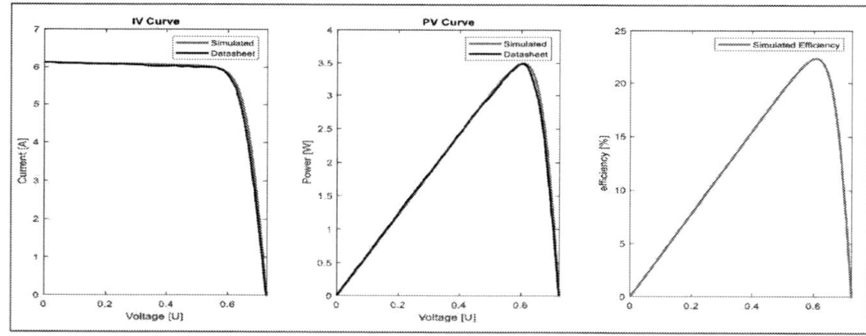

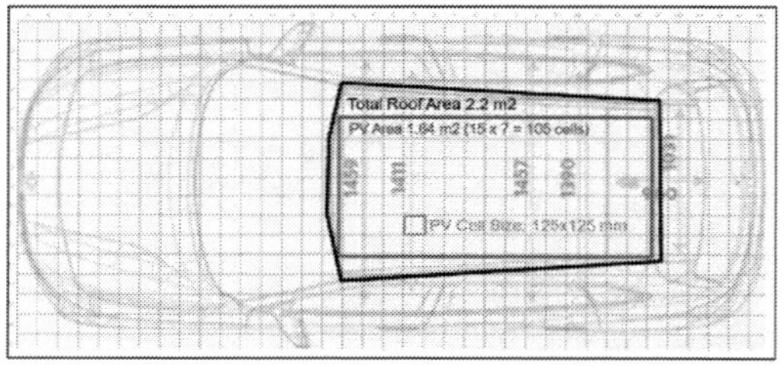

[2]Materials 2022, 15, 8774. https://doi.org/10.3390/ma15248774

25/09/2025

BPD Simulations

- BPD simulations include varying the shading factor (SF), the electrical configuration (EC), and the shading pattern (SP).

- Simulation parameters:
  - Max. voltage = Voc
  - Simulation time: 300 s
  - Logarithmic increase to derive high resolution around Pmax
  - All PV cells connected in series

1. Shading Factor

- From 0 → 0.8
- Refers to the intensity of the shaded object
- The irradiance that reaches the PV cells in each case is: **Irradiance = SF x 1000 W/m2.**

2. Electrical Configuration

	Number of cells / BPD	Number of Modules	Module Dimensions [m2]
Option 1	3	35	0.047
Option 2	7	15	0.11
Option 3	15	7	0.23

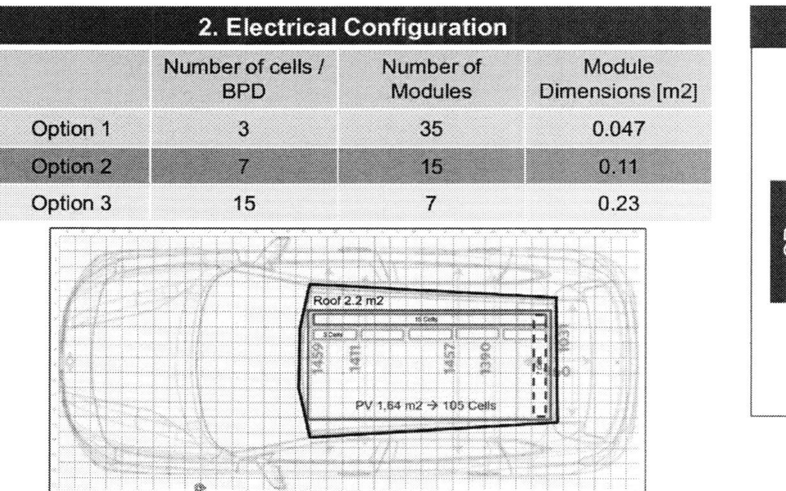

3. Shading Pattern

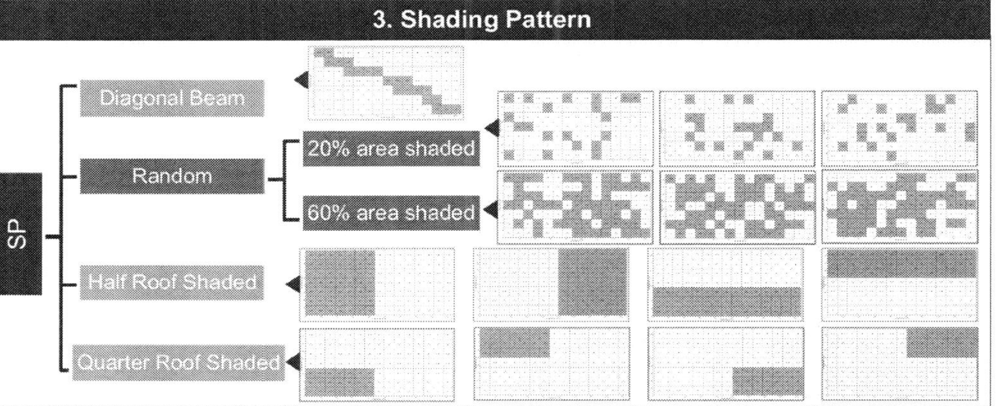

9

BPD TOGG Simulation Results

A- Which electrical configuration reaches the greatest Pmax?

For each SP and SF, the three ECs were compared in terms of maximum power reached.

- With high intensity shading (SF<= 0.3) ➔ 3 cells per BPD (35 BPDs)
- For lower intensity shading (SF >= 0.5) ➔ doesn't matter

B- Effect of Shading Pattern

- Quarter Roof shaded ➔ the location of the shadow does not affect the power. The 3 cells per BPD gives the highest power (except with 0.8 SF).

- Half Roof Shaded ➔ the orientation of the PV modules wrt the shading location determines the EC preference (F + R vs L + Rt).

- 60% random shading ➔ No effect. All 3 scenarios achieve similar Pmax values with any of the ECs since the majority of the roof is shaded.

- 20% shaded area ➔ 4 different SP give different Pmax values, highlighting the effects of not only the amount of the shaded area, but its distribution. However, they all prefer the 3 cells/BPD EC for high intensity shading.

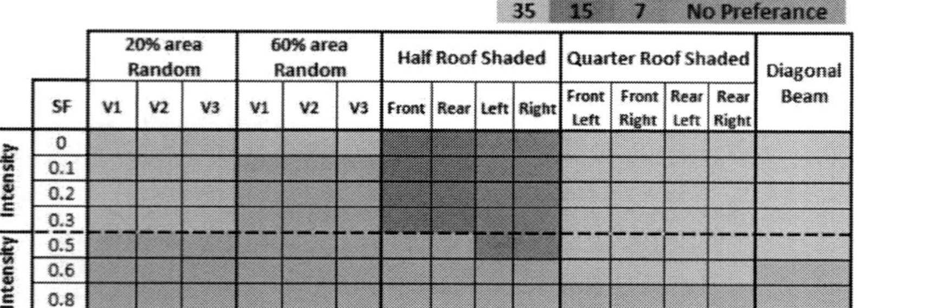

	SF	20% area Random			60% area Random			Half Roof Shaded				Quarter Roof Shaded				Diagonal Beam
		V1	V2	V3	V1	V2	V3	Front	Rear	Left	Right	Front Left	Front Right	Rear Left	Rear Right	
High Intensity	0															
	0.1															
	0.2															
	0.3															
Low Intensity	0.5															
	0.6															
	0.8															

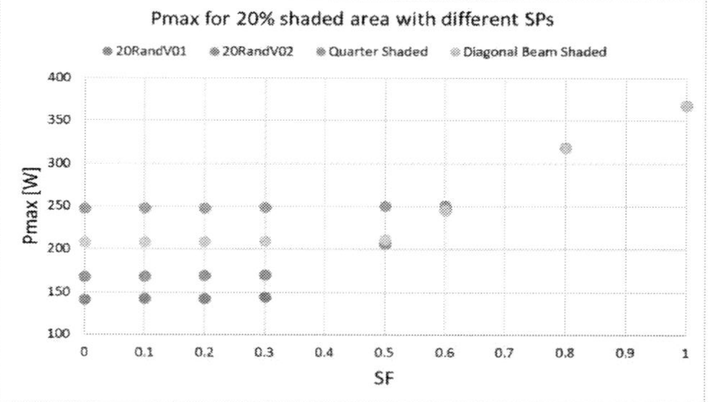

020456-010

BPD Measurement Campaign

virtual vehicle

- Pyranometer: EKO INSTRUMENTS, ML-02
- Software: 'Data Beam'
- PV Cells: CIGS cells from ISC-Konstanz, 160x160 mm
- Bypass Diodes: Schottky-Diode STPS1545D
- Test-Bench provided by TU-Graz

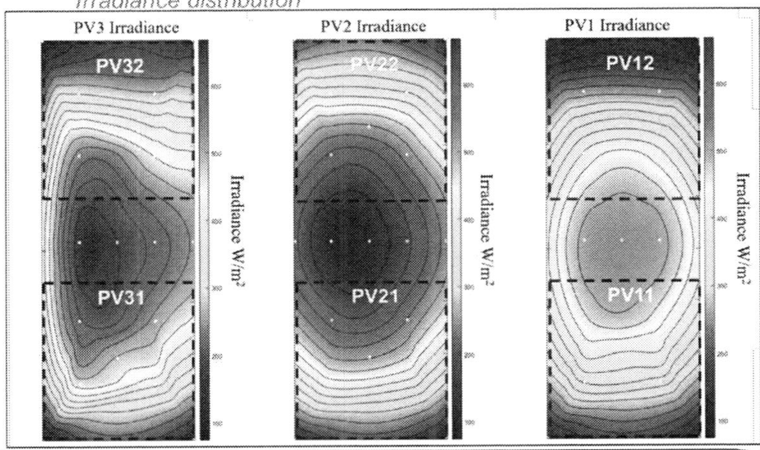

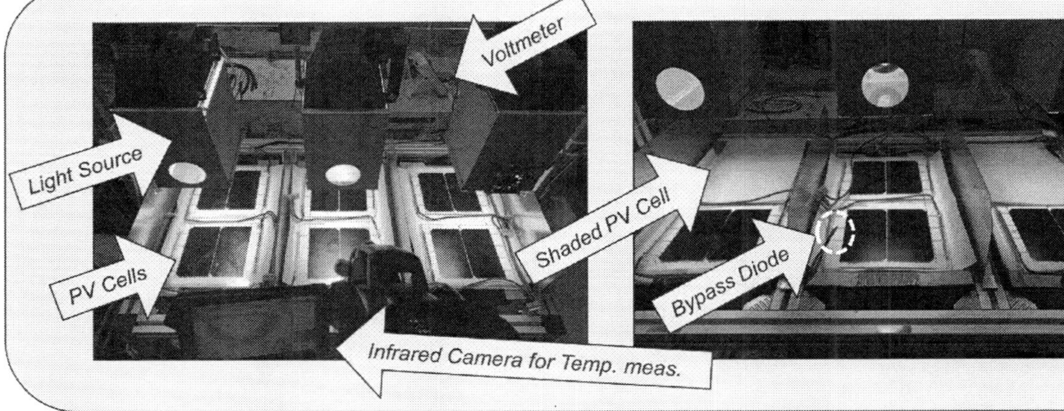

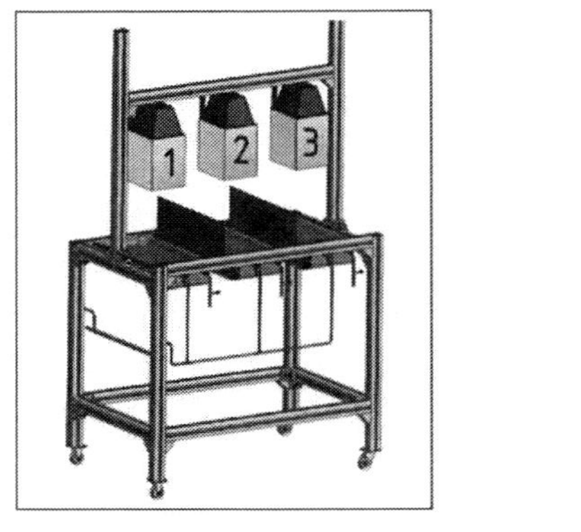

Strasser (2013)

020456-011

BPD Measurement Campaign Results

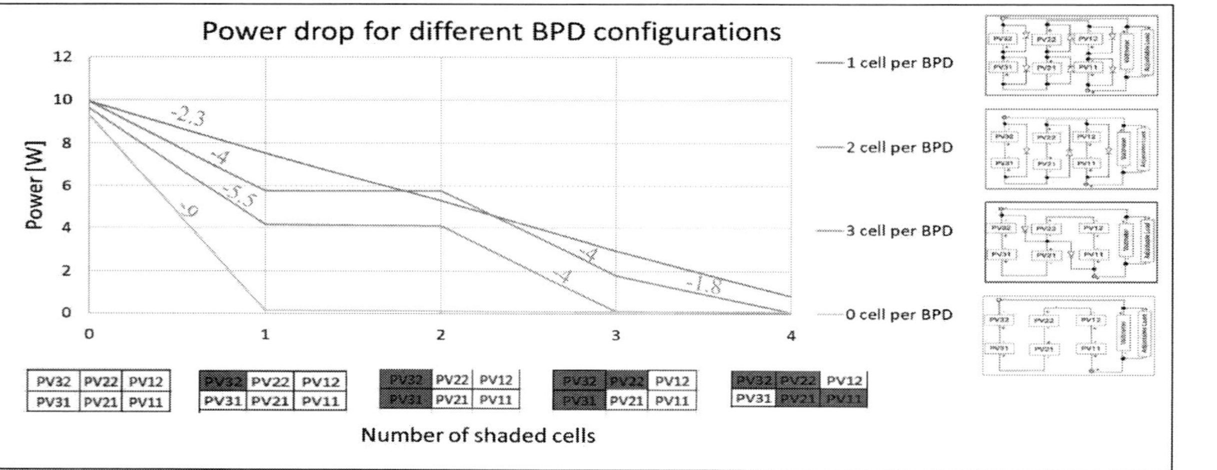

Fixed EC:
- No bypass diodes: Power drop is already drastic with just 1 shaded cell. The power barely decreases with additional shaded cells.
- 1 cell per BPD: Power experiences a steady decline as the number of shaded cells increases.
- 2 and 3 cells per BPD: Similar *non-steady* power drop trends. No change from 1 to 2 cells shaded because the same number of strings is affected.

Fixed SP:
- The 1 cell per BPD achieves the highest power except with 2 shaded cells. This is due the losses in the additional bypass diode.

BPD Measurement Campaign Results

Effect of shading pattern

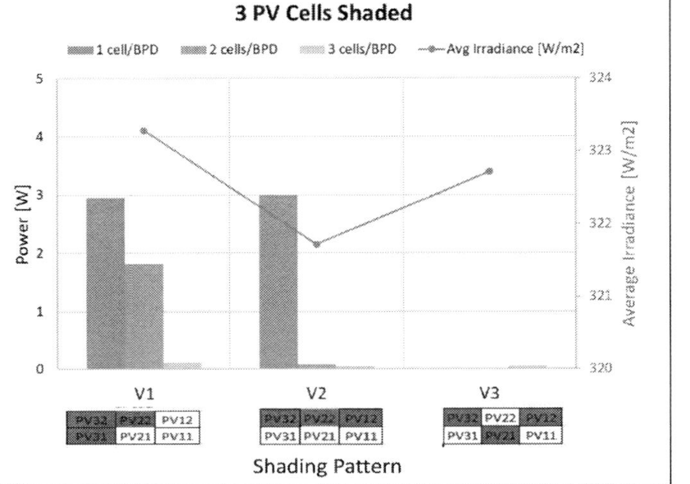

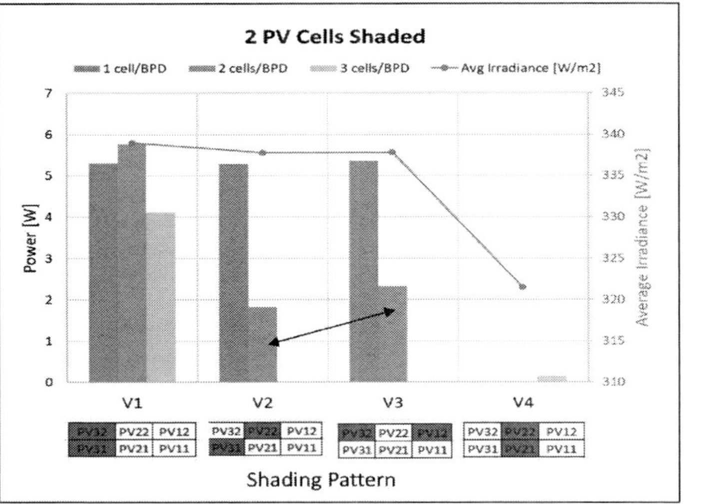

- With 1 cell/BPD, the power is the same independent of the SP.

- With more cells/ BPD, the power depends on the SP and thus the number of strings affected.

- V2 vs V3 for 2 PV cells shaded with 2 cells/BPD is probably due to the distribution of the irradiance, even though the average is the same. *(refer to prev slide with irradiance distribution)*

020456-013

MPPT Comparisons

	Perturb and Observe (P&O)	Particle Swarm Optimization (PSO)
Working principle	• Perturbs the voltage • Observes if +ve or –ve power response	• Bio-inspired (bird flocks/ fish swarms) • Each particle is aware of its personal and global best
With partial shading	Can get stuck on local instead of global MPP which leads to power loss	Iteratively converges towards global MPP

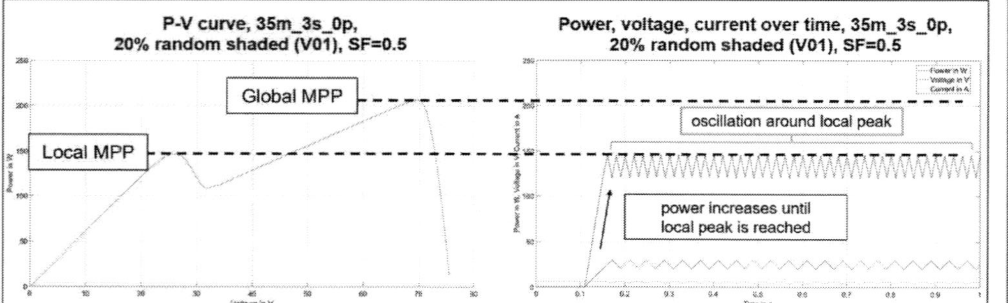

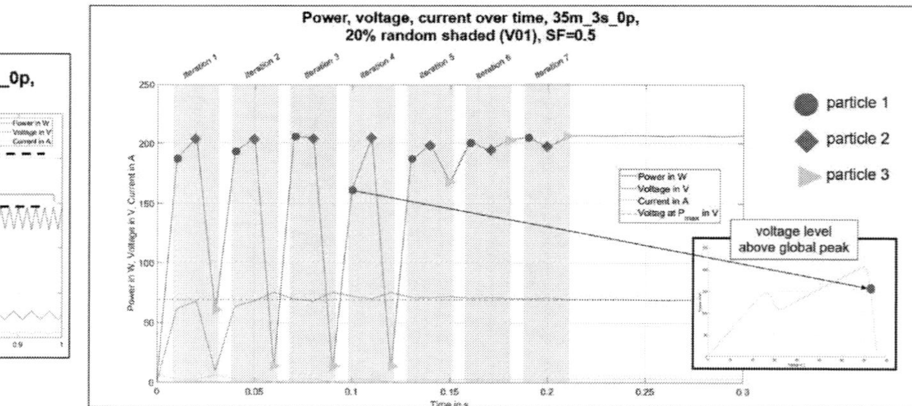

020456-014

MPPT Comparisons

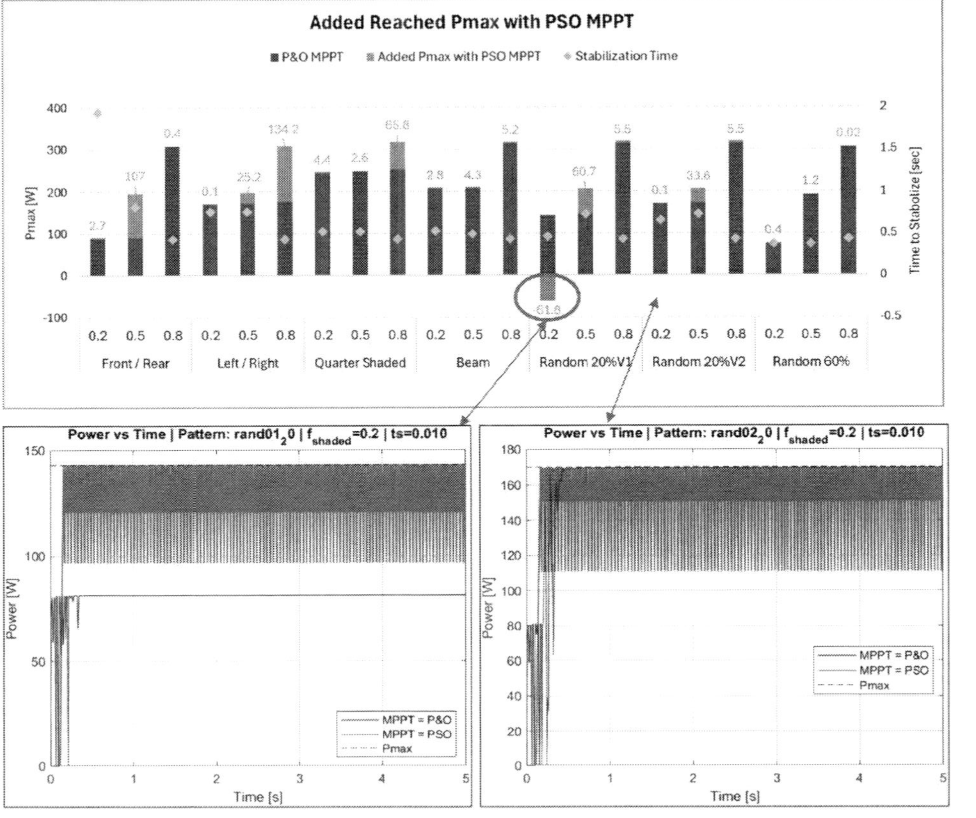

- MPPT simulations include varying the shading factor (SF), the shading pattern (SP), and the MPPT type.

- Simulation parameters:
  - Original irradiance = 1000 W/m2
  - Simulation time: 5 s
  - Time sample = 0.01 s
  - 35 modules, 3 cells per BPD

Results:
- PSO MPPT reaches a higher Pmax than the P&O.
- Some cases are better than others, but there is no clear trend.
- 1 exception is the R20V1 SF0.2 where the P&O behaves better.

Conclusion

- Four driver types with different driving and parking conditions were studied.
- The driven distance and parking location affect the produced PV energy.
- A household with a garage can still benefit from VIPV if its members take shorter trips and park outside during peak sun hours. This is why the Short Distance driver benefitted the most from VIPV.
- Driver type influences VIPV performance in Southern and Central Europe but has little impact in Northern Europe.

- The number of cells bypassed is important primarily with high intensity shading.
- The reached power is not only affected by the size of the shaded area, but also the distribution and location of the shadow.
- PSO is better suited for partial shading than P&O MPPT, even though there is no clear trend wrt shading pattern or factor.

Next Steps:
Simulate partial shading and temperature effects for all exemplary weeks

020456-016

Acknowledgement

The authors would like to acknowledge ISC Konstanz for supplying their CIGS PV cells used in this study's measurement campaign.

This work was conducted in the EFFEREST project that has received funding from the European Union's Horizon Europe research and innovation programme under Grant Agreement No. 101138266. Views and opinions expressed are however those of the author(s) only and do not necessarily reflect those of the European Union or European Climate, Infrastructure and Environment Executive Agency (CINEA). Neither the European Union nor the granting authority can be held responsible for them. The publication was written at Virtual Vehicle Research GmbH in Graz and partially funded within the COMET K2 Competence Centers for Excellent Technologies by the Austrian Federal Ministry for Innovation, Mobility and Infrastructure (BMIMI), Austrian Federal Ministry for Economy, Energy and Tourism (BMWET), the Province of Styria (Dept. 12) and the Styrian Business Promotion Agency (SFG). The Austrian Research Promotion Agency (FFG) has been authorised for the programme management.

020456-017

www.v2c2.at

25/09/2025

Bundesministerium Klimaschutz, Umwelt, Energie, Mobilität, Innovation und Technologie

Bundesministerium Arbeit und Wirtschaft

FFG Promoting Innovation

Das Land Steiermark

SFG

Virtual Vehicle Research GmbH wird im Rahmen von COMET Competence Centers for Excellent Technologies durch BMK, BMAW, Land Steiermark und Steirische Wirtschaftsförderung (SFG) gefördert. Das Programm wird durch die FFG abgewickelt.

18

020456-018

DYNAMIC GIS-BASED 3D SOLAR SIMULATION FRAMEWORK FOR ASSESSING VIPV IN URBAN PUBLIC TRANSPORT USING GTFS AND DRIVING CYCLES

David Pera[1], Christian Braun[1], Philippe Pinheiro[1], Miguel Brito[2] and Ulrich Leopold[1]

[1]Luxembourg Institute of Science and Technology , [2]Faculdade de Ciências da Universidade de Lisboa

david.pera@list.lu, philippe.pinheiro@list.lu, christian.braun@list.lu, mcbrito@fc.ul.pt, ulrich.leopold@list.lu

ABSTRACT: Vehicle-Integrated Photovoltaics (VIPV) represent a promising pathway to reduce the energy demand of electric bus fleets, particularly in urban environments where charging infrastructure constraints and operational costs are critical. This paper introduces a dynamic GIS-based 3D solar simulation framework that integrates General Transit Feed Specification (GTFS) data with advanced irradiation modeling to quantify VIPV potential along real-world bus routes. The methodology combines Copernicus Atmosphere Monitoring Service (CAMS) solar radiation datasets with hemispherical beam-projection shadow casting on standardized CityGML 3D city models, enabling detailed assessment of direct, diffuse, and reflected solar components under complex urban shadowing conditions. To assess the net impact of VIPV integration, GTFS-derived driving cycles are processed in conjunction with vehicle powertrain and consumption models, calibrated against experimental measurements from a field campaign in Luxembourg. This combined workflow provides time-resolved estimates of photovoltaic generation, energy consumption, and resulting battery state-of-charge, allowing direct comparison between baseline and VIPV-equipped operations.
In a case study of TICE Line 1 in Esch-sur-Alzette in Luxembourg, rooftop PV (3.5 kWp, PR = 75 %) covers 2.8–4.1 % of annual traction energy. Summer clear-sky operation reaches daily yields of about 3.9 kWh/kWp. This contribution avoids up to ~146 standard 20–80 % state-of-charge charging cycles per year (about 98 cycles under real-sky conditions) and offers simple payback of 7–10 years at current electricity tariffs. The open-data, standards-based workflow is transferable to other cities and provides a reproducible tool for assessing VIPV in public-transport electrification strategies.
Keywords: Vehicle-Integrated Photovoltaics, GTFS, 3D GIS, Urban Shadowing, Electric Buses

1 AIM AND APPROACH

The transition to electric mobility in public transport fleets introduces new challenges regarding charging demand, operational flexibility, and integration with energy systems. Vehicle-Integrated Photovoltaics (VIPV) have emerged as a complementary technology to reduce battery charging needs, but their deployment in complex urban contexts requires accurate assessment methods. The aim of this work is to present a dynamic GIS-based simulation framework that quantifies VIPV energy yield for buses under real operational conditions, explicitly considering urban shadowing, diffuse reflection, and route-specific driving cycles.

The novelty of this approach lies in the integration of General Transit Feed Specification (GTFS) data [6] with high-resolution 3D solar modeling. GTFS datasets, openly available for most cities worldwide, contain structured information on routes, timetables, and stops. In this framework, GTFS data are converted into continuous spatio-temporal driving cycles, capturing vehicle trajectories, speeds, gradients, and stop durations. These cycles serve as the basis for both solar irradiation and energy consumption simulations.

The irradiation model employs a multi-beam projection collision detection method [2], which computes the incident direct radiation for each time step along the route based on solar geometry. Diffuse radiation is corrected using the Sky View Factor (SVF) derived from a hemispherical viewshed analysis. This method propagates thousands of vectors in a 3D CityGML model [1] to identify visible sky fractions and surrounding surfaces. Each façade or obstacle is assigned an albedo coefficient according to its material properties, enabling the calculation of reflected diffuse components. The radiation datasets are accessed from the Copernicus CAMS Radiation Service (CRS) [3–5], ensuring realistic temporal resolution and spatial coverage for all radiative components.

Parallel to the irradiation estimation, a vehicle energy consumption module simulates the power demand of a battery-electric bus. This includes propulsion requirements, braking recovery, auxiliary systems such as HVAC and lighting, and road slope effects. The photovoltaic contribution is introduced by injecting the VIPV-generated power, corrected for maximum power point tracking and DC/DC conversion efficiencies, into the vehicle's energy balance. This enables a direct comparison between the baseline scenario and the VIPV-equipped case, expressed in terms of net energy demand, state-of-charge trajectories, and avoided charging cycles.

To enhance reliability, the simulation framework has been calibrated and validated with experimental measurements performed in Luxembourg during 2023–2024. The campaign included on-road monitoring with silicon irradiance sensors, GPS tracking, and 4G data transmission, complemented by reference meteorological data from national networks (LIST, ASTA, MeteoLux). These datasets were used to cross-check modelled solar components against ground-truth measurements, improving confidence in the shadow-casting and reflection algorithms.

By combining open GTFS datasets with standardized 3D city models, CAMS-derived solar radiation, and detailed vehicle physics, the framework offers a holistic and transferable workflow for assessing VIPV feasibility in public transport fleets. Its modular structure supports replication in cities with different urban morphologies, from dense canyons to suburban and rural areas. This work therefore provides a practical decision-support tool for transport operators and policymakers, enabling high-level techno-economic evaluations of VIPV deployment as part of fleet electrification strategies.

To clarify novelty versus existing approaches, this work differs from earlier VIPV or mobile PV studies that either extrapolate static rooftop yields or apply generic duty cycles. Here, GTFS-derived second-scale driving cycles are directly coupled to 3D radiative transfer and vehicle energy modelling, allowing every stop, gradient and dwell period to consider both irradiation and consumption. This tight coupling, together with automated façade-albedo attribution in a standardized CityGML context, enables route-level VIPV assessment that has not been possible with previous methods.

2 SCIENTIFIC INNOVATION AND RELEVANCE

Most solar potential assessment tools have been developed for static rooftop installations or rely on generalized assumptions about solar exposure. While these approaches are suitable for building-integrated photovoltaics, they fall short when applied to moving vehicles operating in dense urban environments. The framework proposed in this work advances the state of the art by linking real-world transport operations with detailed solar radiation modelling, thereby enabling a realistic quantification of VIPV applied to public transport fleets.

At the core of this innovation is the direct use of General Transit Feed Specification (GTFS) datasets [6], which describe the actual timetables, stops, and routes of public transport systems. By transforming these data into continuous spatial-temporal driving cycles, the methodology captures the specific motion and idling patterns of buses in daily operation. This allows the solar resource assessment to be tightly coupled with vehicle dynamics, rather than relying on simplified cycles or averaged duty profiles.

The accuracy of the solar model is enhanced through the integration of three-dimensional city representations based on the CityGML standard [1]. These models make it possible to calculate not only direct shading but also the hemispherical view of the sky at every point along the route (Figure 1).

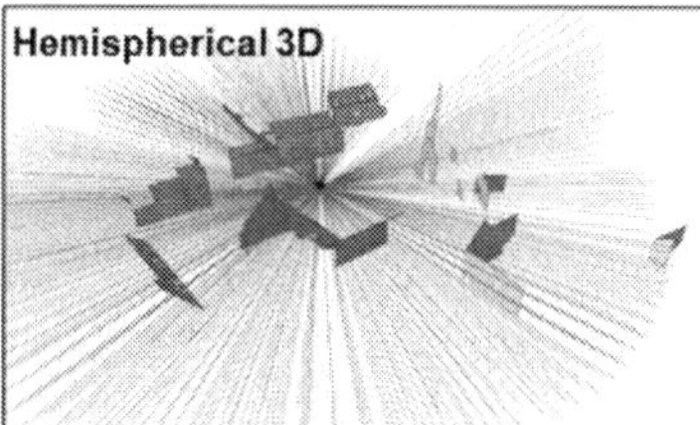

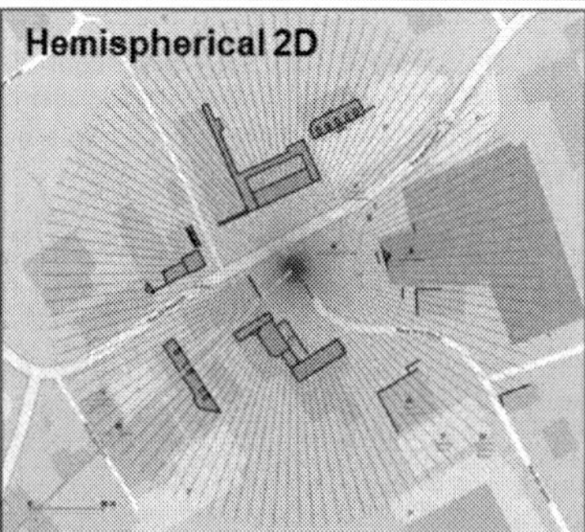

Figure 1: Example of hemispherical viewshed analysis using 3D CityGML models, showing calculation of Sky View Factor and façade reflections in dense urban areas.

(top 3D view, bottom 2D view)

By embedding albedo information into the façades of surrounding infrastructure, the framework accounts for reflected diffuse radiation, which can play an important role in narrow streets and urban canyons. The radiation inputs themselves are obtained from the Copernicus CAMS Radiation Service [3–5], ensuring that cloud cover, atmospheric turbidity, and seasonal effects are consistently represented across different time scales and geographies (Figure 2).

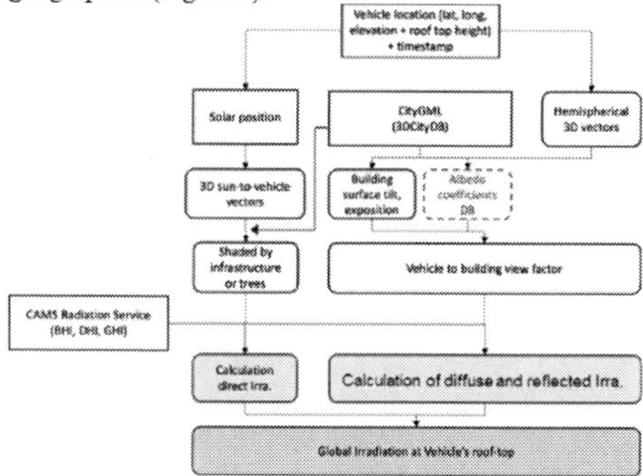

Figure 2: Workflow of the irradiation model integrating direct shading, diffuse sky fraction, and albedo-based façade reflections.

While the irradiation model provides a detailed estimation of the solar resource reaching the vehicle rooftop, a full assessment must also include how this energy interacts with the vehicle itself. This requires a robust description of vehicle power consumption, covering traction, regenerative braking, auxiliary systems, and state-of-charge evolution. For this purpose, the framework makes use of Vehicle Energy Consumption Calculation Tool (VECTO) [7], developed by EC/JRC, which has become the reference methodology for assessing CO_2 emissions and energy consumption in heavy-duty vehicles. Aligning with VECTO ensures that the results are comparable, reproducible, and consistent with European standards, while allowing the direct integration of GTFS-derived driving cycles into energy demand simulations.

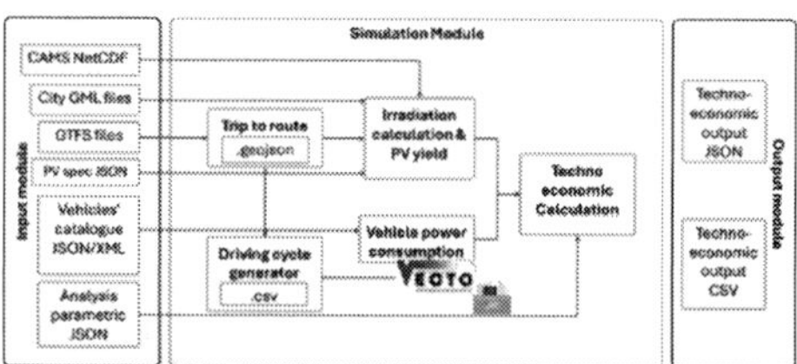

Figure 3: Workflow for Simulation combining the Solar potential assessment of the VIPV systems and the vehicles 'energy consumption.

Figure 3 summarizes how the solar and vehicle modules are combined into a unified workflow. Inputs include CAMS NetCDF irradiance products, CityGML files, GTFS feeds, PV specification JSON, a vehicles' catalogue (JSON/XML), and analysis parameters (JSON). GTFS data are converted in a Trip-to-Route stage to a geospatial trajectory (.geojson). A Driving-Cycle Generator then produces a time series (2-second resolution) representing speeds, stop times, and road gradients. These feed two computational branches: (i) Irradiation calculation & PV yield, and (ii) Vehicle power consumption using VECTO models. The vehicle energy consumption module determine the energy consumption of the vehicle considering, rolling resistance, aerodynamic drag, gear/axle ratios for e-axles, regenerative braking, auxiliary loads, and SoC evolution, providing comparable and reproducible energy baselines. The driving cycles derived directly from GTFS [6], ensure that both energy demand and PV contribution are evaluated under realistic service patterns.

The resulting workflow combines geospatial analysis, radiative transfer modelling, and vehicle physics into a single modular environment. This holistic design provides more than a simple estimation of annual photovoltaic yield; it delivers insights into the operational consequences of installing PV modules on buses, such as reductions in charging frequency, mitigation of peak demand, and potential impacts on battery life. By offering a method that is both transferable, thanks to the widespread availability of GTFS data, and scalable across different cities, the framework has direct relevance for transport operators and policymakers seeking to evaluate the techno-economic feasibility of VIPV adoption.

In this sense, the scientific contribution lies not only in the refinement of solar modelling techniques for mobile platforms, but also in the creation of a decision-support tool that bridges the domains of urban mobility, renewable energy integration, and fleet electrification.

3 RESULTS AND DISCUSSION

The developed framework was applied to TICE Line 1, a high-frequency bus corridor in southern Luxembourg connecting Esch-sur-Alzette and Lamadelaine. The line is particularly suitable for VIPV assessment due to its dense urban morphology, frequent service intervals, and regular operational schedule. Each direction of the route extends for approximately 17–18 km, with 25 and 30 stops and typical trip durations of 40 to 44 minutes, respectively. Up to 63 trips per day are performed in each direction, amounting to more than 41000 trips annually. This high service intensity provides an ideal case to evaluate both the energy yield of rooftop PV systems and their cumulative effect on fleet operations.

3.1 Irradiation and shadowing effects

Simulations performed with CAMS radiation data and 3D CityGML models indicate that the annual clear-sky irradiation potential on the bus rooftop reaches 1409 kWh/kWp. Under real-sky conditions, this value decreases to 944 kWh/kWp, corresponding to an overall reduction of about 33%.

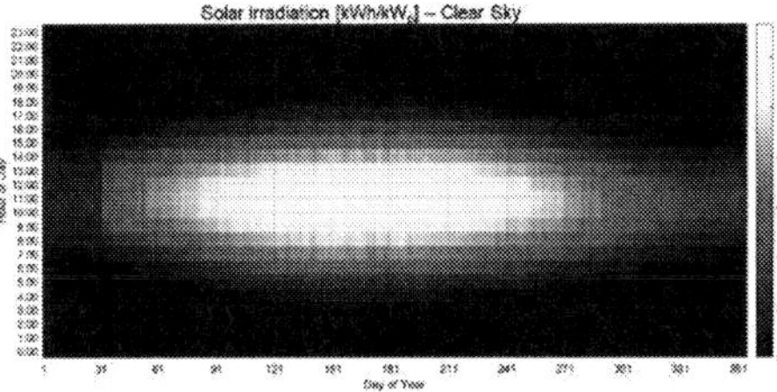

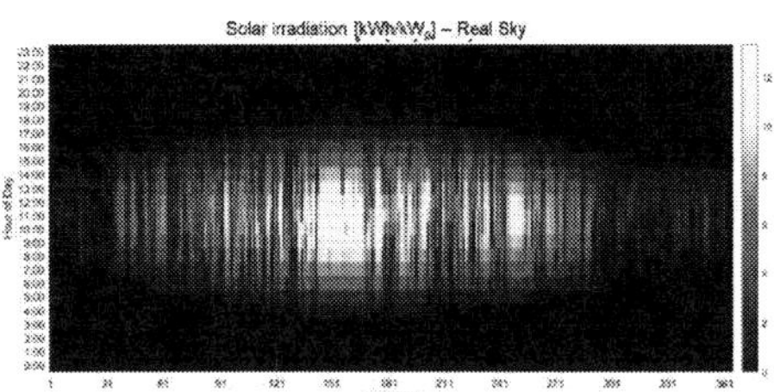

Figure 4: Annual irradiation distribution for TICE Line 1 under clear-sky (top) and real-sky (bottom), with shadowing losses.

The contribution of urban shadowing is non-negligible: losses of 20.5–20.8% were identified, depending on seasonal conditions. These results confirm that urban canyons, building heights, and orientation strongly affect VIPV feasibility and must be explicitly accounted for in yield estimations. Our internal sensitivity check shows that ignoring complex urban shading can overestimate annual production by more than one fifth.

3.2 Energy balance and fleet impact

The case study considered an 12 m Mercedes eCitaro K electric bus with two 125 kW motors, a 330 kWh battery system, and an average auxiliary load of 2–2.5 kW. For this configuration, the average energy demand per one way trip was ~23–24 kWh, corresponding to ~7% state-of-charge depletion. A charging event from 20% to 80% SoC requires ~198 kWh, meaning that multiple trips can be performed between recharges.

A "charging cycle" is counted whenever the cumulative net VIPV energy equals the energy required for a standard 20-80 % state-of-charge recharge (ΔSoC = 60 % of nominal battery capacity). Daily increments of VIPV energy are considered until this threshold is reached, after which the counter resets. This allows direct translation of PV yield into a number of full or partial charging events avoided over time.

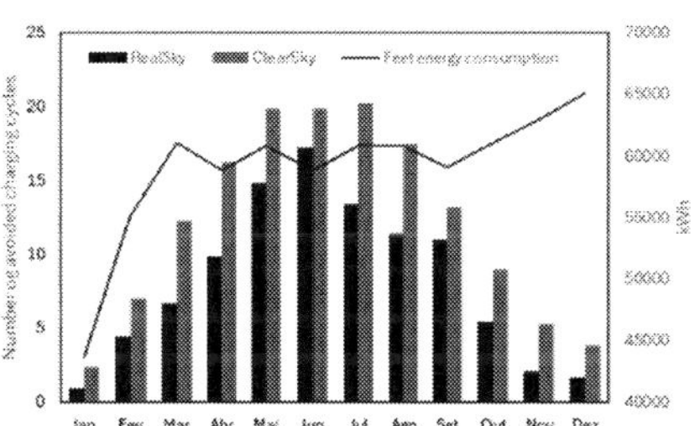

Figure 5: Annual avoided charging cycles (20–80% SoC) under clear-sky and real-sky conditions (bars, left axis) and monthly fleet energy consumption (line, right axis). Totals: 146 cycles (clear-sky), 98 cycles (real-sky), 707.8 MWh fleet demand.

Equipping the bus rooftop with 3.5kWp (considering 80% of the available area) of silicon PV modules and overall performance ratio of 75% (due to mismatch effects, temperature effects, and power conversion losses), yields an annual production covering between 2.8% and 4.1% of the total line energy demand. While modest in absolute terms, this contribution translates into tangible operational benefits. In the most favorable summer month, up to 17 cycles (June, real-sky), highlighting strong seasonality;

annual totals are ~98 cycles (real-sky) versus ~146 cycles for clear-sky upper bound.

3.3 Techno-economic considerations

Considering the VIVP system costs (1.5 €/Wp) and a combined electricity tariff of 0.21 €/kWh, the simple payback time of the VIPV system is estimated to be between 7 and 10 years, depending on degradation, operational intensity, and shadowing conditions. This aligns with the expected service lifetime of bus fleets, indicating that VIPV can approach economic viability under favorable conditions. However, these payback times remain sensitive to several factors: higher installation costs, lower irradiation environments, or reduced vehicle utilization would significantly affect the business case.

While the presented results demonstrate the technical feasibility of VIPV for public transport fleets, the contribution to overall energy demand remains relatively small compared with the size of the traction battery. Ranging from 2.8 to 4.1% of the route's consumption will not fundamentally alter charging infrastructure requirements. Nevertheless, the ability to reduce charging frequency, extend battery lifetimes, and provide distributed generation at the fleet level should not be underestimated, especially in contexts where charging power is constrained.

Moreover, the methodology highlights the importance of urban morphology and shadowing in VIPV studies. The explicit representation of albedo and building façades shows that local geometry can significantly alter the irradiation balance. This suggests that VIPV deployment should be evaluated at the route level, rather than through general average assumptions.

A simple sensitivity analysis indicates that payback is most affected by electricity tariff and installation cost. At ±0.05 €/kWh around the baseline 0.21 €/kWh, payback varies by roughly ±1 year. Likewise, CAPEX shifts of ±20% change payback by approximately ±1.5 years.

From a broader perspective, the integration of GTFS data ensures that results are directly tied to realistic operating conditions, enhancing their relevance for decision makers. However, uncertainties remain. Future work should refine passenger load dynamics and auxiliary power variability (e.g., HVAC demand), which can alter the balance between demand and supply. In addition, further development of automated albedo attribution using open façade datasets could improve accuracy without increasing modeling complexity.

4 CONCLUSIONS

This study introduced a dynamic GIS-based simulation framework to evaluate the feasibility of VIPV for public transport fleets. By integrating GTFS-derived driving cycles, 3D CityGML shadow casting, and CAMS radiation datasets, the workflow delivers high-resolution irradiation profiles along operational bus routes and couples them with VECTO-based vehicle energy modelling. This combination quantifies photovoltaic yield and directly links it to state-of-charge evolution and avoided charging cycles, offering a clear metric for operational impact.

The broader contribution of this work lies in its transferability. GTFS datasets are openly available for most cities, and CityGML or equivalent 3D models are increasingly accessible through public repositories. The method's reliance on open/standardized data makes it well-suited for comparative planning across cities. As such, the framework can be readily applied to diverse geographic and operational contexts, supporting comparative studies across urban densities, climates, and fleet configurations.

Future work will refine passenger load dynamics and better capture seasonal and operational variability in auxiliary energy demand such as heating and cooling. In addition, automated façade albedo attribution will be enhanced to further reduce manual preprocessing. Together, these developments will improve the accuracy and robustness of VIPV yield estimates and energy balance assessments for bus operations.

5 References

[1] Open Geospatial Consortium (OGC), CityGML Standard, available at: https://www.ogc.org/standard/citygml, consulted in February 2025.

[2] Pera, D., Braun, C., Pinheiro, P., Leopold, U., (2023). GIS-based solar irradiance simulation for VIPV applications in a complex urban environment. 40th European Photovoltaic Solar Energy Conference and Exhibition.

[3] Lefèvre, M. et al., (2013). McClear: a new model estimating downwelling solar radiation at ground level in clear-sky conditions. Atmospheric Measurement Techniques, 6, 2403–2418. doi:10.5194/amt-6-2403-2013.

[4] Gschwind, B., et al., (2019). Improving the McClear model estimating the downwelling solar radiation at ground level in cloud-free conditions – McClear-V3. Meteorologische Zeitschrift.doi:10.1127/metz/2019/0946.

[5] Qu, Z. et al., (2017). Fast radiative transfer parameterisation for assessing the surface solar irradiance: The Heliosat-4 method. Meteorologische Zeitschrift, 26, 33–57. doi:10.1127/metz/2016/0781.

[6] GTFS, General Transit Feed Specification Documentation, available at: https://gtfs.org/documentation/,consulted July 2025.

[7] European Commission, Joint Research Centre (JRC). Vehicle Energy Consumption Calculation Tool (VECTO). Available at: https://web.jrc.ec.europa.eu/policy-model-inventory/explore/models/model-vecto/ (consulted July 2025).

Interreg — North-West Europe

Co-funded by the European Union

STEER-NWE

LE GOUVERNEMENT
DU GRAND-DUCHÉ DE LUXEMBOURG
Ministère de l'Environnement, du Climat
et de la Biodiversité

DYNAMIC GIS-BASED 3D SOLAR SIMULATION FRAMEWORK FOR ASSESSING VIPV IN URBAN PUBLIC TRANSPORT USING GTFS AND DRIVING CYCLES

David Pera
ICES Unit, APG Group

david.pera@list.lu

David Pera*[1], C.Braun[1], P.Pinheiro[1], M.C.Brito[2] and U.Leopold[1]

1Luxembourg Institute of Science and Technology
2Faculdade de Ciências da Universidade de Lisboa

LUXEMBOURG
INSTITUTE OF SCIENCE
AND TECHNOLOGY | LIST

020458-001

WHAT IS THE IMPACT OF URBAN SHADOWING ON VIPV?

A USE CASE ON BUSES FOR PUBLIC TRANSPORTATION

EXPERIMENTAL CAMPAIGN IN LUXEMBOURG 2023-2024

Nationwide coverage for a period of 2+ years and further continuation

6 acquisition systems on the road

Cactus

64 Stores and warehouses

- Freight transport
- National Distribution
- Home deliveries

TICE

Public transport company

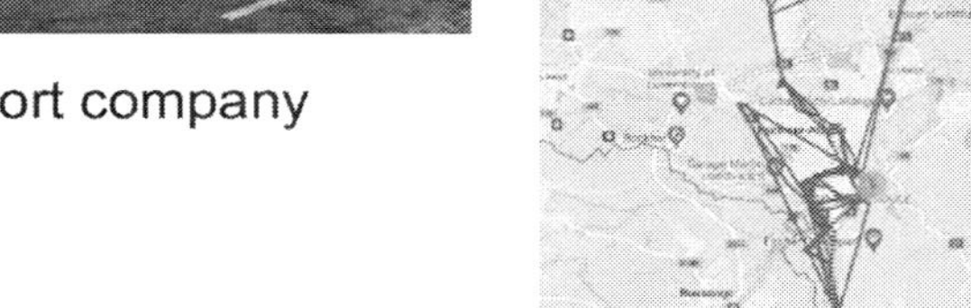

Fast response silicon sen
GPS tracking system
4G communication for dat
transmission

- Historical and real-time Irradiation monitoring
- Sensors' temperature
- Sensors' SoC

The data acquired experimentally, are used for comparison and calibration of the computational models.

LUXEMBOURG INSTITUTE OF SCIENCE AND TECHNOLOGY | LIST

EXPERIMENTAL CAMPAIGN IN LUXEMBOURG 2023-2024

References measurements

Reference solar Irradiation data source: CAMS

- Satellite derived
- GHI, DHI, DNI
- Up to 1 minute resolution
- Time coverage since 2004-02-01
- Spatial coverage: Europe, Africa, Atlantic Ocean, Middle East

Meteorological stations for additional ground validation

- LIST (red)
- ASTA – Admin. Services Tech. de l'Agriculture (green)
- MeteoLux (yellow)

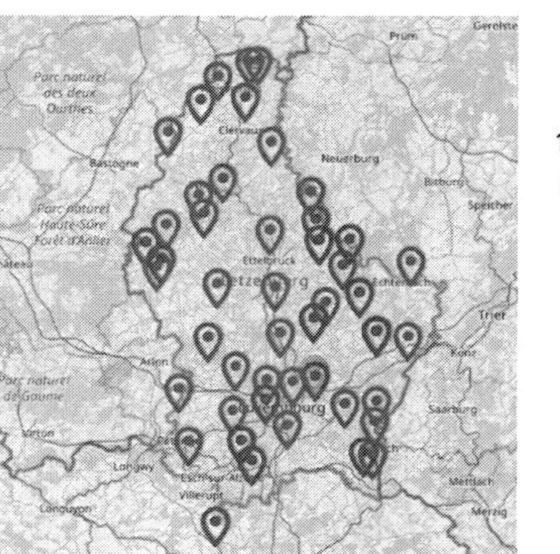

17 stations available
(GHI/DNI/DHI)

LUXEMBOURG
INSTITUTE OF SCIENCE
AND TECHNOLOGY

4

SOLAR POTENTIAL ASSESSMENT

GIS approach using 3D City Models (City GML)in complex urban environments

The method allows to:

- Represent any urban infrastructure and other 3D objects (LoD 2 and LoD3)
- Attributes of surfaces:
  - Textures
  - Optical properties (e.g. albedo reflectivity, transmissivity)
  - other cadaster information…

SOLAR POTENTIAL ASSESSMENT

GIS approach using 3D City Models (City GML)in complex urban environments

Hemispherical viewshed

For each location

- Azimuth steps: 3°
- Zenith steps: 2.5°
- Length: 10000m
- 3D models under 100m radius
- Sum: 4320 hemispherical sectors

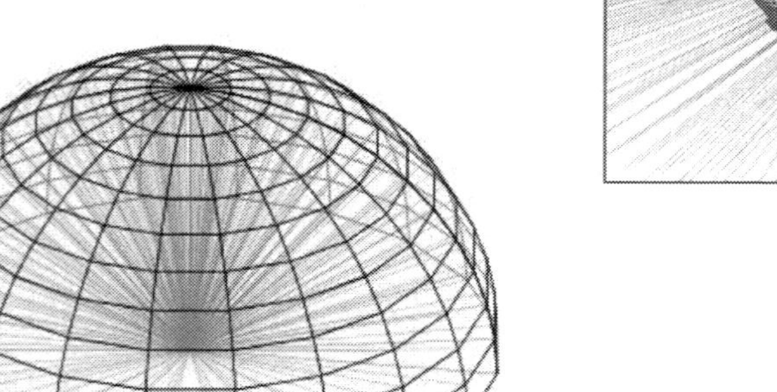

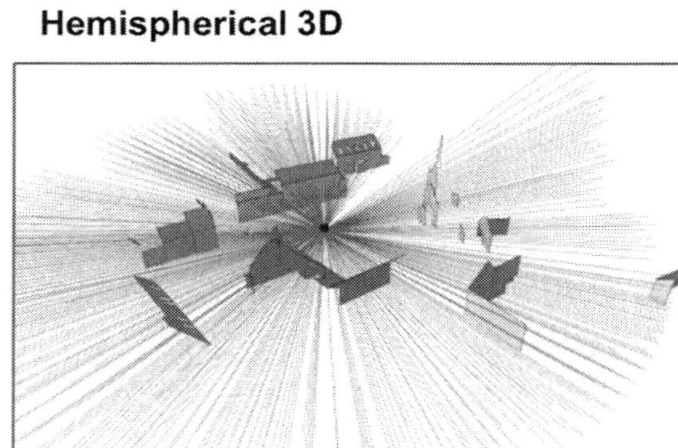

Hemispherical 3D

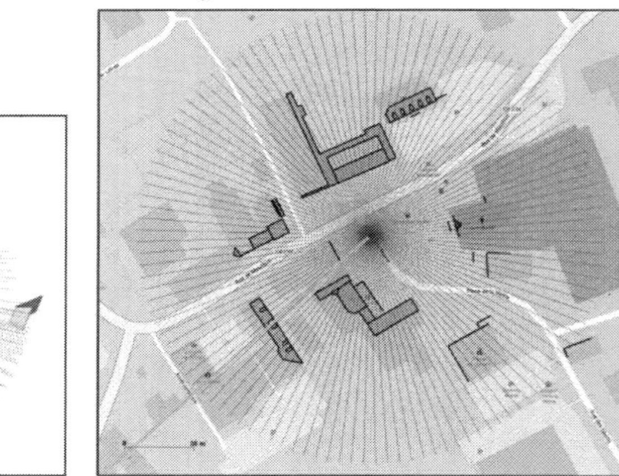

Hemispherical 2D

SOLAR POTENTIAL ASSESSMENT

GIS approach using 3D City Models (City GML)in complex urban environments

Processing workflow

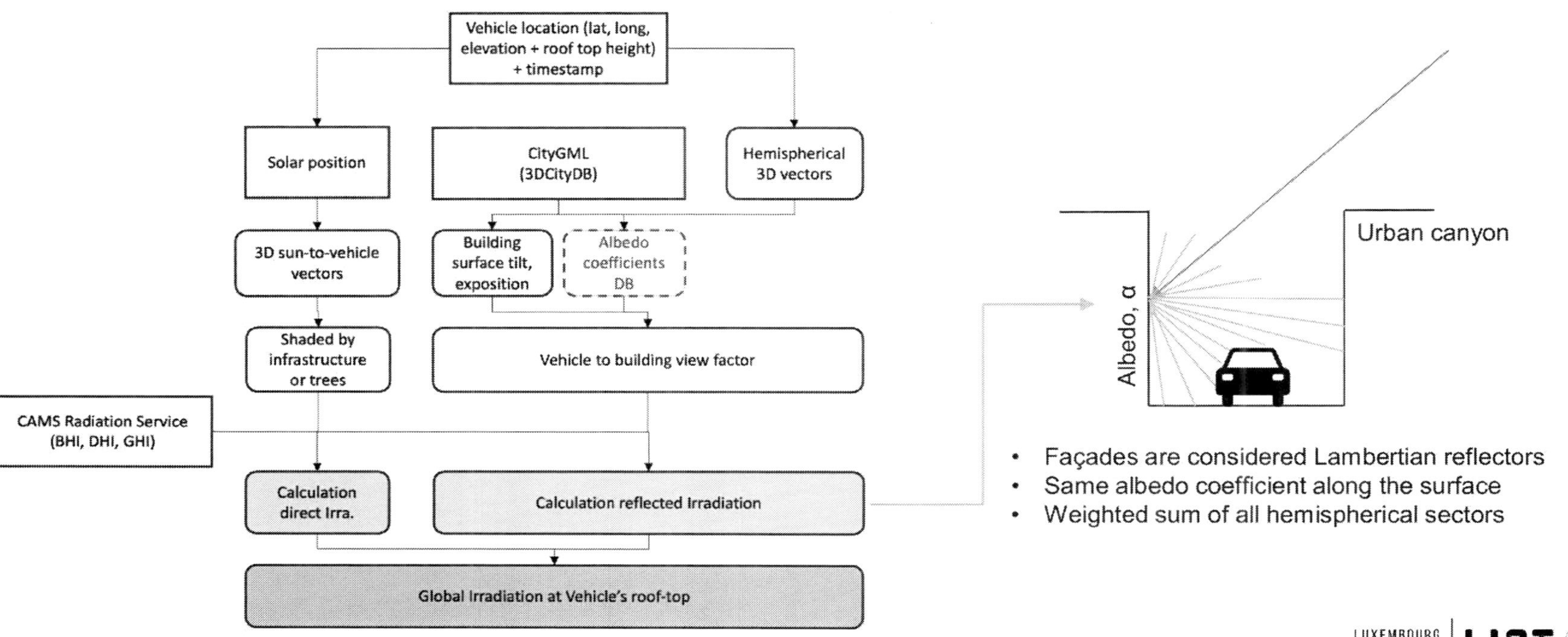

- Façades are considered Lambertian reflectors
- Same albedo coefficient along the surface
- Weighted sum of all hemispherical sectors

SOLAR POTENTIAL ASSESSMENT

GIS approach using 3D City Models (City GML)in complex urban environments

Processing workflow

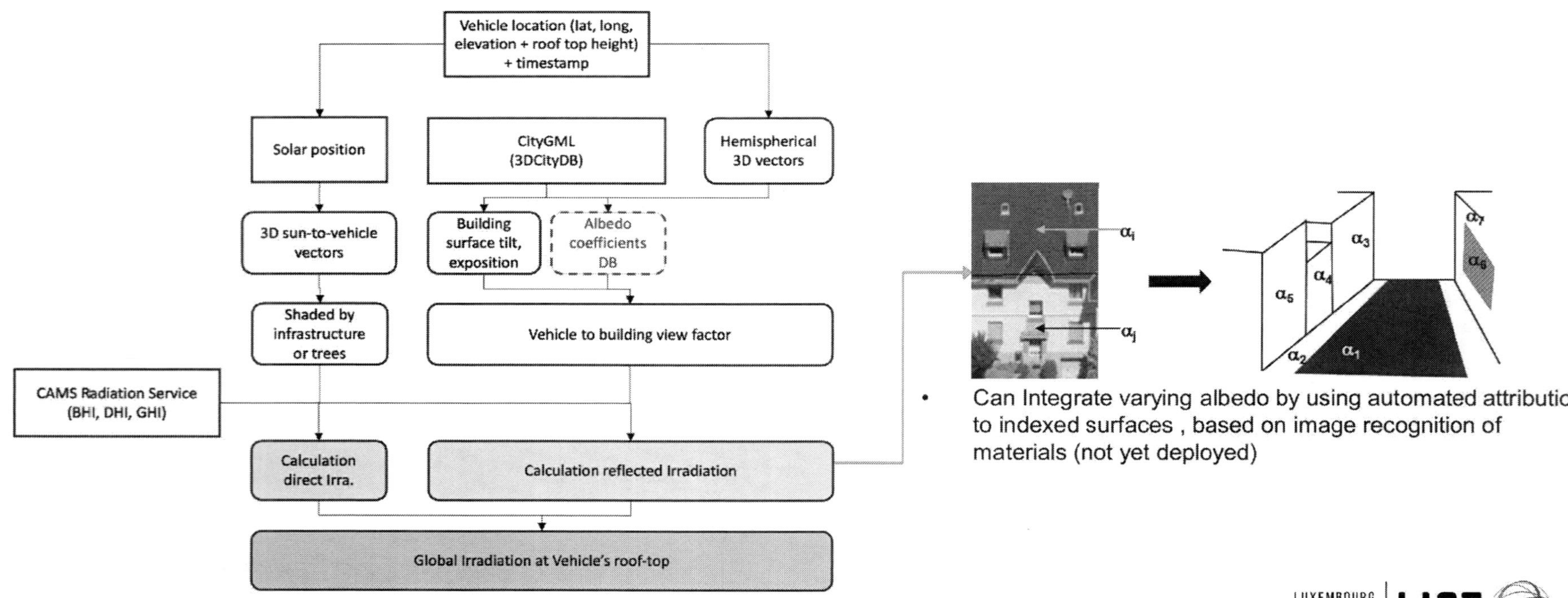

- Can Integrate varying albedo by using automated attribution to indexed surfaces , based on image recognition of materials (not yet deployed)

020458-008

SOLAR POTENTIAL ASSESSMENT

GIS approach using 3D City Models (City GML)in complex urban environments

Simulation Dashboard

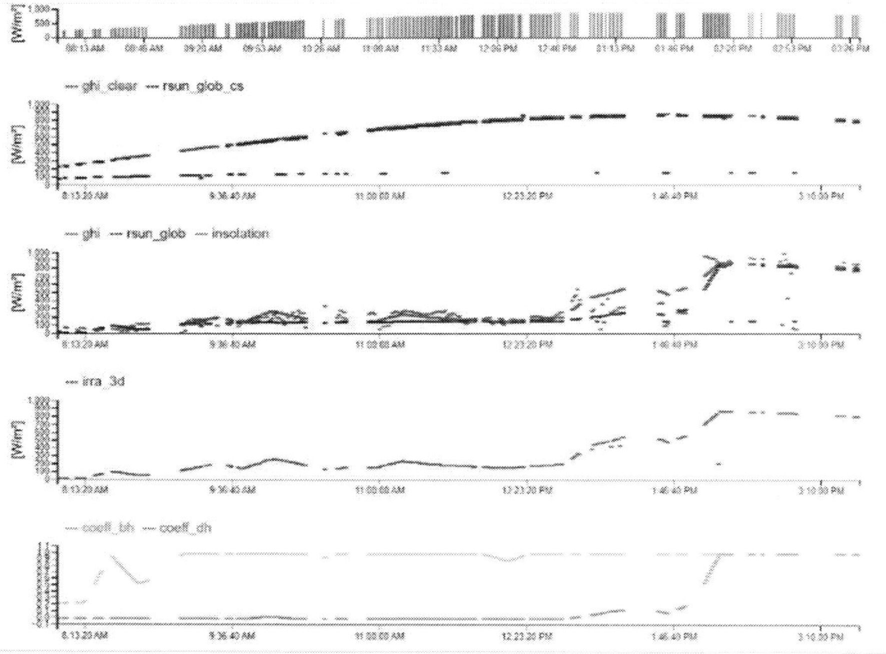

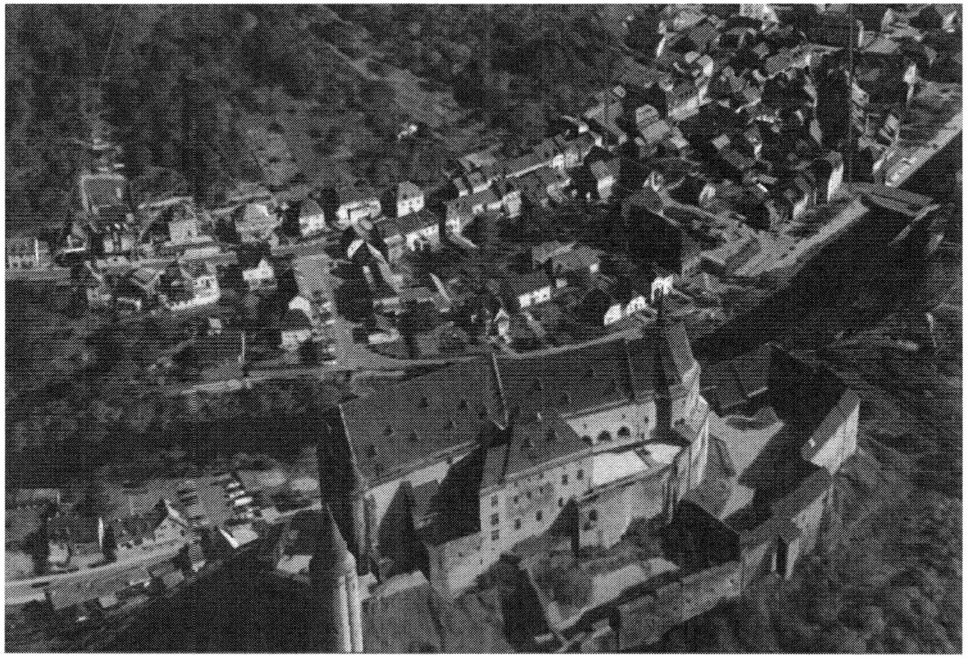

020458-009

SOLAR POTENTIAL ASSESSMENT

GIS approach using 3D City Models (City GML)in complex urban environments

Results – Matching sensor and 3D simulations incl. local diffuse reflection and shading

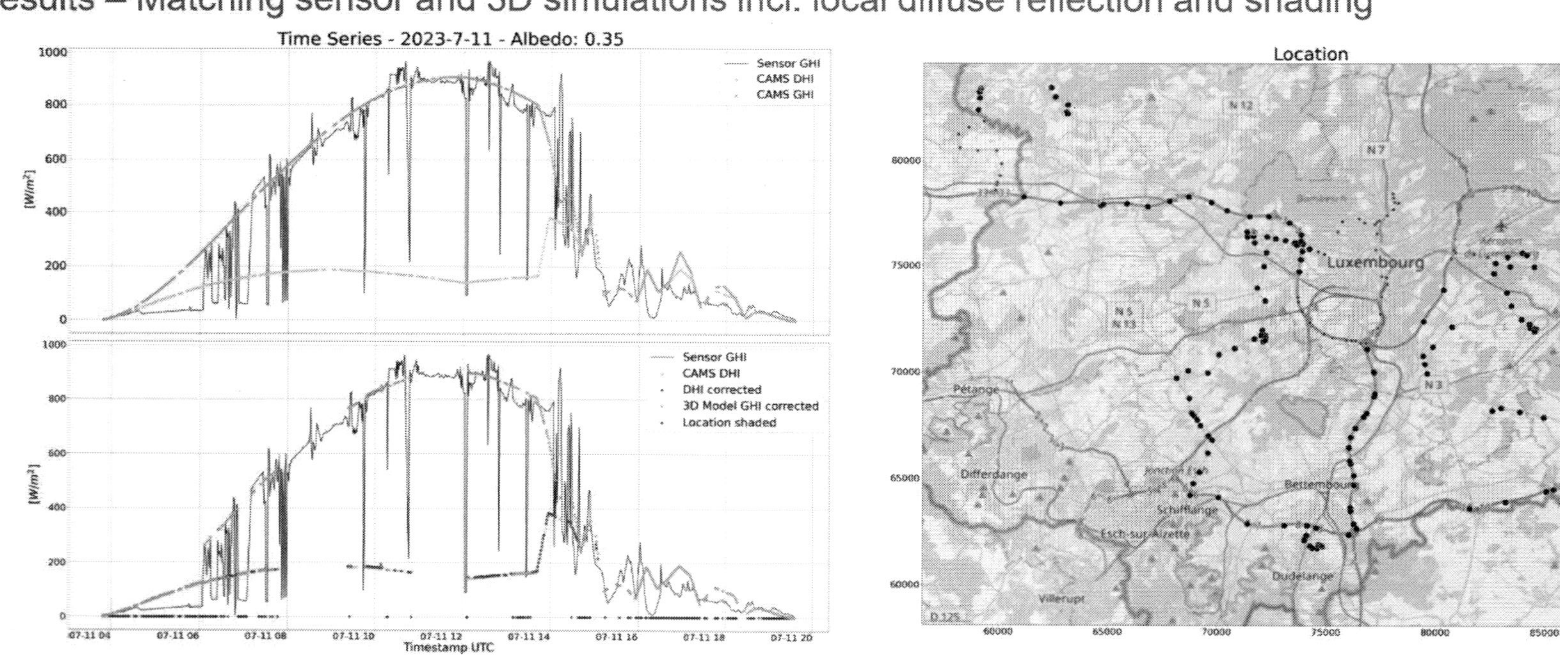

Obtained for a constant albedo coefficient of 0.35 (representative for façades)

020458-010

SOLAR POTENTIAL ASSESSMENT

GIS approach using 3D City Models (City GML)in complex urban environments

Results – Valleys, canyons with forested areas

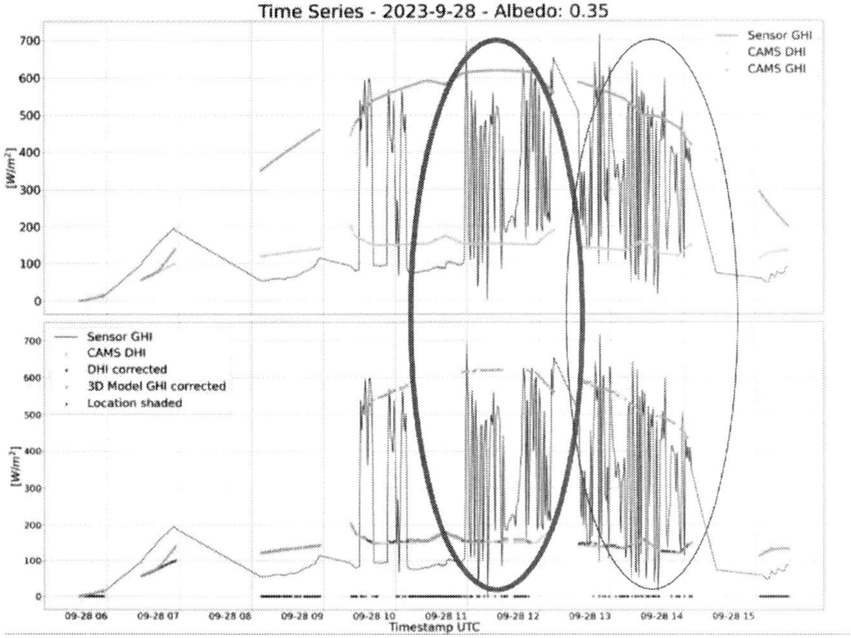

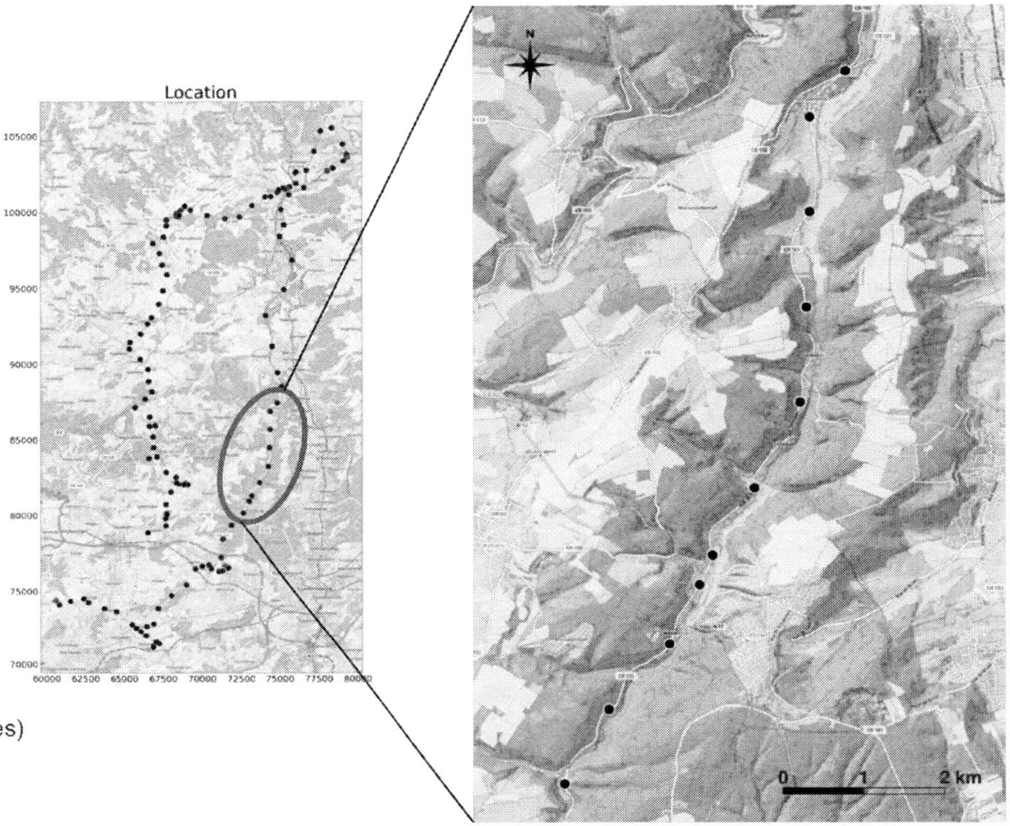

Obtained for a constant albedo coefficient of 0.35 (representative for façades)

11

SOLAR POTENTIAL ASSESSMENT

GIS approach using 3D City Models (City GML)in complex urban environments

Results – Valleys, canyons with forested areas

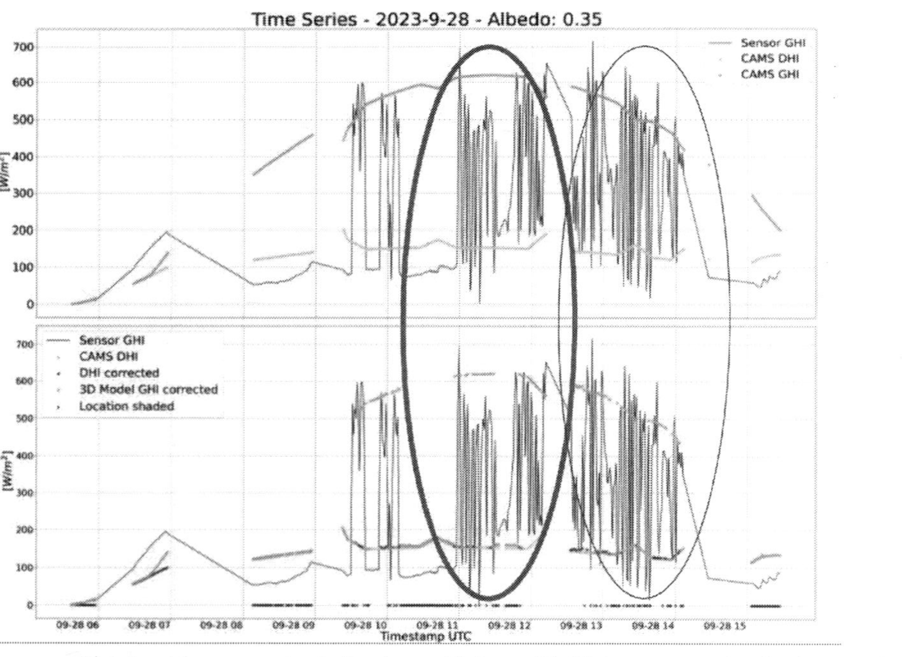

Obtained for a constant albedo coefficient of 0.35 (representative for façades)

cleaned for >20% difference

USING GTFS AND DRIVING CYCLES TO ASSESS VIPV POTENTIAL IN URBAN PUBLIC TRANSPORT

GTFS - General Transit Feed Specification, is an open standard adopted by thousands of public transport providers worldwide, containing information about routes, schedules, fares, and geographic transit details.

Documentation available at gtfs.org.

Use case – TICE Line 1

Direction 1 (D1) – Esch-sur-Alzette (Gare) – Lamadeleine (Pétange)
Distance: 17.4 km
Frequency: each 15 minutes
No stops: 25 (60s)
Typical time: 41 min
Up to 63 trips/day

Direction 2 (D2) –Lamadeleine (Pétange) - Esch-sur-Alzette (Gare)
Distance: 18.3 km
No stops: 30 (60s)
Typical duration: 43.7 min.
Up to 63 trips/day

41169 trips per year
2–8 vehicles simultaneously

USING GTFS AND DRIVING CYCLES TO ASSESS VIPV POTENTIAL IN URBAN PUBLIC TRANSPORT

GTFS based Simulation workflow

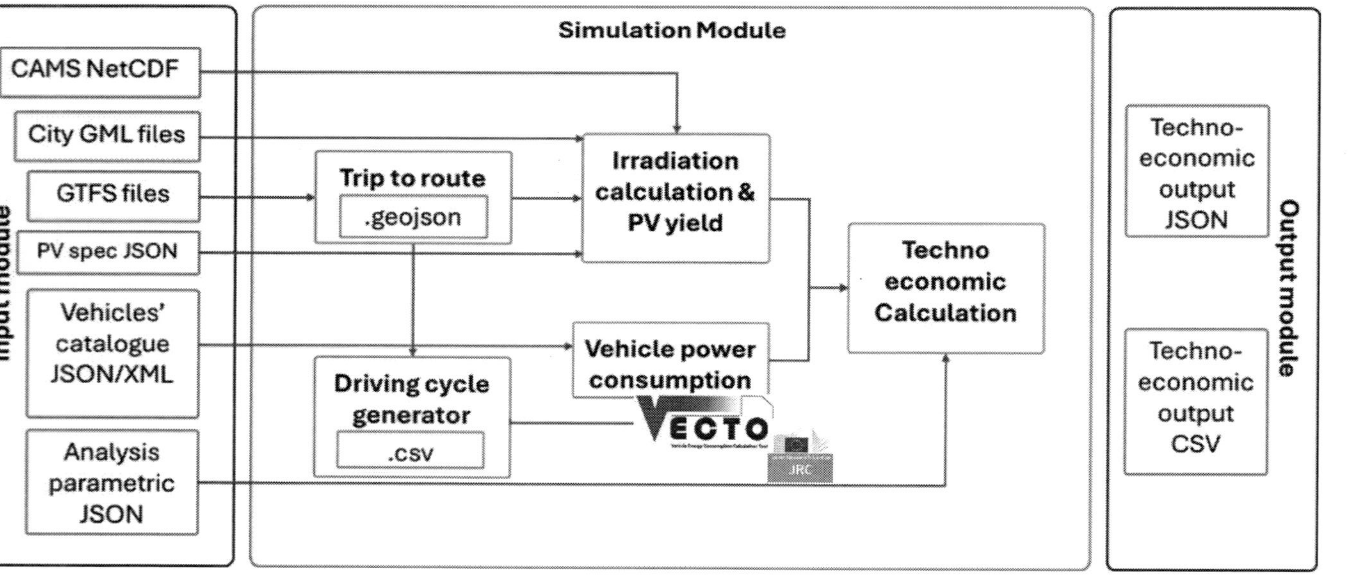

*VECTO is a simulation tool developed by the European Commission to determine CO2 emissions and fuel consumption from heavy-duty vehicles (HDVs).

020458-014

USING GTFS AND DRIVING CYCLES TO ASSESS VIPV POTENTIAL IN URBAN PUBLIC TRANSPORT

Vehicle's Powertrain Components and Model

VECTO Accounts with 26 Powertrain Architectures available:
- ICE
- HEV (9 Parallel Hybrid Electric Vehicle Architectures)
- PEV (4 Pure Electric Vehicle Architectures)

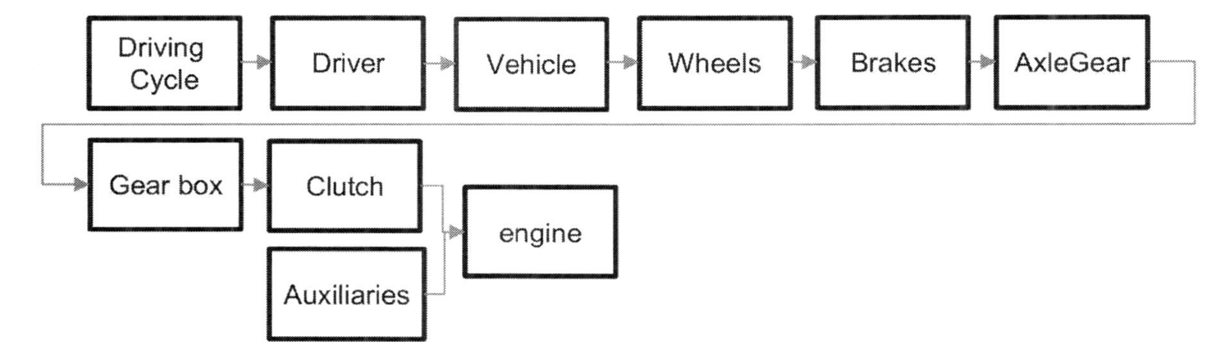

The engine tries to supply the requested power demand (including all power losses occurring in the powertrain and auxiliaries).
If the engine cannot meet the required power demand, the driver reduces acceleration.

15

USING GTFS AND DRIVING CYCLES TO ASSESS VIPV POTENTIAL IN URBAN PUBLIC TRANSPORT

Driving cycle

t [s]	Timestep of the trip
v [km/h]	The target vehicle velocity. >= 0 km/h.
Stop [s]	Stopping Time. After this time, the vehicle tries to accelerate to v.
P_{add} [kW]	Additional auxiliary power demand.
Grad (%)	The road gradient.

Example of processed driving cycle for D1

Simulation parameters : 2s frequency, 10 hypersegments

Vehicle's key parameterisation

- Mass and loading - Corrected Actual Curb Mass and loading
- Cross Sectional Area - Air Resistance and Cross Wind Correction Options
- Effective dynamic Wheel radius - engine speed calculation
- Relative axle load – Rolling resistance coefficient
- Electric machine – porwer and nr. of systems
- Rechargeable Electric Energy Storage System (RESS) parameters

Vehicle:

Mercedez eCitaro K:

- Category:12 m
- Powertrain: 2x 125 kW
- Torque: 2x 484 Nm
- RESS: 330 kWh
- Mass: 28500 kg
- Max occupancy: 158 pax.
- P.aux. 2kW (constant)

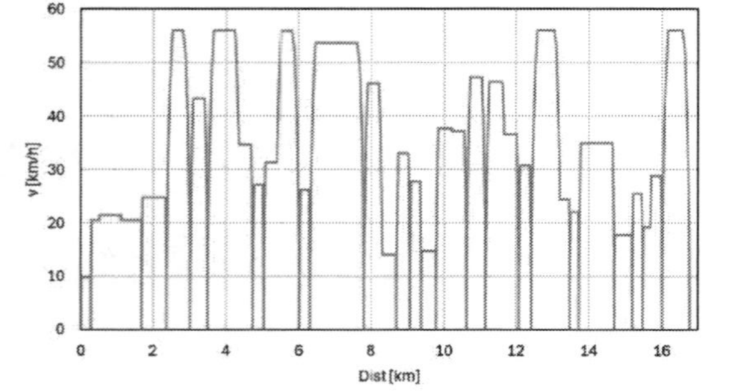

{ "Header": { "CreatedBy": "", "Date": "2025-02-02T14:18:02.0731125Z", "AppVersion": "3", "FileVersion": 10 }, "Body": { "SavedInDeclMode": false, "VehCat": "CityBus", "LegislativeClass": "M3", "CurbWeight": 13440.0, "CurbWeightExtra": 0.0, "MassMax": 11.99, "Loading": 6560.0, "rdyn": 459.0, "CdCorrMode": "CdofVdecl", "CdCorrFile": "", "AxleConfig": { "Type": "4x2", "Axles": [{ "Inertia": 6.5, "wheels": "275/70 R22.5", "AxleWeightShare": 0.38, "TwinTyres": false, "RRCISO": 0.0065, "FzISO": 20850.0, "Type": "VehicleNonDriven", "Steered": false }, { "Inertia": 6.5, "wheels": "275/70 R22.5", "AxleWeightShare": 0.62, "TwinTyres": true, "RRCISO": 0.0075, "FzISO": 20850.0, "Type": "VehicleDriven", "Steered": false }] }, "EngineStopStart": false, "EcoRoll": "None", "PredictiveCruiseControl": "None", "ATEcoRollReleaseLockupClutch": false, "CdA": 4.83, "VehicleHeight": 3.4, "InitialSoC": 80.0, "PowertrainConfiguration": "BatteryElectric", "ElectricMotors": [{ "Count": 2, "Ratio": 22.6, "Position": "E4", "MotorFile": "../GenericVehicleE4/GenericEMotor_125kW_485Nm.vem", "MechanicalEfficiency": 0.97 }], "Batteries": [{ "NumPacks": 2, "BatteryFile": "../GenericVehicleE4/GenericBattery_243kWh_750V.vbat", "StreamId": 0 }], "PTO": { "Type": "None", "LossMap": "", "Cycle": "", "CycleEPTO": "", "CycleDriving": "" } } }

- VIPV 80% rooftop – 3.5 kW$_p$/Bus
- PR – 75% (power losses in MPPT,
- voltage conversion, temperature, curvature, etc…)

LUXEMBOURG INSTITUTE OF SCIENCE AND TECHNOLOGY | LIST

USING GTFS AND DRIVING CYCLES TO ASSESS VIPV POTENTIAL IN URBAN PUBLIC TRANSPORT

Results – TICE Line 1 solar potential

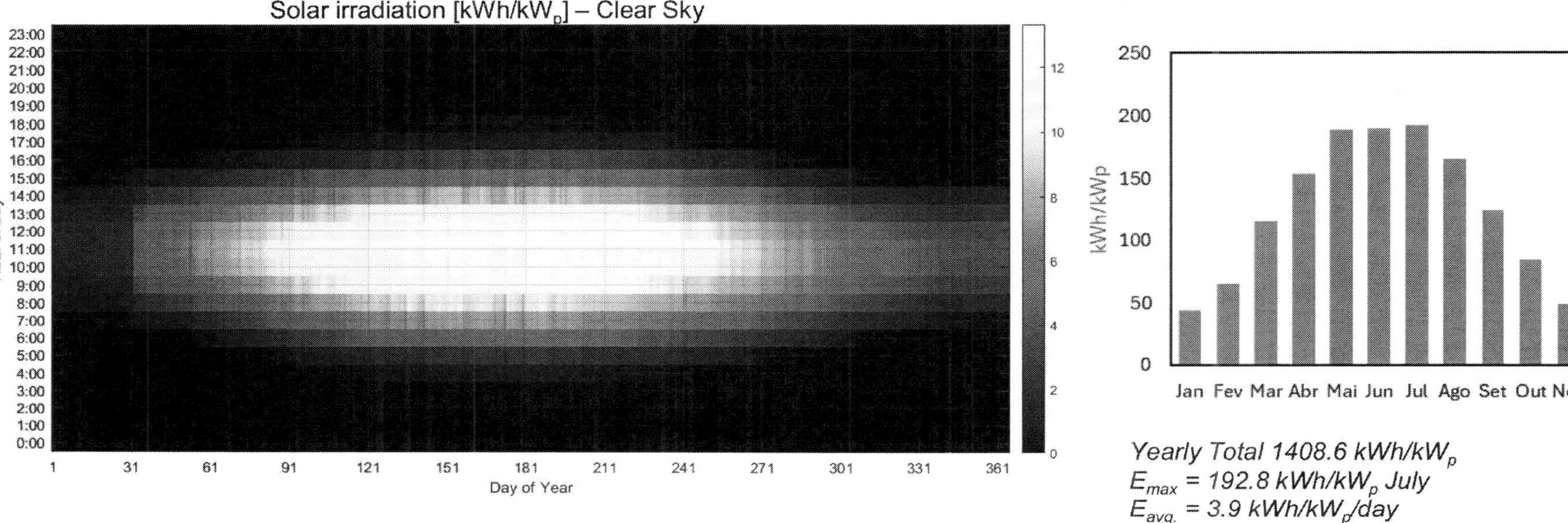

Yearly Total 1408.6 kWh/kW$_p$
E_{max} = 192.8 kWh/kW$_p$ July
$E_{avg.}$ = 3.9 kWh/kW$_p$/day

The shadow losses - 20.5%

USING GTFS AND DRIVING CYCLES TO ASSESS VIPV POTENTIAL IN URBAN PUBLIC TRANSPORT

Results – TICE Line 1 solar potential

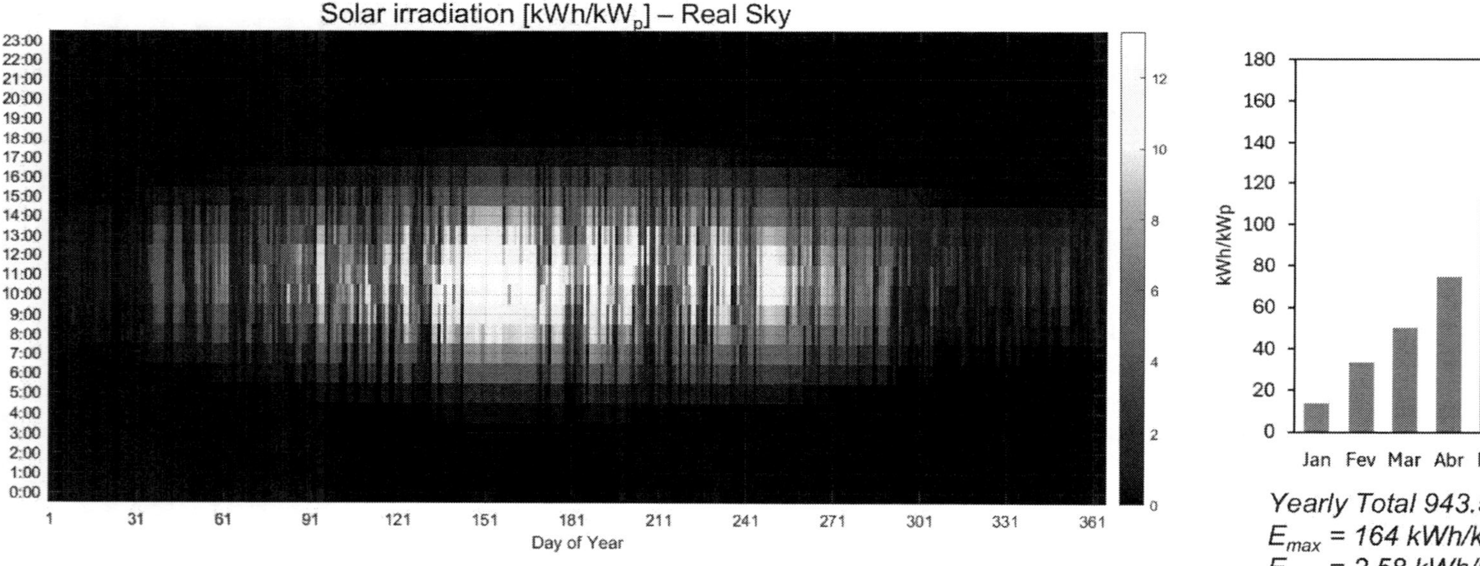

Yearly Total 943.5 kWh/kW$_p$
E_{max} = *164 kWh/kW$_p$ August*
$E_{avg.}$ = *2.58 kWh/kW$_p$/day*

The shadow losses - 20.8%

020458-018

USING GTFS AND DRIVING CYCLES TO ASSESS VIPV POTENTIAL
IN URBAN PUBLIC TRANSPORT
Results — TICE Line 1 VIPV Yield

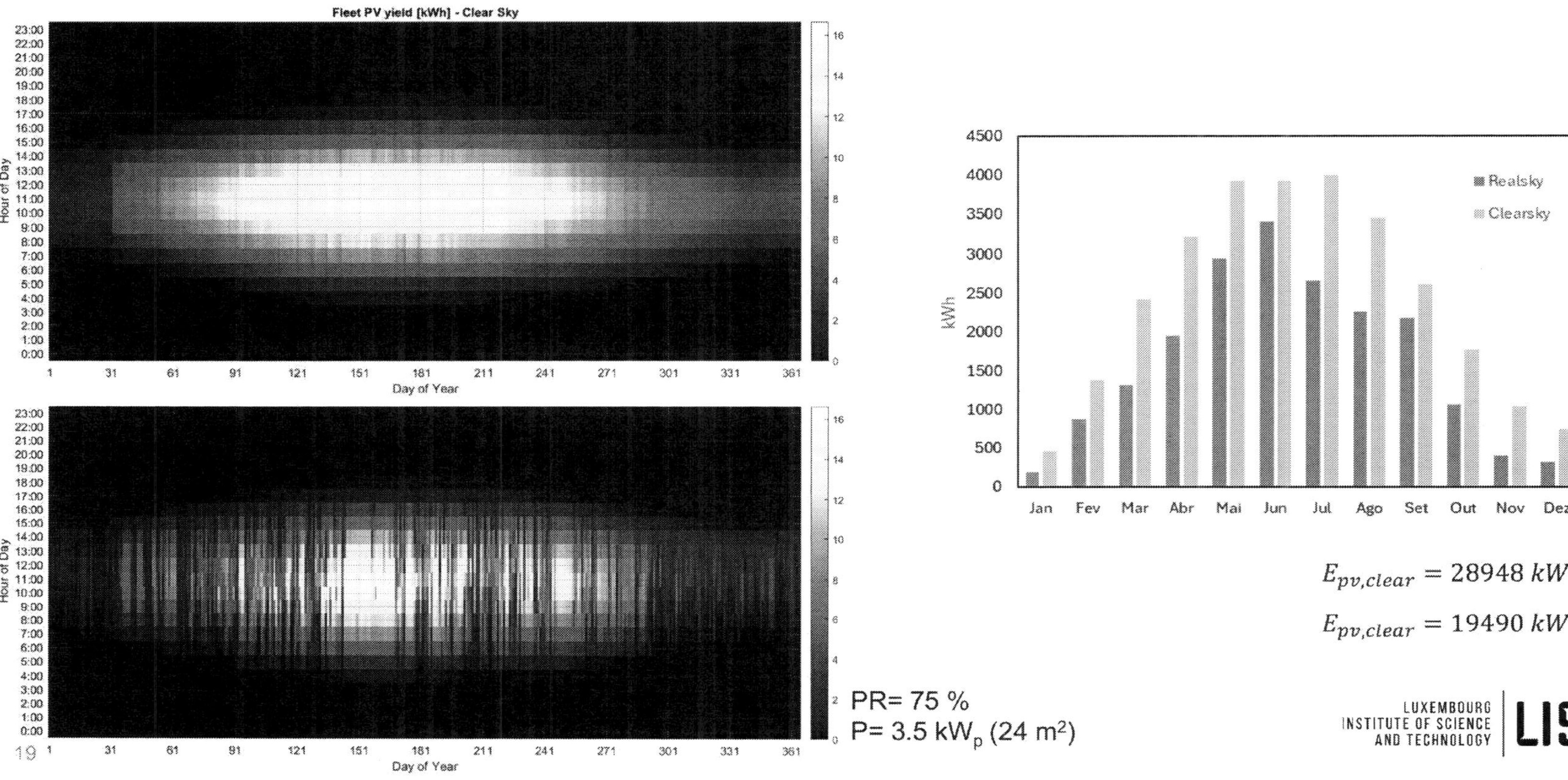

$$E_{pv,clear} = 28948\ kWh$$

$$E_{pv,clear} = 19490\ kWh$$

PR= 75 %
P= 3.5 kW$_p$ (24 m^2)

LUXEMBOURG
INSTITUTE OF SCIENCE
AND TECHNOLOGY | LIST

USING GTFS AND DRIVING CYCLES TO ASSESS VIPV POTENTIAL
IN URBAN PUBLIC TRANSPORT — Results – Energy balance

- Typical Battery discharge per trip:
  - D1 – 23.34 kWh (~7 %SoC)
  - D2 – 23.96 kWh (~ 7 %SoC)

- Charging 20% to 80% = 198 kWh

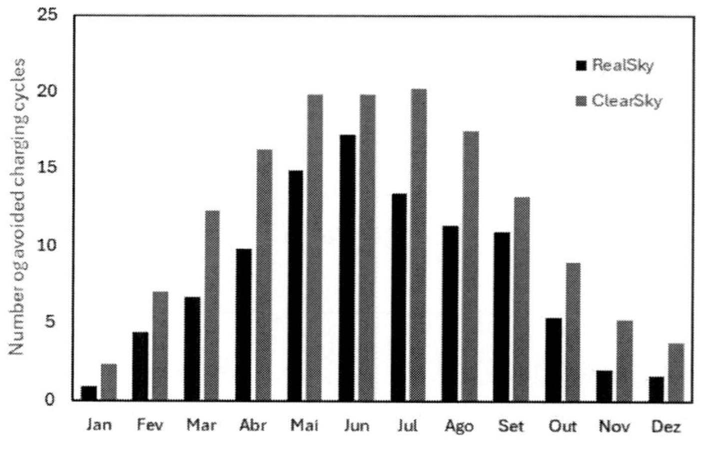

$E_{total} = 707.83 MWh$
$E_{month.avg} = 58.9 MWh$

VIPV system would cover 2.8 % - 4.1% of the TICE line 1 energy demand

Simple payback time ranging 7 -10 years
Energy tariff – 0.21 €/kWh
VIPV cost – 1.5 €/kW_p

LUXEMBOURG
INSTITUTE OF SCIENCE
AND TECHNOLOGY
LIST

USING GTFS AND DRIVING CYCLES TO ASSESS VIPV POTENTIAL IN URBAN PUBLIC TRANSPORT

Next Steps

- Complete the deployment of albedo coefficient indexing for solar the potential assessment, using open datasets based on façade textures.

- Evaluate trips across different urban density levels (low, medium, high), sub-urban, and rural areas.

- Improve vehicle operational parameterization, considering temporal variation of payload (passenger occupancy rates) and auxiliary power demand (e.g., impact on HVAC).

020458-021

thank you

For more info, please contact us

david.pera@list.lu
ulrich.leopold@list.lu

co-funded by:

LE GOUVERNEMENT
DU GRAND-DUCHÉ DE LUXEMBOURG
Ministère de l'Environnement, du Climat
et de la Biodiversité

Interreg
North-West Europe

Co-funded by
the European Union

STEER-NWE

LUXEMBOURG
INSTITUTE OF SCIENCE
AND TECHNOLOGY

LIST

OPTIMIZING ANGULAR PERFORMANCE
OF CURVED VIPV MODULES

F. Martín[1,2], R. Herrero[1], I. Antón[1]
[1]Instituto de Energía Solar – Universidad Politécnica de Madrid (IES-UPM), Madrid, Spain
[2]Solar Added Value (SAV), Madrid, Spain
f.martin.sanagustin@alumnos.upm.es

ABSTRACT: Vehicle-integrated photovoltaics (VIPV) typically operate under non-normal irradiance, making angular performance a critical metric for energy modeling. Because vehicle surfaces often require double curvature for aerodynamic and aesthetic purposes, their angular responses differ from those of flat modules. In addition, not only the curvature but also the electrical configuration influences the angular response. In this work, several electrical configurations of a curved VIPV module have been modeled, their electrical performance simulated, and their angular impact quantified.

The curvature and size of a curved module determine the angular variation across the surface. For this reason, the case study will focus on a large VIPV module of more than 2 m² integrated into a sedan, covering both the roof and rear window. Several electrical configurations were analyzed to assess power output under varying incidence angles, including cell orientation, bypass diode arrangements, and splitting the module into different MPPTs. Results indicate that half-cell orientation and diode parameters have negligible influence. In contrast, dividing the system into MPPT sections enhances overall generation, especially under varying angles of incidence.

For study validation, a commercial VIPV module of 0.87 m² was tested both indoors and outdoors with unique measurement capabilities. The experimental and simulated angular responses are compared, validating the developed model.

Keywords: curved photovoltaic modules, vehicle integrated photovoltaics (VIPV), characterization, relative angular response (RAR).

1 INTRODUCTION

The growth of electric vehicles (EVs) has increased interest in vehicle-integrated photovoltaics (VIPV), a technology that integrates solar panels into vehicle surfaces such as the roof, hood, doors, and windows [1]. These panels must be adapted to the vehicle's shape, which often involves curved and asymmetrical surfaces to maintain both design and aerodynamic needs.

The performance of VIPV systems is influenced by non-uniform light distribution due to these curved surfaces. Factors like shading and the changing angle of sunlight—affected by time of day, season, location, and vehicle position—result in variable energy generation.

The angle of incidence is critical for VIPV modules because it directly affects the irradiance reaching the cells. In flat modules, current is uniform across cells, but in curved modules, varying angles lead to differences in current. Therefore, VIPV module design is critical to reduce mismatch losses caused by both curvature and changing light conditions.

Curvature and shading in VIPV modules may require the integration of a higher number of by-pass diodes than in flat modules, potentially one per cell, to minimize power losses [2],[3]. While diodes are inexpensive, their increased use raises assembly costs, especially in larger modules. However, bypass diodes reduce shading losses and improve performance. The IV curves of VIPV modules show steps due to bypass diodes, indicating uneven illumination across cells. These curves depend on the angle of incidence and the module's electrical design, including cell connections and the number of diodes.

In this context, the objective of this study is to evaluate the angular performance of a sedan's rooftop, including the rear window as an active photovoltaic surface as shown in Fig.1. Specifically, we pointed to investigate potential energy gain of a VIPV module under optimized tilted irradiance conditions.

For this purpose, various electrical configurations were analyzed, including different cell orientations (portrait and landscape), number and breakdown voltage of by-pass diodes, number of MPPTs, etc.

Figure 1: VIPV module evaluated.

2 VALIDATION OF MODELLING TOOL

The validation of our modeling tool was carried out through indoor and outdoor characterization of a curved VIPV module as part of a round-robin activity within the PT600 working group. Further details can be found in [4]

Indoor measurements were performed under STC using a solar simulator designed and built for characterization of curved modules, equipped with a dual-axis rotation structure for varying module angles [5]. An image of the final design of the simulator and a picture of the VIPV module in the rotating structure is presented in Fig.2

Outdoor measurements were taken using a two-axis tracker at the Instituto de Energía Solar facilities in Madrid. VIPV module with its frame is shown in Fig.2.

Figure 2: (up) Collimated solar simulator for curved modules; (left) module and rotating structure; (right) outdoor measurement of VIPV module.

Multiple indoor and outdoor measurements were carried out under various incident angles and compared against simulation results. To perform the angular characterization, the module was intentionally misaligned to the desired positions both in the solar simulator and on the two-axis tracker [6].

To validate the simulations, we also measured the angular response at the P_{mp} and compared it with the experimental data. Extensive validation was conducted across various scenarios, with simulations consistently matching experimental results.

Two representative cases are presented in Fig. 3, showing the excellent agreement between measured and simulated IV curves.

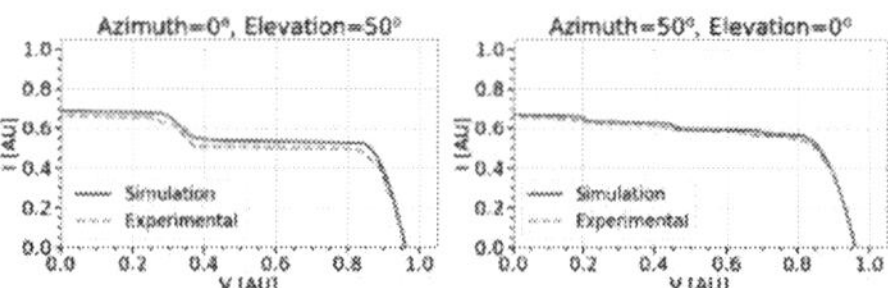

Figure 3: Comparison between measured and simulated IV curves under different angles of incidence.

3 CASE STUDY

This study focuses on the performance of a Vehicle-Integrated Photovoltaics (VIPV) module installed on the rooftop of a sedan, also utilizing the rear window as an active photovoltaic surface as shown in Fig.1. The main objective is to assess the potential energy gain of a VIPV system optimized for tilted irradiance.

It is important to distinguish the module used for experimental validation from the one analyzed in the case study. The validation module had an active area of less than 1 m² and a nominal power below 200 W, and was used to verify the accuracy of the simulation methodology with real data from indoor and outdoor measurements.

In contrast, the case study focuses on a full-scale VIPV module with an active area exceeding 2 m² and a nominal power of approximately 520 W, representative of a realistic integration in a production sedan vehicle.

To introduce the VIPV case study, we first are going to define the angular parameters used in the analysis. α is the incidence angle with respect to the normal at the center of the module, while β represents the azimuth angle as can be seen in Fig. 5.

For clarity in the angular response graphs, a sign convention is adopted for α where positive values indicate light incident from the front of the vehicle and negative values correspond to light from the rear direction.

Figure 5: (left) α: incidence angle relative to the normal at the center of the module; (right) β: azimuth.

Although α remains constant, different β values caused by the changing position of the sun and the movement of the vehicle, can produce significantly different irradiance distributions across the curved VIPV surface.

Due to the module's curvature and asymmetry, β has a significant effect on the irradiance distribution across the surface and cells.

Fig. 6 shows irradiance maps for identical α and varying β angles, highlighting the variation in irradiance patterns induced by β. This non-uniformity strongly impacts PV generation, making the electrical design and interconnection strategy a key aspect in the electrical configurations.

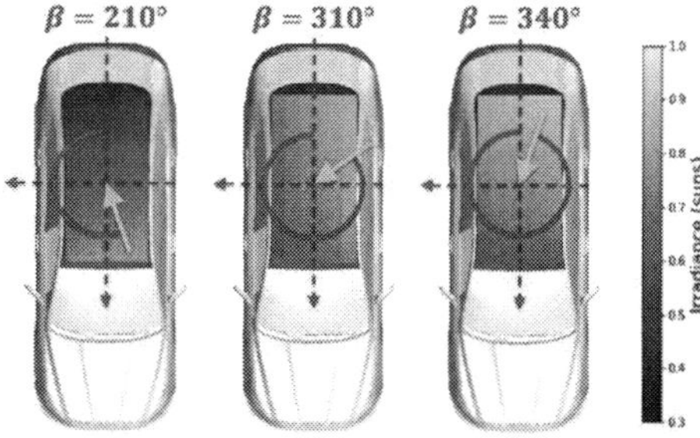

Figure 6: Irradiance variation on the VIPV surface for same α and different β angles.

To evaluate the influence of electrical design on angular performance, various combinations of electrical parameters were analyzed.

The analysis includes different cell orientations (portrait and landscape), bypass diode strategies (number and placement), a range of bypass diode breakdown voltages, and varying numbers of MPPTs per module.

Among the approaches studied, a particularly relevant case involves the use of one bypass diode per cell, not through external components but by leveraging the intrinsic behavior of Interdigitated Back Contact (IBC) cells [7]. These cells can be designed with a low and tunable breakdown voltage, allowing each cell to function as its own bypass element.

This complete analysis will help identify which of these design aspects have the most significant impact on performance and are therefore critical for the case study.

4 RESULTS AND CONCLUSIONS

Results obtained clearly indicate that the number of MPPT sections is the most critical factor for optimizing the angular performance of the VIPV module. Splitting the module into multiple MPPTs significantly improves power output, particularly at high tilted angles.

In contrast, other parameters such as cell orientation, the number of bypass diodes, and diode breakdown voltage have a minimal impact on overall performance.

To analyze these effects in detail, a step-by-step comparison of the angular responses of different configurations is presented in the following figures.

Fig 7. shows the angular response of two configurations where all cells are connected in series, with different orientations: portrait and landscape. The results reveal almost identical angular performance in both cases, with only slight differences at very tilted angles, where the power output is already low.

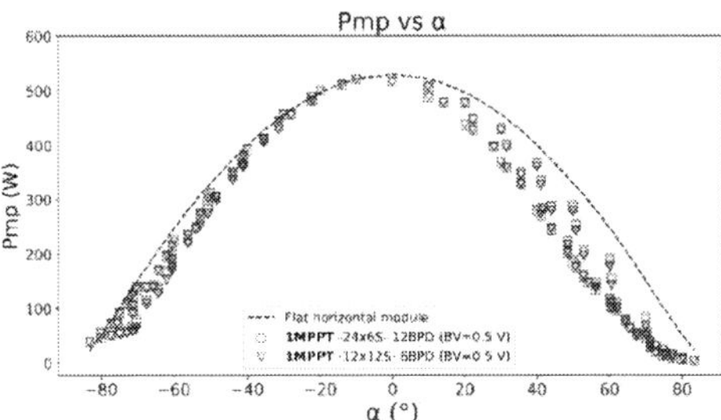

Figure 7: Angular response of VIPV module for different cell orientacion (landscape and portrait).

Fig.8 compares one of the previous configurations with three additional cases using 2 MPPTs. The new configurations are as follows:

- Portrait orientation with 6 bypass diodes (one per string).
- Landscape orientation with IBC cells and a diode breakdown voltage of 0.2 V.
- Same as the previous, but with a breakdown voltage of 1.5 V.

These cases show very similar angular responses. A slight performance improvement is observed in the configuration using IBC cells with 0.2 V breakdown voltage, particularly at highly tilted angles. This suggests that the diode is only activated under extreme angular conditions. Therefore, both the number of bypass diodes and their breakdown voltage provide only marginal benefits in such scenarios.

Additionally, Fig.8 confirms that cell orientation has no significant impact on the power output of the VIPV module under the tested conditions.

Above all, 2 MPPT configurations outperform the 1 MPPT case throughout the entire angular range. The improvement is especially noticeable for positive α angles, corresponding to light coming from the front of the vehicle.

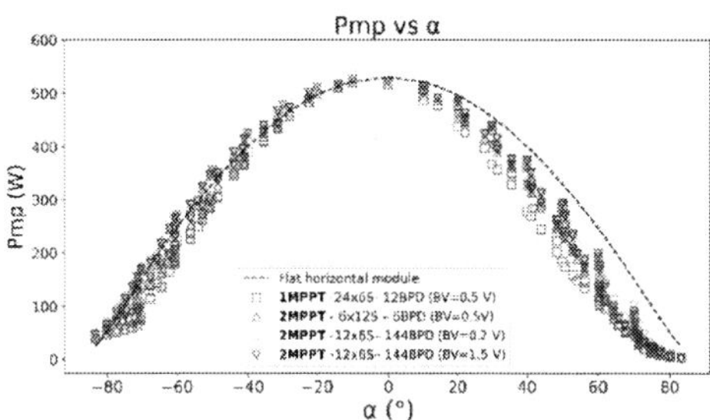

Figure 8: Angular response of VIPV module for different MPPT configurations.

To further validate the impact of MPPT segmentation, Fig.9 compares one of the previous 2 MPPT cases with a new configuration using 3 MPPTs. The results confirm that increasing the number of MPPTs enhances performance, especially at negative α angles, where light comes from the rear of the vehicle.

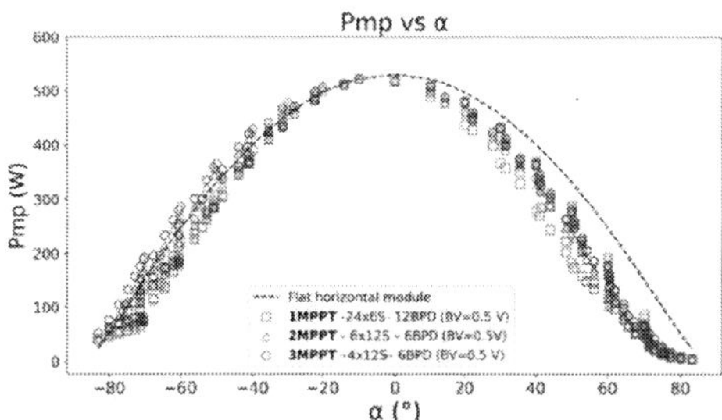

Figure 9: : Angular response of VIPV module for different MPPT configurations.

Overall, the results show distinct behaviors for positive and negative incidence angles:

- Negative α angles (light from the rear): Multi-MPPT configurations offer significant performance gains compared to a single MPPT setup.
- Positive α angles (light from the front): although all configurations perform below the flat module baseline, the single MPPT setup exhibits the greatest power loss. Multi-MPPT configurations mitigate this loss effectively.

In conclusion, optimizing the number of MPPT sections is the most effective strategy to maximize energy harvest in VIPV systems under variable angular and irradiance conditions.

5 ACKNOLEDGMENTS

The authors gratefully acknowledge the DETEC-PV project, Grant PID2021-128853OB-I00, funded by MCIN/AEI/10.13039/501100011033 and "ERDF A way of making Europe."

6   REFERENCES

[1] M. Yamaguchi *et al.*, 'Importance of Developing High-Efficiency Solar Cells for PV-Powered Vehicles', in *2020 47th IEEE Photovoltaic Specialists Conference (PVSC)*, Calgary, AB, Canada: IEEE, Jun. 2020, pp. 0221–0223. doi: 10.1109/PVSC45281.2020.9300413.

[2] Javier Macías,Rebeca Herrero, Luis Javier San José, Rubén Núñez, Ignacio Antón, 'On the optimization of the interconnection of photovoltaic modules integrated in vehicles', *in press*, iScience, 2024.

[3] J. Macias, R. Herrero, R. Nunez, and I. Anton, 'On the effect of cell interconnection in Vehicle Integrated Photovoltaics: modelling energy under different scenarios', in *2021 IEEE 48th Photovoltaic Specialists Conference (PVSC)*, Fort Lauderdale, FL, USA: IEEE, Jun. 2021, pp. 1336–1339. doi: 10.1109/PVSC43889.2021.9518935.

[4] F. Martín *et al.*, 'Relative angular response characterization in VIPV', *Sol. Energy Mater. Sol. Cells*, vol. 276, p. 113063, Oct. 2024, doi: 10.1016/j.solmat.2024.113063.

[5] G. Vallerotto *et al.*, 'Collimated solar simulator for curved PV modules characterization', *Sol. Energy Mater. Sol. Cells*, vol. 258, p. 112418, Aug. 2023, doi: 10.1016/j.solmat.2023.112418.

[6] D. Riley and C. Hansen, 'Sun-Relative Pointing for Dual-Axis Solar Trackers Employing Azimuth and Elevation Rotations', *J. Sol. Energy Eng.*, vol. 137, no. 3, p. 031008, Jun. 2015, doi: 10.1115/1.4029379.

[7] A. Calcabrini *et al.*, 'Low-breakdown-voltage solar cells for shading-tolerant photovoltaic modules', *Cell Rep. Phys. Sci.*, vol. 3, no. 12, p. 101155, Dec. 2022, doi: 10.1016/j.xcrp.2022.101155.

Optimizing angular performance of curved VIPV modules

F. Martín[1,2], R. Herrero[1], I.Antón[1]

[1]Instituto de Energía Solar, Universidad Politécnica de Madrid, Madrid (SPAIN)

[2] Solar Added Value (SAV), Madrid (SPAIN)

020460-001

Motivation

- VIPV surfaces receive **non-normal sunlight**

- Curvature causes **non-uniform irradiance** distribution across cells

- Energy modeling must consider **varying angles of incidence**

- **Module design is critical** for efficient operation

  - Modules operate under **tilted irradiance allways**

  - **Partial shading** conditions only occur **occasionally**

020460-002

Previous works

- Optimization of electrical VIPV module for partial shading (static)

    – Number and Breakdown Voltage of by-pass diodes matters!!

    – Increase the number of MPPTs also helps

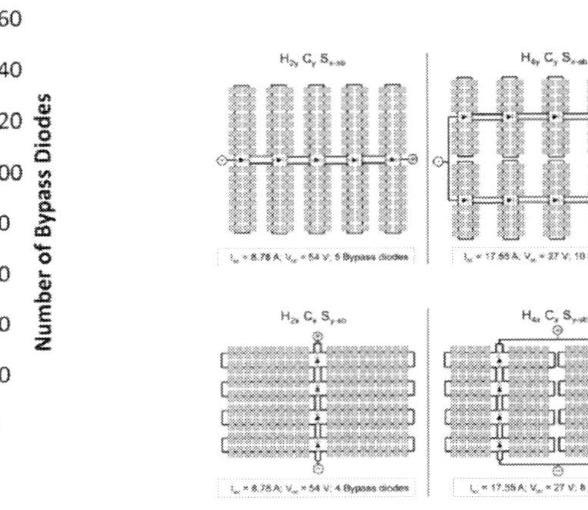

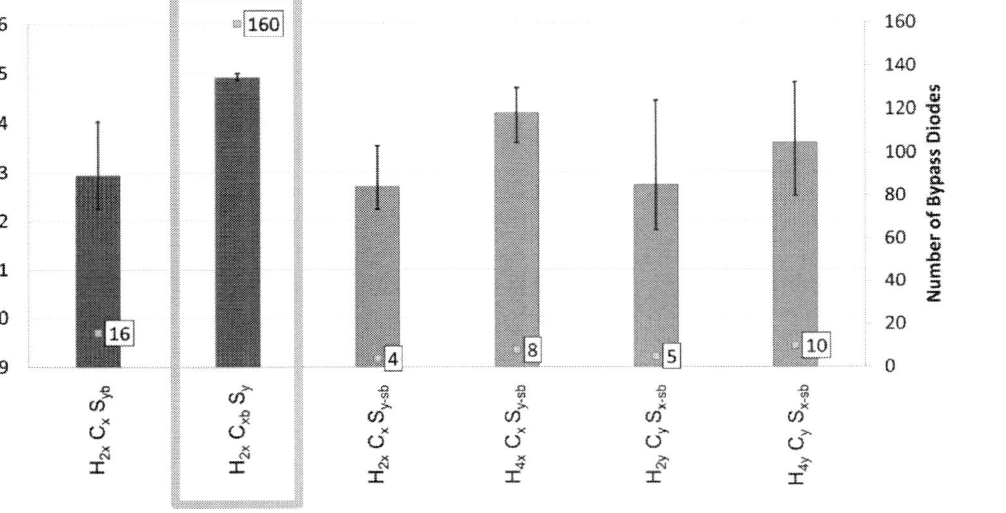

020460-003

Objective

- What is the potential **gain** of VIPV **optimized** for tilted irradiance?

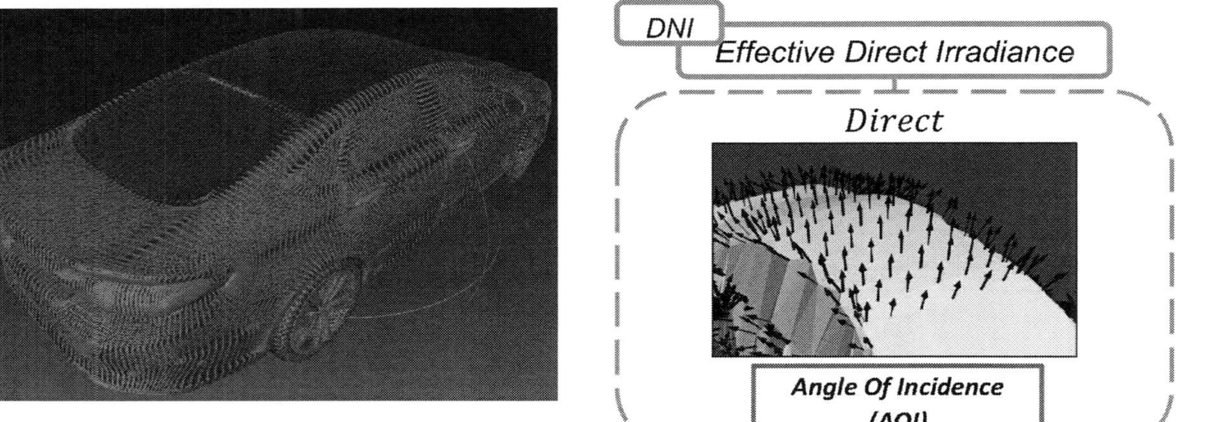

Parameter	Value	Units
Plan view area	2.13	m^2
PV area	2.30	m^2
Number of cells	144	Cells
Cell area	157.2	cm^2
Maximum power	520	W

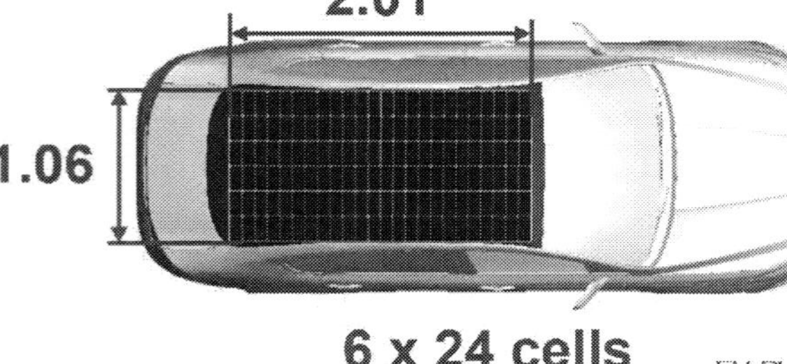

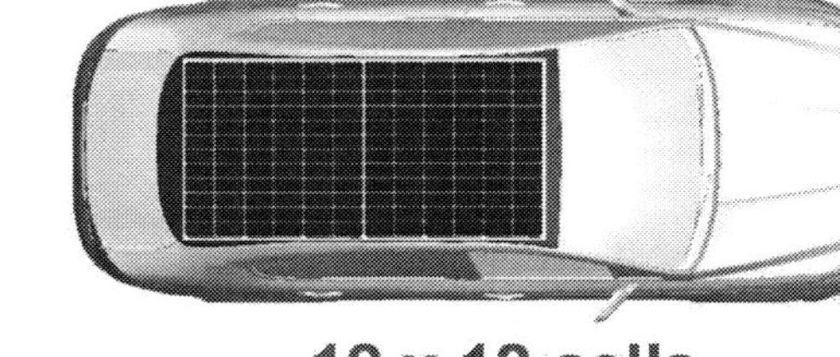

INSTITUTO DE ENERGÍA SOLAR

POLITÉCNICA

020460-004

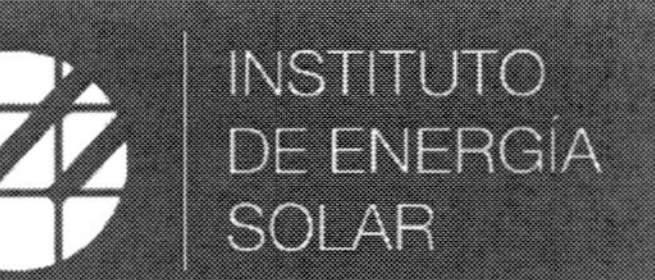

Outline

- Validation of the Modelling Tool from experimental data

- Case Study – Angular performance VIPV integrated in sedan

- Electrical Interconnection Configurations

- Results

  - Tilted Irradiance Optimization.

  - Annual Energy Generation.

- Conclusions

Validation of the Modelling Tool from experimental data

Indoors

Outdoors

More information: 3BO.12.2 Testing VIPV
Curved Modules: Methods and Challenges,
Ricardo Moruno.

Articles

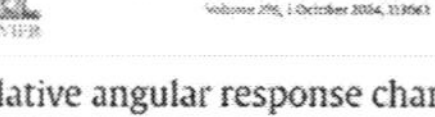

Collimated solar simulator for curved PV modules characterization

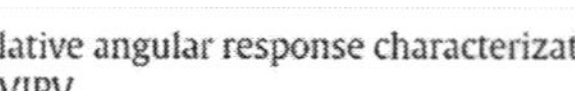

Relative angular response characterization in VIPV

Understanding the impact of sky diffuse irradiance on curved photovoltaic modules

Validation of the Modelling Tool from experimental data

INSTITUTO DE ENERGÍA SOLAR

Module	Active area $[m^2]$	Minimum curvature radius [m]	P_{mp} [W]
Commercial VIPV	0.875	3	<200
VIPV sedan	2.3	3	520

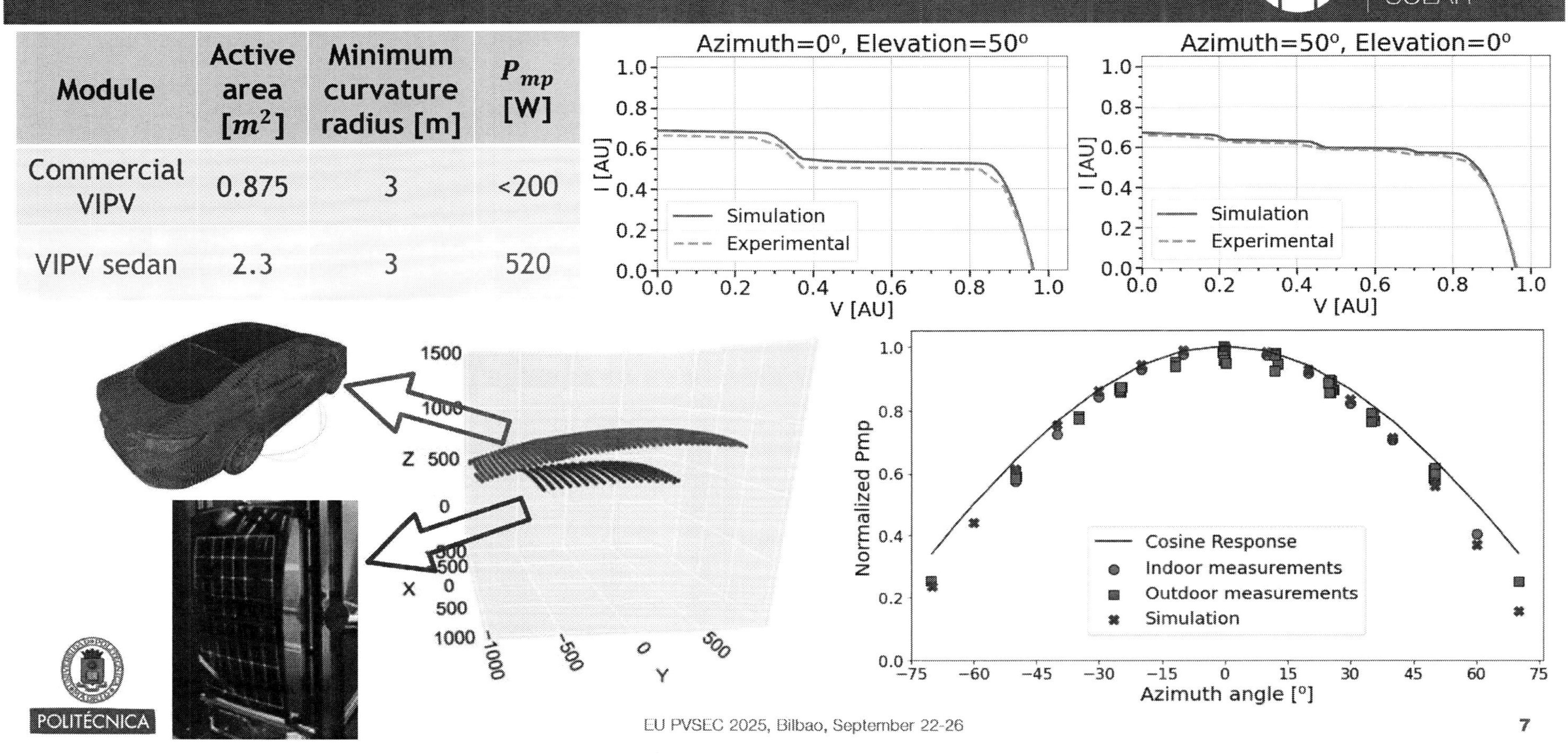

Case Study – Angular performance VIPV integrated in sedan

8

020460-008

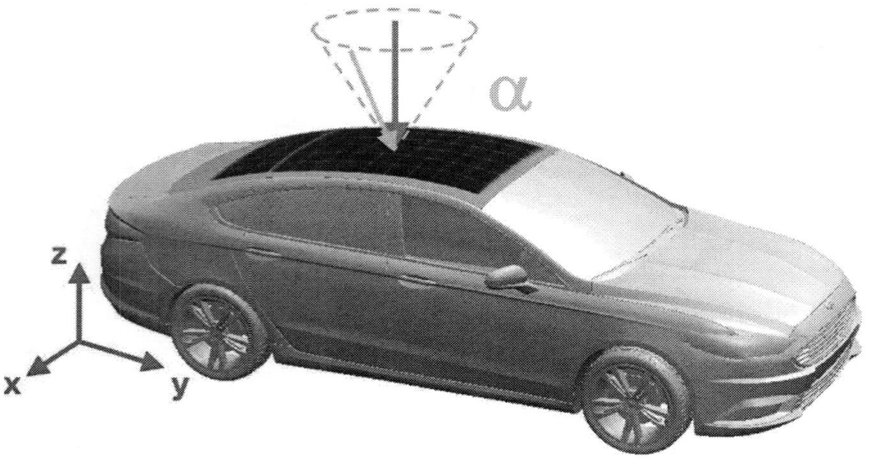

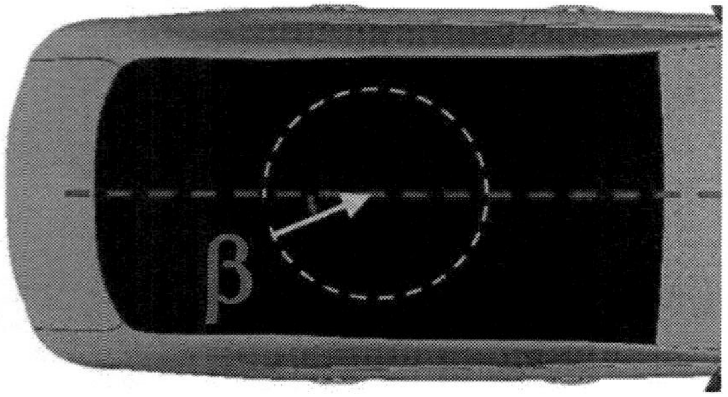

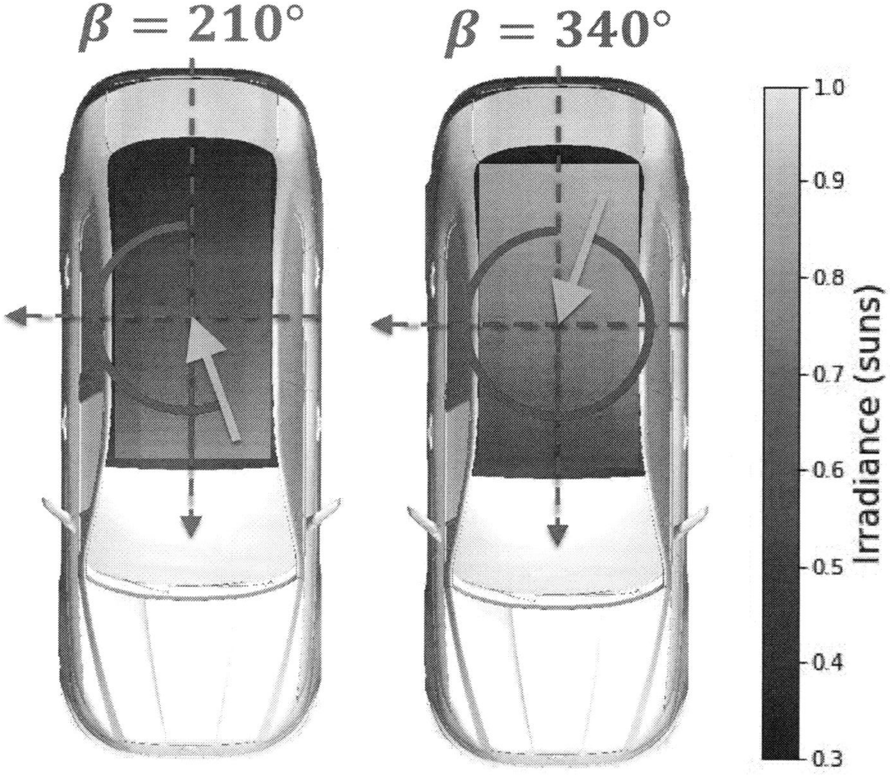

Case Study – Angular performance VIPV integrated in sedan

INSTITUTO
DE ENERGÍA
SOLAR

POLITÉCNICA

9

020460-009

Application cases - Electrical Interconnection Configurations

INSTITUTO DE ENERGÍA SOLAR

6 x 24 cell matrix (landscape)

1MPPT - *24x6S - 12 BPD (BV=0.5V)*

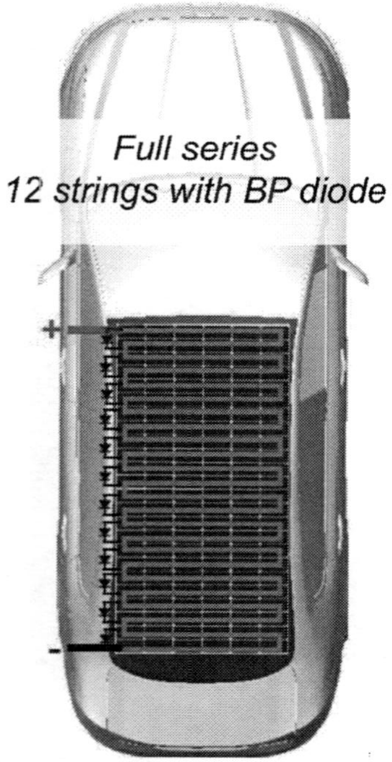

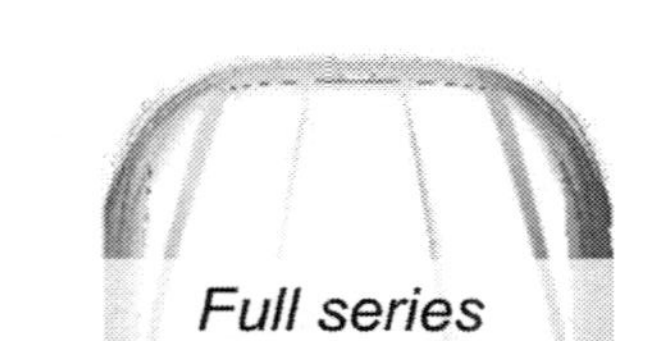

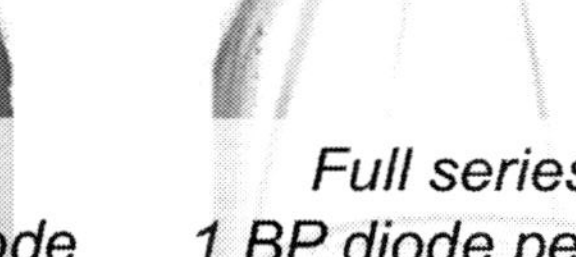

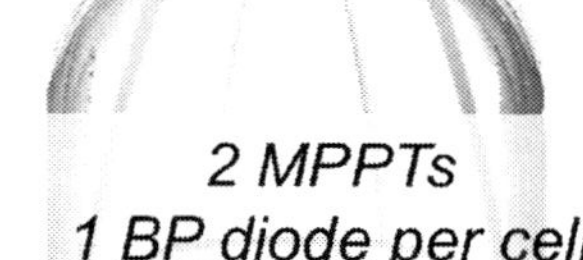

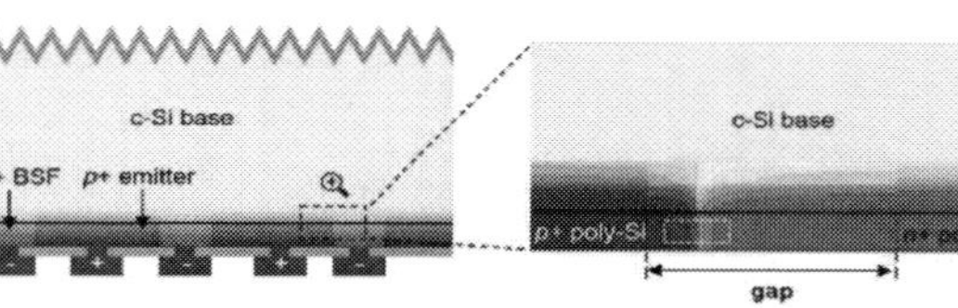

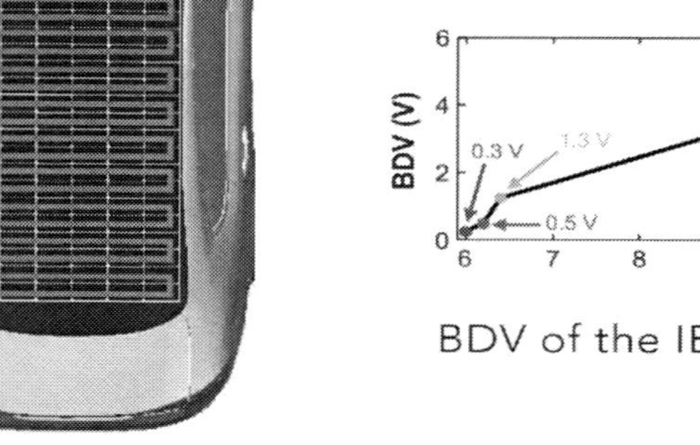

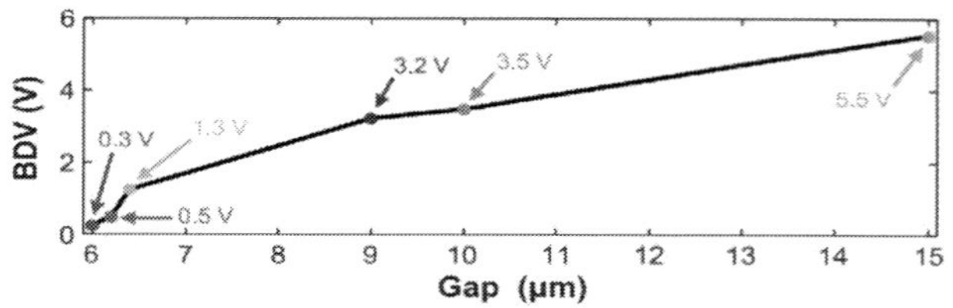

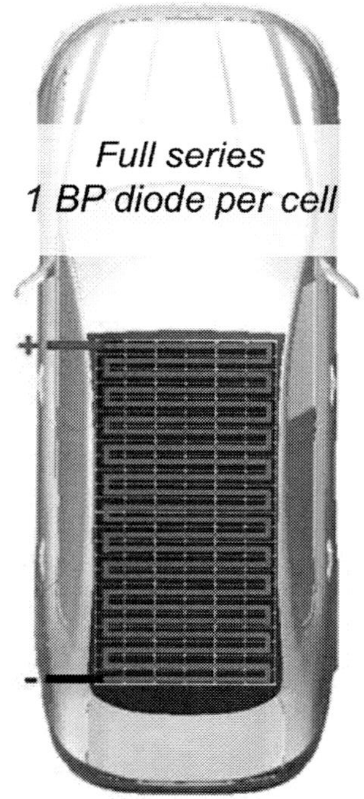

1MPPT - *24x6S – 144 BPD (BV=0.2V)*

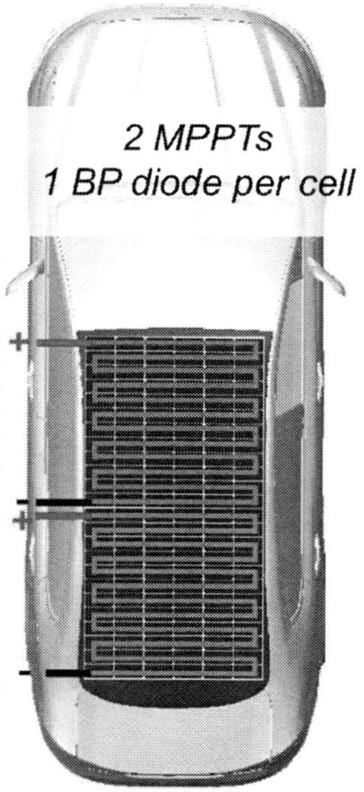

2MPPT - *12x6S – 144 BPD (BV=0.2 V)*
2MPPT - *12x6S – 144 BPD (BV=1.5 V)*

A. Calcabrini et Al, "Low-breakdown-voltage solar cells for shading-tolerant photovoltaic modules", Cell Reports Physical Science, Volume 3, Issue 12, 2022

BDV of the IBC solar cells in dark at 2 A.

POLITÉCNICA

Application cases - Electrical Interconnection Configurations

12 x 12 cell matrix (portrait)

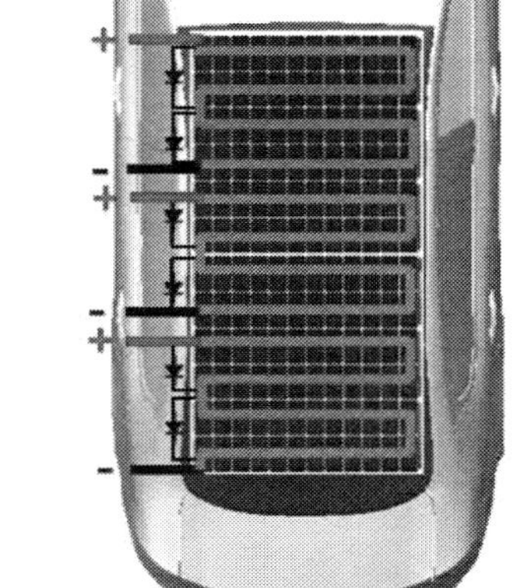

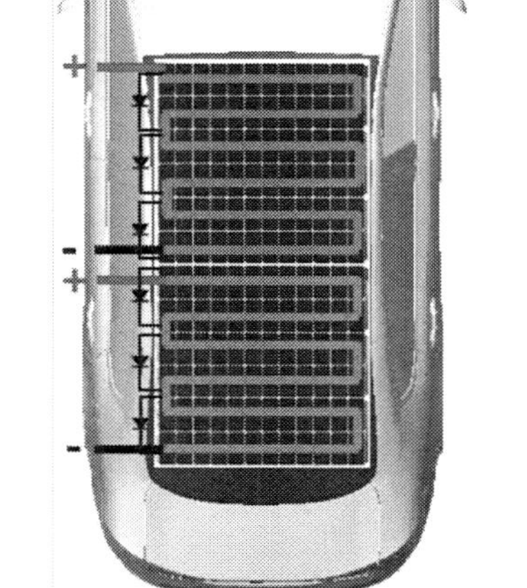

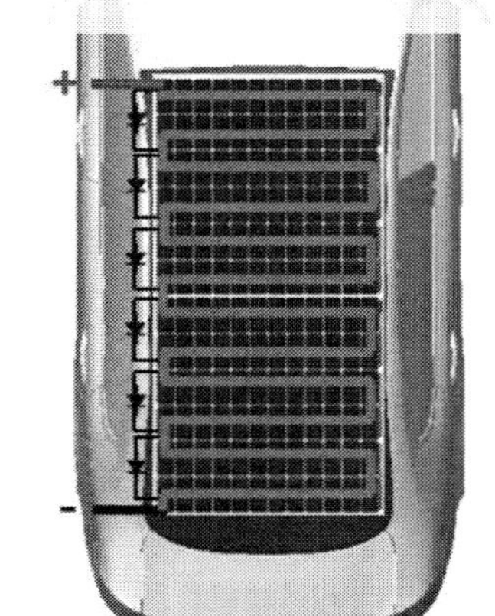

1MPPT - 12x12S – 6 BPD (BV=0.5V)

2MPPT - 6x12S – 6 BPD (BV=0.5V)

3MPPT – 4x12S – 6 BPD (BV=0.5 V)

Results – Tilted Irradiance Optimization

Analysis	Result
Cell orientation	✖
Number of BP diodes	✖
BV of BP diodes	✖
Number of MPPTs	✔

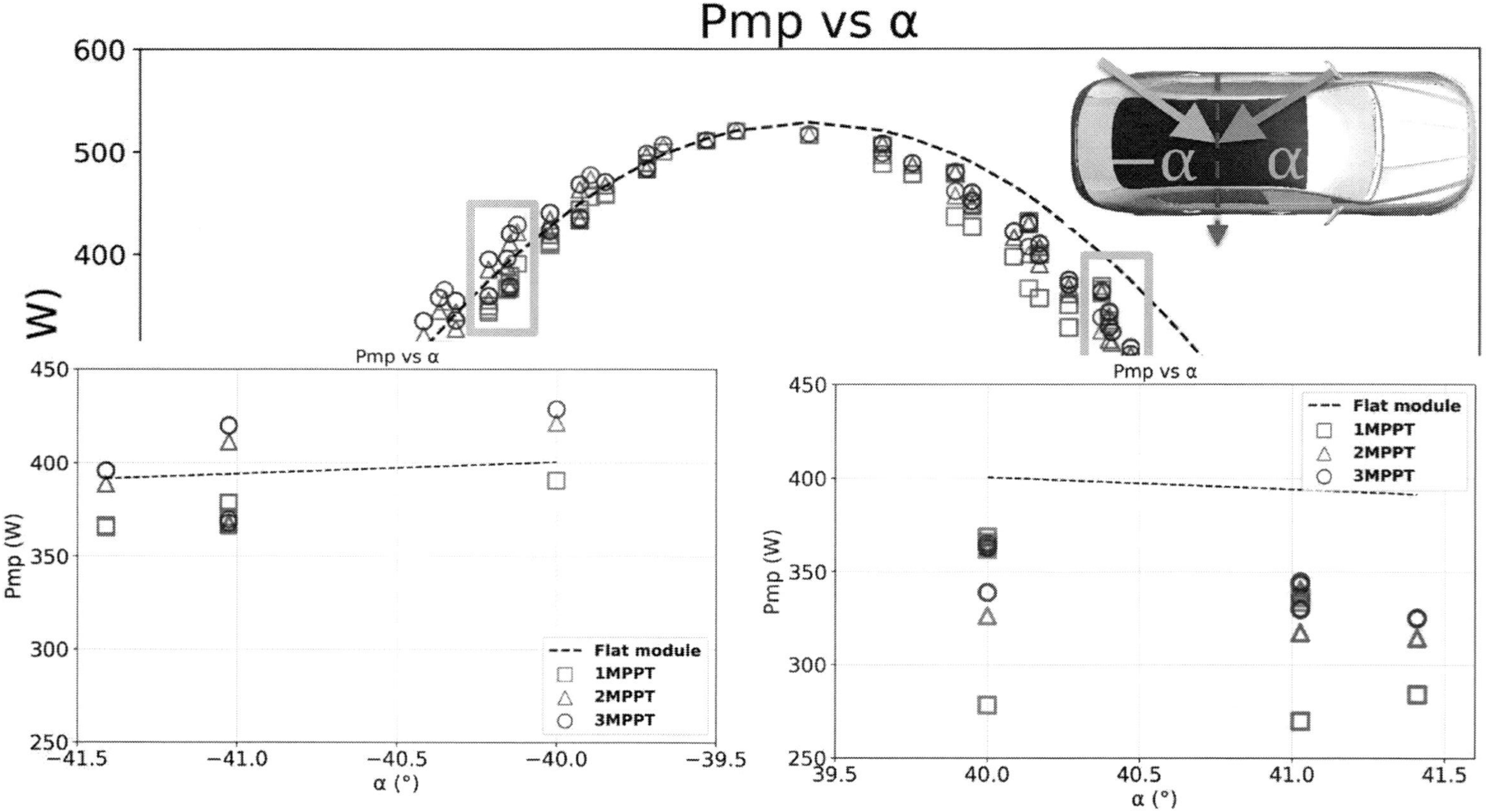

Pmp vs α

POLITÉCNICA

020460-012

12

Results - Annual Energy Generation 

- PV output for one typical meteorological year in Madrid (2005-2023)

- Direct, **diffuse solar radiation** and cells **temperature**

- 15-minute intervals for IV curves

- 8 car positions with azimuth variation of 45 degrees

- **135,596** cases for each electrical configuration

Results - Annual Energy Generation

INSTITUTO DE ENERGÍA SOLAR

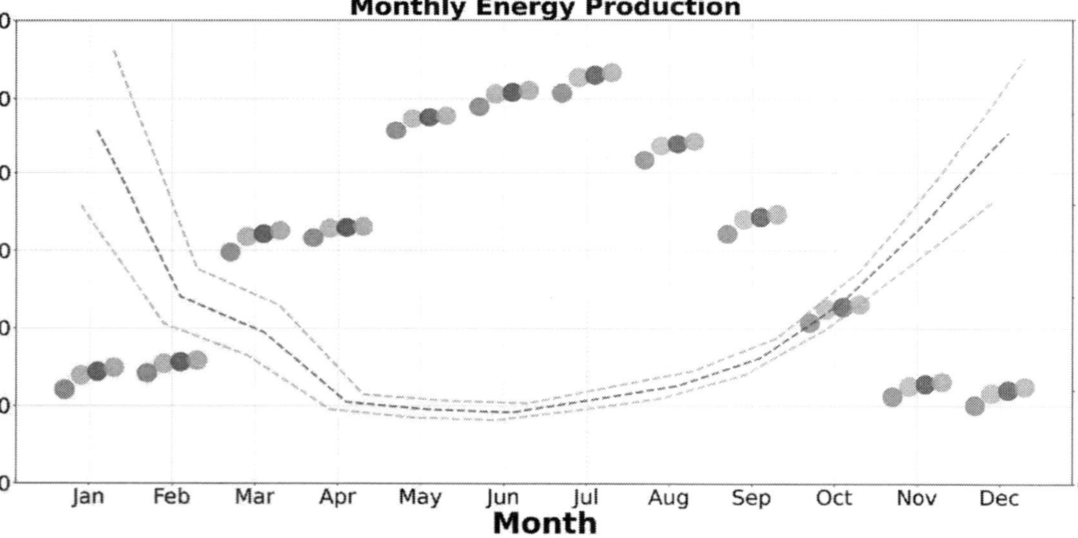

Case	Average Annual production [kWh/year]	Improvement from series [%]
Series	697.9	–
2 MPPTs	737.8	5.7%
3 MPPTs	744.6	6.7%
6 MPPTs	752.1	7.8%

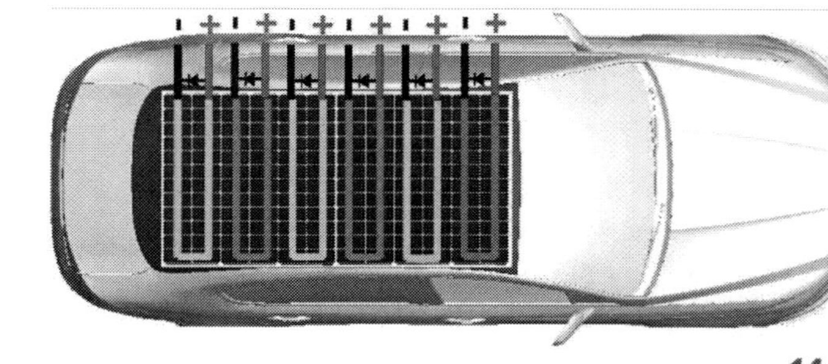

POLITÉCNICA

EU PVSEC 2025, Bilbao, September 22-26

14

Conclusions

- Optimization for angular performance ≠ for partial shading. Do not provide an improvement:

  - Half cell orientation

  - Increasing number of bypass diodes (good for partial shading)

  - Breakdown voltage of bypass diodes (good for partial shading)

- Split module in MPPTs sections

  - 2 MPPTs significantly improves the series connection

  - 3 or 6 MPTTs show similar result, reaching maximum power output

- Energy generation

  - Optimized configuration increases annual yield by ~8% in Madrid climate

020460-015

Thanks for your attention !

Francisco José Martín San Agustín

f.martin.sanagustin@alumnos.upm.es

Happy to take your questions

We gratefully acknowledge the DETEC-PV project, Grant PID2021-128853OB-I00, funded by MCIN/AEI/10.13039/501100011033 and "ERDF A way of making Europe"

The authors express sincere thanks to JEMA and JET program for sponsoring the activities, entrusted by METI (Japan) and carried out under the umbrella of the IEC TC82/PT600 group devoted to Vehicle Integrated Photovoltaic Systems

EU PVSEC 2025, Bilbao, September 22-26

020460-016

INSTITUTO
DE ENERGÍA
SOLAR
Innovation in photovoltaics since 1979

TOWARDS LOW-IMPACT TRIPLE-JUNCTION PEROVSKITE/SILICON TANDEM MODULES

LCA OF PRECURSOR MATERIALS TO DESCRIBE THE INFLUENCE OF BACKGROUND DATA SOURCES

A. Galarza[1] , S. Nold[2] , L. Oberbeck[1,3]

1. Institut Photovoltaïque d'Île-de-France (IPVF)
2. Fraunhofer Institute for Solar Energy Systems ISE
3. TotalEnergies OneTech

EUPVSEC 2025 – 5CO.4 | Bilbao, Spain
September 24, 2025

Outline

1. **Meet IPVF and the TRIUMPH project**
2. Life Cycle Assessment in the PV industry
3. Data availability for perovskite materials
4. Comparison between perovskite compositions
5. Summary

About IPVF

An initiative born from the French State's ambition to drive **scientific excellence** in support of an effective **European photovoltaic industry**, with active partners spanning most of the value chain and collaborating closely with leading academic institutions.

020461-003

About the TRIUMPH project

Triple Junction Solar Module

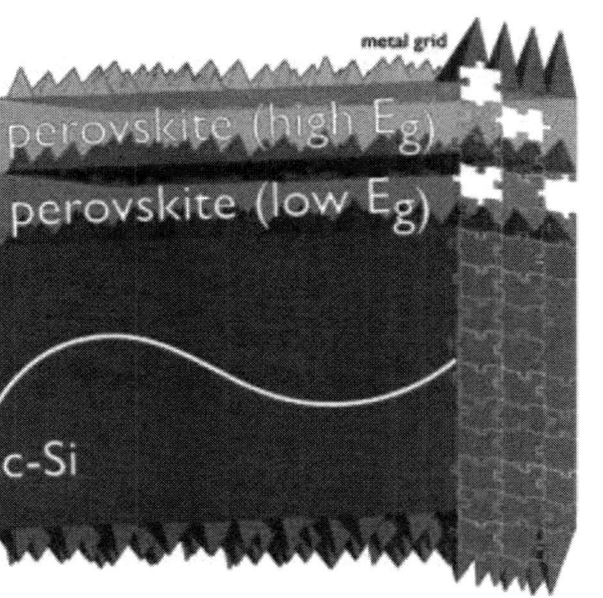

General objectives

1. High efficiencies and stability
   - Target efficiency **>33%** on 1 cm^2
   - Passing accelerated reliability testing.

2. Cost-effective and scalable technology (TRL = 5)
   - Target of **≥100 cm2** using cost-effective and scalable cell processes

3. Design for sustainability
   - Reduction of **critical raw materials** such as Indium and Silver
   - Circular concepts that allow easy recycling

4. Value chain buy-in
   - Establishing the **value chain** within **European Union** for future multi-junction modules.

Find more information →
- *Booth F6*
- *5EO.3: Markets, Costs and Economics (26th Sep – 8h30h-10h)*

020461-004

Outline

1. Meet IPVF and the TRIUMPH project

2. **Life Cycle Assessment in the PV industry**

3. Data availability for perovskite materials

4. Comparison between perovskite compositions

5. Summary

LCA in the PV industry

Life Cycle Assessment (LCA) is the systematic analysis of the potential environmental impacts of products or services during their entire life cycle (manufacturing, distribution, use and end-of-life phases) according to ISO 14040 and 14044

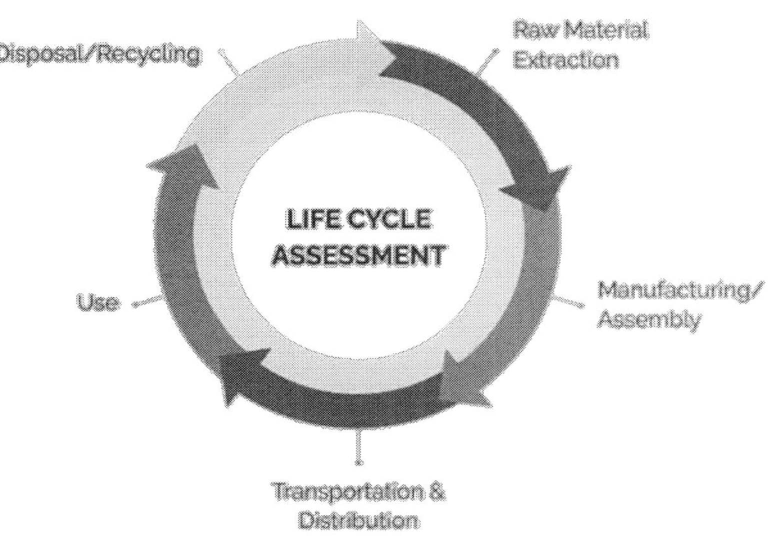

➢ Research and development
➢ Product design or improvement
➢ Process optimization
➢ Legislative compliance
➢ Market positioning

- **Minimization** of the environmental impact of PV technology developed in TRIUMPH
- **Focus** on categories of global warming potential, toxicity, and resource depletion
- **Strategic** material selection & energy use optimization

◻ IPVF

020461-006

Where to find the data for an LCA
Background and Foreground data

Background Data

Energy consumption
Water consumption
Reactants
Source of the reactants
Waste management
(Emissions)

Foreground Data

Process input
- Materials
- Energy

Process output
- PV
- Emissions

SPECIALIZED LCA
DATABASES

+

LITERATURE REVIEW
OR
INDUSTRY INPUT

+

STOICHIOMETRY-BASED
ESTIMATION

Outline

1. Meet IPVF and the TRIUMPH project

2. Life Cycle Assessment in the PV industry

3. **Data availability for perovskite materials**

4. Comparison between perovskite compositions

5. Summary

Availability of background data of precursor materials

Material	Specialized database	Industry (2024)	Alberola-Borras et al. (2018)	Khalifa et al. (2020)	Gong et al. (2015)	Espinosa et al. (2015)	Geisler et al. (2004)
PbBr2			●	●	●		●
PbCl2						●	
PbI2			●	●	●		
FABr		●					
FACl		●					
FAI		●	●	●			●
MABr			●				
MACl		●					
MAI		●	●	●	●	●	
CsBr		●					●
CsI		●	●	●			
DMF	●						
NMP	●						

➢ Most perovskite materials lack standard LCI datasets

➢ Available sources differ on the information provided and represent different production roads

➢ Critical gaps:
  ➢ Organic salts
  ➢ Cesium salts

Does the selection of the sources affect the LCA results?

◻ IPVF

020461-009

Implications of source variation
Environmental assessment for the production of precursors

Scope
- FU: Production 1 kg
- Cradle-to-gate

Methodology
- Simapro 9.5.0.2
- Ecoinvent 3.9.1
- Cut-off allocation
- Environmental Footprint 3.1 method

- Strong variations within materials
- No trends for global high/low impact sources
- Selection of source could be bias

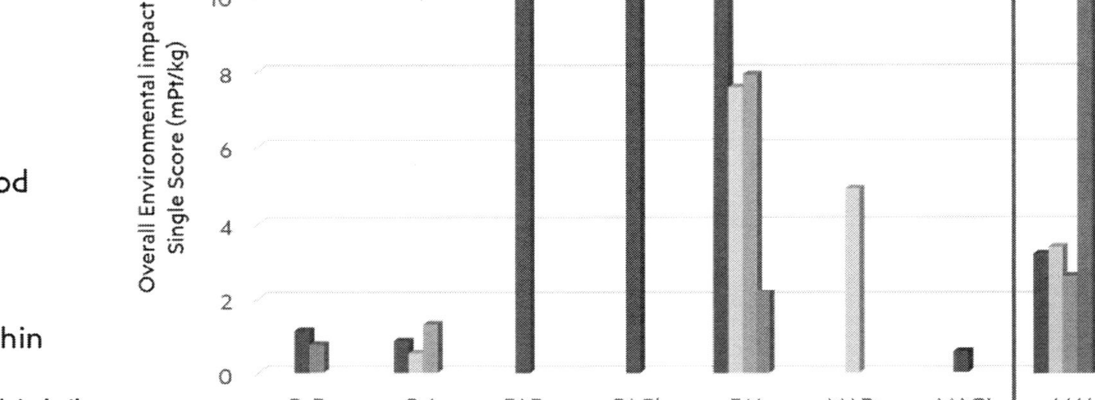

IPVF

020461-010

Case Methylammonium Iodide (MAI)
Distribution per category

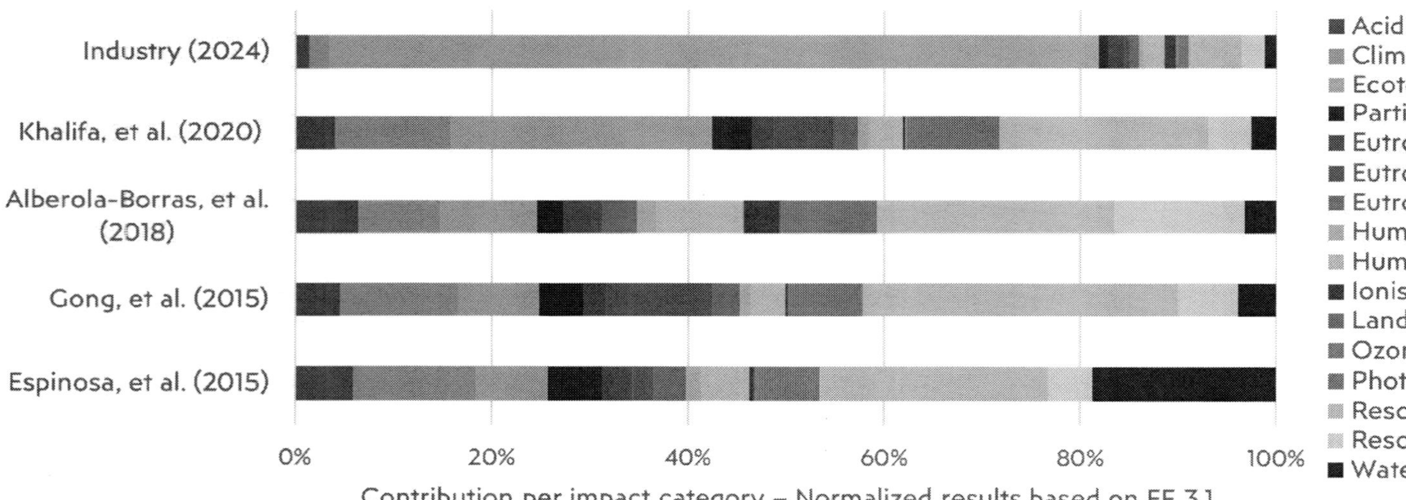

➢ Similar overall impacts could present different impact distribution

➢ Similar impact distribution could present different overall impact

- Variations in industrial processes influence the impact distribution
- High complexity for comparison and reliability determination
- Prioritization of data source selection remains challenging

IPVF

020461-011

Outline

1. Meet IPVF and the TRIUMPH project
2. Life Cycle Assessment in the PV industry
3. Data availability for perovskite materials
4. **Comparison between perovskite compositions**
5. Summary

Effects of source selection in perovskite layers

Process description
- 450 nm layer thickness
- Thermal evaporation
- M10 wafer size

Scope
- FU: Deposition 1 m^2
- Cradle-to-gate

Material	Alberola-Borras et al. (2018)	Khalifa et al. (2020)	Gong et al. (2015)
PbBr2			
PbI2	●	●	●
FAI			
MAI	●	●	●
CsI			

Selected Perovskites
- MAPbI$_3$ (3 sources)
- FAPbI$_3$ (2 sources)
- MAPb(I$_{0.8}$Br$_{0.2}$)$_3$ (2 sources)
- Cs$_{0.15}$FA$_{0.85}$PbI$_3$ (2 sources)

Allow comparison of the effects of source variation for a perovskite layer

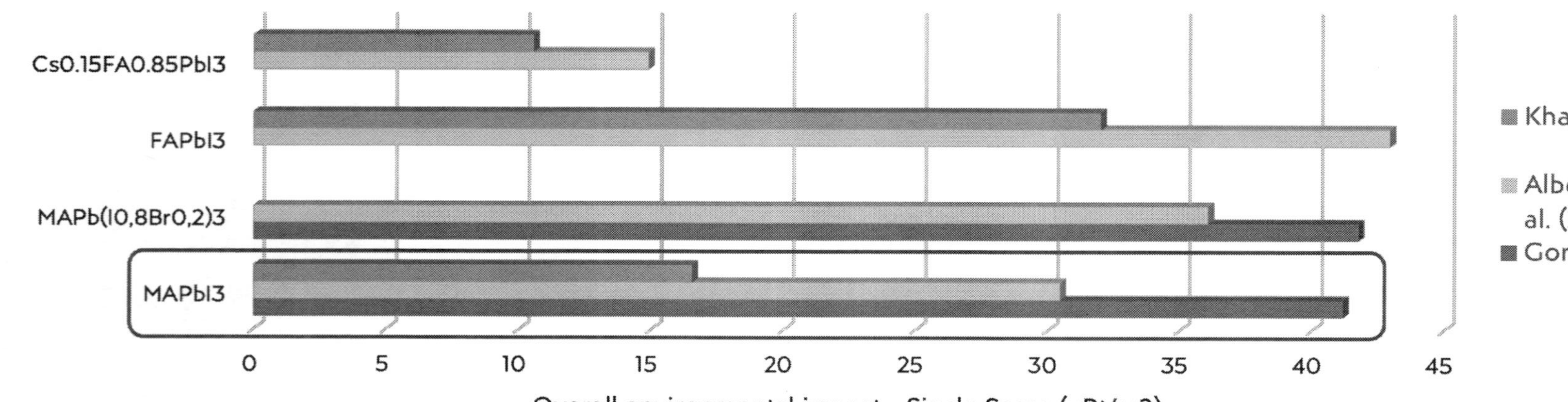

IPVF

020461-013

Case MAPbI3 – Comparison per category

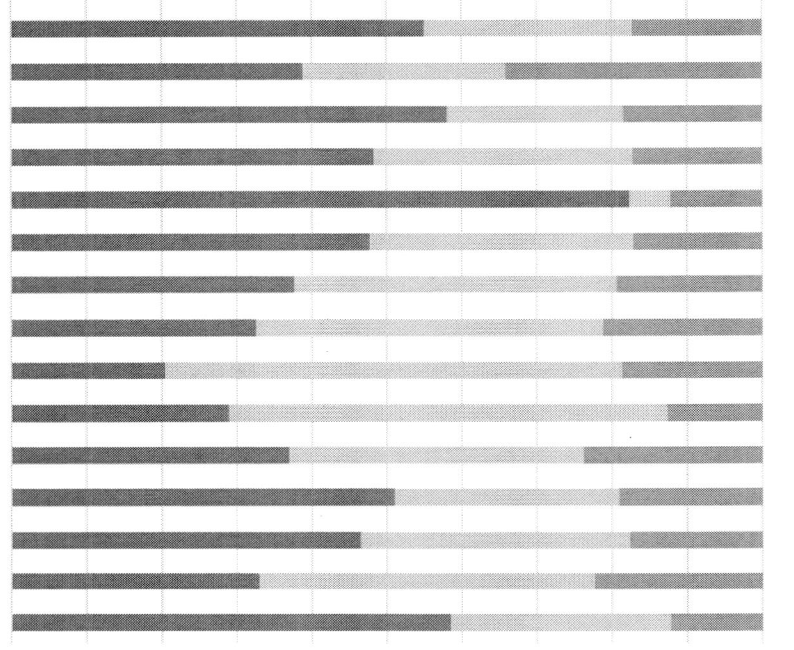

Gong et al. (2015):
406 g CO_2-eq/m^2

Alberola-Borras et al. (2018):
204 g CO_2-eq/m^2

Khalifa, et al. (2020):
127 g CO_2-eq/m^2

- Variations on the characterized result are significant
- Source selection could determine the hotspot categories and LCA conclusions

IPVF

Variation assessment

ACTIONS DONE FOR EACH PEROVSKITE

- Determine potential mix cases
- Characterization results under every case
- Calculation of mean and standard deviation per impact category
- Calculation of coefficient of variation (CV%)

$$CV\% = {SD}/{Mean} * 100$$

- Average of CV%

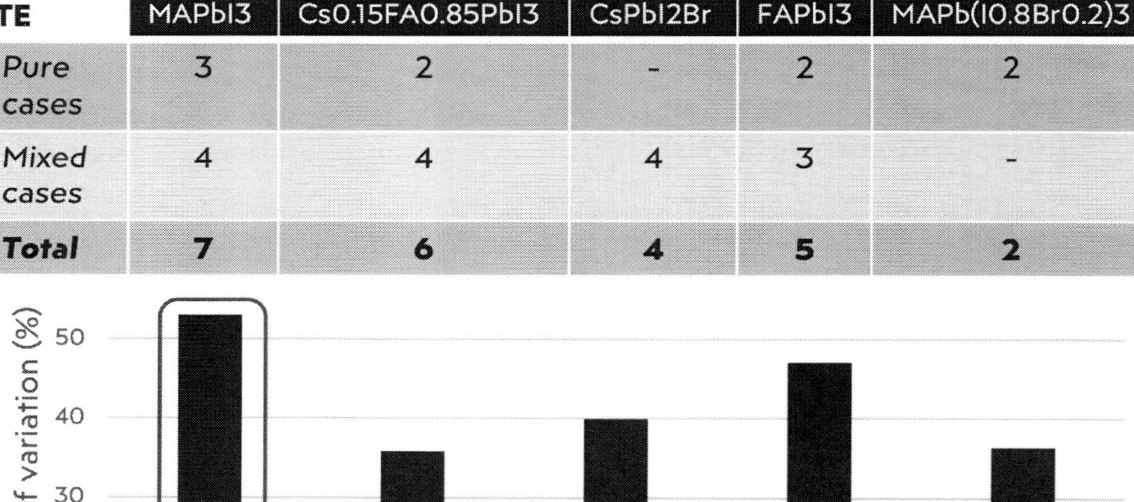

	MAPbI3	Cs0.15FA0.85PbI3	CsPbI2Br	FAPbI3	MAPb(I0.8Br0.2)3
Pure cases	3	2	-	2	2
Mixed cases	4	4	4	3	-
Total	**7**	**6**	**4**	**5**	**2**

IPVF

020461-015

Case MAPbI$_3$ – Coefficient of variation per category

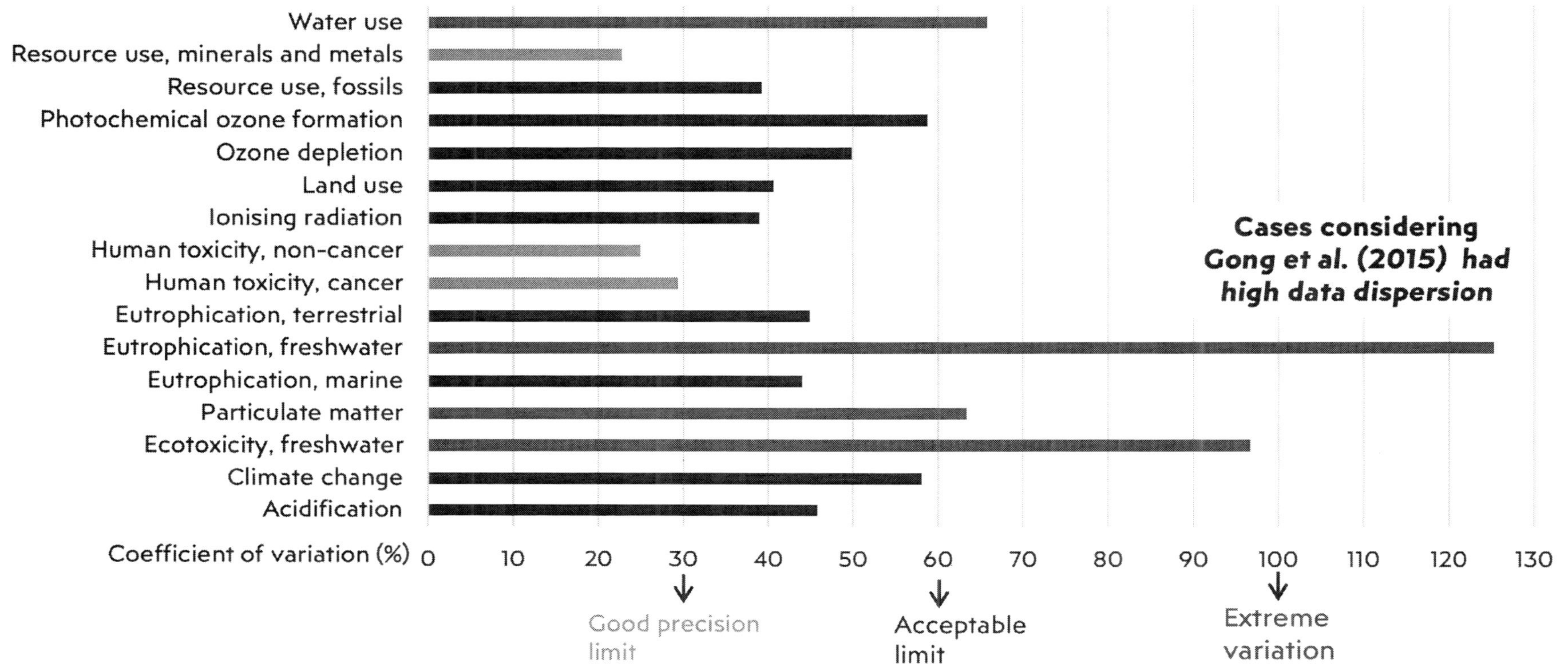

IPVF

020461-016

Outline

1. Meet IPVF and the TRIUMPH project
2. Life Cycle Assessment in the PV industry
3. Data availability for perovskite materials
4. Comparison between perovskite compositions
5. **Summary**

Conclusions

- **High variability in background data and no selection criteria:** Novel PV technologies (e.g., perovskites) show strong variation in material datasets due to lack of maturity and limited reporting.

- **Critical role of source selection:** Dataset selection influences the LCA outcomes. High coefficient of variation represent high LCA uncertainty and challenging comparisons. LCAs should incorporate a range of impact values from multiple sources to facilitate comparability

- **Research need:** Development of harmonized, high-quality LCI datasets for perovskite precursors is essential to improve reliability and comparability of LCAs.

- **Industry–science collaboration:** Closer collaboration is needed to generate trustworthy data and support robust environmental assessments of next-generation PV technologies.

IPVF

020461-018

Thank you for your attention

Further questions?
alejandra.galarza@ipvf.fr

This project is supported at IPVF by the French Government in the frame of the program of investment for the future (Programme d'Investissement d'Avenir – ANR-IEED-002-01)

This work has been co-funded by the European Union under the project TRIUMPH from the European Union's Horizon research and innovation program

020461-019

TRIUMPH

Literature

❑Alberola-Borras, J. A., Vidal, R., & Mora-Sero, I. (2018).
Evaluation of multiple cation/anion perovskite solar cells through life cycle assessment.
❑Khalifa, S. A., Spatari, S., Fafarman, A. T., & Baxter, J. B. (2020).
Environmental sustainability of mixed cation perovskite materials in photovoltaics manufacturing.
❑Gong, J., Darling, S. B., & You, F. (2015).
Perovskite photovoltaics: life-cycle assessment of energy and environmental impacts.
❑Espinosa, N., Serrano-Luján, L., Urbina, A., & Krebs, F. C. (2015).
Solution and vapour deposited lead perovskite solar cells: Ecotoxicity from a life cycle assessment perspective.
❑Geisler, G., Hofstetter, T. B., & Hungerbühler, K. (2004).
Production of fine and speciality chemicals: procedure for the estimation of LCIs

Sustainability Assessment of Perovskite/Silicon Tandem Solar Modules: From Laboratory scale to Industrial implementation

Elisabetta Brivio, Andrea Danelli, Sofia Spagnolo, Pierpaolo Girardi

24/09/2025

020462-001

Index

(1) **Introduction**

(2) **What is an LCA**

(3) LCA of a lab-scale PVSK/Si tandem module

(4) LCA of industrial-scale PVSK/Si tandem module

(5) Potential application in a hypothetical PV plant

Introduction

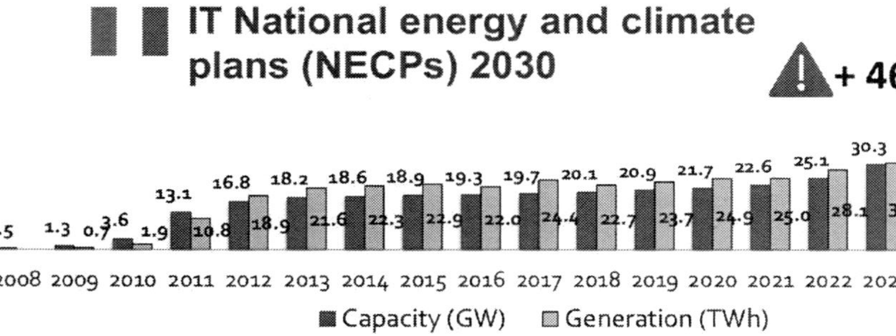

EU solar energy strategy

aims to bring online over **700 GW by 2030.**

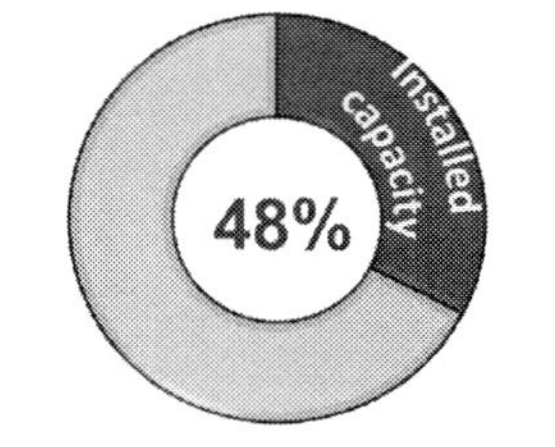

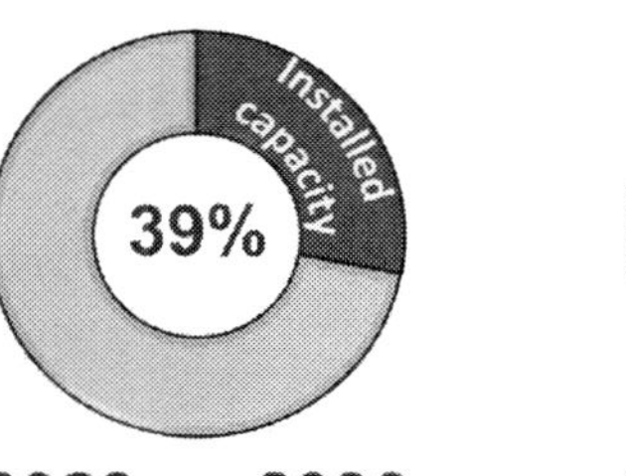

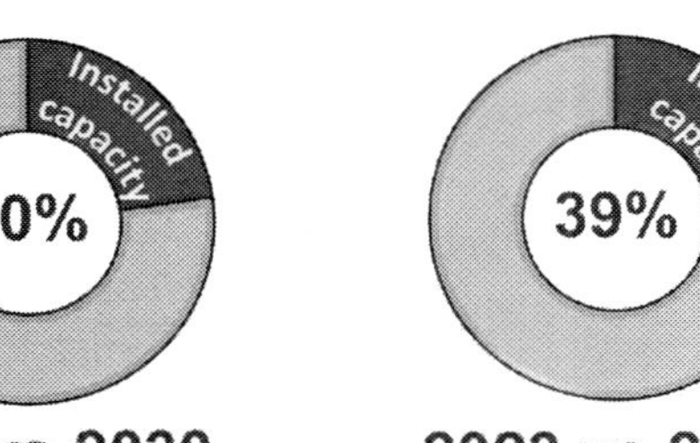

Increase of the PV installed capacity

Improving the efficiency of photovoltaic systems

Mitigating CO_2-equivalent emissions related to the electricity system

Promote environmentally sustainable development of high-efficiency photovoltaic generation systems!

020462-003

Life Cycle Assessment

Methodology description

- LCA is defined by the ISO 14040 as the compilation and evaluation of the inputs, outputs and the potential environmental impacts of a product or system throughout its life cycle.

- It consists in quantifying the **use of resources** ("inputs" such as energy, raw materials, water) and **emissions into the environment** ("outputs" in the air, water and soil) associated with a product, a process or an activity throughout its **life cycle** in order to evaluate the potential environmental impact.

ISO 14040

ISO 14044

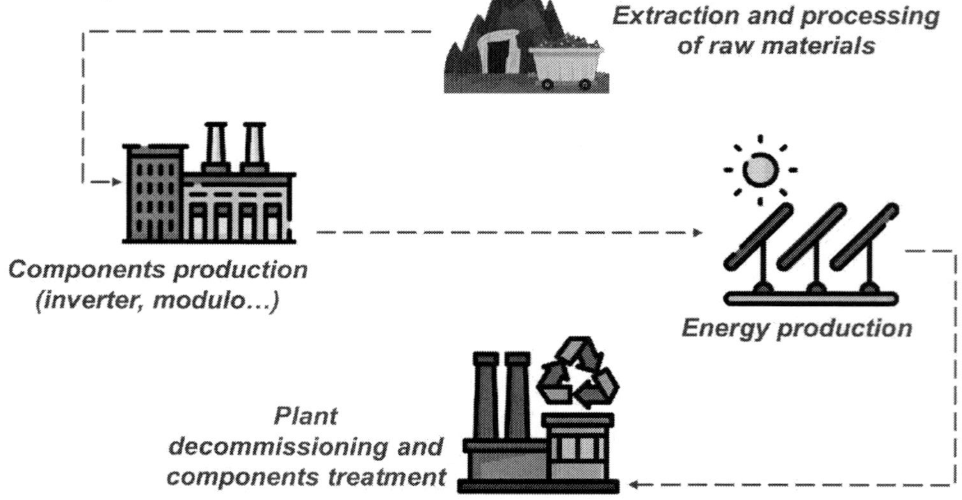

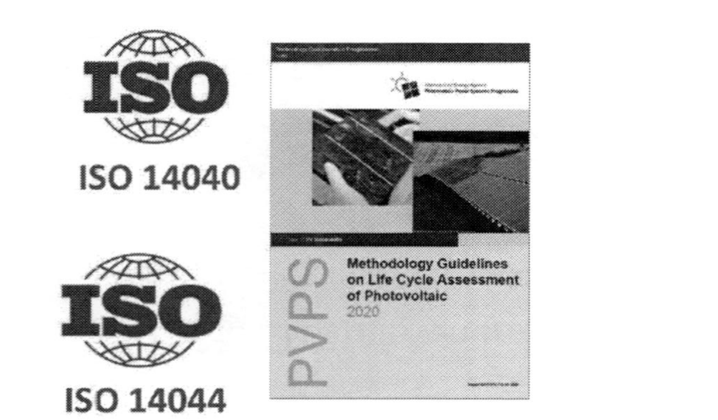

Life Cycle Assessment

Case study description

- The analysis aims to understand the **potential environmental benefit** generated by PVSK/Si tandem technology.
- The study focuses on its **future application**, assuming a system comparable to current silicon-based technologies

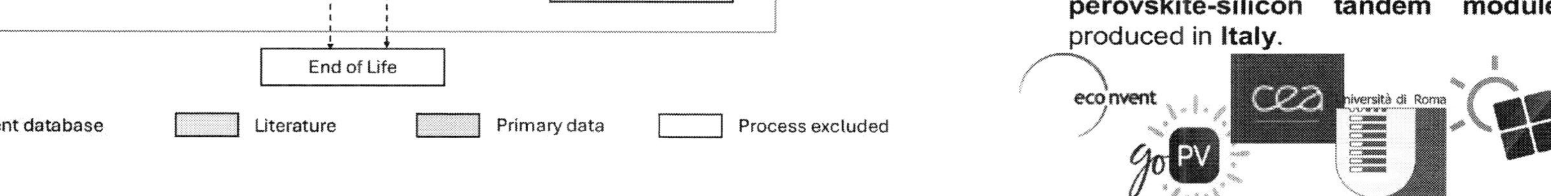

- The background processes are modelled by using the **Ecoinvent database.**
- Silicon cell and perovskite/silicon tandem cell and module production are based on **primary data.**
- Silicon solar grade and wafer are modelled according with **IEA PVPS Task 12 LCI**
- The analysis **considers all the life cycle phases,** from raw material extraction to energy production.
- The **wafer** and **silicon cell** are manufactured in **China**, whereas the **perovskite-silicon tandem module** is produced in **Italy.**

020462-005

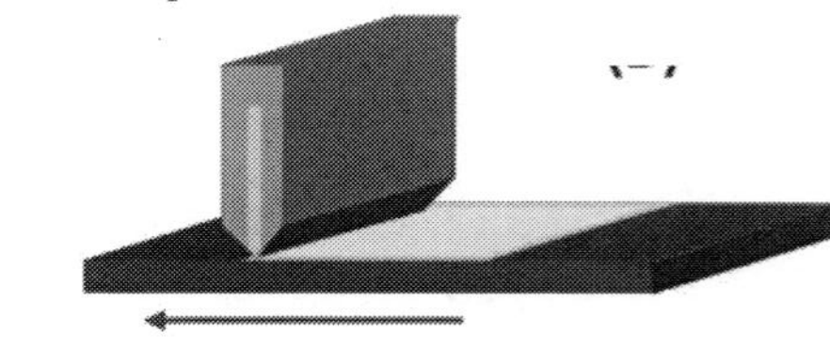

Life Cycle Assessment

PVSK cell production at laboratory scale

The production process includes **11 steps**:

- The perovskite cell is modeled using primary laboratory-scale data

- The **muffle furnace** is used for tin oxide firing and perovskite (PVSK) deposition

- **Layer deposition** is carried out using the **slot-die coating technique**.

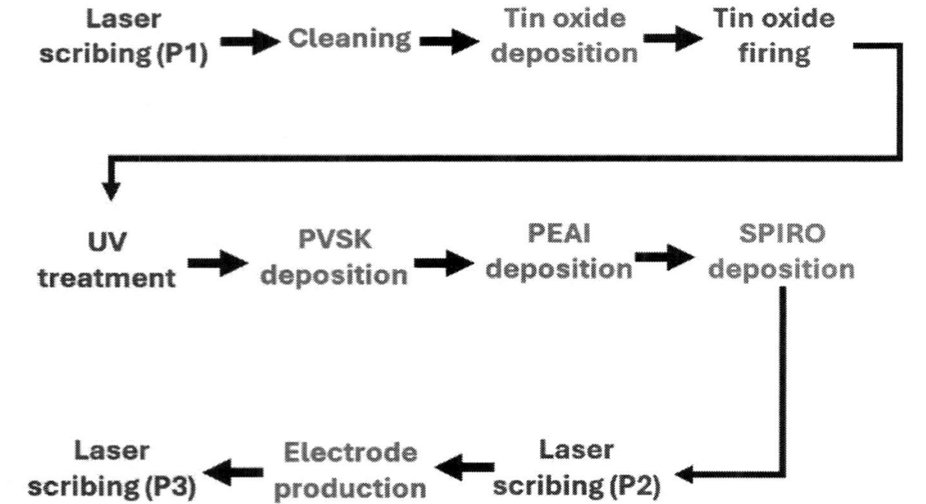

- The study considers **gold electrode**.

RED: this phase includes only energy consumption
BLUE: this phase includes the consumption of both energy and materials/chemicals

Life Cycle Assessment

PVSK cell production at industrial scale

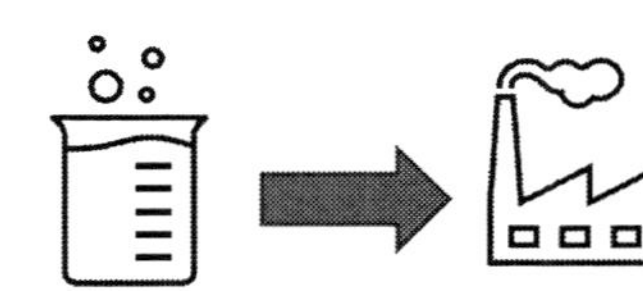

The laboratory-scale data have been adjusted to reflect a potential industrial-scale production scenario.

The **muffle furnace,** used for tin oxide firing and perovskite (PVSK) deposition, has been replaced with a **conveyor furnace.**

The study considers two possible electrode:
1. **SCENARIO A:** Gold/ITO electrode
2. **SCENARIO B:** MoOX/ITO electrode

The use of ITO implies the introduction of a sputtering process.

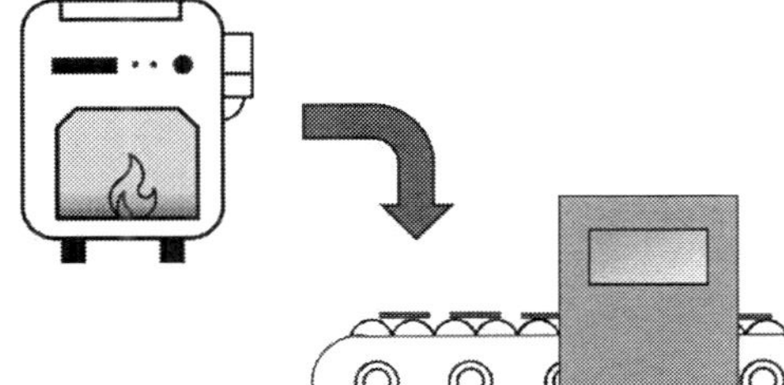

7

Life Cycle Assessment

PVSK/Si tandem module production

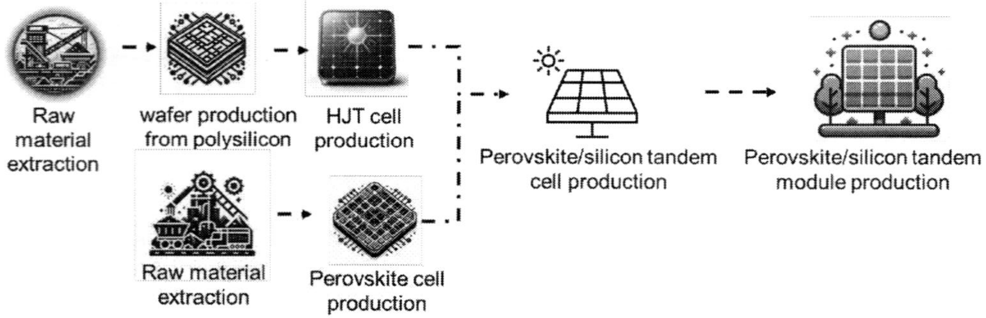

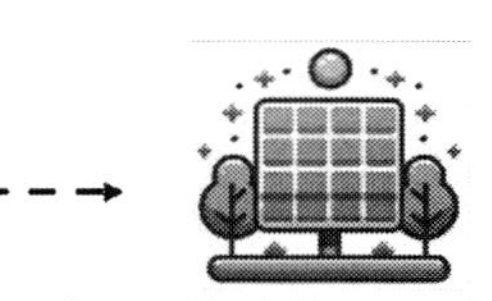

Silicon cell technical information

	HJT
Type	HJT n-Type
Dimension	156 mm x 156 mm
Thickness	185 µm
Efficiency	21.6 %
Power	5.3 W
Production site	China

Module technical information

Type of module	Mechanically stacked Perovskite/Silicon cell
Module efficiency	28.5%
Module power	563 W
Area	1.98 m^2
Type of Si-cell	N-type HJT cell

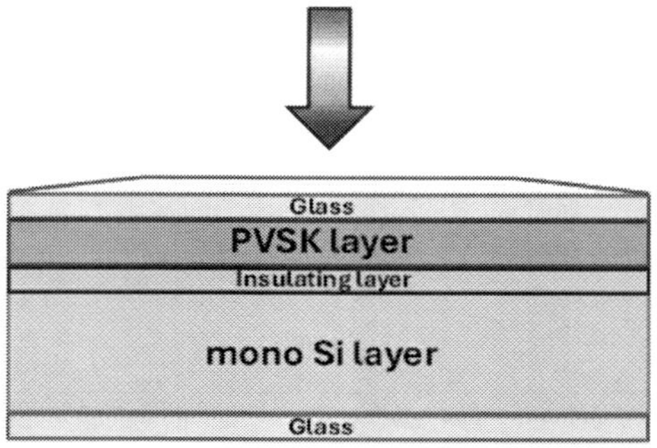

Perovskite/Silicon Tandem module structure

The study assumes a hypothetical **PVSK/Si tandem module comparable** to current **silicon modules** in terms of lifespan and degradation rate, in order to evaluate the technology at an industrial scale.

Life Cycle Assessment

Environmental impact of a tandem module at lab-scale

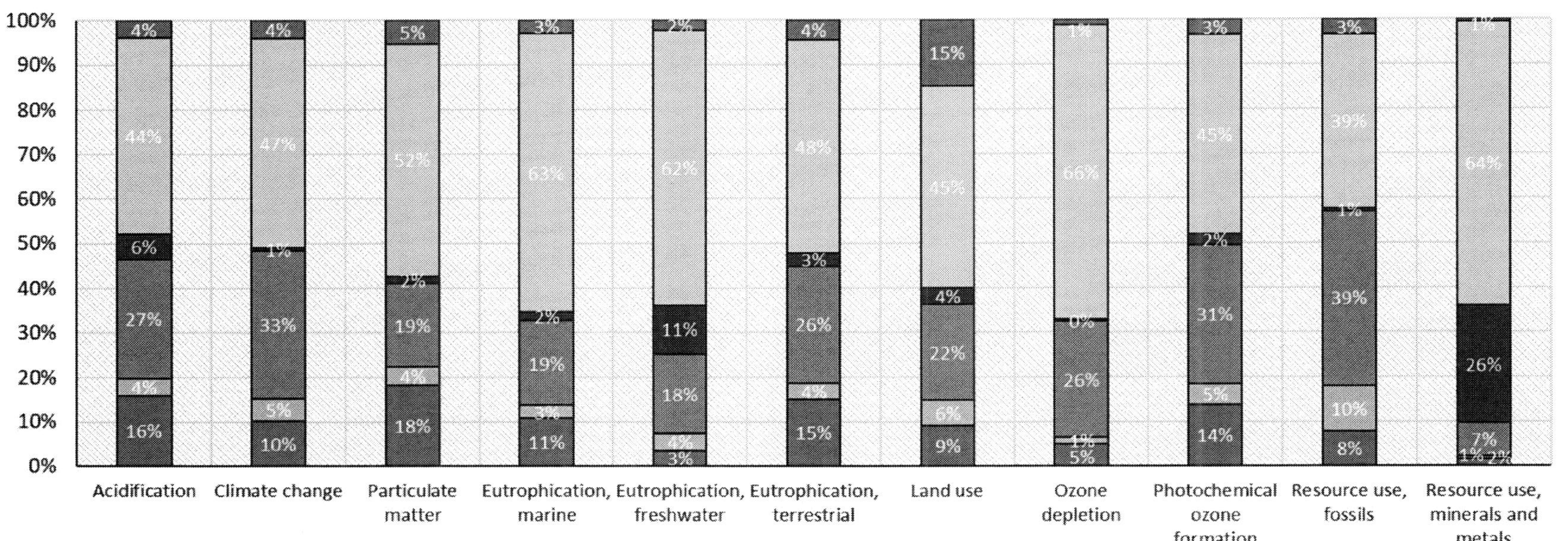

The results are referred to 1 W of module (A: 1.9 8m² and P: 563 W)

EF METHOD SimaPro

Life Cycle Assessment

Environmental impact of a PVSK cell at lab-scale

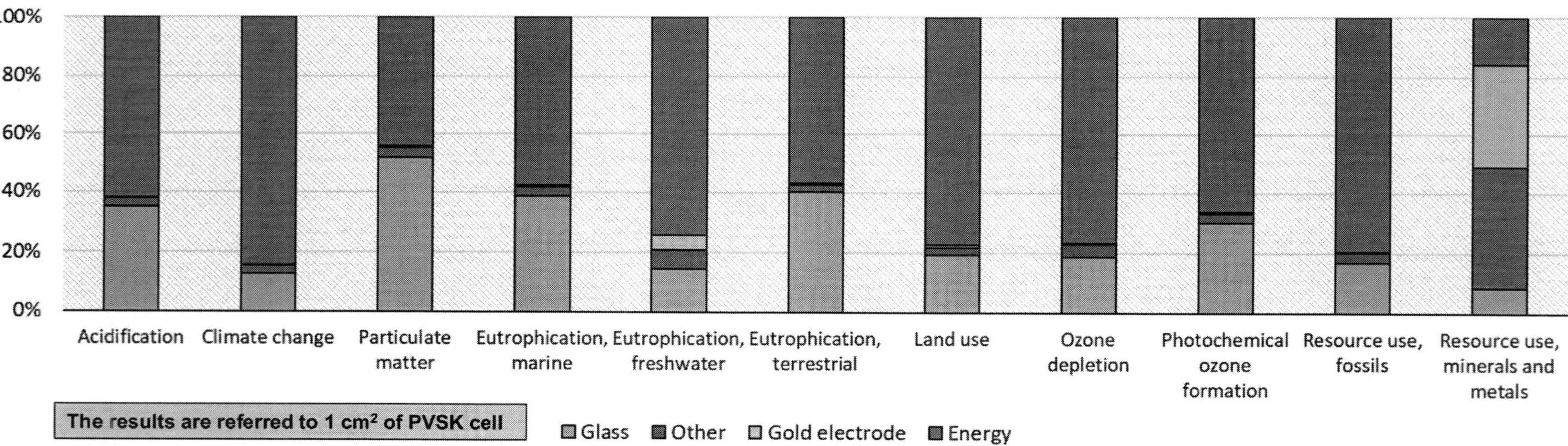

The impact associated with **energy consumption** is mainly due to the energy required for **the electrode deposition process**.
In the Resource use, mineral and metals category, the **electrode material** accounts for **40%** of the impacts.

 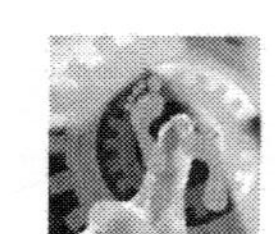

EF METHOD   SimaPro

10

Life Cycle Assessment

Comparison among different electrode scenarios

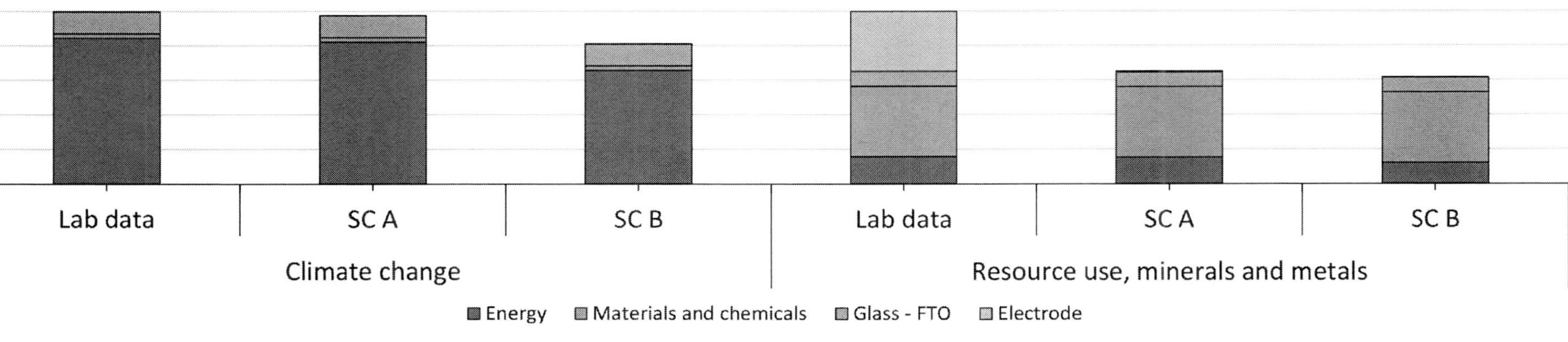

Electrode production accounts for **over 85%** of the total energy consumption

Scenarios A and B involve a **reduced material usage,** resulting in **lower environmental impacts** and a decreased contribution from the electrode

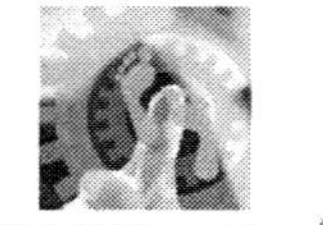

EF METHOD   SimaPro

The results are referred to 1 cm² of perovskite cell. Lab data: PVSK cell modelled by using laboratory data; SC A: scale-up scenario with AU/ITO electrode; SC B: scale-up scenario with MoOx/ITO electrode.

11

Life Cycle Assessment

Comparison among different PVSK/Si module scenarios

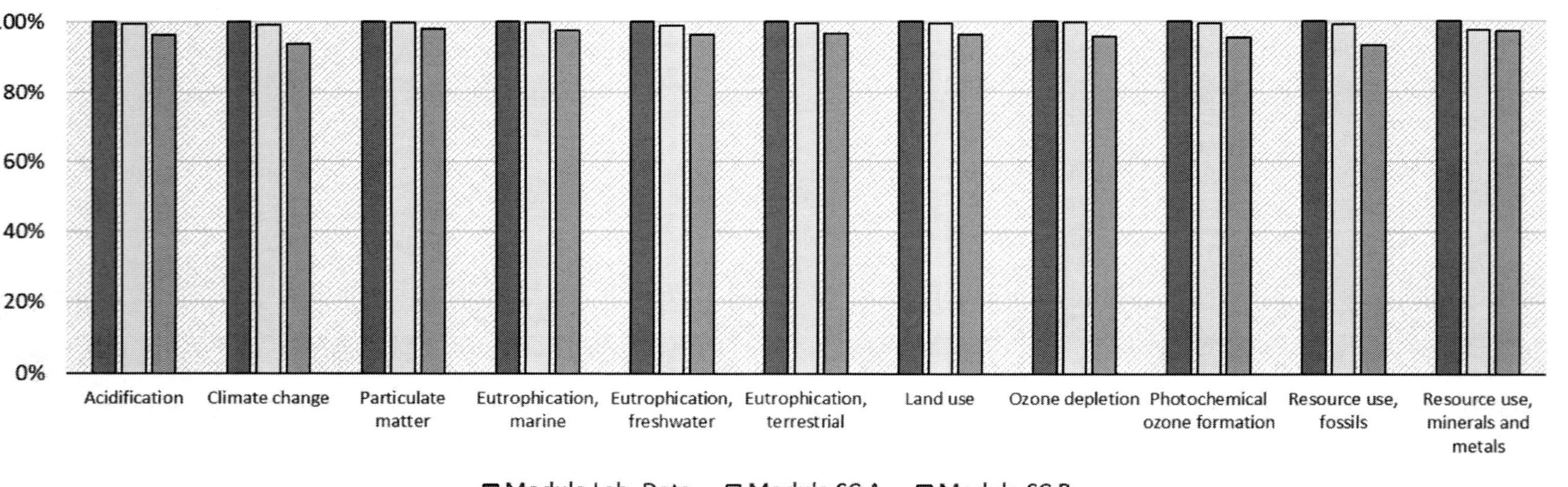

The use of fewer and **alternative materials**, combined with **lower energy consumption**, leads to a slight **reduction in environmental impact**.

EF METHOD SimaPro

The results are referred to 1 W of perovskite/Si module. Lab data: PVSK cell modelled by using laboratory data; SCA: scale-up scenario with AU/ITO electrode; SCB: scale-up scenario with MoOx/ITO electrode.

Life Cycle Assessment

PVSK/Si tandem application in a utility scale plant (Power 84.73 MW $_{DC}$)

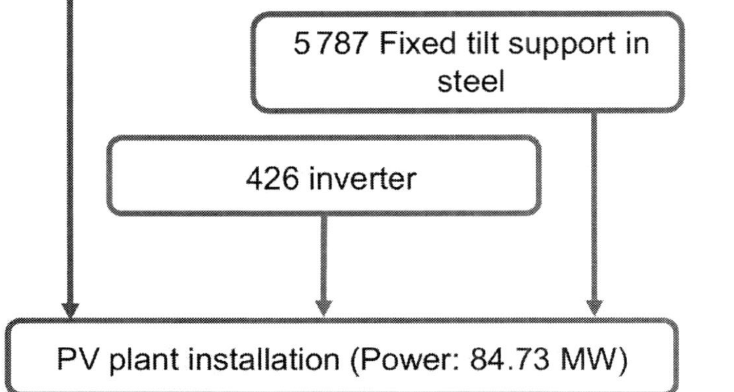

- The analysis considers the **Scenario B (MoOX/ITO electrode)** which is characterised by the lowest impact.

- The **module, module support and inverter** were modelled by using **primary data**.

- The analysis includes the **entire life cycle of the PV plant**, with the **exception** of the **end-of-life** (EOL) phase.

- **Electricity production** was assessed using the average equivalent hours in Italy, recorded as **1101 hours** according to the GSE reports.

- The plant has a **lifetime** of **25 years.**

- The **energy** produced over the lifetime is **2331 GWh**

Type of module	Mechanically stacked Perovskite/Silicon cell
Module efficiency	28.5%
Module power	563 W
Area	1.98 m^2

EF METHOD  SimaPro

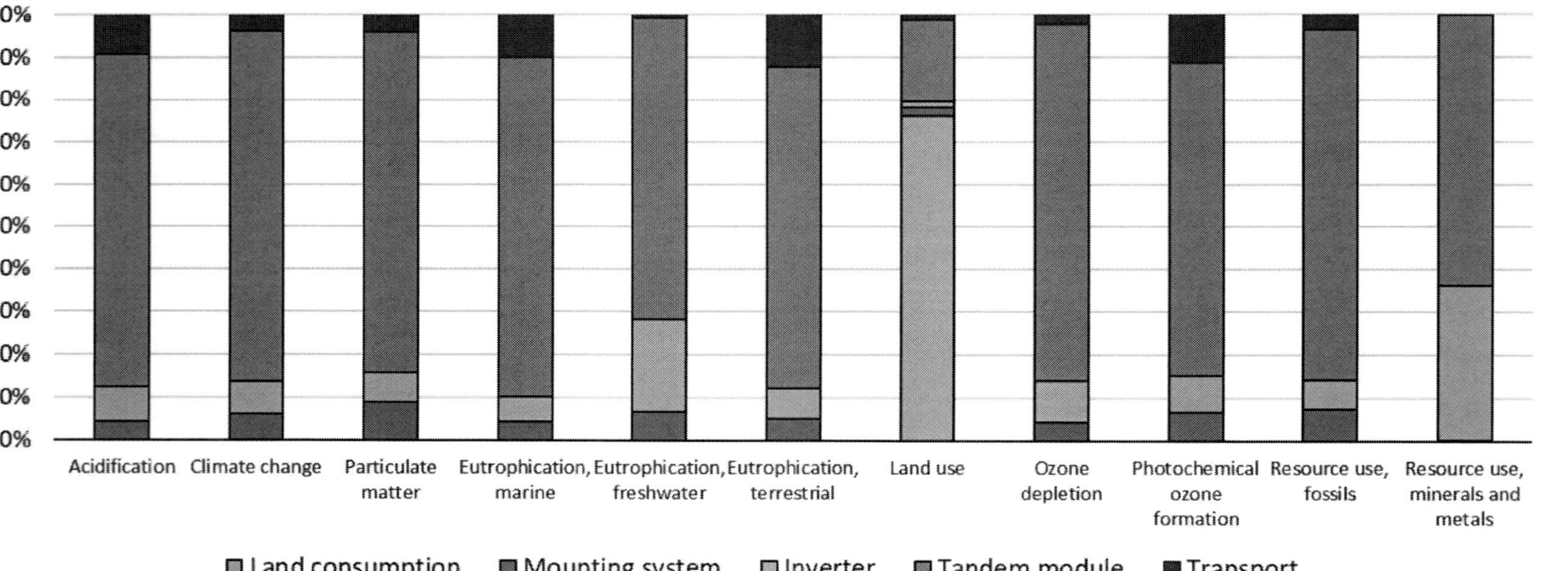

The **higher contribution** is associated to the production **of tandem module**, the only exception is **land use** categories in which the impact are generated to the **land consumption**.

The results are referred to 1 kWh produced – SC B: MoOX/ITO electrode is showed. Energy production over the lifetime: 2331 GWh

EF METHOD   SimaPro

Life Cycle Assessment

PVSK/Si tandem application in a utility scale plant: a comparison with HJT technology

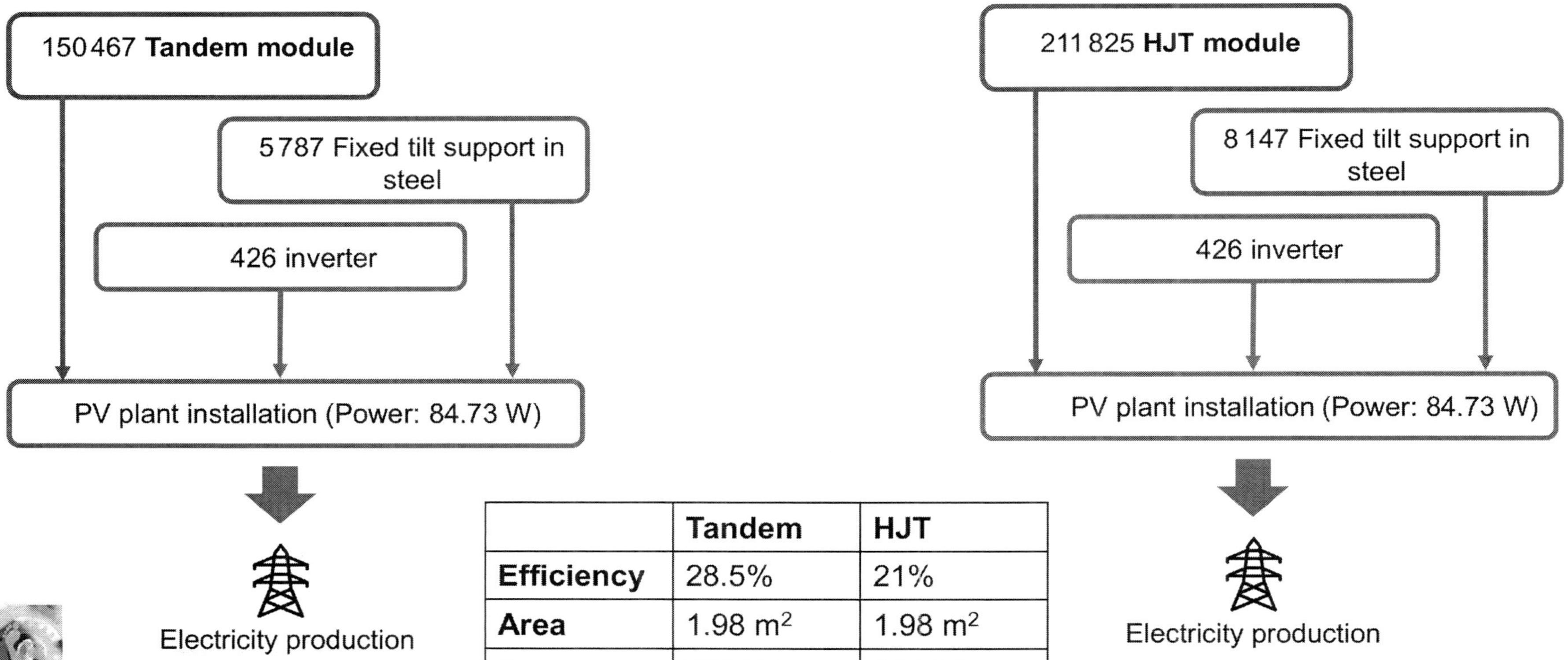

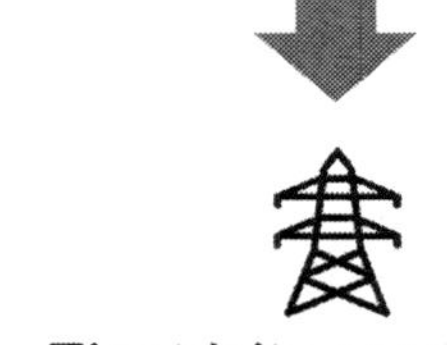

	Tandem	HJT
Efficiency	28.5%	21%
Area	1.98 m^2	1.98 m^2
Power	563 W	400 W

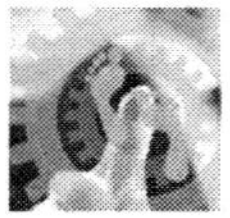

EF METHOD   SimaPro

Life Cycle Assessment

PVSK/Si tandem utility scale plant VS HJT Plant

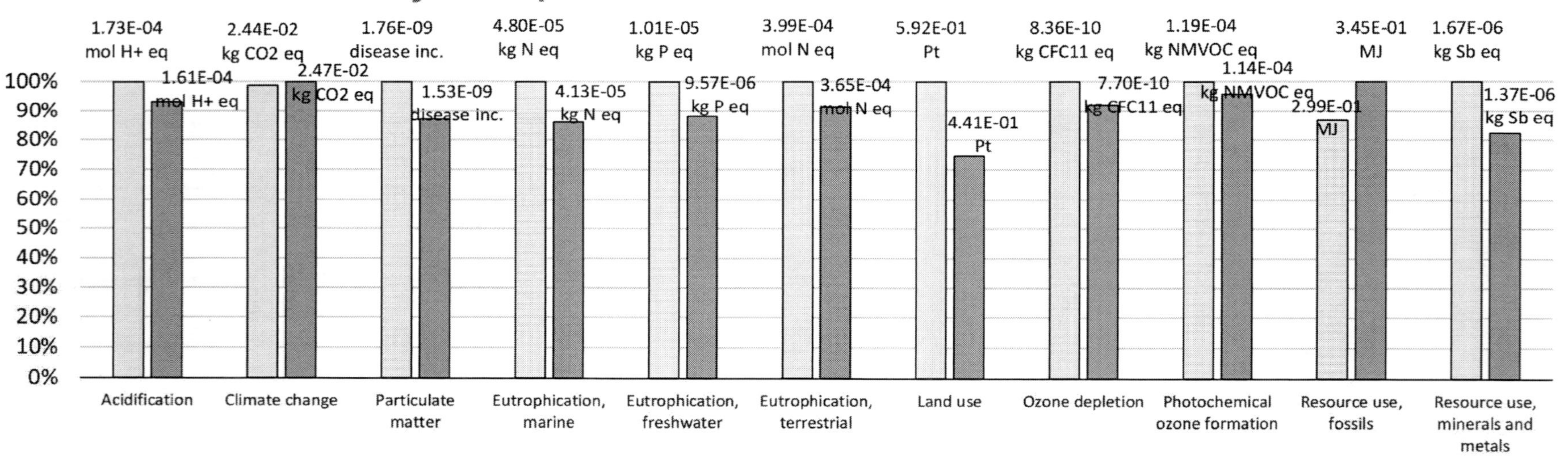

PVSK/Si tandem plant is characterised by **lower impacts** in **9 out of 11 categories**.

In the **Land use category**, the higher efficiency of the tandem module allows **for lower land consumption.**

In the resource use, fossil category, the impact of the tandem system is influenced by the **energy consumption** associated with the production of the **electrode.**

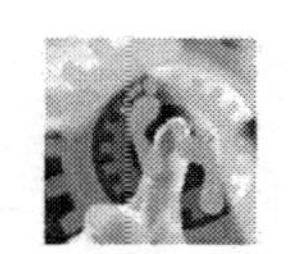

EF METHOD SimaPro

The results are referred to 1 kWh produced – SC B: MoOX/ITO electrode is showed. Energy production over the life: 2331 GWh

Conclusion

- Focusing on the perovskite cell, the analysis highlights a **significant contribution** generated by the **energy consumed** during the **electrode production** phase in the climate change category.

- In the resource use, minerals and metals category, **Scenarios A and B** perform better than the Lab Scenario due to the **reduced quantity of electrode materials** required in the process. The result obtained emphasized the importance of proper material selection.

- The comparative analysis of the two PV plants (tandem and HJT) point out that the **higher efficiency** of the **PVSK/Si tandem** module compared to the HJT module enables the use of fewer modules, resulting in **reduced of land consumption**.

- In general, the photovoltaic is a promising technology that plays a key role in the energy transition process. For this reason, it is important to promote the development of high-efficiency photovoltaic characterized by lower environmental impact, like perovskite/silicon tandem module.

RSE — we move research

Contact

Stay tuned…

#wemoversearch

Elisabetta Brivio

 *Elisabetta.brivio@rse-web.it*

 **www.rse-web.it**

 **@Ricerca sul Sistema Energetico - RSE SpA**

 **@RSEnergetico**

 **RSE SpA - Ricerca sul Sistema Energetico**

This work has been financed by the Research Fund for the Italian Electrical System under the Three-Year Research Plan 2025-2027 (MASE, Decree n.388 of November 6th, 2024), in compliance with the Decree of April 12th, 2024

RCT
solutions
Photovoltaic
Services & Technology
Solutions Partner
LCA Learning Curve for Crystalline Silicon Solar Technologies based on Technology Improvements
Group of companies
RCT solutions
RCT power
RCT hydrogen
Julian Reichle*, Moritz Fath, Sraisth, Amish Kumar Sinha, Mehul Raval, Wolfgang Jooss and Peter Fath
RCT Solutions GmbH, Line - Erd - Str. 1, 78467 Konstanz, Germany
With support of Wolfgang Herbst from ViridisIQ GmbH, Germany
*E-mail: julian.reichle@rct-solutions.com

Motivation
Learning Rate of GWP for Crystalline Silicon Modules was at 10%

RCT
solutions

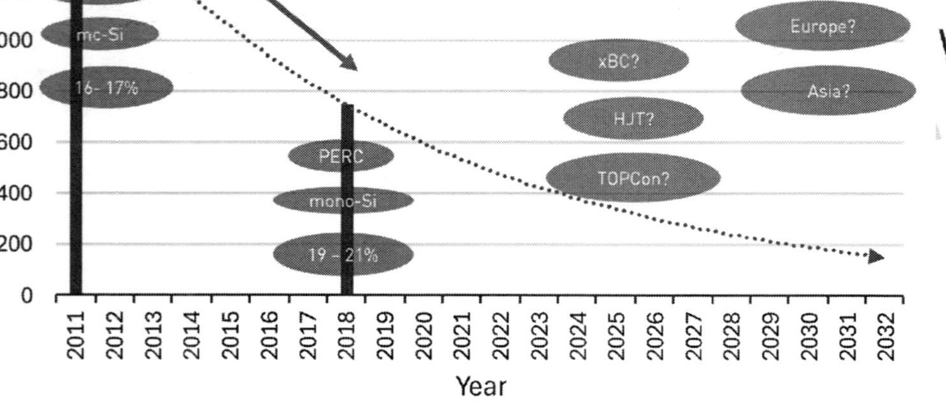

- Reduction from **1660 to 750 kgCO₂-eq/kWp** between 2011 and 2018 [1].

- Technological improvements and deployment of renewables

What does the future hold?

- What **technological advancements** are expected?

- **Global Warming Potential (GWP)** of PV in the next years?

- Maintaining the recent **10% YoY reduction realistic?**

- How LCA guides us trough the engineering process?

[1] L. Wang, T. Qiu, M. Zhang, Q. Cao, W. Qin and S. Wang, "Carbon emissions and reduction performance of photovoltaic systems," Renewable and Sustainable Energy Reviews, 2024.

020463-002

Agenda for this LCA Study
KPIs for Learning Rate combined with LCA

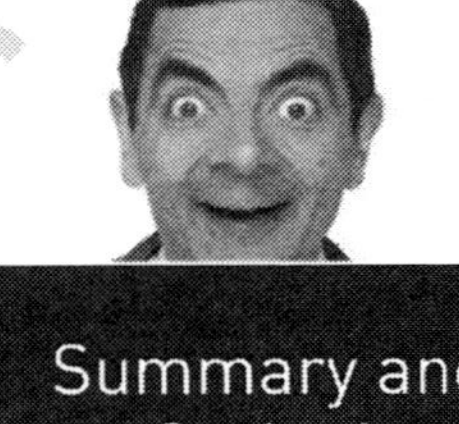

Study Introduction

- Goal & Scope
- Functional Unit
- Boundary Conditions

KPIs for Modelling of Technological Improvements

- mgSi + PolySi
- Ingot & Wafer
- Cell
- Module

Life Cycle Impact Assessment - GWP

- Technology Improvements
- Technology Comparison
- Country Comparison

Summary and Outlook

The RCT Group at a Glance

Conceptual & Detailed Engineering

Training & On-site Installation

Financial & Business Modeling

2012
Founded, privately owned

≈ 100 GW
Supporting PV manufacturing capacity

26+
Countries

62
Factories worldwide

World's First
Fully integrated giga-scale factory installation

76 GW
Ingot & Wafer integration

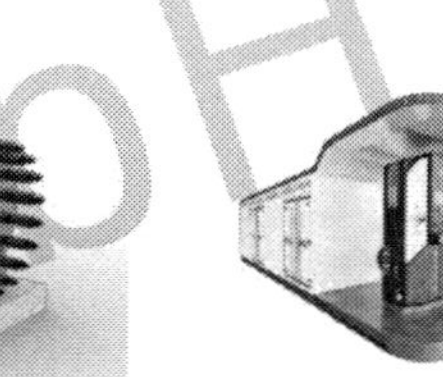

RCT Power Residential Batteries & inverters

2015
Founded, privately owned

20GWh
production capacity, fully automated

Fully EES manufacturing
Residential, commercial, utility scale (from kWh to MWh)

RCT Power C&I/ Utility Battery Energy Storage

>15 GWh (5 GWh USA)
Total shipment

Best Storage
Awarded in Germany

EU–China–USA Based
Battery production & Operations

Electrolyser stack

Re-fueling station

Gas Separation System

Hydrogen Purification System

Made/Engineered in Germany
Hydrogen equipment & engineering service

Factory Output
250MW (Target)

020463-004

Typical Project Phases
RCT Services for PV Manufacturing Project and Detail of Life Cycle Assessment

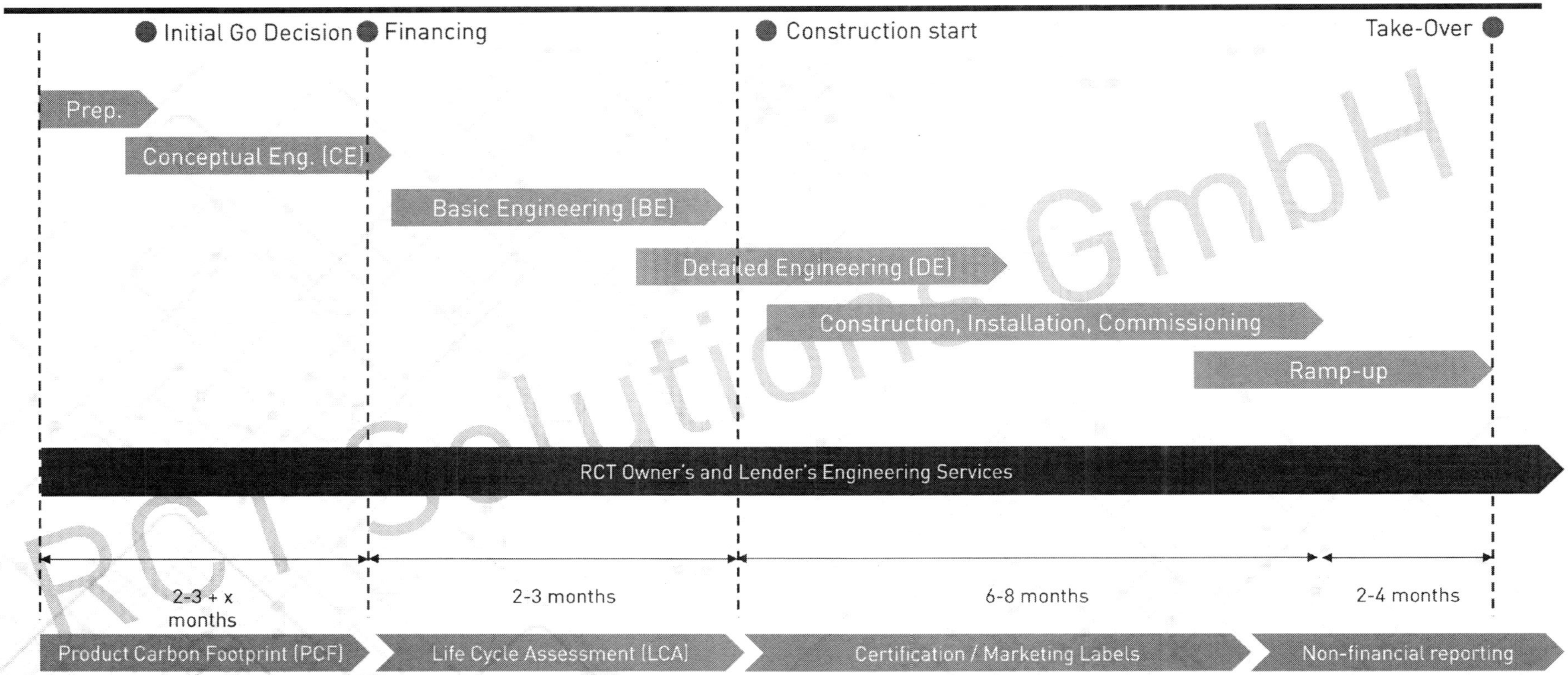

5

020463-005

Study Introduction
Goal and Scope: LCA Learning Curve Technologies and Regions

- **Life Cycle Assessment**
  1. Technological advancements
  2. Different crystalline Silicon PV Module technologies
  3. Regional manufacturing
- Bottom-up and parametric model
- Incorporation of the extensive engineering experience
→ Reliable and valid comparisons.
→ Reflects real-world PV manufacturing

Technologies	TOPCon	HJT	TBC
Description	Tunnel Oxide Passivated Contact Solar Cell with LECO	Silicon Hetero Junction Solar Cell Technology	TOPCon Back Contact Solar Cell with Cu metallization
Cell Eff. (Fab-Theoretical)	25.5% → 27.6% [2]	25.7% → 26.9% [2]	26.0% → 28.0 [2]
Cell structure			

Locations	Germany	China	India
Flag			
Location details	Northern Germany	Inner Mongolia	Western India

[2] Solar Energy Materials & Solar Cells 231 (2021) 111291, – Solar Energy Materials & Solar Cells 238 (2022) 111560

020463-006

Study Introduction
Functional Unit, Boundary Conditions & Methodology

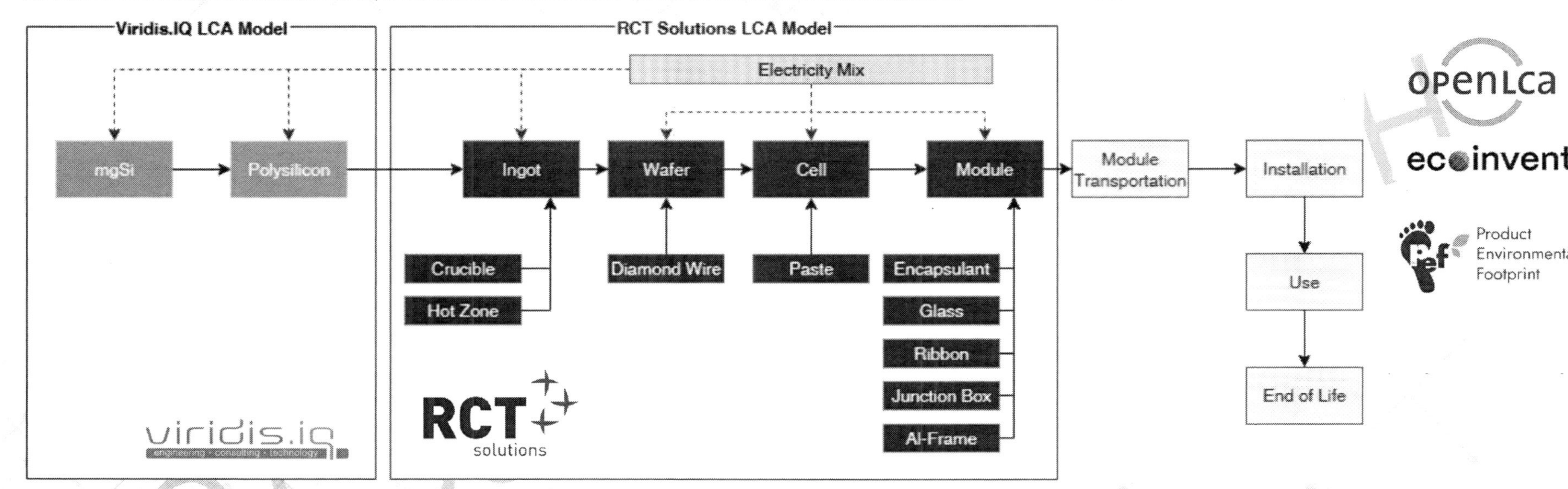

- 1 kilowatt-peak (kWp) photovoltaic (PV) module as functional unit
- Cradle-to-gate approach
- LCIA Method: EF 3.1

- Foreground data: RCT Solutions and Viridi.IQ
- Background data: Ecoinvent 3.11 Cutoff System-Processes
- Software used: openLCA 2.5

020463-007

Global Parameters – Technological improvements
Process improvements considered and excluded

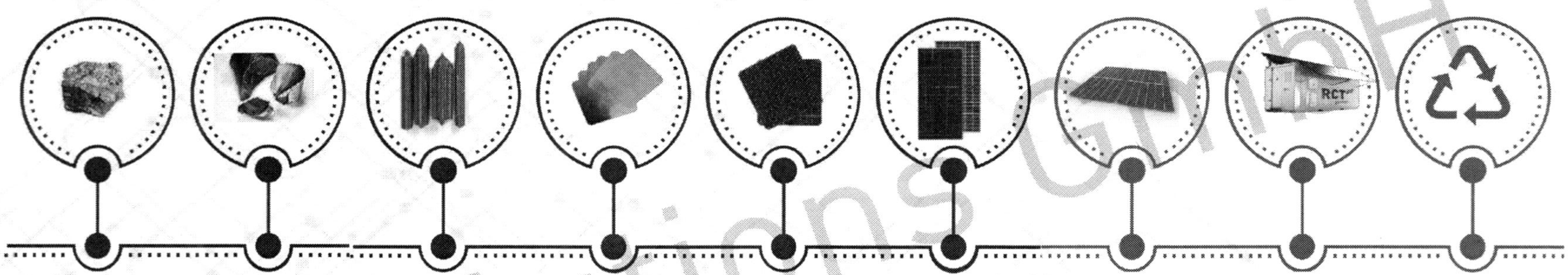

*Electricity includes consumption + energy mix   *Technology depended parameters (also BOM differs)

Global Parameters– Technological improvements
MgSi + Polysilicon - Projected trends

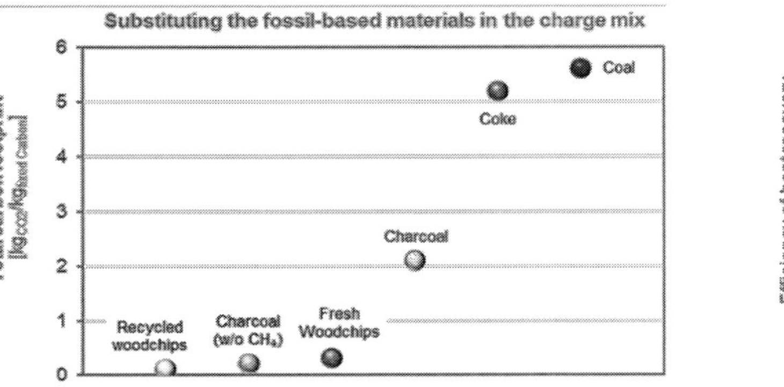

Polysilicon

- Improved TCS production
- Advanced CVD reactor design
- Higher waste heat recovery efficiency

Metallurgical Silicon

- Lower energy consumption
- Changing mix of reductants
- Using metallothermic reduction with the Mg or Al to increase the process yield and to reduce the silica content
- Carbon capture utilization from SAF off-gases

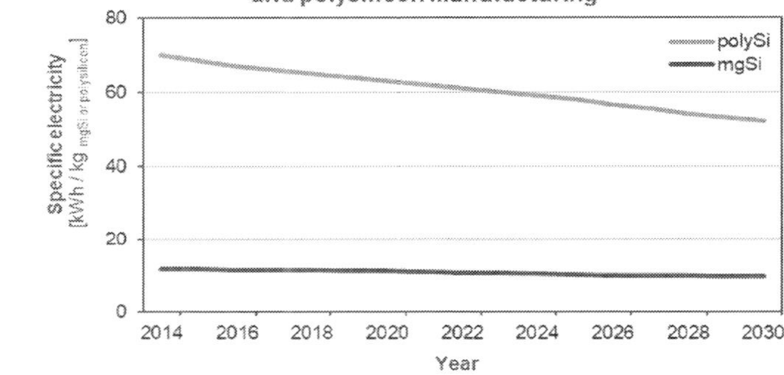

Global Parameters – Technological Improvements
Ingot and Wafering – Wafer Size Increase and Thickness Reduction

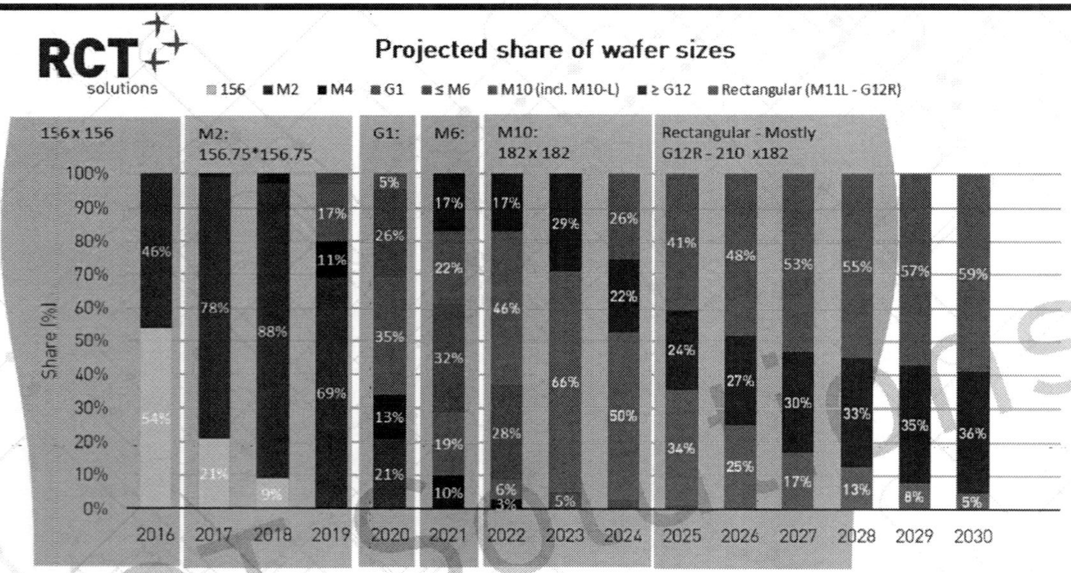

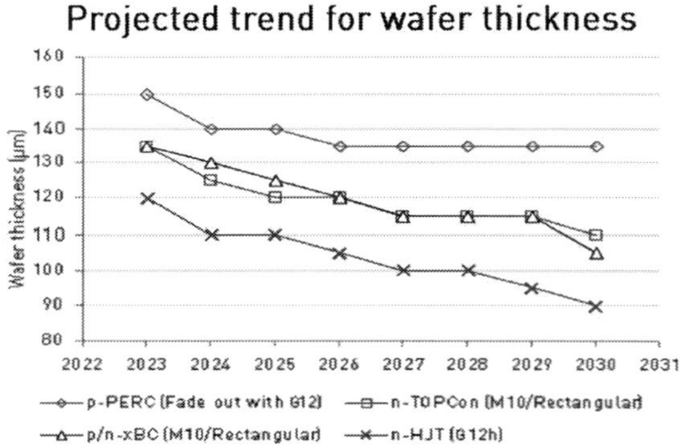

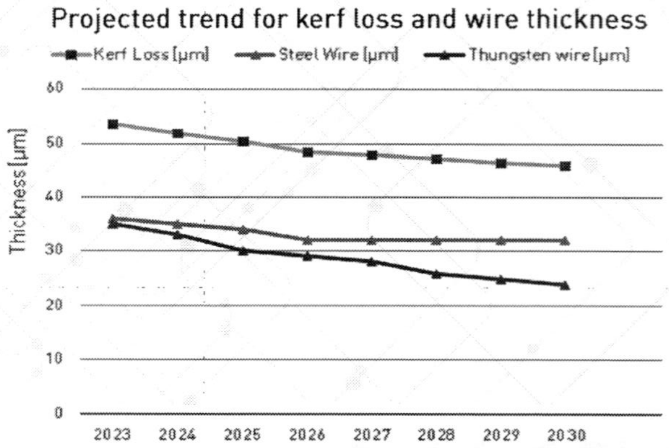

Projected share of wafer sizes

Projected trend for wafer thickness

Projected trend for kerf loss and wire thickness

- TOPCon and xBC → G12R and G12 wafer size
- Wafer thickness is predicted to decrease to 110 µm.
- HJT stay at G12h
- Wafer thickness for HJT → reduce to 90 µm

020463-010

Global Parameters – Technological improvements
Cell - Efficiency increase and paste consumptions

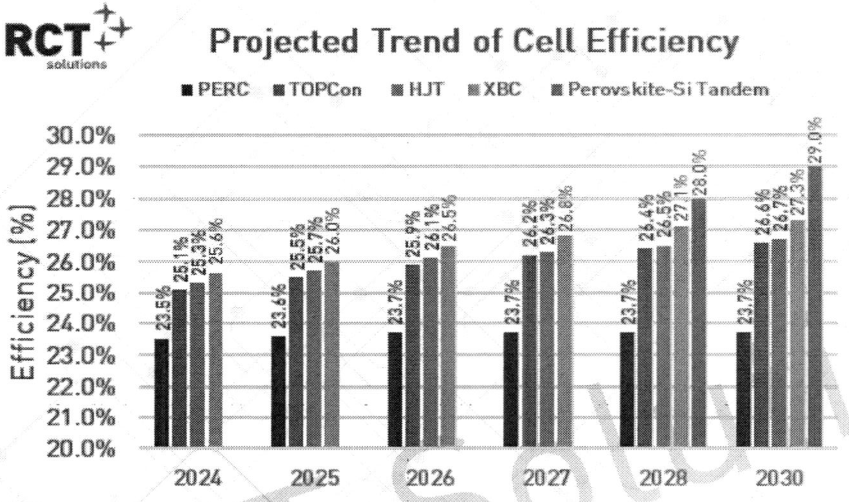

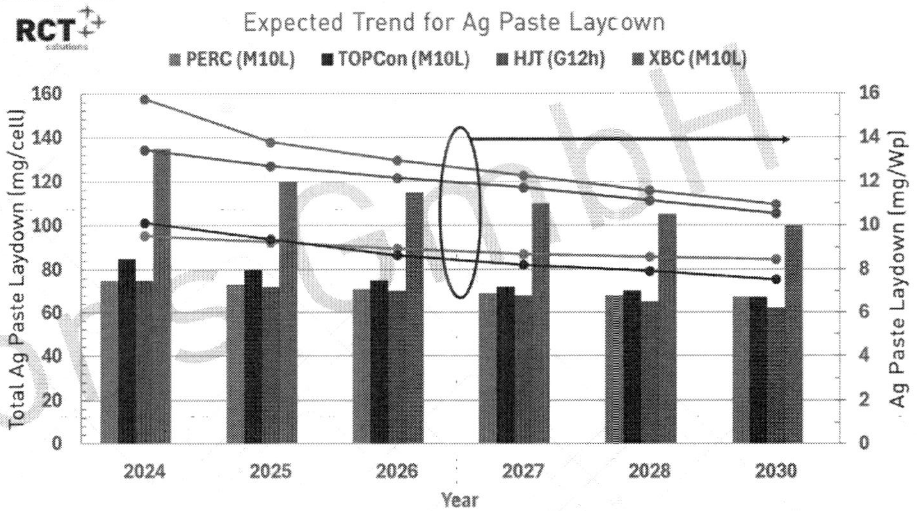

Projected Trend of Cell Efficiency

Expected Trend for Ag Paste Laydown

- Cell Efficiencies for TOPCon 25.5% (2025) up to 26.6% (2030)
- TBC from 26% to 27.3%, HJT from 25.7% to 26.7%

- Paste laydown expected to reduce
- Share of silver content changes

020463-011

Global Parameters – Technological improvements
Module manufacturing – Glass thickness kept at 2mm

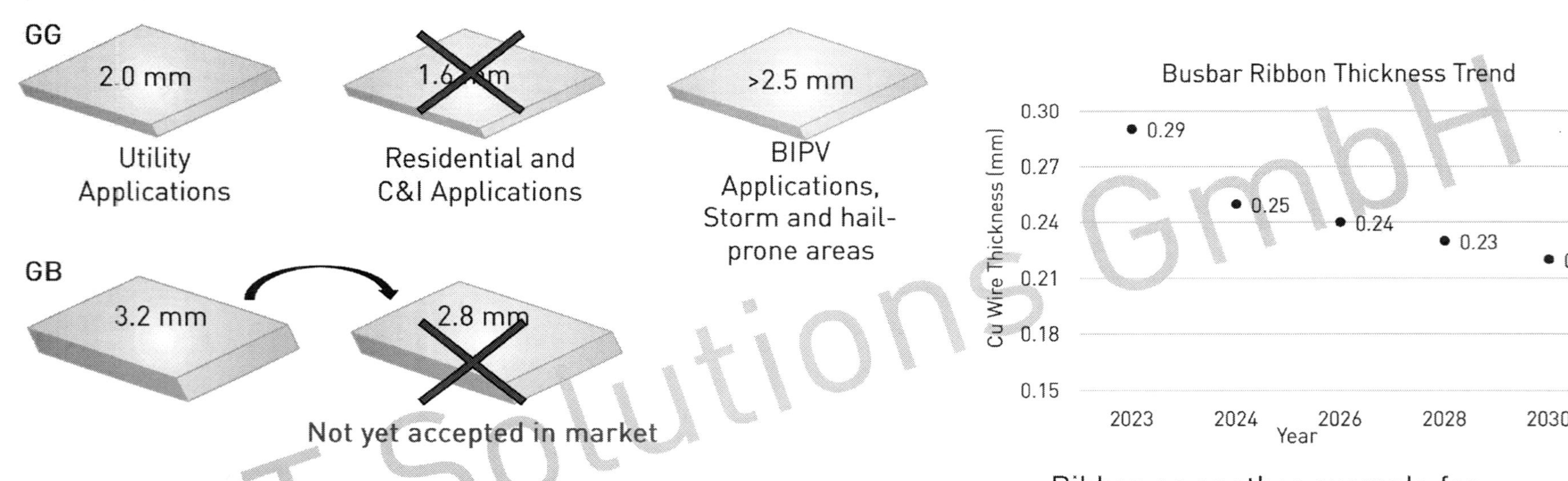

- More than 90% of modules Glass–Glass configuration for power plants
- Glass thinner than 2 mm not excepted for utility-scale power plants, particularly in hail-prone regions

→ The use of 2 mm glass is expected to continue until 2030

- Ribbon as another example for reduction in material use

020463-012

Global Parameters – Technological improvements
General factory level KPIs take

General KPIs			
MgSi Yield	**UOM**	**2025**	**2030**
Process Yield	%	77.7%	76.5%
Polysilicon	**UOM**	**2025**	**2030**
MgSi Demand	%	1.08	1.07
Ingot	**UOM**	**2025**	**2030**
Cycle Load	kg/Cycle	3900	4600
Wafer	**UOM**	**2025**	**2030**
Kerf Loss	µm	50	44
Wafering Yield	µm	95%	95%

Tech. Rel. KPIs		TOPCon		HJT		TBC	
Ingot	**UOM**	**2025**	**2030**	**2025**	**2030**	**2025**	**2030**
Ingot Diameter	mm	258	300	305	300	258	300
Wafer	**UOM**	**2025**	**2030**	**2025**	**2030**	**2025**	**2030**
Wafer Thickness	µm	130	110	110	90	130	110
Wafer Size		M10L	G12	G12h	G12h	M10L	G12
Cell	**UOM**	**2025**	**2030**	**2025**	**2030**	**2025**	**2030**
Efficiency	%	25.5%	26.6%	25.7%	26.7%	26.0%	27.3%
Factory Yield	%	98%	98%	96%	96%	97%	97%
Module	**UOM**	**2025**	**2030**	**2025**	**2030**	**2025**	**2030**
Cells	pcs	72.0	66.0	66.0	66.0	72.0	66.0
CTM	%	98%	98%	98%	98%	98%	98%

020463-013

Results – Technological improvements
Step breakdown for TOPCon (excl. E-mix change)

RCT solutions

- TOPCon GWP 499 to 416 kgCO2 eq./kW in China → 3.7% YoY Improvement

- HJT lower GWP

  1. Low temperature processing

  2. Reduced upstream requirements

- TBC higher GWP

  1. More Process Steps → Higher electricity demand

  2. Increased supply chain volume and complexity

- **Still HJT and TBC** with nearly same YoY improvement of 3.5%/3.8%

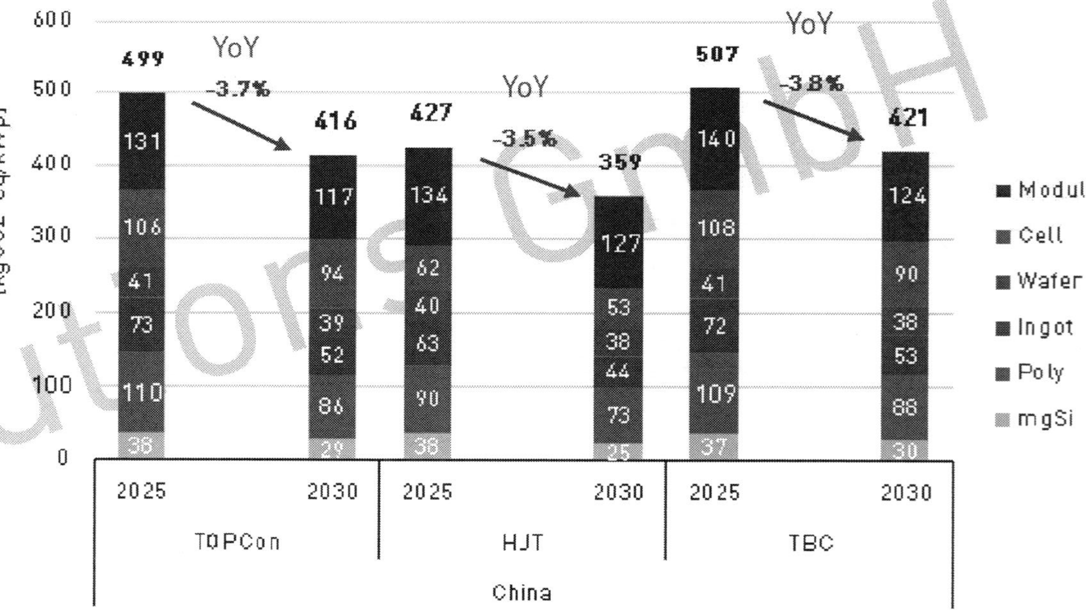

020463-014

Results – Technological improvements
TOPCon, HJT and xBC @ different sites (excl. E-mix change)

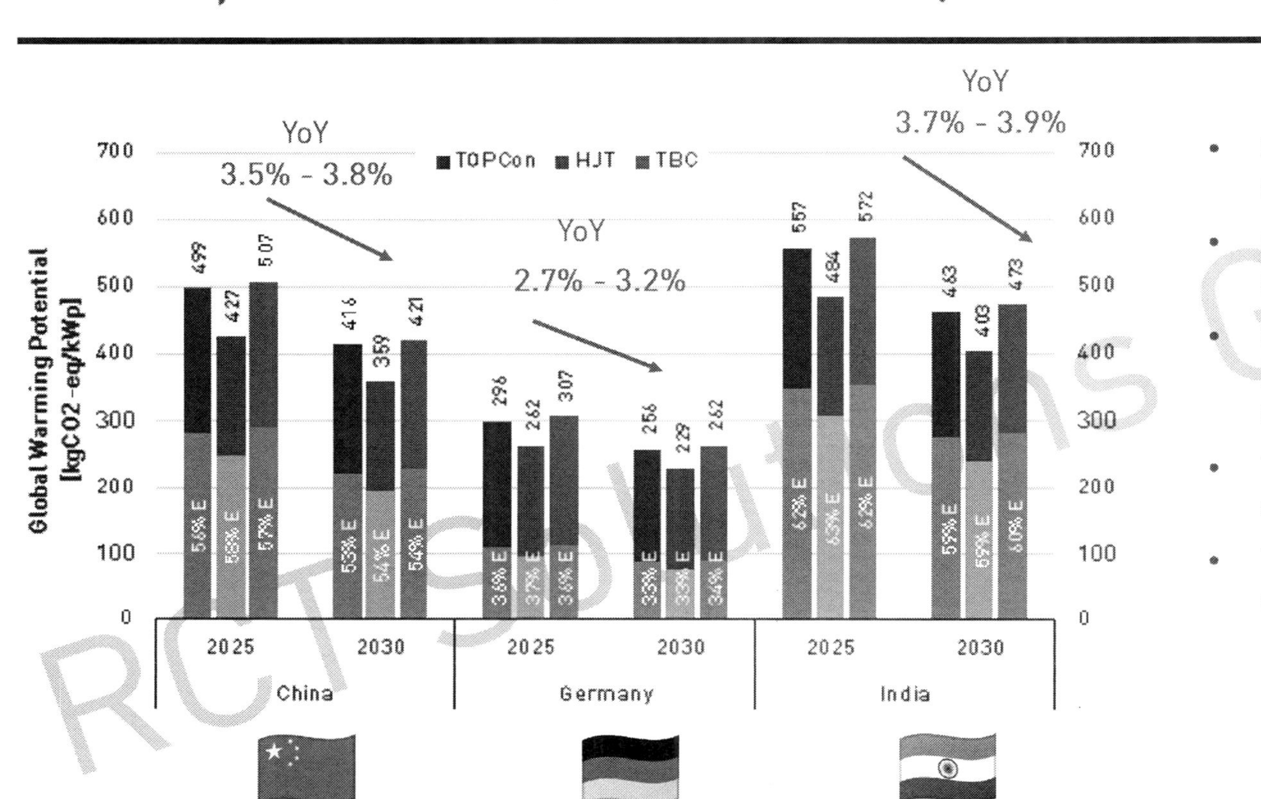

- GWP highest in India → high share of coal in grid mix
- Germany lowest → high share of renewable electricity
- German improvement lower → improvements in electricity have a lower overall impact
- TBC with highest per kWp emissions.
- TBC will get closer to TOPCon depending on the location.

020463-015

Results – Technological improvements
Incorporating the influence of local electricity mix dynamics

RCT solutions

- Integrate changes in electricity mix

- Main processes local and supply chain based on China

- 2024 data: BNetzA (DE), CEA & NPP (IN), and NEA (CN)

- The 2030 projections, from the IEA APS

- Germany Ren.-share 62% to 86%

- India Ren.-share 38% to 43%

- China Ren.-share 38% to 60%

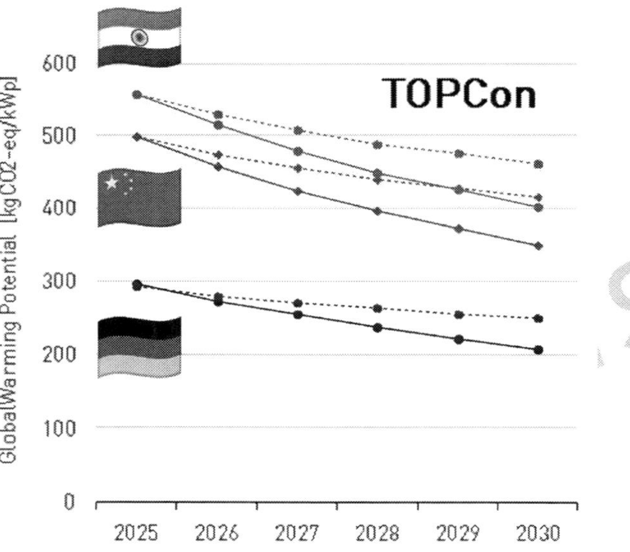

China (CN):

- Improvement 3.5% to 3.8% without E-mix and 7.4% to 7.6% with

→ doubling improvement

Germany (DE):

- Improvement is 2.7% to 3.2% without E-mix, lower impact of the electricity rising to 7.0% to 7.5% with E-mix

→ more than doubling

India (IN):

- Improvement shifts from 3.7% to 3.9% without E-mix, to 6.6% to 6.8% with it

→ only 70–80% higher

020463-016

Results – Technological improvements
Closer look at TBC – GWP will get closer to TOPCon

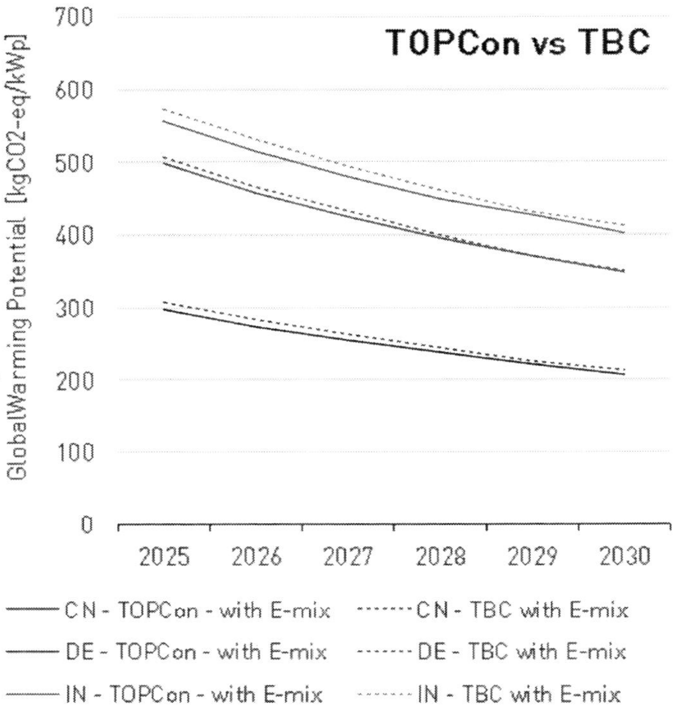

020463-017

Summary
Expected development curves only at around 7% → Not 10% yet

- YOY improvement rate 7% (all countries)

- 3% to 4% without considering E-mix

- PV manufacturing benefits equal strong from technological improvements than from decarbonization of electricity supply

- HJT with lower and TBC with higher GWP

- TBC GWP will get closer to TOPCon

- India in country comparison high GWP – high global competitivity but disadvantage in environmental sensitive markets.

- German/EU with potential for manufacturing low carbon modules – competitiveness disadvantage in current market situation

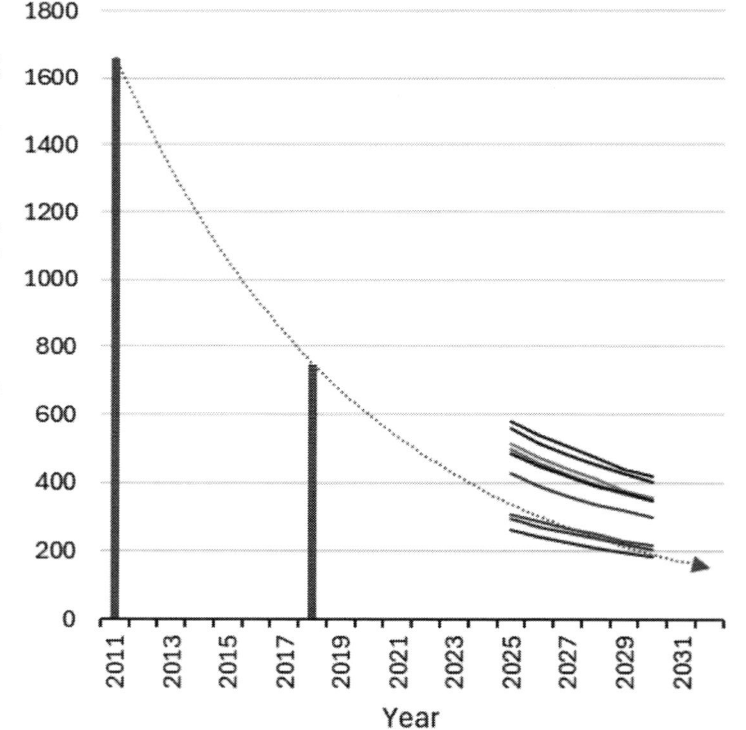

020463-018

Outlook for low carbon modules
Hidden potential in upstream direct emissions and supply chain

- **Decarbonizing** of energy throughout **all steps**
  - Downstream placed in regions with lower share of renewables → Might lower the prediction of a 7% learning rate.
- Reduce **direct process related emissions**
  - e.g., emissions from silicon reduction process trough carbon capturing or non-fossil reductants
- Improving **yield** during production
- Improve the **supply chain**
  - Potential in background data
  - Technological improvements in supply chain
  - Localization

020463-019

Thank you to all RCT Solution colleagues – Join us at Konstanz

020463-020

RCT Solutions GmbH
Line-Eid-Strasse 1
D-78467 Konstanz, Germany

Phone +49 7531 58470 12
info@rct-solutions.com
http://www.rct-solutions.com

Regd. HRB 708952,
Executive Board: Dr. Peter Fath

Confidential

Thank you

Group of companies

RCT solutions **RCT** power **RCT** hydrogen

**OPTIMIZING AGRIPV: A COMPREHENSIVE
ASSESSMENT FRAMEWORK FOR SUSTAINABLE ENERGY AND
AGRICULTURE**

A. Lopes[1], B. Barrionuevo[2], D. P. Albuquerque[3], D. Cordeiro[4], C. Fernandes[3], A. T. Balafoutis[2], R. Castro[5]

[1] IST, University of Lisbon, Lisbon, Portugal
[2] Center for Research and Technology Hellas, Athens, Greece
[3] Centre for New Energy Technologies, SA, Sacavém, Portugal
[4] EDP Gestão da Produção de Energia, SA, Lisbon, Portugal
[5] INESC-ID/IST, University of Lisbon, Lisbon, Portugal

ABSTRACT: By integrating solar panels with agricultural activities, AgriVoltaics (AgriPV) optimizes land use while offering a solution to the increasing demand for food and renewable energy. This dual use approach not only enhances land productivity but also helps regulate microclimatic conditions, reduce water evaporation, and support biodiversity. AgriPV can improve soil conditions in areas with poor agricultural productivity and enable cultivation, transforming this type of land into productive farmland. This positions AgriPV as a promising strategy for the expansion of renewable energy and sustainable agriculture.
Despite its relatively recent emergence, AgriPV has shown significant advancements, though its implementation remains limited across Europe. To support its broader adoption, this study presents a Life Cycle Assessment (LCA) framework to analyze energy production, Greenhouse Gas (GHG) emissions and environmental impacts from raw material extraction to farm-gate, within the context of the EU-funded TALOS project. A comparative sustainability assessment also examines the trade-offs between AgriPV and conventional Photovoltaics (PV) in terms of energy generation, land use efficiency and agricultural productivity. By providing a structured evaluation framework, this research supports policymakers, researchers, and stakeholders in making informed decisions that enhance both energy production and agriculture.
Keywords: AgriPV, LCA, Sustainability

1 INTRODUCTION

AgriPV presents a dual land use strategy that enables the simultaneous generation of solar energy and agricultural production, addressing the increasing global demand for food and clean energy. Despite its potential, the widespread adoption of AgriPV remains constrained by several challenges, among which the absence of standardized and comprehensive sustainability assessment methodologies. This research seeks to overcome these barriers by developing an integrated sustainability assessment framework specifically designed for AgriPV systems.

The primary aim of this research is to establish a comprehensive approach that combines both qualitative and comparative analysis. The LCA framework evaluates GHG emissions, energy generation efficiency, and overall environmental impact across several stages of the lifecycle of the AgriPV systems. This is complemented by a comparative sustainability analysis that evaluates the advantages and trade-offs between AgriPV systems and conventional PV.

This dual functionality enhances the environmental performance and introduces a sustainable model that benefits a diverse range of stakeholders. The framework is designed to be a valuable tool not only for utility companies but also for farmers and other beneficiaries within AgriPV business models, providing additional energy production capabilities and promoting environmentally sustainable agricultural practices.

This work is divided into four parts. Section 2 present a qualitative LCA framework of AgriPV systems, analyzing the cradle-to-gate process to identify impacts, challenges and opportunities to improve. Section 3 a comparison is made between AgriPV systems and conventional PVs, analyzing the main differences in land use, energy production, environmental impacts, and economic factors. Lastly, Section 4 summarizes the key findings. limitations encountered and suggestions for future research.

2 AGRIPV Life Cycle Assessment

This LCA of AgriPV systems is based on the ISO 14040/14044 framework [1] and is divided into four main phases: Goal and Scope Definition, Life Cycle Inventory (LCI), Life Cycle Impact Assessment (LCIA) and Interpretation. These phases are interconnected and provide a structured basis for assessing environmental impacts. This study conducts a qualitative LCA, examining each phase in detail to identify challenges and opportunities for improvement.

2.1 Goal and Scope Definition

The first step in the LCA is to set the study's goal and scope. The goal is to qualitatively evaluate the environmental sustainability of AgriPV systems. The scope includes the entire life cycle of both PV and agricultural components, from raw material extraction to farm-gate. A cradle-to-gate approach is adopted, which includes the production and use phases but not the end of life. AgriPV projects are usually planned to last 25 to 30 years, but limited data exists regarding decommissioning. End of life for conventional PV is already known to be complicated and might need its own study [2], so focusing on the farm gate makes sure that the operational phase gets attention, while acknowledging the importance of disposal and recycling for future research.

Defining the functional unit is challenging because these systems produce both electricity and crops. ISO 14040/14044 [1] recommends functional unit that quantify system performance. From a methodological point of view, this problem of multifunctionality is dealt either through system subdivision, system expansion or allocation, depending on the characteristics of the system, the goals of the study and data availability. In the case of AgriPV, however, given its dual nature, having two different functional units could provide a clearer and more complete assessment of their full environmental impact than by using the methodological steps mentioned above. The units used are expressed in hectare year, including electricity output (kWh) and crop yield (kg). This method guarantees that both products are included, without favoring one output over the other, following recommendations to use multiple functional units for systems with more than one output [3]. Another metric is the Land Equivalent Ratio (LER) [1], which is also seen as a conceptual measure of how well land is used when both food and electricity are made in the same area.

This framework is meant to be useful for a wide range of people, including researchers, policymakers and project developers, as they could benefit from this by evaluating the advantages and disadvantages of their AgriPV projects.

2.2 Life Cycle Inventory

The LCI lists and quantifies all the inputs, outputs, emissions and waste flows of the AgriPV system, including materials and energy. It is organised in chronological order, from getting the raw materials to the use phase.

The first step in the PV subsystem is to get raw materials and turn them into a panel. In this type of systems is normal to use bifacial models and semi-transparent. They are mainly made of silicon for wafers and cells, aluminium and steel for structures, copper for wiring and glass for encapsulation. These processes release pollutants like CO_2, SO_2, Nox, as well as industrial waste[4]. The next step in the manufacturing process uses purified silicon, aluminium profiles, tempered glass and steel beams, requiring significant energy. Outputs include solid waste from cutting wafers, chemicals released during etching and cleaning and more emissions from processes that use a lot of heat. Overhead configurations require taller and stronger structures, so they can provide support and stability for the weight of panels. This increases the steel and aluminium usage relative to standard PV farms.

The environmental impact of making modules depends a lot on where they are made [5]. China is where most of the manufacturing happens and the electricity is mostly made of coal, which means that each module emits a high amount of greenhouse gases. In Europe, on the other hand, the energy is cleaner, which means that the emission of greenhouse gases are lower. One big problem with PV inventories is that Chinese manufacturers provide limited data, which proves to be a challenge regarding gathering information available about how much energy is used, how many chemicals are used and how efficient processes are. In this circumstances, secondary data from LCA databases can be obtained. This, however, can be challenging because datasets based on European averages may not accurately capture the actual environmental impacts of PV panels manufactured in regions like China, where production practices, energy sources, and supply chain may differ significantly, leading to potentially misleading or incomplete estimations.

When transporting PVs and their components, long distance shipping and subsequent land regional distribution via road or rail are required. Fossil fuel combustion during these processes results in more CO_2 emissions. Installation involves site preparation, assembly

of mechanical structures and connection of electrical systems. This stage needs machines and transportation that run on diesel, which means that using the machines and workers travelling will create emissions, as well as waste from the packaging. During the use and maintenance phase, inputs include water and cleaning products for PVs, replacing electrical components if needed and moving people around for agricultural supervision, harvesting and maintenance of the PV system, which could be made by a farmer if provided with proper training, but which would require external services if not. The outputs are the amount of electricity produced per hectare year, the amount of electronic waste and the amount of wastewater from cleaning.

The agricultural subsystem uses seeds, fertilisers, pesticides, irrigation water and systems and energy to run pumps and machines. Outputs include the crop yield in kilogrammes per hectare year, any form of waste and the pollution that gets into the air, soil and water. Fertilisers release nitrous oxide (N_2O) directly, but they can also release it indirectly through volatilisation and nitrate leaching[6]. How minerals dissolve in soil, how much fertiliser is used and how much plants take in all affect how much nitrate leaches. Farm activities and soil management release CO_2. Crop residues increase the amount of organic matter in the soil and the amount of nitrogen that is released. Pesticides and heavy metals from inputs are considered as well as losses from leaching, erosion and harvesting. When nutrients are picked up depends on when they are planted and harvested.

Under AgriPV, these operations might have to change, for example by using smaller machines or changing how they rotate to make room for the PV infrastructure. Using pesticides and fertilisers, burning fuel and leaving organic matter in the field all create waste and emissions. Certain AgriPV systems use grazing animals to control the vegetation beneath or between the panels, which lowers the need for herbicides and diesel fuel for mowing while also producing manure that can partially replace synthetic fertilisers. Crop residues can be used as animal feed or soil amendments. These should be counted as flows that balance out outside inputs in the inventory.

Elevated structures for PV panels change the microclimate, which means that plants get less sunlight. This can slow down the rate of evapotranspiration and the amount of water needed for each unit of yield [7]. These changes can also change how much fertiliser is needed and how well crops grow. Additionally, the cover provided by PV panels can contribute to a reduction of overall moisture levels, which in turn leads to a reduction of fungicides application due to the creation of less favourable conditions for fungal growth.

This study excludes end of life processes due to insufficient data and livestock integration. However, these are significant domains for future investigation.

2.3 Life Cycle Impact Assessment

The LCIA transforms the inventory data for AgriPV systems into possible effects on the environment. ReCiPe model [8] and the EU Product Environmental Footprint (PEF)[7] are examples of standardised methods that give a structured way to measure these effects in many different areas. This is essential for AgriPV systems that can be used for energy and agriculture. ReCiPe uses midpoint indicators like eutrophication, acidification, toxicity, and resource depletion, as well as endpoint indicators that show adverse effects on human health, ecosystems, and resource availability. PEF on the other hand, provides a framework that is especially useful for European applications. Their use allows for a complete sustainability assessment by looking at not only climate change derived from GHG emissions but also pressures on water, soil and resources.

The production of PV modules, which accounts for the majority of the system's carbon footprint, is the main source of climate change consequences. The carbon payback period for PV systems is relatively short as operational energy offsets initial emissions.

Water related effects are also relevant due to the fact that PV modules need to be cleaned, and irrigation is needed for some crops. However, shading from panels can lower evapotranspiration, which can lower the amount of water needed, which is particularly relevant in arid and semi-dry regions where water scarcity is a major problem. Current LCIA methods do not fully capture these positive effects.

In addition to climate change and rising energy demand, other significant issues are based on the eutrophication and acidification from fertiliser use, water shortages from irrigation and cleaning panels and toxicity from pesticides or chemicals used in making PV panels.

Another important effect category for AgriPV is resource depletion. Increased material demand, especially for silicon, steel, aluminium, copper, and other materials, is caused by PV panels and structures manufacturer. There are ways to recycle glass and aluminium, but there is a lack inefficient ways to recover silicon. This indicates that mineral depletion should be prioritized when looking at long-term sustainability.

Using land efficiently is a key feature. The LER is a relevant metric, which shows that AgriPV produces more overall output than just farming or making energy.

2.4 Interpretation

Key findings, trade-offs and limitations are identified during the interpretation phase. The majority of impacts come from the production of PV modules, particularly the processing of silicon, while agriculture contributes using irrigation and fertilisers. AgriPV can improve the soil, save water, make it more resistant to drought and heat extreme events and make land use more efficient. It also gives farmers a new revenue source and lowers the risks of decreasing the crops production. Shading can lower the amount of crops that grow, but the value of electricity often makes up for this. These trade-offs must be considered because lower yields could cancel out environmental benefits.

AgriPV also helps fight climate change by producing renewable energy and helps crops adapt to extreme weather by keeping them safe. LCA indicators do not always show all the benefits, like creating microclimates, using less herbicide through grazing and creating jobs in rural areas, but they are still important.

There is still uncertainty related to the lack of long-term data for vertical and semi-transparent systems. Also, recycling options for PV parts are still under developed and LCA databases do not yet effectively capture the interactions between crops and regional conditions. Future research should be focused on enhanced data quality, demonstrations and investments. To fully unlock the potential of AgriPV as a sustainable alternative to traditional PV, it will be necessary to incorporate policy into land use and energy planning.

3 COMPARISON BETWEEN AGRIPV SYSTEMS AND CONVENTIONAL PV

Traditional PV farms and AgriPV systems represent two distinct approaches to solar installation. Conventional PV systems are only meant for producing electricity and they often take up a lot of land that cannot be used for anything else. AgriPV is made to be used for two things, producing renewable energy and growing crops on the same land. To understand the trade-offs between land use, energy output and agricultural value, as well as how design choices affect sustainability and resource efficiency, it is important to compare these different systems.

3.1 Land Use

The layout of traditional PV systems and AgriPV systems are very different, which affects how land is used. While traditional utility-scale PV commonly occupies cleared sites on low structures frequently with single-axis tracking, which the main objective is to capture as much sunlight as possible, with the aim of producing as much energy as possible. This leads to a high ground covering ratio (GCR), which means that most of the land surface is covered or shaded by panels, making it unsuitable for farming. On the other hand, AgriPV systems are made to be used for dual use of land. The PV panels are either raised several meters above the ground (overhead configuration) or arranged in rows (interspace configuration) with more space between them so that farming can take place underneath and between the panels respectively. For instance, overhead configurations use support structures that are between 2 and 5 meters high, which let tractors and other farm machinery pass through. In the other configuration, interspace, the panels are set up mostly vertically or with wide gaps between them, leaving strips of land open for farming. These configuration choices result in lower GCR, allowing sufficient sunlight to reach the ground for crop growth and development.

This dual use approach also makes it possible to produce solar energy in places where there limited land available for PV projects, since PV systems can coexist with farming instead of competing with it.

AgriPV systems can be adapted to various agricultural environments, such as vineyards, orchards, and greenhouses, facilitating energy production while preserving the land essential agricultural use. AgriPV mitigates the necessity to deforest, transform natural ecosystems or reserve arable land solely for energy generation by facilitating dual land use.

3.2 Energy Production

The way AgriPV is designed to allow farming also affects energy production. AgriPV systems have a lower installed capacity than traditional PV farms on the same area due to fewer panels being installed per hectare. More sunlight can reach crops with semi-transparent modules, but the part of the radiation that gets to plants is no longer available to be turned into electricity. This is why it is so important to find a balance in how radiation is spread out. Too much shade on crops lowers their yields and too much light on plants lowers their electricity output. An AgriPV project that works must make sure that neither energy production nor farming is harmed to the point where it becomes unsustainable. The goal is not to make one output more valuable than the other, but to find a way for both remain productive. Therefore, achieving an even distribution of solar radiation is crucial. Too much shade can stress the plants, which can slow their growth and productivity or even make it impossible to grow it in that place. It is also important to choose the right crops because some are more sensitive to shade, which can lower yields and make the project impossible. A successful AgriPV project must make sure that neither energy production nor farming is harmed that it becomes unviable. An additional factor to take into consideration is the microclimate created by the vegetation beneath the panels. The cultivation of crops decreases the ambient temperature near the modules, relieving thermal stress and enhancing panel efficiency. This cooling effect helps to mitigate the reduced energy produced in AgriPV configurations, which does not figure in conventional PV farms.

A way to increase the energy produced is to use tracking systems, but it remains a concern for keeping a balance between the distribution of the radiation between the panels and the crops, besides the higher Operational expenditure (OPEX) costs associated.

3.3 Material and Infrastructure Requirements

Common mounting methods used by traditional PV farms include fixed tilt racks and single axis trackers. Their designs are standardised and optimised for cost effectiveness and they often use a structural steel needed to support modules that are close to the ground. AgriPV systems, on overhead structures, on the other hand, need more complex structures. Structures that are higher up must be built to withstand wind loads and therefore in places where wind exposure is high, choosing the right site is very important. Because they are so high, they need special tools for cleaning and maintenance, which makes the materials needed and the work more complicated, increasing the overall costs.

Bifacial modules usually cost comparatively more than regular monofacial panels because they have two layers of glass and are more complex to produce. But their ability to capture both direct and reflected light increases the overall yield, which can be very helpful in AgriPV systems with lower density of panels. This higher energy output helps make up for the fact that there are fewer modules per hectare, which can make the system work better overall. Semi-transparent PV is an advanced technology that combines power generation with light transmission. However, the fact that it is more complex to manufacture, increases the costs while reducing energy production [8].

3.4 Environmental Impact

The production phase of regular PV systems has the largest impact on the environment, as module manufacturing requires significant energy and critical raw materials. This stage accounts for most CO_2 emissions over the course of the life cycle, while the operation itself generates almost no emissions. AgriPV systems share the same upstream effects, but add another dimension related to the crops cultivated under the panels. The vegetation cultivated under AgriPV systems absorbs CO_2 from the atmosphere through photosynthesis, temporarily storing biogenic carbon. While this process does not permanently offset the fossil-based emissions associated with PV module production, it may contribute to improving the overall carbon balance of the system, particularly if practices that promote longer-term carbon retention -such as soil carbon sequestration- are simultaneously implemented.

3.5 Economic Considerations

From an economic point of view, conventional PV systems are currently much cheaper to install. They are one of the most cost-effective sources of renewable energy because their design is standardised, their supply chains are well-established and large-scale deployment has lowered the cost per installed megawatt though the years. AgriPV systems, on the other hand, need more complex engineering, more building materials and more demanding maintenance. These factors increase the initial investment and running costs, which often means that capital expenditure (CAPEX) is higher than it is for regular PV farms [9].

In AgriPV, farmers can use the energy produced to meet their own needs, such as irrigation or others agricultural tasks. They can also sell the energy to the grid. Using electricity for personal consumption results in cost savings, while selling it to the grid generates revenue.

Despite these benefits, AgriPV continues to encounter significant regulatory obstacles. Although traditional PV systems benefit from robust legal protocols, dedicated regulations for AgriPV projects are limited in most European countries. This regulatory gap creates uncertainty for investors and blocks project development, frequently leading to protracted approval processes and less access to assistance programs. As legislation evolve to acknowledge AgriPV as a dual use solution, definitive rules will be crucial to achieve its complete economic and social potential.

4 CONCLUSION

Combining solar panels with farming is a promising way to combine renewable energy generation with food production. The LCA results show that producing PV modules, especially made in China, has the biggest impact on the environmental. On the other hand, agriculture has a smaller effect through the use of fertilisers. The analysis also highlights the problem of defining functional units in type of systems. Using both electricity output and crop yield per hectare-year, as well as the Land Equivalent Ratio (LER), gives a more balanced view. This study's LCA framework shows that it is better for land use efficiency and fighting climate change than traditional PV systems. There are still trade-offs to consider regarding, related to shading, lowering yields and lower energy produced compared with conventional PV farms. This means that system design needs to be extremely meticulous to achieve a balance between energy and agricultural production.

In addition to standard indicators, dual-use systems provide additional benefits, such as improved soil conditions, reduced irrigation requirements, greater resilience to extreme weather, and increased income opportunities for farmers. These synergies enhance the overall value of this land management approach for the environment, society, and the economy.

The study also found some important problems, such as lacking sufficient information on PV manufacturing, not having strong end-of-life scenarios, and current LCA databases not being able to include site-specific crop and regional interaction.

AgriPV systems provide a strategy to address the increasing demand for food and renewable energy on limited land. With advancements in solar technology, recyclable designs, and supportive policies, these systems have the potential to scale from individual projects to widespread implementation, enhancing both agricultural productivity and energy generation in the future.

5 ACKNOWLEDGEMENTS

Rui Castro was supported by national funds through FCT, Fundação para a Ciência e a Tecnologia, under project UIDB/50021/2020 (DOI: 10.54499/UIDB/50021/2020).

5 REFERENCES

[1] I. O. f. Standardization, "ISO 14040:2006. Environmental management — life cycle assessment — principles and framework," [Online]. Available: https://www.iso.org/standard/37456.html. [Acessed on 24 07 2025].

[2] R. Sanathi, S. Banerjee, S. Bhowmik, "A technical review of crystalline silicon photovoltaic module recycling", Solar Energy, Volume 281, 2024.

[3] Ai Leon, Keiichi N. Ishihara,"Assessment of new functional units for agrivoltaic systems", Journal of Environmental Management, Volume 226, 2018.

[4] T. Krexner, A. Bauer, A. Gronauer, C. Mikovits, J. Schmidt, I. Kral, "Environmental life cycle assessment of a stilted and vertical bifacial crop-based agrivoltaic multi land-use system and comparison with a mono land-use of agricultural land", Renewable and Sustainable Energy Reviews, Volume 196, 2024.

[5] A. Müller, L. Friedrich, C. Reichel, S. Herceg, M. Mittag, D. Neuhaus, "A comparative life cycle assessment of silicon PV modules: Impact of module design, manufacturing location and inventory", Solar Energy Materials and Solar Cells, Volume 230, 2021.

[6] W Moritz, J Lask, A. Kiesel, I. Lewandowski, A Weselek, P Högy, M Trommsdorff, M Schnaiker, A. Bauerle, "Agrivoltaics: The Environmental Impacts of Combining Food Crop Cultivation and Solar Energy Generation", Agronomy 13, 2023.

[7] G. Barron-Gafford, M. Pavao-Zuckerman, R. Minor, L. Sutter, I. Barnett-Moreno, D. Blackett, M. Thompson, K. Dimond, A. Gerlak, G. Nabhan, J. Macknick, "Agrivoltaics provide mutual benefits across the food–energy–water nexus in drylands", Nature Sustainability, Volume 2, 2019.

[8] S. Gorjian, E. Bousi, Ö. Özdemir, M. Trommsdorff, N. Manoj Kumar, A. Anand, K. Kant, S. Chopra, "Progress and challenges of crop production and

[9] electricity generation in agrivoltaic systems using semi-transparent photovoltaic technology", Renewable and Sustainable Energy Reviews, Volume 158, 2022.
S. Schindele, M. Trommsdorff, A. Schlaak, T. Obergfell, G. Bopp, C. Reise, C. Braun, A. Weselek, A. Bauerle, P. Högy, A. Goetzberger, E. Weber, "Implementation of agrophotovoltaics: Techno-economic analysis of the price-performance ratio and its policy implications", Applied Energy, Volume 265, 2020.

TALOS

AgriPV: A Comprehensive Assessment Framework for Sustainable Energy and Agriculture

Session 5CO.5.1

EU PVSEC Conference 2025

September 24, 2025

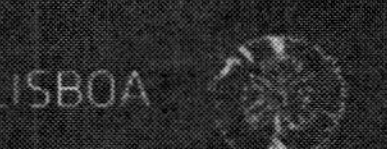

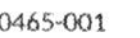

Introduction and Motivation

AgriPV presents a dual land use strategy **combining solar energy generation** and **agricultural production**

Addresses the increasing global **demand for food** and **clean energy**

Adoption remains limited due to lack of standardized sustainability assessment methodologies

This research proposes an **integrated framework** to evaluate energy generation, emissions and environmental impact. **Supports decision-making** for policymakers, researchers and farmers by providing a structured tool to evaluate the feasibility of AgriPV

1. The **Life Cycle Assessment (LCA)** methodology evaluates GHG emissions, energy generation efficiency and overall environmental impact across several stages
2. A **comparative sustainability analysis** between AgriPV and conventional PV complements the LCA

Life Cycle Assessment

This LCA of AgriPV systems is based on the ISO 14040/14044[1] framework and is divided into four main phases:

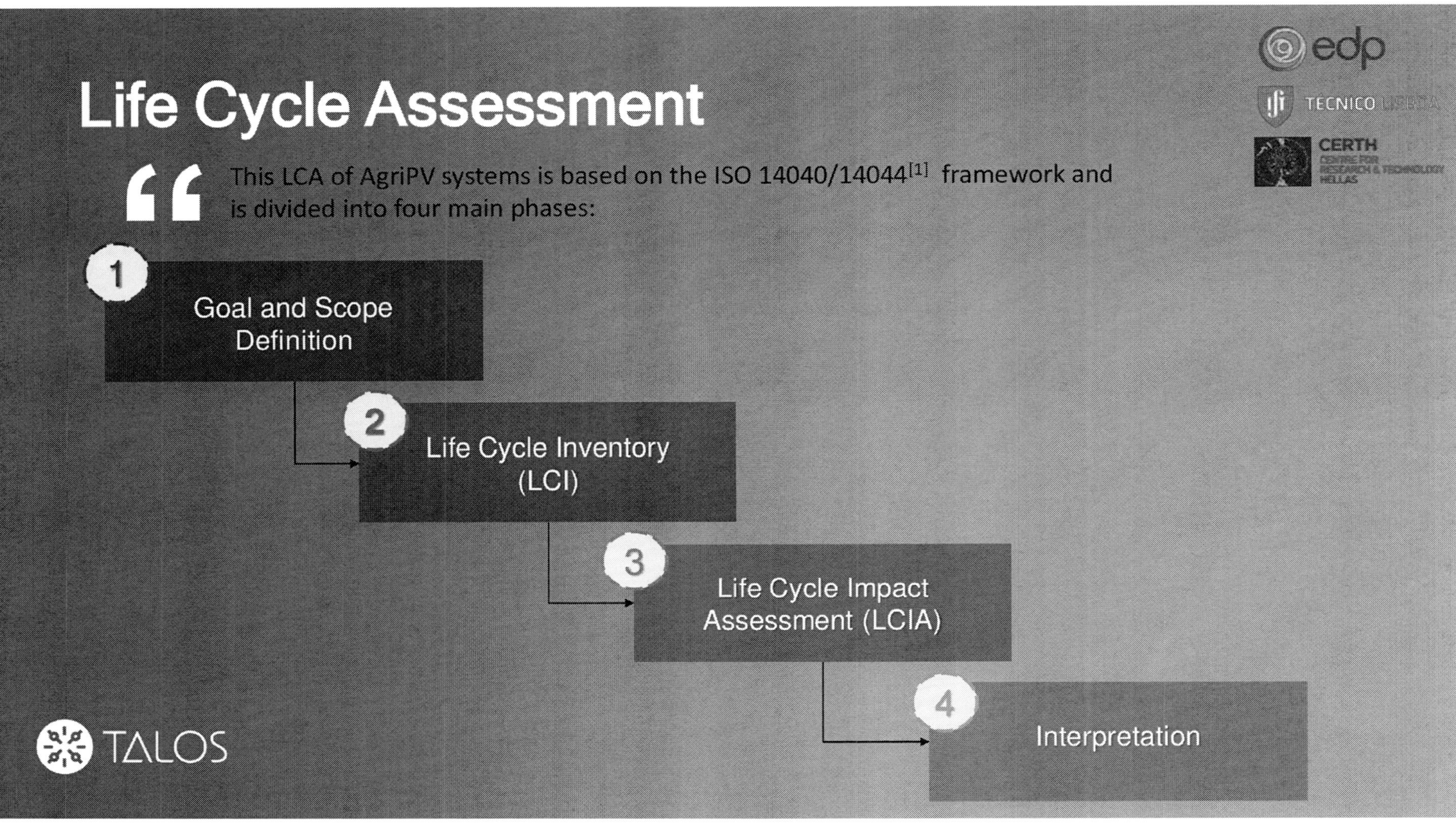

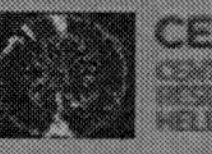

Life Cycle Assessment

This LCA of AgriPV systems is based on the ISO 14040/14044[1] framework and is divided into four main phases:

1

Goal and Scope Definition

Life Cycle Inventory (LCI)

Life Cycle Impact Assessment (LCIA)

Interpretation

Objective
Evaluate environmental sustainability of AgriPV

Boundaries
Cradle-to-gate

Functional units
Electricity (kWh/ha·yr) and Crop yield (kg/ha·yr)
captures both outputs without favoring one

Another Metric
Land Equivalent Ratio (LER)

 TALOS

Life Cycle Assessment

This LCA of AgriPV systems is based on the ISO 14040/14044[1] framework and is divided into four main phases:

Life Cycle Assessment

This LCA of AgriPV systems is based on the ISO 14040/14044[1] framework and is divided into four main phases:

Goal and Scope Definition

Life Cycle Inventory (LCI)

Life Cycle Impact Assessment (LCIA)

Interpretation

Methodologies

ReCiPe (midpoint & endpoint indicators) and EU Product Environmental Footprint (PEF)

Impact categories

- **Climate change**: CO_2 emissions, carbon payback time
- **Water related**: irrigation and panel cleaning, but a reduction from evapotranspiration
- **Eutrophication and acidification**: fertiliser use and runoff
- **Toxicity**: pesticides, chemical processes in PV manufacturing
- **Resource depletion**: silicon, steel, aluminium, copper demand

Key driver

PV module manufacturing dominates carbon footprint

TALOS

Life Cycle Assessment

This LCA of AgriPV systems is based on the ISO 14040/14044[1] framework and is divided into four main phases:

- Goal and Scope Definition
- Life Cycle Inventory (LCI)
- Life Cycle Impact Assessment (LCIA)
- Interpretation

4

Main impacts
Manufacturing of PV modules is the dominant source

Agricultural share
Irrigation and fertilisers add emissions but at a smaller scale

Positive effects
- Improve soil quality
- Reduced water use
- Better resilience to extreme events, like heat and drought

Trade-offs
Balance between crop yield and electricity production critical to maintain overall sustainability

Knowledge gaps
Lack of transparent data from PV manufacturers

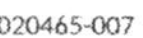

Comparison between Conventional PV vs AgriPV

To better understand the trade-offs between conventional PV and AgriPV, this study compares both systems across five key aspects:

Comparison between Conventional PV vs AgriPV

To better understand the trade-offs between conventional PV and AgriPV, this study compares both systems across five key aspects:

Land Use	Energy Production	Materials and Infrastructure	Environmental Impact	Economic
AgriPV	Elevated structures or interspace layouts allow crop growth	Low Ground Coverage Ratio		Preserves soil, reduces erosion and enables dual land productivity
Conventional PVs	Low-elevation, mainly with fixed-tilt or single-axis tracker	High Ground Coverage Ratio		Land is only used for the energy production purpose

Comparison between Conventional PV vs AgriPV

To better understand the trade-offs between conventional PV and AgriPV, this study compares both systems across five key aspects:

Land Use	Energy Production	Materials and Infrastructure	Environmental Impact	Economic
AgriPV	Fewer panels per hectare: lower installed capacity	Vegetation can reduce temperature improves panel efficiency	Tracking systems can increase production, although they raise OPEX and may affect light distribution	Requires optimised design to balance shading and crop yields
Conventional PVs	Maximum panel density		Stable energy output unaffected by crops or shade	Optimised for only energy production

Comparison between Conventional PV vs AgriPV

To better understand the trade-offs between conventional PV and AgriPV, this study compares both systems across five key aspects:

Land Use	Energy Production	Materials and Infrastructure	Environmental Impact	Economic
 **AgriPV**	Overhead structures have stronger structures and need more material	Installation involves additional equipment (irrigation, sensors)	Special tools needed for cleaning and maintenance	Bifacial and semi-transparent modules add cost but improve performance
 **Convention al PVs**	Standardised and cost-effective mounting systems		Lower consumption of steel and aluminium	

Comparison between Conventional PV vs AgriPV

To better understand the trade-offs between conventional PV and AgriPV, this study compares both systems across five key aspects:

Land Use	Energy Production	Materials and Infrastructure	Environmental Impact	Economic
AgriPV	Creates microclimate that helps crops adapt to heat and drought	Improves soil quality and supports biodiversity under panels	Reduces water evaporation, potentially lowering irrigation needs	
Conventional PVs	Life Cycle Assessment dominated by module production impacts	Land use excludes agriculture and provides no biodiversity benefit	No contribution to soil quality	

Comparison between Conventional PV vs AgriPV

To better understand the trade-offs between conventional PV and AgriPV, this study compares both systems across five key aspects:

	Land Use	Energy Production	Materials and Infrastructure	Environmental Impact	Economics
AgriPV		Higher CAPEX and OPEX due to taller structures and dual-use design	Additional revenue for farmers through crop production and energy sales	Potential cost savings from self-consumption	Regulatory frameworks still under development, leading to longer approval processes
Convention al PVs		Lower CAPEX, simpler design and installation		Fast permitting and standardised incentives	

Conclusion

Next steps

- **AgriPV increases overall land productivity** by combining food and energy generation

- **LCA results:** PV manufacturing is the main contributor to impacts, but carbon payback is short

- **Environmental benefits:** improved soil quality, reduced water use, biodiversity support

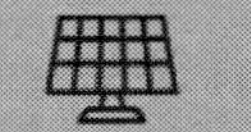

Improve data transparency

Need for detailed and region-specific LCI from PV manufacturers

AgriPV lacks common regulatory and legislative frameworks

EU regulations should evolve to be the same in all State Members as soon as possible

Provide incentives

Financial support and tax benefits for farmers adopting AgriPV.

Grants or feed-in tariffs to speed up deployment and make projects viab

Promote further research

More field trials and pilot studies to optimise design and speed up development

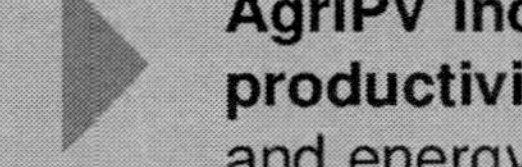
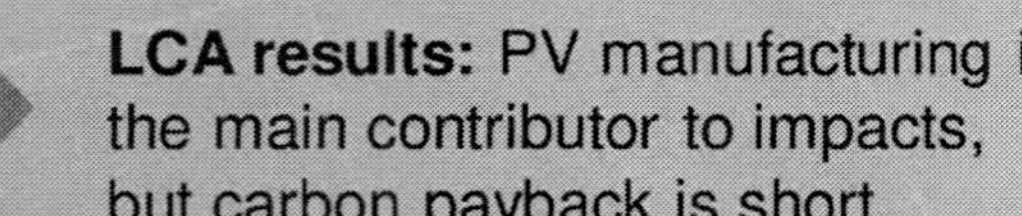
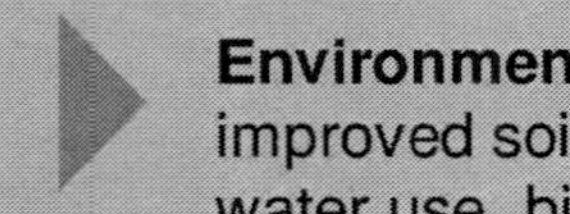

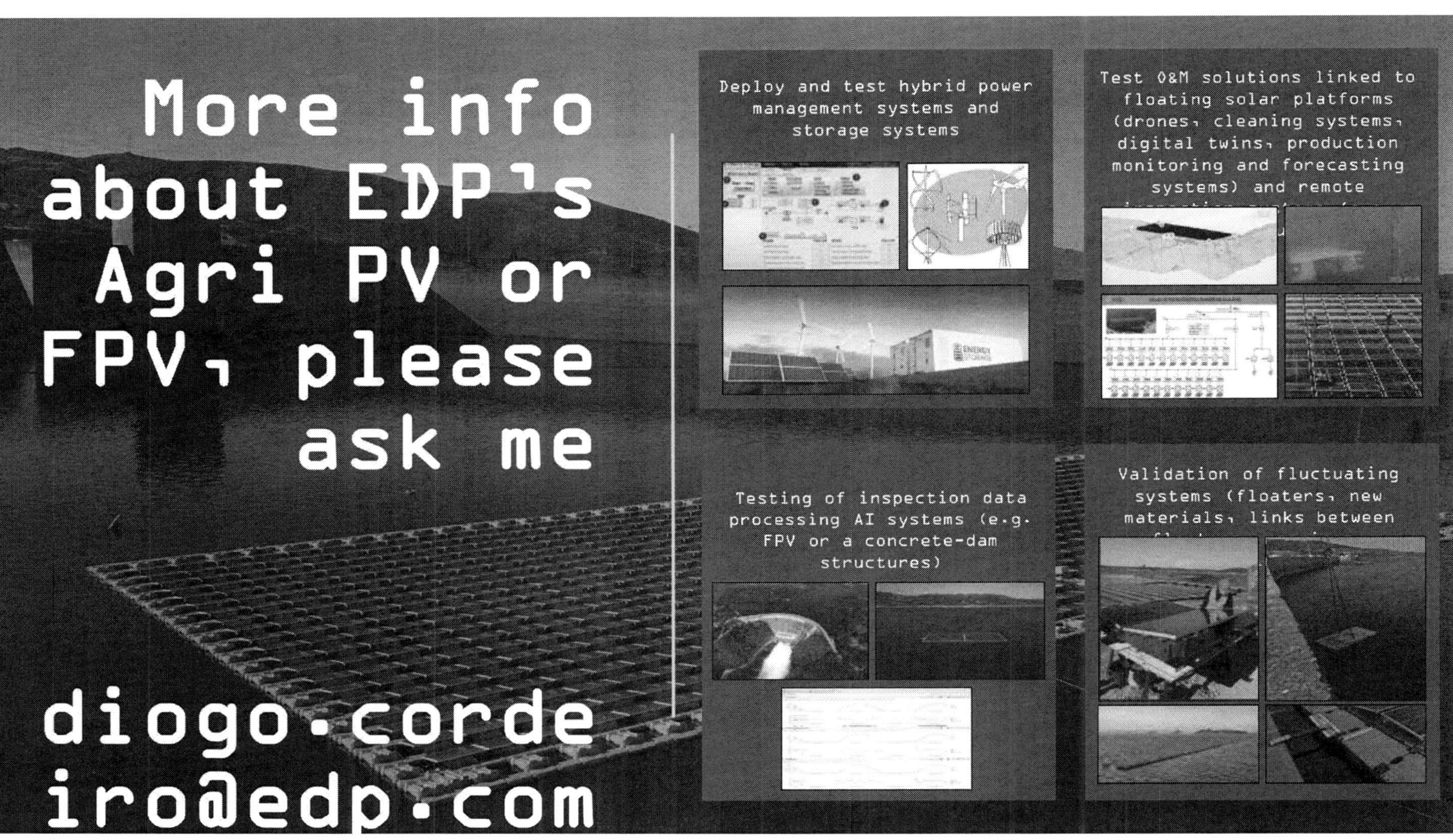

More info about EDP's Agri PV or FPV, please ask me

diogo.corde iro@edp.com

Deploy and test hybrid power management systems and storage systems

Test O&M solutions linked to floating solar platforms (drones, cleaning systems, digital twins, production monitoring and forecasting systems) and remote

Testing of inspection data processing AI systems (e.g. FPV or a concrete-dam structures)

Validation of fluctuating systems (floaters, new materials, links between

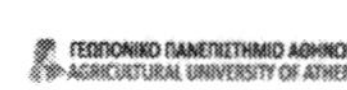
TALOS
roboTics and Artificial intelligence Living labs improving Operations in PV Scenarios

Thank you

talosproject.eu
info@talosproject.eu
@Talos_EUproject
TALOS EU PROJECT

NEW
edp
INESCTEC
DTA THE SMART MOVE
SolarCleano
FundingBox
ICONS
isotrol
alisys
res power for good
WAGENINGEN UNIVERSITY & RESEARCH
CERTH CENTRE FOR RESEARCH & TECHNOLOGY HELLAS
iBO
Eden Core
ΓΕΩΠΟΝΙΚΟ ΠΑΝΕΠΙΣΤΗΜΙΟ ΑΘΗΝΩΝ AGRICULTURAL UNIVERSITY OF ATHENS
Funded by
the European Union

Environmental Sustainability Assessment of Agrivoltaic Systems: A Life Cycle Approach

Maria Anna Cusenza, Andrea Danelli, Sofia Spagnolo, Pierpaolo Girardi

24.09.2025

This work has been financed by the Research Fund for the Italian Electrical System under the Three-Year Research Plan 2025-2027 (MASE, Decree n.388 of November 6th, 2024), in compliance with the Decree of April 12th, 2024.

LCA applied to agrivoltaic system: methodological aspects and research gaps

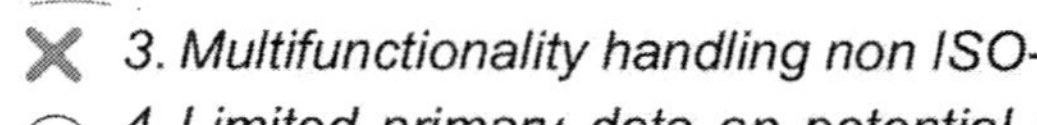

Life Cycle Assessment[1,2]

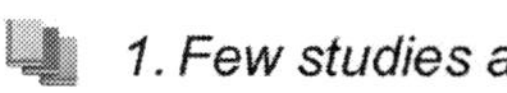

LCA applied to agrivoltaic systems

Agrivoltaic systems are **multifunctional** systems

Key methodological aspects for the application of the LCA methodology to multifunctional systems in compliance with ISO 14040/14044

- ❖ Identification of the main function

- ❖ Selection of the appropriate functional unit

- ❖ Handling of multifunctionality

State of Research on Agrivoltaic LCA: research gaps[3]

1. *Few studies available*
2. *Main function not defined*
3. *Multifunctionality handling non ISO-compliant*
4. *Limited primary data on potential synergies and/or trade-offs*

Contribution to the research gaps

- *LCA fully compliant with ISO 14040/14044 → 1, 2 and 3*

- *Scenario analysis to explore potential synergies and trade-offs → 4*

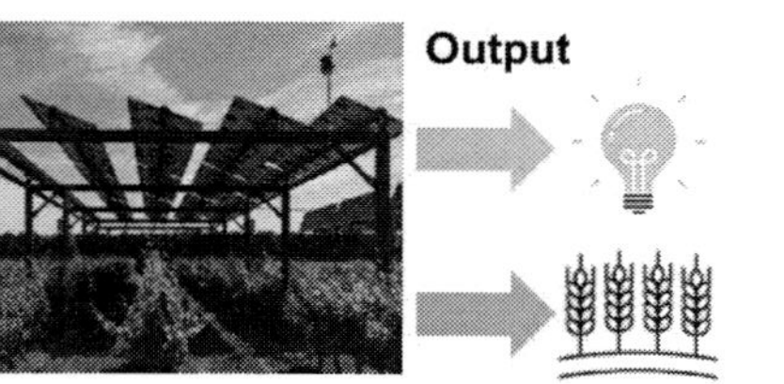

LCA of an agrivoltaic system in Italy

Case study

Overhead agrivoltaic system installed in Robecco sul Naviglio (MI) near a wastewater treatment plant for electricity supply, by CAP Holding.

Main function: Electricity generation

Agrivoltaic system[3]

- Overhead agrivoltaic system
- Agricultural activity takes place underneath the PV modules
- Area (S_{AgriPV}): 15,000 m^2
- Modules at 5 m height from ground
- Row spacing (pitch): 16 m

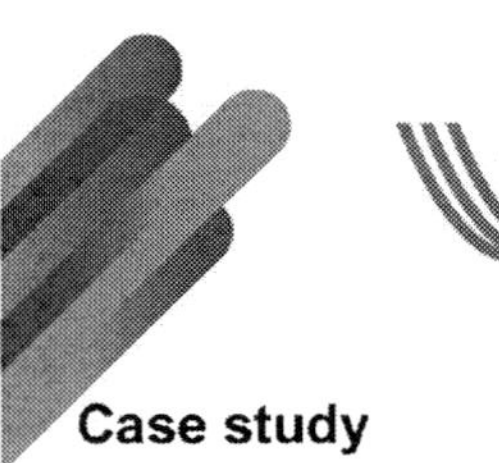

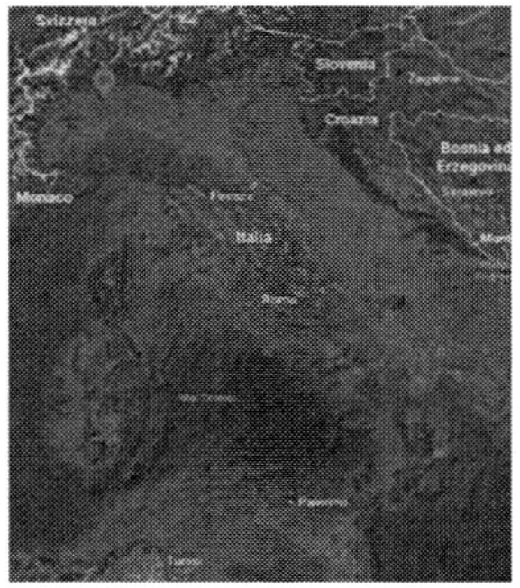

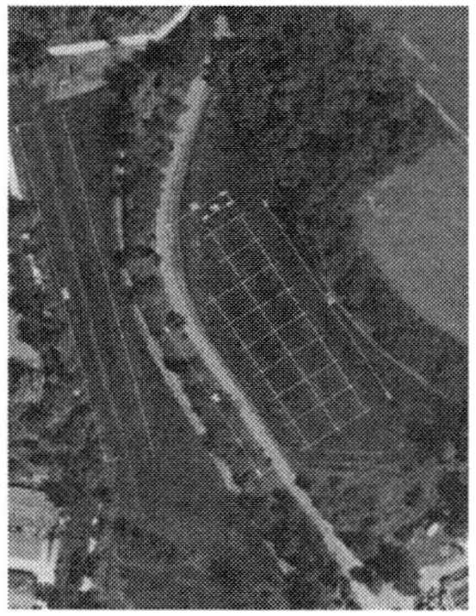

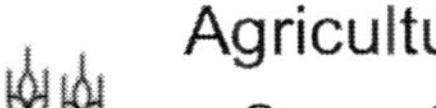

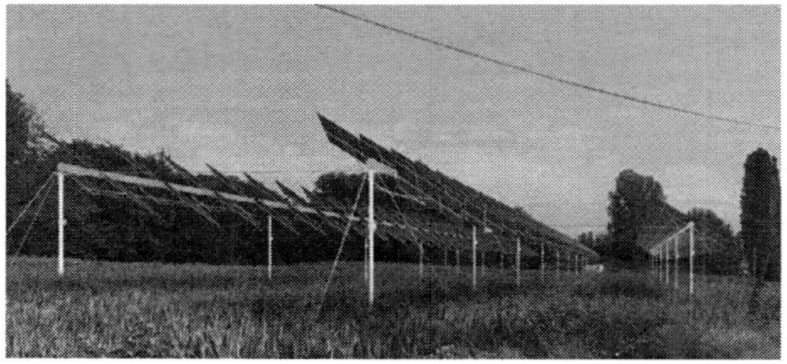

Photovoltaic system

- Installed capacity: 540 kW
- Modules: 816 bifacial PERC monocrystalline (660 W)
- PV modules footprint (S_{PV}): 2,500 m^2
- 34 dual-axis trackers (24 PV modules/tracker), hot-dip galvanized steel
- 2 inverters (320 kW + 225 kW)
- Foundations: Screw piles, steel
- First-year generation: 1,533 kWh/(kW·yr)

Agricultural system

- Conventional maize cultivation
- Agricultural area (S_{Agr}): 13,900 m^2
- Yield reduction: -15% vs full-sun cultivation (literature)

$$S_{Agr} = 92{,}7\% \ of \ S_{AgriPV}$$

LCA of an agrivoltaic system in Italy – Goal and scope

Goal

Environmental sustainability assessment: agrivoltaic vs. conventional PV systems (**reference PV system**)

Scope definition

Functional unit: 1 kWh of electricity delivered to the grid over the plant's lifetime.

Key technical characteristics of the agrivoltaics and the reference PV systems for the comparative LCA

Parameter	Agrivoltaic system	Reference PV system[4]
Plant configuration	Overhead PV system, bi-axial solar tracker	Ground-mounted PV system, mono-axial solar tracker
Location	Robecco sul Naviglio (MI)	Piacenza (PC)
PV technology	PERC (bi-facial)	PERC (mono-facial)
Capacity (MW)	0.54	84.7
Equivalent operating hours (30-year average) (hours)	1,412	1,417

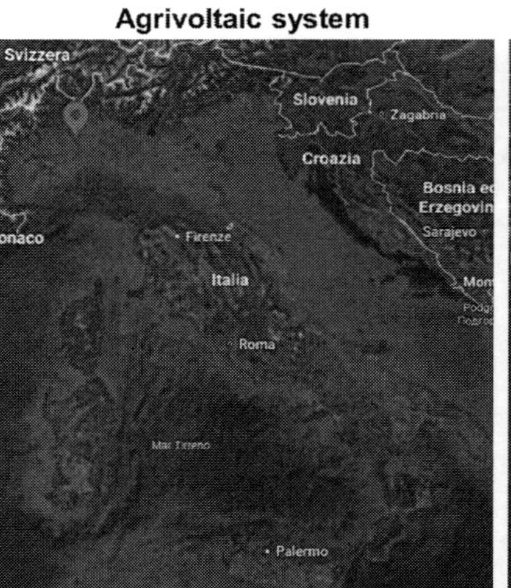
Agrivoltaic system

Reference PV system

LCA of an agrivoltaic system in Italy – Goal and scope

Scope definition

Multifunctionality handling (to make systems functionally comparable): **System expansion**

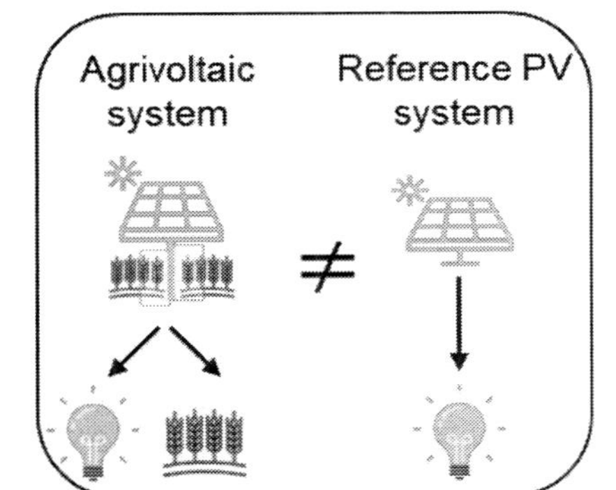

System boundaries

Life cycle impact assessement method

Environmental Footprint 3.1[5]

Impact category; (acronym); [robustness]	Unit
Acidification; (A); [II]	molH⁺eq
Climate change; (CC); [I]	kgCO$_2$eq
Particulate matter; (PM); [I]	Disease incidence
Eutrophication marine; (EU$_M$); [II]	kgNeq
Eutrophication freshwater; (EU$_{FW}$); [II]	kgPeq
Eutrophication terrestrial; (EU$_T$); [II]	molNeq
Land use; (LU); [III]	Pt
Ozone depletion; (OD); [I]	kgCFC-11eq
Photochemical ozone formation human health; (POF); [II]	kgNMVOCeq
Resource use, minerals and metals; (RUMM) [III]	kgSbeq

5

LCA of an agrivoltaic system in Italy - LCI

Construction phase[3,4]

- **PV modules** → RSE dataset: PV datasheets + previous studies on PV modules based on PERC technology (European manufacturer primary data)
- **PV cell** → RSE dataset: based on PERC cell data from a European manufacturer
- **Overhead bi-axial tracker** → RSE dataset: project drawings (CAP holding) + tracker data (European manufacturer primary data).
- **Inverter** → RSE dataset created within the EU GoPV project, based on European manufacturer data
- **Other components** → Modelled consulting RSE experts and Ecoinvent database v. 3.9.1[6]

Operational phase

- **Lifetime electricity (30-years)** → calculated from net annual production provided by the system designer (1,533 kWh/kW/year), considering module degradation

End of Life

- **Inverters, trackers, foundations** → Assumed fully recyclable; recycling excluded from system boundary (cut-off approach) [5]
- **PV modules** → EoL model based on LCI data from IEA PVPS Task 12 activities[7,8,9]

Conventional maize cultivation in the Nothen Italy (Po Valley) – Full sun conditions

- **Yield** → Provided by Università Cattolica del Sacro Cuore – UNICATT (PhD program funded by RSE) (1.2 kg/m^2/year)

Main cultivation operations → Based on standard maize cultivation practices in the Po Valley, from UNICATT with support from literature

Conventional maize cultivation in the Po Valley, Italy – Agrivoltaic conditions

- **Yield** → ~15 % lower than full sun (based on literature)[10]

Upstream and downstream processes

Material and energy inputs, including raw materials, semi-finished products, auxiliary materials, electricity, and fuels, as characterised in Ecoinvent Database v3.9.1

020466-006

LCA of an agrivoltaic system in Italy - LCIA

Environmental impacts associated with the agrivoltaic system. All values are expressed per FU: 1 kWh of electricity.

Impact category	Agrivoltaic PV plant (A)	Maize cultivation - Agrivoltaic conditions (B)	Maize cultivation - Full sun condition (C)	FU (1 kWh of electricity) (A+B+C)/(A+B)
Acidification (Mol H^+eq)	$1.04 \cdot 10^{-4}$	$2.93 \cdot 10^{-4}$	$-2.48 \cdot 10^{-4}$	$\mathbf{1.48 \cdot 10^{-4}}$
Climate change ($kgCO_2$eq)	$1.58 \cdot 10^{-2}$	$7.01 \cdot 10^{-3}$	$-5.95 \cdot 10^{-3}$	$\mathbf{1.68 \cdot 10^{-2}}$
Particulate matter (disease inc.)	$1.18 \cdot 10^{-9}$	$1.97 \cdot 10^{-9}$	$-1.67 \cdot 10^{-9}$	$\mathbf{1.48 \cdot 10^{-9}}$
Eutrophication marine (kgNeq)	$2.91 \cdot 10^{-5}$	$3.67 \cdot 10^{-3}$	$-3.12 \cdot 10^{-4}$	$\mathbf{8.47 \cdot 10^{-5}}$
Eutrophication freshwater (kgPeq)	$7.24 \cdot 10^{-6}$	$7.02 \cdot 10^{-6}$	$-5.96 \cdot 10^{-6}$	$\mathbf{8.30 \cdot 10^{-6}}$
Eutrophication terrestrial (mol Neq)	$2.33 \cdot 10^{-4}$	$1.26 \cdot 10^{-3}$	$-1.07 \cdot 10^{-3}$	$\mathbf{4.23 \cdot 10^{-4}}$
Land use (Pt)	0,101	1.114	-1.197	**0,018**
Ozone depletion (kgCFC11eq)	$3.05 \cdot 10^{-10}$	$9.35 \cdot 10^{-11}$	$-7.94 \cdot 10^{-11}$	$\mathbf{3.19 \cdot 10^{-10}}$
Photochemical ozone formation (kgNMVOCeq)	$7.07 \cdot 10^{-5}$	$2.38 \cdot 10^{-5}$	$-2.02 \cdot 10^{-5}$	$\mathbf{7.43 \cdot 10^{-5}}$
Resource use, minerals and metals (kgSbeq)	$9.44 \cdot 10^{-7}$	$3.80 \cdot 10^{-8}$	$-3.23 \cdot 10^{-8}$	$\mathbf{9.49 \cdot 10^{-7}}$

Shading effects on crop yield (limited primary data)

Percentage contribution of agrivoltaics PV plant, maize cultivation in the agrivoltaic system, and avoided impacts from conventional full-sun maize cultivation, relative to the total system impacts (A + B), set at 100%.

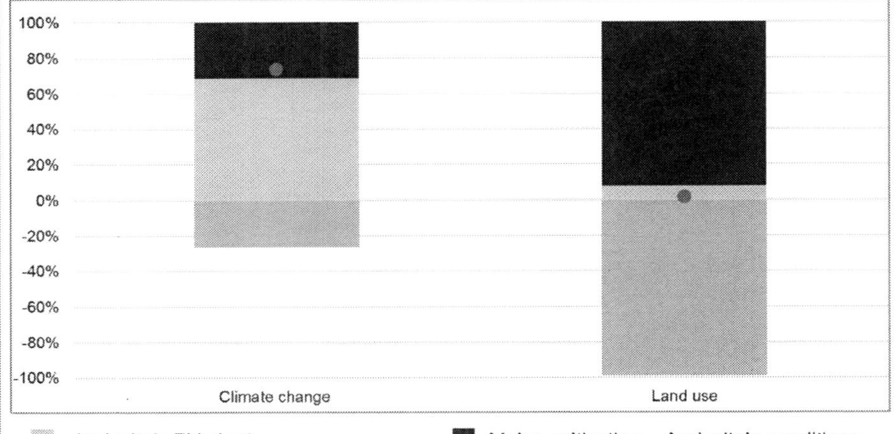

Key considerations:

☑ Land use efficiency: reduced land required per kWh generated

✕ Climate change: lack of synergy between electricity and agriculture systems can increase the overall environmental impact

020466-007

LCA of an agrivoltaic system in Italy - LCIA

Comparative assessment with the reference PV system

Impact category	FU (1 kWh electricity into the grid form the agrivoltaic system)	1 kWh electricity into the grid from the reference PV system
Acidification (Mol H$^+$eq)	$1.48 \cdot 10^{-4}$	$1.00 \cdot 10^{-4}$
Climate change (kgCO$_2$eq)	$1.68 \cdot 10^{-2}$	$1.51 \cdot 10^{-2}$
Particulate matter (disease inc.)	$1.48 \cdot 10^{-9}$	$1.12 \cdot 10^{-9}$
Eutrophication marine (kgNeq)	$8.47 \cdot 10^{-5}$	$2.82 \cdot 10^{-5}$
Eutrophication freshwater (kgPeq)	$8.30 \cdot 10^{-6}$	$6.55 \cdot 10^{-6}$
Eutrophication terrestrial (mol Neq)	$4.23 \cdot 10^{-4}$	$2.23 \cdot 10^{-4}$
Land use (Pt)	$1.87 \cdot 10^{-2}$	$4.51 \cdot 10^{-1}$
Ozone depletion (kgCFC11eq)	$3.19 \cdot 10^{-10}$	$8.12 \cdot 10^{-10}$
Photochemical ozone formation (kgNMVOCeq)	$7.43 \cdot 10^{-5}$	$6.76 \cdot 10^{-5}$
Resource use, minerals and metals (kgSbeq)	$9.49 \cdot 10^{-7}$	$8.34 \cdot 10^{-7}$

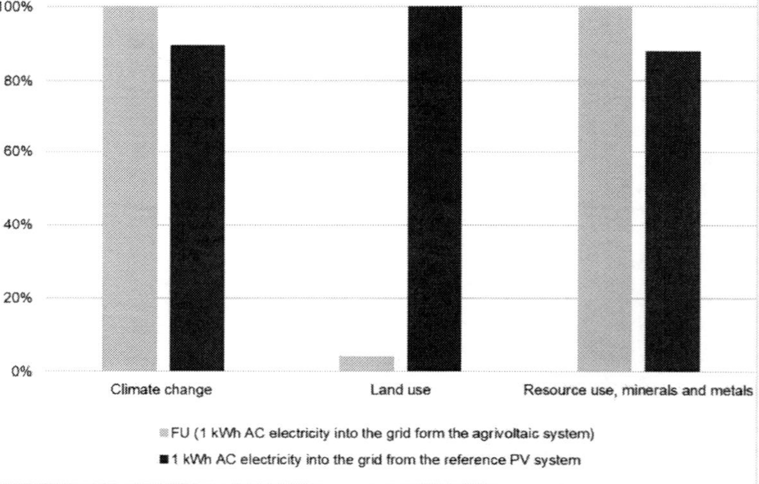

Life cycle impacts of 1 kWh from agrivoltaics vs. reference PV (normalized to 100).

Agrivoltaic systems vs reference PV systems

Land use: - 95% compared to reference PV system **Climate change:** impacts of the same order of magnitude

Beyond yield reduction, higher impacts linked to intrinsic features of the agrivoltaic configuration

- *e.g., more complex structures → higher resource use, minerals and metals*  No additional supply risk

RSE Ricerca Sistema Energetico we move research

LCA of an agrivoltaic system in Italy – scenario analysis

Scenario analysis – impact of PV module shading on maize agricultural yield

Base case	Neutral yield scenario	Enhanced yield scenario
• *15% yield reduction vs. full light cultivation*	• *No yield reduction – shade-tolerant crops*	• *15% yield increase – vs full-light cultivation*

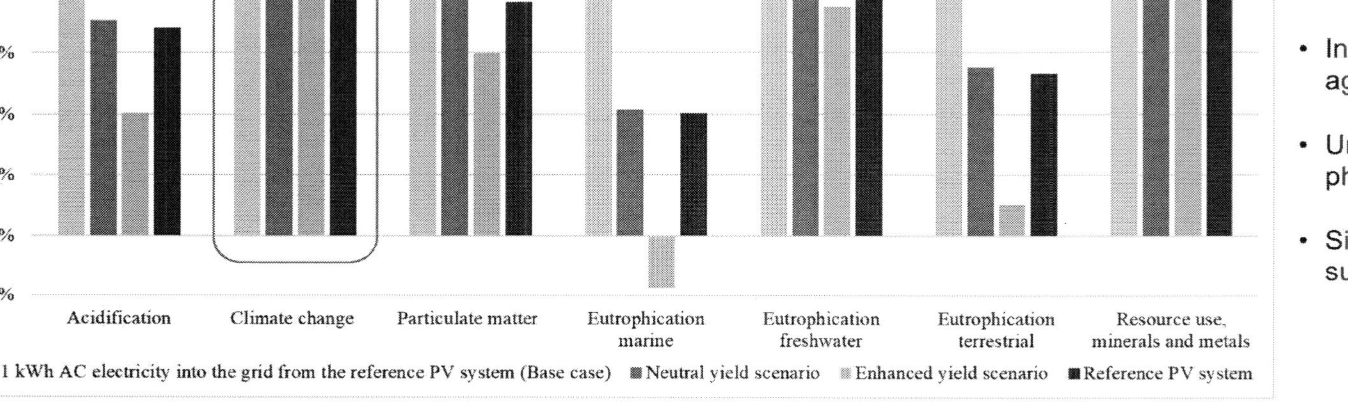

Life cycle impacts of 1 kWh from agrivoltaics vs. reference PV (normalized to 100)

Key considerations:

- Integrated system designs improve agrivoltaics' environmental performance
- Understanding interactions within agro-photovoltaic systems is crucial
- Site-specific data (different climates) support wider adoption

Conclusions and future reasearch

Research innovation

❖ *The study contributes to knowledge in an emerging field*

Environmental sustainability compared to conventional PV

❖ *Significant land use reduction, with comparable climate change impacts*

❖ *Integrated system design maximizes synergies between PV and crops, reducing trade-offs across impact categories*

Strategic implications

❖ *LCA results guide policymakers and industry; more data needed to support sustainable expansion across different climates*

Future research 

- **LCA of agrivoltaic systems across diverse climates:** evaluation of different system configurations and crop varieties.
- **LCA of the RSE experimental agrivoltaic system in Piacenza:** based on primary data collected from the test field, both for the agrivoltaic system and for the corresponding single-use systems.

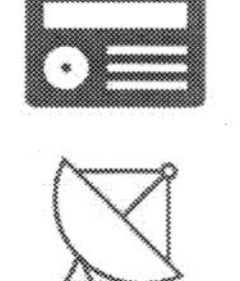

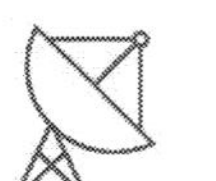

References

1. ISO 14040:2006/A1:2020, 2020. Environmental management - Life cycle assessment - Principles and framework - Amendment 1 (ISO 14040:2006/Amd 1:2020).
2. ISO 14044:2006/A1:2018, 2018. Environmental management - Life cycle assessment - Requirements and guidelines - Amendment 1 (ISO 14044:2006/Amd 1:2017).
3. Cusenza M.A., Danelli A., Spagnolo S., Girardi P. Comparative Life Cycle Assessment of an Overhead Agrivoltaic System: Environmental Impacts and Methodological Insights. Submitted to Journal of cleaner production (under review, JCLEPRO-D-25-23283)
4. Danelli, A., Brivio, E., Girardi, P., Baggio, N., Libal, J., 2024. Environmental Life Cycle Assessment of Passivated Emitter and Rear Contact (PERC) Photovoltaic Module Technology. Report IEA PVPS T12-26:2024. https://doi.org/10.69766/EEMP5995 ISBN: 978-3-907281-47-5.
5. Andreasi Bassi, S., Biganzoli, F., Ferrara, N., Amadei, A., Valente, A., Sala, S., Ardente, F., 2023. Updated characterisation and normalisation factors for the Environmental Footprint 3.1 method. Publications Office of the European Union, Luxembourg. https://doi.org/10.2760/798894.
6. Wernet, G., Bauer, C., Steubing, B., Reinhard, J., Moreno-Ruiz, E., Weidema, B., 2016. The ecoinvent database version 3 (part I): overview and methodology. Int J Life Cycle Assess 21, 1218–1230. https://doi.org/10.1007/s11367-016-1087-8.
7. Frischknecht, R., Heath, G., Raugei, M., Sinha, P., de Wild-Scholten, M., Fthenakis, V., Kim, H.C., Alsema, E., Held, M., 2016. Methodology Guidelines on Life Cycle Assessment of Photovoltaic Electricity, 3rd edition, IEA PVPS Task 12, International Energy Agency Photovoltaic Power Systems Programme. Report IEA-PVPS T12-06:2016.
8. Frischknecht, R., Stolz, P., Heath, G., Raugei, M., Sinha, P., de Wild-Scholten, M., 2020a. Methodology Guidelines on Life Cycle Assessment of Photovoltaic 2020. 4th edition, IEA PVPS Task 12, International Energy Agency Photovoltaic Power Systems Programme.
9. Frischknecht, R., Stolz, P., Krebs, L., de Wild-Scholten, M., Sinha, P., 2020b. Life Cycle Inventories and Life Cycle Assessments of Photovoltaic Systems. Report IEA-PVPS T12-19:2020.
10. Ramos-Fuentes, I.A., Elamri, Y., Cheviron, B., Dejean, C., Belaud, G., Fumey, D., 2023. Effects of shade and deficit irrigation on maize growth and development in fixed and dynamic AgriVoltaic systems. Agricultural Water Management 280, 108187. https://doi.org/10.1016/j.agwat.2023.108187.

Contacts

Thank you for the attention!

Stay informed about RSE

#wemoversearch

Maria Anna Cusenza

 *mariaanna.cusenza@rse-web.it*

 **www.rse-web.it**

 **@Ricerca sul Sistema Energetico - RSE SpA**

 **@RSEnergetico**

 **RSE SpA - Ricerca sul Sistema Energetico**

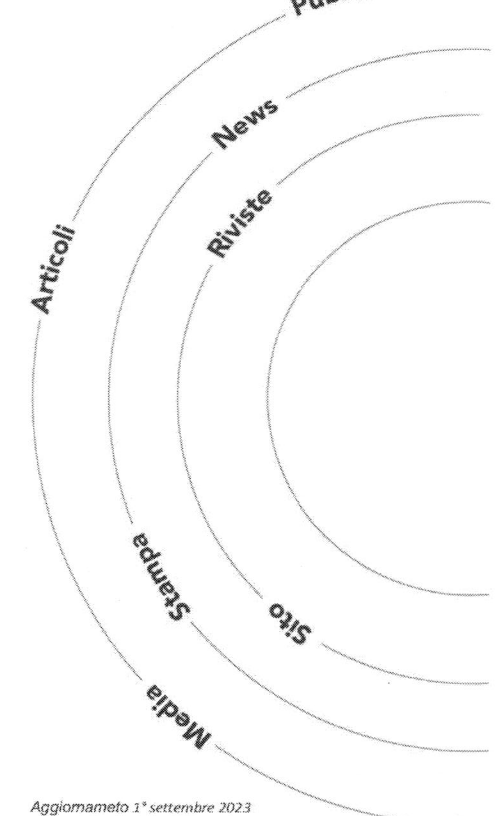

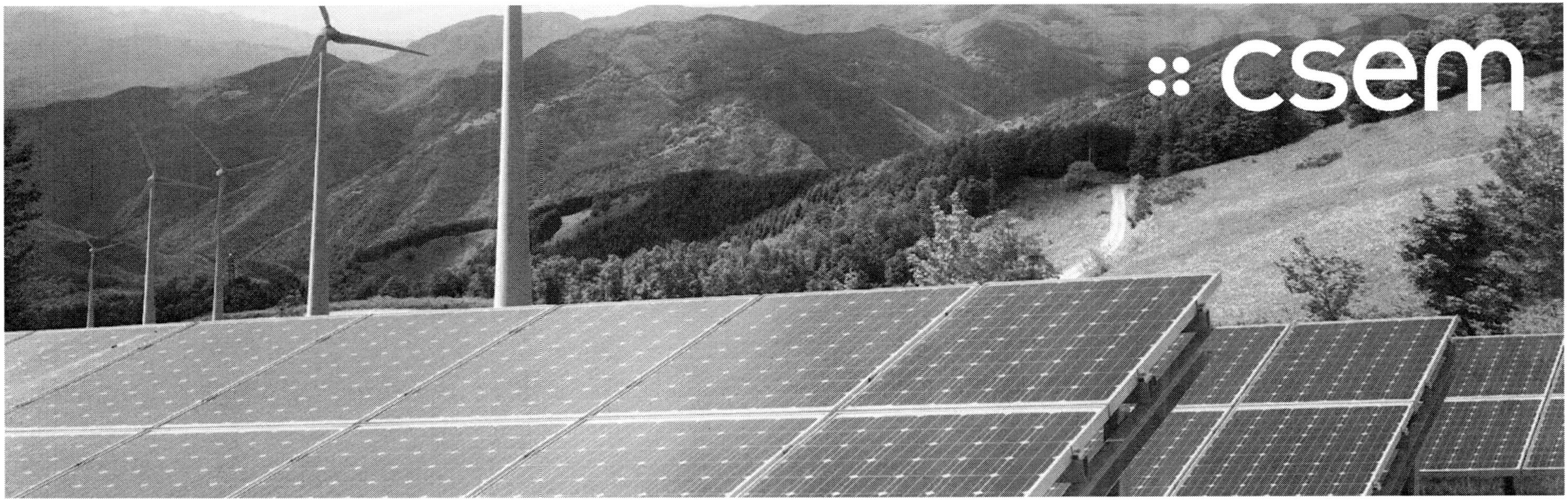

CLOSING THE CIRCLE: INTEGRATING THE CIRCULAR FOOTPRINT FORMULA INTO PV SYSTEM LIFE CYCLE ASSESSMENT

Alexis Barrou, Selin Kandiyoti Eskenazi, Jacques Levrat, Bertrand Paviet-Salomon, Christophe Ballif

CSEM: Swiss Center of Electronic & Microtechnology, Neuchâtel, Switzerland

OUTLINE

- What is the **circular footprint formula** and in which context it happens?

- How to implement the **CFF** for the **LCA** of PV modules and systems?

- What are the preliminary results? Can **CFF** show us how to improve the **environmental footprint** of PV modules and systems?

- What are the main **advantages**, limitations and **next steps**?

- Wrap-up

CONTEXT & MOTIVATIONS

EU policies

EU green deal: climate neutrality in **2050**

Circular economy plan: reuse, recycle, reduce waste

Ecodesign Sustainable Product Regulation:

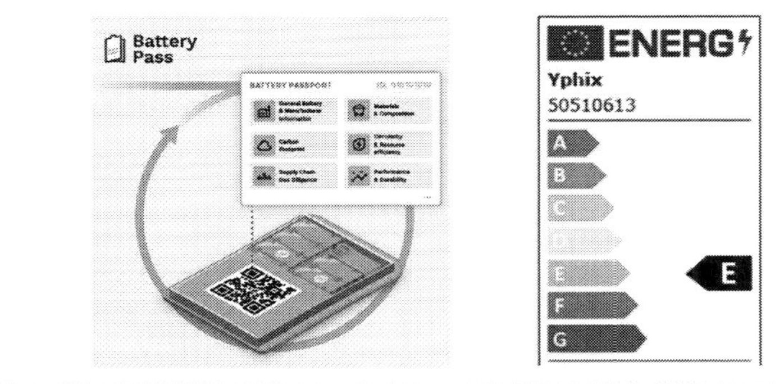
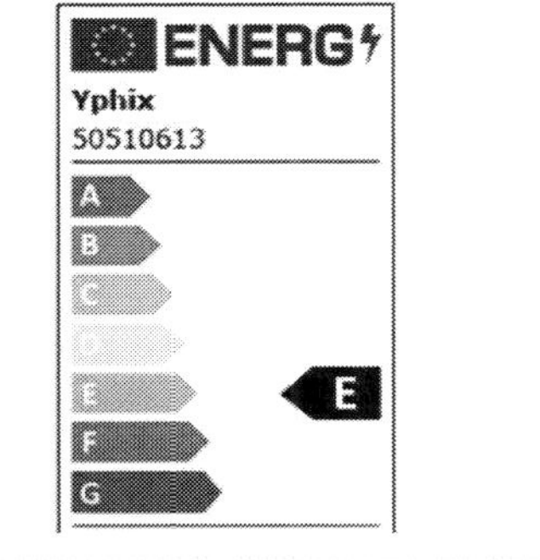

LCA standards for PV

ISO 14040:14044: international standards for LCA

IEA PVPS task 12:
Acknowledged guidelines for PV LCAs

EN15804: EU standards for **Environmental Product Declaration (EPD)** for construction (including PV modules)

EU Product Environmental Footprint (PEF): official LCA methodology for EU products

Introduce the **Circular Footprint Formula (CFF)**

 **Understand & implement CFF for PV module & system LCAs**

CIRCULAR FOOTPRINT FORMULA (CFF) IS A FORMULA USING PARAMETERS & PROCESSES

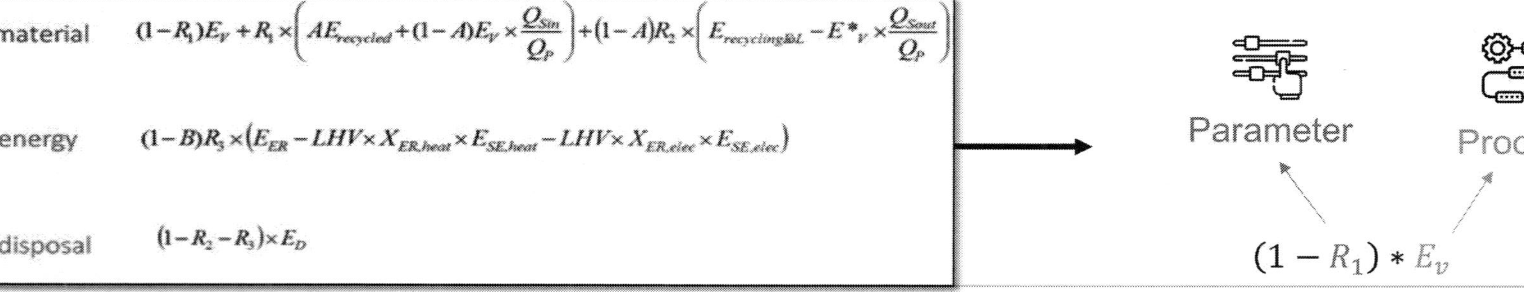

material	$(1-R_1)E_V + R_1 \times \left(AE_{recycled} + (1-A)E_V \times \dfrac{Q_{Sin}}{Q_P} \right) + (1-A)R_2 \times \left(E_{recyclingEoL} - E^*_V \times \dfrac{Q_{Sout}}{Q_P} \right)$
energy	$(1-B)R_3 \times \left(E_{ER} - LHV \times X_{ER,heat} \times E_{SE,heat} - LHV \times X_{ER,elec} \times E_{SE,elec} \right)$
disposal	$(1-R_2-R_3) \times E_D$

The parameters of the Circular Footprint Formula :
A: allocation factor of burdens and credits between supplier and user of recycled materials.
B: allocation factor of energy recovery processes: it applies both to burdens and credits.
Qs_{in}: quality of the ingoing secondary material, i.e. the quality of the recycled material at the point of substitution.
Qs_{out}: quality of the outgoing secondary material, i.e. the quality of the recyclable material at the point of substitution.
Q_p: quality of the primary material, i.e. quality of the virgin material.
R_1: it is the proportion of material in the input to the production that has been recycled from a previous system.
R_2: it is the proportion of the material in the product that will be recycled (or reused) in a subsequent system. R2 shall therefore take into account the inefficiencies in the collection and recycling (or reuse) processes. R2 shall be measured at the output of the recycling plant.
R_3: it is the proportion of the material in the product that is used for energy recovery at EoL.
$E_{recycled}$ (E_{rec}): specific emissions and resources consumed (per unit of analysis) arising from the recycling process of the recycled (reused) material, including collection, sorting and transportation process.
$E_{recyclingEoL}$ (E_{recEoL}): specific emissions and resources consumed (per unit of analysis) arising from the recycling process at EoL, including collection, sorting and transportation process.
E_v: specific emissions and resources consumed (per unit of analysis) arising from the acquisition and pre-processing of virgin material.
E^*_v: specific emissions and resources consumed (per unit of analysis) arising from the acquisition and pre-processing of virgin material assumed to be substituted by recyclable materials.
EER: specific emissions and resources consumed (per unit of analysis) arising from the energy recovery process (e.g. incineration with energy recovery, landfill with energy recovery, …).
$E_{SE,heat}$ and $E_{SE,elec}$: specific emissions and resources consumed (per unit of analysis) that would have arisen from the specific substituted energy source, heat and electricity respectively.
ED: specific emissions and resources consumed (per unit of analysis) arising from disposal of waste material at the EoL of the analysed product, without energy recovery.
$X_{ER,heat}$ and $X_{ER,elec}$: the efficiency of the energy recovery process for both heat and electricity.
LHV: Lower Heating Value of the material in the product that is used for energy recovery.

CIRCULAR FOOTPRINT FORMULA (CFF) IS A FORMULA USING PARAMETERS & PROCESSES

material: $(1-R_1)E_V + R_1 \times \left(AE_{recycled} + (1-A)E_V \times \frac{Q_{Sin}}{Q_P} \right) + (1-A)R_2 \times \left(E_{recyclingEoL} - E^*_V \times \frac{Q_{Sout}}{Q_P} \right)$

energy: $(1-B)R_3 \times \left(E_{ER} - LHV \times X_{ER,heat} \times E_{SE,heat} - LHV \times X_{ER,elec} \times E_{SE,elec} \right)$

disposal: $(1-R_2-R_3) \times E_D$

Parameter   Process

$(1-R_1)*E_v$

	Parameter	Process
Description	**Variable** specific to a material & product type	**Material, energy and waste & pollution** generated to create a product
Exemple	R_1 = % of recycled content of Aluminium	E_v = process to produce 1kg of aluminium from virgin material
Outcome data	**Coefficient (0-1** range oftenly)	**Environmental impact** such as carbon footprint [kg CO2-eq]
Source	Listed by PEFCR or other organisms (JRC) [1]	EF-compliant dataset, to be listed by the **PEFCR** [2]

[1] Joint Research Center, Ardente et al., Harmonised rules for the calculation of the carbon footprint of photovoltaic modules in the context of the EU Ecodesign Directive, 2025
[2] PEFCR for PV modules, 2020

:: csem

CIRCULAR FOOTPRINT FORMULA QUANTIFIES MATERIAL'S MANUFACTURING & END-OF-LIFE ENVIRONMENTAL IMPACTS

- Was created in the context of the **PEF methodology**

- Manages **end-of-life credits** and accounts material's **recycled share**

Parameter   Process

$$(1 - R_1) * E_v$$

Manufacturing   **End-of-life**

Virgin/primary material

$$(1 - R_1) * E_v$$

$1 - R_1$

R_2

Recycling with benefits

$$(1 - A)R_2 * (E_{recyclingEoL} - E_v^* * \frac{Q_{Sout}}{Q_p})$$

Energy recovery

R_3

$$(1 - B)R_3 * (E_{ER} - LHV * X_{ER,heat} * E_{SE,heat} - LHV * X_{ER,elec} * E_{SE,elec})$$

Recycled/secondary material

$$R_1 * (AE_{recycled} + (1 - A)E_v * \frac{Q_{Sin}}{Q_p})$$

R_1

$1 - R_2 - R_3$

Landfill/waste disposal

$$(1 - R_2 - R_3) * E_D$$

HOW TO IMPLEMENT THE CFF FOR THE LCA OF PV MODULES & SYSTEMS?

$R_1, R_2, R_3, A, B, \ldots$ $E_v, E_v^*, E_D, E_{recycled}, E_{recyclingEoL}, \ldots$ …kg/PV module   …kg/PV BOS

47
Ag
Silver

$R_1, R_2, R_3, A, B, \ldots$ $E_v, E_v^*, E_D, E_{recycled}, E_{recyclingEoL}, \ldots$ …kg/PV module   …kg/PV BOS

14
Si
Silicon

$R_1, R_2, R_3, A, B, \ldots$ $E_v, E_v^*, E_D, E_{recycled}, E_{recyclingEoL}, \ldots$ …kg/PV module   …kg/PV BOS

Parameters [1]   **Process environmental impact** *, [2]   **Weight PV module & system** *

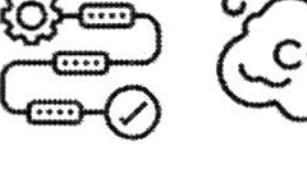

CFF_calculator

CFF_PV_calculator

Impact per kg
- Virgin material
- Recycled material
- EoL Recycling
- EoL energy recovery
- EoL disposal

Impact per PV
- Virgin material
- Recycled material
- EoL Recycling
- EoL energy recovery
- EoL disposal

* Own calculations/sources
[1] Joint Research Center, Ardente et al., Harmonised rules for the calculation of the carbon footprint of photovoltaic modules in the context of the EU Ecodesign Directive, 2025
[2] PEFCR for PV modules, 2020

:: csem

SCOPE OF ANALYSIS

13 materials analyzed   

7 parameters $R_1, R_2, R_3, A, B, \ldots$

16 environmental impact categories 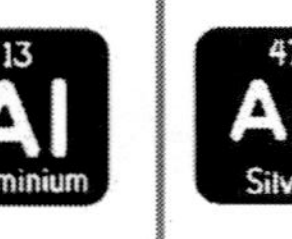

4 PV module types:

- Glass-glass with alu frame
- Glass-glass without alu frame
- Glass-Backsheet with alu frame
- Lightweight without alu fame

Decomposition of the impact

6 PV system configurations:

1. Slanted roof
2.A Flat roof (only racking)
2.B Flat roof (with ballast)
3.A Open-ground (no concrete)
3.B open-ground (with concrete)
4. Façade

:: csem

WEIGHT REPARTITION OF 4 TYPES OF PV MODULES

HJT technology 3.11 m², 132 ½ G12 cells, manufactured in China

- **Glass** = major **contributor** to module **weight** for GG and GBs

- For **lightweight module**: majority of impact is on **polymers**

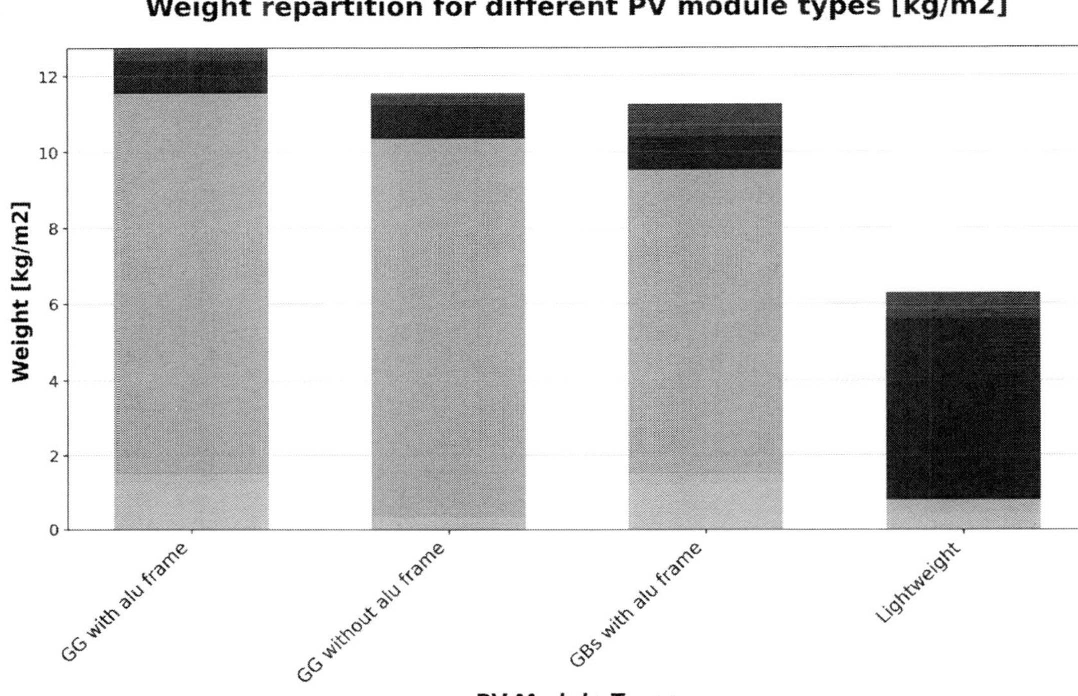

:: csem

PRELIMINARY RESULTS

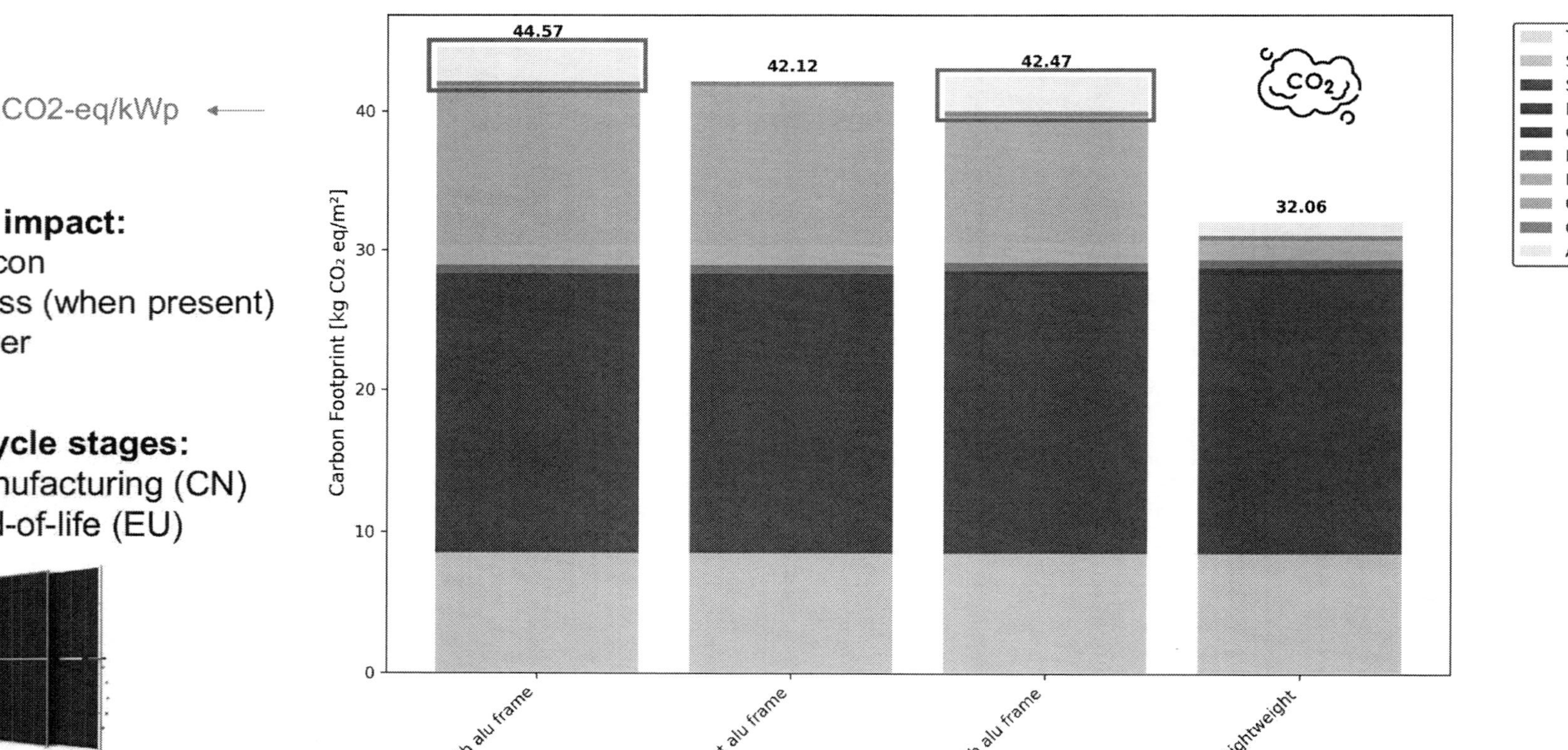

~ 200 kgCO2-eq/kWp

Major impact:
- Silicon
- Glass (when present)
- Silver

Life cycle stages:
- Manufacturing (CN)
- End-of-life (EU)

020467-010

DECOMPOSITION OF ALUMINIUM CARBON FOOTPRINT

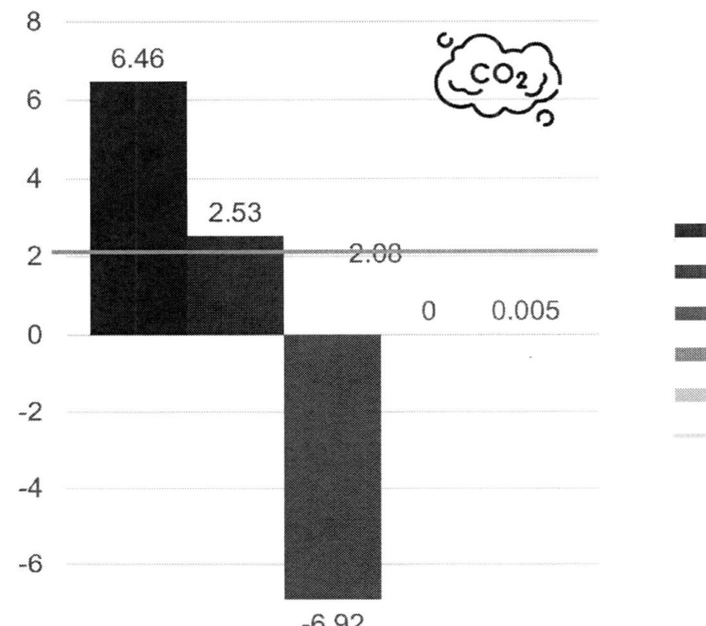

Al
13
Aluminium

CO₂

| EoL energy recovery | > Virgin material

- Important **recycled content** (R1 = 32%)
- **Massive recycling** (R2 = 95%)

- **Recycling has benefits (negative value)** by deleting the need of important quantities of virgin aluminium production

:: csem

PARAMETER SENSITIVITY ANALYSIS WITH ALUMINIUM

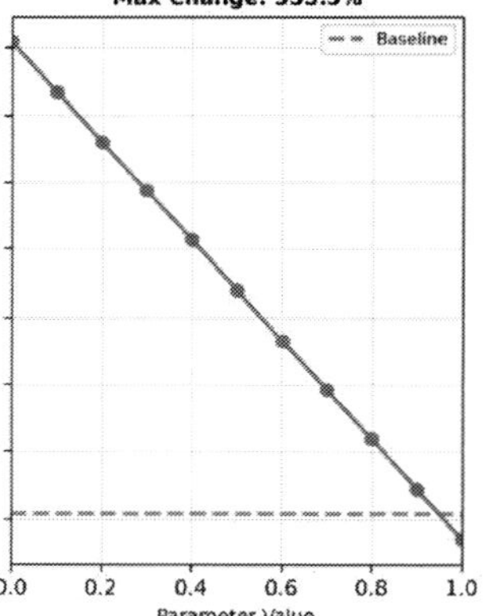

How the **carbon footprint** of 1kg of aluminium would change if **recycled content (R1) = 100%**?

What if **recycling rate (R2)** is reduced?

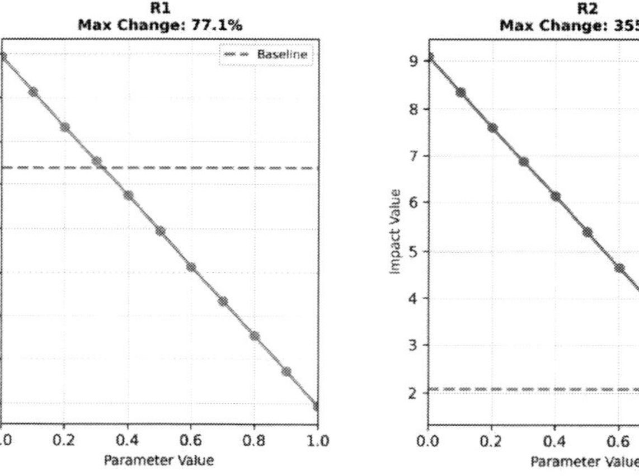

Baseline Parameters: A=0.20 | B=0.00 | R1=0.32 | R2=0.95
R3 (EU)=0.02 | Qs_in_Qp=1.00 | Qs_out_Qp=1.00

Sensitivity Analysis: Aluminum - Climate change (kg CO2 eq)
Baseline Impact: 2.076100

:: csem

PARAMETER SENSITIVITY ANALYSIS WITH ALUMINIUM

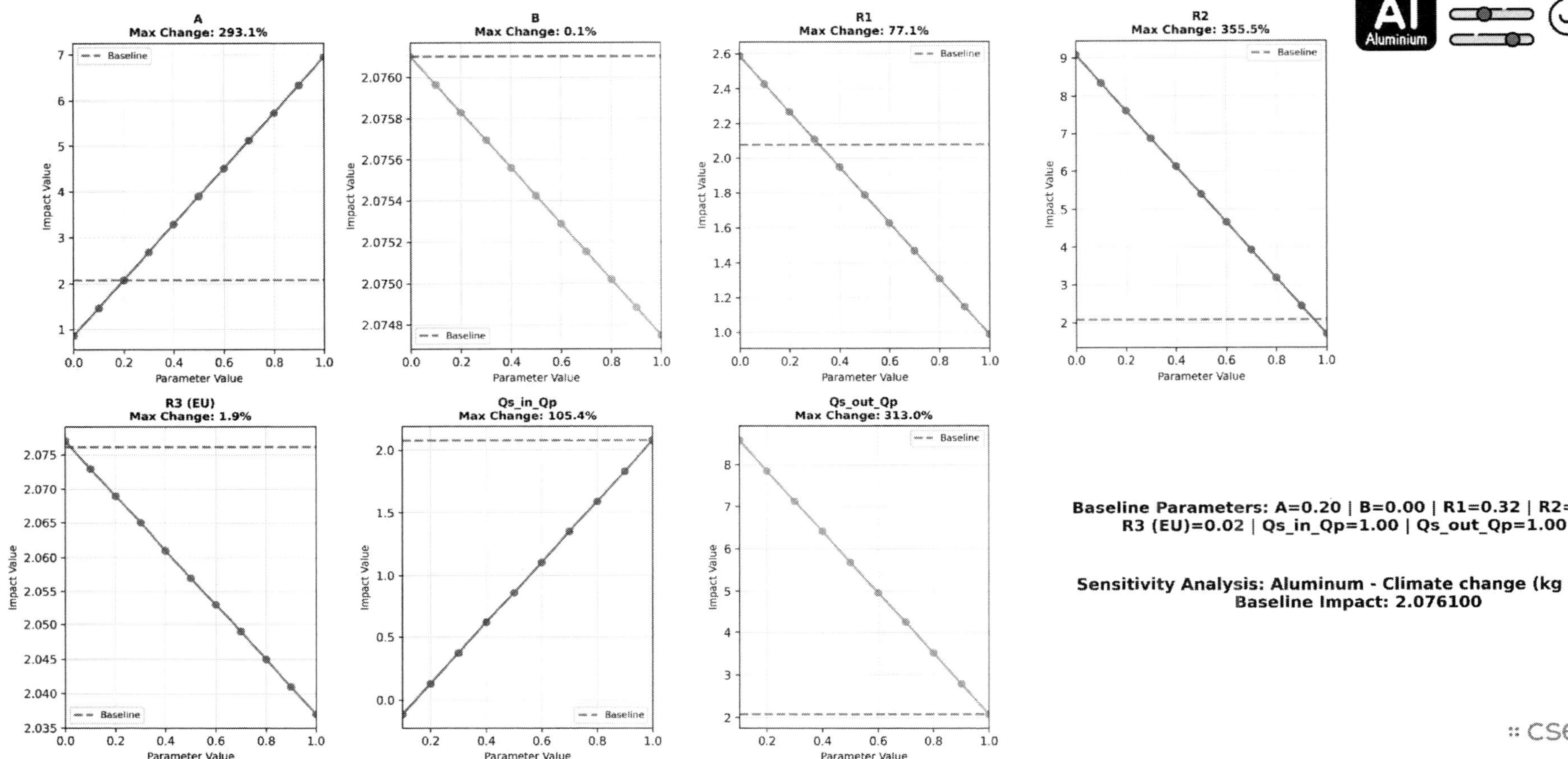

ADVANTAGES, LIMITATIONS & NEXT STEPS

- **Advantages** of CFF:
  - Scenarios evaluation with parametric LCA
  - Decomposes material's environmental footprint along manufacturing & end-of-life

- **Inconvenients** of CFF:
  - Only focuses on materials' environmental footprint
  - Dependent of EF-compliant dataset for parameters & processes
  - LCA softwares do not always include parameters modelisation

- **Next steps & challenges**:
  - Implement the CFF in existing LCA software
  - Find up-to-date and accurate EF-compliant datasets
  - Establish link with other LCA methodologies: ex: EPD (EN15804) [1]

Parameter   Process

$$(1 - R_1) * E_v$$

[1] Durao et al. Assessment and communication of the environmental performance of construction products in Europe

:: csem

WRAP-UP

Circular footprint formula (CFF):

$$(1 - R_1) * E_v$$

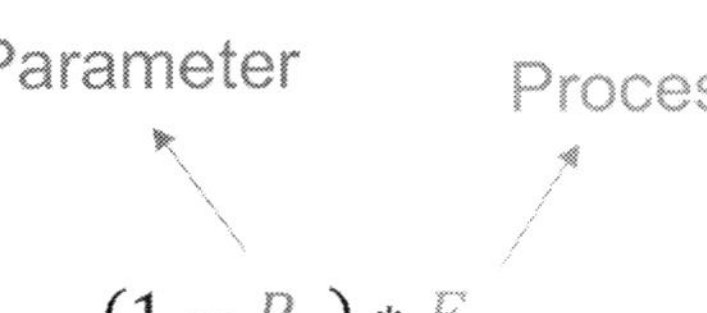

- **Is mandatory** to be PEF compliant, for carbon footprint & ecodesign regulations for PV [1]

- Has parameters & processes specific to a material used for a product

- Evaluates virgin and recycled materials manufacturing additionally to end-of-life

- Is useful to evaluate **circularity** or recyclability index for PV & how to reduce further the **environmental footprint of PV modules & systems**

- need **parameters** & processes EF-compliant datasets updates

- can be implemented in **LCA softwares** allowing parameters settings

[1] Joint Research Center, Ardente et al., Harmonised rules for the calculation of the carbon footprint of photovoltaic modules in the context of the EU Ecodesign Directive, 2025

:: csem

Alexis Barrou , R&D Engineer, CSEM   alexis.barrou@csem.ch

ENVIRONMENTAL BENEFITS OF SILICON KERF SECONDARY PRODUCTS IN PILOT PROCESSES OVER CONVENTIONAL PRODUCTION OF EQUIVALENT PRODUCTS WITH PRIMARY RAW MATERIALS IN CHINA AND EUROPE

René Peche, Matthias Seitz, Markus Schönheits, Karsten Wambach
bifa Umweltinstitut GmbH
Am Mittleren Moos 46, 86167 Augsburg, Germany

ABSTRACT: bifa Umweltinstitut GmbH is evaluating four pilot units newly developed in the ICARUS project for processing silicon kerf waste into secondary materials and marketable products and shows whether an ecological improvement compared to the conventional Chinese and European supply of functionally equivalent materials from primary raw material can be achieved. The evaluation is done using the method of life cycle assessment (LCA). The turning of PV waste silicon kerf into secondary raw materials or marketable products eliminates a large part of the environmental impact associated with the conventional production of equivalent raw materials or products. The reduction in environmental impact ranges from more than 85% for the production of secondary metallurgical grade and solar grade silicon compared to the conventional production in China over more than 75% for the production of secondary metallurgical grade and solar grade silicon compared to the conventional production in Europe to more than 30% for the production of hydrogen and water glass from silicon kerf waste compared to the conventional production in Europe. Thus, the newly developed processes in the ICARUS project not only reduce dependence on supplies from Asia, but also help to reduce harmful emissions into the environment during the production of raw materials.
Keywords: LCA; ecology index; secondary materials; silicon; recycling; PV modules

1 INTRODUCTION

In the ICARUS project, 17 European partners are collaborating to develop innovative methods for processing and refining secondary raw materials from silicon PV manufacturing. This involves transforming the process wastes Si-kerf waste, graphite waste and silica waste from silicon (Si)ingot and wafer production into valuable secondary resources (Figure 1).

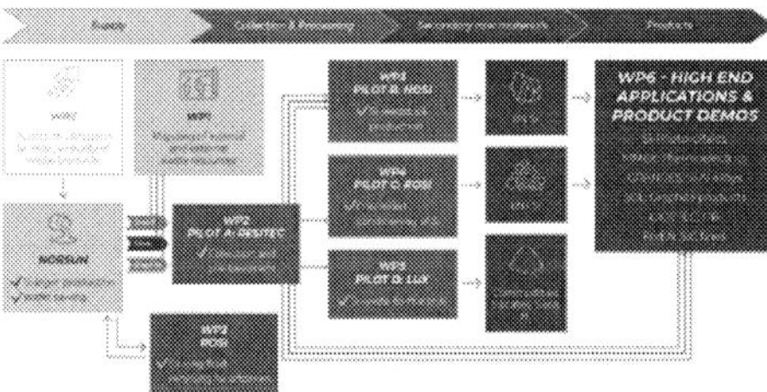

Figure 1: ICARUS project

For filtered Si-Kerf, which is produced during the diamond wire sawing of silicon blocks into wafers, four pilot processes have been developed and operated, demonstrating the relevance of the different technological options and bringing modularity in: (a) Si-kerf recycling and refining (PILOT A, B and C) considering different inputs and purity grades for diverse applications; and (b) revalorisation of Si (PILOT D), transforming Si-kerf into the valuable commodities green hydrogen and water glass. The energy intensity of silicon is strongly related to its purity. Therefore, the ICARUS project will take advantage of the silicon content of the kerf, invested with a lot of energy, and reuse it as secondary raw material. For example, reusing secondary silicon in wafer production can significantly reduce the high energy demands associated with processing primary raw Si into wafers, which accounts for about 75 % of the total energy used in PV module manufacturing.
The LCA conducted in the ICARUS project supports and quantifies the process developments.

2 METHOD

An LCA is a system analysis method for the integrated, media-wide acquisition and evaluation of environment-related matters in connection with products, processes and services. LCA are characterized by the analyses of environmental influences in association with prior or subsequent life cycle stages. Also considered here are inputs and withdrawals of raw materials and energy to and from environmental media, namely water, air and earth. Overall, LCA can make a comprehensive statement on the relevance to the environment of the systems investigated and are therefore optimally suited for environment-related comparison of various systems.

The LCA in the ICARUS project is carried out under the norm specifications for the execution of eco-balances DIN EN ISO 14040 [1] and DIN EN ISO 14044 [2], taken into account the Product Environmental Footprint Category Rules (PEFCR) for photovoltaic modules used in photovoltaic power systems for electricity generation [3,4]. Starting with the definition of goal and scope under the terms of the Life cycle inventory analysis, all relevant parameters are recorded and summarized in the life cycle impact assessment regarding their environmental impact. Figure 2 shows a schematic overview of the basic compilation of an LCA with fields of application.

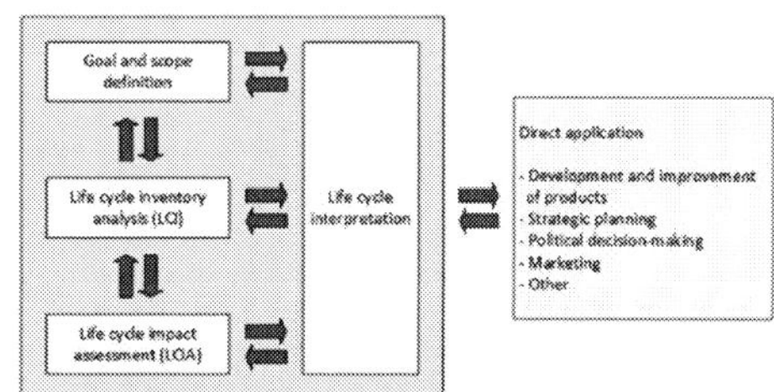

Figure 2: Schematic overview of the basic compilation of an LCA with fields of application

Table 1 shows the thirteen impact categories that are assessed and interpreted in the LCA of the ICARUS project.

Table 1: Applied environmental impact category used in the ICARUS project

Impact category	Unit
Climate change	kg CO_2 eq.
Ozon depletion	kg CF-11 eq.
Particulate matter	Disease Incidence
Ionizing radiation, human health	kBq U^{235} eq.
Photochemical ozone formation, human health	kg NMVOC eq.
Acidification	mole H^+ eq.
Eutrophication, terrestrial	mole N eq.
Eutrophication, freshwater	kg P eq.
Eutrophication, marine	kg N eq.
Land use	Pt
Water use	kg world eq. deprived
Resource use, minerals and metals	kg Sb eq.
Resource use, energy carriers	MJ

The individual results of the impact categories are combined using the normalization and weighting factors published by the European Commission's Joint Research Centre [5,6], to create a dimensionless single ecological indicator – the so-called ecology index.

3   RESULTS

Information and process data for the pilot processes are provided by the project partners. The Chinese and European production processes are modelled using data from IEA PVPS Task 12 [6] and ecoinvent database [7].

The data sets used together with the process data and information to create the LCA models also came from the ecoinvent database.

PILOT A process: Secondary dry silicon compared to conventional metallurgical grade silicon produced in China and Europe

The product of the pilot A process developed by project partner Resitec AS (Norway) is secondary dry silicon with less than 1% moisture. The starting material is filtered Si-kerf containing 47 % moisture from the silicon wafer sawing process.

The comparable conventional product is metallurgical grade silicon, produced from primary silica sand.

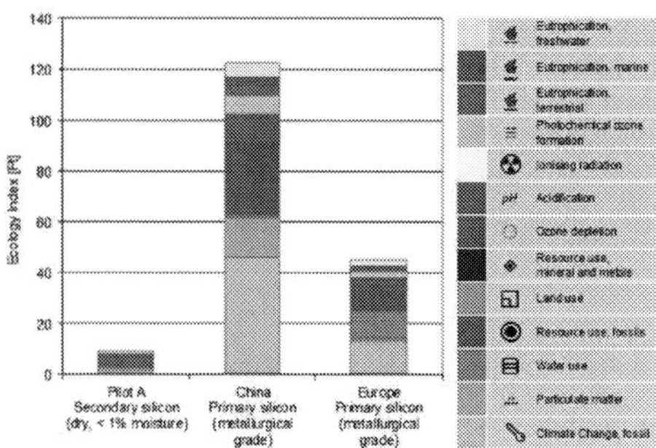

Figure 3: Comparison of the ecological indices of the pilot A process and the conventional production processes in China and Europe

Figure 3 demonstrates that secondary dry silicon has an ecological advantage of more than 90 % over conventional production of metallurgical grade silicon in China, and almost 80% compared to conventional production in Europe

The improved ecology index can be attributed primarily to the lower quantity of energy used in the pilot A process, and secondarily to the use of materials, which is significantly reduced compared to those used in the Chinese and European production processes.

For instance, the electricity consumption for the pilot A process is more than eight times lower than that required for the conventional production of metallurgical grade silicon. Furthermore, unlike the 2 conventional production processes the pilot A process does not require any thermal energy

PILOT B and PILOT C processes: Secondary silicon 6N+ and 8N compared to conventional solar grade silicon produced in China and Europe

The product of the pilot B process developed by project partner ROSI SAS (France) is secondary silicon of 8N purity and the product of the pilot C process developed by project partner Northern Silicon (Norway) is secondary silicon of 6N+ purity.

The comparable conventional product is solar grade silicon, produced from primary metallurgical grade silicon.

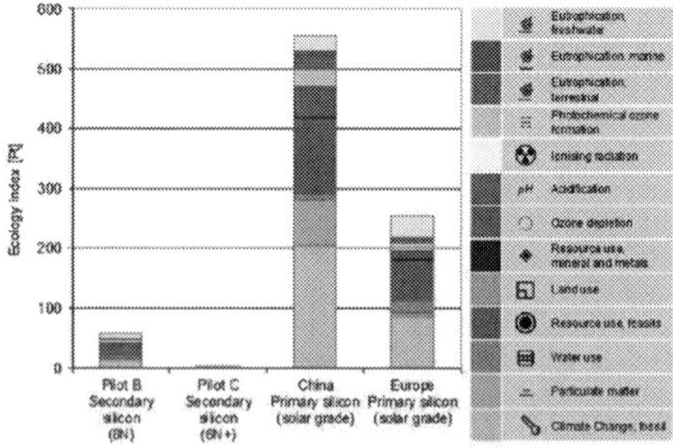

Figure 4: Comparison of the ecological indices of the pilot B and pilot C processes and the conventional production processes in China and Europe

Figure 4 shows that the secondary silicon 8N and 6N+ have an ecological advantage of more than 85 % over the conventional production of solar grade silicon in China and more than 75% over the conventional production in

Europe.

The improved ecological indices are due to the same factors as described for pilot A process. The main reason is the lower quantity of energy used in the pilot processes. In addition, the consumption of primary materials is significantly lower compared to the conventional production processes because of the use of waste as a starting material.

PILOT D process: Hydrogen and water glass produced from silicon kerf compared to conventional hydrogen and sodium silicate produced in Europe

The products of the pilot D process developed by project partner LuxChemtech GmbH (Germany) are hydrogen and water glass. The starting material is the processed Si-kerf from the pilot A process.

In the conventional production processes of hydrogen (produced via the cracking of fossil fuels and chlor-alkali electrolysis) and water glass (produced from the furnace process), the starting materials are natural gas and the silica sand as well as soda ash, respectively.

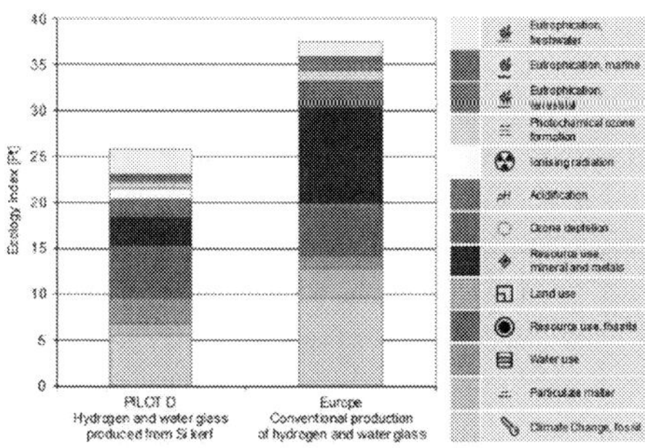

Figure 5: Comparison of the ecological indices of the pilot D process and the conventional production processes in Europe

Figure 5 shows that hydrogen and water glass produced from silicon kerf have an ecological advantage of more than 30 % over the conventional production of the two products in Europe.

The improved ecology index results from the reduction of primary raw materials and the lower consumption of fossil fuels, which are typically required for conventional hydrogen and water glass production.

4 DISCUSSION AND CONCLUSION

The turning of PV waste silicon kerf, which is energy-dense and rich in highly pure silicon, into secondary raw materials or marketable products eliminates a large part of the environmental impact associated with the conventional production of equivalent raw materials or products.

The reduction in environmental impact ranges from more than 85% for the production of secondary metallurgical grade and solar grade silicon compared to the conventional production in China over more than 75% for the production of secondary metallurgical grade and solar grade silicon compared to the conventional production in Europe to more than 30% for the production of hydrogen and water glass from silicon kerf waste compared to the conventional production in Europe.

Thus, the newly developed processes in the ICARUS project not only reduce dependence on supplies from Asia, but also help to reduce harmful emissions into the environment during the production of raw materials.

5 REFERENCES

[1] DIN EN ISO 14040:2021-02: Environmental management - Life cycle assessment - Principles and framework (ISO 14040:2006 + Amd 1:2020), Deutsches Institut für Normung DIN e.V.; 2021

[2] DIN EN ISO 14044:2021-02: Environmental management - Life cycle assessment - Requirements and guidelines (ISO 14044:2006 + Amd 1:2017 + Amd 2:2020), Deutsches Institut für Normung DIN e.V.; 2021

[3] Product Environmental Footprint Category Rules (PEFCR) for photovoltaic modules used in photovoltaic power systems for electricity generation. European Commission's Joint Research Centre - Institute for Environment and Sustainability; 2020

[4] JRC Technical Report - Updated characterisation and normalisation factors for the Environmental Footprint 3.1 method. European Commission's Joint Research Centre - Institute for Environment and Sustainability; 2023

[5] JRC Technical Reports - Development of a weighting approach for the Environmental Footprint. European Commission's Joint Research Centre - Institute for Environment and Sustainability; 2018

[6] Life Cycle Inventory and Life Cycle Assessments of Photovoltaic Systems. Report IEA-PVPS T12-19:2020, International Energy Agency; 2020

[7] Life cycle inventory database ecoinvent v3.8: https://www.ecoinvent.org, Zürich; 2021

6 ACKNOWLEDGEMENTS

This work has received funding from the European Union's Horizon 2020 research and innovation programme under grant agreement No 958365; project ICARUS.

Views and opinions expressed are however those of the authors only and do not necessarily reflect those of the European Union or CINEA. Neither the European Union nor the granting authority can be held responsible for them.

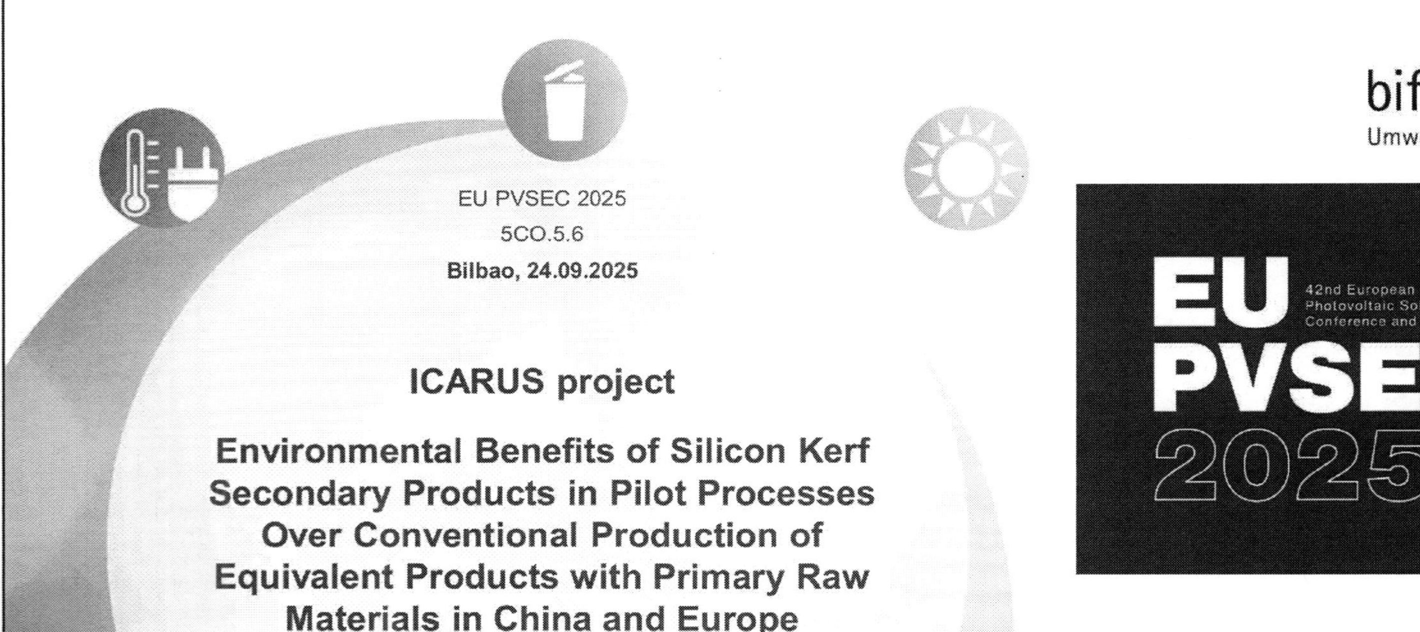
EU PVSEC 2025
5CO.5.6
Bilbao, 24.09.2025

ICARUS project

Environmental Benefits of Silicon Kerf
Secondary Products in Pilot Processes
Over Conventional Production of
Equivalent Products with Primary Raw
Materials in China and Europe

René Peche, Matthias Seitz, Markus Schönheits,
Karsten Wambach

bifa
Umweltinstitut

EU PVSEC 2025
42nd European
Photovoltaic Solar Energy
Conference and Exhibition

www.bifa.de

bifa Umweltinstitut GmbH

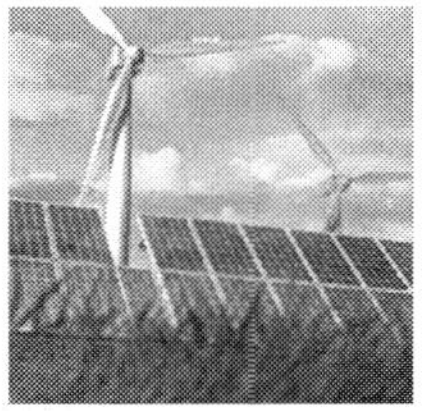

Application-orientated research, development and consulting facility

Our expertise:

- LCA, eco-efficiency analysis, LCC, TEA
- Recycling processes from laboratory to pilot plant scale
- Environmental Analytics
- Waste and circularity Assessment
- Recyclability and circularity Indices
- Ecodesign / design for recycling
- Social acceptance (workshops, surveys, interviews)

Recent and relevant EU Projects

24.09.2025

EU PVSEC 2025

bifa
Umweltinstitut

Outline

1. **ICARUS project**

2. **Life Cycle Assessment (LCA)**

3. **Creation of the ecology index**

4. **Preliminary Results**

5. **Conclusion**

Source: https://www.icarus.eu.com

24.09.2025

3

ICARUS project

bifa
Umweltinstitut

Development of innovative methods for processing and refining secondary raw materials from silicon PV manufacturing

- 17 European partners

- ICARUS will demonstrate:
  - 3 innovative industrial pilots producing silicon, silica and graphite raw materials
  - 1 pilot converting silicon waste into full value industrial commodities

- **bifa's work package in the project:**
  - **Techno economic analysis**
  - **Life cycle assessment**
  - **Social acceptance**

This project has received funding from the European Union's Horizon 2020 research and innovation programme under grant agreement No 958365

24.09.2025

4

Life Cycle Assessment

bifa
Umweltinstitut

1. Define the goal and scope

What is being investigated and what aspects need to be considered?

2. Collect data for all process steps

Which substances are taken from the environment or released into the environment?

3. Create a balance sheet of emissions and resources extracted (LCI)

Which substances are removed from or released into the environment during the life cycle?

4. Assess environmental impacts (LCIA and interpretation)

What are the implications and how are they assessed?

24.09.2025

5

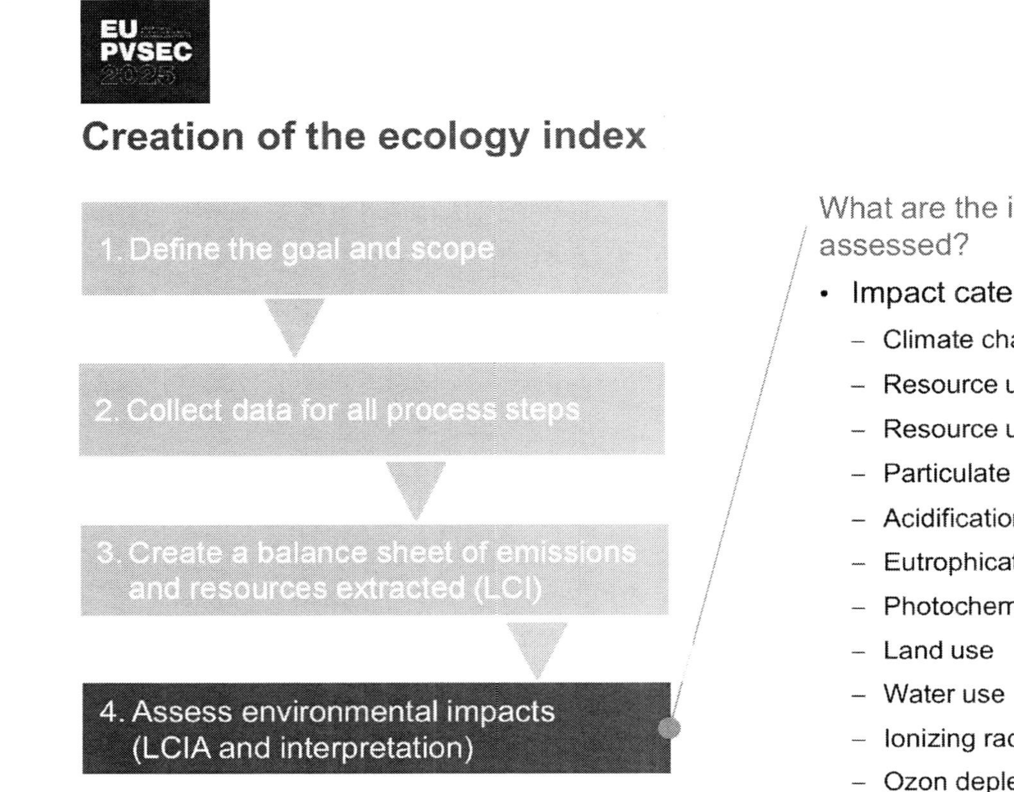

Creation of the ecology index

What are the implications and how are they assessed?

- Impact categories considered
  - Climate change
  - Resource use, energy carriers
  - Resource use, minerals and metals
  - Particulate matter
  - Acidification
  - Eutrophication, marine/freshwater and terrestrial
  - Photochemical ozone formation, human health
  - Land use
  - Water use
  - Ionizing radiation, human health
  - Ozon depletion

24.09.2025

Creation of the ecology index

Combination of individual LCA results (three-step process)

1. **Standardization:** Conversion of the individual results in the common reference unit of "population equivalents"
   - Basis → Normalisation factors in Environmental Footprint 3.1 (EF3.1)
   - Examples → Climate change: 7,550 kg CO_2 eq. / person
     Acidification: 55.6 mol H^+ eq. / person
     Resource use, fossils: 65 GJ / person

2. **Weighting:** Weighting of the individual impact categories
   - Basis → Weighting set for the standardized impact categories in EF3.1
   - Examples → Climate change: 22.19 %
     Acidification: 6.64 %
     Resource use, fossils: 8.92 %

3. **Combining:** Combining the weighted results to create the ecology index
   - Sum of the standardized, weighted impact indicator results to a dimensionless single value

PILOT A process: Secondary dry silicon

bifa
Umweltinstitut

Comparison: **Secondary** *dry silicon with < 1% moisture from ICARUS vs.*
Conventional *metallurgical grade silicon (mg-Si) produced in China / Europe*

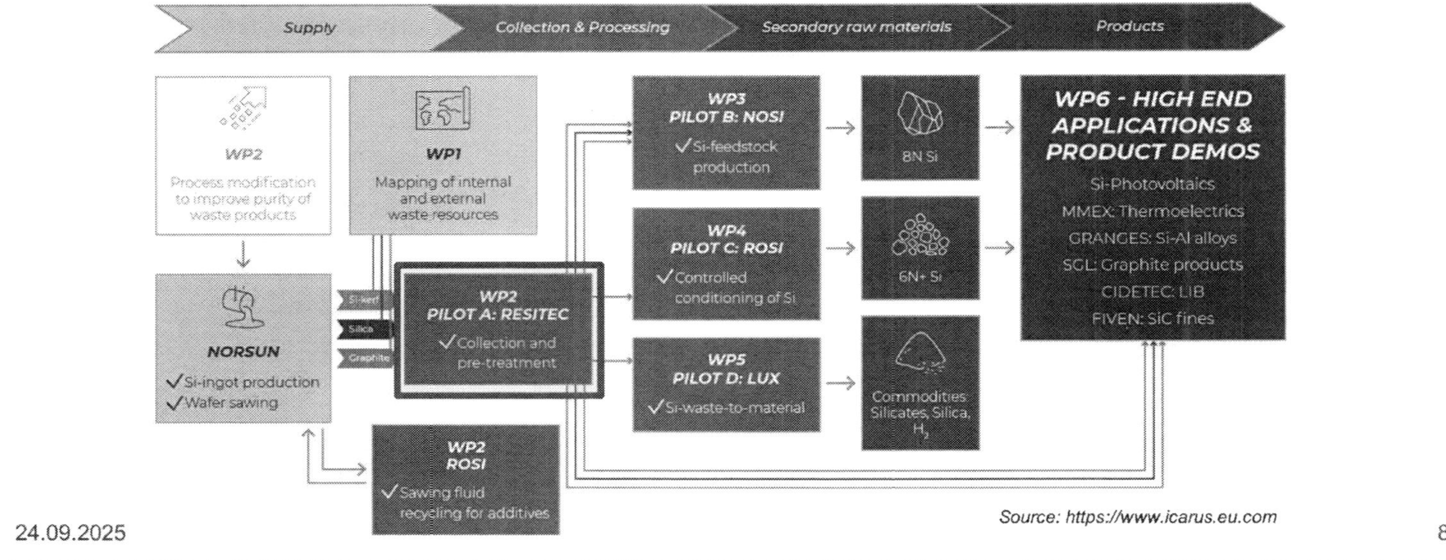

Source: https://www.icarus.eu.com

24.09.2025

8

PILOT A process: Secondary dry silicon

Comparison: **Secondary** *dry silicon with < 1% moisture from ICARUS vs.*
Conventional *metallurgical grade silicon (mg-Si) produced in China / Europe*

PILOT A process:

- Starting material: filtered Si-kerf with 47% moisture from the wafer sawing process
- Process data: provided by project partner

Conventional processes in China/Europe:

- Starting material: primary silica sand
- Process data: IEA PVPS Task 12-19:2020 "LCI and LCA of Photovoltaic Systems"

24.09.2025

9

PILOT A process: Secondary dry silicon

Comparison: **Secondary** *dry silicon with < 1% moisture from ICARUS vs.*
Conventional *metallurgical grade silicon (mg-Si) produced in China / Europe*

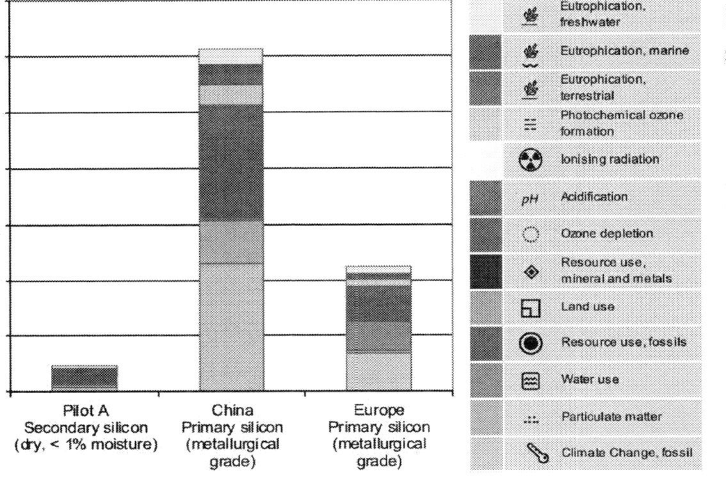

Ecological advantage of secondary dry silicon over primary mg-Si:

- China process: more than 90%
- Europe process: almost 80%

Main reasons for better result of Pilot A process:

- Electricity consumption is more than 8 times lower
- No thermal energy is required
- Starting material is the waste *silicon kerf* instead of the primary raw material *silica sand*

24.09.2025

10

PILOT B/C processes: Secondary silicon 6N+ and 8N

Comparison: **Secondary** *silicon 6N+ and 8N from ICARUS vs.*
Conventional *solar grade silicon (sg-Si) produced in China / Europe*

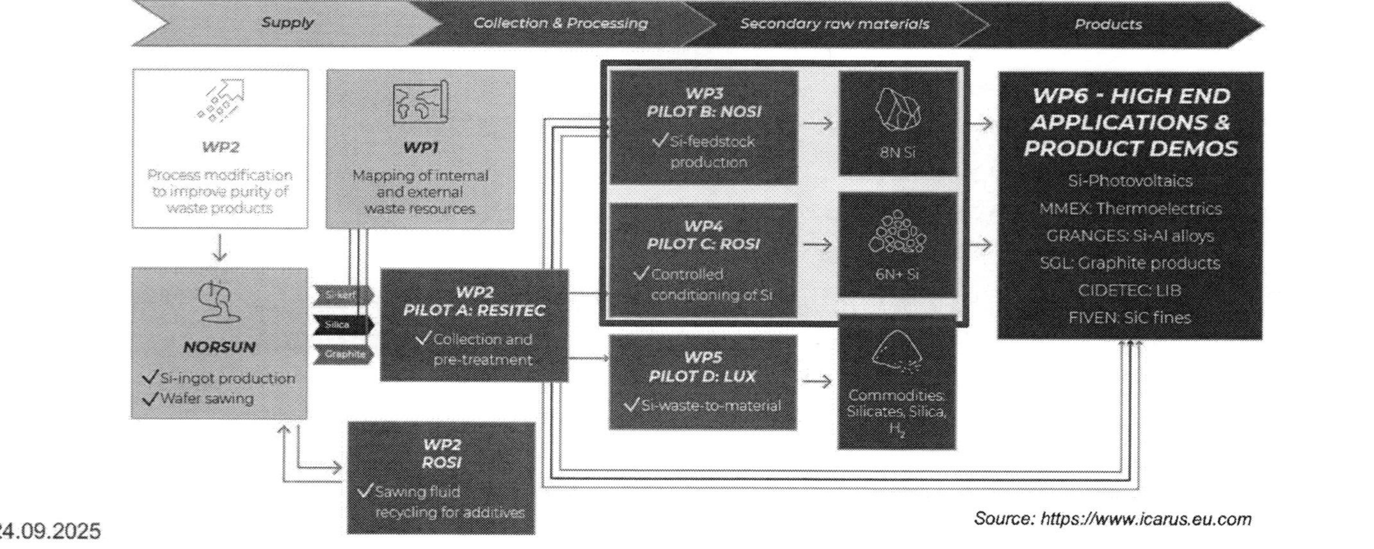

Source: https://www.icarus.eu.com

24.09.2025

11

020469-011

PILOT B/C processes: Secondary silicon 6N+ and 8N

bifa
Umweltinstitut

Comparison: **Secondary** *silicon 8N and 6N+ from ICARUS vs.*
Conventional *solar grade silicon (sg-Si) produced in China / Europe*

PILOT B / PILOT C process:

- Starting material: secondary dry silicon with < 1% moisture from the Pilot A process
- Process data: provided by project partners

Conventional processes in China/Europe:

- Starting material: primary metallurgical grade silicon
- Process data: IEA PVPS Task 12-19:2020 "LCI and LCA of Photovoltaic Systems"

24.09.2025

12

PILOT B/C processes: Secondary silicon 6N+ and 8N

bifa
Umweltinstitut

Comparison: **Secondary** *silicon 6N+ and 8N from ICARUS vs.*
Conventional *solar grade silicon (sg-Si) produced in China / Europe*

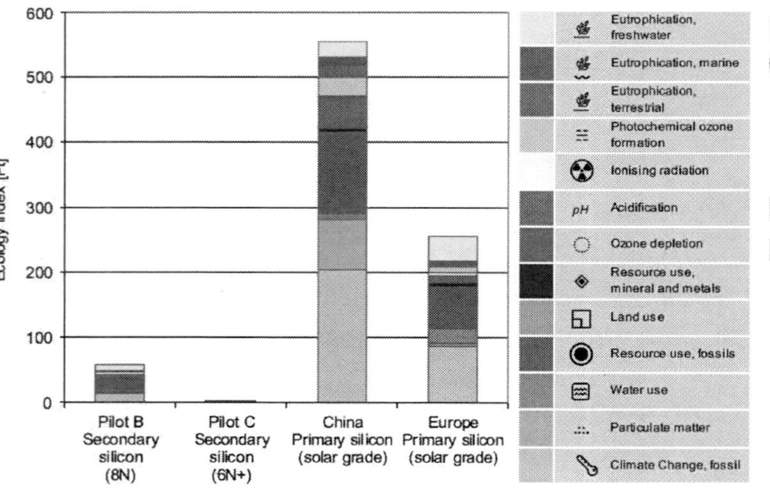

Ecological advantage of secondary silicon 6N+ and 8N over primary sg-Si:

- China process: more than 85%
- Europe process: more than 75%

Main reasons for better results of Pilot B/C processes:

- Electricity consumption is more than 4 times (Pilot B) or 46 times (Pilot C) lower
- No thermal energy is required
- Starting material is the waste *silicon kerf* instead of the primary raw material *mg-Si*

24.09.2025

13

PILOT D process: Hydrogen and water glass

Comparison: **Hydrogen and water glass** *produced* **from Si kerf** *in ICARUS vs.* **Conventional hydrogen and sodium silicate** *produced in Europe*

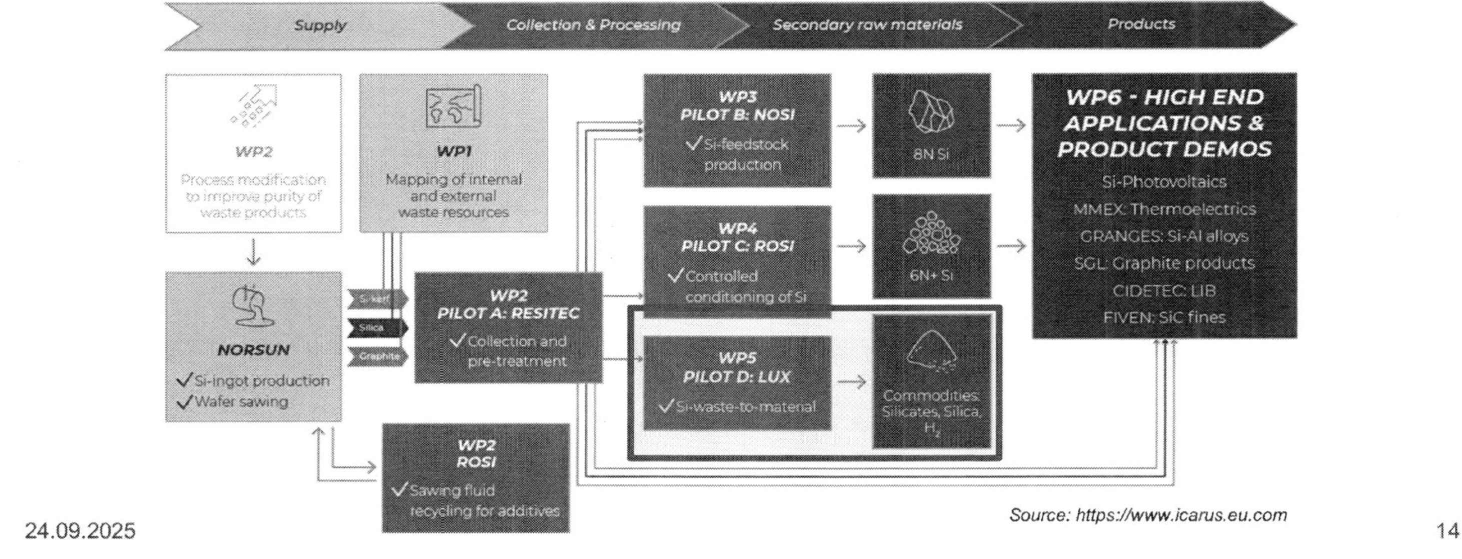

Source: https://www.icarus.eu.com

24.09.2025

14

PILOT D process: Hydrogen and water glass

bifa
Umweltinstitut

Comparison: ***Hydrogen and water glass*** *produced* ***from Si kerf*** *in ICARUS vs.*
Conventional hydrogen and sodium silicate *produced in Europe*

PILOT D process:

- Starting material: secondary dry silicon
  with < 1% moisture from the Pilot A process
- Process data: provided by project partners

Conventional processes in Europe:

- Starting material: natural gas (hydrogen),
  silica sand and soda ash (water glass)
- Process data: ecoinvent data base v3.8

24.09.2025

Detailed information about the process: **5DV.2.12 (25.09.2025 10:30-12:00 Poster Area)** *"Waste 2 Energy and Commodities – an Offbeat use of Silicon Kerf Loss and other Silicon-Based Waste with Amazing Side Effects"*

15

PILOT D process: Hydrogen and water glass

Comparison: **Hydrogen and water glass** *produced* **from Si kerf** *in ICARUS vs.*
Conventional hydrogen and sodium silicate *produced in Europe*

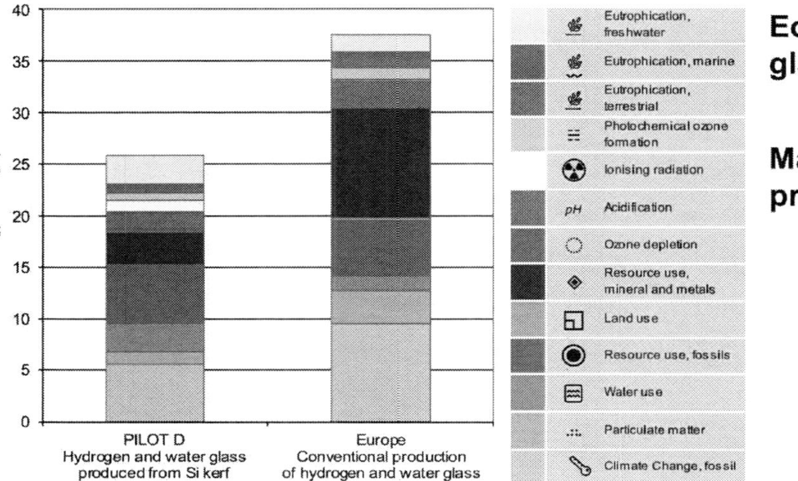

Ecological advantage of hydrogen and water glass produced from Si kerf:

- Europe process: more than 30%

Main reasons for better results of Pilot D process:

- Electricity consumption is more than 10 times lower
- Starting material is the waste *silicon kerf* instead of the primary raw materials *natural gas, petroleum* and *naphtha* (hydrogen) or *silica sand* and *soda ash* (water glass)

Detailed information about the process: **5DV.2.12 (25.09.2025 10:30-12:00 Poster Area)** *"Waste 2 Energy and Commodities – an Offbeat use of Silicon Kerf Loss and other Silicon-Based Waste with Amazing Side Effects"*

24.09.2025

16

Conclusion

- The turning of PV waste, rich in highly pure Si and energy-dense, into a secondary raw material eliminates a large part of the environmental impact associated with the conventional production of equivalent primary raw materials.

- Compared to conventional production
    - → of mg- and sg-silicon in China by more than 85%
    - → of mg- and sg-silicon in Europe by more than 75%
    - → of hydrogen and water glass in Europe by more than 30%

- Thus, the newly developed processes in the ICARUS project not only reduce dependence on supplies from Asia, but also help to reduce harmful emissions into the environment during the production of raw materials.

24.09.2025

17

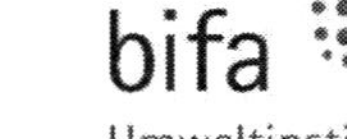

Thank you for your attention!

bifa
Umweltinstitut

This work has received funding from the European Union's Horizon 2020 research and innovation programme under grant agreement No 958365; project ICARUS. Views and opinions expressed are however those of the authors only and do not necessarily reflect those of the European Union or CINEA. Neither the European Union nor the granting authority can be held responsible for them.

**Funded by
the European Union**

bifa Umweltinstitut GmbH
Am Mittleren Moos 46
86167 Augsburg

René Peche
Tel. +49 821 7000-186
rpeche@bifa.de
www.bifa.de

More info:

QUANTIFICATION OF TECHNICAL RECYCLABILITY OF PV MODULES FOR DIFFERENT RECYCLING SCENARIOS

Matthias Hämmer, Kerstin Baumann, Karsten Wambach, Markus Schönheits
bifa Umweltinstitut GmbH
Am Mittleren Moos 46, 86167 Augsburg, Germany

ABSTRACT: In the context of recyclability indices, the highest quality in calculating the recyclability values should be aimed for. Additionally, such high-quality calculations are also of fundamental interest in design for recycling in order to both quantify the status-quo and to monitor potential improvements. Calculations to quantify the recyclability of PV products are standardized by EN 45555. These calculations require detailed material specific recycling rate data for the relevant recycling processes. Frequently, there is lack of such data. Further, these calculations do not discriminate by the quality of recycling. Both challenges, the lack of recycling rate data and the lack of information about recycling quality, undermining the informative value of recyclability results are addressed in this paper. The recycling rate database recently presented by some of the authors is expanded and applied to PV module recycling. Moreover, the typical classification into "recycled" and "lost" is expanded by introducing four recycling categories including the assessment which recycled material can be used in the production of new PV modules. The technical recyclability of exemplary PV modules is calculated for five recycling scenarios ranging from 18% in worst-case mechanical recycling to 80% in advanced recycling facilities.
Keywords: recycling; recyclability; PV modules; ecodesign; circularity

1 INTRODUCTION

In the context of product labelling in EU ecodesign regulation and related aspects within the policy-making process in Europe, the labelling of a product's recyclability in the form of recyclability indices or as part of the digital product passport are extensively discussed [1]. This includes photovoltaic products, i.e. PV modules and inverters [2]. Right now, respective indices are being developed [3]. Naturally, for labelling, high-quality recyclability calculations should be aimed for. To quantify the recyclability of PV products, calculations can be made according to EN 45555 "General methods for assessing the recyclability and recoverability of energy related products" [4]. Yet, these calculations are hampered by the lack of material specific data for the relevant material recovery processes. EN 45555 allows the use of the so-called simplified method when data is missing. Then, unknown material recoverability factors are estimated to be either 1 or 0. Depending on the assumptions made during the simplified method, this yields recyclability values that are either much too small or much too high. Going from such potential recyclability to a more realistic assessment is often difficult due to a lack of data [5]. The recycling rates calculated according to EN 45555 can be considered technical recyclability [6]. Often, theoretical recyclability values are reported by PV module manufacturers. Theoretical recyclability is limited to the material choice and its recyclability properties. Technical recyclability also considers the practical waste quality and treatment, dismantling, size reduction and sorting and – most importantly - the existence of dedicated recycling processes. For the real recyclability, additionally, the aspect of collection as well as the market situation for the secondary raw output materials have to be considered. The differences between theoretical, technical and real recyclability are summarized in Fig. 1.
Besides recyclability indices and respective labelling, the calculation of technical recyclability of PV modules is also relevant as an ecodesign tool for comparison of various PV modules as well as for the quantitative comparison of recycling scenarios and technologies. Finally, such results enable realistic estimates of secondary raw material pro-

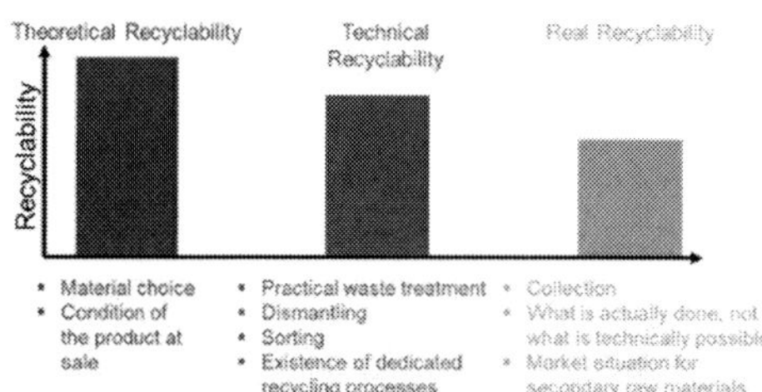

Figure 1: Comparison of the three types of recyclability according to [6]: Going from left to right the respective aspects are considered, additionally.

duction per waste volume input – an essential part of any business plan for PV module recycling companies.

2 METHODS

Commonly, there are two challenges in calculating the technical recyclability according to EN 45555: the lack of (material specific) recycling rate data and the lack of consideration of recycling quality, e.g. downcycling, upcycling and other recycling varieties. Both challenges were addressed in our previous work [7]. Herein, the assessment is adjusted to PV modules using both literature data for various delamination [8-10] and downstream treatment options [7,8,10-12] and pilot line batch test data [10]. Available data for these calculations is scarce and its public availability is even more restricted. To the best of our knowledge, no similar recycling rate database for PV module recycling exists, so far.

Further, the four categories "circular", "recycled", "alternative material recovery" and "lost" are introduced discriminating by the quality of recycling. The "circular" recycling rate describes the rate of recovered material which can be used for the substitution of corresponding virgin material in the production of new PV modules. The "recycled" recycling rate describes the rate of recovered material which can substitute virgin material outside the PV industry. In other words, the category "circular" refers to closed-loop and the category "recycled" to open-loop recycling. The "alternative material recovery" rate describes the rate of material which can replace virgin materials that are not identical to the recovered materials. This includes so-called downcycling, e.g. solar glass recycled in the form of foam glass or slag in road construction. Materials are considered "lost" if they are used for energy recovery or landfilled. The recovery of ashes from waste incineration is neglected.

The discrimination by the quality of recycling enables the assessment which recycled material can be used in the production of new PV modules and, thus, the quantification of the circularity of the PV module value chain. At present, this applies only to recycled material assigned to the "circular" category. This highlights the relevance of the present work for circularity assessments for PV modules. For this study, the circular category's materials are Ag, Cu and Si.

As an example, an average c-Si Al-BSF glass-foil PV module [10] and five different recycling scenarios are considered for the technical recyclability calculations. Table I shows the bill-of-material for the PV module.

Table I: Bill of material for average c-Si Al-BSF glass-foil PV module [10]

Component	Material	wt.-%
Frame	Al	13.1
Cables	Cu	0.2
Cables	Polymer	0.4
Junction Box	Cu	0.3
Junction Box	Polymer	0.6
Glass	Glass	70.4
Encapsulant	EVA	6.5
Backsheet	PVF	2.8
Cells	Si	4.4
Cells	Ag	0.1
Cells	Al	0.3
Interconnectors	Cu	0.9

The five end-of-life scenarios are
S1: Worst-case recycling treatment by non-specialized glass recyclers [9]
S2: State-of-the-art dedicated mechanical recycling [8]
S3: Advanced recycling using pyrolysis delamination [8]
S4: Advanced recycling using water-jet delamination [8]
S5: PHOTORAMA pilot line recycling [10]

The respective flow charts for the five scenarios are shown in Fig. 2 to 6. All scenarios include dismantling, i.e. the removal of frame, cables and junction box prior to the processing of the PV module's laminate as mandatory in the EU according to the WEEE directive [13] and respective national or local legislation. The five scenarios differ as well in the used delamination technique and the downstream treatment as in their technology readiness levels (TRL). S1 and S2 include mechanical treatment for delamination and run at industrial scale (TRL 9). In S3, pyrolysis is used for delamination and S4 and S5 utilize the water-jet technology. The materials silicon and silver from the solar cells are recovered in S3, S4 and S5, only. All three, S3, S4 and S5, are at pilot scale (TRL 7). Further relevant differences in process steps are discussed with the results in the subsequent section. All five recycling scenarios comply with the WEEE directive. Further, waste inputs comprising solely of intact, i.e. non-broken PV modules is assumed. The set of recycling scenarios is not intended to be exhaustive representing exemplary end-of-

life options.

In line with EN45555, the yields of downstream processes like smelting are included in the calculations as indicated by the system boundaries shown in dashed blue in Fig. 2 to 6.

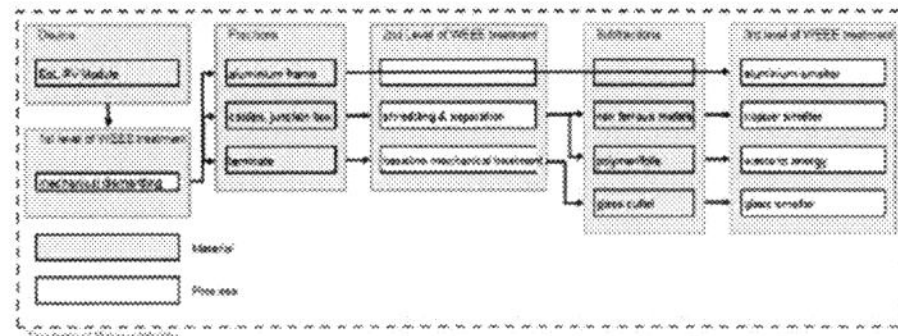

Figure 2: Flow sheet for S1

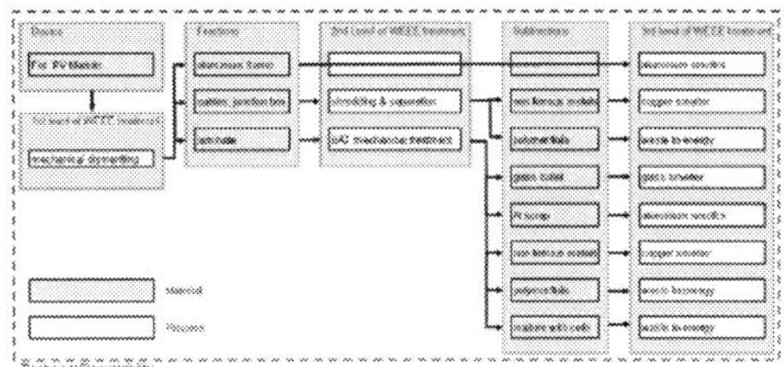

Figure 3: Flow sheet for S2

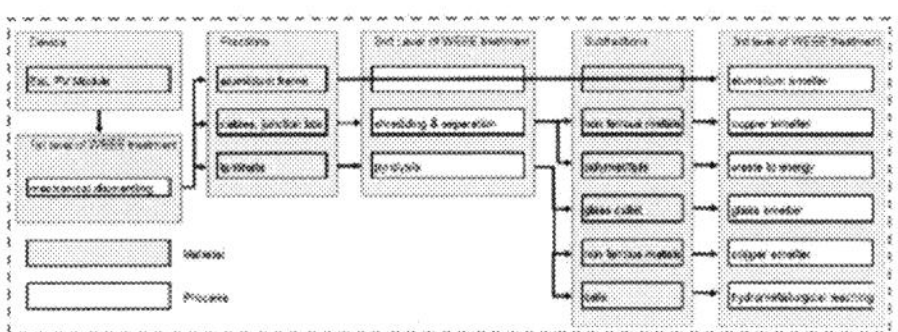

Figure 4: Flow sheet for S3

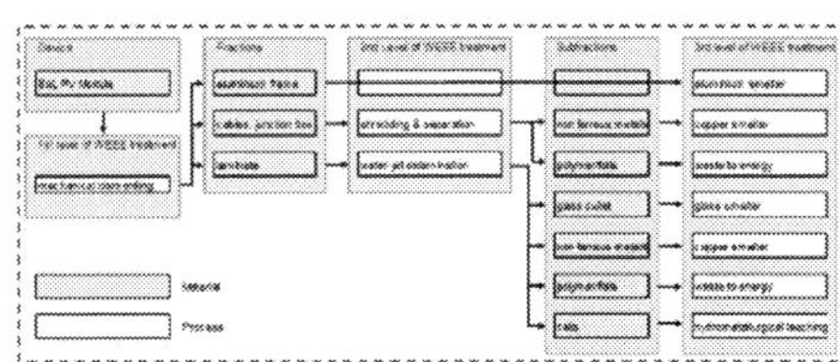

Figure 5: Flow sheet for S4

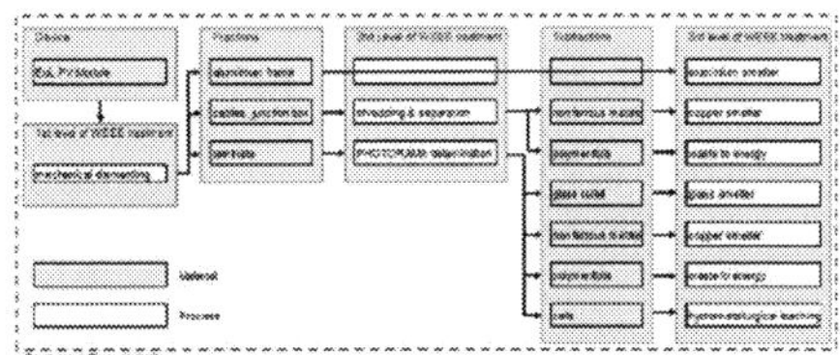

Figure 6: Flow sheet for S5

3 RESULTS

The technical recyclability results are shown in Fig. 7. They range from 18.1% for the worst-case scenario when the module is recycled by non-specialized glass recyclers to 80.2% for the PHOTORAMA pilot line.

In S1, following dismantling, the laminate is shredded and only glass is recovered. Thus, the materials aluminum from the frame, copper from the cables and junction box as well as glass from the laminate are recovered with rather

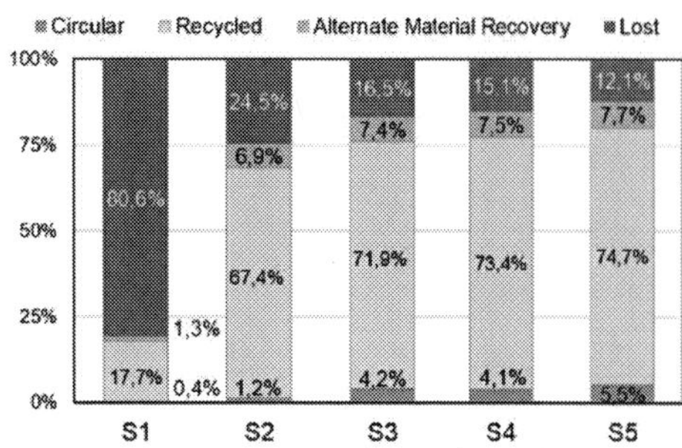

Figure 7: Technical recyclability results for five recycling scenarios for average c-Si Al-BSF glass-foil PV module on module level. For more details, see main text.

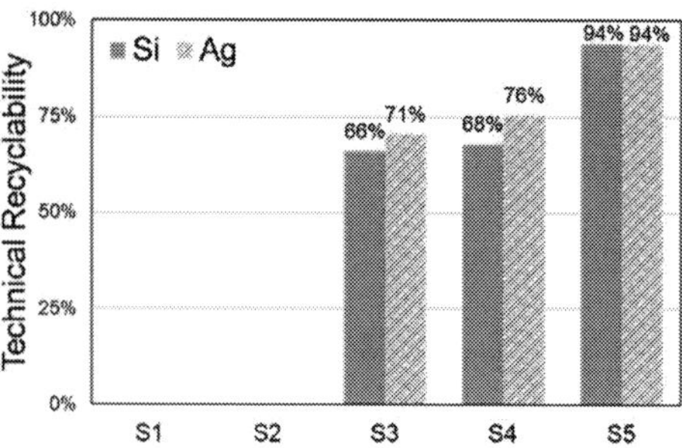

Figure 8: Technical recyclability results for five recycling scenarios for average c-Si Al-BSF glass-foil PV module on material level for silicon and silver. For more details, see main text.

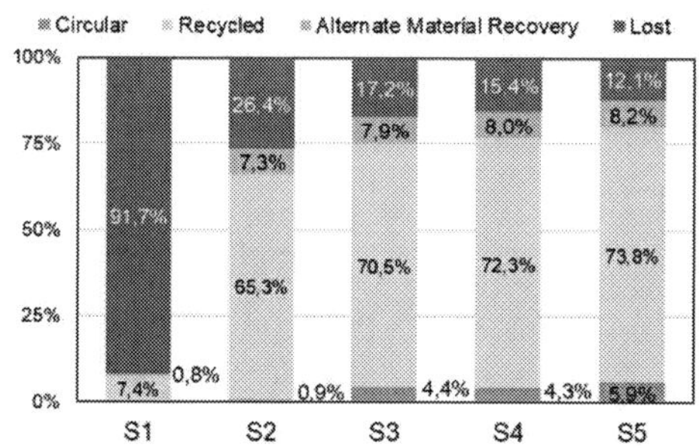

Figure 9: Technical recyclability results for five recycling scenarios for average c-Si Al-BSF glass-foil PV module on fraction level for the laminate fraction. For more details, see main text.

low process yields. In total, this results a technical recyclability of 18.1% with merely 0.4% in the circular category. S1 can be considered worst-case formal recycling of PV modules in the EU. In S2, mechanical delamination is performed, too. However, using state-of-the-art separation and sorting technology non-ferrous metals are recovered from the laminate fraction, too, and the mechanical treatment exhibits higher yields. In sum, this results in a technical recyclability of 68,6% with 1.2% in the circular category.

The remaining scenarios (S3-S5) include more advanced delamination techniques instead of mechanical treatment. However, this is accompanied by reduced - TRL. S1 and S2 can be considered industrial scale with TRL 9 while S3 to S5 reach TRL 7.

In S3, delamination using pyrolysis is performed. Further, dedicated hydrometallurgical downstream treatment enables the recovery of silicon and silver from the solar cells. Overall, the technical recyclability reaches 76.1% with 4.2% in the circular category. S4 utilizes water-jet delamination and state-of-the-art hydrometallurgical downstream treatment for silicon and silver recovery yielding a technical recyclability of 77.4% with 4.1% circular share. Finally, S5 representing the PHOTORAMA pilot line includes an improved combination of diamond wire and water-jet delamination together with optimized hydrometallurgical downstream treatment for silicon and silver extraction. In total, this results in a technical recyclability of 80.2% with 5.5% in the circular category.

The differences between the five recycling scenarios becomes even more obvious on the material (Fig. 8) or fraction level (Fig. 9).

Fig. 8 shows the material specific technical recyclability values for silicon and silver. These results emphasize the improvements in S5. Moreover, Fig. 9 depicts the technical recyclability values on the fraction level of the laminate fraction, i.e. excluding the frame, the cables and the junction box. The scenarios do not differ in the treatment of the excluded fractions. When comparing the technical recyclability results on the laminate fraction's level underlines the importance of delamination since the major differences in recyclability can be found in the laminate fraction.

4 DISCUSSION AND CONCLUSION

As shown above, it is readily possible to quantitatively calculate the technical recyclability of PV modules using the database and methodology presented herein. Such calculations can be applied as an ecodesign tool to compare different PV modules, in recycling technology development to benchmark different recycling approaches as well as in economic assessments by realistically estimating secondary raw material production from PV module recycling.

Thus, it is possible to go from merely material-based theoretical recyclability values to more realistic technical recycling rates. When doing so, it is crucial to ensure the comparability of different results by disclosing the respective end-of-life scenario's details and to use identical system borders. Further, the discrimination between closed-loop and open-loop recycling via the categories "circular" and "recycled" is relevant for overall circularity assessments of PV modules. The result that even the best-case scenario barely exceeds 5% circular share - that means only 5% of the material reaching the end-of-life will have a "second life" in PV modules - highlights the room for improvements in the design for circularity and recycling infrastructure.

Beyond the current work, extended batch tests to be performed in the QUASAR project are expected to even further increase the recycling rate data quality for the two PV module recycling pilots in the QUASAR project using pyrolysis and water-jet delamination.

5 REFERENCES

[1] Regulation (EU) 2024/1781, Ecodesign for Sustainable Products Regulation (ESPR): latest consolidated vers.: 2024-06-28, **2024**.

[2] D. Polverini, F. Alfieri, C. Spiliotopoulos, A. Arcipowska, *Prog Photovolt Res Appl.* **2024**, 1-9. doi: 10.1002/pip.3781.

[3] VIEGAND MAAGØE A/S, *Interim Report - Technical Support for the Development of a Recyclability Index for Photovoltaic Products Specific Contract No CINEA/2023/OP/0007/ SI2.906326*, **2024**.

[4] EN 45555:2020, *General methods for assessing the recyclability and recoverability of energy-related products*, **2020**.

[5] P. M. Mählitz, N. Korf, G. Chryssos, V. S. Rotter, *J of Industrial Ecology* **2022**, *26*, 1061–1077.

[6] R. Pomberger, A. Bezama, *Waste Manag Res* **2024**, *42*, 713–714.

[7] M. Hämmer, K. Wambach, *Sustainability* **2024**, *16*, 8726.

[8] K. Wambach, C. Libby, S. Shaw, *Advances in Photovoltaic Module Recycling: Literature Review and Update to Empirical Life Cycle Inventory Data and Patent Review*, Report IEA-PVPS T12-28:2024, **2024**.

[9] F. Ardente, C. E. L. Latunussa, G. A. Blengini, *Waste Management* **2019**, *91*, 156.

[10] M. Seitz, R. Steber, K. Baumann, M. Hämmer, PHOTORAMA Deliverable D5.5, **2025**, *unpublished*.

[11] C. E. Latunussa, F. Ardente, G. A. Blengini, L. Mancini, *Solar Energy Materials and Solar Cells* **2016**, *156*, 101.

[12] B. Huang, J. Zhao, J. Chai, B. Xue, F. Zhao, X. Wang, *Solar Energy* **2017**, *143*, 132.

[13] Directive 2012/19/EU; Waste Electrical and Electronic Equipment (WEEE): Latest Consolidated Vers.: 2024-04-08. European Union: Brussels, Belgium, **2024**.

6 ACKNOWLEDGEMENTS

This work has received funding from the European Union's Horizon 2020 research and innovation programme under grant agreement No 958223; project PHOTORAMA and from the European Union´s Horizon Europe research and innovation programme under Grant Agreement No 101122298; project QUASAR. Views and opinions expressed are however those of the authors only and do not necessarily reflect those of the European Union or CINEA. Neither the European Union nor the granting authority can be held responsible for them.

bifa
Umweltinstitut

EU PVSEC 2025

5CO.6.4

Bilbao, 24.09.2025

Quantification of Technical Recyclability of PV modules for different recycling scenarios

PHOTORAMA

Quasar

Matthias Hämmer, Kerstin Baumann, Karsten Wambach, Markus Schönheits

www.bifa.de

020471-001

bifa Umweltinstitut GmbH

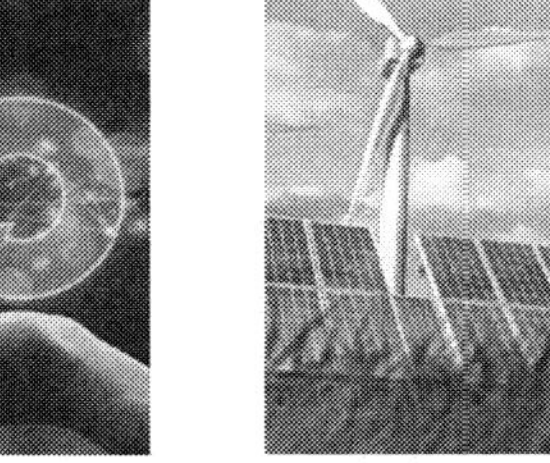

Application-orientated research, development and consulting facility

Our expertise:

- LCA, eco-efficiency analysis, LCC, TEA
- Recycling processes from laboratory to pilot plant scale
- Environmental Analytics
- Waste and circularity Assessment
- Recyclability and circularity Indices (EN4555x and ISO590xx)
- Ecodesign / design for recycling
- Social acceptance (workshops, surveys, interviews)

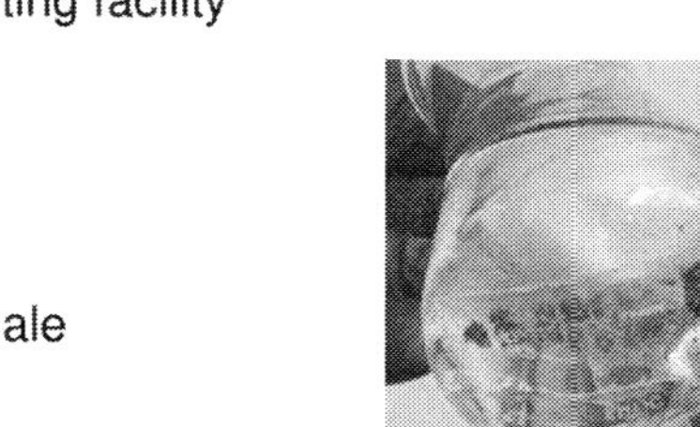

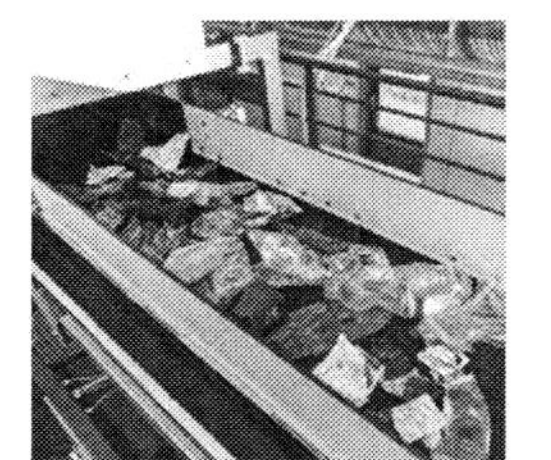

Recent and relevant EU Projects

24.09.2025

Outline

1. **Motivation**

2. **Methodology**

3. **Technical Recyclability Results**

4. **Conclusion**

Ms Tech | Pixel Squid, https://www.technologyreview.com/2021/08 /19/1032215/solar-panels-recycling/ (19.09.2022)

Motivation

bifa
Umweltinstitut

Technical recyclability of PV modules is relevant for

- Recyclability indices
- Ecodesign / design for recycling
- Comparison of PV modules (input)
- Comparison of PV module recycling technologies (output)
- Quantification of secondary raw material production

Methodology

Pomberger, R. *Österr Wasser- und Abfallw* **2021**, *73*, 24–35.
Pomberger, R.; Bezama, A. *Waste Manag. Res.* **2024**, *42*, 713–714.

Methodology

EN45555 describes calculation of technical recyclabilty

$$R = \frac{\sum_{k=1}^{n}\left(m_k \cdot R_k\right)}{m_{\text{tot}}}$$

n — number of materials
m_k — mass of material k
R_k — recyclability factor of material k
m_{tot} — total mass of device

Calculation for each step and each material.

EN 45555:2020, *General methods for assessing the recyclability and recoverability of energy-related products*, **2020**.

020471-006

bifa
Umweltinstitut

Methodology

EN45555 describes calculation of technical recyclabilty

$$R = \frac{\sum_{k=1}^{n} (m_k \cdot R_k)}{m_{\text{tot}}}$$

n	number of materials
m_k	mass of material k
R_k	recyclability factor of material k
m_{tot}	total mass of device

Calculation for each step and each material.

EN 45555:2020, *General methods for assessing the recyclability and recoverability of energy-related products*, **2020**.

24.09.2025

Challenges:
1. Lack of material-specific recycling rate data
2. No consideration of recycling quality

M. Hämmer, K. Wambach, *Sustainability* **2024**, *16*, 8726.

Methodology

24.09.2025

M. Hämmer, K. Wambach, *Sustainability* **2024**, *16*, 8726.

8

EU PVSEC 2025

Methodology

bifa
Umweltinstitut

System Boundaries

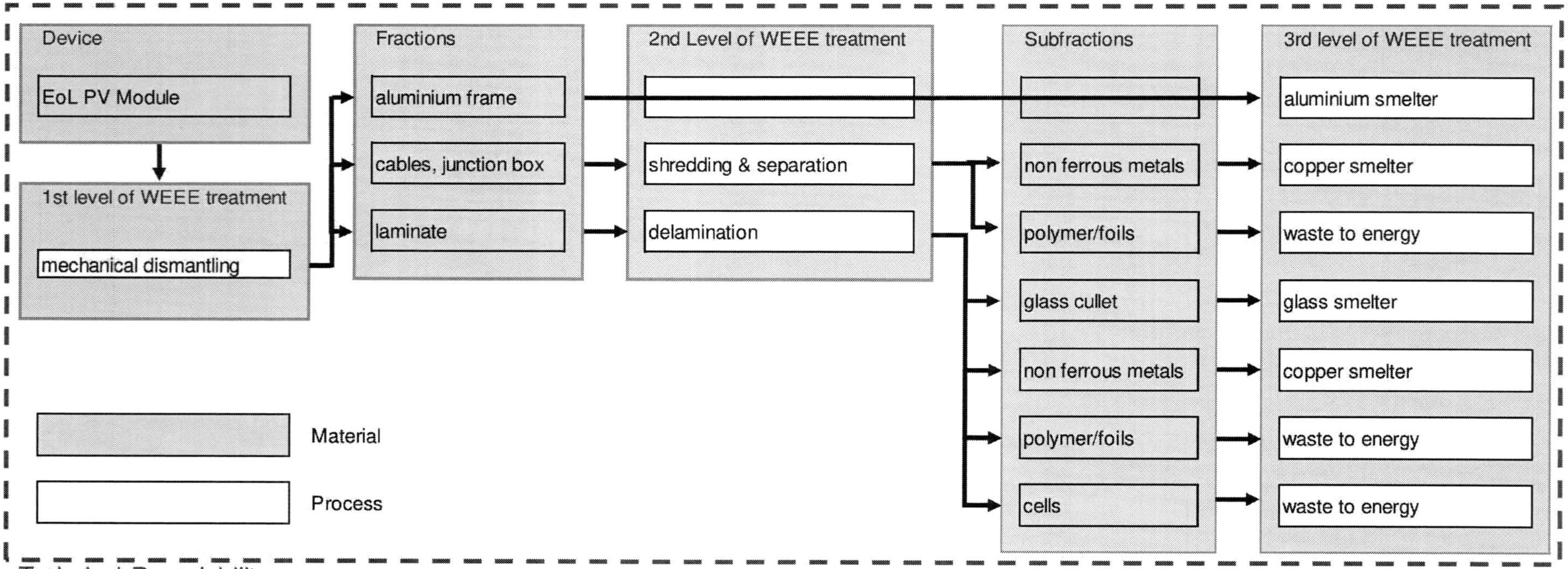

Technical Recyclability

24.09.2025

9

Technical Recyclability Results

Example: Average c-Si Al-BSF glass-foil PV module

End-of-life scenarios:
S1: worst-case mechanical treatment
S2: BAT mechanical treatment
S3: pyrolysis
S4: water-jet delamination
S5: PHOTORAMA pilot

All scenarios include dismantling, i.e. the removal of frame, cables and junction box prior to the processing of the PV module's laminate.
→ Formal treatment as mandatory in the EU (WEEE directive)

Differences: delamination technique and downstream treatment

24.09.2025

10

Technical Recyclability Results

bifa
Umweltinstitut

Flow Chart, Scenarios and References

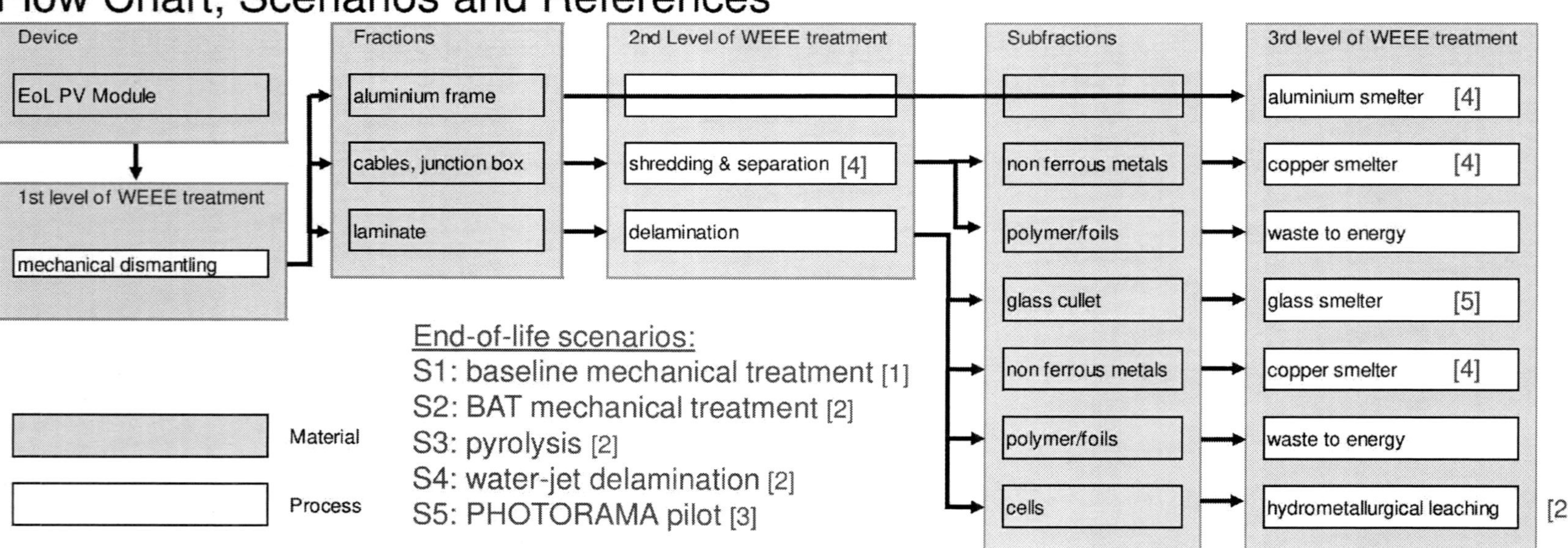

[1] F. Ardente, C. E. L. Latunussa, G. A. Blengini, *Waste Management* **2019**, *91*, 156.
[2] K. Wambach, C. Libby, S. Shaw, *Advances in Photovoltaic Module Recycling*. Report IEA-PVPS T12-28:2024, **2024**.
[3] M. Seitz, R. Steber, K. Baumann, M. Hämmer, PHOTORAMA Deliverable D5.5, **2025**.
[4] M. Hämmer, K. Wambach, *Sustainability* **2024**, *16*, 8726.
[5] C. E. Latunussa, F. Ardente, G. A. Blengini, L. Mancini, *Solar Energy Materials and Solar Cells* **2016**, *156*, 101.
[6] B. Huang, J. Zhao, J. Chai, B. Xue, F. Zhao, X. Wang, *Solar Energy* **2017**, *143*, 132.

24.09.2025

11

Technical Recyclability Results

bifa
Umweltinstitut

Worst-case recycling treatment by non-specialized glass recyclers (S1)

Recovered secondary raw materials

✓ Al (frame)

✓ Cu (cables and junction box)

✓ Glass cullet

End-of-life scenarios:
S1: baseline mechanical treatment
S2: BAT mechanical treatment
S3: pyrolysis
S4: water-jet delamination
S5: PHOTORAMA pilot

F. Ardente, C. E. L. Latunussa, G. A. Blengini, *Waste Management* **2019**, *91*, 156.

24.09.2025

12

020471-012

Technical Recyclability Results

bifa
Umweltinstitut

state-of-the-art dedicated mechanical recycling (S2)

Recovered secondary raw materials

✓ Al (frame)

✓ Cu (cables, junction box and ribbons)

✓ Glass cullet

End-of-life scenarios:
S1: baseline mechanical treatment
S2: BAT mechanical treatment
S3: pyrolysis
S4: water-jet delamination
S5: PHOTORAMA pilot

K. Wambach, C. Libby, S. Shaw, *Advances in Photovoltaic Module Recycling*. Report IEA-PVPS T12-28:2024, **2024**.

24.09.2025

13

Technical Recyclability Results

Advanced recycling pyrolysis (S3)

Recovered secondary raw materials

- ✓ Al (frame)
- ✓ Cu (cables, junction box and ribbons)
- ✓ Glass cullet
- ✓ Si
- ✓ Ag

End-of-life scenarios:
S1: baseline mechanical treatment
S2: BAT mechanical treatment
S3: pyrolysis
S4: water-jet delamination
S5: PHOTORAMA pilot

K. Wambach, C. Libby, S. Shaw, *Advances in Photovoltaic Module Recycling*. Report IEA-PVPS T12-28:2024, **2024**.

24.09.2025

14

Technical Recyclability Results

Advanced recycling water-jet (S4)

Recovered secondary raw materials

✓ Al (frame)

✓ Cu (cables, junction box and ribbons)

✓ Glass cullet

✓ Si

✓ Ag

End-of-life scenarios:
S1: baseline mechanical treatment
S2: BAT mechanical treatment
S3: pyrolysis
S4: water-jet delamination
S5: PHOTORAMA pilot

K. Wambach, C. Libby, S. Shaw, *Advances in Photovoltaic Module Recycling*. Report IEA-PVPS T12-28:2024, **2024**.

24.09.2025

15

Technical Recyclability Results

bifa
Umweltinstitut

PHOTORAMA pilot line recycling (S5)

24.09.2025

M. Seitz, R. Steber, K. Baumann, M. Hämmer, PHOTORAMA Deliverable D5.5, **2025**.

16

020471-016

Technical Recyclability Results

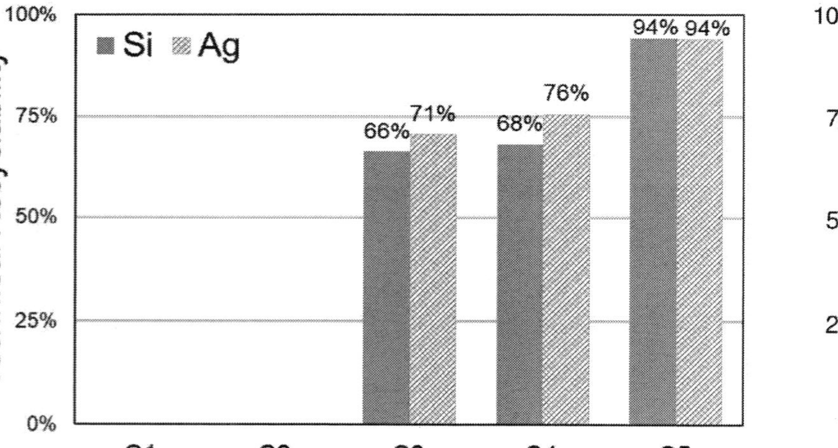

Results on material and fraction level

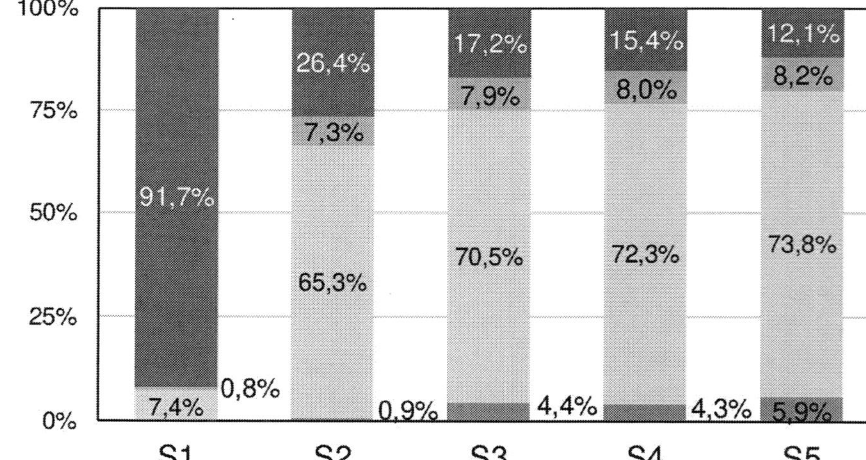

bifa
Umweltinstitut

Fraction: Laminate

Conclusion

bifa
Umweltinstitut

- Quantification of technical recyclability for PV modules possible (with database and methodology)
- Application:
  - Ecodesign (comparison of different modules)
  - Recycling technology development (comparison of different recycling approaches)
  - Economic assessment (realistic quantitative secondary raw material production)
- Extended batch test QUASAR project for better data quality

Thank you for your attention!

bifa
Umweltinstitut

**Funded by
the European Union**

This work has received funding from the European Union's Horizon 2020 research and innovation programme under grant agreement No 958223; project PHOTORAMA and from the European Union´s Horizon Europe research and innovation programme under Grant Agreement No 101122298; project QUASAR. Views and opinions expressed are however those of the authors only and do not necessarily reflect those of the European Union or CINEA. Neither the European Union nor the granting authority can be held responsible for them.

bifa Umweltinstitut GmbH
Am Mittleren Moos 46
86167 Augsburg

Dr. Matthias Hämmer
Tel. +49 821 7000-297
mhaemmer@bifa.de
www.bifa.de

Mehr Infos:

Technical Recyclability Results

Scenarios:
S1: baseline mechanical treatment
S2: BAT mechanical treatment
S3: pyrolysis
S4: water-jet delamination
S5: PHOTORAMA pilot

bifa
Umweltinstitut

Worst-case recycling treatment by not-specialized glass recyclers (S1)

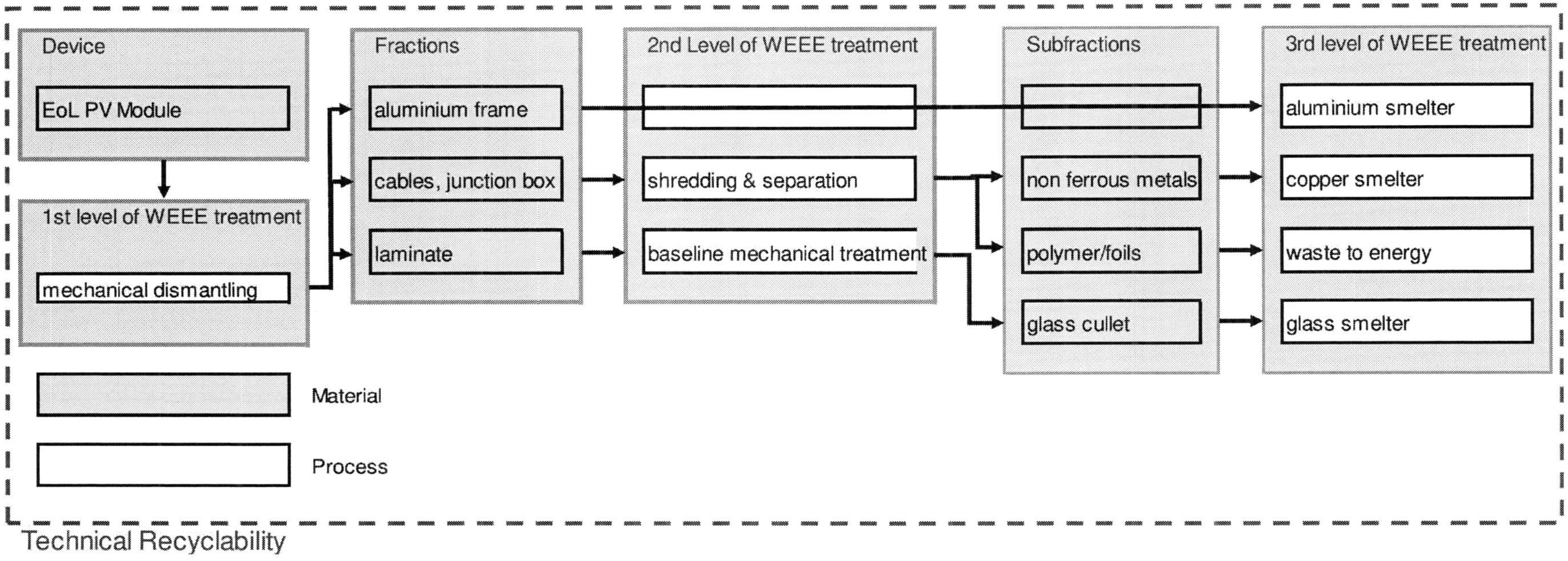

Technical Recyclability

24.09.2025

020471-020

Technical Recyclability Results

Scenarios:
S1: baseline mechanical treatment
S2: BAT mechanical treatment
S3: pyrolysis
S4: water-jet delamination
S5: PHOTORAMA pilot

bifa
Umweltinstitut

state-of-the-art dedicated mechanical recycling (S2)

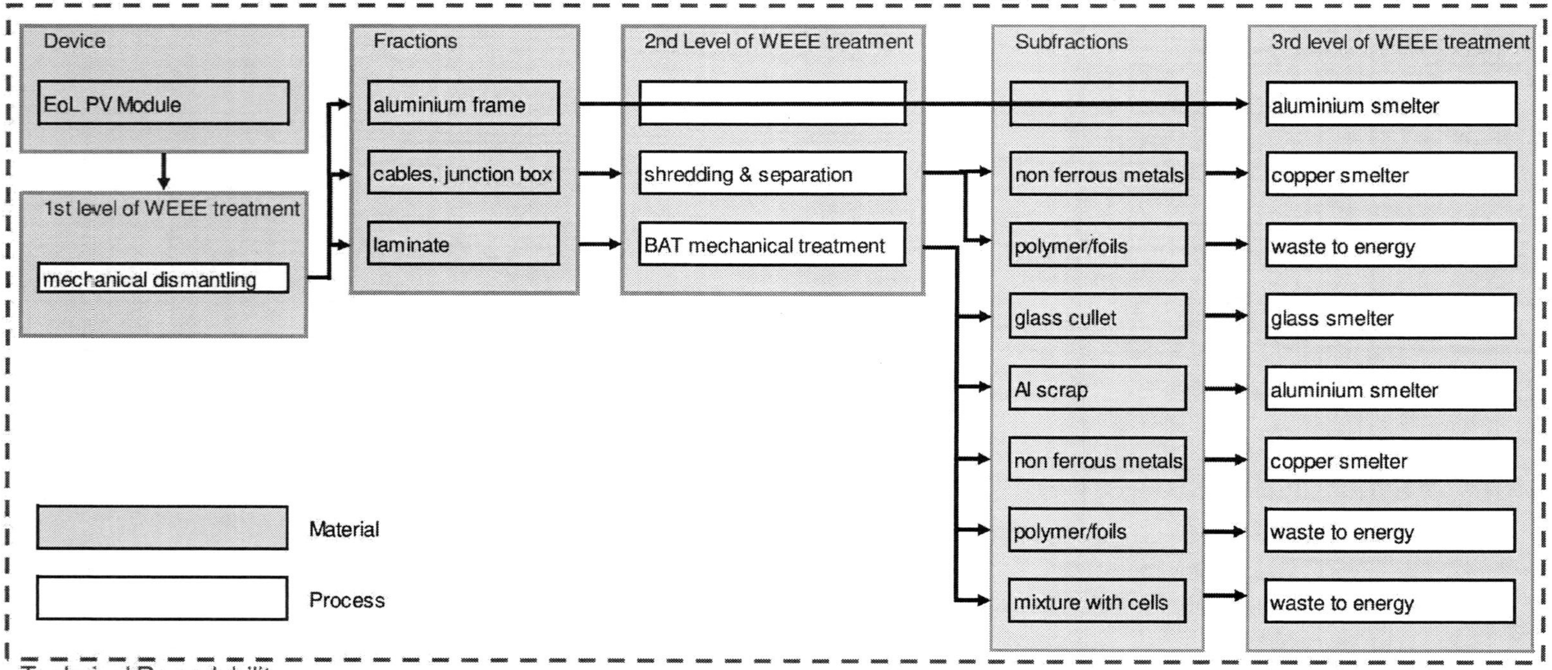

Technical Recyclability
24.09.2025

21

020471-021

Technical Recyclability Results

Advanced recycling pyrolysis (S3)

Technical Recyclability

Technical Recyclability Results

Scenarios:
S1: baseline mechanical treatment
S2: BAT mechanical treatment
S3: pyrolysis
S4: water-jet delamination
S5: PHOTORAMA pilot

bifa Umweltinstitut

Advanced recycling water-jet (S4)

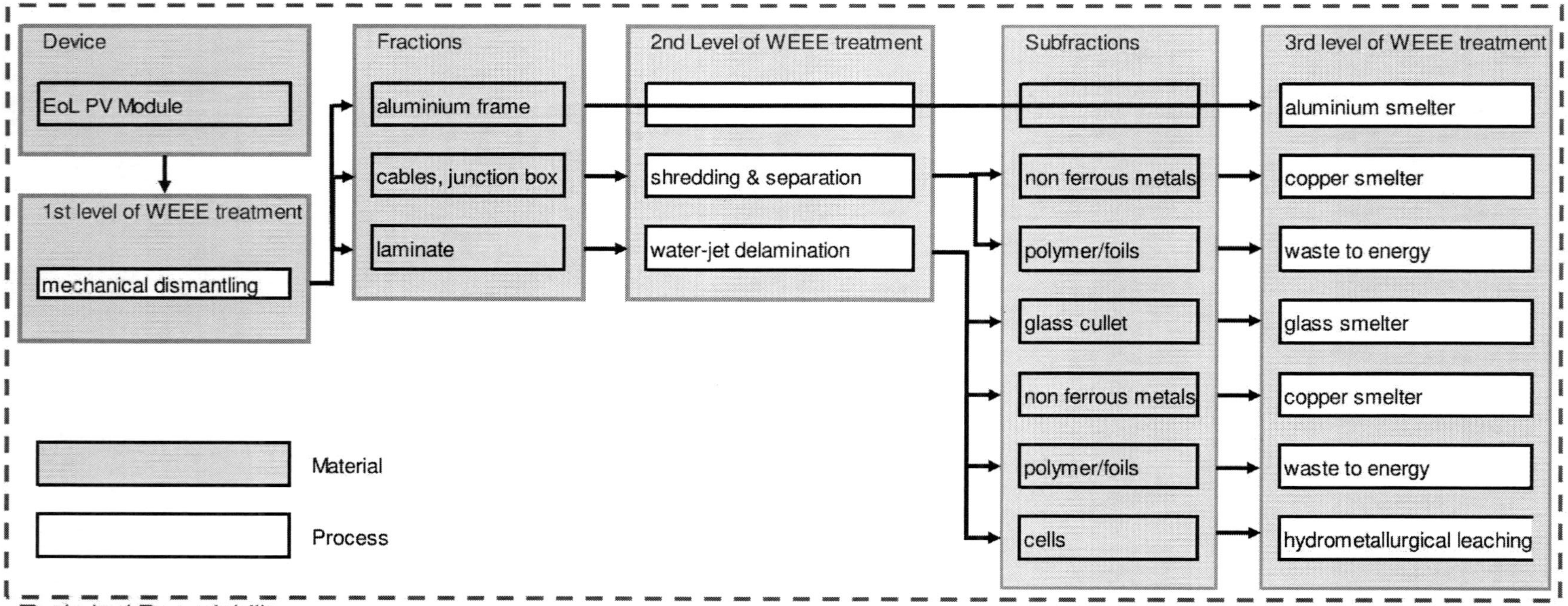

Technical Recyclability

020471-023

Technical Recyclability Results

Scenarios:
S1: baseline mechanical treatment
S2: BAT mechanical treatment
S3: pyrolysis
S4: water-jet delamination
S5: PHOTORAMA pilot

bifa
Umweltinstitut

PHOTORAMA pilot line recycling (S5)

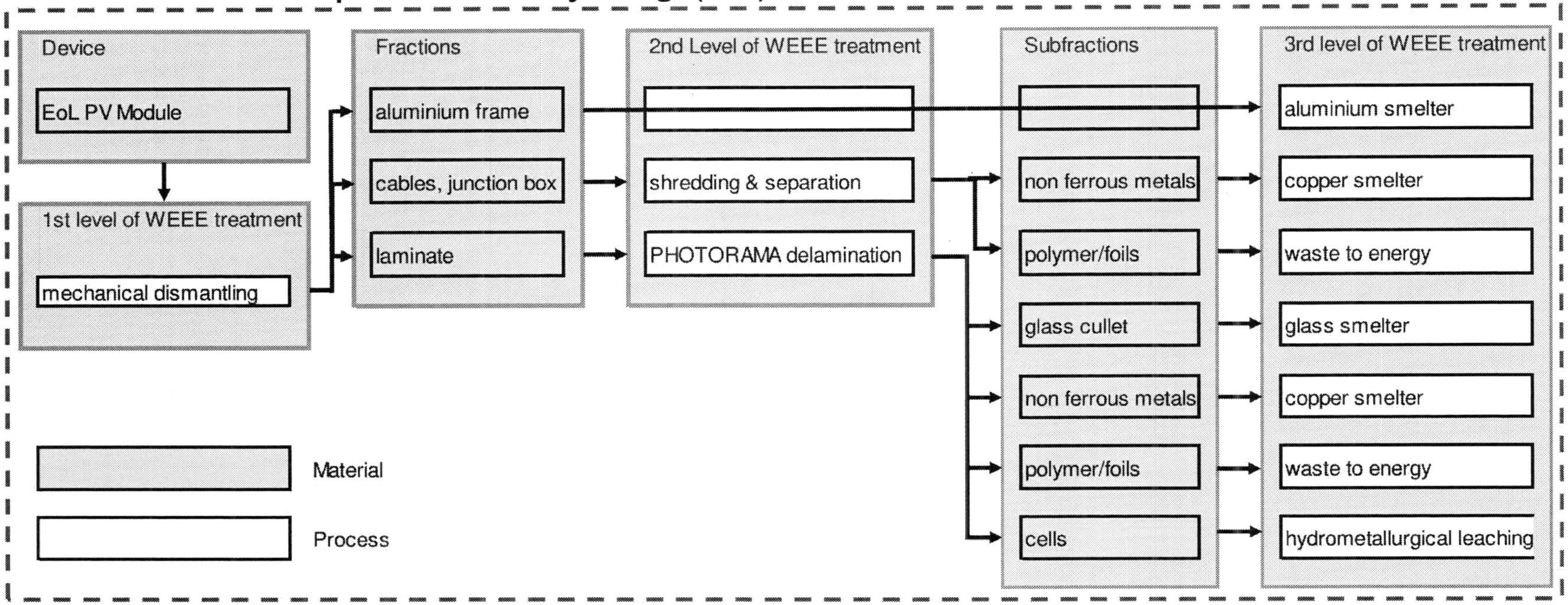

Technical Recyclability
24.09.2025

020471-024

IEC TECHNICAL REPORT 63525 ON THE REUSE OF PV MODULES: FINAL RESULT

Arvid van der Heide[1,2,3], Serge Noels[4], Jan Clyncke[4], Rich Strömberg[5,6]
[1]imec, imo-imomec, Thor Park 8320, 3600 Genk, Belgium
[2]Hasselt University, imo-imomec, Martelarenlaan 42, 3500 Hasselt, Belgium
[3]EnergyVille, imo-imomec, Thor Park 8320, 3600 Genk, Belgium
[4]PV CYCLE, Brand Whitlocklaan 114/5, 1200 Brussels, Belgium
[5]ACEP, University of Alaska Fairbanks, 1764 Tanana loop, Fairbanks, AK 9975, USA
[6]Equitable Solar Solutions, P.O. Box 463, Gunnison CO 81230, USA
e-mail: arvid.vanderheide@imec.be

ABSTRACT: To promote PV sustainability, an IEC project team was created to prepare a Technical Report (TR) 63525 "PV module reuse and circular economy". The TR working draft has been finished recently and includes recommendations for PV module reuse, that can also serve as a basis for the future development of normative documents. The possibility of reducing the on-site inspection work by sampling of PV modules is discussed. Although this is a promising approach, the TR still recommends testing every PV module for possible reuse. The recommended tests (for PV modules without repair) are visual inspection, I-V, EL, bypass diode test and dry insulation test. Although the dry insulation test is not sensitive to all insulation defects, it is not recommended to do the wet insulation test for every PV module. It is only recommended after certain repairs, like junction box replacement or backsheet repair. The remaining power is recommended to be still above the guaranteed value, taking the age of the PV module into account. An additional label should be placed next to the original one, with the new maximum system voltage indicated (either the original or a reduced value when necessary).
Keywords: reuse, re-use, second life, circularity, standardisation

1 INTRODUCTION

Many PV modules will be decommissioned in the next years, either because they are near the end of their designed technical lifetime (20-30 years) or because they are replaced by new PV modules with higher efficiency ("repowering" of PV plants). According to IRENA, 78 million metric tons of PV module waste is expected worldwide by 2050 [1]. Because of this, it is very important to develop strategies to deal with these large numbers of decommissioned PV modules like reuse and recycling.

Currently, most decommissioned PV modules are either disposed of in landfills (but not in the European Union) or sent to waste treatment and recycling facilities [3,13,14]. Considering extending the lifetime of the products that are still functioning (through preparation for reuse) instead of sending them directly to recycling, this has proven to reduce the environmental impact and contributes to higher levels of circularity [2-3].

The main opportunities and advantages of reusing PV modules are listed below [2-12]:

- Prevent premature entry into the waste stream
- Reduce the PV module waste
- Reduce extraction of materials for new PV modules
- Reduce energy and water to produce new PV modules
- Decrease the environmental impact of the overall PV sector and enable wide-spread access to electricity, especially to poorly connected areas

Although the advantages of reusing PV modules are clear, it is a very complex subject. There are concerns about safety, performance, remaining lifetime, financial viability and possible export of PV modules to countries without (proper) waste treatment and recycling infrastructure in general. The first 3 concerns should be addressed by standardising the requirements for reuse of PV modules. For this reason, at the end of 2021, the IEC agreed to install a project team to start drafting a Technical Report (TR) on this subject. A TR is not normative but can give recommendations and can be used to develop future Technical Specifications and/or Standards. The preparation of the working draft has been completed, and it now moves to the committee stage "acceptance of draft". The main contents of the TR will be discussed in this paper.

2 THE CONTENTS OF THE TECHNICAL REPORT

In the TR, a PV module is considered to be fit for reuse only if it is still safe, has sufficient remaining power and a sufficient remaining lifetime. It should also be noted that the TR has been limited to the reuse of crystalline silicon PV modules, since other technologies have always been a small fraction of the installed capacity.

In the following, first the organisation of the TR will be described, followed by a description of the main issues discussed in the TR. These are:

- Testing via sampling or for every PV module
- Visual inspection
- I-V testing
- EL imaging
- Bypass diode testing
- Insulation tests (dry and wet)
- Relabelling
- Repair

2.1 Organisation of the TR

The TR starts with a general description of the technology to manufacture c-Si PV modules and the materials and components that are involved. Also, the reliability issues of PV modules are discussed, since it is an important subject in view of reusing PV modules. Then on-site inspection of PV plants and on-site evaluation methods are discussed including suggestions to select PV modules for reuse based on sampling instead of testing every PV module (although this way of working is considered to be not ready for implementation right now).

The concept of reduced maximum system voltage is introduced for PV modules that might have reduced insulation quality or PV modules that have undergone a certain repair. Then the actual tests for the evaluation of PV modules for reuse are presented. The subjects of repair and relabelling of the PV modules conclude the technical part of the report, and is followed by a few pages about other issues around the reuse of PV modules like legislation and policy. After this main part of the TR that contains 100 pages, several annexes have been added (containing for example some use cases but also pictures to support the visual inspection in the main document text). Including these annexes, the total number of pages in the TR adds up to 163.

2.2 Testing via sampling or testing every PV module

The project team for this TR has investigated the possibility of reducing the amount of effort for selection of PV modules for reuse by applying a sampling approach instead of testing every PV module. This would of course only be justified if the PV modules inside a plant can be assumed to be in similar condition, so not if the plant has been partly destroyed by a weather disaster, for example. For such cases it is suggested that such a sampling could be based on a similar approach as applied by Solar Power Europe for the inspection of newly installed PV plants [15]. Their approach is to use the Acceptable Quality Limit (AQL) sampling described in ISO 2859-1 with different inspection levels depending on the type of test. The idea would be to apply this also for the selection of PV modules for reuse, using the AQL sampling method with slightly stricter inspection levels. Especially in combination with energy yield data for the plant over the past years and drone inspection imaging, this could be an interesting and economically viable approach. However, for the moment it has not yet been determined under which circumstances and with which inspection levels this should be made, and it was decided that this will need to be described in a future technical specification or standard. For this reason, for the moment it is still recommended to test every PV module for its evaluation for reuse.

The recommended test sequence for the testing of every PV module for possible reuse is the following:

- Visual inspection
- I-V testing
- EL imaging
- Bypass diode testing
- Dry insulation test
- Wet insulation test, only in the case of certain repairs

For application in a reuse facility, all of these tests (except the wet insulation test that is not standard included anyway) can in principle be integrated in a "test unit".

2.3 Visual inspection

Before electrical testing, every PV module must be inspected visually since it does not make sense to spend more time on a PV module having unacceptable defects. Figure 1 shows the basic visual inspection.

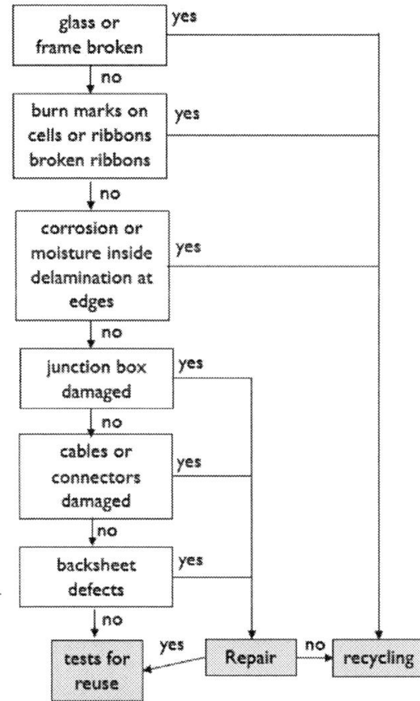

Figure 1: Basic visual inspection decision tree

In the TR, the visual inspection has been further detailed in a table containing recommended pass/fail/deliberate criteria for different components or materials of the PV module. In addition, example pictures to support the visual inspection are available in the annex C of the TR draft. The deliberation of a PV module means it could still be repaired or used at a reduced maximum system voltage.

2.4 I-V testing

Before I-V testing, PV modules have to be sufficiently clean (few % power loss due to soiling at most). The I-V measurement itself can be done outdoor or indoor, either on-site or at a reuse test facility.

The recommendation is to have a remaining measured P_{max} > guaranteed P_{max}, taking into account nameplate negative tolerance (if any), PV module age, guarantee curve from manufacturer and the measuring tolerance (default value 5%).

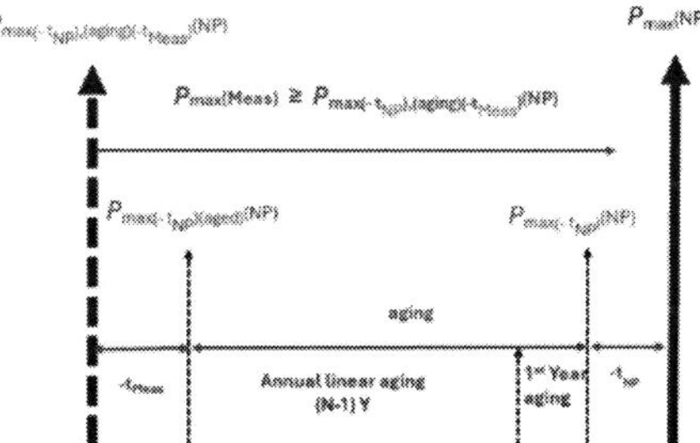

Figure 2: Determination of the remaining minimum power, starting on the right from $P_{max(NP)}$ and subtracting the tolerances and maximum allowed aging according to guarantee.

In some cases, it might also be possible to agree with a lower P_{max}, but only when agreed beforehand with the end user.

2.5 EL imaging

EL imaging is useful to detect cell cracks inside the PV module. In IEC TS 60904-13, cell cracks of different severity have been classified into categories A, B and C. In Figure 3, a cell with cracks from all categories is shown:

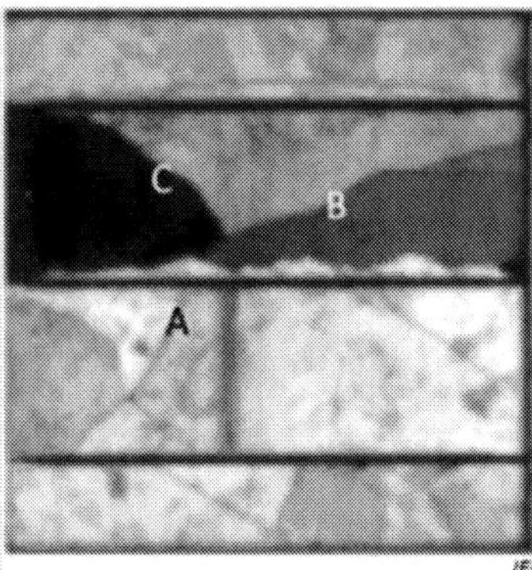

Figure 3: EL image of a cell having cell cracks of all three categories A, B, C used in IEC TS 60904-13

The cracks of the different classes are having the properties listed below:
- A: line defects not isolating cell area
- B: cracks causing partially disconnected regions
- C: cracks causing completely disconnected regions

Cracks of category B cause regions that are quite dark for an injected current that equals the short-circuit current I_{sc}, but that are not so dark for an injected current that equals only 10% of I_{sc}. For category C cracks, the disconnected region is black for any injected current.

The recommended rules for the acceptation of cracks in a PV module for reuse are the following:
- Only accept if < 50% of cells are crack affected
- A cracks are allowed if affected cell area < 1%
- B cracks are allowed if 1% < affected cell area < 20% and this occurs in < 20% of cells
- C cracks are allowed if affected area > 20% but < 5% of the cells.

2.6 Bypass diode test

The recommended bypass diode test is the test named method A in IEC 61215-2. Since it involves reverse biasing of the PV module in the dark, it is recommended to perform this test after the EL test. The reverse current should be swept from 0 A to $1.25I_{sc}$, while recording the required voltage. The expected voltage is now the number of diodes times the forward diode voltage required to pass the current through one diode (take the voltage at the highest current stated in the datasheet). If the total voltage is less (for 3 diodes typically by 1/3 or 2/3) it means that there are short-circuited bypass diodes. When no current can be passed in reverse for the expected forward bias voltage for 3 diodes, it means that one or more of the bypass diodes are open-circuited.

2.7 Dry insulation test

The dry insulation test that has been specified for new PV modules in IEC 61730 consists of two parts. First a voltage stress test of 4 times the maximum system voltage + 2000 V, with a dwell time of 1 minute. Afterwards, the voltage is reduced to the maximum system voltage (or 500 V at least), and after a dwell time of 2 minutes, the insulation resistance is determined. The voltage ramp rate should always remain < 500 V/s. The criteria to pass this test in IEC 61730 are: no breakdown during the first part of the test, and a value of the insulation resistance times the PV module area > 40 MΩm². In the TR, it is recommended to apply this dry insulation test also for testing PV modules for reuse, but with some adaptations to speed up the test: The dwell times are both reduced to only 1 s, and the voltage ramp rate may be > 500 V/s. The recommended criteria for passing the test are the same, although it should be noted that it is possible to select a reduced maximum system voltage for the PV module when it will be reused, which means that the test requirements can now be lower than they had been when the PV modules were still new.

It is very important to realise that certain insulation defects might not lead to failing in the dry insulation test when the PV module is in well dried condition. For this reason, it is important to take care that no insulation defects like (deep) backsheet scratches are overlooked in the visual inspection. Although the research community is investigating ways of insulating testing for reuse that should be both practical and sensitive (for example using steam instead of liquid water), it was decided to not yet include such a method in the current TR draft.

2.8 Wet insulation test

In the first place, it has to be mentioned that the wet insulation test as described in IEC 61730 for new PV modules is very impractical for testing PV modules for reuse. In fact, it is not recommended to apply this test for every PV module, but only if for example the junction box has been replaced or a local back sheet repair has been made.

In IEC 61730, it is mentioned that the PV module has to be placed in a water tank with the front side facing down (water level still below frame height). The electrical test itself is exactly equal to the second part of the dry insulation test, including the criterion for passing. Also here, the recommended adaptations for testing for reuse are the same: dwell time of only 1 s and a voltage ramp rate that is allowed to be > 500 V/s. Also here, the recommended criteria for passing the test are the same as for new ones. It should be noted again that it is possible to select a reduced maximum system voltage for the PV module when it will be reused, which means that the test requirements can now be lower than they had been when the PV modules were still new.

2.9 Relabelling

When a PV module has been found to be fit for reuse, the recommendation is to put an additional label on the PV module next to the original one. On this label, it is also required to specify the maximum system voltage from now on, which can be the original one or a reduced maximum system voltage. The proposed label is shown in Figure 4.

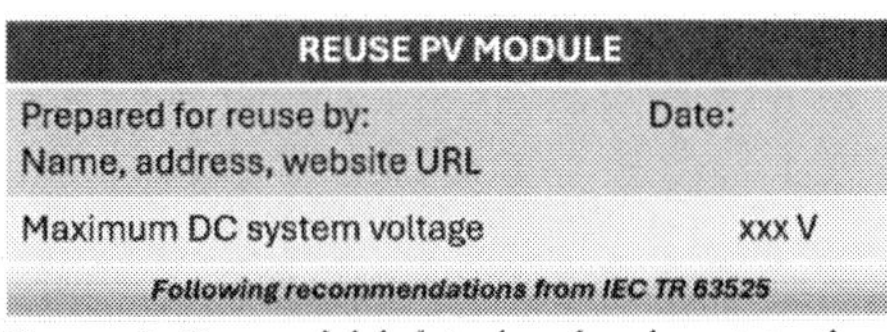

Figure 4: Proposed label to be placed next to the original one on a PV module that is fit for reuse.

Possible repairs should also be indicated on the label, as shown below.

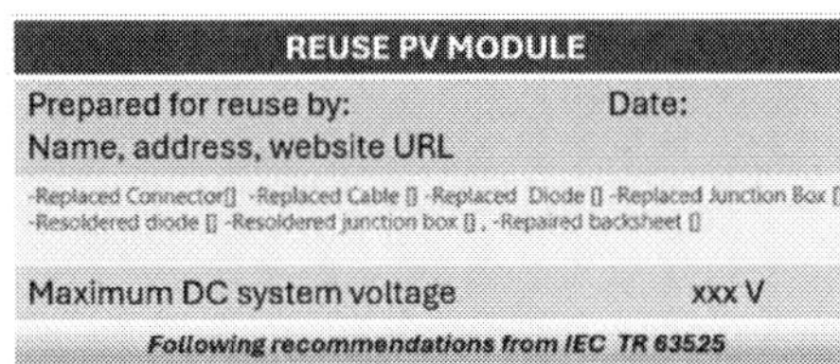

Figure 4: Proposed label to be placed next to the original one on a PV module that is fit for reuse, when the PV module has undergone one or more repairs

On another version of the label (not shown), it is also possible to add the newly measured electrical parameters. This is especially recommended when it has been agreed beforehand with the end user that the remaining power does not need to be higher than the minimum expected value based on the original power guarantee of the manufacturer.

2.10 Repair

Some of the options for repair have been discussed in the TR. While repair is relatively easy concerning liabilities and so on within an existing plant without change of ownership, it gets complicated when PV modules are offered to the market after repair. A simple replacement of connectors should not be a big issue, but replacing bypass diodes by other ones than the original ones is already something different, and certainly the replacement of a junction box is a major repair. In fact, it is a too complex subject to describe in detail in this paper, but different repair options for connectors, cables and backsheet are included in the TR, also recommending wet leakage testing and using the PV module at a reduced maximum system voltage where necessary.

3 CONCLUSIONS

The preparatory phase for the working draft of the IEC TR 63525 "Reuse of PV modules and circular economy" has been finished recently. Suggestions for future sampling of PV modules from large PV plants are given for future standardisation efforts, but for the moment it is recommended to still test every PV module on its properties. The tests that are recommended for every PV module are a visual inspection, I-V testing, EL, bypass diode testing and dry insulation testing. For the remaining power it is recommended to stay above the originally guaranteed power for the current age of the PV module, although it is possible to go below this value if the end user agrees with that beforehand. Concerning EL testing, criteria have been given for the acceptable presence of cracks for the different types A, B and C that have been specified in IEC 60904-13. The bypass diode testing is

rather straightforward and can detect short-circuited or open-circuited diodes. For dry insulation testing, it is acknowledged that it is not perfect and some insulation defects like back sheet scratches can be missed, but it still has an added value for inspecting internal insulation issues. It also means that a good visual inspection is still very important, especially on (deep) back sheet scratches and possible junction box damage.

A new label has to be placed next to the original one and should mention the maximum system voltage, which can be reduced compared to the original value, for example because of a reduced insulation quality or certain repairs.

Repairing PV modules for reuse is in general still a complicated issue. While replacing connectors and cables is still rather straightforward, replacing a junction box or repairing a backsheet is a different thing, especially when the PV module is to be put on the market after the repair. However, since it is such an important topic, the TR does give some recommendations for repair options, including backsheet repair.

4 ACKNOWLEDGEMENTS

The authors thank all the IEC experts of the project team that have contributed to this final working draft.

The contribution to this IEC TR draft by Serge Noels as project team lead and editor of the draft has been funded:
- from Dec 2021 – Nov 2022 by CIRCUSOL. This project has received funding from the European Union's Horizon 2020 research and innovation programme under grant agreement number 776680.
- from Dec 2022 – Sep 2025 by PV CYCLE

The contribution to this IEC TR draft by Arvid van der Heide at imec has been funded in part by the CLOSER project. This project has received funding from the European Union's I3 instrument under grant agreement number 101161109.

5 REFERENCES

[1] IRENA, IEA-PVPS, 2016. End-of-life management: Solar Photovoltaic Panels. p.98.

[2] PVPS, I.E.A., 2021. Preliminary Environmental & Financial Viability Analysis of Circular Economy Scenarios for Satisfying PV System Service Lifetime. p.69 Report IEA-PVPST12-21:2021.

[3] Wim Van Opstal, Anse Smeets, 2022, Circular economy strategies as enablers for solar PV adoption in organizational market segments, Sustainable Production and Consumption, Volume 35, 2023, Pages 40-54, ISSN 2352-5509.

[4] G Oviedo Hernandez et al 2022. Trends and innovations in photovoltaic operations and maintenance. Prog. Energy 4 042002

[5] Majewski P et al 2021 Recycling of solar PV panels-product stewardship and regulatory approaches Energy Policy 149 112062

[6] Tsanakas J A et al 2019 Towards a circular supply chain for PV modules: review of today's challenges in PV recycling, refurbishment and re-certification Prog. Photovolt. Res. Appl. 28 454–64

[7] Lempkowicz B et al 2021 RE-USE of PV modules, challenges and opportunities of the circular economy PV Cycle & IMEC (available at: https://pvcycle.be/wp-content/uploads/Press-Release-Reuse-08032021.pdf)

[8] Dodd N, Espinosa N, Van Tichelen P, Peeters K and Soares A 2020 Preparatory study for solar photovoltaic modules, inverters and systems: final report European Commission Publications Office (available at: https://data.europa.eu/doi/10.2760/852637)

[9] Godinho Ariolli D M 2021 Moving towards a circular photovoltaic economy in Europe: a system approach of the status, drivers, barriers, key policies and opportunities Master Thesis in the framework of the Erasmus Mundus Masters course in Environmental Sciences, Policy and Management (MESPOM)

[10] Hengky K S et al 2019 Drivers, barriers and enablers to end-of-life management of solar photovoltaic and battery energy storage systems: a systematic literature review J. Clean. Prod. 211 537–54

[11] van der Heide A et al 2021 Towards a successful re-use of decommissioned photovoltaic modules Prog. Photovolt. Res. Appl. 2021 1–11

[12] Strategic Research and Innovation Agenda Photovoltaics (SRIA), 2022.

[13] Farrell C C et al (2020). *Technical challenges and opportunities in realizing a circular economy for waste photovoltaic modules.* Renew. Sustain. Energy Rev. 128 109911

[14] Deng, R., Chang, N., Lunardi, M. M., Dias, P., Bilbao, J., Ji, J., & Chong, C. M. (2020). *Remanufacturing end-of-life silicon photovoltaics: Feasibility and viability analysis.* Progress in Photovoltaics: Research and Applications, pip.3376. https://doi.org/10.1002/pip.3376

[15] SolarPower Europe (2021)– *Engineering, Procurement & Construction Best practices guidelines version 2.0*
(https://www.solarpowereurope.org/insights/thematic-reports/epc-best-practice-guidelines-version-2-0

IEC Technical Report 63525 on the reuse of PV modules: final draft

Arvid van der Heide, Serge Noels, Jan Clyncke, Rich Strömberg

Technical Report (TR) on reuse of PV modules in IEC TC82 WG2

IEC TR 63525 : "Reuse of PV modules and circular economy"

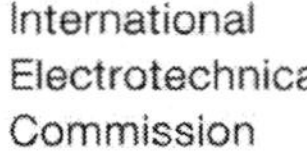

- Project team started 2022, led by Serge Noels, ~ 30 IEC experts involved

- TR: **simplified** project flow but **cannot** be **normative**

- Draft has been completely finished last week

- IEC TC82 "mirror committees" now have to decide about acceptance

- This presentation: summary of the final TR contents

"Acceptance of draft"

"Publication of Technical Report"

2

Basic principles behind this TR

- Safe
- Sufficient power
- Enough remaining lifetime

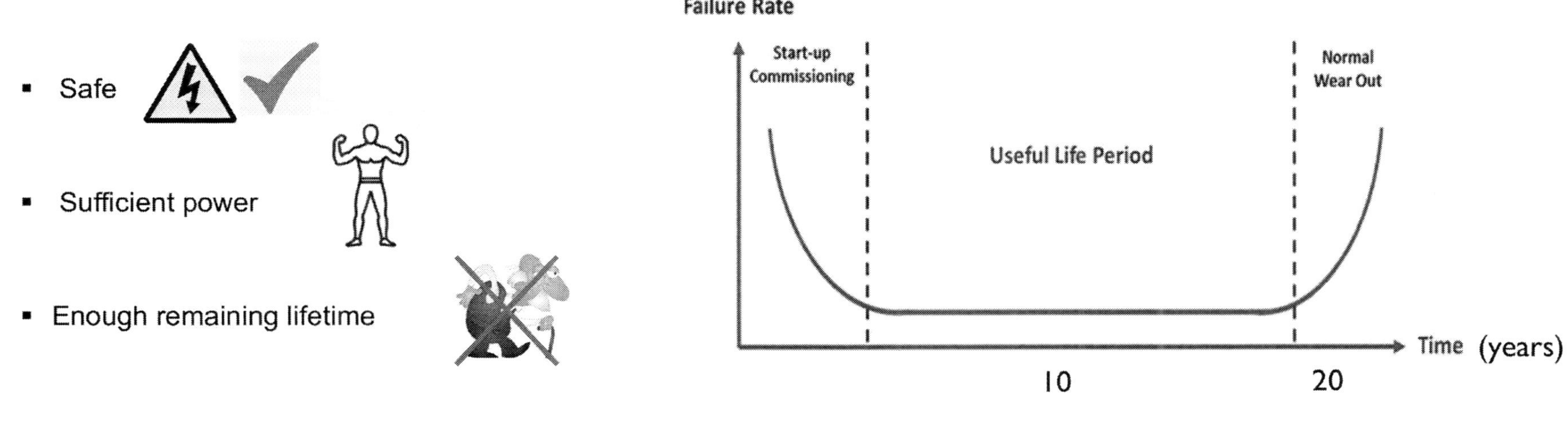

Main issues addressed in TR (100 pages, 163 pages with annexes)

- Testing **via sampling** or **testing every module**

- **Visual inspection** (and additional IR inspection in the field)

- **I-V test** and **remaining power**

- **EL** imaging and criteria on cell cracks

- Bypass diode testing

- **Insulation tests** (dry and wet) and possible reduction of maximum system voltage

- **Relabelling**

- Repair

Subjects in **bold**: will be discussed

Comparison testing based on sampling versus every module

Comparison subject	Sampling	Every module
Applicability	Only intact PV plants, preferably supported by O&M information like performance loss rate, drone images 	OK for testing all used modules 
Advantages	Fast, cheap and efficient	- Easier to standardise (more straightforward) - More guarantee for customer
Disadvantages	- Agreement required about justification for sampling and sampling rates	Slow and more expensive

Comparison testing based on sampling versus every module

Comparison subject	Sampling	Every module
Applicability		OK for testing all used modules
Advantages		- Ea… - More guarantee for customer
Disadvantages		Slow and more expensive

Testing every module

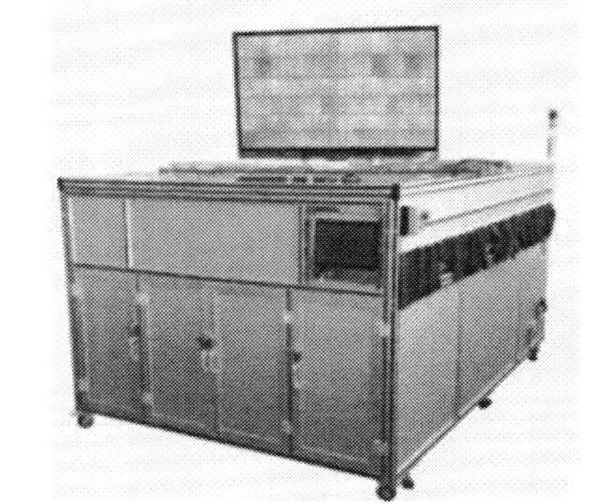

- **Recommended tests** (after initial visual inspection):

    - I-V test
    - dry insulation test
    - (wet insulation test): only in case of certain replacements/repairs
    - bypass diode test (both shorted/open)
    - EL imaging

- Some companies in Germany already use such an approach in a factory line
- Typical speed per line: 60 modules/h
- On site testing typically ~ 20-30 modules/h

IMO-IMOMEC · imec · UHASSELT · Energy Ville · PV CYCLE · UAF UNIVERSITY OF ALASKA FAIRBANKS · ACEP

Visual inspection

Basic principles of the visual inspection

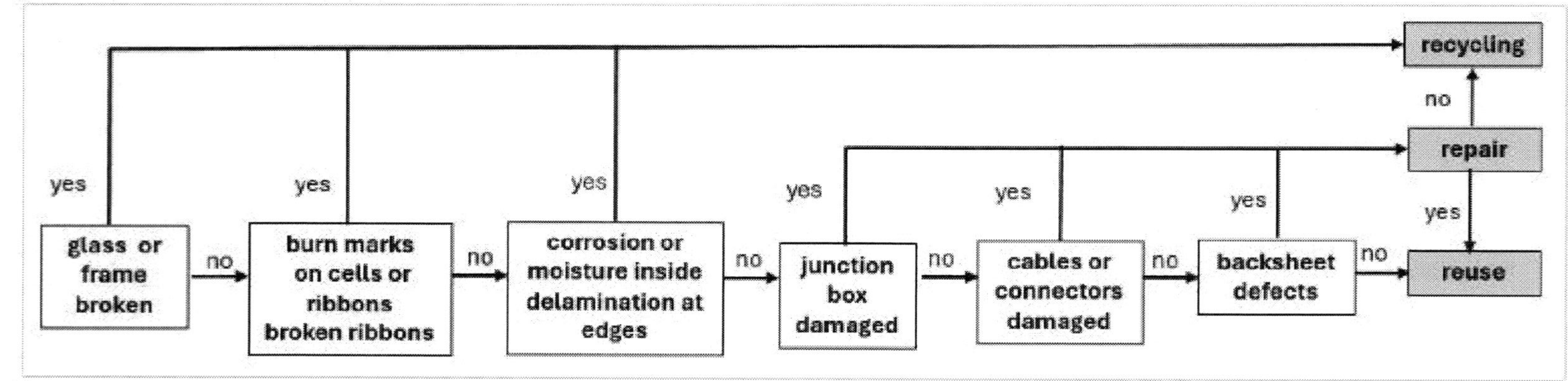

020473-008

Visual inspection

Table with more detailed criteria on recommended pass/fail/deliberation of module

Example part of the table: →

In **Annex C** also pictures have been included (back sheet chalking in this case)

↓

Defect Type	Representative Image
Chalking	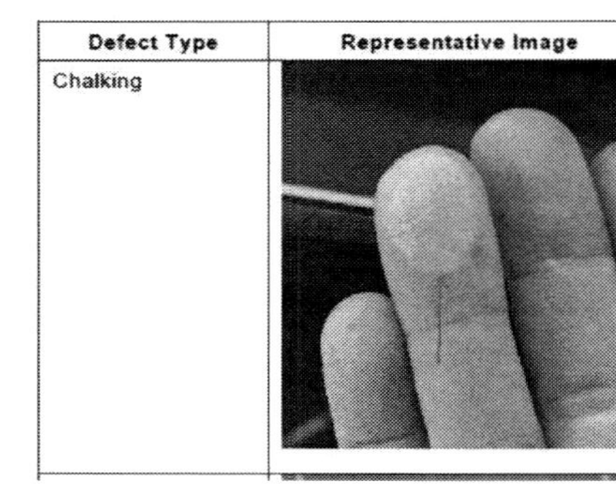

Back-sheet: front & back view	Pass	Appearance and texture are like new.
Back-sheet: front & back view	Fail	Burn marks originating from internally. No repair (3.8) accepted.
Back-sheet: front & back view	Fail	Delamination that can occur from the edge to the centre, from the centre, or near a junction box, creating a void between the back-sheet and encapsulant, or between the layers of the back-sheet. No repair (3.8) accepted.
Back-sheet: front & back view	Fail	If cracks or chalking, along with corrosion visible from the front, are present.
Back-sheet: front & back view	Deliberate	Yellowing should be verified with an *I-V* test to assess performance at the batch level. PV modules should be free of burn marks or other anomalies.
Back-sheet: front & back view	Deliberate	Bubbles between the encapsulant and backsheet if the average bubble size is < 5 mm², the bubble is > 5 cm from the edge, and the total bubble area is < 1 % of the PV module area
Back-sheet: front & back view	Deliberate	Superficial burn marks from an external source (e.g., grass fire) may require a polymer risk assessment for continued use. Individual patch repair (3.8) is possible based on technical and economic considerations. Wet insulation test depending on reuse application.

020473-009

I-V test and remaining power

Recommendations:

- Modules have to be sufficiently clean

- I-V test can be done either **outdoor** or **indoor**, either **on-site** or at a **reuse test facility**

- **Remaining P_{max} > guaranteed P_{max}**, taking into account nameplate negative tolerance, module age and measuring tolerance (default value 5%). Lower P_{max} only when agreed with end user

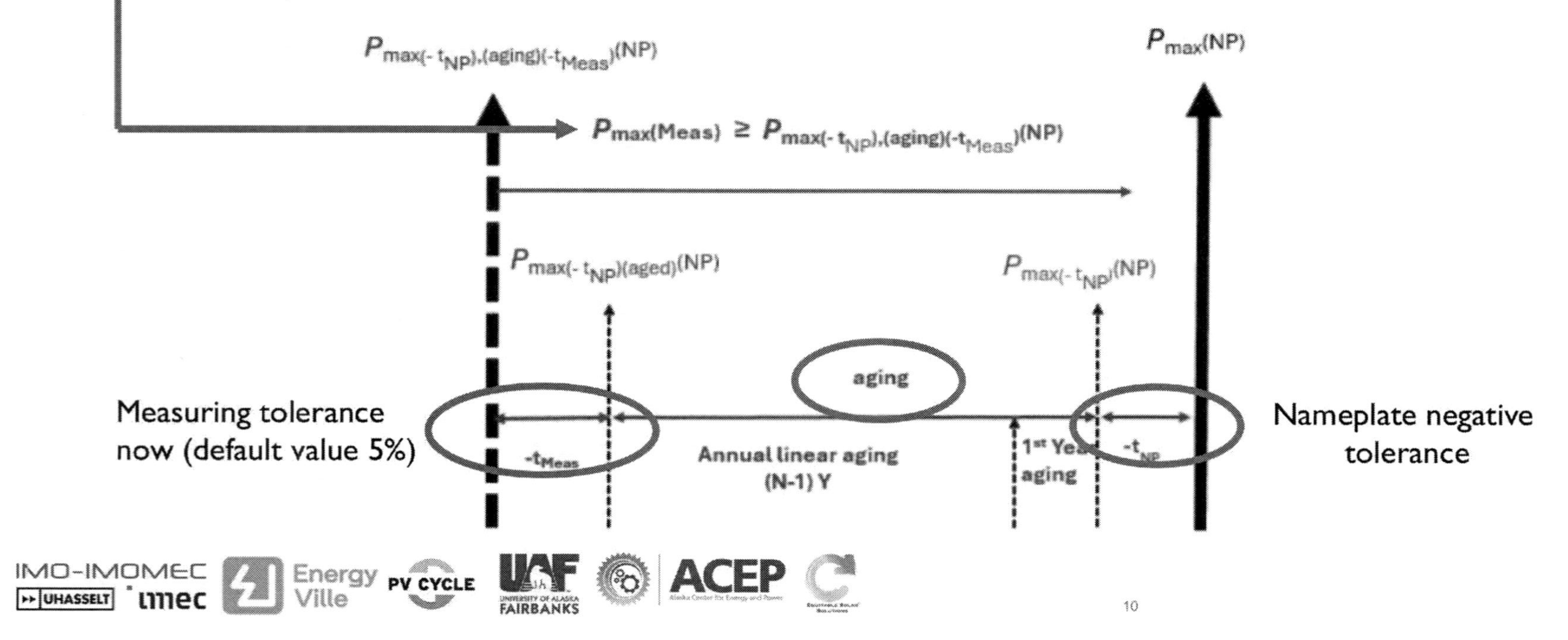

EL imaging and criteria on cell cracks

- Cell crack classification A, B, C conform IEC TS 60904-13
  - A: line defects not isolating cell area
  - B: cracks causing partially disconnected regions
  - C: cracks causing completely disconnected regions

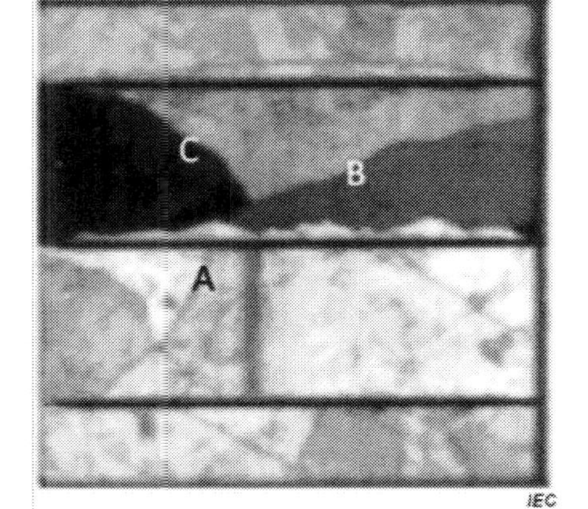

- Recommendation:
  To accept a module for reuse
  - Only if < 50% of cells are crack affected
  - Mode A cracks allowed if affected cell area < 1%
  - Mode B cracks allowed if 1% < affected cell area < 20% and in < 20% of cells
  - Mode C cracks allowed if affected area > 20% but < 5% of the cells

11

Insulation testing

Insulation test	IEC 61730 (class II modules)	Recommended adaptations
Dry insulation test	$2000\,V + 4*V_{sys,max}$ for 1 min (ramping up < 500 V/s) Followed by $V_{sys,max}$ for 2 min, then measuring R_{iso} Required: no breakdown & R_{iso}*area > 40 MΩm^2	Dwell time 1 s, ramp up optional > 500 V/s Dwell time 1 s, then measuring R_{iso}
Wet leakage current test	Immersion of module in shallow water tank $V_{sys,max}$ for 2 min, then measuring R_{iso} Required: no breakdown & R_{iso}*area > 40 MΩm^2	On site: water spraying (ASTM E2047-10) Indoor: water tank (or optional spraying) Dwell time 1 s, then measuring R_{iso}

Remarks:

Earlier determination R_{iso} : worst-case scenario, leakage current can be higher at start (capacitances)

Dry insulation test: for testing every module

Wet insulation test: not practical, only after certain repairs or sampling in PV plants

Detection limitations of insulation tests

Limitations dry insulation test:

- Result depends on storage condition (humidity) before testing: drying helps to pass

- "Dried modules" can still pass with damage (e.g. backsheet cracks): visual inspection also important

Limitation wet insulation test:

- Some defects not penetrated by liquid water, but sensitive to humid air

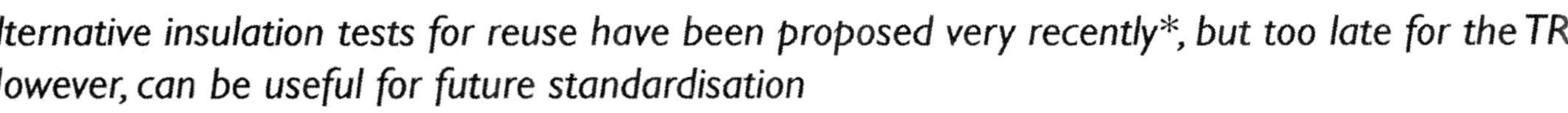

Alternative insulation tests for reuse have been proposed very recently, but too late for the TR*
However, can be useful for future standardisation

- E.R. Anagha et. al, Solar Energy Materials and Solar Cells, Volume 292, 2025
- Maximilian Engel et.al, this conference 3AV.3.21

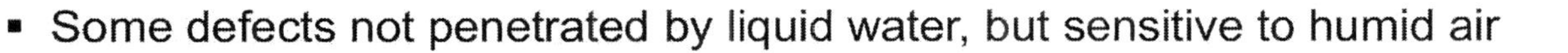

Relabelling

- Next to original label

- Always with maximum system voltage (possibly reduced for reduced insulation quality)

- Label in the case of repair

- Also new electric parameters can be mentioned (below)

REUSE PV MODULE		
Prepared for reuse by: Name, address, website URL		Date:
Maximum DC system voltage		xxx V
Following recommendations from IEC TR 63525		

REUSE PV MODULE		
Prepared for reuse by: Name, address, website URL		Date:
-Replaced Connector[] -Replaced Cable [] -Replaced Diode [] -Replaced Junction Box [] -Resoldered diode [] -Resoldered junction box [] , -Repaired backsheet []		
Maximum DC system voltage		xxx V
Following recommendations from IEC TR 63525		

REUSE PV MODULE		
Prepared for reuse by: Name, address, website URL		Date:
Maximum power	P_{max}	xxx W
Maximum power voltage	V_{mp}	xxx V
Maximum power current	I_{mp}	xxx A
Open circuit voltage	V_{OC}	xxx V
Short circuit current	I_{SC}	xxx A
Maximum DC system voltage		xxx V
Following recommendations from IEC TR 63525		

020473-014

Summary

- TR working draft text finished

- Recommended to test every module until standard for sampling approach will be available

- Visual inspection list including example pictures in Annex provided

- Tests and criteria have been described for: I-V, (fast) dry/wet insulation test, bypass diode test, EL

- Minimum remaining P_{max}: based on age, still > guaranteed P_{max} , including nameplate tolerance and measuring uncertainty

- Reduced maximum system voltage for certain repairs and lower insulation quality

Acknowledgements

The authors thank **all the IEC experts of the project team** that have contributed to this final working draft

The contribution to this IEC TR draft by Serge Noels as project team lead and editor of the draft has been funded from

Dec 2021 – Nov 2022 : By **CIRCUSOL** - This project has received funding from the European Union's Horizon 2020 research and innovation programme under grant agreement number 776680

Dec 2022 – Sep 2025 : By **PV CYCLE**

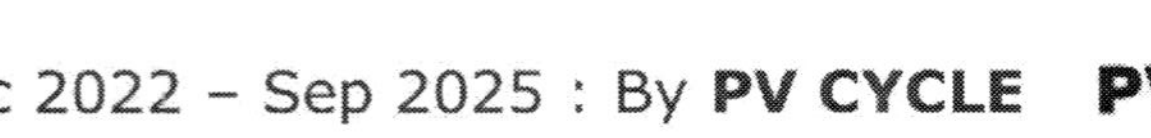

The contribution to this IEC TR draft by Arvid van der Heide at imec has been funded in part by the **CLOSER** project.

This project has received funding from the European Union's I3 instrument under grant agreement number 101161109

020473-016

BECQUEREL INSTITUTE
Strategy Consulting in Solar PV

Business model optimization for European Solar PV: A study on costs & commercial strategies

Ian Kenchington[a], Philippe Macé[a], Gaëtan Masson[a], Joris Libal[b]

[a] Becquerel Institute (Belgium)
[b] ISC Konstanz (Germany)

This project has received funding from the European Union's Horizon Europe under grant agreement № 101084259

Funded by the European Union

020474-001

Becquerel Institute at a Glance

- Est. 2014 in **Brussels, Belgium**
- Est. 2022 in **France**
- Est. 2023 in **Spain**
- Est. 2025 in **Italy**
- Focused on **solar PV**

 Strategy Consulting

 Technical Assistance

 Applied Research

They Trust Us

Project Developers

Manufacturers

Associations

Researchers

BECQUEREL INSTITUTE
Strategic Consulting in Solar PV

Table of Contents

1 | Context

2 | Research Questions

3 | Our Approach

4 | Main Results

5 | Takeaways

020474-003

BECQUEREL INSTITUTE

Table of Contents

1 | Context

2 | Research Questions

3 | Our Approach

4 | Main Results

5 | Takeaways

020474-004

BECQUEREL INSTITUTE
Strategy Consulting in Solar PV

Prices of PV modules collapsed to unstainable levels as production has largely outpaced market demand and competition among Chinese manufacturers has been as fierce as ever

Weekly evolution of PV *modules* average spot prices (in USD/Wp)

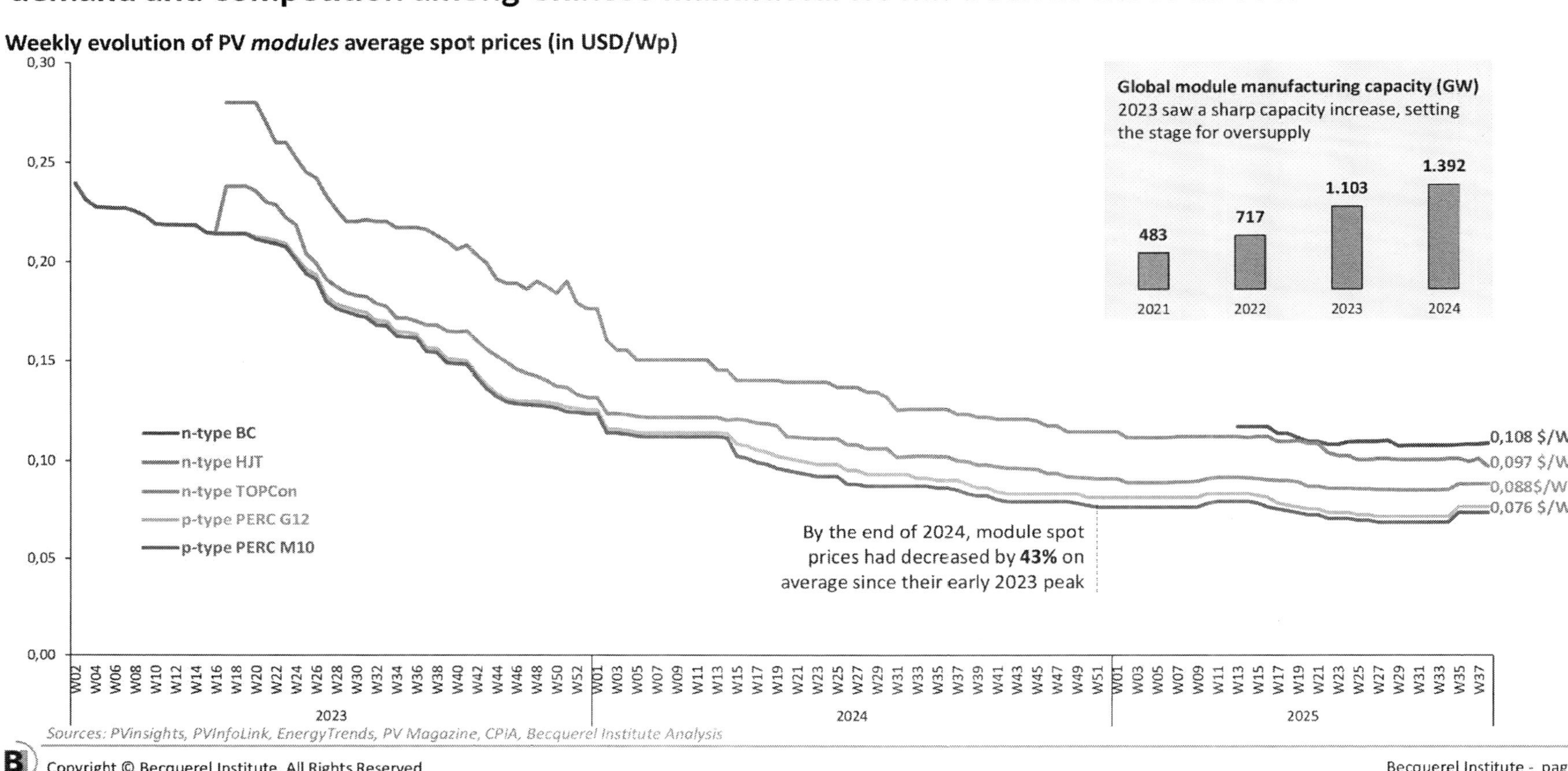

Sources: PVinsights, PVInfoLink, EnergyTrends, PV Magazine, CPIA, Becquerel Institute Analysis

020474-005

1 | Context

Spot prices seen since mid-2024 are below production costs, leading to heavy losses and threatening the existence of many actors, even the biggest ones

Average production cost* in FY 2024 (US$/Wp)

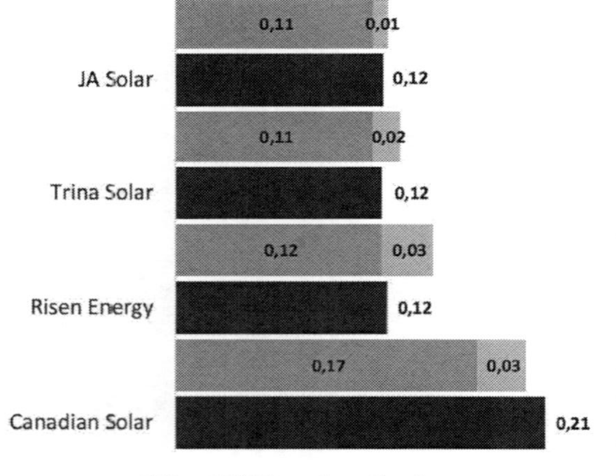

*Factory gate manufacturing cost, i.e. without margin and without transportation costs
**Canadian Solar calculations are made out of the revenues, COGS and operational expenses from the business unit CSI Solar that produces more than just solar PV modules.

1 | Context

Spot prices seen since mid-2024 are below production costs, leading to heavy losses and threatening the existence of many actors, even the biggest ones

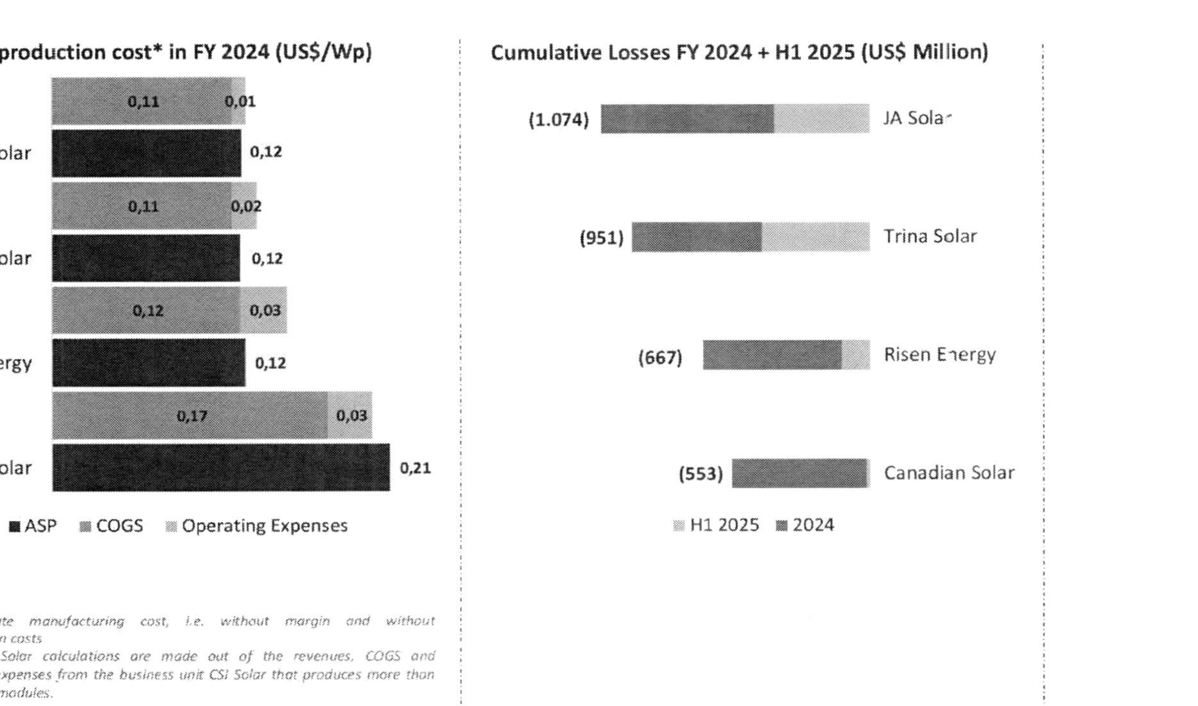

*Factory gate manufacturing cost, i.e. without margin and without transportation costs
**Canadian Solar calculations are made out of the revenues, COGS and operational expenses from the business unit CSI Solar that produces more than just solar PV modules.

1 | Context

Spot prices seen since mid-2024 are below production costs, leading to heavy losses and threatening the existence of many actors, even the biggest ones

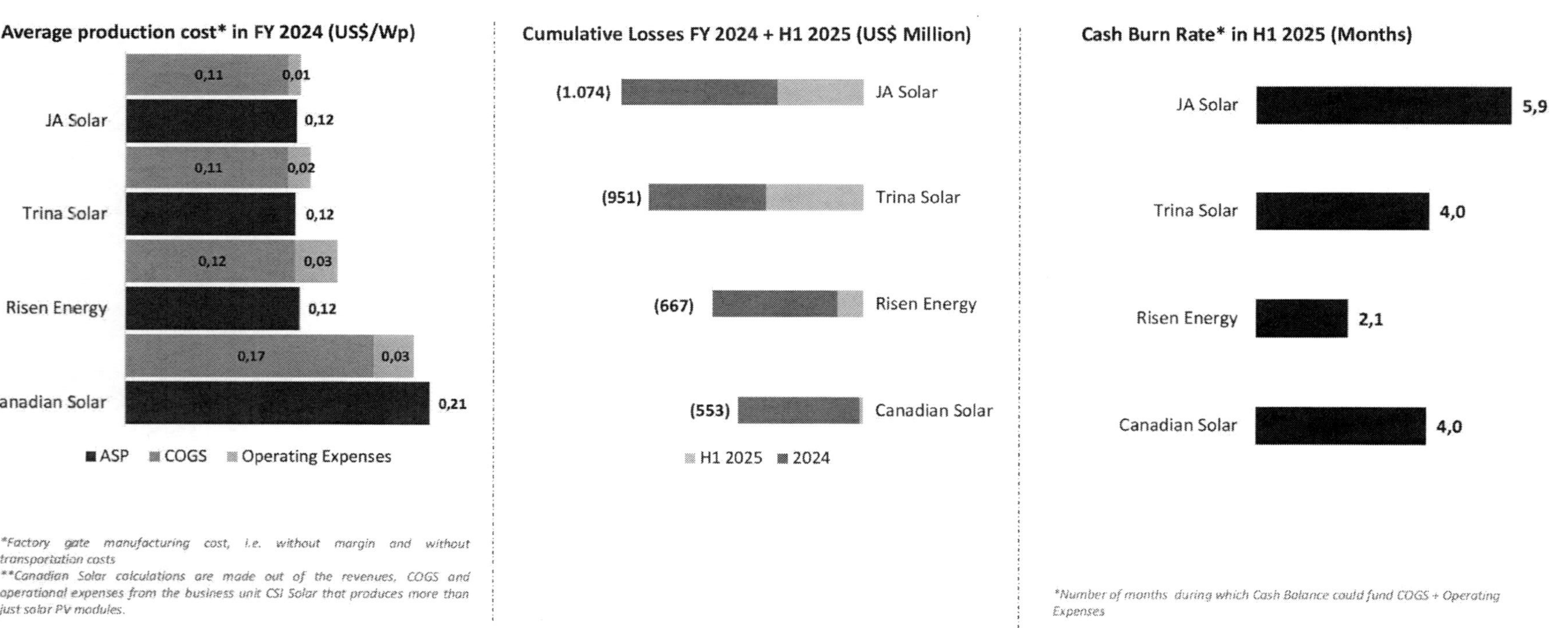

*Factory gate manufacturing cost, i.e. without margin and without transportation costs
**Canadian Solar calculations are made out of the revenues, COGS and operational expenses from the business unit CSI Solar that produces more than just solar PV modules.

*Number of months during which Cash Balance could fund COGS + Operating Expenses

1 | Context

The European solar manufacturing sector suffers collateral damage from global overcapacity, with multiple closures in the last 18 months

Meyer Burger to cease PV module production in Germany

Meyer Burger, a Switzerland-based heterojunction cell and panel manufacturer, says it will stop making PV modules in Germany, but it will continue to produce solar cells in the country to support its panel production operations in the United States.

JANUARY 17, 2024 EMILIANO BELLINI

Exasun files for insolvency

Exasun, a Dutch manufacturer that specializes in building-integrated photovoltaics (BIPV), has blamed Chinese rivals for its decision to launch insolvency proceedings.

JANUARY 22, 2024 EMILIANO BELLINI

French PV module maker Systovi goes into liquidation

Systovi has gone into liquidation, as the commercial court in Nantes, France, has issued an order to do so, citing the solar panel manufacturer's failure to find new investors, despite its 80 MW of panel manufacturing capacity.

APRIL 18, 2024 GWÉNAËLLE DEBOUTTE

Aleo Solar to halt production at PV module factory in Germany

Aleo Solar says it will halt production at its solar panel factory in Prenzlau, Germany, affecting 110 employees. The manufacturer is a unit of Taiwan's Sino-American Silicon.

MARCH 10, 2025 SANDRA ENKHARDT

Solarwatt to close German solar module factory in August

The module manufacturing facility is located in Dresden, eastern Germany, and has an annual capacity of 300 MW.

APRIL 29, 2024 SANDRA ENKHARDT

BECQUEREL INSTITUTE
Strategy Consulting in Solar PV

Table of Contents

1 | Context

2 | Research Questions

3 | Our Approach

4 | Main Results

5 | Takeaways

020474-010

BECQUEREL INSTITUTE
Strategy Consulting in Solar PV

How to minimise the cost gap with Chinese competitors...

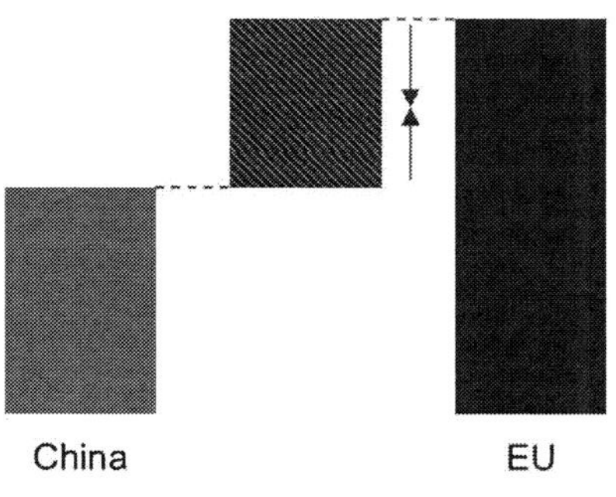

- *Location choice*
- *Bill of materials*
- *Level of integration*

BECQUEREL INSTITUTE
Strategy Consulting in Solar PV

How to minimise the cost gap with Chinese competitors...

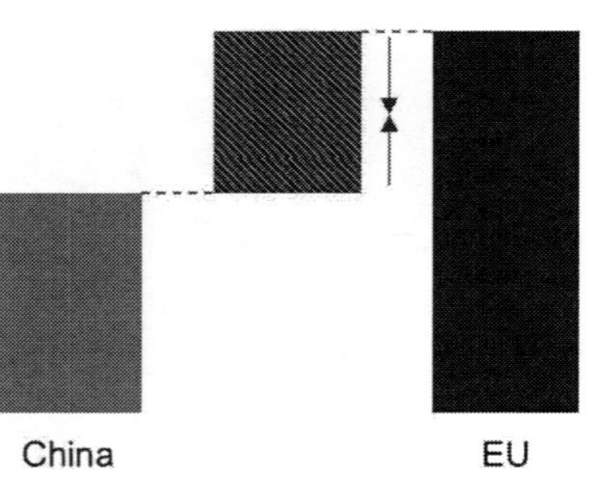

- *Location choice*
- *Bill of materials*
- *Level of integration*

...and maximise the chances of reaching a sustainable business...

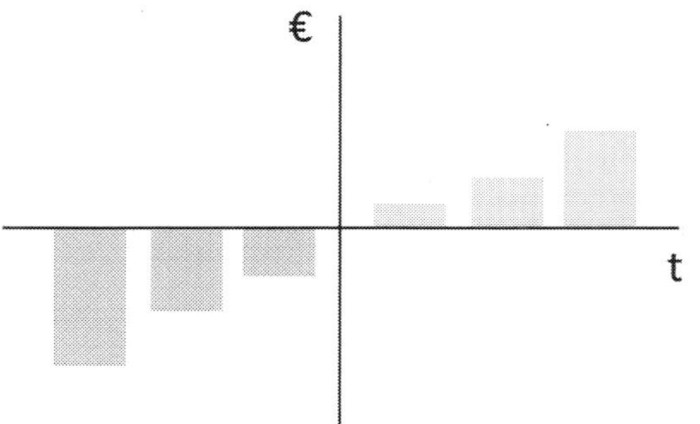

- *Equipment procurement*
- *Supplier relationships*
- *Choice of market segments*

020474-012

2 | Research Questions

BECQUEREL INSTITUTE

How to minimise the cost gap with Chinese competitors...

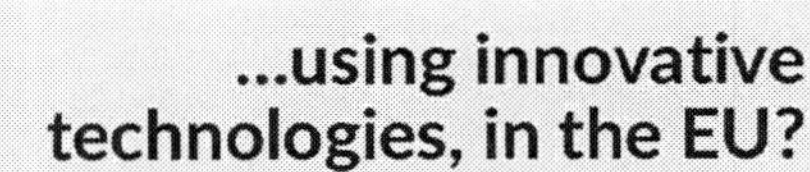

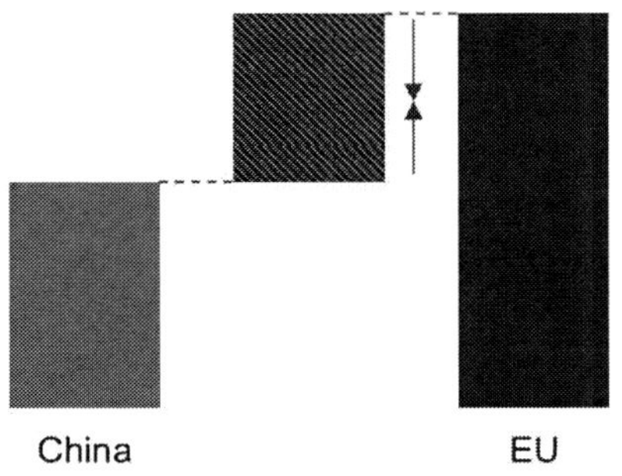

- *Location choice*
- *Bill of materials*
- *Level of integration*

...and maximise the chances of reaching a sustainable business...

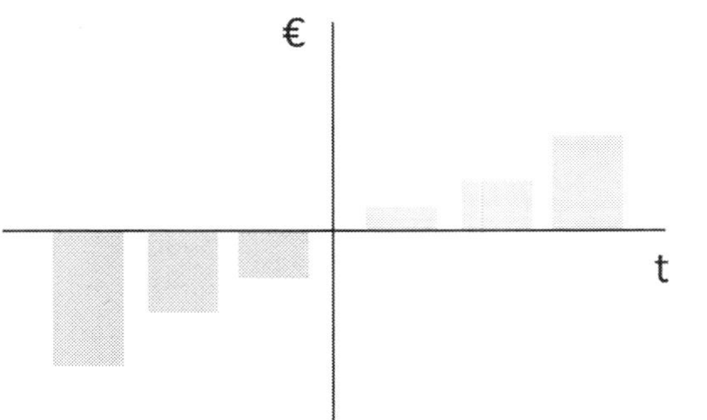

- *Equipment procurement*
- *Supplier relationships*
- *Choice of market segments*

...using innovative technologies, in the EU?

- *BC cells and modules*
- *EU BOM when possible*
- *Copper replacing silver*

BECQUEREL INSTITUTE
Strategy Consulting in Solar PV

Table of Contents

1 | Context

2 | Research Questions

3 | Our Approach

4 | Main Results

5 | Takeaways

020474-014

BECQUEREL INSTITUTE
Strategy Consulting in Solar PV

By using a Business Model Canvas approach, we can identify key business activities within manufacturing that affect business performance

Key Partnerships

- Material suppliers
- Equip. Manufacturers
- Distributors
- Research institutions
- Logistic companies

Key Activities

- Manufacturing
- R&D
- Quality control
- SC management
- Sales & marketing

Key Resources

- Manufacturing plants
- Tech & IP
- Skilled workforce
- Raw materials
- Financial capitals

Value Proposition

- High-efficiency modules
- Long-term warranties
- Sustainability
- Cost-effective solutions

Channels

- Distributors
- Direct sales
- Online platforms
- Trade shows & exhibitions

Customer Relationships

- B2B sales: EPC, contractors & utility companies
- After-sales service
- Customer support

Customer Segments

- Utility scale
- C&I
- Residential
- Distributors & EPC
- IPV

Cost Structure

- Raw materials costs
- Manufacturing costs
- R&D costs
- Sales & marketing expenses
- Logistics

Revenue Streams

- Module sales
- Licensing technology

020474-015

3 | Our Approach

We broke down the analysis into three analytical steps

Key Partnerships
- Material suppliers
- Equip. Manufacturers
- Distributors
- Research institutions
- Logistic companies

Key Activities
- Manufacturing
- R&D
- Quality control
- SC management
- Sales & marketing

Key Resources
- Manufacturing plants
- Tech & IP
- Skilled workforce
- Raw materials
- Financial capitals

Value Proposition
- High-efficiency modules
- Long-term warranties
- Sustainability
- Cost-effective solutions

Channels
- Distributors
- Direct sales
- Online platforms
- Trade shows & exhibitions

Customer Relationships
- B2B sales: EPC, contractors & utility companies
- After-sales service
- Customer support

Customer Segments
- Utility scale
- C&I
- Residential
- Distributors & EPC
- IPV

Cost Structure
- Raw materials costs
- Manufacturing costs
- R&D costs
- Sales & marketing expenses
- Logistics

Revenue Streams
- Module sales
- Licensing technology

1st Step

BECQUEREL INSTITUTE
Strategy Consulting in Solar PV

We broke down the analysis into three analytical steps

Key Partnerships

- Material suppliers
- Equip. Manufacturers
- Distributors
- Research institutions
- Logistic companies

Key Activities

- Manufacturing
- R&D
- Quality control
- SC management
- Sales & marketing

Key Resources

- Manufacturing plants
- Tech & IP
- Skilled workforce
- Raw materials
- Financial capitals

Value Proposition

- High-efficiency modules
- Long-term warranties
- Sustainability
- Cost-effective solutions

Channels

- Distributors
- Direct sales
- Online platforms
- Trade shows & exhibitions

Customer Relationships

- B2B sales: EPC, contractors & utility companies
- After-sales service
- Customer support

Customer Segments

- Utility scale
- C&I
- Residential
- Distributors & EPC
- IPV

Cost Structure

- Raw materials costs
- Manufacturing costs
- R&D costs
- Sales & marketing expenses
- Logistics

Revenue Streams

- Module sales
- Licensing technology

2nd Step

1st Step

020474-017

We broke down the analysis into three analytical steps

Key Partnerships
- Material suppliers
- Equip. Manufacturers
- Distributors
- Research institutions
- Logistic companies

Key Activities
- Manufacturing
- R&D
- Quality control
- SC management
- Sales & marketing

Key Resources
- Manufacturing plants
- Tech & IP
- Skilled workforce
- Raw materials
- Financial capitals

Value Proposition
- High-efficiency modules
- Long-term warranties
- Sustainability
- Cost-effective solutions

Channels
- Distributors
- Direct sales
- Online platforms
- Trade shows & exhibitions

Customer Relationships
- B2B sales: EPC, contractors & utility companies
- After-sales service
- Customer support

Customer Segments
- Utility scale
- C&I
- Residential
- Distributors & EPC
- IPV

Cost Structure
- Raw materials costs
- Manufacturing costs
- R&D costs
- Sales & marketing expenses
- Logistics

Revenue Streams
- Module sales
- Licensing technology

1st Step

2nd Step

3rd Step

020474-018

3 | Our Approach

BECQUEREL INSTITUTE
Strategy Consulting in Solar PV

Our methodology combines ISC Konstanz technical expertise in upstream cost assessment, with Becquerel Institute's experience in module cost evaluation and business models

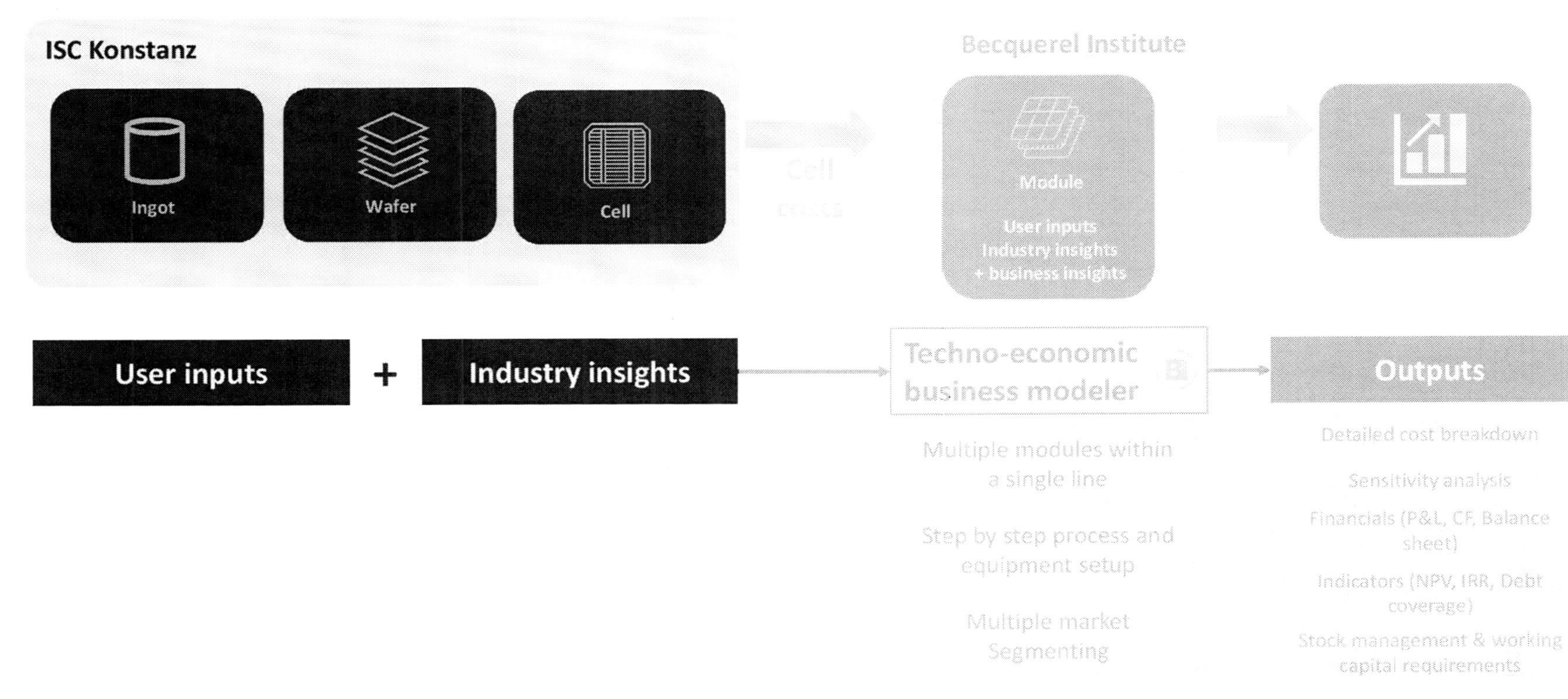

020474-019

BECQUEREL INSTITUTE
Strategy Consulting in Solar PV

Our methodology combines ISC Konstanz technical expertise in upstream cost assessment, with Becquerel Institute's experience in module cost evaluation and business models

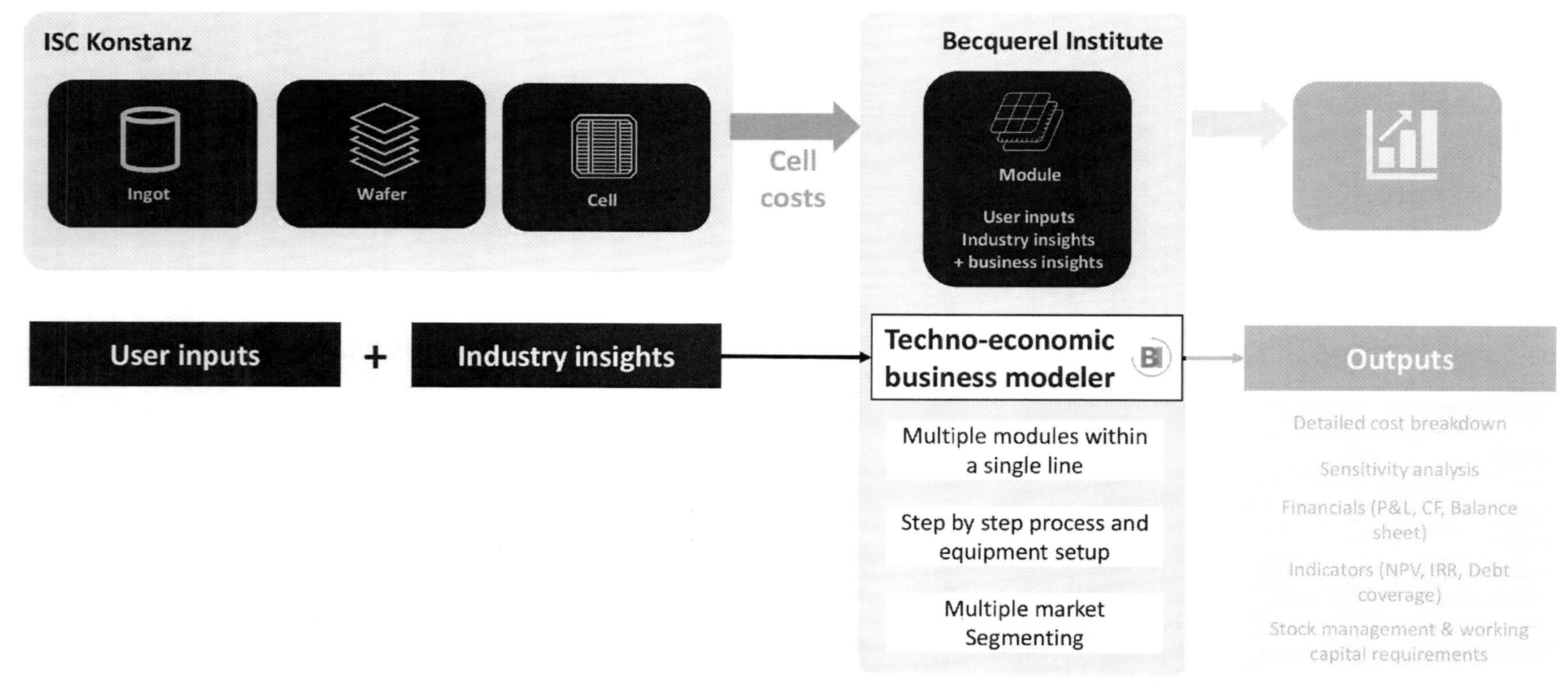

020474-020

BECQUEREL INSTITUTE
Strategy Consulting in Solar PV

Our methodology combines ISC Konstanz technical expertise in upstream cost assessment, with Becquerel Institute's experience in module cost evaluation and business models

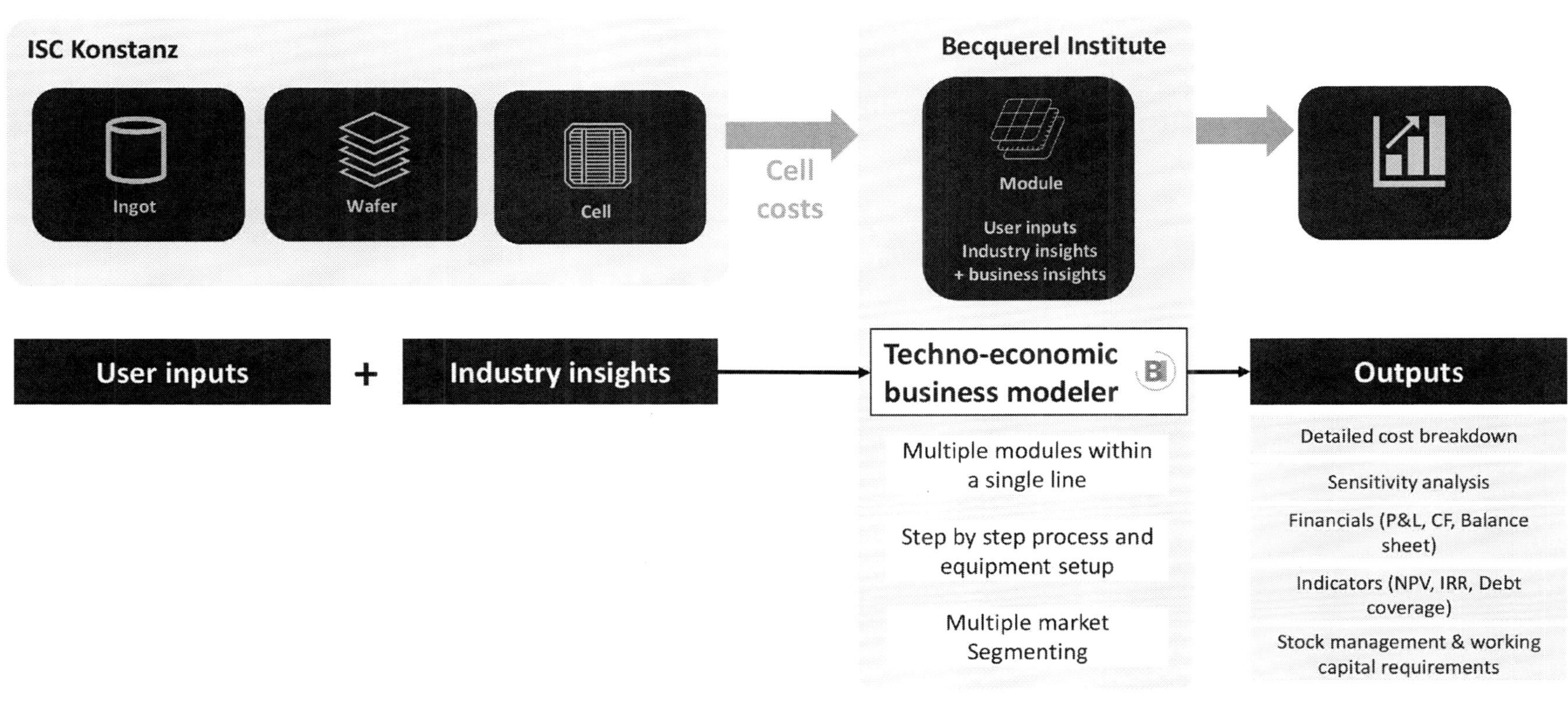

BECQUEREL INSTITUTE
Strategy Consulting in Solar PV

Table of Contents

1 | Context

2 | Research Questions

3 | Our Approach

4 | Main Results

5 | Takeaways

020474-022

4 | Main Results

BECQUEREL INSTITUTE
Strategy Consulting in Solar PV

First step: What to make, where to make it
Before addressing the full business model, cost structures are first studied

- **Location choice**: EU low-cost or high-cost country
- **Materials used**: Mainstream Ag metallisation or innovative Cu alternative
- **Level of integration**: Importing cells from abroad, using EU-made cells, or fully EU-made value chain.

020474-023

BECQUEREL INSTITUTE
Strategy Consulting in Solar PV

First step: What to make, where to make it
Before addressing the full business model, cost structures are first studied

- **Location choice**: EU low-cost or high-cost country
- **Materials used**: Mainstream Ag metallisation or innovative Cu alternative
- **Level of integration**: Importing cells from abroad, using EU-made cells, or fully EU-made value chain.

Modules - Total Cost of Ownership (€cent /Wp) per level of integration and metallisation choice
Bars represent cost range between location

EU Modules	ex-EU TOPCon (Benchmark)	Low: 16,5 — High: 17,6
	ex-EU IBC	Low: 21,2 — High: 22,4
EU Cells + Modules	Copper	Low: 24,1 EU Cells High: 27,2
	Silver	Low: 26,4 EU Cells High: 29,4
EU Ingots + Wafers + Cells + Modules	Copper	Low: 28,8 EU Ingot/Wafer/Cells High: 35,0
	Silver	Low: 31,0 EU Ingot/Wafer/Cells High: 37,2

020474-024

BECQUEREL INSTITUTE
Strategy Consulting in Solar PV

First step: What to make, where to make it
Before addressing the full business model, cost structures are first studied

- **Location choice**: EU low-cost or high-cost country
- **Materials used**: Mainstream Ag metallisation or innovative Cu alternative
- **Level of integration**: Importing cells from abroad, using EU-made cells, or fully EU-made value chain.

Modules - Total Cost of Ownership (€cent /Wp) per level of integration and metallisation choice
Bars represent cost range between location

EU Modules	ex-EU TOPCon (Benchmark)	Low: 16,5 — High: 17,6
	ex-EU IBC	Low: 21,2 — High: 22,4
EU Cells + Modules	Copper	Low: 24,1 EU Cells High: 27,2
	Silver	Low: 26,4 EU Cells High: 29,4
EU Ingots + Wafers + Cells + Modules	Copper	Low: 28,8 EU Ingot/Wafer/Cells High: 35,0
	Silver	Low: 31,0 EU Ingot/Wafer/Cells High: 37,2

1 Operations must be in a low-cost location

2 Cell cost reductions are the main priority

3 Integration should be minimal at first to reach competitive costs

020474-025

BECQUEREL INSTITUTE
Strategy Consulting in Solar PV

First step: What to make, where to make it
Before addressing the full business model, cost structures are first studied

- **Location choice**: EU low-cost or high-cost country
- **Materials used**: Mainstream Ag metallisation or innovative Cu alternative
- **Level of integration**: Importing cells from abroad, using EU-made cells, or fully EU-made value chain.

Modules - Total Cost of Ownership (€cent /Wp) per level of integration and metallisation choice
Bars represent cost range between location

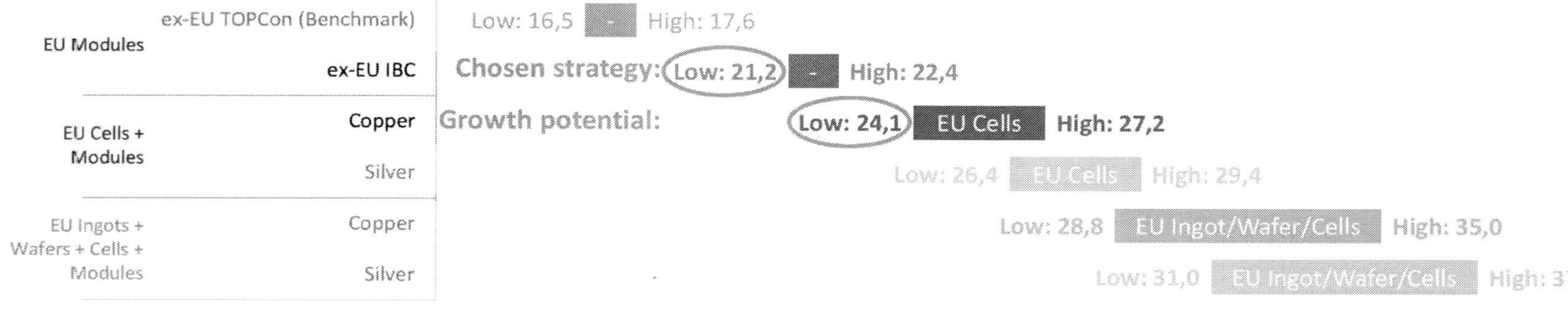

1 Operations must be in a low-cost location

2 Cell cost reductions are the main priority

3 Integration should be minimal at first to reach competitive costs

020474-026

BECQUEREL INSTITUTE
Strategy Consulting in Solar PV

Second and Third step: We set out scenarios to test their impact in business performance
With starting strategy: Imported BC cells, low-cost EU location for modules' assembling

 ## A. Cash management

B. Sales optimisation 

A.1 Equipment acquisition strategy
Operational lease instead of purchase

Alternative market segments B.1
Carports, agrivoltaics, BIPV

A.2 Just in Time manufacturing
Reducing inventory levels

Downwards integration B.2
Direct end-user sales

A.3 Favourable payment conditions
Deferring a fraction of payments

Aggressive diversified sales B.3
Alternative markets + end-user sales

A.4 Grants
Reducing total CAPEX required

Sales de-risking B.4
Acting as OEM for third companies

BECQUEREL INSTITUTE
Strategy Consulting in Solar PV

Scenarios are developed through iterations from a defined business case

A.1

A.2

A.3

A.4

B.1

B.2

B.3

B.4

Base Case

NPV	IRR
0,4 M€	**7,5 %**

Targeting three segments:

Residential (Small 54 GB), **50% prod.**
- Channels: Distributors, installers

Commercial (Medium 60 GB), **30% prod.**
- Channels: Distributors, installers

Utility (Large 72 GG), **20% prod.**
- Channels: EPCs, developers

Yearly Cumulative Cash Flow after debt servicing (CFADS), in M€

Segment	Channel	Selling price /Wp
Residential	Distributors	22,8 €ct
C&I	Distributors	20,7 €ct
C&I	Installers	23,0 €ct
Utility	EPC	20,0 €ct
Utility	Developers	20,7 €ct

020474-028

BECQUEREL INSTITUTE
Strategy Consulting in Solar PV

Operational leasing reduces CAPEX, but turns depreciation into cash expenses

A.1

A.2

A.3

A.4

B.1

B.2

B.3

B.4

A.1 Leased Equipment

NPV
▼(2,6 M€)

IRR
▼5,1 %

? Instead of **purchasing** equipment, it is acquired via **operational leasing.**

+ Lower CAPEX (reduced early cash outflow, which can be crucial in a time of limited available financing)

− Reduced total cash from operations (lease payments). Interests can be very high due to the high risk perception & limited number of actors

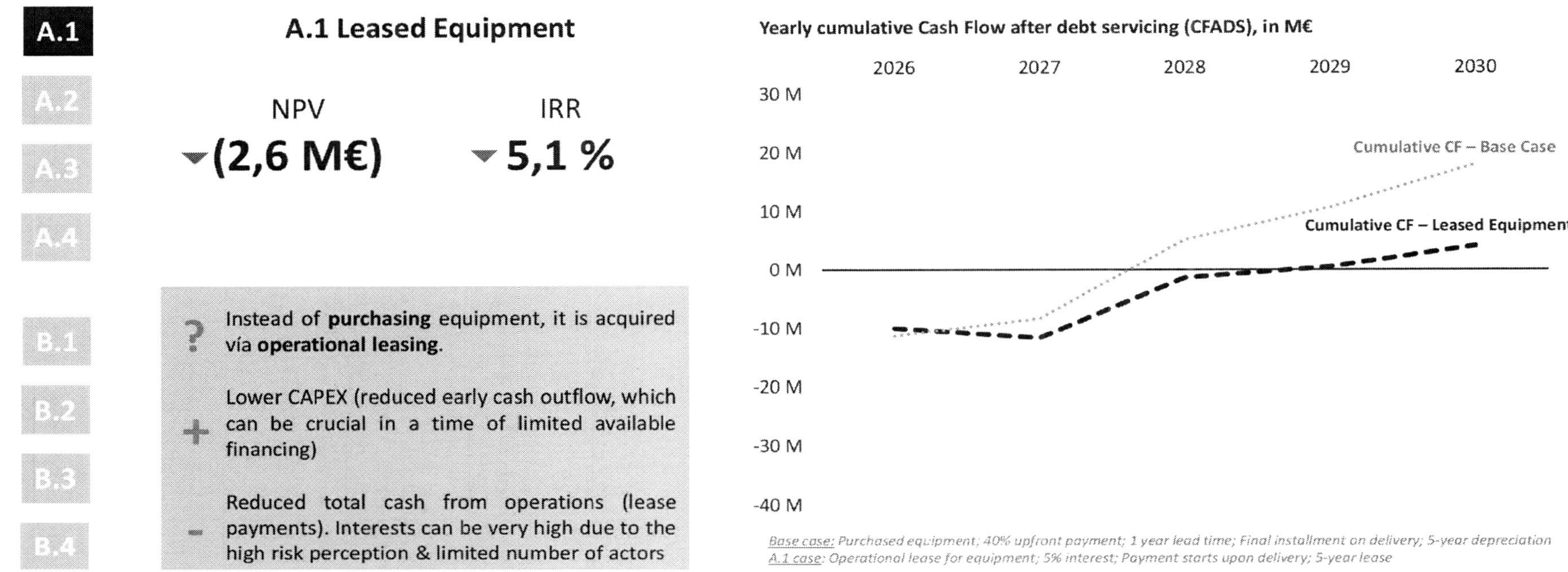

020474-029

BECQUEREL INSTITUTE
Strategy Consulting in Solar PV

Minimizing inventory levels keeps manufacturing costs lean on cash

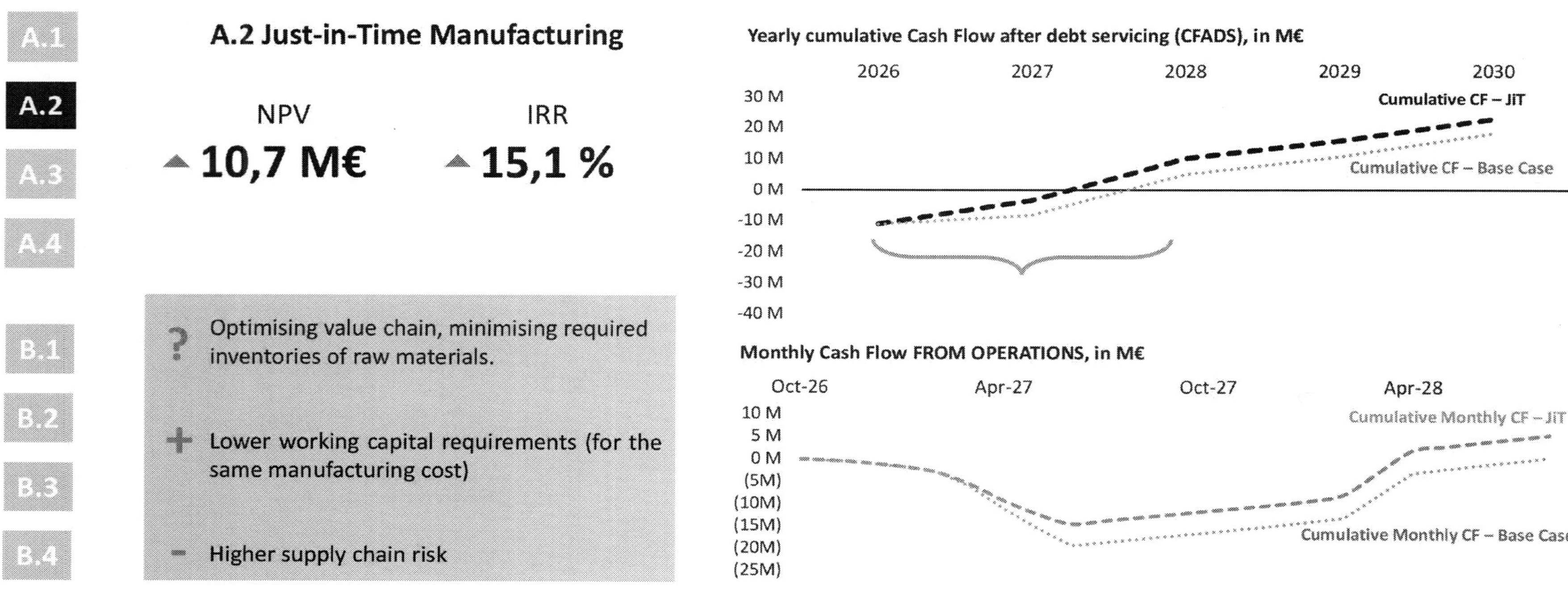

020474-030

BECQUEREL INSTITUTE
Strategy Consulting in Solar PV

Better supplier relationships reduce working capital requirements

A.1
A.2
A.3
A.4

B.1
B.2
B.3
B.4

A.3 Favourable Payment Conditions

NPV

IRR

▲ **1,1 M€**

▲ **8,2 %**

? Initially, everything is paid upfront. After 4 months, 50% upfront only.

+ Deferring payments reduces early BOM investments, increasing cash savings from operations (in blue)

− Difficulties to find accepting suppliers, and it may come with a risk premium

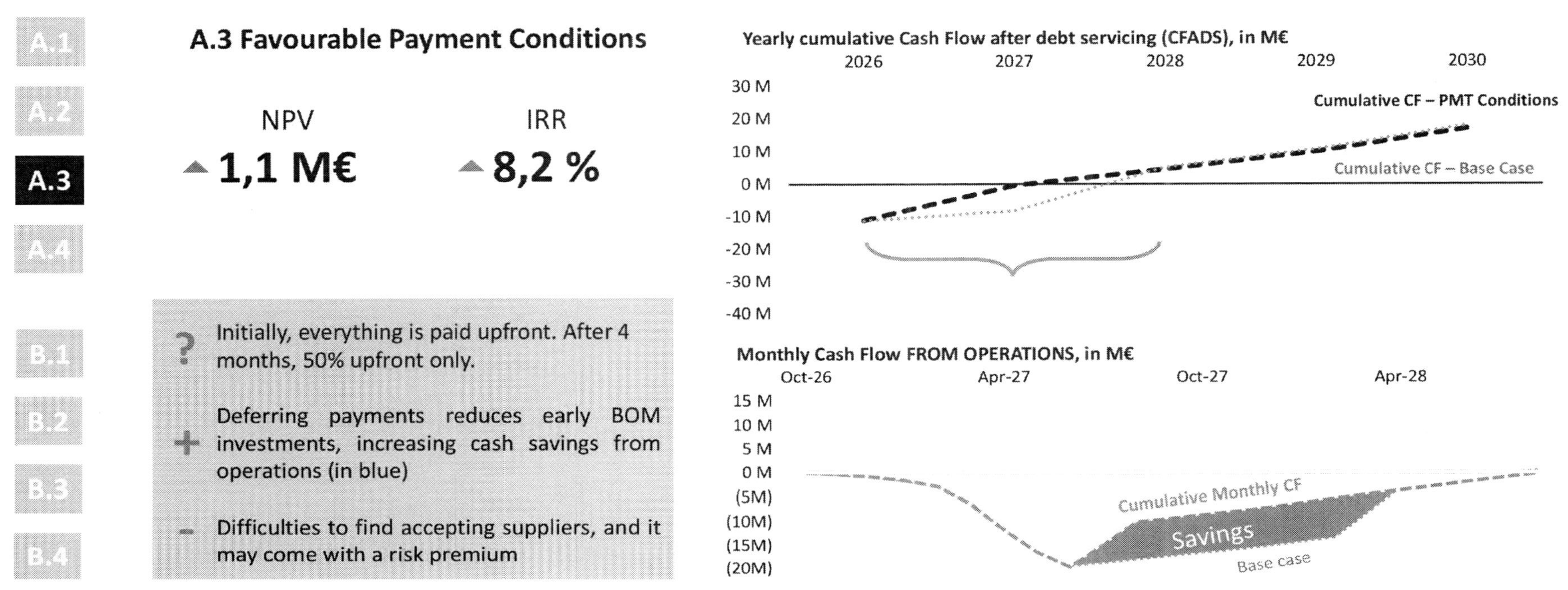

Base case: After 12 months, materials are paid 50% upfront and 50% on delivery
A.3 case: After 4 months, materials are paid 50% upfront and 50% on delivery

020474-031

BECQUEREL INSTITUTE
Strategy Consulting in Solar PV

CAPEX grants' benefits are twofold, with no drawbacks for manufacturers.

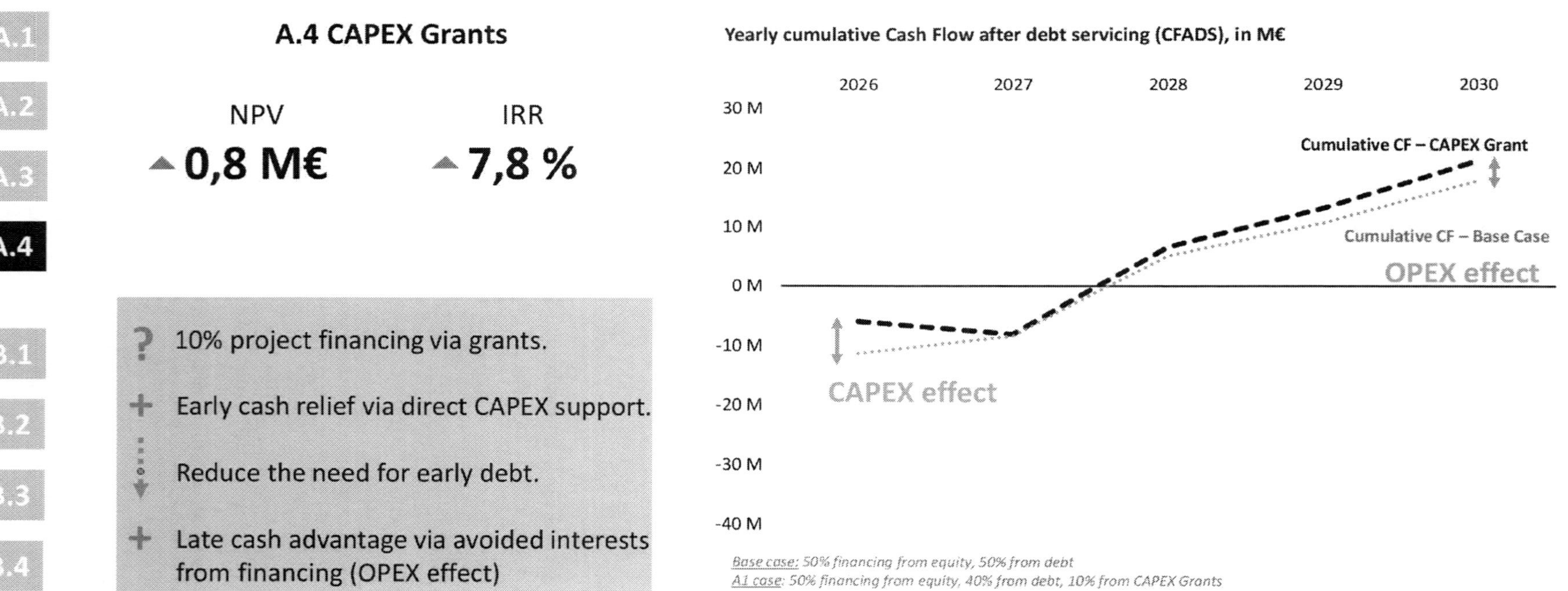

High-cost, premium alternative markets can yield better margins, but sales conversion cost almost offset the gains

A.1

A.2

A.3

A.4

B.1

B.2

B.3

B.4

B.1 Extended portfolio

NPV	IRR
▲ **1,4 M€**	▲ **8,2 %**

? Target **additional** alternative markets with greater potential margins:

Carports (Distributors, installers), **AgriPV** (Distributors), **BIPV** (Distributors)

+ Higher margins, and diversified sales less prone to demand shocks

– Higher sales conversion cost

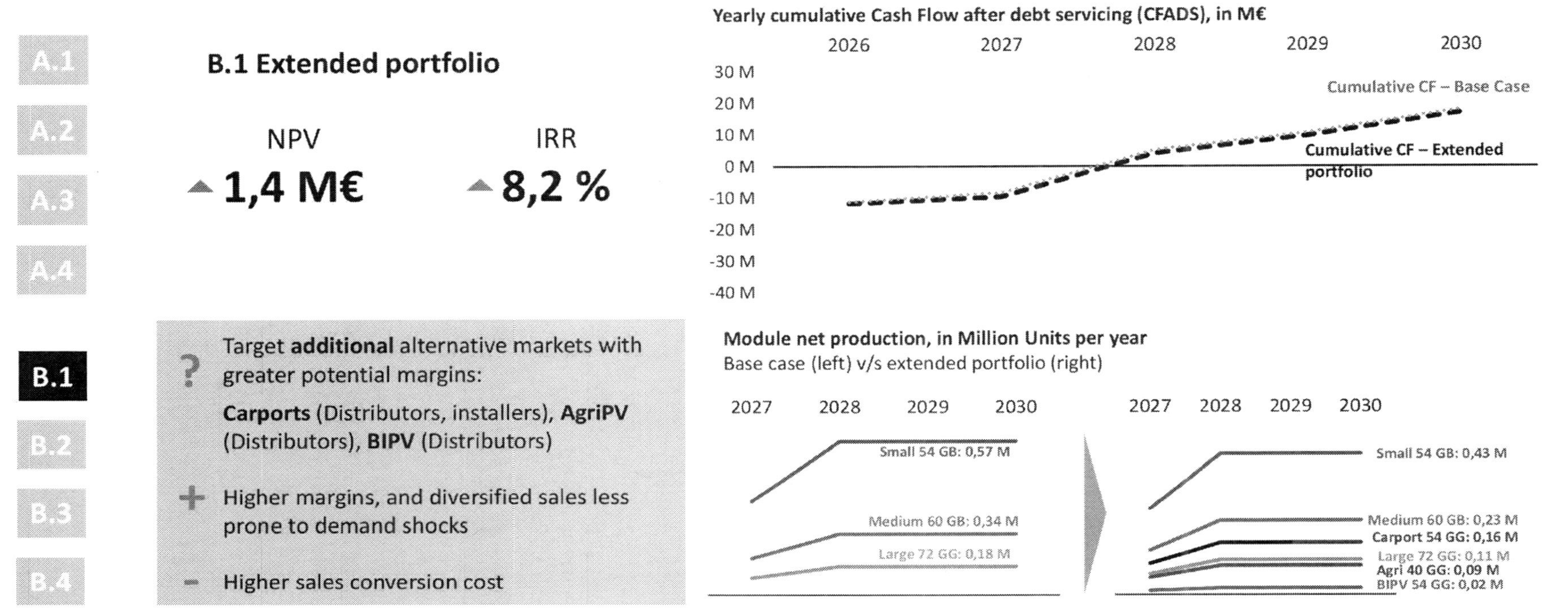

020474-033

BECQUEREL INSTITUTE
Strategy Consulting in Solar PV

Greater prices for end-users are outshined by high sales conversion costs

A.1
A.2
A.3
A.4
B.1
B.2
B.3
B.4

B.2 Downwards integration

NPV
▼ **(5,0 M€)**

IRR
▼ **4,1 %**

? Products are also sold to end-users.

+ Higher prices

– Sales conversion costs have the potential to outweigh end-user pricings.

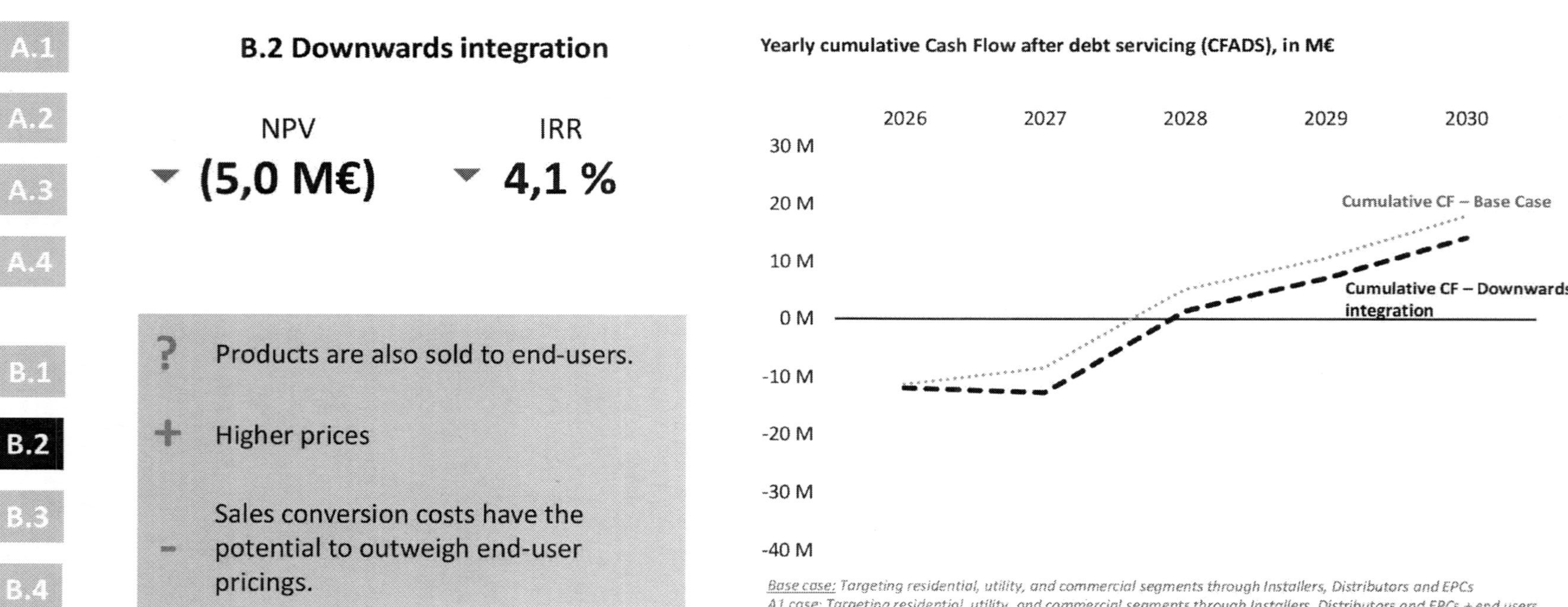

Base case: Targeting residential, utility, and commercial segments through Installers, Distributors and EPCs
A1 case: Targeting residential, utility, and commercial segments through Installers, Distributors and EPCs + end users

020474-034

BECQUEREL INSTITUTE
Strategy Consulting in Solar PV

Alternative markets with direct end-user sales are strategies that cannibalise each other

A.1
A.2
A.3
A.4

B.1
B.2
B.3
B.4

B.3 Extended portfolio (B.1)
+ Downwards integration (B.2)

NPV | IRR
▼ **(3,2 M€)** | ▼ **5,2 %**

? Targeting all alternative markets and conducting downwards integration (target end-users for conventional markets, installers for alternative ones)

– Alternative markets' extra income **cannot offset losses** from downstream integration.

Yearly cumulative Cash Flow after debt servicing (CFADS), in M€

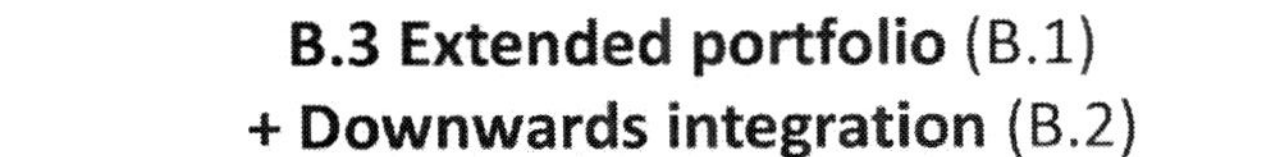

Base case: Targeting residential, utility, and commercial segments through Installers, Distributors and EPCs
A1 case: Targeting alternative markets (scenario B1) + downward integration (scenario B2)

020474-035

BECQUEREL INSTITUTE
Strategy Consulting in Solar PV

Fully de-risking operative costs by acting as original equipment manufacturer (OEM)

A.1
A.2
A.3
A.4
B.1
B.2
B.3
B.4

B.4 Acting as OEM

NPV
▼ **(7,6 M€)**

IRR
▼ **1,8 %**

? 1/3rd of each segment production is being sold as OEM.

+ Lower risks on volumes

− Savings from SG&A cannot compensate nearly at-cost selling.

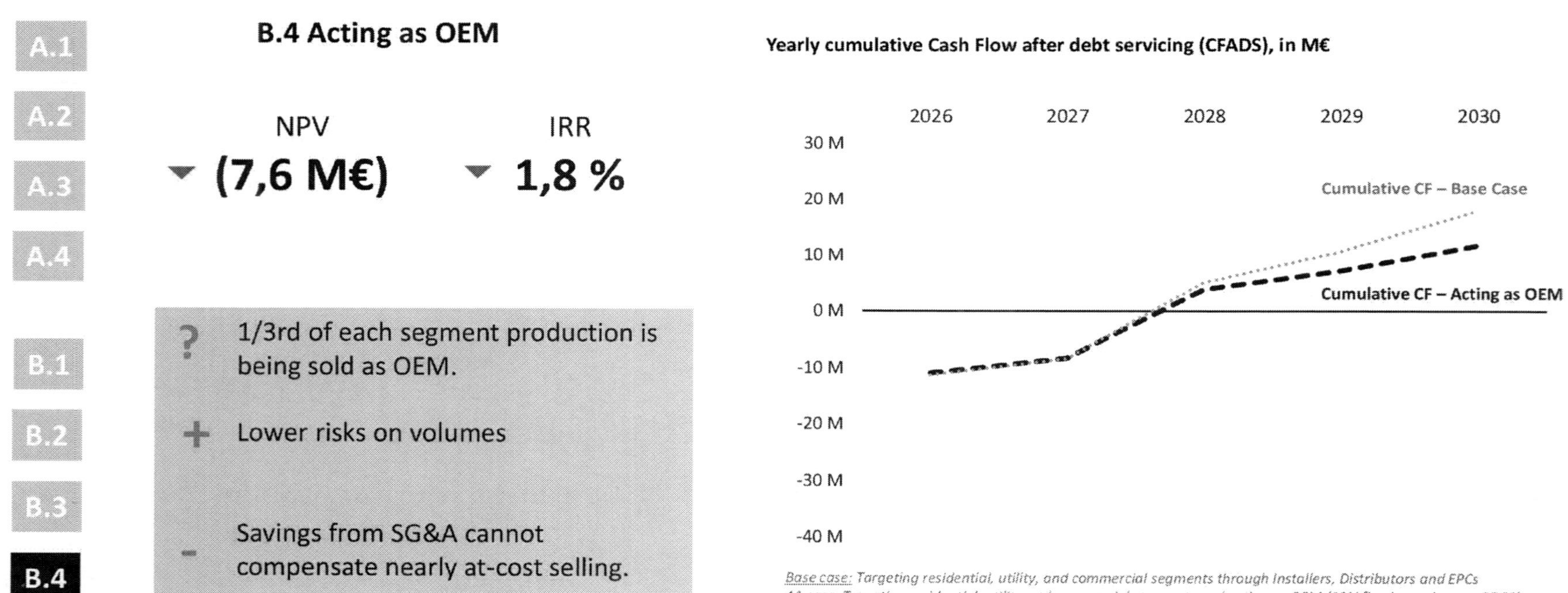

Base case: Targeting residential, utility, and commercial segments through Installers, Distributors and EPCs
A1 case: Targeting residential, utility and commercial segments and acting as OEM (12% fixed margin over COGS)

Final stage: Choosing compatible strategies
By simultaneously implementing best strategies, companies can reduce risks

 **A. Cash management**

 **B. Sales optimisation**

A.1 **Equipment acquisition strategy**
Operational lease instead of purchase

A.2 **Just in Time manufacturing**
Reducing inventory levels

A.3 **Favourable payment conditions**
Deferring a fraction of payments

A.4 **Grants**
Reducing total CAPEX required

B.1 **Alternative market segments**
Carports, agrivoltaics, BIPV

B.2 **Downwards integration**
Direct end-user sales

B.3 **Aggressive diversified sales**
Alternative markets + end-user sales

B.4 **Sales de-risking**
Acting as OEM for third companies

B BECQUEREL INSTITUTE
Strategy Consulting in Solar PV

Final stage: Choosing compatible strategies
Example: Efficient cash management & commercial strategies enable lower pricing

Optimised business strategy

NPV   IRR

▲ **0,5 M€**   ▲ **7,7 %**

Effective cash management and **well-designed sales strategies** ease cash flow constraints, enabling manufacturers to **adjust pricing** and **strengthen competitiveness** in their target segments without sacrificing profitability, even when **manufacturing costs remain constrained.**

While these module prices may seem high compared to today's levels, they represent only a **minor increase at system price level**, allowing to reach **competitive LCOE.**

Yearly Cash Flow after debt servicing (CFADS), in M€

Cumulative CF – Improved Case
Cumulative CF – Base Case

Segment	Channel	Base Price /Wp	New Price /Wp
Residential	Distributors	22,8 €ct	**22,1** ↓↓ 0,7 €ct
C&I	Distributors	20,7 €ct	20,7 €ct
C&I	Installers	23,0 €ct	**22,7** ↓↓ 0,3 €ct
Utility	EPC	20,0 €ct	20,0 €ct
Utility	Developers	20,7 €ct	20,7 €ct
Carports	Distributors	26,0 €ct	**25,3** ↓↓ 0,7 €ct
Carports	Installers	31,0 €ct	**29,8** ↓↓ 1,2 €ct
AgriPV	Distributors	31,0 €ct	**29,9** ↓↓ 1,1 €ct
BIPV	Distributors	44,0 €ct	**42,6** ↓↓ 1,4 €ct

BECQUEREL INSTITUTE
Strategy Consulting in Solar PV

Table of Contents

1 | Context

2 | Research Questions

3 | Our Approach

4 | Main Results

5 | Takeaways

020474-039

BECQUEREL INSTITUTE
Strategy Consulting in Solar PV

Once we understand how we can optimise our business models, we have to turn them into strategic and tactical activities

Key Partnerships

Supplier payment partnerships (A.3)

Logistic partners with reliable JiT delivery systems (A.2)

Key Activities

JiT logistics (A.2)

Key Resources

Flexible capital to optimize cash flow (A.1)

Financial support from grants (A.4)

Value Proposition

Offering customisable PV modules for emerging markets (B.1)

Channels

Specialised distributors and installers (B.1)

Customer Relationships

Building consultative and educational relationships with niche markets (B.1)

Customer Segments

Residential, C&I:
Distributors, installers
Agri, BIPV:
Distributors (B.1)

Cost Structure

Potentially higher negotiated costs for BOM flexibility (A.3)
JiT: Investment in real-time logistics systems and supplier coordination (A.2)

Revenue Streams

Premium pricing in niche markets with lower price elasticity (B.1)

020474-040

BECQUEREL INSTITUTE
Strategy Consulting in Solar PV

Profitability for the EU PV industry has become nearly impossible amid persistent market distortions
Urgent, ambitious policies are needed to break the "high risk, low reward" deadlock and create a level playing field

1 Cost-competitive manufacturing in the EU is currently **out of reach**, but the gap can be narrowed through smart **factory localization** and **phased vertical integration**, while leveraging current Asia's below-cost pricing

2 Adopting innovative technologies—such as back-contact cells, copper metallization instead of silver, or partial EU BOM—can **provide differentiation but does not necessarily enhance cost** competitiveness.

3 Strategic **levers beyond cost do exist**, but **not all are equally beneficial**; only by identifying the most effective and **combining those that are compatible** can economic sustainability be improved.

Even under optimized business strategies, the **path to success remains extremely narrow**, almost impossible, due to **persistent and severe market distortions**

Indeed, the **usual rules of economics seem no longer to apply to the PV sector** and have not for some time, as shown by the financial results of Asian players, who manage to survive regardless of market conditions.

How can we repair what is broken? **Political intervention is essential to break the 'high risk, low reward' deadlock**, especially in such a capital-intensive industry. Without it, private capital will remain unavailable, creating a **critical bottleneck with no solution**.

A. Cover risks that private actors cannot bear

- Guarantees, low to no interest loans
- Grants
- Production-linked incentives

B. Reduce risks by re-establishing fair rules

- Local content incentives or requirements, with quality and performance criteria
- Financial fairness criteria

020474-041

BECQUEREL INSTITUTE

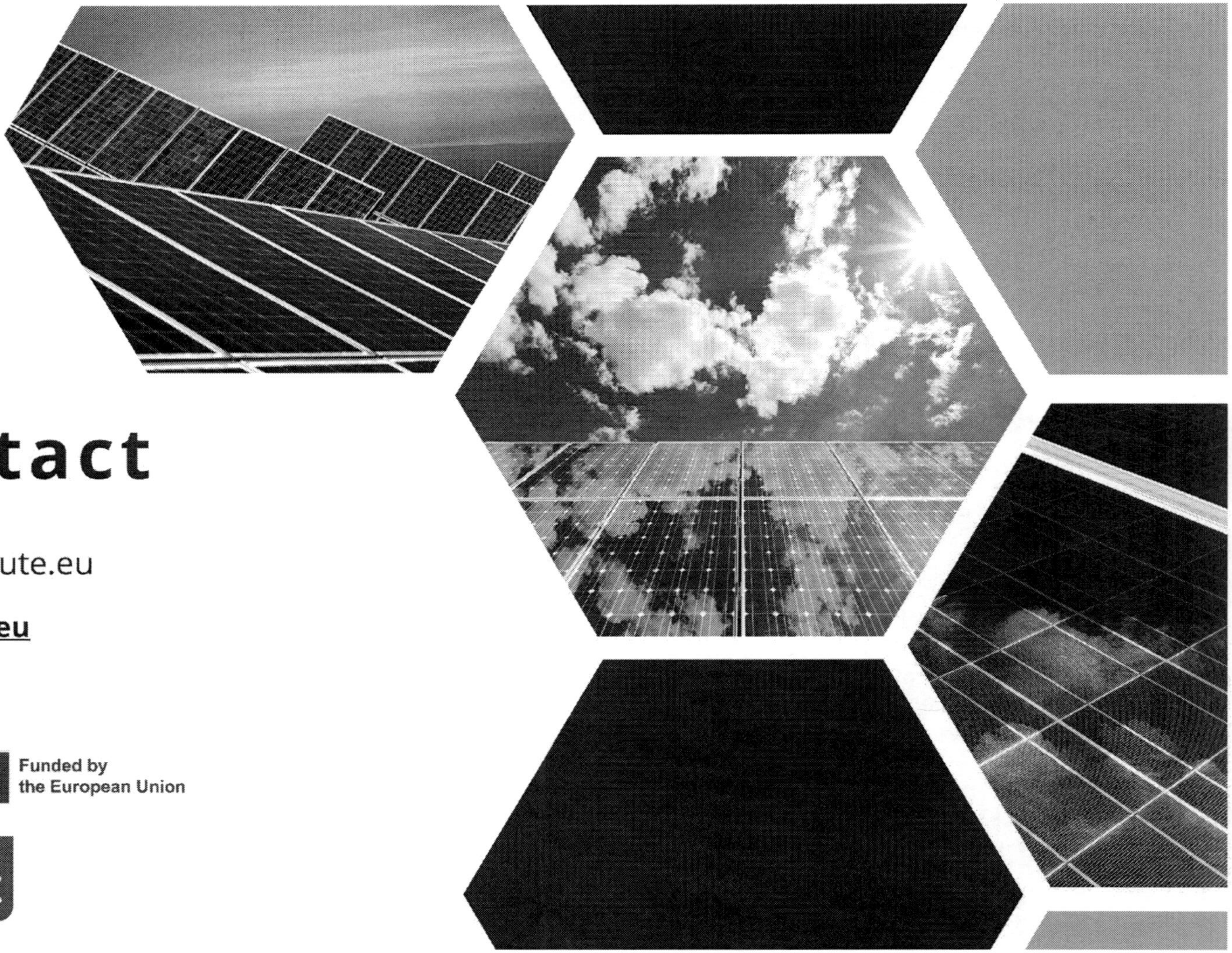

Your contact

Philippe Macé
p.mace@becquerelinstitute.eu

www.becquerelinstitute.eu

This project has received funding from the European Union's Horizon Europe under grant agreement Nº 101084259

Funded by the European Union

IBC4EU

ISC

EU PVSEC

22 — 26
September

BEC
Bilbao Exhibition Centre

Bilbao
Spain

EU
PVSEC
2025

42nd European
Photovoltaic Solar Energy
Conference and Exhibition

030001-001

Conference Highlights

Robert Kenny
European Commission Joint Research Centre
EU PVSEC Technical Programme Chair

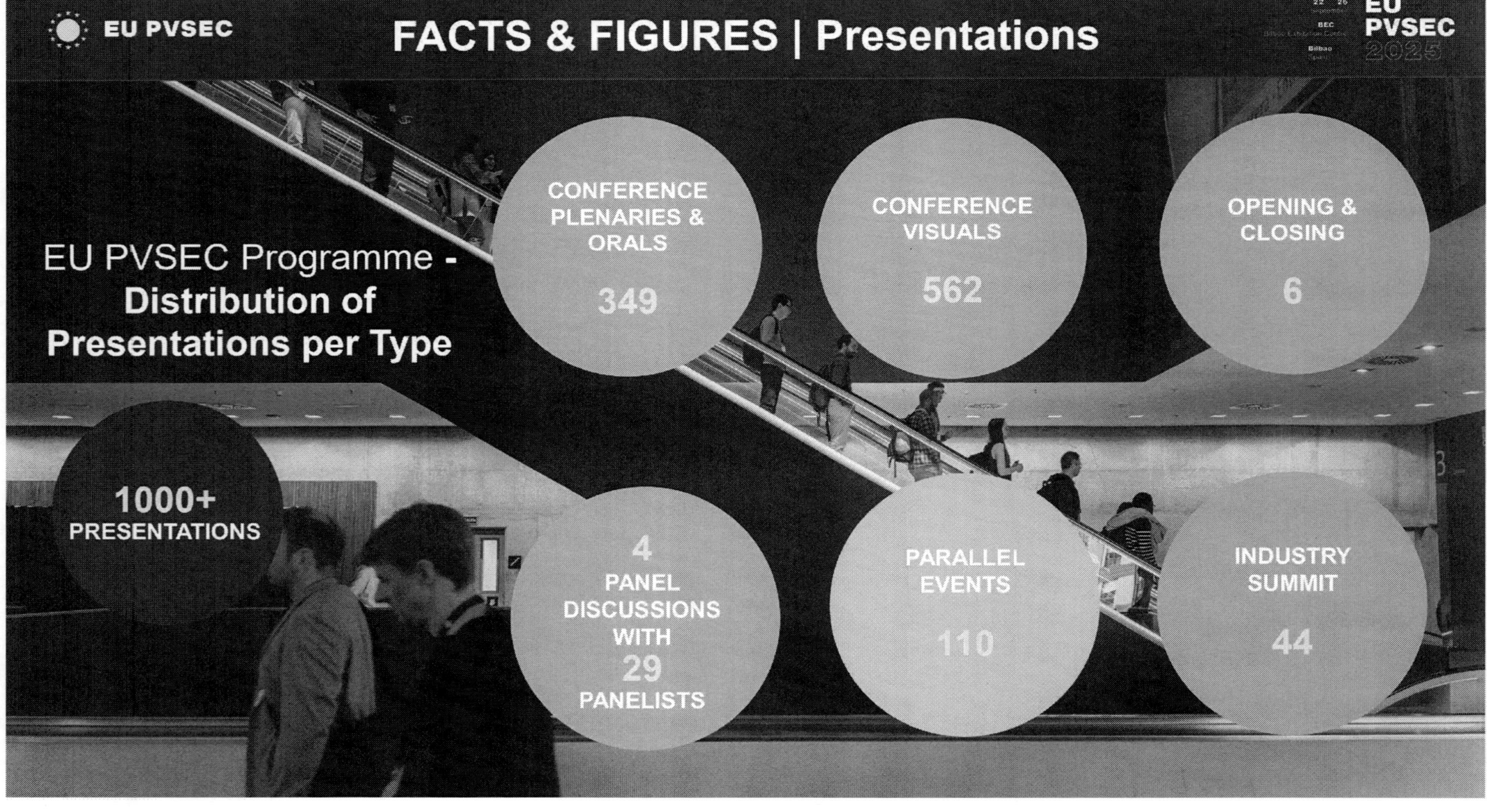

EU PVSEC
FACTS & FIGURES | Presentations
22 26
BEC
Bilbao
EU PVSEC 2025
EU PVSEC Programme -
Distribution of
Presentations per Type
1000+
PRESENTATIONS
CONFERENCE PLENARIES & ORALS
349
CONFERENCE VISUALS
562
OPENING & CLOSING
6
4 PANEL DISCUSSIONS WITH 29 PANELISTS
PARALLEL EVENTS
110
INDUSTRY SUMMIT
44

EU PVSEC
FACTS & FIGURES | Presentations
EU PVSEC 2025
EU PVSEC Scientific Conference Programme - Distribution of Presentations per Topic
TOPIC 5:
Photovoltaics in the Energy Transition
18%
TOPIC 1:
Silicon Materials and Cells
12%
TOPIC 2:
Thin Films and New Concepts
20%
TOPIC 4:
Photovoltaic Systems
32%
TOPIC 3:
Photovoltaic Modules
18%
030001-005

FACTS & FIGURES | Participants

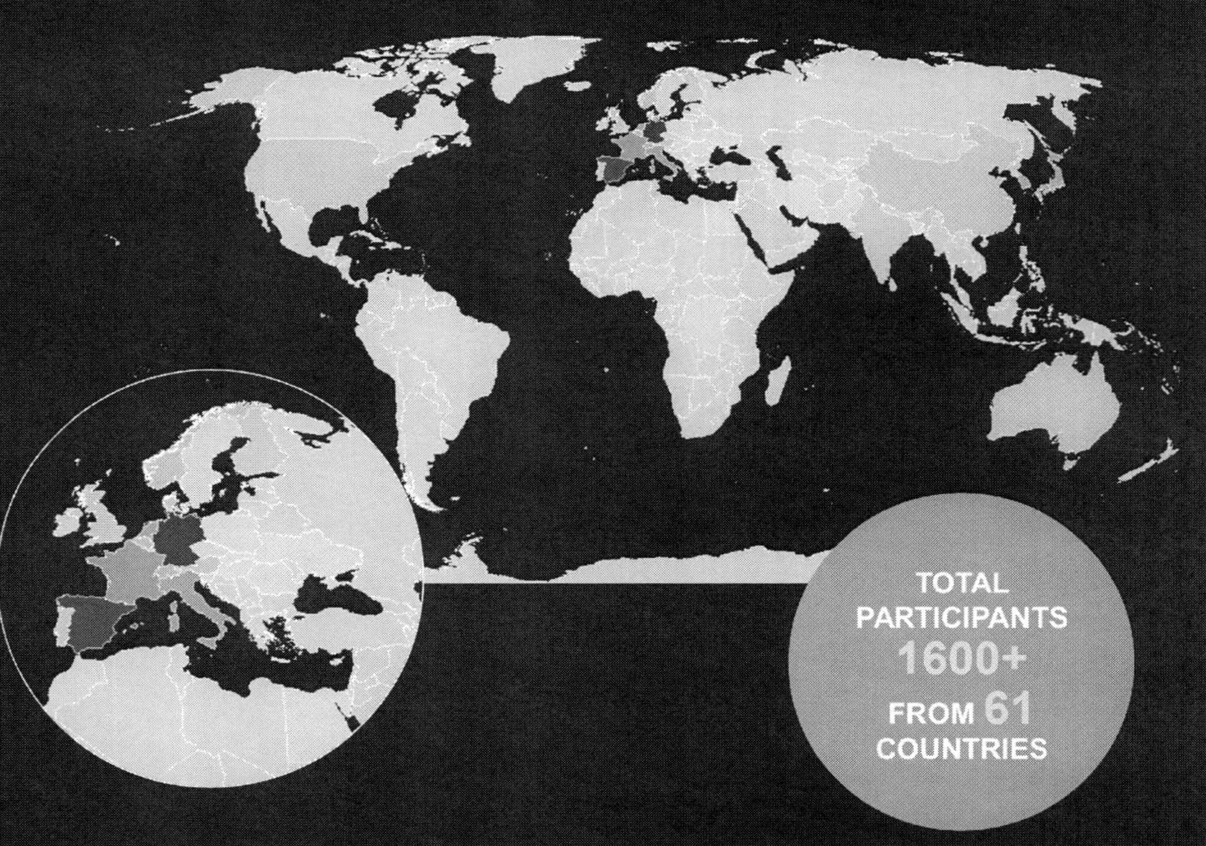

Participants by Countries
Top 10

No	Country	Participants
1	Germany	310
2	Spain	270
3	France	108
4	Italy	90
5	The Netherlands	76
6	South Korea	67
7	Switzerland	62
8	Japan	55
9	Belgium	44
10	Norway	35

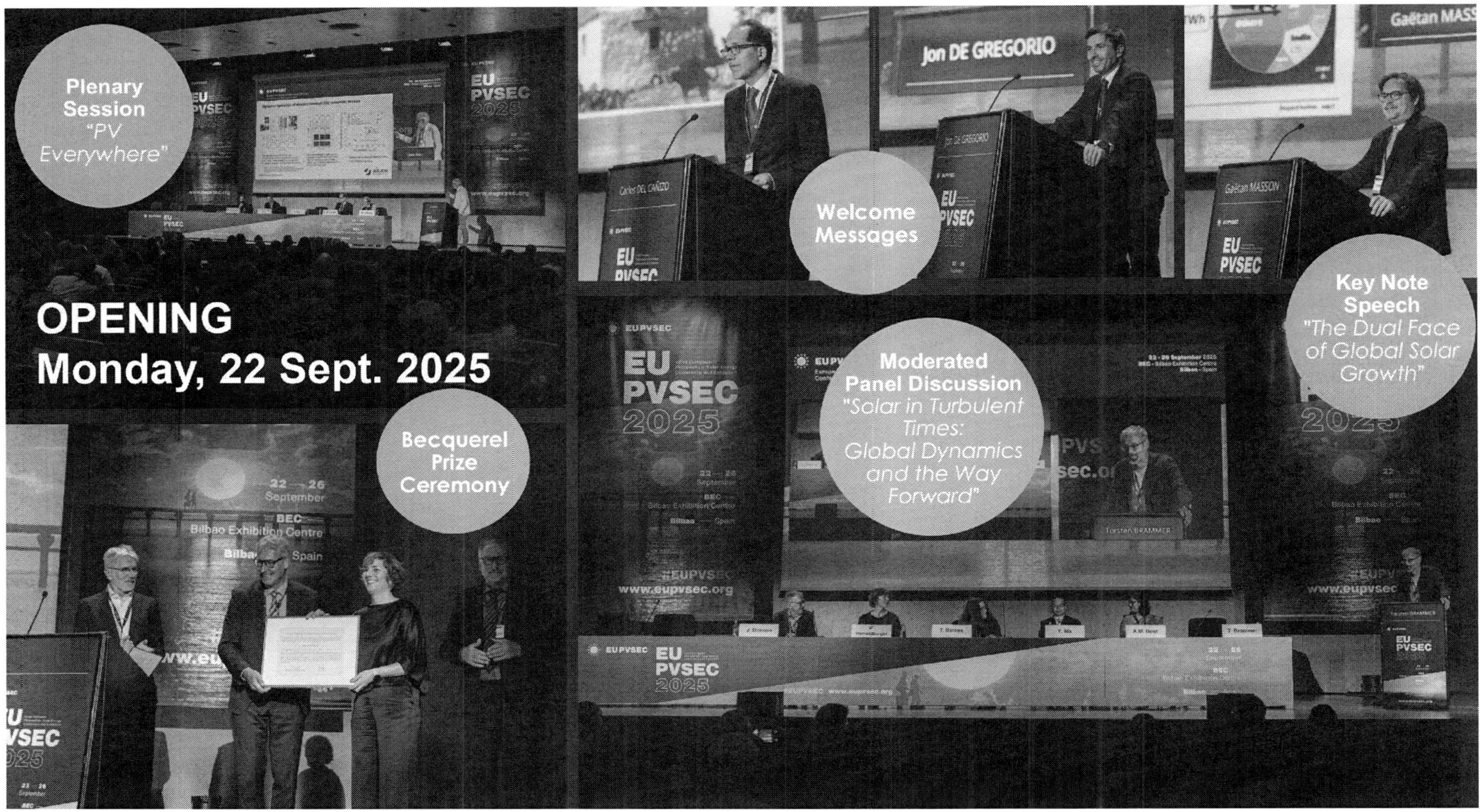

Plenary Session "PV Everywhere"
OPENING
Monday, 22 Sept. 2025
Becquerel Prize Ceremony
Welcome Messages
Jon DE GREGORIO
Carlos DEL CAÑIZO
Gaëtan MASSON
Key Note Speech "The Dual Face of Global Solar Growth"
Moderated Panel Discussion "Solar in Turbulent Times: Global Dynamics and the Way Forward"
Torsten BRAMMER

EU PVSEC
PANEL DISCUSSIONS
22 26 September
BEC
Bilbao Exhibition Centre
Bilbao Spain
EU PVSEC 2025

BO.13 Reliability and Bankability in PV
"The rapid developments of PV technology require increased attention to be paid to reliability testing."

CO.7 Challenges and Opportunities of PV up to 2030
"PV Technology is already reliable and cost effective, and even though improvements are welcome, key blockages are storage and grid strengthening. AI and robotics are essential to meet the scale of developments needed."

DO.13 Scalability and Manufacturability Prospects in Europe for New Technologies
"The prospects for reaching the 30GW target for PV module manufacturing in Europe were discussed and policy measures proposed."

EU PVSEC
EU PVSEC
2025
22 26
Switzerland
BEC
Bilbao Exhibition Centre
Bilbao
Spain

CONFERENCE

KEY
MESSAGES

Cross-cutting themes emerged throughout the programme, showcasing how solar technologies can be applied everywhere, from traditional to emerging fields.

• Sustainability and circularity remain central, with research focused on reducing material use, such as replacing silver with copper, and advancing end-of-life management of modules.

• Ensuring long-term stability and predictable energy yield is equally essential, with studies of degradation mechanisms such as UVID carried out.

• The role of AI across the PV value chain is rapidly expanding, from design to operations and maintenance, including drone applications.

CONFERENCE

TOPIC 1:
SILICON
MATERIALS
AND CELLS

Enhancements in IV measurement procedures

- Michael Rauer, Fraunhofer ISE: 1AO.4.5 *Universal Contacting Approaches for the Characterization of Solar Cells*
- Shuai Nie, UNSW: 1AO.4.6 *Contact-Free J-V: a Simple Technique for Universal State-of-the-Art Solar Cells*

Replacement of critical by sustainable materials:

- Reduced Ag consumpion e.g. by replacing by Cu (plating)
- In-free SHJ solar cells and Pero-Si tandems

EU PVSEC

EU PVSEC 2025

CONFERENCE

TOPIC 1:
SILICON
MATERIALS
AND CELLS

Great advance in understanding of UV induced degradation and Hydrogen related degradation

- Excellent PLENARY by Bram Hoex (presenting for Muhammad Umair Khan), UNSW: 1CP.3.5 *Understanding the Root Cause of UV-Induced Degradation in TOPCon and PERC Solar Cells*

Further high quality orals:

- Christina Hollemann, ISFH: 1AO.4.2 *Mitigating UV-Induced Degradation: Impact of PECVD and PEALD AlOx Layers Deposited in a Tube-Type Direct Plasma-Enhanced Chemical Vapor Deposition System*
- Hugo Lajoie, CEA: 1AO.4.3 *New Insights on UV-Induced Degradation of SHJ Solar Cells*
- Byungsul Min, ISFH: 1BO.3.6 *UV Stable Passivation Stack with Plasma-Enhanced Atomic Layer Deposition of Aluminum Oxide from an Industrial Tube-Type Direct Plasma-Enhanced Chemical Vapor Deposition System*
- Wolfram Kwapil, Fraunhofer ISE: 1AO.5.6 *Impact of Illumination on Solar Cell Properties: Insights into Atomic Hydrogen Release*

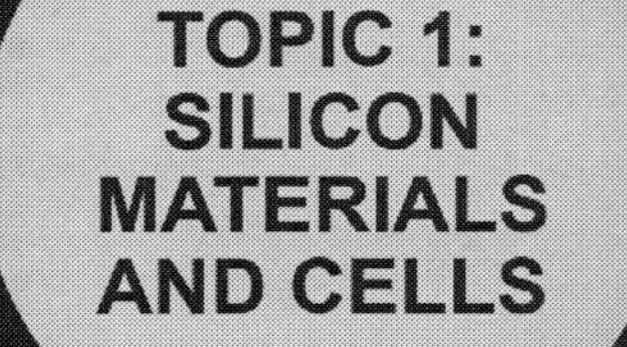

CONFERENCE

Advances in TOPCon and SHJ technology → Pushing the Limits of Performance

- Fantastic keynote lecture (PLENARY) on heterojunction solar cells by Dr. Guangtao Yang, Trina: 1CP.1.1 *Silicon Surface and Interface Study for >27% Efficient SHJ Solar Cell*
  - Deep insight into technological aspects eg. influence of rear side polishing on cell performance
  - Very high efficiencies for both-sides contacted HJT > 27%
  - Issues with CAPEX, sustainibility (Ag, In)
  - Pero-Si tandem cells on large area and modules

Late News Presentation on 27.8% efficient back contact silicon solar cells by Hua Wu, Longhi: 1DO.9.1 *Hybrid Interdigitated Back Contact Silicon Solar Cells with Superior Efficiency*

Late News Presentation as TOPCon for Bottom Solar Cells in Pero-Si Tandem devices by Jana Polzin-Isabelle Polzin, Fraunhofer ISE: 1DO.9.3 *Silicon Solar Cells – From High Efficiency Single-junction to Bottom Cells in Two-Terminal Perovskite-Silicon Tandem Devices*

EU PVSEC
EU PVSEC
2025
Bilbao
CONFERENCE
TOPIC 1:
SILICON
MATERIALS
AND CELLS

Further high quality orals:

- Hua Wu, Longhi: 1DO.9.1 *Hybrid Interdigitated Back Contact Silicon Solar Cells with Superior Efficiency*
- Daming Chen, Trina: 1AO.5.1 *Large Area i-TOPCon Solar Cells with 25.9% Record Efficiency*
- Maysa Sarsour, UNSW: 1AO.6.1 *Evaluating Silicon Heterojunction Solar Cell Stability under Industrial Illuminated Hydrogenation Conditions*

Bottom cell optimization for Pero-Si tandems

030001-013

CONFERENCE

TOPIC 2: THIN FILMS AND NEW CONCEPTS

A lot of focus on the long-term stability improvement and upscaling of tandem devices based on a variety of materials (hence not only pero-Si).

Many companies (e.g. Hanwha Q-cells, Oxford PV, Microquanta Seminconductor, Jinko Solar, Longi, etc. non-exhaustive list) presented impressive results on industrial size single-junction pero modules and pero-based tandem modules. A highlight here was the plenary talk from Hanwha Q-cells showing a record large area (M10) pilot-scale Pk/Si tandem cell of 28.6% efficiency.

EU PVSEC

EU PVSEC
22 26 September
BEC
Bilbao Exhibition Centre
Bilbao Spain
2025

CONFERENCE

TOPIC 2:
THIN FILMS
AND NEW
CONCEPTS

In the field of pero-Si tandems, there is clearly more focus on improving the stability of the tandem devices than before with many contributions doing in-depth investigations into the different degradation mechanisms that can occur in pero-Si tandems.

In this respect, 2DO9.5 presented a consensus statement about reliability testing of perovskite-based tandems that is endorsed by specialists worldwide from both industry and research and presents a kind of minimum that should be done in terms of testing and reporting concerning the stability and lifetime of perovskite-based tandem devices.

More and more advanced characterization methods for perovskite and perovskite - silicon tandem solar cells are being used, hyperspectral imaging methods identify non-uniformities by layer for processing development.

CONFERENCE

Another clear trend is that pero-TOPCon cells are nearing the same record efficiencies as pero-Heterojunction cells. A highlight talk here was the certified 34.22% efficiency perovskite/ topcon tandem solar cell(1cm2) by Jinko Solar 2CO2.1

Another highlight was the 30.5% triple junction pero/pero/silicon cell by EPFL (2CO2.3)

In the field of perovskite single junction devices, 2DO.7.3 showed perovskite devices with remarkable reliability, withstanding 4 years of outdoor exposure. The degradation mechanism is attributed to the diurnal behaviour, also verified and replicated with indoor experiments.

2AO3.6 investigated experimental degradation and recovery of perovskite solar cells, improving the comprehension of instability's dynamics, to extend the lifetime of devices.

CONFERENCE

**TOPIC 2:
THIN FILMS
AND NEW
CONCEPTS**

In the field of compound semiconductors, there were many presentations on alternative materials for perovskite in tandems. In this way, first monolithic (AgCu)(InGa)Se2 on Si tandem cells were demonstrated as well as 16.1% semitransparent Ag doped Cu(InGa)S2 sulfide top cells.

An exciting highlight in this field was 2BO8.2 in which UPC Barcelona achieved 18% efficiency under indoor lighting for kesterite solar cells with alkali doping

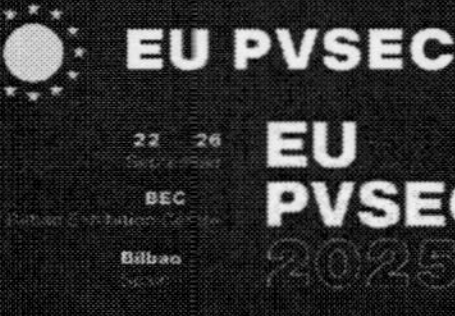

EU PVSEC
22-26 September
BEC
Bilbao Exhibition Centre
Bilbao
EU PVSEC 2025
CONFERENCE
TOPIC 3:
PHOTOVOLTAIC MODULES
"Reliable packaging to Maximize the energy yield from high efficiency cells"
big theme: Optimizing module materials and packaging for long lifetime and predictable energy yield from high efficiency cells. The industry and research community are moving quickly to assess and improve reliability.
• Understanding, accelerated testing, and mitigating UV-ID in n-type cells and modules
• How do you develop accelerated tests for constantly changing BOMs - new encapsulants, new metallization, thinner glass, and high efficiency cells

EU PVSEC
22 26 September
BEC
Bilbao Exhibition Centre
Bilbao Spain
EU PVSEC 2025

CONFERENCE

TOPIC 3:
PHOTOVOLTAIC
MODULES

- Degradation and metastability in packaged perovskite tandems - understanding energy yield and realistic degradation rates

- Characterization out of the lab and into the field and factory - accurate outdoor performance, online quality control measurements for encapsulant cross linking

- Reducing silver content and metallization temperatures - reliability of low temperature and low silver metallization

- Developing glass qualification requirements to minimize breakage

030001-019

CONFERENCE

TOPIC 4:
PHOTOVOLTAIC
SYSTEMS

Advances in O&M of PV systems

(4CV.1) focuses on fault detection, cleaning optimization, soiling (and snow 4CO.8), UAV for autonomous monitoring and digital twin.

Data driven and AI based O&M (4CO.9) including a medicine-like workflow in Autonomous multi-AI agent system for health monitoring: a fully automated O&M pipeline with field robotics (4CO.9.4 D. Moser, EURAC)

PV Everywhere from space to agricultural applications like integration in vineyards (Mo, Opening plenary) and many other **integrated options** as we have seen throughout the week. On Thursday (4DO.4) agriPV, noise barriers and floating integrated systems. AgriPV technologies (4DO.2), BIPV

PV needs solar energy. **Solar resource and forecasting** (Mo, 4AO.7-9 & Tu 4BV.3). Shortly IEA PVPS T16 will publish minute irradiance data, some including GT over 220 stations worldwide with. Same format and quality controlled. (*Worldwide solar radiation measurement database with quality-control added value*, Anne Forstinger CSP Services, 4AO.7.1)

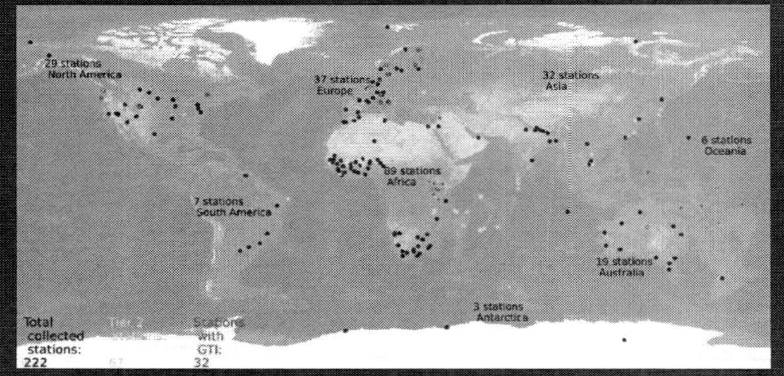

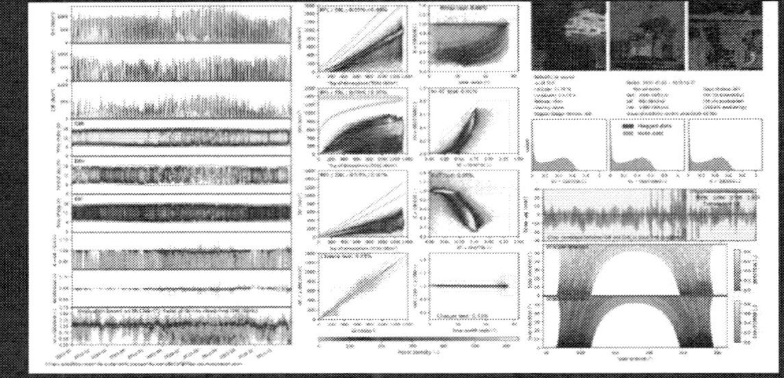

(4BV.3). Poster winner 4BV.3.12 *Advancing Very Short-Term Solar Irradiance Forecasting in Africa: A Low-Cost Sky Imaging and Machine Learning-Based Approach*, implications for PV deployment and grid integration (Martin Ansong, KIT). Runner-up 4BV.3.25 *Evaluating the Suitability of Köppen-Geiger Climate Classifications for Photovoltaic Systems: Micro-climate Analysis and Risk Assessment Maps,* with worldwide distribution of humidity related risk assessment for PV performance (Pavan Kumar Panda, Anhalt University of Applied Sciences).

Integrated PV

BIPV (4BO.16) examples of coloured modules (which was main topic of the poster session along with fire concerns of BIPV, 4BV.4), lightweight solutions (4BO.5) and modelling partial shading effects 4BO.17.1, *Modelling partial shading at the cell level on PV modules,* Jean-Paul Calin, ENSTA) and 4BO.17.3, *Comparing the energy yield and degradation rates of smart PV modules compared to conventional PV system designs in shaded urban scenario's,* Youri Blom, TU DELF.

AgriPV 4DO.2 the room was fully packed showing the interest in the topic. 5 talks were on new ways of sharing light (2 spectral splitting before the PV conversion, 2 semitransparent PV modules both c-Si and CdTe, 1 on downshifting encapsulate) + 1 new AgrivPV like application with Algae instead of crops.

4DO.4 also included AgriPV and **Others types of integration like noise barriers and floating.** In addition to performance other aspects like (*Hydrological and ecological effects on floating PV,* Konstantin Ilgen, FHO ISe) have been highlighted this week

BOS and tracking systems (4DO.1) focused on backtracking strategies and terrains with complex topography.

4DO.1.4

4DO4.2

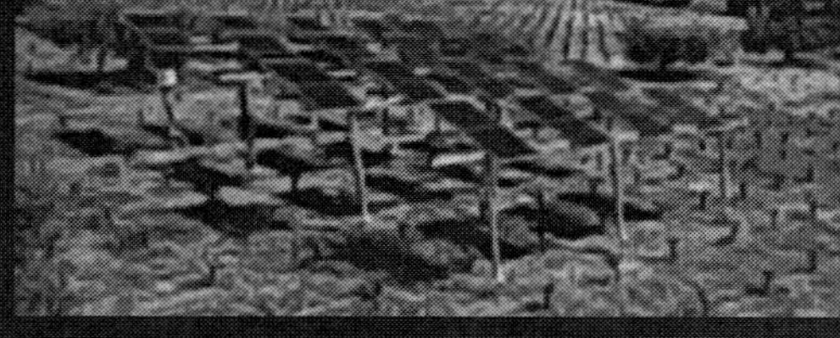

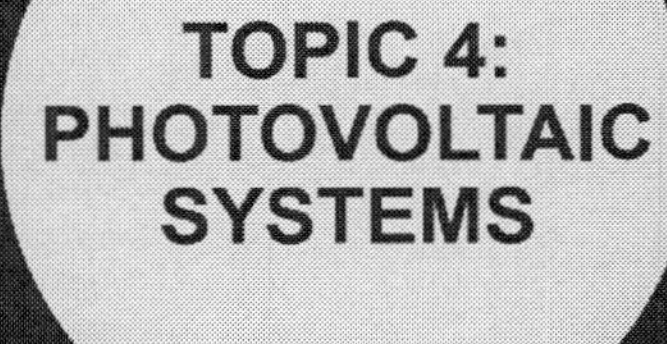

CONFERENCE

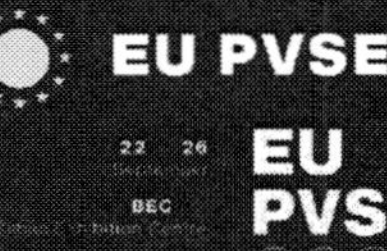

Reliability of PV systems

Several presentations focused long-term monitored degradation, failure modes and degradation modes identification techniques (non-destructive, aerial images, AI-based)

4BO.6.1 *Three decades, three climates: insights and lessons on PV reliability*. Good BOM offer very high reliability in power production, with 30-35 years old modules showing 0.24% degradation rate per year.

4BO.6.3 *Non-destructive detection of water ingress in solar modules using NIR spectroscopy* (Oleksandr Mashkow HI ERN) proved near-infrared absorption (NIRA) technique to detect water ingress in modules in the field, which correlated with the module degradation.

4BO.7.2 *Robust PV performance loss rate calculation for high latitudes* (Lauri Karttunen, Meteo Inst Helsinki) and 4BO.7. 3 *Detailed analysis of degradation rates of operating PV assets in tropical climate conditions* (Xioaqi Xu, Seris Singapore) Performance loss rates reported for high latitudes and tropics based on solid data sets. PLR in the tropics -1.4%/year

4DO.3.6 PV system design and assessment highlighted how inverter safety issues are extremely important and how more research about inverter safety and reliability is needed.

EU PVSEC
EU PVSEC 2025
22 - 26 September
BEC
Bilbao Spain
CONFERENCE
TOPIC 5:
PHOTOVOLTAICS
IN THE ENERGY
TRANSITION
Main topics of interest :
• Flexibility
• Artificial intelligence
• EoL management
030001-024

TOPIC 5: PHOTOVOLTAICS IN THE ENERGY TRANSITION

5.1 Grid Integration and Flexibility Enablers (2 sessions)

- Smoothing effect related to different orientations of PV systems in a given area allows 10 to 15% additional hosting capacity of the distribution grid compared to the conservative calculation that consists in summing the AC power. Such accurate calculation enabled by high resolution large area images and LIDAR and induces therefore very low costs.

5.2 Sustainability of PV (4 sessions)

- New inventories LCI and LCA for emerging technologies even though lack of data for perovskites, LCA showing a way for low environmental Impacts with technology improvement and localisation. / Technological improvements will contribute to the reduction of environmental Impact / Grid Efficiency has an Impact on the environmental Footprint.

- Manufacturing optimization / Reuse & recycling: results from the perspective of economic performance – would it convince manufacturer to consider it if economic benefit ?

- EoL Management /recycling -> emerging field attracting lots of activities / mainly EU projects (EVERPV / ICARUS / QASAR) – highlight on polymer, interesting question came up and to be debated for the next decade: is it worth it to consider polymer (EVA/ backsheet) recycling ?

- Major progress in methodology and indicators to assess sustainable design & circularity and improve transparency recyclability index, technical recyclability, digital passport)

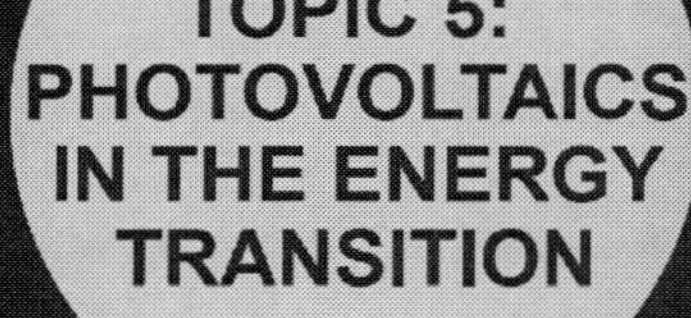

CONFERENCE

5.3 Scenarios for Renewables, Policy, Global Challenges (1 session)

- wide scope of contributions on the way to massive, medium- to long-term PV deployment -> should not be taken for granted despite positive projections since there can be limiting factors such as public acceptance / regulatory restrictions and effect of climate change

5.4 Costs, Economics, Finance and Markets (1 session)

- Annual installed capacity over 400 GWp / total cumulative installed capacity worldwide over 2.1 TWp / Clear mismatch between PV module installations rate worldwide and PV module production rate leading to bunch of inventories and drastically reduced prices.

5.6 Societal Challenges; Citizens' Participation, Awareness (1 session)

- data and analysis in gender aspects are emerging in PV! (poster session) + Highlight on innovation in education! On example that targets students & skilled workers -> mobile Lab for advanced experimental training PV-related to bring skills and characterization tools everywhere.

PARALLEL
EVENTS
Collaborat Network
Diversity
Prejudice
Justificat
Change
Needs — Profile Match
Avoid Blind Spots
Job loss?
Integration
Lack of Attractiveness
Resilience (people + company)
Creativity
Different Communicat°
Internal Friction
More effort

EU PVSEC

EU PVSEC 2025

22–26 September
BEC
Bilbao Exhibition Centre
Bilbao, Spain

PARALLEL EVENTS

- Perovskite Innovation Roundtable: Driving EU Leadership in Perovskite Innovation
- Women in PV presents: Leading with Inclusion – Embracing the 6 Traits of Inclusive Leadership
- Unlocking the Potential of Integrated Photovoltaic Systems - European R&D Approach
- Why Do PV Plants Perform Lower than Expected? (Estimating losses by backtracking algorithms in undulating terrain & Analysis of the loss chain and identification of deviations from initial expectations)
- PV Made in the EU: How Do Companies Die and How Can They Thrive?

22 — 26 September
BEC — Bilbao Exhibition Centre
Bilbao — Spain
EU PVSEC 2025
42nd European Photovoltaic Solar Energy Conference and Exhibition
GEOPOLITICS & PV MANUFACTURING CHALLENGES
EXHIBITION FORUM
INDUSTRY SUMMIT
The road to a sustainable future

Industry Summit Opening (session I)

Session Title: Solar PV production in Europe - the way forward

Moderators: Begoña Molinete, Walburga Hemetsberger

Key Takeaway:

This session discussed the state of play of European manufacturing projects and whether there is enough European support. It was clear that political support is further lacking – only 3 Member States have developed schemes to support European manufacturing. While the Net Zero Industry Act is helpful to diversify supplies, it will not particularly support European manufacturing.

All panellists agreed that apart from further policy support (financing, derisking) collaboration is the way forward.

Session II
Session Title: International corporations in the light of changing geopolitics
Moderators: Radovan Kopecek, Puzant Baliozian

Key takeaway:
EU machine builders are still supporting mostly Indian but also US and EU projects with their technology and expertise. The major arguments for choosing EU tech are quality, training, support and low OPEX.

Session III
Session Title: PV Systems: How do we get the produced electricity in Europe into the grid?
Moderators: Catarina Augusto, Peter Fath

Key Takeaway:
Hybrid PV + storage systems (co-located or distributed) are essential for integrating PV into electricity grids. Storage adds flexibility and stabilizes the grid, making it a cornerstone of resilient energy systems; while the technology is mature, scalable and bankable revenue models remain the key gap for widespread deployment.

LIST OF EXHIBITORS
(in alphabetical order)

Company name	Country
2nd Cycle FlexCo	Austria
9-Tech	Italy
Avalon ST / Pasan	Switzerland
BASQUENERGY Cluster	Spain
Becquerel Institute	Belgium
ECOPROGETTI	Italy
EKIENERGY	Spain
ESMC Pavilion	Belgium
Eternal Sun I WAVELABS	The Netherlands
EU PVSEC Startup Pavilion	
European Commission JRC	Italy
exateq	Germany
FLUXiM AG	Switzerland
G2V Optics	Canada
GALEA	Spain
halm elektronik	Germany
HighLine Technology	Germany
IEA PVPS	
Innovations in Optics, Inc.	United States of America
ISC Konstanz	Germany
LAB14	Germany
MBJ Solutions	Germany
Mondragon Assembly	Spain
Nagase Chemtex America	United States of America
NEO Messtechnik Holding	Austria
ODTÜ GÜNAM	Türkiye
Phoenixolar	China
PSE Instruments	Germany
PVsyst	Switzerland
RCT Future	Germany
RCT Solutions	Germany
RENA	Germany
ReNewPV-CA21148 / 5GSOLAR	Estonia
SALD B.V.	The Netherlands

SCIPRIOS	Germany
SEMILAB	Hungary
SINGULUS TECHNOLOGIES	Germany
Sinton Instruments	United States of America
SOLAR MATERIALS	Germany
SolarNL	The Netherlands
Soli Tek R&D	Lithuania
TAMURA ELSOLD	Germany
TECNALIA	Spain
The Netherlands Pavilion	The Netherlands
TNO	The Netherlands
University of the Basque Country	Spain
Vector Energy	Spain
VON ARDENNE	Germany
WCPEC-9	South Korea
WIP Renewable Energies	Germany
ZSW	Germany

We thank the EU PVSEC 2025 Sponsors

Platinum

Gold

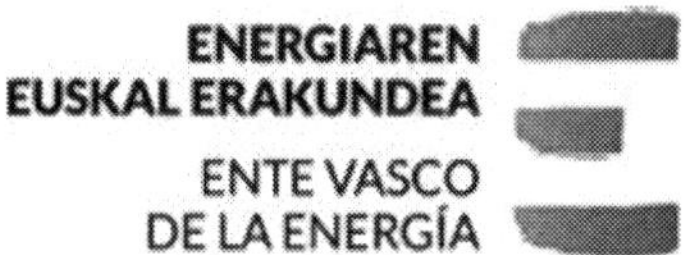

Silver

Bronze

AUTHORS OF EU PVSEC 2025 PROCEEDINGS PAPERS

A. dos Reis Benatto, Gisele
DTU, Roskilde, Denmark

020028, 020037, 020039, 020191, 020265, 020376, 020477

Aaltonen, Lauri
Tampere University, Tampere, Finland

020537

Abad Alcaraz, Verónica
University of Almería, La Cañada de San Urbano, Spain

020336

Abbott, Malcolm D.
PV Lighthouse, Coledale, Australia

020396

Abbotto, Alessandro
University of Milano-Bicocca, Milan, Italy

020077

Abdallah, Amir A.
QEERI, Doha, Qatar

020146, 020166

Abdel Nour, Christine
EDF R&D, Moret Loing Orvanne, France

020188

Abdelrahim, Mohamed
QEERI, Doha, Qatar

020166

Abdou-Tankari, Mahamadou
Paris-East Créteil University, Créteil, France

020562

Abrego, Gillen
ALLOTARRA, Allo, Spain

020392

Acciarri, Maurizio
University of Milano-Bicocca, Milan, Italy

020087

Acevedo Devoto, M. Ignacia
ISC Konstanz, Konstanz, Germany

020220

Achenbach, Jannik
University of Applied Science Cologne, Cologne, Germany

020522

Acinas, Victor
Applied Materials, Dublin, Ireland

020019

Adachi, Satoru
NIED, Shinjo, Japan

020436

Aden, Samira
HZB, Berlin, Germany

020513

Adinolfi Borea, Riccardo
University of Bologna, Bologna, Italy

020314

Adnan Hameed, Mohammed
Martin-Luther-University Halle-Wittenberg, Halle, Germany

020156

Adothu, Baloji
DEWA, Dubai, United Arab Emirates

020229

Aghaei, Mohammadreza
NTNU, Aalesund, Norway

020335, 020356

Aghaei, Mohammadreza
NTNU, Ålesund, Norway

020374, 020375

Aghamohammadi, Amirhossain 020356
Amirkabir University of Technology, Tehran, Iran

Aguirre, Aranzazu 020064
Hasselt Unversity, Genk, Belgium

Ahmadi, Mehdi 020066
CNR-IMM, Catania, Italy

Aiello, Andrea 020255
ACCA Software, Cosenza, Italy

Aimé, Jérémie 020217, 020311
CEA / INES, Le Bourget-du-Lac, France

Aissa, Brahim 020042, 020075, 020108, 020109, 020146,
QEERI, Doha, Qatar 020147

Aizpurua, Jon 020139
Tecnalia, Donostia - San Sebastián, Spain

Akbayrak, Serdar 020020
Necmettin Erbakan University, Konya, Türkiye

Akram, M. Waqar 020164
Hohai University, Changzhou, China

Al Katrib, Mirella 020116
IPVF, Palaiseau, France

Alam, Habeel 020394
Lancaster University, Lancaster, United Kingdom

Alberts, Vivian 020229
DEWA, Dubai, United Arab Emirates

Albuquerque, Daniel P. 020464
Centre for New Energy Technologies, Sacavém, Portugal

Alet, Pierre-Jean 020238, 020544
CSEM, Neuchâtel, Switzerland

Alexandris, Nikos 020210
European Commission JRC, Ispra, Italy

Alfieri, Felice 020497
Viegand Maagøe, Copenhagen, Denmark

Ali, Adnan 020147
QEERI, Doha, Qatar

Allen, Vince 020048
SunDrive Solar, Kurnell, Australia

Alloji, Esma 020020
Necmettin Erbakan University, Konya, Türkiye

Almeida Silva, José 020565
University of Évora, Évora, Portugal

Almuneau, Guilhem 020074
LAAS-CNRS, Toulouse, France

Alonso, Ricardo 020197, 020198, 020353, 020358
TECNALIA, Derio, Spain

Alonso-Montesinos, Joaquín 020100
University of Almeria, Almeria, Spain

Alonso-Montesinos, Joaquín 020336
University of Almería, La Cañada de San Urbano, Spain

Álvarez Hervás, José Domingo 020336
University of Almería, La Cañada de San Urbano, Spain

Alvarez, José 020040, 020058
CNRS, Gif-sur-Yvette, France

Álvarez, Marta 020300
CENER, Sarriguren, Spain

Álvarez-Pérez, Guillem 020062
IPVF, Palaiseau, France

Alvaro Høye, Ingar 020443
Solkraft Sør, Øyslebø, Norway

Alves e Silva, Kiane 020439, 020535, 020567, 020575
UPM, Madrid, Spain

Amaro e Silva, Rodrigo 020490
University of Lisbon, Lisbon, Portugal

Amatriain, Irati 020392
CENER, Sarriguren, Spain

Anamiati, Gaetana 020448, 020481
GreenPowerMonitor a DNV company, Barcelona, Spain

Anaya, Julian 020191, 020205
University of Valladolid, Valladolid, Spain

Ancillao, Andrea 020079
Polytechnic University of Turin, Turin, Italy

Anderlini, Alessandro 020155
Coveme, Gorizia, Italy

Andersen, Nanna L. 020250
DTU, Roskilde, Denmark

Andersen, Nanna Lysgaard 020306
DTU, Roskilde, Denmark

Andrade-Arvizu, Jacob 020094
IREC, Barcelona, Spain

Andreozzi, Federico 020494
University of Rome Tor Vergata, Rome, Italy

Anefnaf, Ikram 020093
University of Verona, Verona, Italy

Ansong, Martin 020272
KIT, Eggenstein-Leopoldshafen, Germany

Antognini, Luca 020196
PVsyst, Geneva, Switzerland

Antoine, C. 020508
IMDEA Nanoscience Institute, Madrid, Spain

Antón, Ignacio 020209, 020246, 020257, 020453, 020459
UPM, Madrid, Spain

Antonucci, Daniele 020551
Eurac Research, Bolzano, Italy

Apostoleris, Harry   020487
EPRI, Dubai, United Arab Emirates

Arakawa, Hayato   020436
NIED, Shinjo, Japan

Aranguren, Gerardo   020289, 020353
UPV/EHU, Bilbao, Spain

Arbaretaz, Sebastien   020317
CEA INES, Le Bourget-du-Lac, France

Ardissone, Bastien J. J.   020396
PV Lighthouse, Coledale, Australia

Arduino, Daniele   020079
Polytechnic University of Turin, Turin, Italy

Ariolli, Daniela Maria Godinho   020325
BayWa r.e, Rome, Italy

Ariza Camacho, Maria Jesus   020100
University of Almeria, Almería, Spain

Armstrong, Alona   020394
Lancaster University, Lancaster, United Kingdom

Arribat, Mathieu   020074
LAAS-CNRS, Toulouse, France

Arrizabalaga, Igor   020139
Tecnalia, Donostia - San Sebastián, Spain

Artegiani, Elisa   020057, 020089, 020093
University of Verona, Verona, Italy

Arumughan, Jayaprasad   020569
ISC Konstanz, Konstanz, Germany

Asaa, Shu-Ngwa   020393
imo-imomec, Genk, Belgium

Ascencio-Vásquez, Julián   020371
Univers, Courbevoie, France

Askins, Steve   020209, 020257
UPM, Madrid, Spain

Assaid, El Mahdi   020171
University of Chouaib Doukkali, El Jadida, Morocco

Aste, Niccolò   020249
Polytechnic University of Milan, Milan, Italy

Astigarraga, Alexander   020226
Eurac Research, Bolzano, Italy

Athienitis, Andreas   020248
Concordia University, Montreal, Canada

Aurrekoetxea, Olaia   020302
TECNALIA, Saint Sebastian, Spain

Awadallah, Carlos   020536
Wattkraft, Madrid, Spain

Azkona, Nekane   020055, 020097, 020153, 020287
UPV/EHU, Bilbao, Spain

Azzopardi, Brian   020318, 020334, 020520
FIR, Birkirkara, Malta

Azzopardi, Carmel   020334
FIR, Birkirkara, Malta

Babich, Francesco   020551
Eurac Research, Bolzano, Italy

Babics, Maxime   020217
CEA / INES, Le Bourget-du-Lac, France

Babin, Markus   020249, 020250, 020306, 020477
DTU, Roskilde, Denmark

Bachour, Dunia A.   020275, 020278
QEERI, Doha, Qatar

Bachour, Dunia   020291
QEERI, Doha, Qatar

Baderiya, Naman   020390
MARIN, Wageningen, The Netherlands

Badosa Franch, Jordi   020214
Polytechnic Institute of Paris, Palaiseau, France

Baeck, Pieter-Jan   020511
Flemish Institute for Technological Research (VITO), Genk,
Belgium

Bai, Jianbo   020164
Hohai University, Changzhou, China

Bailache, Simon   020303
CSTB, Marne-la-Vallée, France

Bakhtiari, Afshin   020121
AESOLAR, Koenigsbrunn, Germany

Balafoutis, Athanasios T.   020464
CERTH, Athens, Greece

Bald, Juan   020514
AZTI, PASAIA, Spain

Baldacchino, Alex J.   020065
UNSW, Sydney, Australia

Baležentienė, Skirmantė   020380
The Applied Research Institute for Prospective
Technologies, Vilnius, Lithuania

Baležentis, Algirdas   020380
The Applied Research Institute for Prospective
Technologies, Vilnius, Lithuania

Ballif, Christophe   020467
CSEM, Neuchâtel, Switzerland

Ballif, Christophe   020251
EPFL, Neuchâtel, Switzerland

Bandaru, Narendra   020039, 020043, 020104
Aarhus University, Aarhus, Denmark

Bang, Ole   020043
Technical University of Denmark, Copenhagen, Denmark

Barakel, Damien   020188
Toulon University, Marseille, France

Baraket, Mira   020039
ATLANT 3D, Taastrup, Denmark

Baranek, Philippe   020060
EDF R&D, Palaiseau, France

Barchi, Grazia   020485, 020489, 020544
Eurac Research, Bolzano, Italy

Bardizza, Giorgio   020181
TÜV Rheinland Italia, Milan, Italy

Bardizza, Giorgio   020208
TÜV Rheinland Solar, Cologne, Germany

Bardizza, Giorgio   020144
TÜV Rheinland, Cologne, Germany

Barguès, Anna   020505
Becquerel Institute France, Lyon, France

Barguès, Anna   020558
Becquerel Institute, Brussels, Belgium

Barnscheidt, Verena   020063, 020114
ISFH, Emmerthal, Germany

Barretta, Chiara   020325
PCCL, Leoben, Austria

Barrionuevo, Bruno   020464
CERTH, Athens, Greece

Barroso, João   020565
University of Évora, Évora, Portugal

Barrou, Alexis   020467
CSEM, Neuchâtel, Switzerland

Barrutia, Laura   020446, 020536
UPM, Madrid, Spain

Barth, Vincent   020134
CEA / INES, Le Bourget-du-Lac, France

Barth, Vincent   020019
CEA, Le Bourget-du-Lac, France

Barth, Vincent   020226
CEA/ INES, Le Bourget-du-Lac, France

Bartholomäus, Martin   020346
DTU, Roskilde, Denmark

Bartolo, Brian   020334
FIR, Birkirkara, Malta

Basta, Beata   020068
Roltec, Poznań, Poland

Basta, Marek   020068
Roltec, Poznań, Poland

Battisti, Kurt   020255
A-Null Development, Vienna, Austria

Bauhuis, Gerard   020067
Radboud University, Nijmegen, The Netherlands

Baumann, Kerstin   020470
bifa Umweltinstitut, Augsburg, Germany

Baumann, Sara   020063
ISFH, Emmerthal, Germany

Baumann, Ulrike   020006
ISFH, Emmerthal, Germany

Baur, Carsten   020246
European Space Agency, Noordwijk, The Netherlands

Beaucarne, Guy   020384
Dow Silicones Belgium, Seneffe, Belgium

Becker, Carl   020331
DLR, Almería, Spain

Behrensdorff Poulsen, Peter   020037
DTU, Lyngby, Denmark

Beinert, Andreas J.   020123
Fraunhofer ISE, Freiburg, Germany

Bejat, Timea   020225, 020500
CEA, Le Bourget-du-Lac, France

Belawadi, Aditya Girish   020231
Fraunhofer ISE, Freiburg, Germany

Belferkous, Brahim Anis   020325
PCCL, Leoben, Austria

Bellmann, Martin   020495, 020510
SINTEF, Trondheim, Norway

Bellvert, Eduard   020139
Tecnalia, Donostia - San Sebastián, Spain

Beltran-Condori, Sonia   020129, 020417
University of Antofagasta, Antofagasta, Chile

Belzunce, María Jesús   020514
AZTI, PASAIA, Spain

Bendix, Peter   020388
Next2Sun Technology, Dillingen, Germany

Bengoechea, Jaione   020181, 020300
CENER, Sarriguren, Spain

Bermudez Benito, Veronica   020146
QEERI, Doha, Qatar

Bermudez-Garcia, Anderson   020246
Thales Alenia Space, Cannes, France

Berrian, Djaber   020492
Belectric, Kolitzheim, Germany

Berson, Solenn   020134
CEA / INES, Le Bourget-du-Lac, France

Bolink, Henk J. 020226
University of Valencia, Paterna, Spain

Bonal, Victor 020085
UAM, Madrid, Spain

Bonnet, Martin 020141
University of Applied Science Cologne, Cologne, Germany

Bonnet-Eymard, Bénédicte 020251
CSEM, Neuchâtel, Switzerland

Borgers, Tom 020225
IMEC, Genk, Belgium

Borgna, Luciano 020369
BFH, Burgdorf, Switzerland

Borie, Benjamin 020039
ATLANT 3D, Taastrup, Denmark

Borowski, Peter 020307
Avancis, Munich, Germany

Borriello, Aniello 020378
ENEA, Portici, Italy

Borzi, Giovanni 020019
Enginsoft, Padua, Italy

Bosch, Elina 020252, 020543, 020564, 020573
Becquerel Institute, Brussels, Belgium

Bosma, Theo 020571
DNV, Arnhem, The Netherlands

Bothe, Karsten 020236
ISFH, Emmerthal, Germany

Bou-Nassif, Liliane 020338
CETHIL, Villeurbanne, France

Bouchier, Daniel 020058
CNRS, Palaiseau, France

Bouguerra, Sara 020156, 020294, 020389, 020393
imec, Genk, Belgium

Bourdin, Vincent 020406
CNRS, Paris, France

Bourgeois, Antoine 020102
SERIS, Singapore, Singapore

Bovesecchi, Gianluigi 020494
University of Rome Tor Vergata, Rome, Italy

Brabec, Christoph J. 020117
HI ERN, Erlangen, Germany

Bradford, David Roy 020077
Newcastle University, Newcastle upon Tyne, United
Kingdom

Brailovsky, Peter Henri 020475
Fraunhofer ISE, Freiburg, Germany

Braña, Alejandro F. 020508
Autonomous University of Madrid, Madrid, Spain

Brandstätter, Andreas Lenzing Plastics, Lenzing, Austria	020227
Braun, Christian Luxembourg Institute of Science and Technology, Esch-sur-Alzette, Luxembourg	020457
Brecl, Kristijan University of Ljubljana, Ljubljana, Slovenia	020269, 020319
Bredemeier, Dennis Leibniz University Hannover, Hannover, Germany	020240
Breitenbücher, Marian Highline Technologies, Freiburg, Germany	020225
Brendel, Rolf ISFH, Emmerthal, Germany	020006, 020008, 020236, 020240, 020260, 020482
Brendstrup Møller, Clara Bolette DTU, Roskilde, Denmark	020028
Bretzel, Tamara Fraunhofer ISE, Freiburg, Germany	020195
Breyer, Christian LUT University, Lappeenranta, Finland	020479
Brito, Miguel University of Lisbon, Lisbon, Portugal	020457
Brivio, Elisabetta RSE, Milan, Italy	020462
Brockmann, Lukas ISFH, Emmerthal, Germany	020063
Brodnicke, Linda ETH, Zurich, Switzerland	020296
Brueckner, Emanuel ISFH, Emmerthal, Germany	020063
Bründlinger, Roland AIT, Vienna, Austria	020369
Brun, Gonzalo ENDEF, Zaragoza, Spain	020414, 020517
Bruno, Maddalena Fraunhofer ISE, Freiburg, Germany	020452
Buceta, Alicia CENER, Sarriguren, Spain	020300
Bucher, Christof BFH, Burgdorf, Switzerland	020179, 020322, 020359, 020369, 020386
Buchholz, Florian ISC Konstanz, Konstanz, Germany	020035, 020225, 020569
Buchmann, Johanna Berlin University of Applied Sciences, Berlin, Germany	020309
Buck, Thomas ISC Konstanz, Konstanz, Germany	020033

Buckland, Daniel Henkel, Düsseldorf, Germany	020119, 020218
Buddana, Viswa Harinath DLR, Oldenburg, Germany	020482
Bühlmann, Gian-Luca ZHAW, Winterthur, Switzerland	020385
Buerhop, Claudia HI ERN, Erlangen, Germany	020149, 020150, 020377
Buerhop-Lutz, Claudia HI ERN, Erlangen, Germany	020185, 020230
Burgers, Antonius R. TNO, Petten, The Netherlands	020405
Burri, Matthias BFH, Burgdorf, Switzerland	020179
Busto, Chiara Eni, Novara, Italy	020521
Butrichi, Fabio University of Milano-Bicocca, Milan, Italy	020087
Butt, Nauman Lahore University of Management Sciences, Lahore, Pakistan	020394

C. Tavares, Fabiele Federal University of Rio de Janeiro, Duque de Caxias, Brazil	020090
Cabal, Raphael University Grenoble Alpes, Le Bourget-du-Lac, France	020034
Caballero, Luis Jaime UPM, Madrid, Spain	020501, 020508
Caballero, Raquel CSIC, Madrid, Spain	020094
Caballero, Raquel IO-CSIC, Madrid, Spain	020085
Cabecinha, Vasco Nova University Lisbon, Lisbon, Portugal	020565
Cabello, Fatima IO-CSIC, Madrid, Spain	020085
Caçapietra Pires da Silva, Lucas Teixeira PUCRS, Porto Alegre, Brazil	020025
Caccavelli, Dominique CSTB, Bussy-Saint Georges, France	020551
Caccivio, Mauro SUPSI, Mendrisio, Switzerland	020204, 020574
Caffari, Francesca ENEA, Ispra, Italy	020551
Calabrese, Nicolandrea ENEA, Ispra, Italy	020551

Carroy, Perrine CEA/ INES, Le Bourget-du-Lac, France	020226
Carstens, Justus ISC Konstanz, Konstanz, Germany	020003
Cartenì, Fabrizio University of Naples Federico II, Naples, Italy	020378
Casappa, Michele National Research Council, Parma, Italy	020087
Casasola Paesa, Marta Hasselt University, Diepenbeek, Belgium	020389
Castilla Nieto, María del Mar University of Almería, La Cañada de San Urbano, Spain	020336
Castillo Patton, Daniel Jason Enertis Applus+, Madrid, Spain	020326
Castro, Luis Guilherme Casa dos Ventos, Fortaleza, Brazil	020530
Castro, Rui University of Lisbon, Lisbon, Portugal	020464
Castro-Gallardo, Fernando University of Antofagasta, Antofagasta, Chile	020417, 020422
Cavaco, Afonso University of Évora, Évora, Portugal	020304, 020565
Cebecauer, Tomas Solargis, Bratislava, Slovakia	020274
Çekerek, Gamze Kalyon PV, Ankara, Türkiye	020006
Celik, Duygu WIP Renewable Energies, Munich, Germany	020551
Çeliktaş, Melih Soner Ege University, İzmir, Türkiye	020559
Centazzo, Massimo EnPV, Karlsruhe, Germany	020006
Centeno Brito, Miguel University of Lisbon, Lisbon, Portugal	020421, 020490
Cereceda, Eneko UPV/EHU, Bilbao, Spain	020055, 020097, 020153, 020287
Ceretti, Mattia SUPSI, Mendrisio, Switzerland	020204
Cesar, I. TNO, Petten, The Netherlands	020405
Ceuppens, Ignas BUILD`UP, Aarschot, Belgium	020302
Chatterji, Nithin SVNIT, Surat, India	020071
Chen, Daniel SunDrive Solar, Kurnell, Australia	020048

Chen, Syh-Homg 020161
ITRI, Hsinchu, Taiwan

Chen, Xiang 020111
Hohai University, Changzhou, China

Cheung, Kak Pong 020313
Kiel University of Applied Sciences, Kiel, Germany

Chhapia, Gaurang 020492
Belectric, Kolitzheim, Germany

Chiba, Takahiro 020436
Hokkaido University of Science, Sapporo, Japan

Chichignoud, Guy 020495
13Institut Polytechnique De Grenoble, Grenoble, France

Chicote, Beatriz 020289
Mondragon University, Arrasate-Mondragon, Spain

Chiesa, Matteo 020487
Khalifa University, Abu Dhabi, United Arab Emirates

Chini de Freitas, Felipe 020023
PUCRS, Porto Alegre, Brazil

Cho, Yunae 020045
KIER, Daejeon, South Korea

Choi, Kwan Bum 020102
SERIS, Singapore, Singapore

Chouder, Aissa 020301
University of M'sila, M'sila, Algeria

Chowdhury, Gofran 020276, 020544
3E, Brussels, Belgium

Christ, Anja 020063
ISFH, Emmerthal, Germany

Chrkavy, Daniel 020262
Solargis, Bratislava, Slovakia

Chueh, Wei-Lo 020021
TSEC, Hsinchu, Taiwan

Ciesla, Alison 020065
UNSW, Sydney, Australia

Cirimele, Vincenzo 020314
University of Bologna, Bologna, Italy

Clausing, Roland 020063, 020114
ISFH, Emmerthal, Germany

Clochard, Laurent 020031
Nines Photovoltaics, Dublin, Germany

Clochard, Laurent 020007
Nines Photovoltaics, Dublin, Ireland

Clyncke, Jan 020472, 020513
PV CYCLE, Brussels, Belgium

Coşkun, Özlem 020006, 020027, 020225
Kalyon PV, Ankara, Türkiye

Colberts, Fallon Zuyd University, Heerlen, The Netherlands	020389
Colin, Hervé CEA / INES, Le Bourget-du-Lac, France	020217, 020262
Collin, Stéphane C2N, Palaiseau, France	020074
Colwell, Jack SunDrive Solar, Kurnell, Australia	020048
Comak, Mertcan ISC Konstanz, Konstanz, Germany	020003
Connolly, James Patrick CNRS, Gif-sur-Yvette, France	020058, 020060
Cordeiro, Diogo EDP, Lisbon, Portugal	020464
Cornago, Iñaki CENER, Sarriguren, Spain	020392
Cornaro, Cristina University of Rome Tor Vergata, Rome, Italy	020494
Correa, Guillermo Gonvarri MS R&D, Corvera - Asturias, Spain	020412
Correia, Joana University of Évora, Évora, Portugal	020565
Couderc, Romain CEA / INES, Le Bourget-du-Lac, France	020217, 020311, 020546
Coutel, John SOLAÏS, Valbonne, France	020244
Cowan, Don Kiwa PI Berlin, Hudson, United States of America	020230
Cox, Joel D. SDU Climate Cluster, Odense, Denmark	020250
Cox, Joel D SDU Climate Cluster, Odense, Denmark	020306
Coz, Pier Luigi European Space Agency, Noordwijk, The Netherlands	020246
Crespo, Carolina University of Lisbon, Lisbon, Portugal	020490
Cristiane Pan, Aline UFRGS, Tramandaí, Brazil	020548
Cristóbal, Ana Belén UPM, Madrid, Spain	020491, 020535, 020575
Crozier McCleland, Jacqueline Nelson Mandela University, Port Elizabeth, South Africa	020185, 020344
Cuadra, Juan Manuel CENER, Sarigurren, Spain	020318
Cui, Jindan Tokyo University of Science, Tokyo, Japan	020320, 020525

Culot, Dominique 020384
Dow Silicones Belgium, Seneffe, Belgium

Curon, Jonathan 020384
Dow Silicones Belgium, Seneffe, Belgium

Cusenza, Maria Anna 020466
RSE, Milan, Italy

D. Pinto, Luciana 020090
Federal University of Rio de Janeiro, Rio de Janeiro, Brazil

Daenen, Michael 020156, 020389, 020393
imec, Genk, Belgium

Dagla, Anastasia 020276
3E, Brussels, Belgium

Dahle, Arne 020225, 020495
Norsun, Oslo, Norway

Dahlioui, Dounia 020443
University of Agder, Grimstad, Norway

Dalibor, Thomas 020307
Avancis, Munich, Germany

Dalla Maria, Enrico 020485
Eurac Research, Bolzano, Italy

Dalla Torre, Francesco 020010
Applied Materials, Treviso, Italy

Dalmazzone, Didier 020251
ENSTA Paris, Palaiseau, France

Damon, Keanu 020382
7SecondSolar, Cape Town, South Africa

Danelli, Andrea 020462, 020466
RSE, Milan, Italy

Darsene Dimd, Berhane 020270
SINTEF, Trondheim, Norway

Das, Gourab 020005, 020222, 020463
RCT Solutions, Konstanz, Germany

Dasilva-Villanueva, Nerea 020014, 020501, 020508
UPM, Madrid, Spain

Daßler, David 020313
Fraunhofer CSP, Halle, Germany

Daßler, David 020355
Fraunhofer IMWS, Halle, Germany

Daume, Darwin 020361
pvnode, Rosenheim, Germany

Davidsen, Rasmus Schmidt 020028, 020039, 020043
Aarhus University, Aarhus, Denmark

De Almeida, Laura 020074
LAAS-CNRS, Toulouse, France

De Biasio, Martin Silicon Austria Labs, Villach, Austria	020504
De Blasi, Mariam Enel Green Power, Pisa, Italy	020378
de Graaf, Gertjan J. TNO, Petten, The Netherlands	020405
de Groot, Koen M. TNO, Petten, The Netherlands	020405
De Gruijter, Alvaro Eurac Research, Bolzano, Italy	020254
de Jong, Minne M. TNO, Eindhoven, The Netherlands	020169, 020425
De Jong, Richard imec, Genk, Belgium	020156, 020294, 020389
de l'Epine, Mélodie Becquerel Institute France, Lyon, France	020252, 020505, 020543, 020564
de l'Epine, Melodie Becquerel Institute, Brussels, Belgium	020225, 020334, 020520, 020558
de l'Epine, Melodie IEA PVPS Task 1, Lyon, France	020570
de la Casa Higueras, Juan University of Jaén, Jaén, Spain	020269
de la Viuda, Eva University of Valladolid, Valladolid, Spain	020205
de Meatza, Iratxe CIDETEC, San Sebastián, Spain	020495
De Rose, Angela Fraunhofer ISE, Freiburg, Germany	020123
De Rose, Jonas Fraunhofer ISE, Freiburg, Germany	020010
Debastiani Benato, Betina AMIRES, Prague, Czech Republic	020019
Deepti, SRM University, Sonipat, India	020563
Del Campo, Valeria Federico Santa María Technical University, Valparaiso, Chile	020311
del Cañizo, Carlos UPM, Madrid, Spain	020014, 020501, 020507, 020508
Del Pero, Claudio Polytechnic University of Milan, Milan, Italy	020249
Del Pozo, Alberto TECNALIA, Derio, Spain	020197, 020198
del Prado Santamaria, Rodrigo DTU, Roskilde, Denmark	020191, 020376
del Ser, Javier UPV/EHU, Bilbao, Spain	020358

Delgado-Sanchez, Jose Maria   020089
University of Seville, Seville, Spain

Delli Veneri, Paola   020378
ENEA, Naples, Italy

Denafas, Julius   020225, 020353
Solitek, Vilnius, Lithuania

Deniz, Engin   020559
Ege University, İzmir, Türkiye

Denke, Sebastian   020236
ISFH, Emmerthal, Germany

Dentz, Laurie   020058
CNRS, Palaiseau, France

Derin Gure, Pinar   020513, 020521, 020556
ODTU GUNAM, Ankara, Türkiye

Derj, Anyssa   020116
IPVF, Palaiseau, France

Dessi, Alessio   020077
CNR-ICCOM, Sesto Fiorentino, Italy

Devenson, Jan   020157
Center for Physical Sciences and Technology (FTMC),
Vilnius, Lithuania

Dhimish, Mahmoud   020346, 020376
DTU, Roskilde, Denmark

Di Matteo, Alfredo   020010
Enel Green Power, Catania, Italy

Diab, Mohanad   020203
Eurac Research, Bolzano, Italy

Diano, Marcello   020378
M2M Engineering, Naples, Italy

Diaz, Roberto   020300
Notio Association, Toledo, Spain

Díaz, Sara   020365, 020366
CENER, Sarriguren, Spain

Dietrich, Andreas   020355
DiSUN Deutsche Solarservice, Werder, Germany

Díez Alcántara, Eduardo   020501
UCM, Madrid, Spain

Díez, Eduardo   020508
UCM, Madrid, Spain

Dimd, Berhane Darsene   020495, 020510
SINTEF, Trondheim, Norway

Ding, Kaining   020233
FZJ, Jülich, Germany

Ding, Kung   020111
Hohai University, Changzhou, China

Dittmann, Sebastian   020318
Anhalt University of Applied Sciences, Köthen, Germany

Dittrich, Arne   020240
ISFH, Emmerthal, Germany

Dizier, Antoine   020373
INES, Le Bourget-du-Lac, France

Djeukeu, Ivanol Jaurece   020050
halm elektronik, Frankfurt am Main, Germany

Dobreva, Petja   020193
University of Namibia, Windhoek, Namibia

Dörenkämper, Maarten   020169
TNO, Eindhoven, The Netherlands

Dörn, Markus   020255
A-Null Development, Vienna, Austria

Doi, Minh Thong   020317
CEA INES, Le Bourget-du-Lac, France

Domínguez, César   020209, 020246, 020257
UPM, Madrid, Spain

Donadello, Alessandro   020485, 020489
Edyna, Bolzano, Italy

Donėlienė, Jolanta   020157
Applied Research Institute for Prospective Technologies,
Vilnius, Lithuania

Donoso, José   020570
UNEF, Madrid, Spain

Doppler, Christian   020455
Virtual Vehicle, Graz, Austria

dos Reis, Givaldo   020348
University of São Paulo, São Paulo, Brazil

dos Santos, Jeremias   020409
University of Évora, Évora, Portugal

Doucet, Jean-Baptiste   020074
LAAS-CNRS, Toulouse, France

Dovesi, Roberto   020060
Academy of Sciences of Turin, Torino, Italy

Driesse, Anton   020211, 020293, 020452
PV Performance Labs, Freiburg, Germany

Duarte, Dorivaldo   020418, 020565
University of Evora, Évora, Portugal

Dubois, Sebastien   020034
University Grenoble Alpes, Le Bourget-du-Lac, France

Dubravskij, Piotr   020157
Applied Research Institute for Prospective Technologies,
Vilnius, Lithuania

Dubravskij, Piotr   020380
Modern E-Technologies, Vilnius, Lithuania

Duerinckx, Filip   020064, 020225
Hasselt Unversity, Genk, Belgium

Düz, Cansel   020135
Kalyon PV, Ankara, Türkiye

Dullweber, Thorsten   020006, 020007, 020008, 020225
ISFH, Emmerthal, Germany

Dunlop, Ewan D.   020173, 020210, 020213
European Commission JRC, Ispra, Italy

Dupon, Olivier   020294
imec, Genk, Belgium

Dupuis, Julien   020188
EDF R&D, Moret Loing Orvanne, France

Dutykh, Denys   020338
Khalifa University, Abu Dhabi, United Arab Emirates

Duzellier, Sophie   020073
University of Toulouse, Toulouse, France

Dypvik Sødahl, Elin   020340
IFE, Kjeller, Norway

Ebert, Matthias   020426
Fraunhofer CSP, Halle, Germany

Ebert, Matthias   020355
Fraunhofer IMWS, Halle, Germany

Ebner, Rita   020318, 020334, 020521
AIT, Vienna, Austria

Echeverria, Oihane   020139
Tecnalia, Donostia - San Sebastián, Spain

Eder, Gabriele C.   020160, 020162, 020249, 020500, 020504
OFI, Vienna, Austria

Eelma, Tonis   020302
IBS, Tartu, Estonia

Efthymiou, Venizelos   020544
EPL Technology Frontiers, Dhali, Cyprus

Egan, Renate   020048
UNSW, Sydney, Australia

Egido, Miguel-Ángel   020407
UPM, Madrid, Spain

Eidtmann, Maximilian   020385
ZHAW, Winterthur, Switzerland

Eijgelaar, Marcel   020571
DNV, Arnhem, The Netherlands

Eikelboom, Erik   020225
Futurasun, Citadella, Italy

Einhaus, Roland   020312
ZSW, Stuttgart, Germany

Eisenacher, Matthias   020141
University of Applied Science Cologne, Cologne, Germany

Eiternick, Stefan   020004, 020052
Fraunhofer CSP, Halle (Saale), Germany

Ekins-Daukes, Nicholas J.   020065
UNSW, Sydney, Australia

El Ainaoui, Khadija   020171
Green Energy Park, Benguerir, Morocco

El mrabet, Yasmine   020171
Green Energy Park, Benguerir, Morocco

Elgaili, Mohamed   020166
QEERI, Doha, Qatar

Elhamaoui, Said   020171
Green Energy Park, Benguerir, Morocco

Ellis, Hanna   020213
European Commission JRC, Ispra, Italy

Engelen, Tine   020389
Hasselt University, Diepenbeek, Belgium

Erber, Alexander   020386
BFH, Burgdorf, Switzerland

Eryılmaz, Hande   020521
ODTÜ-GÜNAM, Ankara, Türkiye

Escudero, Ana   020414
IaSol, Zaragoza, Spain

Esmailifar, Seyyed Majid   020335, 020356, 020374, 020375
Amirkabir University of Technology, Tehran, Iran

Espinosa, Nieves   020497, 020506
University of Murcia, Murcia, Spain

Essam T. Mohammed, Sarah   020546
EU SOLARIS, Almeria, Spain

Esteras, Miguel   020358
TECNALIA, Derio, Spain

Eyhorn, Steffen   020369
Fraunhofer ISE, Freiburg, Germany

Fabel, Yann   020235, 020237, 020239
DLR, Almería, Spain

Fabris, Francesca   020225
Futurasun, Citadella, Italy

Faes, Antonin   020251
CSEM, Neuchâtel, Switzerland

Falangas, Alexandros   020210
TRASIS International, Brussels, Belgium

Fang, Xue   020525
Tokyo University of Science, Tokyo, Japan

Fano, Vanesa   020055, 020097, 020153, 020287
UPV/EHU, Bilbao, Spain

Farhat, Mohammad   020428
Australian University, Kuwait City, Kuwait

Farina, Andrea   020066
CNR-IFN, Milan, Italy

Farrias-Basulto, Guillermo   020101
HZB, Berlin, Germany

Fath, Moritz   020463
RCT Solutions, Konstanz, Germany

Fath, Peter   020005, 020463
RCT Solutions, Konstanz, Germany

Fava, Henrique   020565
University of Évora, Évora, Portugal

Feichtner, Markus   020255
Sonnenkraft Energie, St. Veit/Glan, Austria

Feichtner, Markus   020160
Sonnenkraft Energy, St. Veit/Glan, Austria

Feldbacher, Sonja   020136, 020500
PCCL, Leoben, Austria

Feldhof, Anne Maren   020522
University of Applied Science Cologne, Cologne, Germany

Fernandes, Cláudia   020464
Centre for New Energy Technologies, Sacavém, Portugal

Fernández Solas, Álvaro   020331
DLR, Almería, Spain

Ferrando, Jorge   020226
University of Valencia, Paterna, Spain

Ferreira, Catarina G.   020250
SDU Climate Cluster, Odense, Denmark

Ferreira, Catarina   020306
SDU Climate Cluster, Odense, Denmark

Ferrero, Sergio   020079
Polytechnic University of Turin, Turin, Italy

Feuerherdt, Niels   020309
Berlin University of Applied Sciences, Berlin, Germany

Fialho, Luis   020203, 020254, 020261, 020304, 020403,
Eurac Research, Bolzano, Italy   020409, 020418, 020420, 020565

Figueroa, Andrés   020339
National University of Colombia, Bogotá, Colombia

Fischer, Stefan   020495
SGL Carbon, Meitingen, Germany

Fleischanderl, Martin   020136
voestalpine Stahl, Linz, Austria

Fleury, Perine   020513, 020521
Biosphere Solar, Delft, The Netherlands

Flouchi, Imane   020171
Green Energy Park, Benguerir, Morocco

Fodor, Nikoletta
SolarPower Europe, Brussels, Belgium
020521

Fontani, Daniela
CNR-INO, Florence, Italy
020066

Forster, Jacob
Fraunhofer ISE, Freiburg, Germany
020135

Forstinger, Anne
CSP Services, Cologne, Germany
020331

Franch, Jordi Badosa
Ecole Polytechnique, Palaiseau, France
020406

Franchi, Daniele
CNR-ICCOM, Sesto Fiorentino, Italy
020077

Franquet, Erwin
Côte d'Azur University, Nice, France
020259, 020428

Frasson, Nicola
Applied Materials, San Biagio di Callalta, Italy
020019

Freer, Solomon
PV Lighthouse, Coledale, Australia
020396

Freitag, Marina
Newcastle University, Newcastle upon Tyne, United Kingdom
020077

Freund, Timo
EnBW, Karlsruhe, Germany
020312

Friansyah, Rizal
DTU, Roskilde, Denmark
020376

Friesen, Gabi
SUPSI, Mendrisio, Switzerland
020160, 020249, 020574

Friesen, Thomas
Megasol Energie, Deitingen, Switzerland
020249

Fritz Muñoz, Benjamín
UPV, Valencia, Spain
020099

Froebel, Jens
Fraunhofer CSP, Halle, Germany
020121, 020142, 020192, 020223

Frontini, Francesco
SUPSI, Mendrisio, Switzerland
020249, 020253

Fuentealba-Vidal, Edward
University of Antofagasta, Antofagasta, Chile
020129, 020311, 020342, 020417, 020422

Füreder-Kitzmüller, Friedrich
voestalpine Stahl, Linz, Austria
020136

Fuertes Marrón, David
UPM, Madrid, Spain
020014, 020501, 020507, 020508

Fuertes, David
IES-UPM, Madrid, Spain
020097

Furnari, Alessandro
Enel Green Power, Catania, Italy
020010

Fuß, Michael
MBJ Solutions, Ahrensburg, Germany
020206

Gabor, Andrew M.   020166
BrightSpot Automation, Boulder, United States of America

Gaete, Martin   020311
University of Antofagasta, Antofagasta, Chile

Gafert, Michael   020369
AIT, Vienna, Austria

Gageot, Tristan   020040
CEA / INES, Le Bourget-du-Lac, France

Gainza, Eusebio   020392
ALLOTARRA, Allo, Spain

Galarza, Alejandra   020461
IPVF, Palaiseau, France

Galbiati, Giuseppe   020119, 020218
Henkel, Düsseldorf, Germany

Galdikas, Algirdas   020157
Applied Research Institute for Prospective Technologies,
Vilnius, Lithuania

Galiana, Beatriz   020085
Charles III University of Madrid, Madrid, Spain

Galiazzo, Marco   020019
Applied Materials, San Biagio di Callalta, Italy

Gall, Stefan   020101
HZB, Berlin, Germany

Gallmetzer, Sandra   020261, 020509
Eurac Research, Bolzano, Italy

Galparsoro, Ibon   020514
AZTI, PASAIA, Spain

Gamarra, Ana Rosa   020502
CIEMAT, Madrid, Spain

Ganter, Alissa   020296
ETH, Zurich, Switzerland

Gaona García, Elvis Eduardo   020279
District University of Bogotá, Bogotá, Colombia

Garabetian, Thomas   020551
SolarPower Europe, Brussels, Belgium

García Campos, Enrique   020336
University of Almería, La Cañada de San Urbano, Spain

García, Fernando   020326
UC3M, Madrid, Spain

García, Sonia   020139
Tecnalia, Donostia - San Sebastián, Spain

García-Cañas, Alejandro   020257
IMDEA Nanoscience, Madrid, Spain

García-Salinas, María José   020100
University of Almeria, Almería, Spain

Garcia-Sanchez, Almudena   020246, 020257
UPM, Madrid, Spain

Garg, Vivek   020069, 020071, 020081
SVNIT, Surat, India

Garraín, Daniel   020502
CIEMAT, Madrid, Spain

Gasse, Hugues   020073
University of Toulouse, Toulouse, France

Gassner, Anika   020160, 020162, 020500, 020504
OFI, Vienna, Austria

Gatti, Cesare   020541
PedersoliGattai, Milan, Italy

Gattu, Apoorva   020003
ISC Konstanz, Konstanz, Germany

Gautier, Damien   020505
Becquerel Institute, Brussels, Belgium

Gauvin, Xavier   020302
Bouygues Construction, Saint-Quentin-en-Yvelines, France

Ge, Hua   020249
Concordia University, Montreal, Canada

Gebhardt, Paul   020195
Fraunhofer ISE, Freiburg, Germany

Geerligs, L. J.   020030
TNO, Petten, The Netherlands

Gehrlein, Janek   020522
University of Applied Science Cologne, Cologne, Germany

Geier, Jutta   020234
PCCL, Leoben, Austria

Geml, Fabian   020031
University of Konstanz, Constance, Germany

Genovese, Maria   020378
Enel Green Power, Pisa, Italy

Georghiou, George E.   020534
University of Cyprus, Nicosia, Cyprus

Germani, Simone   020302
CEI, Milan, Italy

Getsiou, Maria   020181
Directorate General for Research and Innovation, Brussels,
Belgium

Geymayer, Lukas   020136
voestalpine Stahl, Linz, Austria

Ghahremani, Amirreza   020335, 020374
Amirkabir University of Technology, Tehran, Iran

Ghennioui, Abdellatif   020171
Green Energy Park, Benguerir, Morocco

Ghosh, Saptak   020519
CSTEP, Bengaluru, India

Girardi, Pierpaolo RSE, Milan, Italy	020462, 020466
Giroux-Julien, Stephanie CNRS, Villeurbanne, France	020338
Gissler, Antoine EDF R&D, Palaiseau, France	020060
Göckeritz, Robert Fraunhofer CSP, Halle, Germany	020119
Gohil, Hardik RCT Solutions, Konstanz, Germany	020222
Gomes de Venuto, Vitor PUCRS, Porto Alegre, Brazil	020025
Gomez Trillos, Juan Camilo DLR, Oldenburg, Germany	020482
Gomez-Lazaro, Emilio University of Castilla-La Mancha, Albacete, Spain	020562
Gonnella, Gabriella Eurac research, Bolzano, Italy	020249, 020254
González Pérez, Sara ULL, San Cristóbal de La Laguna, Spain	020151
González Rodríguez, Brais University of Vigo, Vigo, Spain	020243
González, Miguel Ángel University of Valladolid, Valladolid, Spain	020205
González-Díaz, Benjamín ULL, San Cristóbal de La Laguna, Spain	020151
Goraya, Baljeet Singh Fraunhofer ISE, Freiburg, Germany	020475
Gordillo, Gerardo National University of Colombia, Bogotá, Colombia	020110
Gordon, Ivan imec, Genk, Belgium	020521
Gottschalg, Ralph Anhalt University of Applied Sciences, Köthen, Germany	020158
Gottschalg, Ralph Fraunhofer CSP, Halle, Germany	020056, 020201, 020229, 020233, 020284, 020574
Govaerts, Jonathan imec, Genk, Belgium	020019
Gracia Amillo, Ana María CENER, Pamplona, Spain	020211
Gracia Amillo, Ana María CENER, Sarigurren, Spain	020318
Gracia Amillo, Ana María CENER, Sarriguren, Spain	020181, 020365, 020366, 020497
Gregory, Geoffrey EnPV, Karlsruhe, Germany	020006

Greslou, Olivier   020551
CSTB, Bussy-Saint Georges, France

Grommes, Eva-Maria   020522, 020523
University of Applied Science Cologne, Cologne, Germany

Grosser, Stephan   020119, 020142, 020218
Fraunhofer CSP, Halle, Germany

Grünsteidl, Stefan   020307
Avancis, Munich, Germany

Gruginskie, Natasha   020067
Radboud University, Nijmegen, The Netherlands

Guedea, Isabel   020127, 020517
ENDEF, Zaragoza, Spain

Gülsoy, Eren Cihan   020521
METU, Ankara, Türkiye

Gümüs Çiftci, Burcu   020027
Kalyon PV, Ankara, Türkiye

Guerra, Gerardo   020448, 020481
GreenPowerMonitor a DNV company, Barcelona, Spain

Guidetti, Giulia   020541
Green Horse Advisory, Milan, Italy

Guillemoles, Jean François   020062
IPVF, Palaiseau, France

Guillevin, Nicolas   020225
TNO, Petten, The Netherlands

Gunbas, Gorkem   020113
ODTÜ-GÜNAM, Ankara, Türkiye

Gupta, Akshit   020551
Eurac Research, Bolzano, Italy

Gutierrez, Jose Ruben   020055, 020097, 020153, 020287
UPV/EHU, Bilbao, Spain

Gutjahr, Astrid   020030
TNO, Petten, The Netherlands

Haaland, Petry Kristine Nøttum   020476
NTNU, Trondheim, Norway

Haase, Felix   020063
ISFH, Emmerthal, Germany

Hadiwidjaja, Stella   020102
SERIS, Singapore, Singapore

Hadjipanayi, Maria   020064
University of Cyprus, Nicosia, Cyprus

Haedrich, Ingrid   020195, 020231
Fraunhofer ISE, Freiburg, Germany

Hämmer, Matthias   020470
bifa Umweltinstitut, Augsburg, Germany

Hafidi, Elias   020511
Inflights BV, Brussels, Belgium

Hagemann, Elizabeth M.   020416
Nelson Mandela University, Port Elizabeth, South Africa

Hallais, Géraldine   020058
CNRS, Palaiseau, France

Halle, Lasse   020359
BFH, Burgdorf, Switzerland

Hallensleben, Carina   020220
TAMURA-ELSOLD, Ilsenburg, Germany

Halm, Andreas   020218, 020220, 020221
ISC Konstanz, Konstanz, Germany

Halme, Janne   020249
Aalto University, Espoo, Finland

Hamada, Toshiyuki   020190
Osaka Electro-Communication University, Osaka, Japan

Hammer, Annette   020239
DLR, Oldenburg, Germany

Hamouda, Frederic   020058
CNRS, Palaiseau, France

Hanifi, Hamed   020121, 020125, 020137, 020223
AESOLAR, Koenigsbrunn, Germany

Hansen, Per-Anders   020017, 020503
Institute for Energy Technology, Kjeller, Norway

Harit, Amit Kumar   020064
Hasselt Unversity, Genk, Belgium

Harrison, Samuel   020225
CEA, Le Bourget-du-Lac, France

Hashem, Ahmad   020056, 020201
Anhalt University of Applied Sciences, Köthen, Germany

Hategan, Sergiu Mihai   020283
West University of Timisoara, Timisoara, Romania

Hauch, Jens   020117, 020149, 020150
HI ERN, Erlangen, Germany

Hauer, Martin   020255
Bartenbach, Vienna, Austria

Haverkamp, Helge   020008
centrotherm international, Blaubeuren, Germany

Hee Lee, Sang   020045
KIER, Daejeon, South Korea

Heidrich, Robert   020233
Fraunhofer CSP, Halle, Germany

Heikkinen, Kyösti   020423
VTT Technical Research Centre of Finland, Oulu, Finland

Heiser, Moritz   020230
Kiwa PI Berlin, Berlin, Germany

Helbig, Matthias   020220
ISC Konstanz, Konstanz, Germany

Helten, David   020331
CSP Services, Cologne, Germany

Hennig, Carsten   020313, 020355
saferay holding, Berlin, Germany

Hennig, Patrick   020313
Kiel University of Applied Sciences, Kiel, Germany

Heras, Jesús   020536
Wattkraft, Madrid, Spain

Hermle, Martin   020475
Fraunhofer ISE, Freiburg, Germany

Hernández Mora, Johann Alexander   020279, 020441
District University of Bogotá, Bogotá, Colombia

Hernández, Jaime J.   020257
IMDEA Nanoscience, Madrid, Spain

Hernández, Johann   020526
Francisco José de Caldas District University, Bogota,
Colombia

Herodotou, Panayiotis   020534
University of Cyprus, Nicosia, Cyprus

Herrera Leon, Fernando Augusto   020339, 020546
National University of Colombia, Bogotá, Colombia

Herrero, Leire   020139
Tecnalia, Donostia - San Sebastián, Spain

Herrero, Rebeca   020209, 020453, 020459
UPM, Madrid, Spain

Herrmann, Werner   020208
TÜV Rheinland Solar, Cologne, Germany

Herteleer, Bert   020329, 020351
KU Leuven, Ghent, Belgium

Herteleer, Bert   020574
SUPSI, Mendrisio, Switzerland

Hessler-Wyser, Aïcha   020251
EPFL, Neuchâtel, Switzerland

Heydari, Azim   020485
Eurac Research, Bolzano, Italy

Hinken, David   020236
ISFH, Emmerthal, Germany

Hladys, Bertrand   020010
CEA, Grenoble, France

Hoex, Bram   020065
UNSW, Sydney, Australia

Hofer, Leo   020322
BFH, Burgdorf, Switzerland

Hoffmann, Erik   020006
EnPV, Karlsruhe, Germany

Hogan Almeida, Rita
UPM, Madrid, Spain

020535, 020567

Hollemann, Christina
ISFH, Emmerthal, Germany

020008

Holovský, Jakub
Czech Technical University, Prague, Czech Republic

020107

Honrubia-Escribano, Andrés
University of Castilla-La Mancha, Albacete, Spain

020562

Hopp, Tobias
Sunman Energy, Frankfurt, Germany

020384

Horn, Jonas
halm elektronik, Frankfurt am Main, Germany

020050

Horta, Pedro
University of Évora, Évora, Portugal

020304, 020403, 020409, 020418, 020420, 020565

Hosatte, Mikaël
SEGTON Advanced Technology, Versailles, France

020068

Hoß, Jan
ISC Konstanz, Konstanz, Germany

020004, 020035

Hossain, Mohammad Istiaque
QEERI, Doha, Qatar

020042, 020075, 020108, 020109, 020146, 020147

Hou, Yi
SERIS, Singapore, Singapore

020102

Hsiao, Pei-Chieh
UNSW, Sydney, Australia

020048

Hsieh, Cho Fan
ITRI, Hsinchu, Taiwan

020083, 020161, 020163

Hu, Shuaifeng
University of Oxford, Oxford, United Kingdom

020226

Huang, Chris
SunDrive Solar, Kurnell, Australia

020048

Huang, Gan
KIT, Eggenstein-Leopoldshafen, Germany

020272

Huang, Lu-Jan
TNO, Leiden, The Netherlands

020425

Huang, Tzu-Yen
National Synchrotron Radiation Research Center, Hsinchu, Taiwan

020096

Hügi, Matthias
BFH, Burgdorf, Switzerland

020322

Huemer, Martin
University of Linz, Linz, Austria

020227

Huerta, Hugo E.
TUAS, Turku, Finland

020286, 020400

Hüttl, Bernd
Coburg University of Applied Sciences, Coburg, Germany

020361

Hulik Jansova, Marketa
Solargis, Bratislava, Slovakia
020274

Hung, Tzu Han
ITRI, Taipei City, Taiwan
020552

Hutterer-Tik, Thomas
Watt Analytics, Vienna, Austria
020347

Hwang, Hye-Mi
KIER, Daejeon, South Korea
020324, 020357, 020561

Iglesias, Unai
Tecnalia, Donostia - San Sebastián, Spain
020139

Ikeda, Kazuaki
AIST, Koriyama, Japan
020436

Infante, Paulo
University of Évora, Évora, Portugal
020420

Isabella, Olindo
TU Delft, Delft, The Netherlands
020515

Ishikawa, Ryousuke
Tokyo City University, Setagaya, Japan
020106, 020115

Iwaszko, Victorien
ROSI Solar, Saint-Martin-d'Hères, France
020495

Izquierdo-Roca, Victor
IREC, Barcelona, Spain
020094

J. N. Soares, Guillermo
Federal University of Rio de Janeiro, Duque de Caxias, Brazil
020090

Jacob, Julieu
METABUILD, Berlin, Germany
020302

Jacobs, Ayesha
Zutari, Cape Town, South Africa
020382

Jaeckel, Bengt
Fraunhofer CSP, Halle, Germany
020056, 020119, 020121, 020140, 020142, 020175, 020192, 020201, 020223, 020229

Jäger Waldau, Arnulf
European Commission, Rome, Italy
020570

Jäger, Philip
ISFH, Emmerthal, Germany
020006

Jäggi, Adrian
BFH, Burgdorf, Switzerland
020179

Järventausta, Pertti
Tampere University, Tampere, Finland
020445

Jaffré, Alexandre
CNRS, Gif-sur-Yvette, France
020058

Jahn, Ulrike
Fraunhofer CSP, Halle, Germany
020521, 020574

Jahn, Ulrike — 020355
Fraunhofer IMWS, Halle, Germany

Jahreis, Sophia — 020142, 020192
Fraunhofer CSP, Halle, Germany

Jakomin, Roberto — 020090
Federal University of Rio de Janeiro, Duque de Caxias, Brazil

Jakubik, Martin — 020274
Solargis, Bratislava, Slovakia

Jakuza, Paola — 020089
University of Padova, Padova, Italy

Jalkh, Judy — 020455
Virtual Vehicle, Graz, Austria

Jandl, Ralf — 020204
FFHS, Zurich, Switzerland

Jankovec, Marko — 020197
University of Ljubljana, Ljubljana, Slovenia

Jaworczak, Kamil — 020402
Technology Innovation Institute, Abu Dhabi, United Arab Emirates

Jensen, Adam R. — 020267
DTU, Kongens Lyngby, Denmark

Jeong, Jungi — 020323
K-water, Daejeon, South Korea

Jeong, Kyung Taek — 020045
KIER, Daejeon, South Korea

Jeong, Minsoo — 020045
KIER, Daejeon, South Korea

Jeronimo, Pedro — 020010
CEA, Grenoble, France

Jiang, Zonghan — 020158, 020201
Anhalt University of Applied Sciences, Köthen, Germany

Jimenez, Maria — 020302
Onyx Solar, Avila, Spain

Jimeno, Juan Carlos — 020055, 020097, 020153, 020287, 020289, 020353
UPV/EHU, Bilbao, Spain

Jo, Hyunsik — 020323
K-water, Daejeon, South Korea

Job, Enzo — 020231
Fraunhofer ISE, Freiburg, Germany

Johnson, Mark Robert — 020546
Institut Laue-Langevin (ILL), Grenoble, France

Joo, Dongmyoung — 020449
KETI, Wonmi-gu, South Korea

Jooss, Wolfgang — 020005, 020222, 020463
RCT Solutions, Konstanz, Germany

Joseph, Daniel Christopher   020123
Fraunhofer ISE, Freiburg, Germany

Joshi, Deepak   020069, 020081
SVNIT, Surat, India

Joss, David   020359, 020369, 020386
BFH, Burgdorf, Switzerland

Jouini, Anis   020034
ECM Technologies, Grenoble, France

Jouttijärvi, Sami   020286, 020298, 020398
University of Turku, Turku, Finland

Joziak, Roman   020230
Kiwa PI Berlin, Berlin, Germany

Ju, Young-Chul   020324, 020357, 020561
KIER, Daejeon, South Korea

Jugo, Josu   020437
UPV/EHU, Leioa, Spain

Junge, Sebastian   020008, 020482
ISFH, Emmerthal, Germany

Kaaya, Ismail   020156, 020294, 020389, 020393
imec, Genk, Belgium

Kähler, Jan-Dirk   020482
Centrotherm International, Blaubeuren, Germany

Kahraman, Mert   020027
Kalyon PV, Ankara, Türkiye

Kainz, Konrad   020430
AIT, Vienna, Austria

Kaiser, Martin   020215
Fraunhofer ISE, Freiburg, Germany

Kaizuka, Izumi   020570
RTS Corporation, Tokyo, Japan

Kajari-Schröder, Sarah   020063
ISFH, Emmerthal, Germany

Kallioharju, Kari   020444, 020445
TUAS, Tampere, Finland

Kalliojärvi, Heidi   020194
Tampere University, Tampere, Finland

Kalshetty, Mahesh   020519
CSTEP, Bengaluru, India

Kaltenbach, Thomas   020195
Fraunhofer ISE, Freiburg, Germany

Kamphues, Joshua   020031
University of Konstanz, Constance, Germany

Kandiyoti-Eskenazi, Selin   020467
CSEM, Neuchâtel, Switzerland

Kang, Min Gu 020045
KIER, Daejeon, South Korea

Kapetanovic, Viktor 020367
Nextracker, Fremont, United States of America

Karhu, Juha 020286
Finnish Meteorological Institute, Helsinki, Finland

Kari, Thøger 020191, 020376
DTU, Roskilde, Denmark

Karimy, Hedayatullah 020052
Fraunhofer CSP, Halle (Saale), Germany

Karttunen, Lauri 020298, 020398
University of Turku, Turku, Finland

Kasper, Ruth 020167, 020232
University of Applied Sciences Cologne, Cologne, Germany

Katouli, Tannaz 020195
Fraunhofer ISE, Freiburg, Germany

Kaufmann, Kai 020355
DENKweit, Halle, Germany

Kawabata, Rudy 020092
PUC-Rio, Rio de Janeiro, Brazil

Kemp, Linda 020390
MARIN, Wageningen, The Netherlands

Kenchington, Ian 020225, 020474, 020558
Becquerel Institute, Brussels, Belgium

Kenny, Robert 020210
European Commission JRC, Ispra, Italy

Khan, Abeer Ali 020513
First Solar, Mainz, Germany

Khosravi, Arash 020381
Mälardalen University, Västerås, Sweden

Kikkert, Benjamin W. J. 020405
TNO, Petten, The Netherlands

Kilickaya, Seda 020020
ODTÜ-GÜNAM, Ankara, Türkiye

Kim, Jin-Hong 020449
KETI, Wonmi-gu, South Korea

Kim, Jun-Tae 020249
Kongju National University, Chungnam, South Korea

Kim, Kihwan 020112
KIER, Daejeon, South Korea

Kim, Seok Won 020449
KETI, Wonmi-gu, South Korea

Kim, Yong-Jin 020045
KIER, Daejeon, South Korea

Kinge, Sachin 020117
Toyota Motors Europe, Brussels, Belgium

Kitamura, Ibuki
Osaka Electro-Communication University, Osaka, Japan   020190

Kitzberger, Gregor
voestalpine Stahl, Linz, Austria   020136

Kivambe, Maulid
QEERI, Doha, Qatar   020166

Kizukuri, Rihoko
TAMURA-ELSOLD, Ilsenburg, Germany   020220

Kladas, Anastasios
KU Leuven, Ghent, Belgium   020329, 020351

Kleider, Jean-Paul
CNRS, Gif-sur-Yvette, France   020040, 020058

Kleissl, Jan
University of California, San Diego, United States of   020528
America

Klengel, Robert
Fraunhofer IMWS, Halle, Germany   020355

Klenk, Markus
ZHAW, Winterthur, Switzerland   020385

Klos, Christine
Buhck Re.Energy, Hamburg, Norway   020510

Kluska, Sven
Fraunhofer ISE, Freiburg, Germany   020019

Klute, Carola
Fraunhofer IMWS, Halle, Germany   020355

Knausdorf, Christian
Coburg University of Applied Sciences, Coburg, Germany   020361

Ko, Seok-whan
KIER, Daejeon, South Korea   020561

Ko, Suk Whan
KIER, Daejeon, South Korea   020324, 020357

Koc, Timurhan
DTU, Roskilde, Denmark   020376

Koduvelikulathu, Lejo Joseph
ISC Konstanz, Konstanz, Germany   020035, 020068

Koduvelikulathu, Lejo
ISC Konstanz, Konstanz, Germany   020003

Köntges, Marc
ISFH, Emmerthal, Germany   020206

Koepge, Ringo
Fraunhofer CSP, Halle, Germany   020142, 020192

Koester, Lukas
Eurac Research, Bolzano, Italy   020203, 020261, 020325

Kohlenberg, Heike
ISFH, Emmerthal, Germany   020063

Kohno, Tohru
Hitachi, Tokyo, Japan   020186

Kolahi, Mohammad					020356, 020375
University of Isfahan, Isfahan, Iran

Konagai, Makoto					020106, 020115
Tokyo City University, Setagaya, Japan

Kono, Toru						020484
Hitachi, Kokubunji, Japan

Konu, Christopher Bruce				020132
HTW Berlin, Berlin, Germany

Kopecek, Radovan					020569
ISC Konstanz, Konstanz, Germany

Kopp, Nils						020220
TAMURA-ELSOLD, Ilsenburg, Germany

Korkmaz Arslan, Melisa				020020
ODTÜ-GÜNAM, Ankara, Türkiye

Korpås, Magnus					020476
NTNU, Trondheim, Norway

Kortetmäki, Aki					020444, 020445
TUAS, Tampere, Finland

Koskela, Juha					020444, 020445, 020554
Tampere University, Tampere, Finland

Kossen, Eric J.					020030
TNO, Petten, The Netherlands

Kowalski, Julia					020237
RWTH, Aachen, Germany

Kräling, Ulli					020215
Fraunhofer ISE, Freiburg, Germany

Kraft, Thomas M.					020423
VTT Technical Research Centre of Finland, Oulu, Finland

Krainer, Diana Maria				020430
AIT, Vienna, Austria

Krasilnikov, Inga					020379
Tel Aviv University, Tel Aviv, Israel

Krever Lopes, Bruno				020023
PUCRS, Porto Alegre, Brazil

Kribus, Abraham					020379
Tel Aviv University, Tel Aviv, Israel

Krishnan, Sasikumar				020361
Coburg University of Applied Sciences, Coburg, Germany

Kroon, Jan						020225
TNO, Petten, The Netherlands

Kuan, Ta-Ming					020021, 020053
TSEC, Hsinchu, Taiwan

Kubicek, Bernhard					020281, 020318, 020334, 020347, 020430
AIT, Vienna, Austria

Kucuk, E. Busra					020030
TNO, Petten, The Netherlands

Lachowicz, Agata 020039
CSEM, Neuchâtel, Switzerland

Lahr, Simon 020388
Next2Sun Technology, Dillingen, Germany

Lahr, Simon 020411
Next2Sun, Dillingen, Germany

Lajunen, Antti 020400
University of Helsinki, Helsinki, Finland

Lambertz, Andreas 020233
FZJ, Jülich, Germany

Lamblot, Hervé 020302
Sunstyle, Paris, France

Lamghari, Fouad 020402
Fujairah Research Centre, Fujairah, United Arab Emirates

Lamminaho, Jani 020250, 020306
SDU Climate Cluster, Odense, Denmark

Landaas, Christian 020495
Northern Silicon, Meråker, Norway

Landberg, Lars 020448
DNV Denmark, Hellerup, Denmark

Landberg, Lars 020481
DNV Denmark, Hellerup, Spain

Landes, Dieter 020361
Coburg University of Applied Sciences, Coburg, Germany

Landová, Lucie 020107
Czech Technical University, Prague, Czech Republic

Lansade, David 020073
University of Toulouse, Toulouse, France

Lappalainen, Kari 020194, 020528, 020537
Tampere University, Tampere, Finland

Lara, Yolanda 020127, 020414, 020517
ENDEF, Zaragoza, Spain

Larionova, Yevgeniya 020006, 020007, 020225
ISFH, Emmerthal, Germany

Låstad, Jonas 020011
NTNU, Trondheim, Norway

Laurens-Berge, Clarisse 020034
University Grenoble Alpes, Le Bourget-du-Lac, France

Laurikėnas, Paulius 020353
Solitek, Vilnius, Lithuania

Lauwaert, Johan 020064
Ghent University, Ghent, Belgium

Lazaro-Castrillon, Luna 020085
IO-CSIC, Madrid, Spain

Le Bossenec, Hugo 020116
IPVF, Palaiseau, France

Le Brun, Anton   020096
Australian Nuclear Science and Technology Organisation,
Lucas Heights, Australia

Lechón, Yolanda   020502
CIEMAT, Madrid, Spain

Ledesma, Javier R.   020337
UPM, Madrid, Spain

Ledesma, Javier   020446
UPM, Madrid, Spain

Lee, Chun-Wei   020021
TSEC, Hsinchu, Taiwan

Lee, Hyunju   020046
Meiji University, Kanagawa, Japan

Lee, Jieun   020323
K-water, Daejeon, South Korea

Lee, Jin-Seok   020324, 020357, 020561
KIER, Daejeon, South Korea

Legarrea, Aritz   020365
CENER, Sarriguren, Spain

Lelievre, Jean-Francois   020373
INES, Le Bourget-du-Lac, France

Lelong, Benoit   020373
Cythelia Energy, La Motte-Servolex, France

Leloux, Jonathan   020262
LuciSun, Villers-la-Ville, Belgium

Lenain, Philippe   020495
benkei, Lyon, France

Lennon, Alison   020048
UNSW, Sydney, Australia

Lenz, Markus   020226
School of Life Sciences FHNW, Muttenz, Switzerland

Lenzmann, Frank   020019
TNO Energy Transition, Petten, The Netherlands

Leone, Sander   020405
Novar, Rotterdam, The Netherlands

Leonforte, Fabrizio   020249
Polytechnic University of Milan, Milan, Italy

Leopold, Ulrich   020457
Luxembourg Institute of Science and Technology, Esch-sur-
Alzette, Luxembourg

Levrat, Jacques   020251, 020467
CSEM, Neuchâtel, Switzerland

Levtchenko, Alexandra   020116
IPVF, Palaiseau, France

Lewandowski, Simon   020073
University of Toulouse, Toulouse, France

Liu, Huiping GRÄNGES, Finspång, Sweden	020495
Liu, Mengdi TÜV Rheinland, Shanghai, China	020144, 020208
Liu, Yung-Tsung ITRI, Hsinchu, Taiwan	020053, 020083
Livera, Andreas University of Cyprus, Nicosia, Cyprus	020534
Lizin, Sebastien UHasselt, Hasselt, Belgium	020513, 020521
Llarena, María Elena ITER, Granadilla de Abona, Spain	020151
Loeckenhoff, Ruediger F. AZUR SPACE Solar Power, Heilbronn, Germany	020416
Löhning, Martha ISFH, Emmerthal, Germany	020063
Löhr, Johannes ISFH, Emmerthal, Germany	020063, 020114
Lokhat, Ismaël Cythelia Energy, La Motte-Servolex, France	020262
Lokhat, Ismael Trace Software, Saint-Romain-de-Colbosc, France	020373
Lombardo, Salvatore CNR-IMM, Catania, Italy	020066
Long, Yean-San ITRI, Hsinchu, Taiwan	020053, 020083
Longo, Giulia UPV, Valencia, Spain	020099
Lopes Gomes, Carlos Javier Sunveon, Madrid, Spain	020432, 020434
Lopes, Ana Patrícia University of Lisbon, Lisbon, Portugal	020464
López Cuéllar, Juan Manuel UCM, Madrid, Spain	020501
López Dalmau, Daniel Sunveon, Madrid, Spain	020432, 020434
López, Nuria DTU, Roskilde, Denmark	020451
Lorenz, Dieter MBJ Solutions, Ahrensburg, Germany	020206
Lorenzo Pigueiras, Eduardo UPM, Madrid, Spain	020363
Lorenzo, Celena UPM, Madrid, Spain	020337, 020536
Lorenzo, Eduardo UPM, Madrid, Spain	020439, 020446

Lossen, Jan   020003, 020035
ISC Konstanz, Konstanz, Germany

Louwen, Atse   020203, 020226, 020261, 020509, 020546
Eurac Research, Bolzano, Italy

Louwen, Atse   020316
RISE, Boras, Sweden

Lu, Huan-Wu   020161
ITRI, Hsinchu, Taiwan

Lu, Matthew   020230
Kiwa PI Berlin, Shanghai, China

Lucea, Aingeru   020197, 020198
TECNALIA, Derio, Spain

Lüdemann, Marius   020233
Fraunhofer CSP, Halle, Germany

Luís, Margarida   020421
University of Lisbon, Lisbon, Portugal

Lustoza de Souza, Patricia   020092
UFRJ, Rio de Janeiro, Brazil

Ly, Moussa   020023, 020025
PUCRS, Porto Alegre, Brazil

Lyubenova, Teodora   020210
European Commission JRC, Ispra, Italy

M. Bazilio, Willian   020092
PUC-Rio, Rio de Janeiro, Brazil

M. S. Kawabata, Rudy   020090
Pontifical Catholic University of Rio de Janeiro, Rio de
Janeiro, Brazil

M. Torelly, Guilherme   020090
Pontifical Catholic University of Rio de Janeiro, Rio de
Janeiro, Brazil

Ma Lu, Silvia   020381
Mälardalen University, Västerås, Sweden

Ma, Xiang   020011
SINTEF, Oslo, Norway

Macé, Philippe   020225, 020252, 020474, 020505, 020543,
Becquerel Institute, Brussels, Belgium   020558, 020573

Mack, Sebastian   020031
Fraunhofer ISE, Freiburg, Germany

Madsen, Morten   020250, 020306
SDU Climate Cluster, Odense, Denmark

Mahmood, Aysha   020265, 020376
DTU, Roskilde, Denmark

Maixner, Andreas   020121, 020125, 020137, 020223
AESOLAR, Koenigsbrunn, Germany

Maiz, Alexander UPV/EHU, Vitoria-Gasteiz, Spain	020437
Majak, Martyna Roltec, Poznań, Poland	020068
Makrides, George University of Cyprus, Nicosia, Cyprus	020534
Malarkannan, Lavanya National Physical Laboratory, Teddington, United Kingdom	020210
Malcorps, Philippe 3E, Brussels, Belgium	020276
Malik, Stephanie Fraunhofer CSP, Halle, Germany	020313
Malik, Stephanie Fraunhofer IMWS, Halle, Germany	020355
Maliutina, Kristina University of Applied Science Cologne, Cologne, Germany	020141
Malo, Javier UPM, Madrid, Spain	020209
Mancini, Simone TNO, Eindhoven, The Netherlands	020425
Mandiola, Gotzon AZTI, PASAIA, Spain	020514
Manganiello, Patrizio Hasselt University, Diepenbeek, Belgium	020389
Manganiello, Patrizio imec, Genk, Belgium	020294
Manito, Alex University of São Paulo, São Paulo, Brazil	020348
Manochehrian, Rasoul Frankfurt University of Applied Sciences, Frankfurt am Main, Germany	020539
Manzolini, Giampaolo Polytechnic University of Milan, Milan, Italy	020261
Maqsood, Ayman HZB, Berlin, Germany	020101
Marangis, Demetris University of Cyprus, Nicosia, Cyprus	020534
Marcos-Castro, Ana CIEMAT, Madrid, Spain	020297
Marechal, Philippe CEA / INES, Le Bourget-du-Lac, France	020217
Marí Soucase, Bernabé UPV, Valencia, Spain	020099
Markert, Jochen Fraunhofer ISE, Freiburg, Germany	020231
Marquardt, Cornelia ISFH, Emmerthal, Germany	020063

Marteau, Baptiste   020034
ECM Technologies, Grenoble, France

Martín Rueda, Javier   020535
UPM, Madrid, Spain

Martín, Francisco José   020459
UPM, Madrid, Spain

Martín, Francisco   020209
UPM, Madrid, Spain

Martín-Chivelet, Nuria   020297
CIEMAT, Madrid, Spain

Martín-Rueda, Javier   020337, 020363
UPM, Madrid, Spain

Martínez González, Mario   020326
Enertis Applus+, Madrid, Spain

Martinez, Juan Ignacio   020252
Becquerel Institute Spain, San Sebastian, Spain

Martinez, Oscar   020191, 020205
University of Valladolid, Valladolid, Spain

Martínez-Barbeito, María   020243
ieco.io, Vigo, Spain

Maruyama, Rodrigo P.   020154, 020348
University of São Paulo, São Paulo, Brazil

Marzo, Aitor   020311, 020546
University of Granada, Granada, Spain

Mashkov, Oleksandr   020149, 020150, 020377
HI ERN, Erlangen, Germany

Massaro, Lorenzo   020541
PedersoliGattai, Milan, Italy

Masson, Gaëtan   020474, 020558, 020564, 020573
Becquerel Institute, Brussels, Belgium

Masson, Gaëtan   020570
IEA PVPS Task 1, Brussels, Belgium

Mateos, Yeray   020055, 020153
UPV/EHU, Bilbao, Spain

Maturi, Laura   020249, 020254, 020551
Eurac Research, Bolzano, Italy

Mayer-Ullmann, Philipp   020430
AIT, Vienna, Austria

Mazzoleni, Stefano   020378
University of Naples Federico II, Naples, Italy

McIntosh, Keith R.   020396
PV Lighthouse, Coledale, Australia

McNab, Shona   020065
UNSW, Sydney, Australia

Meereboer, Martijn   020225
Energyra, Westknollendam, The Netherlands

Meier, Rico   020132
HTW Berlin, Berlin, Germany

Meixner, Michael   020050
halm elektronik, Frankfurt am Main, Germany

Mekhaldi, Bouchra   020406
Ecole Polytechnique, Palaiseau, France

Melges de Andrade, Adnei   020154
University of São Paulo, São Paulo, Brazil

Melino, Francesco   020314
University of Bologna, Bologna, Italy

Mellone, Celeste   020541
Green Horse Advisory, Rome, Italy

Menard, Lionel   020291
MINES Paris, Nice, France

Mencaraglia, Denis   020058
CNRS, Gif-sur-Yvette, France

Menchaca, Iratxe   020514
AZTI, PASAIA, Spain

Mendes Ferreira Gomes, Amanda   020548
UFSC, Florianopolis, Brazil

Mendikoa, Iñigo   020514
Tecnalia, BRTA, Derio, Spain

Meneghini, Matteo   020089
University of Padova, Padova, Italy

Ménézo, Christophe   020317
LOCIE, Le Bourget-du-Lac, France

Menghini, Mariela   020508
IMDEA Nanoscience Institute, Madrid, Spain

Mercade Ruiz, Pau   020448, 020481
GreenPowerMonitor a DNV company, Barcelona, Spain

Merino, Amanda   020040
CEA / INES, Le Bourget-du-Lac, France

Merino, José Manuel   020085
UAM, Madrid, Spain

Mermoud, André   020196
PVsyst, Geneva, Switzerland

Merodio, Pablo   020337
UPM, Madrid, Spain

Mertens, Jan   020389
imec, Genk, Belgium

Mertens, Verena   020006, 020008
ISFH, Emmerthal, Germany

Meßmer, Marius   020031
Fraunhofer ISE, Freiburg, Germany

Messmer, Tobias   020218, 020221, 020225
ISC Konstanz, Konstanz, Germany

Messner, Christian
AIT, Vienna, Austria

020369

Mettner, Larissa
ISFH, Emmerthal, Germany

020063, 020114

Meusel, Manuel
Fraunhofer CSP, Halle (Saale), Germany

020052

Meyer, Kevin
ISFH, Emmerthal, Germany

020260

Meza, Carlos
Anhalt University of Applied Sciences, Köthen, Germany

020318, 020334, 020426, 020520

Mezzasalma, Frédéric
CEA / INES, Le Bourget-du-Lac, France

020217

Micha, Daniel
CEFET/RJ, Petrópolis, Brazil

020092

Michael, Poland
Nelson Mandela University, Port Elizabeth, South Africa

020193

Miclea, Paul-Tiberiu
Fraunhofer CSP, Halle, Germany

020233

Midtgård, Ole-Morten
NTNU, Trondheim, Norway

020476

Miettunen, Kati
University of Turku, Turku, Finland

020286, 020298, 020398

Migan-Dubois, Anne
CNRS, Gif-sur-Yvette, France

020406

Mignonac, Alexandre
CEA / INES, Le Bourget-du-Lac, France

020217

Mignonac, Alexandre
CEA, Cadarache, France

020334

Mignonac, Alexandre
CEA, Saint-Paul-Lez-Durance, France

020318

Miguel Laborda, María
IaSol, Zaragoza, Spain

020414

Mihailetchi, Valentin Dan
ISC Konstanz, Konstanz, Germany

020033

Mihailetchi, Valentin
ISC Konstanz, Konstanz, Germany

020225

Mihaylov, Blago
European Commission JRC, Ispra, Italy

020210

Milani, Emanuele
Marelli Europe, Venaria Reala, Italy

020495

Milesi, Frédéric
CEA, Grenoble, France

020068

Min, Byungsul
ISFH, Emmerthal, Germany

020008, 020482

Mirandona López, Haritz
Sunveon, Madrid, Spain

020432, 020434

Miró-Llorente, Marta 020094
IREC, Barcelona, Spain

Misra, Prashant 020429
NISE, Gurugram, India

Miszczuk, Andrzej 020068
Roltec, Poznań, Poland

Mittag, Max 020137
Fraunhofer ISE, Freiburg, Germany

Mittal, Ankit 020318
AIT, Vienna, Austria

Mittelman, Gur 020379
Afeka Tel-Aviv Academic College of Engineering, Tel
Aviv, Israel

Mizushima, Io 020028
IPU P/S, Virum, Denmark

Mizushima, Io 020037
IPU, Virum, Denmark

Mngomezulu, Ndumiso 020344
PVinsight, Port Elizabeth, South Africa

Mo, Alvin 020065
UNSW, Sydney, Australia

Mockeviciute-Azzopardi, Austeja 020334
FIR, Birkirkara, Malta

Moe Nygård, Magnus 020340
IFE, Kjeller, Norway

Moehlecke, Adriano 020023, 020025
PUCRS, Porto Alegre, Brazil

Mohammadi, Mohammad Hossein 020037, 020104
Aarhus University, Aarhus, Denmark

Mollier, Stéphane 020262
CEA / INES, Le Bourget-du-Lac, France

Moltke, Asbjørn 020043
Technical University of Denmark, Copenhagen, Denmark

Mondaca-Cuevas, Gino 020422
University of Antofagasta, Antofagasta, Chile

Monokroussos, Christos 020181
TÜV Rheinland Shanghai, Shanghai, China

Monokroussos, Christos 020144, 020208
TÜV Rheinland, Shanghai, China

Monteiro Martins, Filipa 020317
Galp Energia, Lisbon, Portugal

Montes, Carlos 020151
ITER, Granadilla de Abona, Spain

Montoya, Josefa 020311
University of Antofagasta, Antofagasta, Chile

Morabito, Floriana 020066
CNR-IFN, Milan, Italy

Moradi Sizkouhi, Amirmohammad   020356, 020375
Concordia University, Montreal, Canada

Moradi Zavie Kord, Soroush   020400
University of Helsinki, Helsinki, Finland

Morales, Sergio   020491
UPM, Madrid, Spain

Morantes Quintana, Giobertti Raul   020551
Eurac Research, Bolzano, Italy

Mordvinkin, Anton   020233
Fraunhofer CSP, Halle, Germany

Moreda, Guillermo P.   020407
UPM, Madrid, Spain

Morin, Claire   020551
SolarPower Europe, Brussels, Belgium

Morisset, Audrey   020068
CSEM, Neuchâtel, Switzerland

Morlier, Arnaud   020156
Hasselt University, Genk, Belgium

Morlier, Arnaud   020294, 020389
imec, Genk, Belgium

Mortazavifar, Leila   020056, 020158, 020201, 020284
Anhalt University of Applied Sciences, Köthen, Germany

Moruno, Ricardo   020209, 020453
UPM, Madrid, Spain

Mosel, Frank   020015
PVA TePla, Wettenberg, Germany

Moser, David   020573
Becquerel Institute Italy, Trento, Italy

Moser, David   020316
Becquerel Institute, Bolzano, Italy

Moser, David   020254
Bequerel Institute, Trento, Italy

Moser, David   020203, 020226, 020261, 020325, 020485,
Eurac Research, Bolzano, Italy   020489, 020546

Mouhoubi, Felicia   020134
CEA / INES, Le Bourget-du-Lac, France

Müllejans, Harald   020208, 020213
European Commission JRC, Ispra, Italy

Müller, Alexander   020119
Fraunhofer CSP, Halle, Germany

Müller, Larissa   020523
University of Applied Sciences Cologne, Cologne, Germany

Mugica, Maikel   020139
Tecnalia, Donostia - San Sebastián, Spain

Mujovi, Fahradin   020251
CSEM, Neuchâtel, Switzerland

Mukherjee, Srijani   020338
CEA / INES, Le Bourget-du-Lac, France

Mukhtar, Mariyam   020057
University of Verona, Verona, Italy

Mulder, Peter   020067
Radboud University, Nijmegen, The Netherlands

Muller, Matthew   020314
NREL, Denver, United States of America

Munkhammar, Joakim   020532
Uppsala University, Uppsala, Sweden

Muñoz Cerón, Emilio   020269
University of Jaén, Jaén, Spain

Muñoz, Delfina   020040, 020311, 020546
CEA / INES, Le Bourget-du-Lac, France

Muñoz, Delfina   020521
CEA, Le Bourget-du-Lac, France

Muñoz, Delfina   020226
CEA/ INES, Le Bourget-du-Lac, France

Muñoz, Ildefonso   020365, 020366, 020392
CENER, Sarriguren, Spain

Muñoz, Jesús Ángel   020508
UCM, Madrid, Spain

Muñoz-García, Miguel-Ángel   020407
UPM, Madrid, Spain

Murano, Giovanni   020551
ENEA, Ispra, Italy

Murillo, Asier   020497
CENER, Sarriguren, Spain

Musembi, Robinson J.   020272
University of Nairobi, Nairobi, Kenya

Nabipouor, Mohammad   020426
Anhalt University of Applied Sciences, Köthen, Germany

Nagel, Henning   020475
Fraunhofer ISE, Freiburg, Germany

Nakamura, Kyotaro   020046
Toyota Technological Institute, Nagoya, Japan

Nanno, Ikuo   020190
Nanno Energy Research Center, Yamaguchi, Japan

Nargelienė, Viktorija   020157
Center for Physical Sciences and Technology (FTMC),
Vilnius, Lithuania

Narsi Patel, Hitarth   020069
SVNIT, Surat, India

Narvarte, Luis   020337, 020446, 020491, 020535, 020536,
UPM, Madrid, Spain   020567, 020575

Nascimento, Lucas 020377
Solar Energy Research Laboratory Fotovoltaica/ UFSC, Florianópolis, Brazil

Nasebandt, Lasse 020063
ISFH, Emmerthal, Germany

Nasser, Hisham 020226
ODTÜ-GÜNAM, Ankara, Türkiye

Naveiro, José Manuel 020414
ENDEF, Zaragoza, Spain

Nazififard, Mohammad 020259, 020428
Côte d'Azur University, Nice, France

Nejim, Ahmed 020058
SILVACO, St. Ives, United Kingdom

Nel, Paul 020382
7SecondSolar, Cape Town, South Africa

Nelson, Jenny 020394
Imperial College London, London, United Kingdom

Neuba, Adam 020114
Paderborn University, Paderborn, Germany

Neuber, Viola 020031
Fraunhofer ISE, Freiburg, Germany

Neuhaus, Holger 020123, 020140
Fraunhofer ISE, Freiburg, Germany

Neumaier, Lukas 020504
Silicon Austria Labs, Villach, Austria

Neussl, Vassilissa 020318, 020430
AIT, Vienna, Austria

Neykova, Neda 020107
Czech Technical University, Prague, Czech Republic

Nezhad, Mahyar 020230
Kiwa PI Berlin, Hudson, United States of America

Nguyen, Viet Xuan 020008
centrotherm international, Blaubeuren, Germany

Nicolet-dit-Félix, Kléber 020251
EPFL, Neuchâtel, Switzerland

Nicot-Senneville, Zoltan 020102
SERIS, Singapore, Singapore

Nielsen, Michael P. 020065
UNSW, Sydney, Australia

Nissen, Hauke 020313
Wattmanufactur, Galmsbüll, Germany

Nitsche, Tobias 020119, 020218
Henkel, Düsseldorf, Germany

Nobre, André M. 020263
PV Doctor, Singapore, Singapore

Noels, Serge 020472
PV CYCLE, Brussels, Belgium

Noh, Yong-Su   020449
KETI, Wonmi-gu, South Korea

Nold, Sebastian   020461
Fraunhofer ISE, Freiburg, France

Nold, Sebastian   020475
Fraunhofer ISE, Freiburg, Germany

Nordboe, Eirik   020495
Fiven Norge, Lillesand, Norway

Norde Santos, Fernanda   020331
DLR, Almería, Spain

Nouri, Bijan   020235, 020237, 020239
DLR, Almería, Spain

Nova, David   020339
National University of Colombia, Bogotá, Colombia

Núñez, Rubén   020209, 020453
UPM, Madrid, Spain

Núñez-Osorio, Alessia   020100
University of Almeria, Almeria, Spain

Nurmesjärvi, Antti   020423
VTT Technical Research Centre of Finland, Oulu, Finland

Nussbaumer, Hartmut   020385
ZHAW, Winterthur, Switzerland

Nyang'onda, Thomas N.   020272
University of Nairobi, Nairobi, Kenya

Obeidavi, Sahereh   020361
Coburg University of Applied Sciences, Coburg, Germany

Oberbeck, Lars   020461
TotalEnergies OneTech, Paris, France

Oberegger Filippi, Ulrich   020551
Eurac Research, Bolzano, Italy

Ocaña, Luis Manuel   020151
ITER, Granadilla de Abona, Spain

Ockert, Ajka   020312
EnBW, Karlsruhe, Germany

Odilio dos Santos, Daniel   020548
UFSC, Florianopolis, Brazil

Öhgren, Gustav   020532
Becquerel Sweden, Knívsta, Sweden

Öttl, Christian   020347
Watt Analytics, Vienna, Austria

Öz, Aksel Kaan   020135
Fraunhofer ISE, Freiburg, Germany

Özden, Talat   020226
ODTÜ-GÜNAM, Ankara, Türkiye

Özkalay, Ebrar   020160, 020204
SUPSI, Mendrisio, Switzerland

Ogura, Atsushi   020046
Meiji University, Kanagawa, Japan

Ohdaira, Keisuke   020131
JAIST, Ishikawa, Japan

Ohshita, Yoshio   020046
Toyota Technological Institute, Nagoya, Japan

Ojala, Aleksi   020554
Solarigo Systems, Pirkkala, Finland

Okawa, Hayato   020115
Tokyo City University, Setagaya, Japan

Okel, Lars A. G.   020030
TNO, Petten, The Netherlands

Oksanen, Jani   020067
Aalto University, Espoo, Finland

Oliosi, Michele   020196
PVsyst, Geneva, Switzerland

Olivares, Douglas   020311
University of Antofagasta, Antofagasta, Chile

Olivares, Gregorio   020365, 020366, 020392
CENER, Sarriguren, Spain

Oliveira Santos, João Victor   020188
EDF R&D, Moret Loing Orvanne, France

Oliveira, Helena   020420
University of Évora, Évora, Portugal

Oller Westerberg, Amelia   020570
Becquerel Sweden, Knivsta, Sweden

Ollo, Olatz   020139
Tecnalia, Donostia - San Sebastián, Spain

Oozeki, Takashi   020436, 020525
AIST, Koriyama, Japan

Opatovsky, Martin   020241, 020262
Solargis, Bratislava, Slovakia

Oreski, Gernot   020136, 020234, 020325, 020500, 020574
PCCL, Leoben, Austria

Ortega, Eneko   020055, 020153, 020287, 020353
UPV/EHU, Bilbao, Spain

Ortega, Eneko   020289, 020437
UPV/EHU, Leioa, Spain

Ortega, Pascal   020214
University of French Polynesia, Faa'a, French Polynesia

Ortiz-Pena, Aaron   020562
University of Castilla-La Mancha, Albacete, Spain

Ory, Daniel   020188
EDF R&D, Palaiseau, France

Ory, Daniel
EDF, Palaiseau, France
020116

Osman, Alaa
ISFH, Emmerthal, Germany
020006

Osuna, Jose Antonio
MAGTEL, Córdoba, Spain
020358

Osvald, Oliver
Solargis, Bratislava, Slovakia
020274

Otaegi, Aloña
UPV/EHU, Bilbao, Spain
020055, 020097, 020153, 020287

Otnes, Gaute
Institute for Energy Technology, Kjeller, Norway
020169

Otto, Nicolas
HTW, Berlin, Germany
020101

Otto, William
MARIN, Wageningen, The Netherlands
020390

Ou, Chao-Wei
National Chin-Yi University of Technology, Taichung, Taiwan
020350

Ovaitt, Silvana
NREL, Denver, United States of America
020314

Ovaitt, Silvana
NREL, Golden, United States of America
020574

Oviedo Hernandez, Guillermo
BayWa r.e, Rome, Italy
020325

Ozer, Shay
Agricultural Research Organization, Rishon LeZion, Israel
020379

P. Pires, Maurício
Federal University of Rio de Janeiro, Rio de Janeiro, Brazil
020090

Pabiou, Herve
CETHIL, Villeurbanne, France
020338

Pabst, Elena
ZSW, Stuttgart, Germany
020312

Paiva, Lúcio
Casa dos Ventos, Fortaleza, Brazil
020530

Palais, Olivier
Toulon University, Marseille, France
020188

Palitzsch, Wolfram
LuxChemTech, Freiberg, Germany
020225, 020495

Palomino, Laura
UPM, Madrid, Spain
020491, 020535

Pamir Aly, Shahzada
DEWA, Dubai, United Arab Emirates
020229

Pamula, Bindu
SVNIT, Surat, India
020069

Panda, Pavan Kumar   020284
Anhalt University of Applied Sciences, Köthen, Germany

Pandar, Matthias   020229
Fraunhofer CSP, Halle, Germany

Pander, Matthias   020121, 020142, 020175, 020192, 020218,
Fraunhofer CSP, Halle, Germany   020223, 020232

Panduri, Fabio   020322
BFH, Burgdorf, Switzerland

Pantoja, Jaime   020526
Francisco José de Caldas District University, Bogota,
Colombia

Papantoni, Veatriki   020482
DLR, Oldenburg, Germany

Paraficz, Danuta   020204
FFHS, Zurich, Switzerland

Paraskeva, Vasiliki   020064
University of Cyprus, Nicosia, Cyprus

Pardo, Eduardo   020414
Tecnova, Almeira, Spain

Parfeniukas, Karolis   020039
ATLANT 3D, Taastrup, Denmark

Parion, Jonathan   020064
Hasselt Unversity, Genk, Belgium

Park, Hyeonwook   020112
KENTECH, Naju-Si, South Korea

Parmar, Richa   020429
NISE, Gurugram, India

Parra, Johan   020406
Ecole Polytechnique, Palaiseau, France

Parra, Johan   020214
Polytechnic Institute of Paris, Palaiseau, France

Parrilla, Carlos G.   020402
Fujairah Research Centre, Fujairah, United Arab Emirates

Pascual Gallego, Valero   020407
UPM, Madrid, Spain

Pasquier, Mathis   020451
DTU, Roskilde, Denmark

Passaro, Marcello   020513
Sunzest Solar, Rotterdam, The Netherlands

Patel, Dharm   020355
Fraunhofer IMWS, Halle, Germany

Paul, Ananta   020250, 020306
SDU Climate Cluster, Odense, Denmark

Paulescu, Marius   020283
West University of Timisoara, Timisoara, Romania

Paviet-Salomon, Bertrand CSEM, Neuchâtel, Switzerland	020068, 020467
Payno, David UAM, Madrid, Spain	020085, 020094
Pearce, Pheobe UNSW, Sydney, Australia	020065
Peche, René bifa Umweltinstitut, Augsburg, Germany	020468, 020495
Pehlivanli, Ezgi METU, Ankara, Türkiye	020521
Peibst, Robby ISFH, Emmerthal, Germany	020006, 020063, 020114
Pelfort Ojer, Marta Solargis, Bratislava, Slovakia	020241
Pelland, Sophie Natural Resources Canada, Varennes, Canada	020211
Pelle, Martina Eurac Research, Bolzano, Italy	020249, 020254
Peña-Bermudez, Julian University of the Caribbean, Santo Domingo, Dominican Republic	020110
Peng, Cheng-Yu National Chin-Yi University of Technology, Taichung, Taiwan	020350
Pera, David Luxembourg Institute of Science and Technology, Esch-sur-Alzette, Luxembourg	020457
Perani, Martina FFHS, Zurich, Switzerland	020204
Peraticos, Elias University of Cyprus, Nicosia, Cyprus	020064
Pereda, Ainhoa TECNALIA, Derio, Spain	020198, 020358
Pereira Fialho, Luis Andre Eurac Research, Bolzano, Italy	020509
Pereira, Sara University of Évora, Évora, Portugal	020403, 020418, 020565
Pérez García, Manuel University of Almería, La Cañada de San Urbano, Spain	020336
Pérez, Ernesto National University of Colombia, Bogotá, Colombia	020339
Pérez, Jairo Gonvarri AgroTech, Corvera - Asturias, Spain	020412
Pérez, Jorge Gonvarri AgroTech, Corvera - Asturias, Spain	020412
Pérez, Luis Gonvarri MS R&D, Corvera - Asturias, Spain	020412

Perez, Richard University at Albany, Albany, United States of America	020494
Perez-Astudillo, Daniel QEERI, Doha, Qatar	020275, 020278, 020291
Pérez-García, Manuel University of Almeria, Almería, Spain	020100
Pérez-Rodríguez, Alejandro IREC, Barcelona, Spain	020085, 020094
Pernas, Tomás Gonvarri AgroTech, Corvera - Asturias, Spain	020412
Pernau, Thomas centrotherm international, Blaubeuren, Germany	020008
Perrin, Marion Energy Pool, Le Bourget-du-Lac, France	020544
Pervan, Nikolina PCCL, Leoben, Austria	020136, 020234
Peter Amalathas, Amalraj University of Jaffna, Jaffna, Sri Lanka	020107
Peter, Kristian ISC Konstanz, Konstanz, Germany	020569
Peters, Ian Marius Forschungszentrum Jülich, Erlangen, Germany	020230, 020263
Peters, Ian Marius HI ERN, Erlangen, Germany	020149, 020150, 020377, 020574
Petersons, Karlis Stensborg, Roskilde, Denmark	020250, 020306
Petkovski, Emil DNV, Arnhem, The Netherlands	020571
Petzschmann, Jonas ZSW, Stuttgart, Germany	020312
Pfau, Jan Hendrik Leibniz University Hannover, Hannover, Germany	020240
Pfeiffer, Oliver University of Applied Science Cologne, Cologne, Germany	020141
Pfeiffer, Oliver University of Applied Sciences Cologne, Cologne, Germany	020140
Philipp, Daniel Fraunhofer ISE, Freiburg, Germany	020215, 020231
Pierro, Marco Eurac Research, Bolzano, Italy	020489, 020494
Pieters, Bart E. FZJ, Jülich, Germany	020180
Pieterse, Marco Chemconserve, Bussum, The Netherlands	020495
Pietralunga, Silvia Maria CNR-IFN, Milan, Italy	020066

Pietsch, Veith   020331
Aquila Capital, Hamburg, Germany

Pilat, Eric   020311
CEA / INES, Le Bourget-du-Lac, France

Pilat, Eric   020317
CEA INES, Le Bourget-du-Lac, France

Pillai, Akhildev   020558
Becquerel Institute, Brussels, Belgium

Pinheiro, Philippe   020457
Luxembourg Institute of Science and Technology, Esch-sur-
Alzette, Luxembourg

Pinho Almeida, Marcelo   020348
University of São Paulo, São Paulo, Brazil

Pinto, Cristina Leyre   020497
CENER, Sarriguren, Spain

Pinto, Luciana   020092
UFRJ, Rio de Janeiro, Brazil

Pitaval, Sébastien   020244
SOLAÏS, Valbonne, France

Pitz-Paal, Robert   020237, 020331
DLR, Cologne, Germany

Plakhotnyuk, Maksym   020039
ATLANT 3D, Taastrup, Denmark

Platero Gaona, Carlos A.   020332
UPM, Madrid, Spain

Plaza, Caroline   020543, 020564, 020573
Becquerel Institute France, Lyon, France

Polacchi, Cristina   020509, 020513
Eurac Research, Bolzano, Italy

Polo, Jaime   020300
CENER, Sarriguren, Spain

Polo, Jesús   020297
CIEMAT, Madrid, Spain

Polverini, Davide   020181
Directorate General for Internal Market, Industry,
Entrepreneurship and SMEs, Brussels, Belgium

Polverini, Davide   020497
European Comission, Brussels, Belgium

Pongthanacharoenkul, Nattapark   020230
Kiwa PI Berlin, Berlin, Germany

Poortmans, Jef   020064
Hasselt Unversity, Genk, Belgium

Popescu, Lacramioara   020068
ISC Konstanz, Konstanz, Germany

Pospischil, Maximilian   020225
Highline Technologies, Freiburg, Germany

Poulsen, Peter B.   020039
DTU, Copenhagen, Denmark

Poulsen, Peter B.   020250, 020265, 020267, 020376, 020451
DTU, Roskilde, Denmark

Poulsen, Peter Behrensdorff   020028, 020306, 020346
DTU, Roskilde, Denmark

Pourshafi, Pouya   020121, 020125, 020137
AESOLAR, Koenigsbrunn, Germany

Pozza, Cristian   020551
Eurac Research, Bolzano, Italy

Prakash, Jai   020429
NISE, Gurugram, India

Prando, Davide   020485, 020489
Edyna, Bolzano, Italy

Prasad, Manjunath   020225
ISC Konstanz, Konstanz, Germany

Pravettoni, Mauro   020402
Technology Innovation Institute, Abu Dhabi, United Arab
Emirates

Preis, Pirmin   020003
ISC Konstanz, Konstanz, Germany

Preu, Ralf   020475
Fraunhofer ISE, Freiburg, Germany

Preuschoff, Jonas   020101
HTW, Berlin, Germany

Protti, Alexander Aguilar   020140
Fraunhofer ISE, Freiburg, Germany

Protti, Alexander   020137
Fraunhofer ISE, Freiburg, Germany

Provost, Marion   020116
IPVF, Palaiseau, France

Puel, Jean Baptiste   020062
IPVF, Palaiseau, France

Puertas López, Antonio Manuel   020100
University of Almeria, Almeria, Spain

Puttock, Claire   020367
Nextracker, Fremont, United States of America

Queste, Samuel   020068
Marie and Louis Pasteur University, Besançon, France

Quiroz, Mónica   020328
Qualifying Photovoltaics, Madrid, Spain

R. Ledesma, Javier   020363
UPM, Madrid, Spain

Rabanal Arabach, Jorge   020183
University of Antofagasta, Antofagasta, Chile

Rabanal-Arabach, Jorge   020129, 020342, 020417, 020422
University of Antofagasta, Antofagasta, Chile

Rabiei, Hossein   020063
ISFH, Emmerthal, Germany

Rachdi, Lazhar   020035, 020068
ISC Konstanz, Konstanz, Germany

Radzevicius, Aurimas   020225
Valoe Cells, Vilnius, Lithuania

Rafiee, Hossein   020539
Frankfurt University of Applied Sciences, Frankfurt am
Main, Germany

Raginskis, Justinas   020380
Kaunas University of Technology, Kaunas, Lithuania

Raievska, Oleksandra   020117, 020149
HI ERN, Erlangen, Germany

Rajan, S. Prithivi   020262
LuciSun, Villers-la-Ville, Belgium

Rajkiewicz, Katarzyna   020551
NAPE, Warsaw, Poland

Rakotoniaina, Jean Patrice   020311
CEA / INES, Le Bourget-du-Lac, France

Ramachandran Nair, Jishnu   020233
Fraunhofer CSP, Halle, Germany

Ramesh, Santhosh   020389
imec, Genk, Belgium

Ramírez Ledesma, Javier   020535
UPM, Madrid, Spain

Ramirez, S.   020396
PV Lighthouse, Coledale, Australia

Rampino, Stefano   020087
National Research Council, Parma, Italy

Ramspeck, Klaus   020050
halm elektronik, Frankfurt am Main, Germany

Ranisch, Tadeus   020101
HTW, Berlin, Germany

Ranta, Samuli   020286, 020400
TUAS, Turku, Finland

Ranta, Samuli   020298, 020398
Turku University of Applied Sciences, Turku, Finland

Raposo, Mauro   020565
University of Évora, Évora, Portugal

Ratnagiri, Abhinav   020367
Nextracker, Fremont, United States of America

Raugewitz, Annika   020063, 020114
ISFH, Emmerthal, Germany

Riaño, Sandra						020197, 020358
TECNALIA, Derio, Spain

Richards, Bryce S.						020272
KIT, Karlsruhe, Germany

Riechelman, Stefan						020181
PTB, Braunschweig, Germany

Riechelmann, Stefan						020177, 020199, 020211
PTB, Braunschweig, Germany

Riedel-Lyngskær, Nicholas					020451
DTU, Roskilde, Denmark

Rienäcker, Michael						020063
ISFH, Emmerthal, Germany

Rindert, Sören						020230
Kiwa PI Berlin, Berlin, Germany

Ríos Moral, Lucia						020501
UCM, Madrid, Spain

Ríos-Ledesma, Felipe						020446
UPM, Madrid, Spain

Ripke, Melanie						020006
ISFH, Emmerthal, Germany

Riva, Roland							020495
CEA, Le Bourget-du-Lac, France

Rivas Rodríguez, José Manuel					020326
Enertis Applus+, Madrid, Spain

Robledo, Jesús						020262
LuciSun, Villers-la-Ville, Belgium

Rodríguez Lucas, Delia						020407
EkiLabs, Boston, United States of America

Rodríguez Plaza, José Luis					020508
Autonomous University of Madrid, Madrid, Spain

Rodríguez Rodríguez, Araceli					020501
UCM, Madrid, Spain

Rodríguez Salazar, David Leonardo				020441
District University of Bogotá, Bogotá, Colombia

Rodríguez, Araceli						020508
UCM, Madrid, Spain

Rodríguez, Diego Julián					020526
Francisco José de Caldas District University, Bogota,
Colombia

Rodríguez, Isabel						020257
IMDEA Nanoscience, Madrid, Spain

Rodriguez, Sonia Maria						020289
UPV/EHU, Leioa, Spain

Rodríguez, Velia						020097
UPV/EHU, Bilbao, Spain

Rodríguez-Conde, Sofía						020326
Enertis Applus+, Madrid, Spain

Rudzikas, Matas   020380
The Applied Research Institute for Prospective
Technologies, Vilnius, Lithuania

Rüther, Ricardo   020377
Solar Energy Research Laboratory Fotovoltaica/ UFSC,
Florianópolis, Brazil

Rüther, Ricardo   020548
UFSC, Florianopolis, Brazil

Ruf, Manuel   020455
Robert Bosch, Stuttgart, Germany

Ruiz Donoso, Elena   020331
DLR, Almería, Spain

S. Sousa, Graciana   020090
Federal University of Rio de Janeiro, Rio de Janeiro, Brazil

Safarian, Jafar   020011
NTNU, Trondheim, Norway

Sah, Dheeraj   020039
Aarhus University, Aarhus, Denmark

Sahin, Hasret   020479
LUT University, Lappeenranta, Finland

Saito, Kimihiko   020106
Tokyo City University, Setagaya, Japan

Salem, Mohammad   020428
Australian University, Kuwait City, Kuwait

Salerno, Giorgia   020077
University of Milano-Bicocca, Milan, Italy

Salis, Fabio   020541
Iberdrola, Rome, Italy

Salvador, Antonio   020358
MAGTEL, Córdoba, Spain

Sample, Tony   020213
European Commission JRC, Ispra, Italy

Samuolienė, Giedrė   020380
The Lithuanian Research Centre for Agriculture and
Forestry, Kaunas, Lithuania

San José, Luis Javier   020209, 020453
UPM, Madrid, Spain

Sánchez de León Peque, Miguel   020243
ieco.io, Vigo, Spain

Sanchez Garcia, Alfredo   020270
SINTEF, Trondheim, Norway

Sanchez, Hugo   020056, 020158, 020284
Anhalt University of Applied Sciences, Köthen, Germany

Sanchez, Jesus   020437
UPV/EHU, Vitoria-Gasteiz, Spain

Sanchez, Laura   020437
UPV/EHU, Leioa, Spain

Sánchez, Yudania   020085
IREC, Barcelona, Spain

Sanchez-Friera, Paula   020412, 020513, 020521
Solkeys, Gijón, Spain

Sanchez-Ruiz, Alain   020437
UPV/EHU, Vitoria-Gasteiz, Spain

Sansavini, Giovanni   020296
ETH, Zurich, Switzerland

Sansoni, Paola   020066
CNR-INO, Florence, Italy

Santamaría Fernández, Susanna   020249
TECNALIA, Derio, Spain

Santamaría-Sancho, Juan   020363
UPM, Madrid, Spain

Santos, Jose Domingo   020197, 020198, 020358
TECNALIA, Derio, Spain

Santos, Rodrigo   020530
Casa dos Ventos, Fortaleza, Brazil

Sanz Martinez, Asier   020546
Tecnalia, Bilbao, Spain

Sanz, Asier   020514
Tecnalia, BRTA, Derio, Spain

Sanz, Asier   020197
TECNALIA, Derio, Spain

Sanz-Cuadrado, Cristina   020575
UPM, Madrid, Spain

Sanz-Saiz, Carlos   020297
CIEMAT, Madrid, Spain

Sarafijanovic-Djukic, Natasa   020204
FFHS, Regensdorf, Switzerland

Saretti, Angelica   020301
Polytechnic University of Bari, Bari, Italy

Sarkadi, Monika   020569
ISC Konstanz, Konstanz, Germany

Sauer, Thomas   020140
EXXERGY, Gräfelfing, Germany

Saura, Juan Antonio   020506
University of Murcia, Murcia, Spain

Savisalo, Tuukka   020225
Valoe, Mikkeli, Finland

Saw, Min Hsian   020402
Technology Innovation Institute, Abu Dhabi, United Arab
Emirates

Saxena, Anmol Ratan   020429
NIT, Delhi, India

Sayed, Abdullah Abu   020180, 020230
Kiwa PI Berlin, Berlin, Germany

Scaltrito, Luciano   020079
Polytechnic University of Turin, Turin, Italy

Scerri, Kenneth   020334
University of Malta, Msida, Malta

Schading, Steve   020443
University of Agder, Grimstad, Norway

Schäfer, Aysim   020388
Next2Sun Technology, Dillingen, Germany

Schäfer, Sebastian   020539
Frankfurt University of Applied Sciences, Frankfurt am
Main, Germany

Schenk, Paul   020192
Fraunhofer CSP, Halle, Germany

Schermer, John   020067
Radboud University, Nijmegen, The Netherlands

Scherret, Jacqueline   020255
A-Null Development, Vienna, Austria

Schifferegger, Raffael   020162
OFI, Vienna, Austria

Schimanke, Sabrina   020006
ISFH, Emmerthal, Germany

Schirmer, Yoko   020101
HTW, Berlin, Germany

Schläger, Christian   020240
Leibniz University Hannover, Hannover, Germany

Schlatmann, Rutger   020101
HTW, Berlin, Germany

Schmidt Davidsen, Rasmus   020037, 020104
Aarhus University, Aarhus, Denmark

Schnaus, Dominik   020237
TUM, Garching, Germany

Schneider, Andreas   020129, 020183
University of Applied Sciences Gelsenkirchen,
Gelsenkirchen, Germany

Schneider, Astrid   020255
TU Wien, Vienna, Austria

Schneider, Friedrich   020482
LPKF SolarQuipment, Suhl, Germany

Schneider, Marc Gabriel   020522
University of Applied Science Cologne, Cologne, Germany

Schneiderlöchner, Eric   020033
VON ARDENNE, Dresden, Germany

Schnierer, Branislav   020262
Solargis, Bratislava, Slovakia

Schönau, Maximilian   020361
Coburg University of Applied Sciences, Coburg, Germany

Schönau, Maximilian   020544
smartblue, Munich, Germany

Schönheits, Markus   020468, 020470
bifa Umweltinstitut, Augsburg, Germany

Schranz, Christian   020255
TU Wien, Vienna, Austria

Schrempf, Michael   020199
PTB, Braunschweig, Germany

Schrijvers, Patrick   020390
MARIN, Wageningen, The Netherlands

Schröter, Nick   020142
Fraunhofer CSP, Halle, Germany

Schubert, Martin C.   020475
Fraunhofer ISE, Freiburg, Germany

Schubnel, Baptiste   020238
CSEM, Neuchâtel, Switzerland

Schüler, Marc Andre   020388
Next2Sun Technology, Dillingen, Germany

Schüler, Marc Andre   020411
Next2Sun, Dillingen, Germany

Schueler, Nadine   020015
Freiberger Instruments, Freiberg, Germany

Schulte-Huxel, Henning   020008, 020260
ISFH, Emmerthal, Germany

Schultz, Christof   020101
HTW, Berlin, Germany

Schulz, Philip   020060
IPVF, Palaiseau, France

Schulze, Achim   020361
Rosenheim Technical University of Applied Sciences,
Rosenheim, Germany

Schulze, Patricia S.C.   020475
Fraunhofer ISE, Freiburg, Germany

Schwenke, Almut   020495
SGL Battery Solutions, Meitingen, Germany

Sciuto, Marcello   020010
Enel Green Power, Catania, Italy

Scognamiglio, Alessandra   020541
ENEA, Naples, Italy

Scognamiglio, Alessandra   020378
ENEA, Portici, Italy

Sedaghat, Ahmad   020428
Australian University, Kuwait City, Kuwait

Seiffert, Christoph   020169
Institute for Energy Technology, Kjeller, Norway

Seiffert, Daniela   020008
centrotherm international, Blaubeuren, Germany

Seitz, Matthias   020468
bifa Umweltinstitut, Augsburg, Germany

Selj, Josefine H.   020169
Institute for Energy Technology, Kjeller, Norway

Senno, Maximiliano Alejandro   020226
University of Valencia, Paterna, Spain

Senturk, Bilge   020556
ODTU GUNAM, Ankara, Türkiye

Setien, Eneko   020198
TECNALIA, Derio, Spain

Šetkus, Arūnas   020157
Center for Physical Sciences and Technology (FTMC),
Vilnius, Lithuania

Shaaban, Ahmed   020402
Technology Innovation Institute, Abu Dhabi, United Arab
Emirates

Shah, Syed Fawad Ali   020112
KENTECH, Naju-Si, South Korea

Shanmugam, Raphael   020218, 020220
ISC Konstanz, Konstanz, Germany

Sharma, Rajesh Kumar   020071, 020081
SVNIT, Surat, India

Sharma, Sushma   020563
SRM University, Sonipat, India

Shen, Xinyi   020226
University of Oxford, Oxford, United Kingdom

Shen, Zhenjue   020001
YIST, Jiangyin, China

Shin, Donghyeop   020112
KIER, Daejeon, South Korea

Shin, Woo Gyun   020324, 020357
KIER, Daejeon, South Korea

Shin, Woo-gyun   020561
KIER, Daejeon, South Korea

Shirai, Yasuhiro   020115
NIMS, Tsukuba, Japan

Shirazi, Elham   020544
University of Twente, Enschede, The Netherlands

Shishavan, Amir Asgharzadeh   020367
Nextracker, Fremont, United States of America

Shishido, Hirotaka   020106
Tokyo City University, Setagaya, Japan

Shochet, Ofer   020225
Copprint, Jerusalem, Israel

Shyong, Yung-Jen 020163
ITRI, Hsinchu, Taiwan

Sicot, Lionel 020217
CEA / INES, Le Bourget-du-Lac, France

Sidler, Anika 020226
School of Life Sciences FHNW, Muttenz, Switzerland

Siebert, Michael 020206
ISFH, Emmerthal, Germany

Siefer, Gerald 020246
Fraunhofer ISE, Freiburg, Germany

Sierra, Daniel 020491
UPM, Madrid, Spain

Sigounis, Anna-Maria 020248, 020249
Concordia University, Montreal, Canada

Søiland, Anne-Karin 020495
ReSiTec, Kristiansand, Norway

Silva, José A. 020304, 020409, 020420
University of Évora, Évora, Portugal

Silva, José 020403
University of Évora, Évora, Portugal

Silvestre, Santiago 020301
UPC, Barcelona, Spain

Simeunovic, Jelena 020238
CSEM, Neuchâtel, Switzerland

Simón-Allué, Raquel 020127, 020414, 020517
ENDEF, Zaragoza, Spain

Singh, Ravi 020571
DNV, Arnhem, The Netherlands

Sinha, Amish Kumar 020463
RCT Solutions, Konstanz, Germany

Sinopoli, Alessandro 020042
QEERI, Doha, Qatar

Sivaramakrishnan Radhakrishnan, Hariharsudan 020064
Hasselt Unversity, Genk, Belgium

Sivaramakrishnan, Hariharsudan 020225
IMEC, Genk, Belgium

Snaith, Henry 020226
University of Oxford, Oxford, United Kingdom

Søndenå, Rune 020503
Institute for Energy Technology, Kjeller, Norway

Sobajima, Yasushi 020131
Gifu University, Gifu, Japan

Soler Toledo, Denet 020509
University of Antofagasta, Antofagasta, Chile

Solomon, Asfaw A. 020479
LUT University, Lappeenranta, Finland

Solórzano, Jorge	020328
Qualifying Photovoltaics, Madrid, Spain

Sondoqah, Mousa	020316
Becquerel Institute, Bolzano, Italy

Sondoqah, Mousa	020261
Eurac Research, Bolzano, Italy

Song, Hee-eun	020045
KIER, Daejeon, South Korea

Spagnolo, Sofia	020462, 020466
RSE, Milan, Italy

Spataru, Sergiu V.	020265, 020267, 020283, 020376, 020451
DTU, Roskilde, Denmark

Spataru, Sergiu Viorel	020346
DTU, Roskilde, Denmark

Spera, Fabian	020411
Next2Sun, Dillingen, Germany

Spihola, Jan	020355
DiSUN Deutsche Solarservice, Werder, Germany

Sraisth,	020005, 020222
RCT Solutions, Konstanz, Germany

Sraisth, Sraisth	020463
RCT Solutions, Konstanz, Germany

Staňková, Tereza	020107
Czech Technical University, Prague, Czech Republic

Steckenreiter, Verena	020063
ISFH, Emmerthal, Germany

Stegemann, Bert	020309
Berlin University of Applied Sciences, Berlin, Germany

Stegemann, Bert	020101
HTW, Berlin, Germany

Stellbogen, Dirk	020312
ZSW, Stuttgart, Germany

Stensborg, Jan F.	020250
Stensborg, Roskilde, Denmark

Stensborg, Jan	020306
Stensborg, Roskilde, Denmark

Stieldorf, Karin	020255
TU Wien, Vienna, Austria

Stierstorfer, Johannes	020225
WIP - Renewable Energies, Munich, Germany

Stierstorfer, Johannes	020551
WIP Renewable Energies, Munich, Germany

Stivanello, Juan José	020226
Eurac Research, Bolzano, Italy

Stoicescu, Liviu	020198
Solarzentrum Stuttgart, Stuttgart, Germany

Stowhas-Villa, Alejandro020422
Federico Santa María Technical University, Valparaiso, Chile

Stoyanova Lyubenova, Teodora020173
European Commission JRC, Ispra, Italy

Sträter, Hendrik020211
PTB, Braunschweig, Germany

Strey, Jessica020063, 020114
ISFH, Emmerthal, Germany

Strömberg, Rich020472
University of Alaska, Fairbanks, United States of America

Stroyuk, Oleksander020185
HI ERN, Erlangen, Germany

Stroyuk, Oleksandr020117, 020149, 020150
HI ERN, Erlangen, Germany

Suárez Sánchez, Sergio020326
Enertis Applus+, Madrid, Spain

Subasi, Dilara Maria020475
Fraunhofer ISE, Freiburg, Germany

Sudbury, Ben A.020396
PV Lighthouse, Coledale, Australia

Suemitsu, Issei020484
Hitachi, Kokubunji, Japan

Suhonen, Riikka020423
VTT Technical Research Centre of Finland, Oulu, Finland

Sulca, Kabir Paúl020191, 020205
University of Valladolid, Valladolid, Spain

Svatos, Jan020250
DTU, Roskilde, Denmark

Sylla, David020063
ISFH, Emmerthal, Germany

Syre Wiig, Marie020340
IFE, Kjeller, Norway

Szarek, Magda020298, 020398
University of Turku, Turku, Finland

Taghipour Kani, Ghaem020335, 020374
Amirkabir University of Technology, Tehran, Iran

Takahashi, Kanji020106
Tokyo City University, Setagaya, Japan

Talvi, Micke020528
Tampere University, Tampere, Finland

Tanahashi, Tadanori020436
AIST, Koriyama, Japan

Tang, Kai020011
SINTEF, Trondheim, Norway

Torelly, Guilherme	020092
PUC-Rio, Rio de Janeiro, Brazil

Torre, Gorka	020437
UPV/EHU, Leioa, Spain

Torres Aguilar, Moira Itzel	020214
CentraleSupélec, Gif-sur-Yvette, France

Torres Aguilar, Moira Itzel	020406
CNRS, Gif-sur-Yvette, France

Torres Silva, Nicole	020546
ATAMOSTEC, Santiago, Chile

Torres, Oscar	020110
National University of Colombia, Bogotá, Colombia

Tosi, Irene	020037
IPU, Virum, Denmark

Tran Caliste, Thu Nhi	020546
European Synchrotron Radiation Facility (ESRF), Grenoble,
France

Treberspurg, Christoph	020255
Treberspurg und Partner Ziviltechniker, Vienna, Austria

Treberspurg, Martin	020255
Treberspurg und Partner Ziviltechniker, Vienna, Austria

Trefzer, Aaron	020135
Fraunhofer ISE, Freiburg, Germany

Trifiletti, Vanira	020087
University of Milano-Bicocca, Milan, Italy

Trigo-Gonzalez, Mauricio	020342, 020422
University of Antofagasta, Antofagasta, Chile

Tsai, Min-An	020053, 020083, 020161, 020163
ITRI, Hsinchu, Taiwan

Tsanakas, Ioannis (John) A.	020262
CEA / INES, Le Bourget-du-Lac, France

Tsanakas, Ioannis (John) A.	020544
CEA, Le Bourget-du-Lac, France

Tsanakas, Ioannis (John)	020546
CEA / INES, Le Bourget-du-Lac, France

Tsanakas, Ioannis (John)	020317
CEA INES, Le Bourget-du-Lac, France

Tsanakas, Ioannis (John)	020513, 020521
CEA, Le Bourget-du-Lac, France

Tsanakas, Ioannis	020217, 020338
CEA / INES, Le Bourget-du-Lac, France

Tsanakas, Ioannis	020500
CEA, Le Bourget-du-Lac, France

Tsanakas, John A.	020311
CEA / INES, Le Bourget-du-Lac, France

Tseberlidis, Giorgio	020093
University of Milano Bicocca, Milan, Italy

Tseberlidis, Giorgio   020087
University of Milano-Bicocca, Milan, Italy

Tsoi, Konstantin   020113
ODTÜ-GÜNAM, Ankara, Türkiye

Tsombou, Francois M.   020402
Fujairah Research Centre, Fujairah, United Arab Emirates

Tsuno, Yuki   020436
AIST, Koriyama, Japan

Tsunoda, Jun   020484
Hitachi, Kokubunji, Japan

Tsunoda, Jun   020186
Hitachi, Tokyo, Japan

Tulinski, Lona   020385
ZHAW, Winterthur, Switzerland

Tune, Daniel   020220, 020221, 020225
ISC Konstanz, Konstanz, Germany

Turcu, Mircea   020063
ISFH, Emmerthal, Germany

Turek, Marko   020004, 020052
Fraunhofer CSP, Halle (Saale), Germany

Ueda, Yuzuru   020320, 020525
Tokyo University of Science, Tokyo, Japan

Ujvari, Gusztav   020318, 020430
AIT, Vienna, Austria

Ulbikaitė, Vaidvilė   020157
Applied Research Institute for Prospective Technologies,
Vilnius, Lithuania

Ulbikas, Juras   020225
Protechnology, Vilnius, Lithuania

Ulyashin, Alexander G.   020011
SINTEF, Oslo, Norway

Unsur, Veysel   020020
ODTÜ-GÜNAM, Ankara, Türkiye

Urban, Harald   020255
TU Wien, Vienna, Austria

Useni, Yannick   020393
University of Lubumbashi, Lubumbashi, Congo (DRC)

Uzuner, Bahri Eren   020113
ODTÜ-GÜNAM, Ankara, Türkiye

Väisänen, Kaisa-Leena   020423
VTT Technical Research Centre of Finland, Oulu, Finland

Vaicikauskas, Viktoras   020157
Center for Physical Sciences and Technology (FTMC),
Vilnius, Lithuania

Valaski, Rogério   020090
National Institute of Metrology Quality and Technology,
Rio de Janeiro, Brazil

Valencia, Felipe   020342, 020546
AtamosTec, Santiago, Chile

Vallerotto, Guido   020209, 020246, 020257
UPM, Madrid, Spain

van Aken, Bas B.   020405
TNO, Petten, The Netherlands

van der Heide, Arvid   020472
imec, Genk, Belgium

van der Zee, Friso F.   020405
Wageningen University and Research, Wageningen, The
Netherlands

Van Dyck, Rik   020225
IMEC, Genk, Belgium

van Dyk, E. Ernest   020193, 020416
Nelson Mandela University, Port Elizabeth, South Africa

van Dyk, Ernest E.   020344
Nelson Mandela University, Port Elizabeth, South Africa

Van Overstraeten, Julien   020543
Becquerel Institute France, Lyon, France

Van Overstraeten, Julien   020252
Becquerel Institute, Brussels, Belgium

vanBaal, Rene   020492
Belectric, Kolitzheim, Germany

Vanhanen, Tuomas   020225
Valoe, Mikkeli, Finland

Vargas, Renzo   020348
University of São Paulo, São Paulo, Brazil

Varney, Valérie   020522
University of Applied Science Cologne, Cologne, Germany

Varney, Valérie   020523
University of Applied Sciences Cologne, Cologne, Germany

vas Dyk, Ernest   020185
Nelson Mandela University, Port Elizabeth, South Africa

Vasconcelos, Letícia   020530
Casa dos Ventos, Fortaleza, Brazil

Vavilkin, Tatjana   020302
Soltech, Genk, Belgium

Vázquez Adán, Alejandra   020501
UCM, Madrid, Spain

Vázquez, A.   020508
UCM, Madrid, Spain

Veas, Christian   020136, 020234
PCCL, Leoben, Austria

Vecino, Fernando Román   020346
DTU, Roskilde, Denmark

Veerman, Sebastian   020035
ISC Konstanz, Konstanz, Germany

Vega de Seoane, José Maria   020252
Becquerel Institute Spain, San Sebastian, Spain

Vega de Seoane, Jose   020546
Becquerel Institute, Brussels, Belgium

Vega-Herrera, Jorge   020342
University of Antofagasta, Antofagasta, Chile

Vehus, Tore Sandnes   020443
University of Agder, Grimstad, Norway

Veirman, Jordi   020203, 020226, 020254
Eurac Research, Bolzano, Italy

Velasco, Angel   020367
Nextracker, Fremont, United States of America

Veludo, Jorge   020317
Galp Energia, Lisbon, Portugal

Veneri, Alessandro   020093
University of Verona, Verona, Italy

Vergura, Silvano   020301
Polytechnic University of Bari, Bari, Italy

Verlinden, Pierre   020001
YIST, Jiangyin, China

Vermang, Bart   020064
Hasselt Unversity, Genk, Belgium

Vernay, Christophe   020244
SOLAÏS, Valbonne, France

Vero, Giuseppe   020301
Polytechnic University of Bari, Bari, Italy

Veronese, Elisa   020513
Eurac Research, Bolzano, Italy

Veurman, Welmoed   020063
ISFH, Emmerthal, Germany

Viani, Lucas   020326
Enertis Applus+, Madrid, Spain

Vicente-Laiglesia, Pablo   020181
European Climate, Infrastructure and Environment
Executive Agency, Brussels, Belgium

Vidal de Oliveira, Aline   020377
Solar Energy Research Laboratory Fotovoltaica/ UFSC,
Florianópolis, Brazil

Vidal, Beatriz Muñoz   020414
IaSol, Zaragoza, Spain

Vidal-Fuentes, Pedro   020094
IREC, Barcelona, Spain

Videla-Magnata, Natalia
Universidad de Antofagasta, Antofagasta, Chile
020129

Videla-Magnata, Natalia
University of Antofagasta, Antofagasta, Chile
020417

Vilches, Anna Morales
Next2Sun Technology, Dillingen, Germany
020388

Villalonga Palou, Joan Tomás
Sunveon, Madrid, Spain
020432, 020434

Villén, Raúl
ENDEF, Zaragoza, Spain
020127, 020414, 020517

Villodas, Aritz
TECNALIA, Derio, Spain
020198

Vincent, Laetitia
CNRS, Palaiseau, France
020058

Vincent, Robin
PVsyst, Geneva, Switzerland
020196

Viorel Spataru, Sergiu
DTU, Roskilde, Denmark
020191

Viriyaroj, Bergpob
Aalto University, Espoo, Finland
020298

Viti, Valeria
Legance, Milan, Italy
020541

Vitoshkin, Helena
Agricultural Research Organization, Rishon LeZion, Israel
020379

Vögeli, Pascal
ZHAW, Winterthur, Switzerland
020385

Vogt, Malte R.
TU Delft, Delft, The Netherlands
020515

Vogt, Thomas
DLR, Oldenburg, Germany
020482

Vollbrecht, Joachim
ISFH, Emmerthal, Germany
020063, 020114

Voltan, Alessandro
Applied Materials, Treviso, Italy
020010

von Friedeburg, Christoph
CF Energy Research-Consulting-Operation, Berlin,
Germany
020557

Voronko, Yuliya
OFI, Vienna, Austria
020162, 020249

Vorster, Frederik J.
Nelson Mandela University, Port Elizabeth, South Africa
020193, 020344, 020416

Vorster, Frederik
Nelson Mandela University, Port Elizabeth, South Africa
020185

Vuillon, Laurent
CNRS, Chambery, France
020338

Vulic, Natasa   020296
Univesity of Applied Arts and Sciences Northwestern
Switzerland, Muttenz, Switzerland

Vumbugwa, Monphias   020185, 020193, 020344
Nelson Mandela University, Port Elizabeth, South Africa

Waibel, Christoph   020511
Flemish Institute for Technological Research (VITO), Genk,
Belgium

Wakabayashi, Ryo   020484
Hitachi, Kokubunji, Japan

Wakazono, Kouzen   020131
Gifu University, Gifu, Japan

Wallner, Gernot M.   020227
University of Linz, Linz, Austria

Walpita, Harsha   020169
University of Oslo, Kjeller, Norway

Walsh, Yoselyn   020520
Costa Rica Institute of Technology, Cartago, Costa Rica

Wambach, Karsten   020468, 020470
bifa Umweltinstitut, Augsburg, Germany

Wang, Chia-Chen   020549
ITRI, Hsinchu, Taiwan

Wang, Shuo   020286, 020400
TUAS, Turku, Finland

Wang, Tzuya   020549
ITRI, Hsinchu, Taiwan

Wang, Xiaolin   020381
Mälardalen University, Västerås, Sweden

Wannenwetsch, Jann   020312
EnBW, Karlsruhe, Germany

Wargocki, Pawel   020551
DTU, Roskilde, Denmark

Waschl, Alfred   020255
buildingSMART, Vienna, Austria

Weber, Thomas   020180, 020230
Kiwa PI Berlin, Berlin, Germany

Weeber, Arthur W.   020515
TU Delft, Delft, The Netherlands

Wei, Wenpeng   020484
Hitachi, Kokubunji, Japan

Weihs, Philipp   020281
BOKU, Vienna, Austria

Weinrich, Frank   020177
PTB, Braunschweig, Germany

Weiß, Marius   020361
Coburg University of Applied Sciences, Coburg, Germany

Wellens, Christine   020135
Fraunhofer ISE, Freiburg, Germany

Whyatt, Duncan   020394
Lancaster University, Lancaster, United Kingdom

Wienands, Karl   020218, 020220, 020221
ISC Konstanz, Konstanz, Germany

Wiesenfarth, Maike   020246
Fraunhofer ISE, Freiburg, Germany

Wietler, Tobias   020063
ISFH, Emmerthal, Germany

Wilbert, Stefan   020235, 020237, 020239, 020331
DLR, Almería, Spain

Willers, Guido   020201
Fraunhofer CSP, Halle, Germany

Wilson, Helen R.   020249
Fraunhofer ISE, Freiburg, Germany

Winter, Renate   020063
ISFH, Emmerthal, Germany

Winter, Stefan   020177, 020181
PTB, Braunschweig, Germany

Wirtz, Wiebke   020260
ISFH, Emmerthal, Germany

Witkowska, Agnieszka   020498
Gdansk University of Technology, Gdansk, Poland

Wittmer, Bruno   020196
PVsyst, Geneva, Switzerland

Wolf, Andreas   020031
Fraunhofer ISE, Freiburg, Germany

Wong, Craig   020230
Kiwa PI Berlin, Berlin, Germany

Wu, Li-Guo   020021
TSEC, Hsinchu, Taiwan

Wu, Yu   020030
TNO, Petten, The Netherlands

Wyss, Philippe   020068
CSEM, Neuchâtel, Switzerland

Xiong, Weizhen   020320
Tokyo University of Science, Tokyo, Japan

Xu, Jiahui   020001
YIST, Jiangyin, China

Xu, Wenhao   020144, 020208
TÜV Rheinland, Shanghai, China

Xu, Xiaoqi   020263
SERIS, Singapore, Singapore

Xu, Yu   020263
SERIS, Singapore, Singapore
Xuereb, Steven   020180, 020230
Kiwa PI Berlin, Berlin, Germany

Yadav, Shivendra   020071, 020081
SVNIT, Surat, India
Yamaguchi, Yosuke   020484
Hitachi, Kokubunji, Japan
Yanagida, Masatoshi   020115
NIMS, Tsukuba, Japan
Yanar, T. Meriç   020027
Kalyon PV, Ankara, Türkiye
Yang, Donggeon   020323
K-water, Daejeon, South Korea
Yang, Hyoung-Kyu   020449
KETI, Wonmi-gu, South Korea
Yde, Leif   020250, 020306
Stensborg, Roskilde, Denmark
Ye, JiaYi   020102
SERIS, Singapore, Singapore
Yerci, Selcuk   020113
ODTÜ-GÜNAM, Ankara, Türkiye
Ylikunnari, Mari   020423
VTT Technical Research Centre of Finland, Oulu, Finland
Ylinen, Marko   020444
Satakunta University of Applied Sciences, Pori, Finland
Ylipaino, Juho   020444, 020445, 020554
TUAS, Tampere, Finland
Yılmaz, Büşra   020521
Kameleon Solar, Roosendaal, The Netherlands
Yordadov, Georgi   020389
imec, Diepenbeek, Belgium
Younes, Kareem   020487
Khalifa University, Abu Dhabi, United Arab Emirates
Yu, Cheng-Yeh   020021, 020053
TSEC, Hsinchu, Taiwan
Yu, Shusen   020406
Ecole Polytechnique, Palaiseau, France
Yuan, Xiao   020001
YIST, Jiangyin, China
Yun, Jae Ho   020112
KENTECH, Naju-si, South Korea

Zaimi, Mhammed   020171
University of Chouaib Doukkali, El Jadida, Morocco

Zanatta Britto, João Victor 020025
PUCRS, Porto Alegre, Brazil

Zanesco, Izete 020023, 020025
PUCRS, Porto Alegre, Brazil

Zaror, Yasmin 020225
WIP - Renewable Energies, Munich, Germany

Zarzalejo, Luis F. 020237, 020331
CIEMAT, Madrid, Spain

Zekri, Atef 020146
QEERI, Doha, Qatar

Zerafa, Steve 020334
PIXAM, Msida, Malta

Zhang, Geng 020001
Jolywood (ShanXi) Solar Technology, Taiyuan, China

Zhang, Jingwei 020111
Hohai University, Changzhou, China

Zhang, Kai 020233
FZJ, Jülich, Germany

Zhang, Wenjing 020001
YIST, Jiangyin, China

Zhang, Wuai 020101
HZB, Berlin, Germany

Zhang, Yating 020144, 020208
TÜV Rheinland, Shanghai, China

Zhou, Qilin 020102
SERIS, Singapore, Singapore

Zhu, Junjie 020017
Institute for Energy Technology, Kjeller, Norway

Ziaullah, Abdul Wahab 020278, 020291
QEERI, Doha, Qatar

Zilles, Roberto 020154, 020348
University of São Paulo, São Paulo, Brazil

Zimmermann, Iwan 020116
IPVF, Palaiseau, France

Zubillaga, Oihana 020139
Tecnalia, Donostia - San Sebastián, Spain

Zugasti, Eugenia 020334
CENER, Pamplona, Spain

Zugasti, Eugenia 020300
CENER, Sarriguren, Spain

Zwahlen, Theo 020369
BFH, Burgdorf, Switzerland

KEYWORDS OF EU PVSEC 2025 PROCEEDINGS PAPERS

3D GIS	020457
3D Microstructure	020119
3D Shading Model	020432
Accelerated Aging	020254
Accuracy	020276
Adhesion	020384
Adhesive	020384
Adhesives	020127
Adoption vs. Implementation	020563
Aesthetic	020306
Africa	020272
AgBiS2	020071
Agri-photovoltaics	020396
Agriculture	020409
AgriPV	020464
Agrivoltaic	020398, 020407, 020541
Agrivoltaics	020378, 020379, 020388, 020394, 020400, 020402, 020403, 020409, 020412, 020543, 020565
Albedo	020443
Albedo Measurement	020287
Alkaline Leaching	020011
All-Sky Imagers	020267
AlN	020131
Alternative Materials	020020
Aluminium Frame Removal	020497
Aluminium-backed Modules	020192
Aluminum Oxide	020008
Amorphous Silicon	020043
Amorphous Silicon Carbide Crystallization	020079
Ancillary Services	020571
Anion Exchange	020117
Anomaly Detection	020358
Antimony	020140
Antimony Selenide	020087
Antimony-Doping	020015

Characteristics Addition 020081
Characterization 020050, 020119, 020121, 020151, 020166, 020459
CIGS 020097
CIGS/Perovskite Solar Cell 020104
Circular Economy 020141, 020504, 020510, 020517
Circularity 020470, 020472, 020507, 020517
Citizen Participation 020491, 020575
Clay 020300
Clean Firm Power 020487
Clean Transportation 020428
Cleaning 020332
Cleaning Frequency 020348
Cleaning Optimization Asset Management 020339
Clear-sky 020278
Clear-Sky Detection 020340
Climate Change 020402
Climate-dependent Degradation 020150
Climate-responsive Design 020259
Climate-Specific PV O&M 020546
Cloud Detection 020267
Clustering 020243
Co-Extruded EPE 020135
Co-Visibility 020244
Collective Self-consumption 020490
Color Stability 020254
Colored Photovoltaics 020556
ColorFoil 020306
Comfort 020302
Compact Furnace 020025
Comparative Life Cycle Assessment (LCA) 020303
Competitiveness 020573
Compliance 020444
Composite Encapsulant 020139
Composites 020498
Computational Efficiency 020432
Computer Vision 020336, 020511
COMSOL 020104

Concentrator Photovoltaics   020257, 020416

Concentrator Photovoltaics (CPV)   020246

Condition Monitoring   020194, 020289, 020353

Conductive Adhesive   020220

Constitutive Model   020048

Constrained-Off   020530

Constructability   020302

Contact-failure   020055

Controller   020534

Convolutional Neural Networks   020374
(CNNs)

Cooling Load Reduction   020259

Cooperation   020541

Copper Metallization   020035

Correction Factor   020446

Cost of Ownership   020482

Crack Detection   020201

Cracking   020151

Critical Minerals   020559

Cross-lateral Approach   020541

Crosslinking   020158

Crystalline Silicon   020175, 020265

Cu Contact   020020

Cu Plating   020028

Cu-plated Metallization   020037

Current-Voltage Curve   020185

Current–voltage Curve   020194

Curtailment   020332, 020530

Curved Photovoltaic Modules   020459

Czochralski Process   020015

Data Aggregation   020243

Data Center Energy Supply   020487

Data Evaluation   020183

Data Pipeline   020275

Data Quality   020275, 020371

Daylight Electroluminescence   020191

Daylight Luminescence   020205

DC-DC Converters   020422

ECA	020119
Ecodesign	020470
Ecology Index	020468
Economic Feasibility	020394
Economic Valuation	020492
Economic Value Assessment	020486
Education	020548
Education for Sustainable Development (ESD)	020569
Educational Resources	020100
Effects of Temperature and Irradiance	020171
Efficiency Forecast	020279
EL Images Outdoors	020186
EL Imaging	020185, 020510
EL Signal-to-Noise Ratio	020191
Electric Buses	020422, 020457
Electric Mobility	020420
Electric Vehicle Charging	020441
Electric Vehicle Charging Infrastructure	020526
Electrical Mismatch	020265
Electrically Conductive Adhesive	020218
Electricity Demand Coverage	020562
Electricity Market	020332
Electricity Price	020298
Electroluminescence	020188, 020201, 020205, 020206
Electroluminescence (EL) Images	020164
Electrolyzer	020426
Electron Multiplication	020068
Emitter Sheet Resistance	020025
Encapsulant Defects	020157
Encapsulants	020150
Encapsulation	020227
End-of-life PV	020510
Energy Balance	020439
Energy Communities	020445, 020535, 020575
Energy Community	020567
Energy Curtailment	020492
Energy Loss	020223

Energy Management System	020534
Energy Management System (EMS)	020536
Energy Performance Directive	020477
Energy Performance of Buildings Directive (EPBD)	020551
Energy Poverty	020564
Energy Rating	020173, 020177, 020211
Energy Sharing	020564
Energy Storage	020428, 020487, 020534
Energy Testing	020171
Energy Transition	020479, 020537, 020541
Energy Yield	020175, 020181, 020210, 020286, 020318, 020443, 020453
Energy Yield Estimation	020294
Energy Yield Overestimation	020363
Energy Yield Simulations	020262
Environmental Impact	020418
Environmental Psychology	020523
Epitaxial Lateral Overgrowth	020058
Epoxy Bonding	020092
Epoxy–Fiberglass	020417
EROI	020479
ET	020522
Etching	020007, 020031
EU-LAC Collaboration	020546
Eurocode	020167
EV Charging	020428
Evaporation	020015
Experimental Testing	020127
Exports	020563

Facade-Integrated Photovoltaics (FIPV)	020192
Facade-mounted PV	020359
Failures	020328
Fault Analysis	020217
Fault Clustering	020351
Fault Detection	020337, 020346, 020353, 020375, 020511
Fault Signatures	020351
Field Measurements	020377

Grating Structure	020104
Green Hydrogen	020426
Green Purchase Behavior	020523
Greenhouses	020412
Grid Capacity	020486
Grid Integration	020530
Grid Services	020536
Grid-friendly PV Generation	020388
Ground Reflectors	020443
G–T Performance Matrix	020361
GTFS	020457

Half-Cut Cell Module	020193
Headroom Setting	020525
Heat Transfer Modelling	020127
Hemispheric Cameras	020267
Heterojunction	020010, 020515
Heterojunction PV Modules	020173
High Latitude	020400
High-Efficiency	020013
Home Energy Management System	020490
Hor Mirror	020379
Hosting Capacity	020537
Hot Electrons	020013
Hot-Spot	020223
Hotspot	020056
HP-RTM Process	020139
Hybrid Models	020358
Hybrid Photovoltaic-Thermal (PV-T) Collector	020127
Hybrid Photovoltaic-thermal (PVT) Collectors	020517
Hybrid Power Plants	020487, 020530
Hyperspectral Imaging	020504

IAM	020446
IBC	020006, 020055
IBC Cell	020221
IEA PVPS	020570

Irregular Terrain	020434
ISOS Protocols	020064
IV	020346
I–V and EL	020417
I–V Curve Emulation	020369
IV Data	020510
IV Testing	020050
IWO/SiO2 Stack	020046
Junction Box	020129
KPI	020302
Laboratory Measurements	020386
Laboratory Practices	020100
Lamination Monitoring	020132
Land Use	020398, 020543
Land Use Requirements	020476
Landscape	020549
Large Language Model	020544
Large-Size PV Modules	020161
Laser Processing	020023
Laser-grooved BC Technology	020037
LCA	020464, 020468, 020499, 020515
LCOE	020304
LCOE Reduction	020358
LCOH	020426
Lessons Learned	020567
Levelized Cost of Electricity	020482
Li-ion Batteries	020536
LID	020215
LiDAR	020262
Life Cycle Assessment	020511
Life Cycle Impact Assessment	020479
Life-Cycle Assessment	020559
Lifetime Financial Analysis	020367
Light Emitting Diodes	020067
Light Soaking	020010
Light Trapping (LT)	020104

Lightweight	020384
Long-Term Degradation Rate	020181
Low Intensity Low Temperature (LILT)	020246
Low-Cost Sky Imager	020272
Low-energy Secondary Generation and Multiplication	020013
Luminescence	020206
Machine Learning	020337, 020342, 020355, 020434, 020510, 020522
Machine Learning (ML)	020317
Machine Learning Model	020279
Manufacturing	020007, 020558
Market	020570
Market Potential	020252
Market Uptake	020556
Market Value	020539
Mask	020031
Mass Production	020021
Material Classification	020504
Material Qualification	020574
Maximum Power Line	020449
Maximum Power Point Tracking	020437, 020449
McClear	020278
Mechanical Load Test	020167
Mechanical Loads	020231
Mediterranean Climate PV Performance	020334
Metal Recovery	020501, 020508
Metallization	020020, 020028
Metastability	020215
MgO	020131
Micro-Concentrator Optics	020257
Microalgae	020378
Microclimate	020403, 020565
Microinverter	020386
Minimum Sustainable Price	020482
Mismatch	020056, 020396
Mismatch Losses	020432
Mitigation strategies	020573

Modeling	020265
Modelling	020211, 020250
Module Array Design	020394
Module Degradation	020344
Module Design	020154
Module Inspection	020205
Module Integration	020220
Module Reliability	020254
Module Testing for Lifetime	020574
Modules	020129
Modules Testing	020157
Monitoring	020336, 020346, 020403, 020565
Monolithic Interconnection	020094
Monte Carlo Simulation	020441
MPPT	020422, 020453, 020455
MQTT Protocol	020491
Multi-Dwelling Buildings	020445
Multi-junction Solar Cell	020416
Multi-orientation Analysis	020192
Multi-Site Measurements	020334
Multi-Site PV Plant	020525
Multi-source Solar Simulator	020102
Multiple Linear Regression	020342
Nanocrystalline Silicon	020040
Nanostructure	020001
Nanostructures	020068
Natural Language Processing	020522
Near-infrared Absorption Spectroscopy	020149
Negative Electricity Prices	020492
Negative prices	020573
Neural Network	020186
Ni Contacts	020020
Non-destructive Analysis	020504
Non-Uniform UV Illumination	020158
Nordic	020443
Novel Module Structure	020131

Ray-tracing	020250
RCA	020230
Re-Use	020472
Real Monitoring Data	020562
Real-Time Monitoring	020335
Recyclability	020470
Recycling	020468, 020470, 020495, 020499, 020501, 020504, 020507, 020508
Regulatory Constraints	020543
Relative Angular Response (RAR)	020459
Reliability	020144, 020169, 020206, 020218, 020223, 020230, 020233, 020260, 020574
Remote Meteorological Data	020320
Remote Sensing	020486, 020511, 020532
Renewable Energy	020309, 020428
Renewable Energy Communities (REC)	020491
Renewable Energy Integration	020259
Renewable Energy Policy	020549, 020552
Repair	020129, 020511
RES	020476
Research Infrastructures	020546
Reserve Markets	020554
Reserve Power	020525
Residential	020304
Residential Photovoltaic Systems	020294
Residential PV	020490
Resistivity Distribution	020015
Resource	020276
Reuse	020472
Reverse Bias	020056, 020223
Risk	020573
Roll-to-Roll Sputtered System	020306
ROMP	020141
Roof Tile	020300
Round-Robin Study	020262
S-shape	020064
Safety and Quality	020444
Safety Assessment	020386

Silicon	020007, 020058, 020097, 020468, 020495, 020501, 020507, 020508, 020515
Silicon Heterojunction	020040
Silicon Heterojunction Cell	020046
Silicon Kerf	020495
Silicon Photovoltaics	020144
Silicon Solar Cell	020001, 020013, 020023
Silicon Solar Cells	020006, 020068
Silicone	020384
Silver Recovery	020498
Simulation	020255, 020301
Simulation Acceleration	020243
Single-Axis Tracker Reliability	020314
Sizing Optimization	020530
Smart City	020420
Smart Energy System	020544
Smart Inverter IV Tracing	020361
SMARTS2	020278
Social Cognitive Career Theory (SCCT)	020569
Social Housing	020564
Social Innovation	020575
Social Risks	020505
Socio-Economics	020476
Software Tool	020183
Soil	020403, 020565
Soiling	020311, 020332, 020339, 020361
Soiling Loss Modeling	020317
Soiling Losses	020311, 020348
Soiling Mitigation	020311
Solar	020188, 020276
Solar Array Simulator Evaluation	020369
Solar Cell	020007, 020053, 020083
Solar Cells	020090, 020501, 020508
Solar Energy	020526
Solar Glass	020140
Solar Irradiance	020286
Solar Irradiance Forecasting	020267
Solar Irradiation	020412

Value Chain	020505
Vehicle Integrated Photovoltaics (VIPV)	020459
Vehicle-Integrated Photovoltaics	020453, 020457
Vehicle-Integrated Photovoltaics (VIPV)	020422
Vertical Bifacial PV	020262
Vertical PV	020388, 020400
Very Short-term Solar Forecasting	020272
Vibration Durability	020417
VIPV	020417, 020455
Virtual Power Plant	020554
Virtual Power Plants	020535
Visual inspection	020169, 020185
Water Quality	020418
Weather Station	020371
Weather Variables	020279
Wet Etching	020028
Yield	020180, 020307, 020396
YOLO Classifiers	020335, 020374
ZnSnO	020085